What Is an "Integrated Approach"?

One of the key themes in this book is that the body is an integrated set of systems. One of your tasks as you study will be to construct for yourself this global view of the body, its systems, and the many processes that keep the systems working.

Top Ten Ways to Succeed in Classes that Use Active Learning

By Marilla Svinicki, Ph.D., Director
University of Texas Center for Teaching Effectiveness

1. Make the switch from an authority-based conception of learning to a self-regulated conception of learning. Recognize and accept your own responsibility for learning.

2. Be willing to take risks and go beyond what is presented in class or the text.

3. Be able to tolerate ambiguity and frustration in the interest of understanding.

4. See errors as opportunities to learn rather than failures. Be willing to make mistakes in class or in study groups so that you can learn from them.

5. Engage in active listening to what's happening in class.

6. Trust the instructor's experience in designing class activities and participate willingly if not enthusiastically.

7. Be willing to express an opinion or hazard a guess.

8. Accept feedback in the spirit of learning rather than as a reflection of you as a person.

9. Prepare for class physically, mentally, and materially (do the reading, work the problems, etc.).

10. Provide support for your classmate's attempts to learn. The best way to learn something well is to teach it to someone who doesn't understand.

Dr. Dee's Eleventh Rule:
DON'T PANIC! Pushing yourself beyond the comfort zone is scary, but you have to do it in order to improve.

Word Roots for Physiology

a- or **an-** without, absence
anti- against
ase signifies an enzyme
auto self
bi two
brady slow
cardio- heart
cephalo- head
cerebro- brain
contra- against
-crine a secretion
crypt- hidden
cutan- skin
-cyte or **cyto-** cell
de- without, lacking
di- two
dys- difficult, faulty
-elle small
-emia blood
endo- inside or within
epi- over
erythro- red
exo- outside
extra- outside
gastro- stomach
-gen, -genic produce
gluco-, glyco- sugar or sweet
hemi- half
hemo- blood
hepato- liver
homo- same
hydro- water
hyper- above or excess
hypo- beneath or deficient
inter- between
intra- within
-itis inflammation of
kali- potassium
leuko- white
lipo- fat
lumen inside of a hollow tube
-lysis split apart or rupture
macro- large
micro- small
mono- one
multi- many
myo- muscle
oligo- little, few
para- near, close
patho-, -pathy related to disease
peri- around
poly- many
post- after
pre- before
pro- before
pseudo- false
re- again
retro- backward or behind
semi- half
sub- below
super- above, beyond
supra- above, on top of
tachy- rapid
trans- across, through

Improve Your Grade!

Access included with every new book.

Get help with exam prep!

REGISTER NOW!

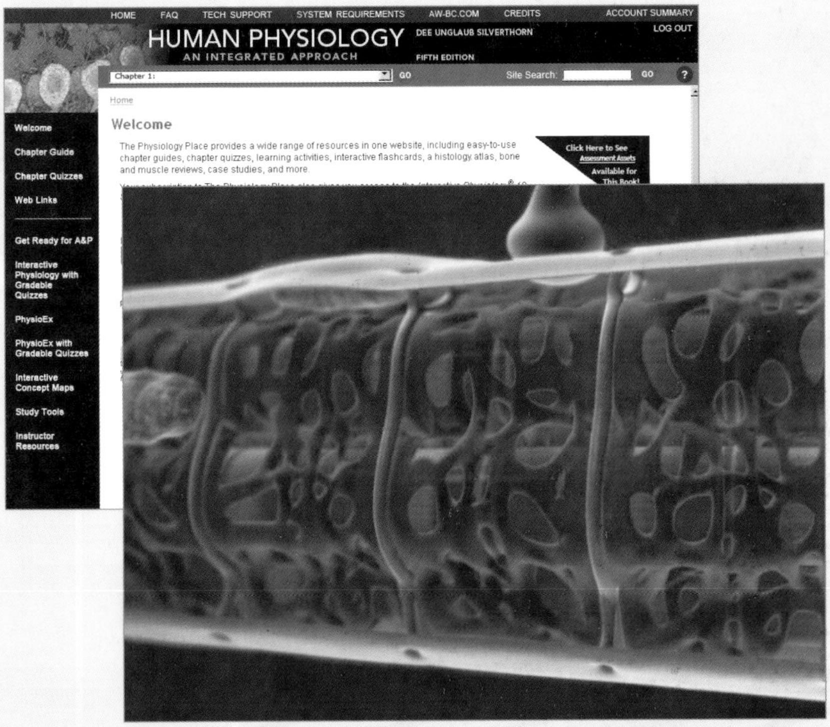

Registration will let you:

- Prepare for exams using pre- and post-tests
- Grasp difficult concepts with animations and tutorials
- Learn at your pace using self-study and practice exercises
- Master key terms and vocabulary
- Access your text online 24/7

www.physiologyplace.com

TO REGISTER

1. Go to **www.physiologyplace.com**
2. Select your book cover and click "Register" under "Students."
3. Follow the on-screen instructions to create your login name and password.

Your Access Code is:

Note: If there is no silver foil covering the access code, it may already have been redeemed, and therefore may no longer be valid. In that case, you can purchase access online using a major credit card or PayPal account. To do so, go to www.physiologyplace.com, click on "Buy Access," and follow the on-screen instructions.

TO LOG IN

1. Go to **www.physiologyplace.com**
2. Click "Log In."
3. Pick your book cover.
4. Enter your login name and password.
5. Click "Log In."

Hint:
Remember to bookmark the site after you log in.

Technical Support:
http://247pearsoned.custhelp.com

HUMAN PHYSIOLOGY

AN INTEGRATED APPROACH

Dee Unglaub Silverthorn

Custom Edition for the University of California, Irvine
Human Physiology
Bio E109

Taken from:
Human Physiology: An Integrated Approach, Fifth Edition
by Dee Unglaub Silverthorn

Custom Publishing

New York Boston San Francisco
London Toronto Sydney Tokyo Singapore Madrid
Mexico City Munich Paris Cape Town Hong Kong Montreal

Cover Art: *Contemplative Figures,* by Robin McDonald–Foley

Taken from:

Human Physiology: An Integrated Approach, Fifth Edition
by Dee Unglaub Silverthorn

Published by Benjamin Cummings
San Francisco, California 94111

This special edition published in cooperation with Pearson Custom Publishing.

Printed in the United States of America

10 9 8 7 6 5 4 3 2 1

2009140386

AK

Pearson
Custom Publishing
is a division of

PEARSON

www.pearsonhighered.com

ISBN 10: 0-558-33929-8
ISBN 13: 978-0-558-33929-6

Contents in Brief

Contents

UNIT 1

BASIC CELL PROCESSES: Integration and Coordination

UNIT 2

HOMEOSTASIS AND CONTROL

UNIT 3

INTEGRATION OF FUNCTION

Owner's Manual: How to Use This Book

WELCOME TO HUMAN PHYSIOLOGY!

As you begin your study of the human body, you should be prepared to make maximum use of the resources available to you, including your instructor, the library, the Internet, and your textbook. One of my goals in this book is to provide you not only with information about how the human body functions but also with tips for studying and problem solving. Many of these study aids have been developed with the input of my students, so I think you may find them particularly helpful. On the following pages, I have put together a brief tour of the special features of the book, especially those that you may not have encountered previously in textbooks. Please take a few minutes to read about them so that you can make optimum use of the book as you study.

One of your tasks as you study will be to construct for yourself a global view of the body, its systems, and the many processes that keep the systems working. This "big picture" is what physiologists call the integration of systems, and it is a key theme in the book. In order to integrate information, however, you must do more than simply memorize it. You need to truly understand it and be able to use it to solve problems that you have never encountered before. If you are headed for a career in the health professions, you will do this in the clinics. If you are headed for a career in biology, you will solve problems in the laboratory, field, or classroom. Analyzing, synthesizing, and evaluating information are skills you need to develop while you are in school, and I hope that the features of this book will help you with this goal.

In this edition we have continued to update and focus on basic themes and concepts of physiology. Chapter 1 introduces you to the key concepts in physiology that you encounter repeatedly as you study different organ systems. It also includes several special features: one on mapping, a useful study skill that is also used for decision-making in the clinics; one on constructing and interpreting graphs, and a third on how to search and read scientific literature.

We have also retained the four approaches to learning physiology that proved so popular since this book was first published in 1998.

1. Cellular and Molecular Physiology

Most physiological research today is being done at the cellular and molecular level, and there have been many exciting developments in molecular medicine and physiology in the ten years since the first edition. For example, now scientists have discovered that our gut senses the composition of a meal using the same receptor proteins that our tongues use to tell us what we're eating. Look for similar links between molecular biology, physiology, and medicine throughout the book.

2. Physiology as a Dynamic Field

Physiology is a dynamic discipline, with numerous unanswered questions that merit further investigation and research. Many of the "facts" presented in this text are really only our current theories, so you should be prepared to change your mental models as new information emerges from scientific research.

3. An Emphasis on Integration

The organ systems of the body do not work in isolation, although we study them one at a time. To emphasize the integrative nature of physiology, three chapters (Chapters 13, 20, and 25) focus on how the physiological processes of multiple organ systems coordinate with each other, especially when homeostasis is challenged.

4. A Focus on Problem Solving

One of the most valuable life skills students should acquire is the ability to think critically and use information to solve problems. As you study physiology, you should be prepared to practice these skills. You will find a number of features in this book, such as the Concept Checks and Figure and Graph Questions, that are designed to challenge your critical thinking and analysis skills. In each chapter, read the Running Problems as you work through the text and see if you can apply what you're reading to the clinical scenario described in the problem.

Also, be sure to look at the back of the text, where we have combined indeand glossary to save time when you are looking up unfamiliar words. The appendices have the answers to the end-of-chapter questions, as well as reviews of physics, logarithms, and basic genetics. The back end papers include a periodic table of the elements, diagrams of anatomical positions of the body, and tables with conversions and normal values of blood components. Take a few minutes to look at all these features so that you can make optimum use of them.

It is my hope that by reading this book, you will develop an integrated view of physiology that allows you to enter your chosen professions with respect for the complexity of the human body and a clear vision of the potential of physiological and biomedical research.

May you learn to love physiology as I do. Good luck with your studies!

Warmest regards,

Dr. Dee (as my students call me)

silverthorn@mail.utexas.edu

Engaging Art Helps You Visualize Physiological Processes and Concepts

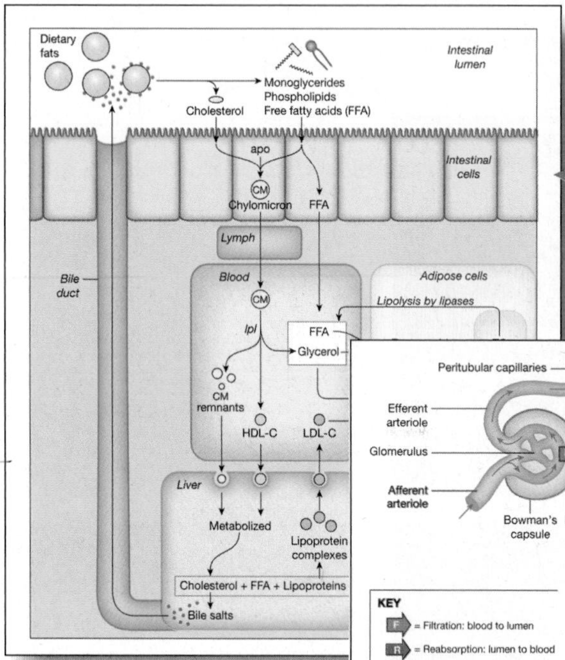

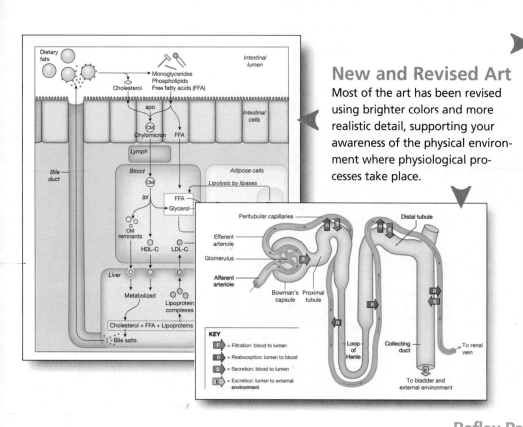

New and Revised Art

Most of the art has been revised using brighter colors and more realistic detail, supporting your awareness of the physical environment where physiological processes take place.

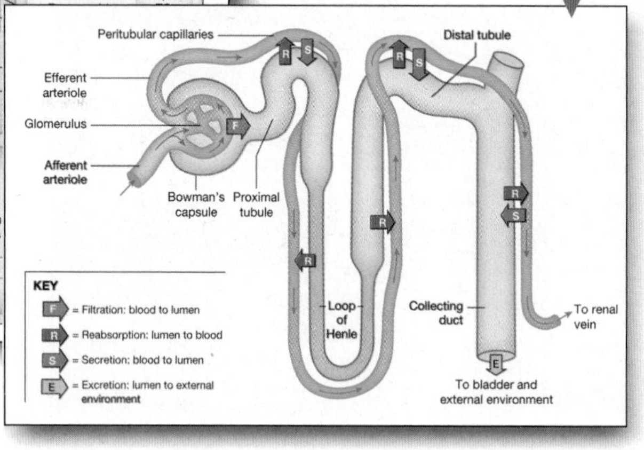

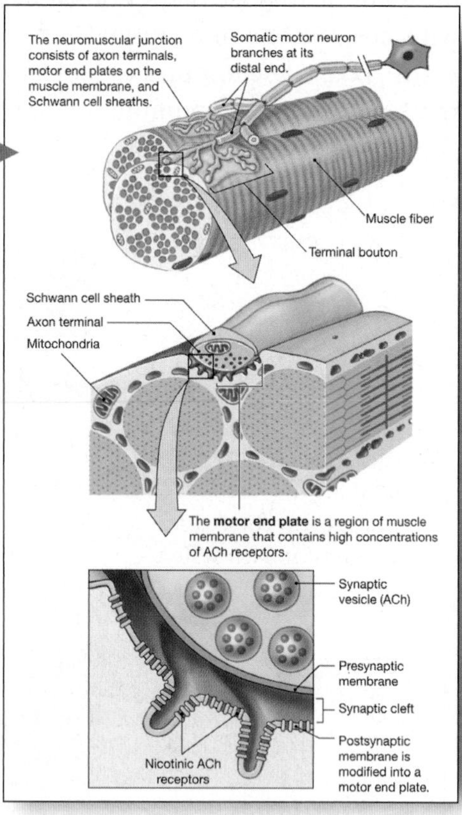

Reflex Pathways & Concept Maps organize physiological processes and details into a logical, consistent visual format. These figures use consistent colors and shapes to represent processes and will guide you to a better understanding of coordinated physiological function. New interactive reflex pathways are available for online study on the companion website.

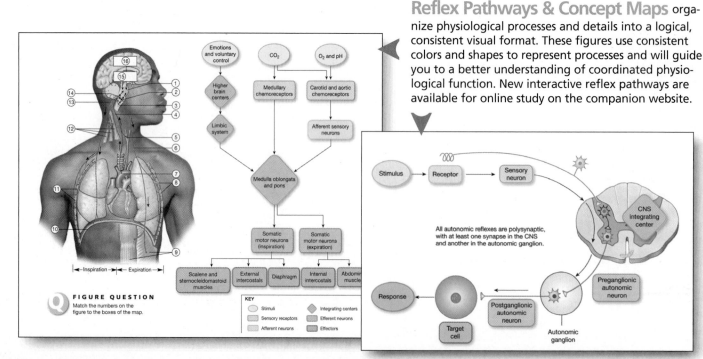

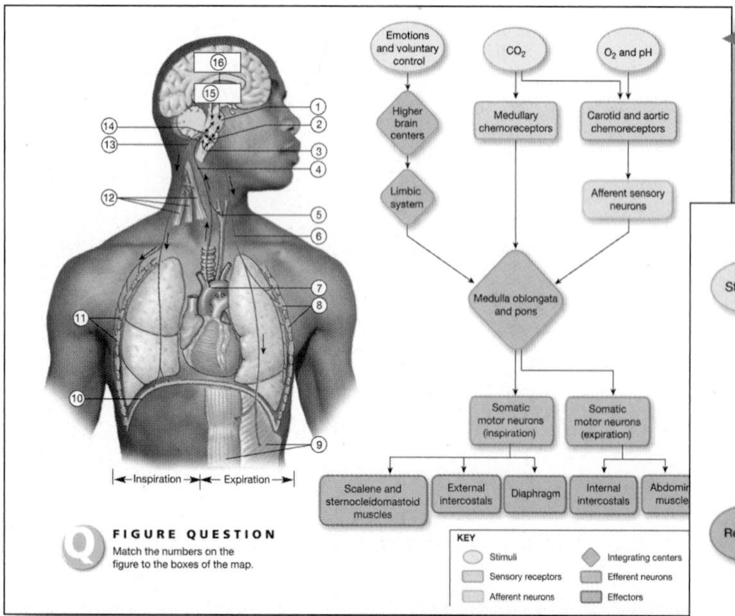

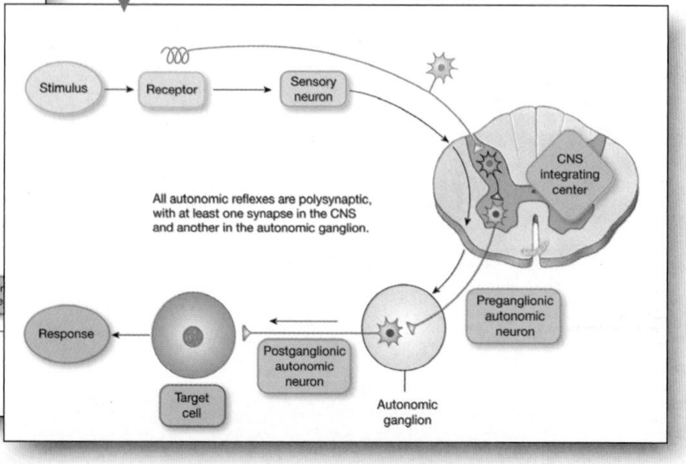

Focus On... figures highlight the anatomy and physiology of organs that are often overlooked in physiology texts, including the skin, the liver, and the pineal gland.

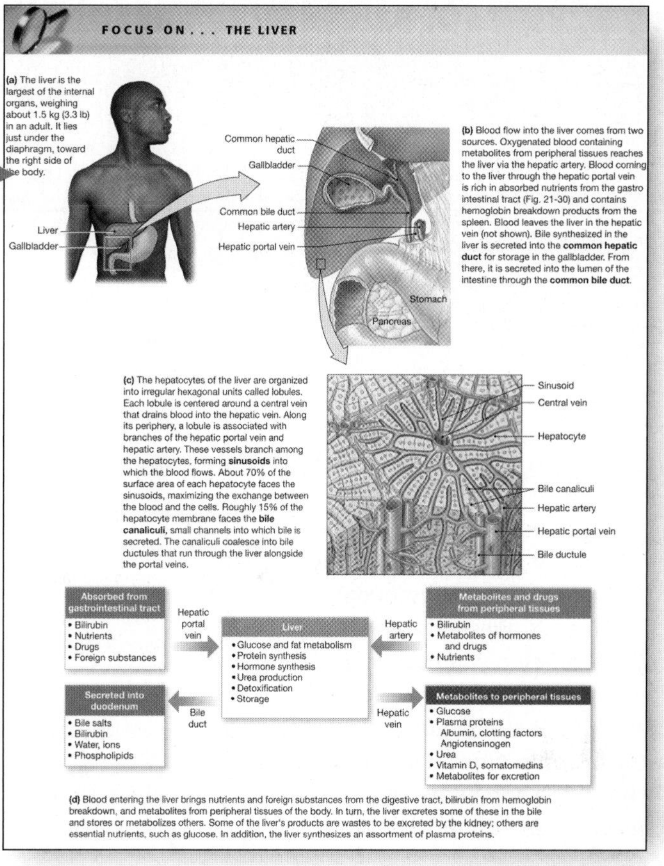

Anatomy Summaries provide succinct visual overviews of a physiological system from a macro to micro perspective. Whether learning the anatomy for the first time or refreshing your memory, these summaries show you the essential features of each system in a single figure.

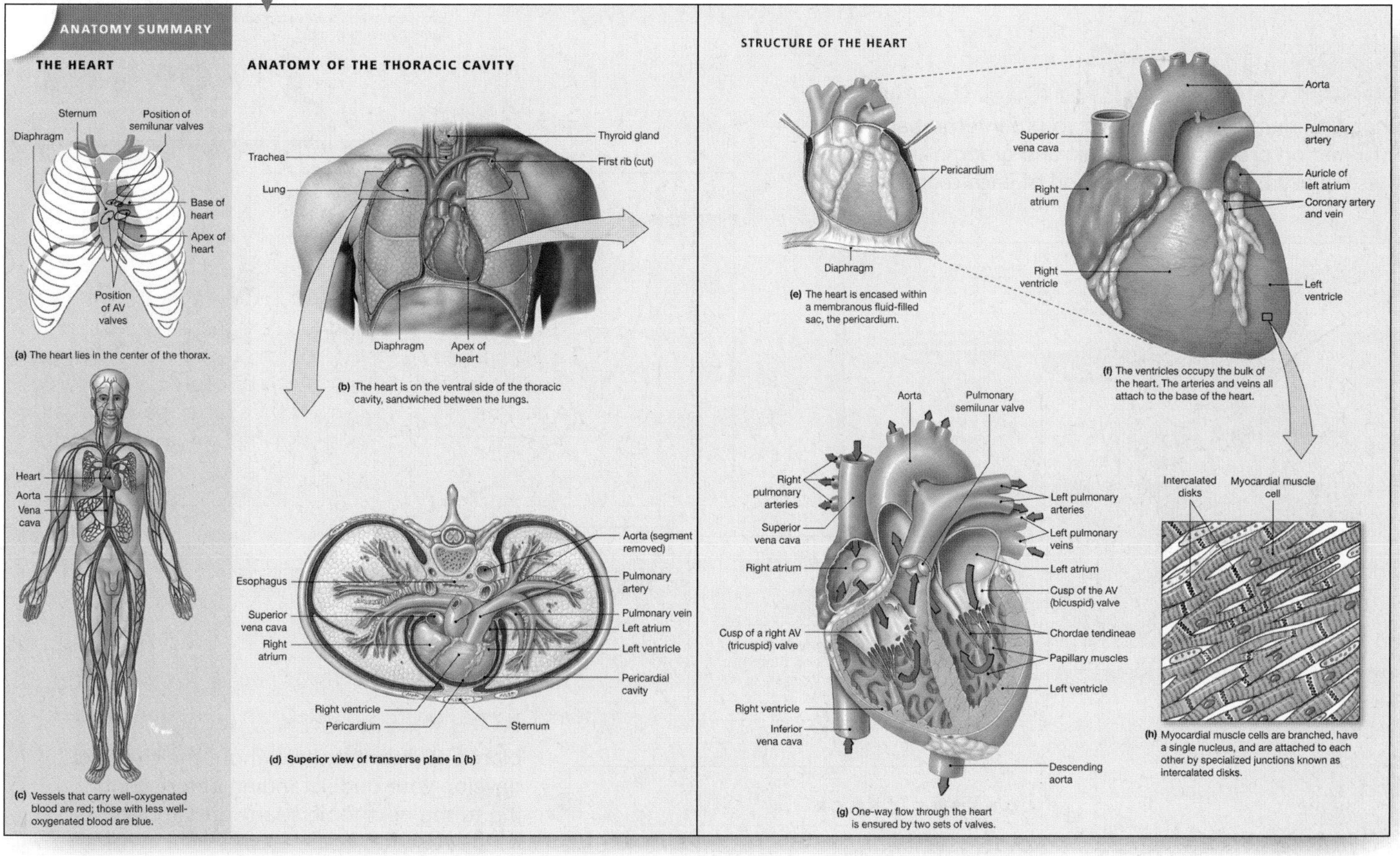

In-Text Tools Develop Your Critical Thinking Skills

Running Problems

Each chapter begins with a relevant, real-life problem involving a disease or disorder that unfolds in segments on subsequent pages. Each segment's questions require you to apply information you have learned from reading the text. You can check your answers against the Problem Conclusion at the end of the chapter. A new Running Problem covering the human papillomavirus appears in this edition.

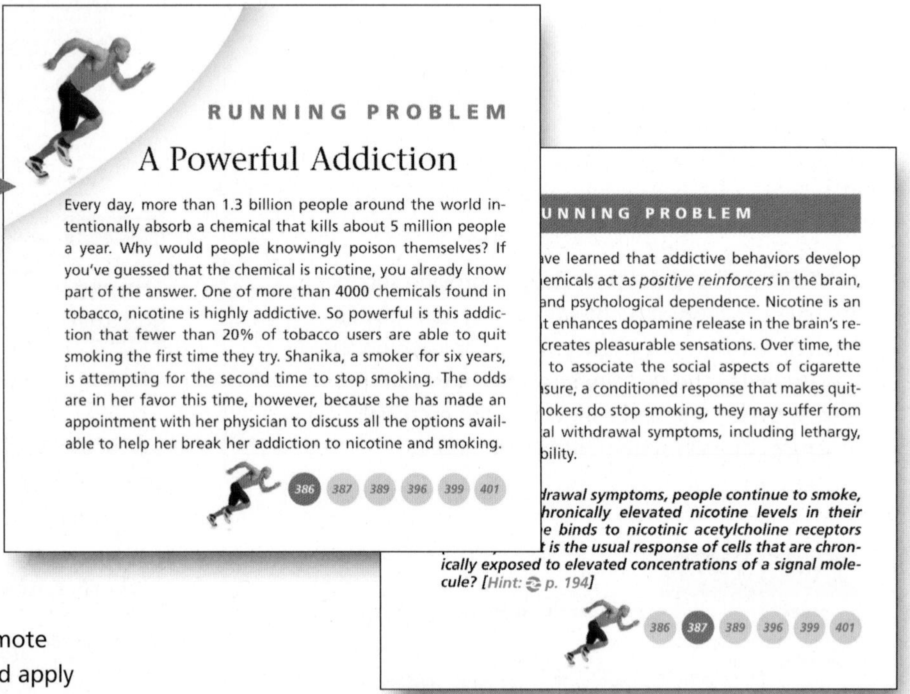
RUNNING PROBLEM

A Powerful Addiction

Every day, more than 1.3 billion people around the world intentionally absorb a chemical that kills about 5 million people a year. Why would people knowingly poison themselves? If you've guessed that the chemical is nicotine, you already know part of the answer. One of more than 4000 chemicals found in tobacco, nicotine is highly addictive. So powerful is this addiction that fewer than 20% of tobacco users are able to quit smoking the first time they try. Shanika, a smoker for six years, is attempting for the second time to stop smoking. The odds are in her favor this time, however, because she has made an appointment with her physician to discuss all the options available to help her break her addiction to nicotine and smoking.

386 387 389 396 399 401

UNNING PROBLEM

ve learned that addictive behaviors develop emicals act as *positive reinforcers* in the brain, and psychological dependence. Nicotine is an t enhances dopamine release in the brain's re- creates pleasurable sensations. Over time, the to associate the social aspects of cigarette sure, a conditioned response that makes quit- okers do stop smoking, they may suffer from al withdrawal symptoms, including lethargy, bility.

drawal symptoms, people continue to smoke, hronically elevated nicotine levels in their e binds to nicotinic acetylcholine receptors t is the usual response of cells that are chronically exposed to elevated concentrations of a signal molecule? [Hint: p. 194]

386 387 389 396 399 401

Figure and Graph Questions

Figure and Graph Questions promote analytical skills by encouraging you to interpret and apply information presented in the art and graphs. Answers to these questions appear at the end of each chapter.

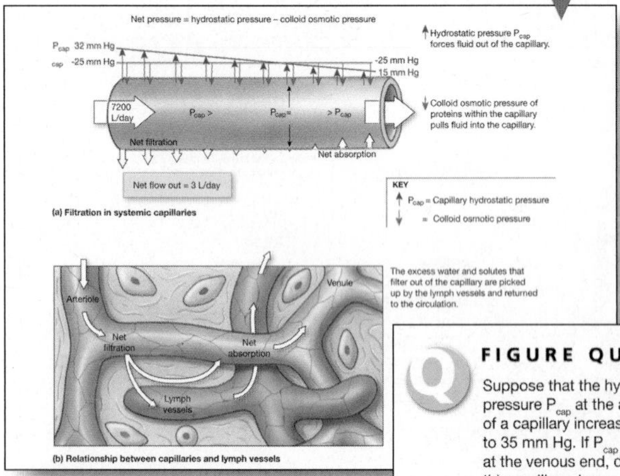
Net pressure = hydrostatic pressure – colloid osmotic pressure
Hydrostatic pressure P_{cap} forces fluid out of the capillary.
Colloid osmotic pressure of proteins within the capillary pulls fluid into the capillary.
Net filtration
Net absorption
Net flow out = 3 L/day
KEY
P_{cap} = Capillary hydrostatic pressure
= Colloid osmotic pressure
The excess water and solutes that filter out of the capillary are picked up by the lymph vessels and returned to the circulation.
Arteriole
Venule
Net filtration
Net absorption
Lymph vessels
(a) Filtration in systemic capillaries

(b) Relationship between capillaries and lymph vessels

FIGURE QUESTION

Suppose that the hydrostatic pressure P_{cap} at the arterial end of a capillary increases from 32 mm Hg to 35 mm Hg. If P_{cap} remains 15 mm Hg at the venous end, does net filtration in this capillary decrease, increase, or stay the same?

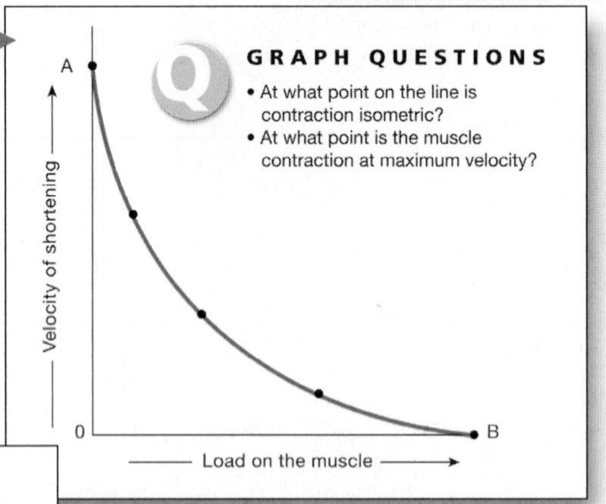
A
B
0
Velocity of shortening
Load on the muscle

GRAPH QUESTIONS

- At what point on the line is contraction isometric?
- At what point is the muscle contraction at maximum velocity?

Concept Check Questions,

placed at intervals throughout the chapters, develop your understanding before continuing to the next topic. Many questions have been revised to better develop your critical thinking skills. You can check your answers using the key at the end of each chapter.

CONCEPT CHECK

12. A drug that blocks all Ca^{2+} channels in the myocardial cell membrane is placed in the solution around the cell. What happens to the force of contraction in that cell? Answers: p. 570

New Study Tools Help You Grasp the Material

The End-of-Chapter, 4-Level Learning System helps build your confidence and understanding by progressing from factual questions to conceptual problems to analytical exercises to quantitative questions. Answers to Level 1 and 2 questions are found in Appendix A at the back of the book; answers to Level 3 and 4 questions are found on the book companion website.

LEVEL ONE **REVIEWING FACTS AND TERMS**

1. List the three functional classes of neurons, and explain how they differ structurally and functionally.
2. Somatic motor neurons control __________, __________ neurons

LEVEL TWO **REVIEWING CONCEPTS**

22. Create a map showing the organization of the nervous system using the following terms, plus any terms you choose to add:

afferent signals	neuron
astrocyte	neurotransmitter

LEVEL THREE **PROBLEM SOLVING**

31. If human babies' muscles and neurons are fully developed and functional at birth, why can't they focus their eyes, sit up, or learn to crawl within hours of being born? (*Hint:* Muscle strength is not the problem.)

LEVEL FOUR **QUANTITATIVE PROBLEMS**

36. The GHK equation is sometimes abbreviated to exclude chloride, which plays a minimal role in membrane potential for most cells. In addition, because it is difficult to determine absolute membrane permeability values for Na^+ and K^+, the equation is revised to use the ratio of the two ion permeabilities as $\alpha = P_{Na}/P_K$:

$$V_m = 61 \log \frac{[K^+]_{out} + \alpha[Na^+]_{out}}{[K^+]_{in} + \alpha[Na^+]_{in}}$$

Thus, if you know the relative membrane permeabilities of the two ions and their intracellular (ICF) and extracellular (ECF) concentrations, you can predict the membrane potential for a cell.

(a) A resting cell has an alpha value of 0.025 and the following ion concentrations:

Na^+: ICF = 5 mM, ECF = 135 mM
K^+: ICF = 150 mM, ECF = 4 mM

Concept Links are encircled "chain-links" that connect concepts to topics discussed earlier in the text. Concept Links will help you find material that you may have forgotten or that may be helpful for understanding new information.

Smooth muscle has less sarcoplasmic reticulum than skeletal muscle does, although the amount varies from one type of smooth muscle to another. The primary Ca^{2+} release channel in smooth muscle sarcoplasmic reticulum is an **IP_3-receptor channel.** *Inositol trisphosphate* (IP_3) is a second messenger created in the phospholipase C pathway [p. 188]. The calcium-storage function of the sarcoplasmic reticulum may be supplemented by *caveolae* [p. 154], small vesicles that cluster close to the cell membrane (Fig. 12-26 ●).

Figure Reference Locators function as place markers to make it easier to connect illustrations with the running narrative that describes the figure.

Background Basics, found on the chapter opening page, reviews topics you will need to master for understanding the material that follows. The page references will save valuable study time.

BACKGROUND BASICS

Tendons: **81** Kinases and phosphatases: **104** Isozymes: **100** Anaerobic and aerobic metabolism: **107** Glycolysis: **107** Fatty acid metabolism: **115** Tonic control: **196** Nitric oxide: **191** Threshold: **200** Summation: **283** Autonomic neurons: **388** Somatic motor neurons: **398** Neuromuscular junction: **398**

Clear Explanations Relate Physiology to Everyday Life

Analogies help you understand difficult concepts

Human physiology includes amazing and complex processes that occur on such a microscopic level, they are difficult to conceptualize. To help you understand how these processes operate, the text uses clear and helpful analogies.

For an analogy, think of the carriers as doors into a concert hall. Each door has a maximum number of people that it can allow to enter the hall in a given period of time. Suppose all the doors together can allow a maximum of 100 people per minute to enter the hall. This is the maximum transport rate, also called the **transport maximum**. When the concert hall is empty, three maintenance people enter the doors every hour. The transport rate is 3 people/60 minutes, or 0.05 people/minute, well under the maximum. For a local dance recital, about 50 people per minute go through the doors, still well under the maximum. When the most popular rock group of the day appears in concert, however, thousands of people gather outside. When the doors open, thousands of people are clamoring to get in, but the doors will allow only 100 people/minute into the hall. The doors are working at the maximum rate, so it does not matter whether there are 1000 or 3000 people trying to get in. The transport rate is saturated at 100 people/minute.

Why does the fastest pacemaker determine the pace of the heartbeat? Consider the following analogy. A group of people are playing "follow the leader" as they walk. Initially, everyone is walking at a different pace—some fast, some slow. When the game starts, everyone must match his or her pace to the pace of the person who is walking the fastest. The fastest person in the group is the SA node, walking at 70 steps per minute. Everyone else in the group (autorhythmic and contractile cells) sees that the SA node is fastest, and so they pick up their pace and follow the leader. In the heart, the cue to follow the leader is the electrical signal sent from the SA node to the other cells.

Now suppose the SA node gets tired and drops out of the group. The role of leader defaults to the next fastest person, the AV node, who is walking at a rate of 50 steps per minute. The group slows to match the pace of the AV node, but everyone is still following the fastest walker.

What happens if the group divides? Suppose that when they reach a corner, the AV node leader goes left but a renegade Purkinje fiber decides to go right. Those people who follow the AV node continue to walk at 50 steps per minute, but the people who follow the Purkinje fiber slow down to match his pace

Active Learning examples help you "see for yourself"

Mini-experiments you can perform nearly anywhere are incorporated into the text to give you a concrete understanding of how processes work. (Additional examples are available via the Instructor's Resource Guide.)

If the walls of a fluid-filled container contract, the pressure exerted on the fluid in the container increases. You can demonstrate this principle by filling a balloon with water and squeezing the water balloon in your hand. Water is minimally compressible, and so the pressure you apply to the balloon is transmitted throughout the fluid. As you squeeze, higher pressure in the fluid causes parts of the balloon to bulge. If the pressure becomes high enough, the stress on the balloon causes it to pop. The water volume inside the balloon did not change, but the pressure in the fluid increased.

In the human heart, contraction of the blood-filled ventricles is similar to squeezing a water balloon: pressure created by the contracting muscle is transferred to the blood. This high-

By the time blood reaches the veins, pressure has fallen because of friction, and a pressure wave no longer exists. Low-pressure blood in veins below the heart must flow "uphill," or against gravity, to return to the heart. Try holding your arm straight down without moving for several minutes and notice how the veins in the back of your hand begin to stand out as they fill with blood. (This effect may be more evident in older people, whose subcutaneous connective tissue has lost elasticity). Then raise your hand so that gravity assists the venous flow and watch the bulging veins disappear.

Focus Boxes Highlight Physiology as a Dynamic Field of Research and Application

Three kinds of focus boxes were developed with the goal of helping you understand the role of physiology in science and medicine today.

BIOTECHNOLOGY

COCHLEAR IMPLANTS

One technique used to treat sensorineural hearing loss is the cochlear implant. The newest cochlear implants have multiple components. Externally, a microphone, tiny computerized speech processor, and transmitter fit behind the ear like a conventional hearing aid. The speech processor is a transducer that converts sound into electrical impulses. The transmitter converts the processor's electrical impulses into radio waves and sends these signals to a receiver and 8–24 electrodes, which are surgically placed under the skin. The electrodes take electrical signals directly into the cochlea and stimulate the sensory nerves. After surgery, recipients go through therapy so that they can learn to understand the sounds they hear. Cochlear implants have been remarkably successful for many profoundly deaf people, allowing them to hear loud noises and modulate their own voices. In the most successful cases, individuals can even use the telephone. To learn more about cochlear implants, visit the web site of the National Institute for Deafness and Other Communication Disorders (*www.nidcd.nih.gov/health/hearing*).

Biotechnology boxes discuss physiology related applications and laboratory techniques from the fast-moving world of biotechnology.

CLINICAL FOCUS

DIABETES

THE DISCOVERY OF INSULIN

Diabetes mellitus, the metabolic condition associated with pathologies of insulin function, has been known since ancient times. Detailed clinical descriptions of insulin-deficient diabetes were available to physicians, but they had no means of treating the disease, and patients invariably died. However, in a series of classic experiments in endocrine physiology, Oscar Minkowski at the University of Strasbourg (Germany) pinpointed the relationship between diabetes and the pancreas. In 1889, Minkowski surgically removed the pancreas from dogs (*pancreatectomy*) and noticed that they developed symptoms that mimicked diabetes. He also found that implanting pieces of pancreas under the dogs' skin would prevent development of diabetes. Subsequently, in 1921 Fredrick G. Banting and Charles H. Best (Toronto, Canada) identified an antidiabetic substance in pancreas extracts. Banting and Best and others injected pancreatic extracts into diabetic animals and found that the extracts reversed the elevated blood glucose levels of diabetes. From there, it was a relatively short process until, in 1922, purified insulin was used in the first clinical trials.

Clinical Focus boxes concentrate on clinical applications and pathologies, helping you understand how to apply your learning in a clinical setting. Revised content includes information on gustation. An additional feature to this box is a **DIABETES THEME**, which is used to illustrate the application of physiology to a clinical situation. Because diabetes has such a widespread effect on the body, it makes a perfect example of integrated physiology.

EMERGING CONCEPTS

TRANSPORTER GENE FAMILIES

One outcome of the Human Genome project has been the recognition that many proteins are closely related to each other, both within and across species. As a result, scientists have discovered that most membrane transporters for organic solutes belong to one of two gene "super-families": the ATP-binding cassette (ABC) superfamily or the solute carrier (SLC) superfamily. The ABC family transporters use ATP's energy to transport small organic molecules across membranes. Interestingly, the CFTR chloride channel is also a member of the ABC family and is the only known ion channel in that superfamily. The 43 families of the SLC superfamily family include most facilitated diffusion carriers, such as the GLUTs, as well as the secondary active transporters shown in Table 5-3.

Emerging Concepts boxes describe upcoming advances in physiological research. Revised content includes information on transporter gene families, and anti-Müllerian hormone and polycystic ovary syndrome.

Unparalleled Student Supplements Make Learning Fun

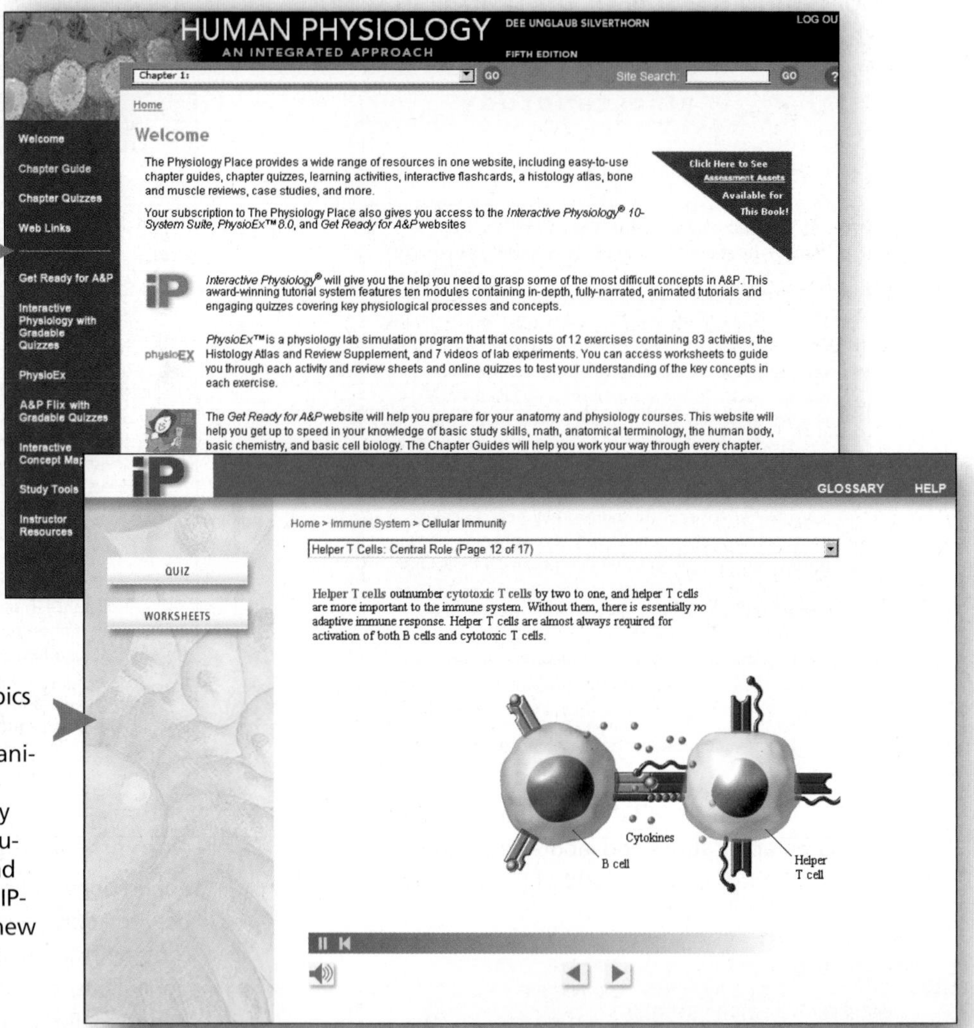

The Physiology Place has been updated to include the new A&P Flix animations in 3D that bring difficult-to-understand physiology concepts to life (see following page for details). Also on the website are new Interactive Concept Maps, chapter guides, chapter quizzes, and web links for every chapter. Access to ***Get Ready for A&P***, an invaluable aid for preparing to study physiology, is included. Online Study Tools include Interactive Case Studies, Flashcards, Answers to Level 3 and 4 end-of-chapter questions, a Glossary, Muscle and Bone Review, ***IP-10***, ***PhysioEx 8.0***, and an Histology Atlas.

Interactive Physiology® 10-System Suite provides an audio/visual presentation of complex topics that you can study from as often as you need. IP-10 features narrated, full-color animated tutorials that thoroughly demonstrate difficult physiology concepts, many of which occur at the cellular and molecular level. Extensive interactive quizzes and games reinforce the material. A copy of IP-10 is automatically included with every new copy of the text and an online version is available via the website.

physioEX™ VERSION 8

PhysioEx 8.0 is an easy-to-use laboratory simulation program consisting of 11 exercises containing 79 activities for you to use to prepare and practice for your physiology lab. PhysioEx 8.0 allows you to repeat labs as often as you like, perform experiments without harming live animals, and conduct experiments that may be difficult to perform in real life due to time, cost, or safety concerns. Access to PhysioEx is included via the Physiology Place.

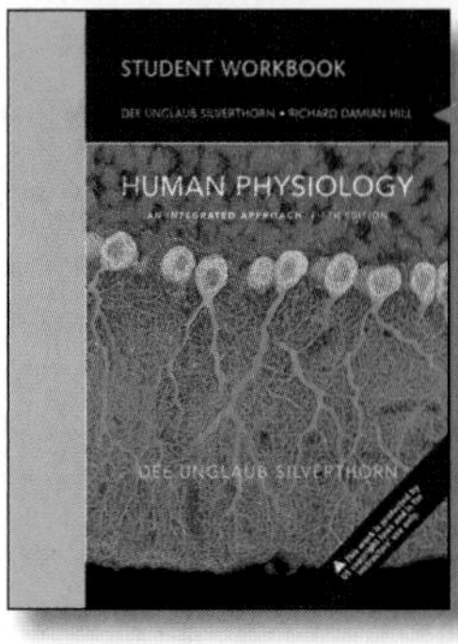

Student Workbook, co-written by Dee Silverthorn, is your personal tutor, assisting you with your preparation for lecture, helping you go over your lecture notes and reinforcing the material you have learned in class. The Student Workbook guides you through the complex field of physiology, providing you with a list of Learning Objectives for each chapter; Teach Yourself the Basics, a series of study questions; Talk the Talk vocabulary lists; Quantitative Physiology, posing quantitative problems with a guide through the solution process; Practice Makes Perfect questions that cover chapter material over a range of skill levels; and Beyond the Pages additional references, background information, and chapter-related activities.

Everything You Need to Teach Your Course Your Way

The Instructor Resource DVD Makes Creating Dynamic Lecture Presentations Easier Than Ever

A&P Flix

Brand new, 3D-quality **A&P Flix** animations (including gradable quizzes and printable study sheets) provide carefully developed, step-by-step explanations with dramatic 3D representations of structures that show action and movement of processes, bringing difficult-to-teach A&P concepts to life. Each animation will be available in PowerPoint with PRS-enabled quiz questions for use with personal response systems (clickers). The A&P Flix are also available on the Physiology Place for students to review on their own.

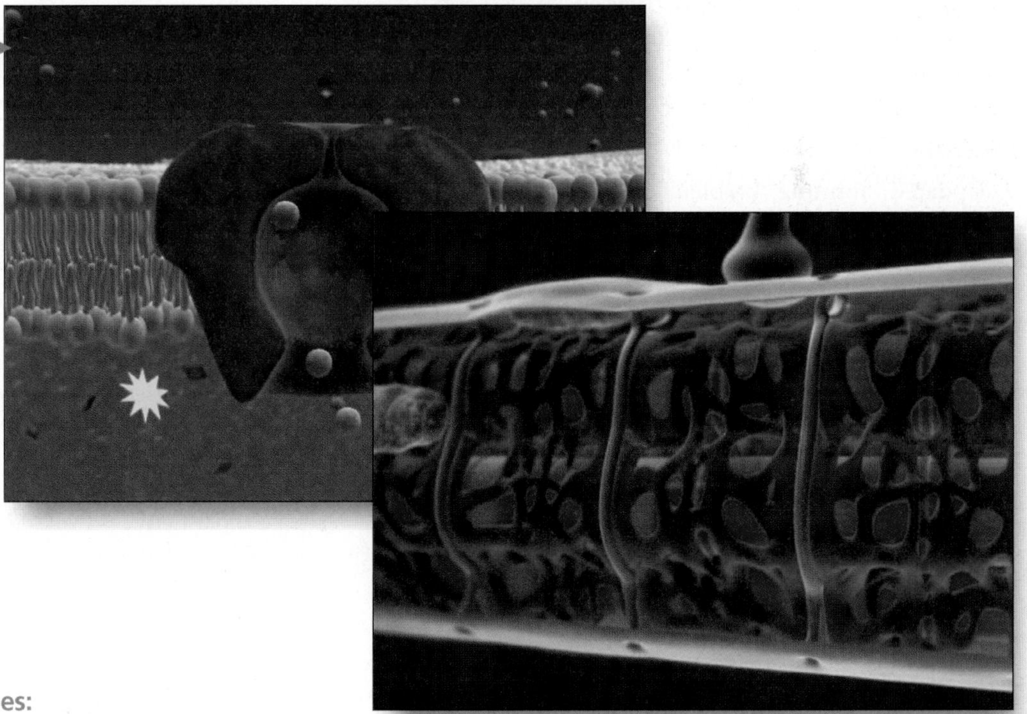

Instructor Resource DVD also includes:

- **JPEG and PowerPoint®** files of all illustrations, photos, and tables from the book.
- **PowerPoint slides** with all images (labeled and unlabeled) with select items in customizable Label Edit PowerPoint and Step Edit PowerPoint format; Lecture Outlines; Active Lecture Questions (PRS-enabled); and Physiology Review Quiz Show Games and Quiz Show Game template.
- **Microsoft Word® documents** with Lecture Outlines, chapter test questions from the Test Bank, Instructor Resource Manual, IP Exercise Sheets, IP Exercise Sheets Answer Key, IP Assignment Sheets, and Quick Reference Guide.
- **Podcast How-To Instructions** to help you create dynamic content students can use to review lectures at their convenience, anywhere they happen to be.

CourseCompass™

Bb Blackboard www.blackboard.com

WebCT

Other Tools to Help You Teach

CourseCompass, WebCT, and **Blackboard** courses offer pre-loaded content including testing and assessment plus assets from The Physiology Place website. These three course management systems are available as pre-built, easy-to-use courses. Professors can use these powerful tools to create sophisticated web-based educational programs.

IRM and **Transparencies** are also available.

New to This Edition

The fifth edition of *Human Physiology: An Integrated Approach* builds upon the thorough coverage of integrative and molecular physiology topics that have been the foundation of this book since its first publication. The text has been revised with extensive content updates and a substantial revision of the art has created clearer figures and diagrams, along with new figures to help clarify confusing concepts.

Chapter-by-Chapter Content Updates

Chapter 1

- Added discussion of difference between "model" and "theory"
- New information on pharmacogenomics and evidence-based medicine
- Updated meta-analysis for glucosamine-chondroitin studies

Chapter 2

- Updated Running Problem information on chromium picolinate

Chapter 3

- New information on immunoliposomes
- Updated information on CAMs
- Introduced paracellular pathway
- Updated Running Problem on Pap tests to include updated collection method and role of HPV in abnormal pap tests and cervical cancer

Chapter 4

- Updated information on RNA, protein synthesis, and protein sorting
- New information on microRNA and RNA interference
- Added enzyme classes to Table 4-4
- Added mnemonic for oxidation-reduction reactions
- New figure on energy yields for glucose metabolism
- New Figure Question

Chapter 5

- Introduced biological transport as a recurring theme
- New section on fluids and bulk flow
- New summary figure of membrane transporters
- Added nuclear pores complexes and gap junctions to discussion of membrane channels
- New section on paracellular and transcellular transport
- Updated discussion of pores in tight junctions
- Updated information on prognosis for patients with cystic fibrosis
- New Emerging Concepts box "Transporter Gene Families," including ATP-binding cassette (ABC), transporter superfamily, and solute carrier (SLC) superfamily
- New Concept Check question

Chapter 6

- Updated information on cytokines, cytokine receptors, and pathways, such as Janus kinase (JAK)
- New information on hydrogen sulfide as a gaseous signal molecule
- New information on sphingolipids as extracellular lipid signals
- Revised Fig. 6-29 on circadian rhythms using data from peer-reviewed literature
- New Level 3 Problem Solving question

Chapter 7

- Updated information about control of prolactin secretion
- Updated terminology for hypothalamic hormones
- Updated information on melatonin
- Added adiponectin and resistin, adipose tissue hormones
- Revised nomenclature for amino-acid derived hormones
- New Concept Check question on glucagon
- New figure of hypothalamic-hypophyseal portal system (Fig. 7-16)

Chapter 8

- New information on etiology of AMAN in Running Problem
- Updated glial cell function and role in pathologies
- Added channel kinetics and channel inactivation
- Added rectifying synapses
- Added information on oxidative stress and reactive oxygen species (ROS)
- Updated information on long-term and short-term synaptic plasticity
- Updated information on mechanisms of long-term potentiation and long-term depression
- Updated channelopathies causing long QT syndrome
- Updated information on neural stem cells and stem cell transplants for Batten disease
- Added role of dissociation in termination of NT action
- New photograph of Purkinje cell
- New image of dendritic spines
- Updated Table 8-4 with neurocrines and receptors
- Revised Fig. 8-21 to reflect docking protein structure
- New Figure Question in Fig. 8-17
- Added additional Level 3 and Level 4 questions

Chapter 9

- Updated information on brain-computer interfaces
- Added information on factors contributing to major depression, such as brain-derived neurotrophic factor (BDNF)
- New Figure Questions and end-of-chapter questions

Chapter 10

- Updated discussions of pain and itch
- Revised model for taste transduction, including type III (presynaptic) cells and type II (receptor) cells, CD36 fat receptors, and T1R sweet-umami receptors in the gut

- Two new figures for taste
- New figures for olfactory and auditory pathways
- New information on cyclic nucleotide-gated (CNG) channels in rods
- New information on phantom limb pain, endolymphatic hydrops, and diabetic neuropathy
- Five new Figure Questions and four new Level Three and Four questions

Chapter 11

- Updated information on adrenergic receptor antagonists
- Updated information on nAChR receptor structure and receptor-channel inactivation
- Updated nicotine addiction in Running Problem
- Revised data on teen smoking

Chapter 12

- Added information on DHP receptors as L-type Ca^{2+} channels
- Added two cross-bridge states to discussion of sliding filament theory
- Updated control of store-operated Ca^{2+} channels
- Updated theories of causes of muscle fatigue
- Revised figure of contraction-relaxation cycle
- Added information on role of channelopathies in periodic paralyses
- New Concept Check question

Chapter 13

- Updated discussions of central pattern generators
- Two new Figure Questions

Chapter 14

- Updated information on cardiac stem cells
- Added information on NCX Na-Ca exchanger and L-type Ca^{2+} channels
- New Concept Check question and four new Figure Questions
- New information on atrial fibrillation

Chapter 15

- Added information on nitric oxide
- Added concept of arteries as pressure reservoir and veins as volume reservoir
- Updated information on angiogenesis
- Added information on liver sinusoids
- Added pre-eclampsia
- Updated information on cardiovascular disease and hypertension in text and Running Problem
- New summary map figure of factors influencing blood flow
- New Figure Questions

Chapter 16

- Updated information on stem cells and cord blood
- Added information on warnings on EPO-like drugs

Chapter 17

- Introduced kilopascals as an alternate unit for pressures
- Added discussion of positive pressure ventilation and obstructive sleep apnea
- Added forced expiratory volume in 1 second (FEV_1)
- New discussion of alveolar fluid transport
- Added idiopathic pulmonary fibrosis
- Included ideal gas law in gas law table
- Revised anatomical art to show scalenes and sternocleidomastoid
- Expanded and updated discussion of COPD in Running Problem

Chapter 18

- Revised model of neural control of breathing, including pre-Bötzinger complex, pontine respiratory group, and nucleus tractus solitarius (NTS)
- Added phrenic, intercostal, vagus, and glossopharyngeal nerves
- New figure showing brainstem centers for ventilation
- New section on alveolar flooding and adult respiratory distress syndrome (ARDS)
- Updated information on glomus cell neurotransmitters
- Updated role of Hering-Breuer reflex in humans
- New Level Three question on alveolar fluid transport
- New Figure Question

Chapter 19

- Updated information on urate transport, including organic anion exchanger (OAT), urate transporter 1 (URAT1), and urate transporter (UAT)
- Added new proteins nephrin and podocin to discussion of filtration slits
- Added megalin to discussion of renal protein reabsorption

Chapter 20

- New Concept Check question on peripheral osmoreceptors
- Added discussion of direct renin inhibitor drugs and vasopressin receptor antagonists
- Updated model of osmoreceptor activation
- Added Level Three question about vasopressin receptor antagonists
- New information about luminal carbonic anhydrase
- Added discussion of cell volume regulation
- New Concept Check questions

Chapter 21

- Updated information on detection and treatment of *H. pylori*
- Added information on ICCs as pacemakers and possible role in functional bowel disorders
- Updated information on transporters, including oligopeptide transporter Pep T1 and oligopeptides
- Updated information on cholesterol transport, including NPCILI cholesterol transporter and ezetimibe
- Added information about sucralose
- Added iron absorption, including divalent metal transporter 1 (DMT1), ferroportin, and hepcidin
- Updated information on gastroparesis and gastric pacemakers
- New information on taste receptors in the gut
- New mapping question and Level Three question on hemochromatosis
- New Figure and Concept Check questions

Chapter 22

- New Concept Check question on DPP-4 inhibitors
- Updated information on control of appetite and food intake, including adipocytokines and obestatin
- Updated information on drugs for diabetes, including dipeptidyl peptidase-4, DPP-4 inhibitors, and sitagliptin
- Updated diabetes statistics

Chapter 23

- Updated information on thyroid cell function, including pendrin (SLC26A4) and sodium-iodide symporter (NIS)
- New Figure Question

Chapter 24

- Substantially revised art
- Updated information on natural killer cell function
- Updated AIDS treatment: HAART (highly active antiretroviral therapy) cocktail
- Added pathogen-associated molecular patterns (PAMP), toll-like receptors (TLRs), and pattern recognition receptors (PRRs)
- Updated clonal deletion and antibody-mediated immunity
- New Figure Questions

Chapter 25

- Updated information on exercise and disease
- Revised heat stroke running problem
- New Concept Check question

Chapter 26

- New information on AMH in ovaries
- Added role of kisspeptin in gonadotropin release
- Role of insulin and IFG-1 in reproduction
- Updated information on contraceptive methods (NuvaRing)
- New Concept Check questions, including one on timing of ovulation based on cycle length
- New Emerging Concepts box on AMH as a follicular marker and role in polycystic ovary syndrome (PCOS)

Acknowledgments

Writing, editing, and publishing a textbook is a group project that requires the talent and expertise of many people. I particularly want to acknowledge Bruce Johnson, Cornell University, Department of Neurobiology and Behavior, a superb neurobiologist and educator, who once again contributed his expertise to ensure that the chapters on neurobiology are accurate and reflect the latest developments in that rapidly changing field.

Many other people devoted time and energy to making this book a reality, and I would like to thank them all, collectively and individually. I apologize in advance to anyone whose name I've left out.

REVIEWERS

I am particularly grateful to the instructors who reviewed one or more chapters of the third edition. There were many suggestions in their thoughtful reviews that I was unable to include in the text but I appreciate the time and thought that went into their comments. The reviewers for this edition include:

Anthony (Tony) Apostolidis, San Joaquin Delta College
Heather Ashworth, Utah Valley State College
Albert Herrera, University of Southern California
Chris Glembotski, San Diego State University
Jennifer Lundmark, California State University, Sacramento
Charles Miller, Colorado State University
Gemma Niermann, St. Mary's College of California
Chris Ward, Queen's University
Carola Wright, Mt. San Antonio College

Many other instructors and students took time to write or email queries or suggestions for clarification. I am always delighted to have input, and I apologize that I do not have room to acknowledge them individually.

SPECIALTY REVIEWS

No one can be an expert in every area of physiology, and I am deeply thankful for my friends and colleagues who reviewed entire chapters or answered specific questions. Even with their help, there may be errors, for which I take full responsibility. The specialty reviewers for this edition were:

George Brooks, University of California, Berkeley
Helen Cooke, Ohio State University
Glenn Hatton, University of California, Riverside
Michael G. Levitzky, Louisiana State University Health Sciences Center
Stan Lindstedt, Northern Arizona University
Jeffrey Pommerville, Maricopa Community Colleges
Frank Powell, University of California, San Diego
Roy Russ, Mercer University School of Medicine

The following individuals contributed analogies, figure suggestions, and ideas that appear in this edition:

Jean Hardwick, Ithaca College
Albert Berger, University of Washington
Andy Bass, Cornell University
Ken Wright, University of Colorado
Hootan Khatami, Merck & Co., Inc.

PHOTOGRAPHS

I would like to thank the following colleagues who generously provided micrographs from their research:

Kristen Harris, University of Texas
Flora M. Love, University of Texas
Jane Lubisher, University of Texas
Young-Jin Son, University of Texas

SUPPLEMENTS

I am very grateful to my friends and colleagues who worked this edition's supplements: Joanna Disnmore, Peter English, Paul Findell, Meg Flemming, Gary Heisermann, Sarah Kennedy,Catherine Loudon, Jennifer Lundmark, Jan Machart, Alice Martin, and Cheryl Smith. They all know how I teach and think, and I believe their work allows the supplements to the book to reflect the style of the text. Damian Hill once again worked with me to revise and improve the Instructor's Resource Guide and Student Workbook.

THE DEVELOPMENT AND PRODUCTION TEAM

Writing a manuscript is only a first step in the long and complicated process that results in a bound book with all its ancillaries. In this edition I was delighted to work once again with Anne A. Reid, development editor *extraodinaire* who makes revisions as painless as they can be. I also enjoyed working for the first time with Antonio Padial, my copy editor, who made my life easier by providing me with excellent style sheets. As usual, Bill Ober and Claire Garrison, my art coauthors, used their considerable talents to improve the art in this edition. Yvo Riezebos was the talented designer who created the cover and interior page designs.

The team at Benjamin Cummings worked tirelessly to see this edition move from manuscript to bound book. My Executive Editor, Deirdre Espinoza, produced a baby at the same time as this edition, so in her absence much of the work of shepherding the fifth edition fell into the able hands of Katy German, my Project Editor. Katy gently but firmly kept me and everyone else on schedule. Shannon Cutt was the Assistant Editor who coordinated the print supplements and assisted Katy. Once again it was a real pleasure to work with Karen Gulliver, Production Editor, and Maureen Sphuler, Photo Editor, who simplified the production as much as is possible for a project this size. Aimee Pavy was the Media Producer who kept my supplements authors on task and on schedule.

Christy Lawrence is the Executive Marketing Manager who works with the excellent sales teams at Benjamin Cummings and Pearson International.

SPECIAL THANKS

As always, I would like to thank my students and colleagues who looked for errors and areas that needed improvement. My graduate teaching assistants have played a huge role in my teaching ever since I arrived at the University of Texas, and their input has helped shape how I teach. Many of them are now faculty members themselves. I would particularly like to thank:

Lynn Cialdella, M.S., M.B.A.
Patti Thorn, Ph.D.
Karina Loyo-Garcia, Ph. D.
Jan M. Machart, Ph.D.
Ari Berman, Ph.D.
Kurt Venator, Ph.D.
Peter English, Ph.D.
Kira Wenstrom, Ph.D.
Lawrence Brewer, Ph.D.
Carol C. Linder, Ph.D.

Finally, special thanks to my colleagues in the American Physiological Society and the Human Anatomy & Physiology Society, whose experiences in the classroom have enriched my own understanding of how to teach physiology. I would also like to recognize a special group of friends for their continuing support: Ruth Buskirk, Judy Edmiston, Jeanne Lagowski, Jan M. Machart and Marilla Svinicki (University of Texas), Penelope Hansen (Memorial University, St. John's), Mary Anne Rokitka (SUNY Buffalo), Rob Carroll (East Carolina University School of Medicine), Cindy Gill (Hampshire College), and Joel Michael (Rush Medical College).

As always, I thank my family and friends for their patience, understanding, and support during the chaos that seems inevitable with book revisions. The biggest thank you goes to my husband Andy, who keeps me focused on what's really important in life.

A WORK IN PROGRESS

One of the most rewarding aspects of writing a textbook is the opportunity it has given me to meet or communicate with other instructors and students. In the years since the first edition was published, I have heard from people around the world, and have had the pleasure of hearing how the book has been incorporated into their teaching and learning.

Because science textbooks are revised every three or four years, they are always works in progress. I invite you to contact me or my publisher with any suggestions, corrections, or comments about this fourth edition. I am most reachable through e-mail at *silverthorn@mail.utexas.edu*. You can reach my editor at the following address:

Applied Sciences
Benjamin Cummings
1301 Sansome Street
San Francisco, CA 94111

Dee U. Silverthorn
University of Texas
Austin, Texas

25. According to the chemiosmotic theory, energy is trapped in a hydrogen ion concentration gradient and selectively released as the ions travel across the membrane separating the mitochondrial matrix from the intermembrane space.

Page 116

26. The digestion is more likely a hydrolysis reaction because large molecules are split into smaller molecules by the addition of water.
27. Deaminases remove amino acids.

Page 117

28. Hexokinase adds a phosphate group; glucose 6-phosphatase removes a phosphate group.

Page 122

29. The DNA triplets are ATT, ATC, and ACT.
30. RNA polymerase makes polymers of RNA.

Page 123

31. During mRNA processing, base sequences called introns are cut out of the mRNA. The remaining segments, the exons, are spliced back together and provide the code for a protein.

Page 126

32. Removal of a phosphate group is dephosphorylation.
33. Three types of post-translational modification are cleavage, addition of groups, and cross-linking.
34. Hemoglobin is a tetramer because it contains four protein chains.

Answers to Figure and Graph Questions

Page 100

Fig. 4-6: The graph shows an endergonic reaction.

Page 101

Fig. 4-7: When pH decreases from 8 to 7.4, enzyme activity increases.

Page 107

Fig. 4-12: The enzyme is glucose-6 phosphatase.

Page 114

Fig. 4-20: 1. Reaction (b) is a hydrolysis reaction, as is reaction (a). 2. Hydrolases add water.

Page 118

Fig. 4-23: Most fatty acids have an even number of carbons because they are made from 2-carbon acyl units. Some fatty acids with odd numbers of carbons are found in marine organisms.

Answer to Running Problem Conclusion

Page 127

Question 3. Factors other than a defective gene that could alter enzyme levels include decreased protein synthesis or increased protein breakdown in the cell. Such changes could occur even though the gene was normal.

5

Membrane Dynamics

BACKGROUND BASICS

Polar and nonpolar molecules: **25** Protein and lipid structure: **31** Cell junctions: **72** Molarity: **37** Solutions: **36** Membrane structure: **56** Cytoskeleton: **66** Types of epithelia: **74** Enzymes: **100**

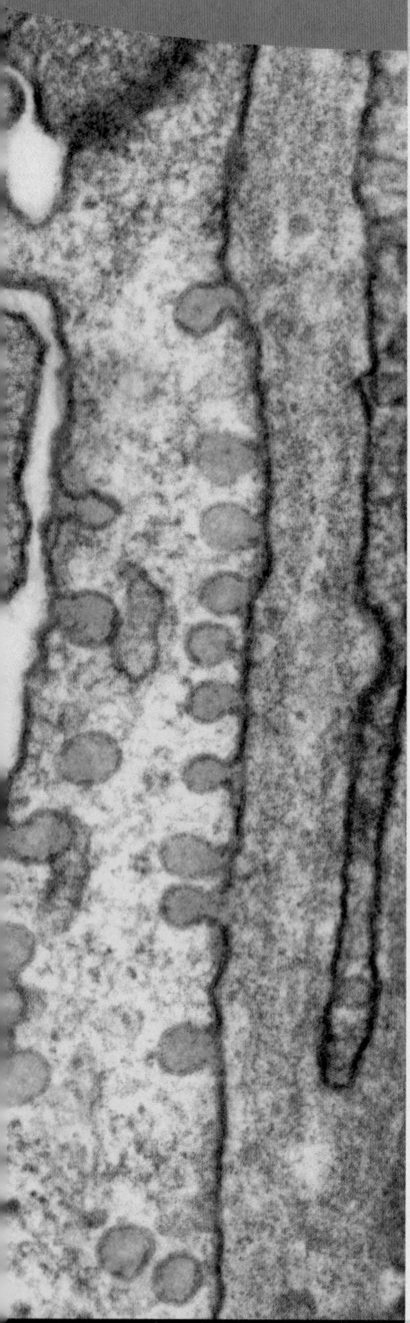

A capillary endothelial cell (yellow) with caveolae and transport vesicles.

Controversy surrounds the exact arrangements of molecules in cell membranes.

—Robert D. DeVoe, in *Mountcastle's Medical Physiology*, 1974

RUNNING PROBLEM

Cystic Fibrosis

Over 100 years ago, midwives performed an unusual test on the infants they delivered: the midwife would lick the infant's forehead. A salty taste meant that the child was destined to die of a mysterious disease that withered the flesh and robbed the breath. Today, a similar "sweat test" will be performed in a major hospital—this time with state-of-the-art techniques—on Daniel Biller, a 2-year-old with a history of weight loss and respiratory problems. The name of the mysterious disease? Cystic fibrosis.

133 144 156 161 165 171

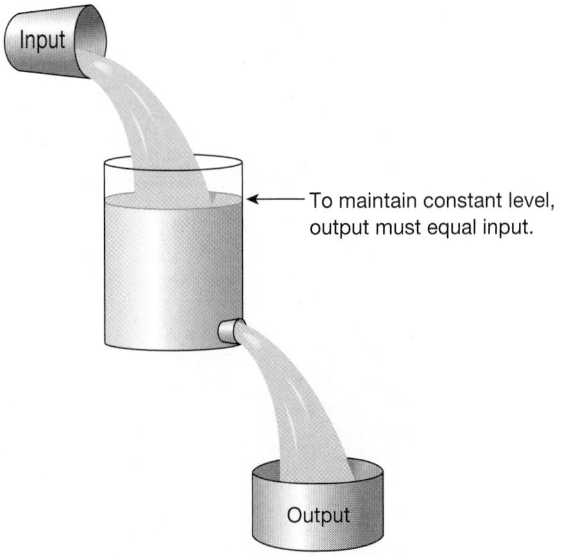

● **FIGURE 5-1** ***Mass balance in an open system***

In the 1960s a group of conspiracy theorists obtained a lock of Napoleon Bonaparte's hair and sent it for chemical analysis in an attempt to show that he had been poisoned to death. Somewhere in Manhattan's Little Italy, a group of friends savor a delicious dinner and joke about the garlic odor on their breath. At first glance these two scenarios appear to have little in common, but in fact, Napoleon's hair and garlic breath both demonstrate how the human body works to maintain the balance that we call homeostasis.

MASS BALANCE AND HOMEOSTASIS

You learned in the previous chapter that the body is an open system that exchanges heat and materials with the outside environment. To maintain a state of homeostasis—a relatively constant internal environment—the body utilizes the principle of mass balance. The **law of mass balance** says that if the amount of a substance in the body is to remain constant, any gain must be offset by an equal loss (Fig. 5-1 ●). For example, to maintain constant body concentration, water loss to the external environment (output) must be balanced by water intake from the external environment and metabolic water production (input). Other substances whose concentrations are maintained through mass balance include oxygen and carbon dioxide, salts, and hydrogen ions (pH). The law of mass balance is summarized by the following equation:

Total amount (or **load**) of substance *x* in the body
= intake + production − excretion − metabolism

Most substances enter the body from the outside environment, but some (such as carbon dioxide) can be produced internally through metabolism (Fig. 5-2 ●). In general, water and nutrients enter the body as food and drink absorbed through the intestine. Oxygen and other gases and volatile molecules enter through the lungs, and a few lipid-soluble chemicals make their way to the internal environment by penetrating the barrier of the skin [p. 86].

To maintain mass balance, the body has two options for output. The simplest option is simply to excrete the material. **Excretion** is defined as the elimination of material from the body, and it usually takes place through the urine, feces, lungs, or skin. For example, carbon dioxide produced during metabolism is excreted by the lungs. Many foreign substances that enter the body, such as drugs or artificial food additives, are excreted by the liver and kidneys. (Any foreign substance in the body is called a *xenobiotic,* from the Greek word *xenos,* a stranger).

A second output option for maintaining mass balance is to metabolize the substance to a different substance. Nutrients that enter the body become the starting substrates in metabolic pathways, as you learned in Chapter 4. Metabolism converts the original nutrient to a different substance but in doing so creates a new mass balance disturbance by adding more of the *metabolite* to the body. (*Metabolite* is the general term for any product created in a metabolic pathway.)

Excretion Clears Substances from the Body

The rate at which a molecule disappears from the body by excretion, metabolism, or both is called the molecule's **clearance**. The quantitative expression of clearance will be introduced in Chapter 19, but it will be easier to understand that discussion if you already know that the kidney is only one organ of several that clear solutes from the body. The liver is the other major organ involved in clearing materials, especially xenobiotics. *Hepatocytes* [*hepaticus,* pertaining to the liver + *cyte,* cell], or liver cells, metabolize many different types of molecules, including hormones and drugs. The resulting metabolites may be

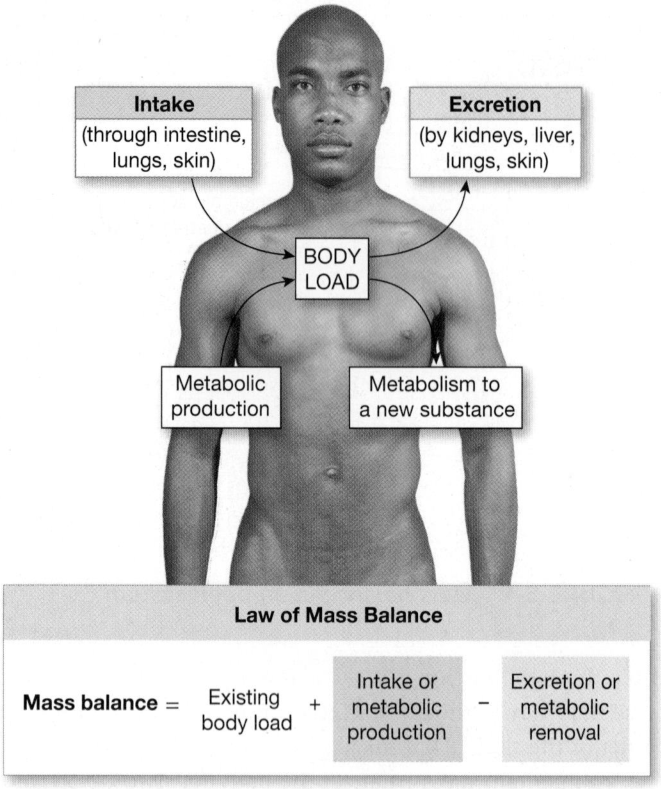

● **FIGURE 5-2** ***Mass balance in the body.*** Materials either enter the body by various routes or are produced through metabolism. Materials leave the body either by excretion or by metabolism.

secreted into the intestine for excretion in the feces or released into the blood for excretion by the kidneys.

Saliva, sweat, breast milk, and hair also contain solutes that have been cleared from the body. Salivary secretion of the hormone *cortisol* provides a simple noninvasive source of hormone for monitoring chronic stress. Drugs and alcohol excreted into breast milk are important because a breast-feeding infant will ingest these substances. Hair analysis can be used to test for arsenic in the body, and the 1960s analysis of Napoleon Bonaparte's hair showed significant concentrations of the poison. (The question remains whether Napoleon was murdered, was poisoned accidentally, or died from stomach cancer.)

The lungs clear volatile lipid-soluble materials from the blood when these substances pass into the airways and are expelled during breathing. One everyday example of lung clearance is "garlic breath." Ethanol also is cleared by the lungs, and exhaled alcohol is the basis of the "breathalyzer" test used by law enforcement agencies.

Clearance is usually expressed as a volume of blood plasma *cleared* of substance *x* per unit of time. For this reason clearance is only an indirect measure of how substance *x* is eliminated. A more direct way to follow substance *x* is **mass flow:**

$$\underset{(\text{amount } x/\text{min})}{\text{Mass flow}} = \underset{(\text{amount } x/\text{vol})}{\text{concentration}} \times \underset{(\text{vol/min})}{\text{volume flow}}$$

Mass flow can be used to determine the rate of intake, output, or production of *x*. For example, suppose a person is given an intravenous infusion of glucose solution that has a concentration of 50 grams of glucose per liter. If the infusion is given at a rate of 2 milliliters per minute, the mass flow of glucose into the body is:

$$50 \text{ g glucose}/1000 \text{ mL solution} \times 2 \text{ mL solution/min} = 0.1 \text{ g glucose/min}$$

Mass flow applies not only to the entry, production, and removal of substances but also to the movement of substances from one compartment in the body to another. Recall from Chapter 3 [p. 54] that we can divide the body into two major compartments: the extracellular fluid and the intracellular fluid. Materials enter the body by crossing an epithelium, then becoming part of the extracellular fluid. How a substance is distributed after that depends on whether or not it can cross the barrier of the cell membrane and enter the cells.

CONCEPT CHECK

1. If a person eats 12 milligrams of salt in a day and excretes 11 milligrams of it in the urine, what happened to the remaining 1 milligram?
2. Glucose is aerobically metabolized to CO_2 and water. Explain the effect of this glucose metabolism on mass balance in the body.

Answers: p. 176

Homeostasis Does Not Mean Equilibrium

When physiologists talk about homeostasis, they are often speaking of the stability of the body's *internal environment*—in other words, the stability of the extracellular fluid compartment (ECF), which consists of the blood plasma and the interstitial fluid [Fig. 3-2, p. 56]. One reason for focusing on extracellular fluid homeostasis is that it is relatively easy to monitor. It is much more difficult to follow what is taking place in the intracellular fluid compartment (ICF), although cells do maintain *cellular homeostasis.*

In a state of homeostasis, the composition of both body compartments is relatively stable. But if we compare the individual solutes in the two compartments, we find that their concentrations are different in the ECF and ICF. Because of these concentration gradients, the fluid compartments usually exist in a state that might best be called a *dynamic disequilibrium.*

Water is essentially the only molecule that moves freely between cells and the extracellular fluid. Because of this free movement of water, the extracellular and intracellular compartments can reach a state of **osmotic equilibrium** [*osmos,* push or thrust], in which the total amount of solute per volume of fluid is equal on the two sides of the cell membrane. At the same time, however, the body is in a state of **chemical disequilibrium,** in which certain solutes are more concentrated in one of the two body compartments than in the other (Fig. 5-3 ●).

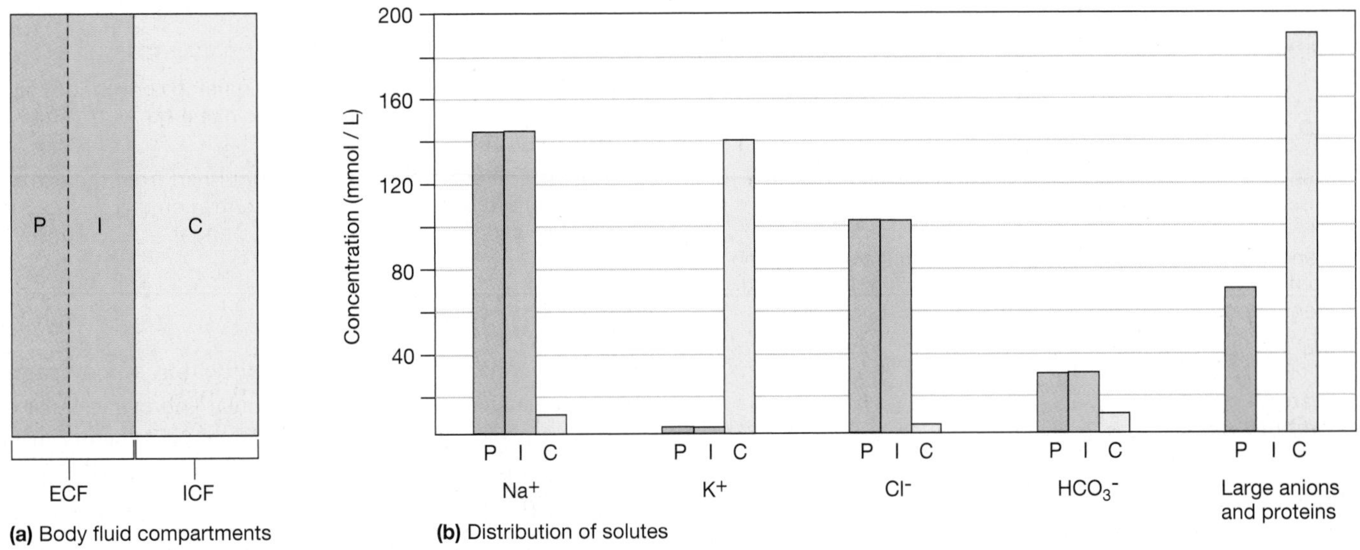

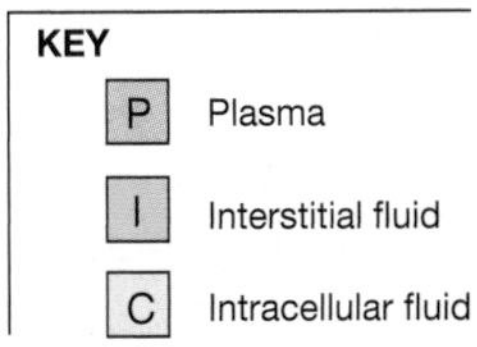

GRAPH QUESTIONS

- How does plasma differ from interstitial fluid?
- What are the major differences between extracellular compartments and intracellular compartments?

● **FIGURE 5-3** ***Distribution of solutes in the body fluid compartments.*** The extracellular fluid (ECF) is composed of the blood plasma plus interstitial fluid. The compartments of the body are in a state of chemical disequilibrium.

Figure 5-3 shows the uneven distribution of major solutes among the body fluid compartments. For example, sodium, chloride, and bicarbonate (HCO_3^-) ions are more concentrated in extracellular fluid than in intracellular fluid. Potassium ions are more concentrated inside the cell. Calcium (not shown in the figure) is more concentrated in the extracellular fluid than in the cytosol, although many cells store Ca^{2+} inside organelles such as the endoplasmic reticulum and mitochondria.

Even the extracellular fluid is not at equilibrium between its two subcompartments [Fig. 3-2, p. 56]. Proteins and other large anions are concentrated in the plasma but almost absent from the interstitial fluid because they are unable to cross the endothelium [p. 76].

The concentration differences of chemical disequilibrium are a hallmark of a living organism, as only the continual input of energy keeps the body in this state. If solutes leak across the cell membrane dividing the intracellular and extracellular compartments, energy is required to return them to the compartments they left. For example, K^+ ions that leak out of the cell and Na^+ ions that leak into the cell are returned to their original compartments by an energy-utilizing enzyme known as the *Na^+-K^+-ATPase*. When cells die and cannot use energy, they obey the second law of thermodynamics [p. 97] and return to a state of randomness that is marked by loss of chemical disequilibrium.

Many body solutes mentioned so far are ions, and for this reason we must also consider the distribution of electrical charge between the intracellular and extracellular compartments. The body as a whole is electrically neutral, but a few extra negative ions are found in the intracellular fluid, while their matching positive ions are located in the extracellular fluid. As a result, the inside of cells is slightly negative relative to the extracellular fluid. This ionic imbalance results in a state of **electrical disequilibrium**, and changes in the disequilibrium create electrical signals. We discuss this topic in more detail later in this chapter.

In summary, note that homeostasis is not the same as equilibrium. The intracellular and extracellular compartments of the body are in osmotic equilibrium, but in chemical and electrical disequilibrium. Furthermore, osmotic equilibrium and the two disequilibria are dynamic *steady states*. The modifier *dynamic* indicates that materials are constantly moving back and forth between the two compartments, but in a *steady state,* there is no *net* movement of materials between the compartments. The goal of homeostasis is to maintain the dynamic steady states of the body's compartments.

In the remainder of this chapter, we discuss how transport mechanisms and the selective permeability of cell membranes are responsible for a body in which the intracellular and extracellular compartments are chemically and electrically different but have the same total concentration of solutes.

CONCEPT CHECK

3. Clinically we monitor homeostasis of various substances such as ions, blood gases, and organic solutes by taking a blood sample and analyzing its plasma. For each of the following substances, predict whether knowing its plasma concentration also tells you its concentration in the ECF and the ICF. Defend your answer.
   (a) Na^+
   (b) K^+
   (c) water
   (d) proteins

Answers: p. 176

Transport Occurs Within and Between Compartments

Humans are large complex organisms, and the movement of material within and between body compartments is necessary for communication. This movement requires a variety of transport mechanisms. Some require an outside source of energy, such as that stored in the high-energy bond of ATP [p. 34], while other transport processes use only the kinetic or potential energy already in the system [p. 96]. Movement between compartments usually means a molecule must cross one or more cell membranes. Movement within a compartment is less restricted. For this reason biological transport is another theme that you will encounter repeatedly as you study the organ systems.

The most general form of biological transport is the **bulk flow** of fluids within a compartment. Although many people equate **fluids** with liquids, in physics both gases and liquids are considered fluids because they flow. The main difference between the two fluids is that gases are compressible because their molecules are so far apart in space. Liquids, especially water, are not compressible. (Think of squeezing on a water balloon.)

In bulk flow, a *pressure gradient* causes fluid to flow from regions of higher pressure to regions of lower pressure. As the fluid flows, it carries with it all of its component parts, including substances dissolved or suspended in it. Blood moving through the circulatory system is an excellent example of bulk flow. The heart acts as a pump that creates a region of high pressure, pushing plasma with its dissolved solutes and the suspended blood cells through the blood vessels. Air flow in the lungs is another example of bulk flow that you will encounter as you study physiology.

Other forms of transport are more specific than bulk flow and when we discuss them, we must name the molecule or molecules that are moving. Transport mechanisms you will learn about in the following sections include diffusion, protein-mediated transport, vesicular transport, and osmosis.

CONCEPT CHECK

4. Using what you learned about the naming conventions for enzymes [p. 103], explain what the name *Na^+-K^+-ATPase* tells you about this enzyme's actions.
5. The intracellular fluid can be distinguished from the extracellular fluid by the ICF's high concentration of ________ ion and low concentration of ________, and ________ ions.

Answers: p. 176

DIFFUSION

Although many materials move freely within a body compartment, exchange between the intracellular and extracellular compartments is restricted by the cell membrane. Whether or not a substance enters a cell depends on the properties of the cell membrane and those of the substance. Cell membranes are **selectively permeable**; in other words, the lipid and protein composition of a given cell membrane determines which molecules will enter the cell and which will leave [p. 56]. If a membrane allows a substance to pass through it, the membrane is said to be **permeable** to that substance [*permeare,* to pass through]. If a membrane does not allow a substance to pass, the membrane is said to be **impermeable** [*im-*, not] to that substance.

Membrane permeability is variable and can be changed by altering the proteins or lipids of the membrane. Some molecules, such as oxygen, carbon dioxide, and lipids, move easily across most cell membranes. On the other hand, ions, most polar molecules, and very large molecules (such as proteins), enter cells with more difficulty or may not enter at all.

Two properties of a molecule influence its movement across cell membranes: the size of the molecule and its lipid solubility [p. 25]. Very small molecules and those that are lipid soluble can cross directly through the phospholipid bilayer. Larger and less lipid-soluble molecules usually do not enter or leave a cell unless the cell has specific membrane proteins to transport these molecules across the lipid bilayer. Very large lipophobic molecules cannot be transported on proteins and must enter and leave cells in vesicles [p. 68].

There are two ways to categorize how molecules move across membranes. One scheme, just described, separates movement according to physical requirements: whether it takes place through the phospholipid bilayer, with the aid of a membrane protein, or by using vesicles (bottom of Fig. 5-4 ●). A second scheme classifies movement according to its energy requirements (top of Fig. 5-4). **Passive transport** does not require the input of energy. **Active transport** requires the input of energy from some outside source, such as the high-energy phosphate bond of ATP.

Diffusion Uses Only the Energy of Molecular Movement

Passive transport across membranes uses the kinetic energy [p. 96] inherent in molecules. Gas molecules and molecules

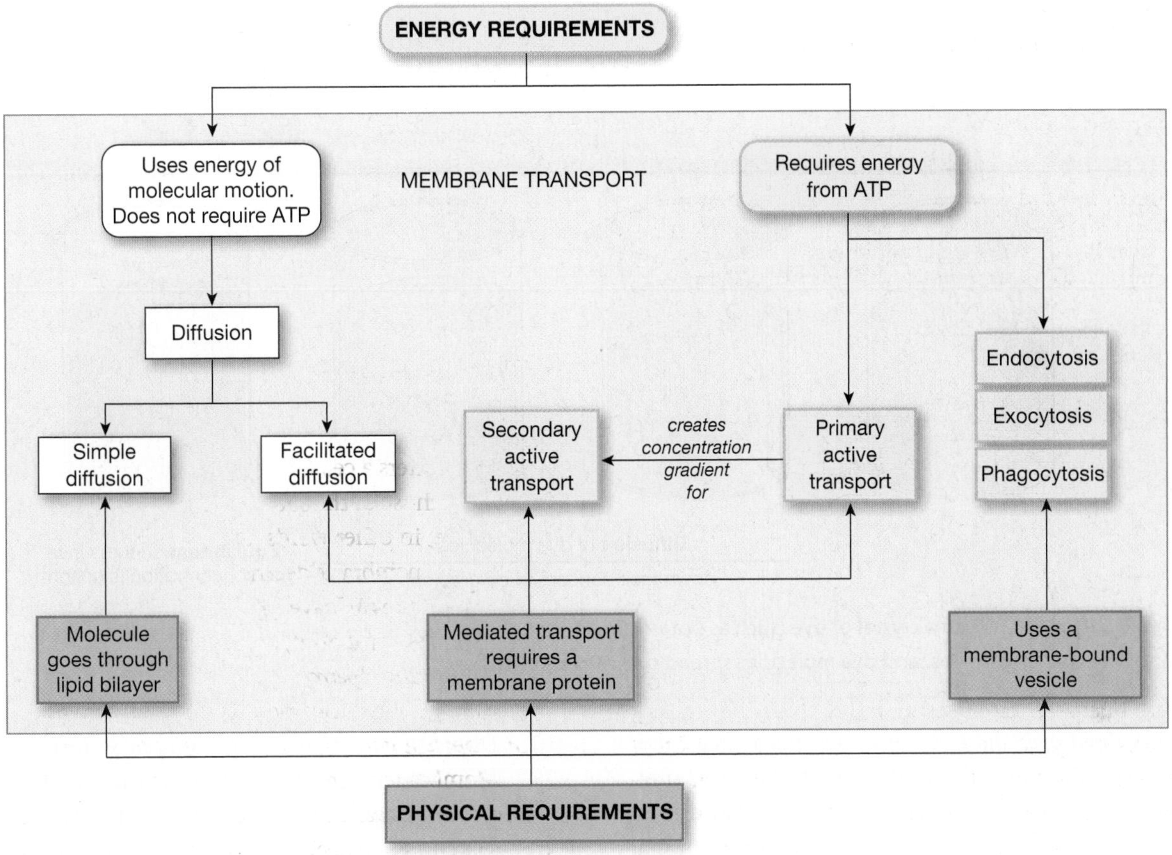

● **FIGURE 5-4** ***Map of membrane transport.*** Movement of substances across cell membranes can be classified either by the energy requirements of transport (top part of map) or according to whether transport uses diffusion, a membrane protein, or a vesicle (bottom part of map).

in solution constantly move from one place to another, bouncing off other molecules or off the sides of any container holding them. When molecules start out concentrated in one area of an enclosed space, their motion causes them to spread out gradually until they are evenly distributed throughout the available space. This process is known as diffusion.

Diffusion [*diffundere,* to pour out] may be defined as the movement of molecules from an area of higher concentration of the molecules to an area of lower concentration of the molecules.* If you leave a bottle of cologne open and later notice its fragrance across the room, it is because the aromatic molecules in the cologne have diffused from where they are more concentrated (in the bottle) to where they are less concentrated (across the room).

Diffusion has the following seven properties:

1. *Diffusion is a passive process.* By *passive,* we mean that diffusion does not require the input of energy from some outside source. Diffusion uses only the kinetic energy possessed by all molecules.

*Some texts use the term *diffusion* to mean any random movement of molecules and call molecular movement along a concentration gradient *net diffusion.* To simplify matters, we will use the term *diffusion* to mean movement down a concentration gradient.

2. *Molecules move from an area of higher concentration to an area of lower concentration.* A difference in the concentration of a substance between two places is called a concentration gradient [p. 95], also known as a **chemical gradient**. We say that molecules diffuse *down the gradient,* from higher concentration to lower concentration (Fig. 5-5 ●). The rate of diffusion depends on the magnitude of the concentration gradient. The larger the concentration difference, the faster diffusion takes place. For example, when you open a bottle of cologne, the rate of diffusion is most rapid as the molecules first escape from the bottle into the air. Later, when the cologne has spread evenly throughout the room, the rate of diffusion has dropped to zero because there is no longer a concentration gradient.
3. *Net movement of molecules occurs until the concentration is equal everywhere.* Once molecules of a given substance have distributed themselves evenly, the system reaches equilibrium and diffusion stops. Individual molecules are still moving at equilibrium, but for each molecule that exits an area, another one enters. The *dynamic equilibrium* state in diffusion means that the concentration has equalized throughout the system but molecules continue to move.

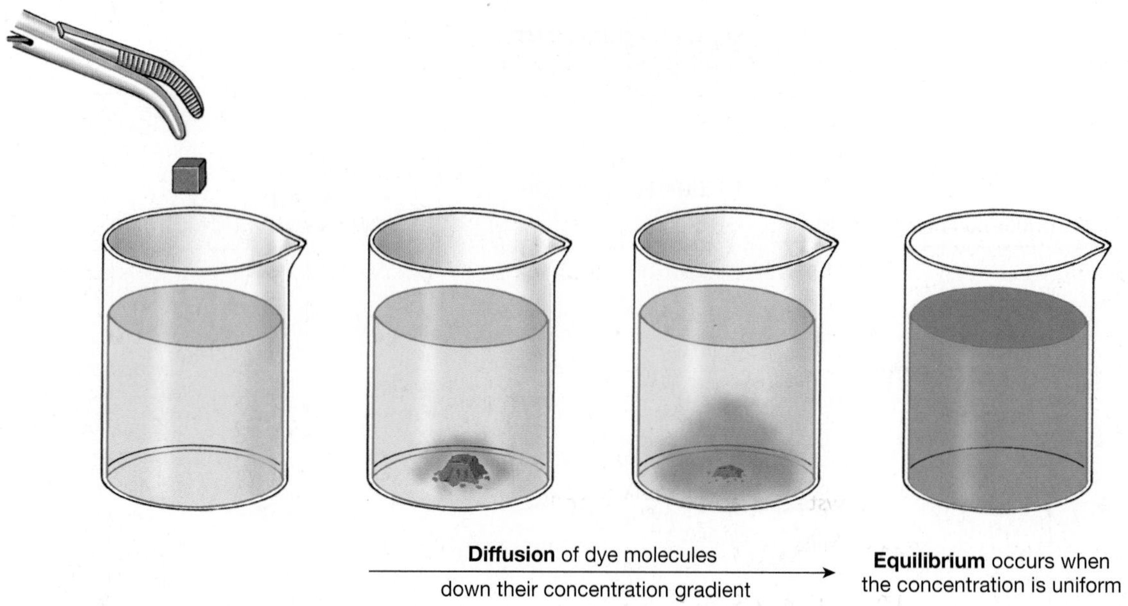

Diffusion of dye molecules
down their concentration gradient
Equilibrium occurs when
the concentration is uniform

● **FIGURE 5-5** ***Diffusion.*** When a crystal of dye (such as potassium permanganate) is placed in water, the crystal dissolves, and dye molecules spread outward by diffusion.

4. *Diffusion is rapid over short distances but much slower over long distances.* Albert Einstein studied the diffusion of molecules in solution and found that the time required for a molecule to diffuse from point A to point B is proportional to the square of the distance from A to B. In other words, if the distance doubles from 1 to 2, the time needed for diffusion increases from 1^2 to 2^2.

   What does the slow rate of diffusion over long distances mean for biological systems? In humans, nutrients take five seconds to diffuse from the blood to a cell that is 100 μm from the nearest capillary. At that rate, it would take years for nutrients to diffuse from the small intestine to cells in the big toe, and the cells would starve to death. To overcome the limitations of diffusion over distance, organisms have developed various transport mechanisms that speed up the movement of molecules. Most multicellular organisms have some form of circulatory system to bring oxygen and nutrients rapidly from the point at which they enter the body to the cells.
5. *Diffusion is directly related to temperature.* At higher temperatures, molecules move faster. Because diffusion results from molecular movement, the rate of diffusion increases as temperature increases. Generally, changes in temperature do not significantly affect diffusion rates in humans because we maintain a relatively constant body temperature.
6. *Diffusion rate is inversely related to molecular size.* Einstein showed that friction between the surface of a particle and the medium through which it diffuses is a source of resistance to movement. He calculated that diffusion is inversely proportional to the radius of the molecule: the larger the molecule, the slower its diffusion through a given medium.
7. *Diffusion can take place in an open system or across a partition that separates two systems.* Diffusion of cologne within a room is an example of diffusion taking place in an open system. There are no barriers to molecular movement, and the molecules spread out to fill the entire system. Diffusion can also take place between two systems, such as the intracellular and extracellular compartments, but only if the partition dividing the two compartments allows the diffusing molecules to cross.

For example, if you close the top of an open bottle of cologne, the molecules cannot diffuse out into the room because neither the bottle nor the cap is permeable to the cologne. However, if you replace the metal cap with a plastic bag that has tiny holes in it, you will begin to smell the cologne in the room because the bag is permeable to the molecules. Similarly, if a cell membrane is permeable to a molecule, that molecule can enter or leave the cell by diffusion. If the membrane is not permeable to that particular molecule, the molecule cannot cross. Table 5-1 ● summarizes these points.

An important point to note: ions do not move by diffusion, even though you will read and hear about ions *diffusing across membranes*. Diffusion is random molecular motion down a *concentration* gradient. Ion movement is influenced by *electrical* gradients because of the attraction of opposite charges and repulsion of like charges. For this reason, ions move in response to combined electrical and concentration gradients, or *electrochemical gradients*. This electrochemical movement is a more complex process than diffusion resulting solely from a concentration gradient, and the two processes should not be confused. We discuss ions and electrochemical gradients in more detail at the end of this chapter.

TABLE 5-1 Rules for Diffusion of Uncharged Molecules

General Properties of Diffusion

1. Diffusion uses the kinetic energy of molecular movement and does not require an outside energy source.
2. Molecules diffuse from an area of higher concentration to an area of lower concentration.
3. Diffusion continues until concentrations come to equilibrium. Molecular movement continues, however, after equilibrium has been reached.
4. Diffusion is faster
—along higher concentration gradients.
—over shorter distances.
—at higher temperatures.
—for smaller molecules.
5. Diffusion can take place in an open system or across a partition that separates two systems.

Simple Diffusion Across a Membrane

6. The rate of diffusion through a membrane is faster if
—the membrane's surface area is larger.
—the membrane is thinner.
—the concentration gradient is larger.
—the membrane is more permeable to the molecule.
7. Membrane permeability to a molecule depends on
—the molecule's lipid solubility.
—the molecule's size.
—the lipid composition of the membrane.

In summary, diffusion is the passive movement of uncharged molecules down their concentration gradient due to random molecular movement. Diffusion is slower over long distances and slower for large molecules. When the concentration of the diffusing molecules is the same throughout a system, the system has come to chemical equilibrium, although the random movement of molecules continues.

CONCEPT CHECK

6. If the distance over which a molecule must diffuse triples from 1 to 3, diffusion takes how many times as long? Answers: p. 176

Lipophilic Molecules Can Diffuse Through the Phospholipid Bilayer

Diffusion across membranes is a little more complicated than diffusion in an open system. Water is the primary solvent of the body, and many vital nutrients, ions, and other molecules dissolve in water because of its polar nature. However, substances that are hydrophilic and dissolve in water are lipo*phobic* as a rule: they do not readily dissolve in lipids. For this reason, the hydrophobic lipid core of the cell membrane acts as a barrier that prevents hydrophilic molecules from crossing.

Substances that can pass through the lipid center of a membrane move by diffusion. Diffusion directly across the phospholipid bilayer of a membrane is called **simple diffusion** and has the following properties in addition to the properties of diffusion listed earlier.

1. *The rate of diffusion depends on the ability of the diffusing molecule to dissolve in the lipid layer of the membrane.* Another way to say this is that the diffusion rate depends on how permeable the membrane is to the diffusing molecules. Most molecules in solution can mingle with the polar phosphate-glycerol heads of the bilayer [p. 56], but only nonpolar molecules that are lipid-soluble (lipophilic) can dissolve in the central lipid core of the membrane. As a rule, only lipids, steroids, and small lipophilic molecules can move across membranes by simple diffusion.

One important exception to this statement concerns water. Water, although a polar molecule, may diffuse slowly across some phospholipid membranes. For years it was thought that the polar nature of the water molecule prevented it from moving through the lipid center of the bilayer, but experiments done with artificial membranes have shown that the small size of the water molecule allows it to slip between the lipid tails in some membranes.

How readily water passes through the membrane depends on the composition of the phospholipid bilayer. Membranes with high cholesterol content are less permeable to water than those with low cholesterol content,

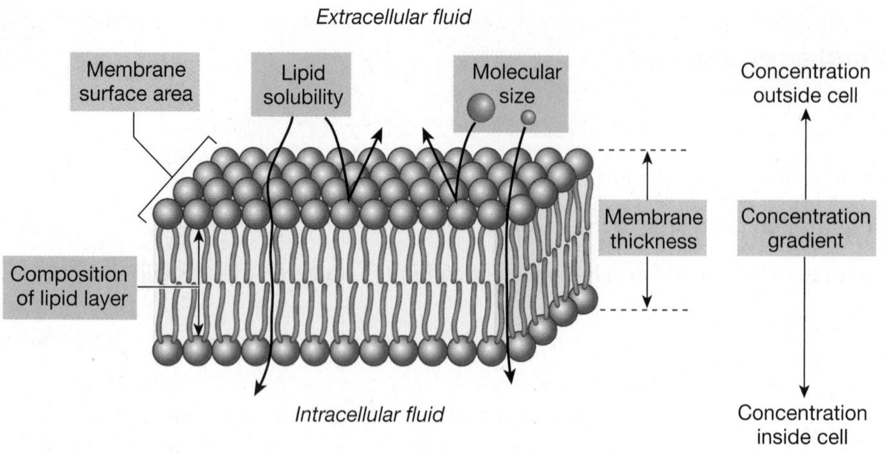

Factors affecting rate of diffusion through a cell membrane:

- Lipid solubility
- Molecular size
- Cell membrane thickness
- Concentration gradient
- Membrane surface area
- Composition of lipid layer

Fick's Law of Diffusion says:

$$\textbf{Rate of diffusion} \propto \frac{\text{surface area} \bullet \text{concentration gradient} \bullet \text{membrane permeability}}{\text{membrane thickness}}$$

Membrane permeability

$$\text{Membrane permeability} \propto \frac{\text{lipid solubility}}{\text{molecular size}}$$

Changing the composition of the lipid layer can increase or decrease membrane permeability.

● **FIGURE 5-6** ***Fick's law of diffusion.*** This law mathematically relates factors that influence the rate of simple diffusion across a membrane.

presumably because the lipid-soluble cholesterol molecules fill spaces between the fatty acid tails of the lipid bilayer and thus exclude water. For example, the cell membranes of some sections of the kidney are essentially impermeable to water unless the cells insert special water channel proteins into the phospholipid bilayer. Most water movement across membranes takes place through protein channels.

2. *The rate of diffusion across a membrane is directly proportional to the surface area of the membrane.* In other words, the larger the membrane's surface area, the more molecules can diffuse across per unit time. This fact may seem obvious, but it has important implications in physiology. One striking example of how a change in surface area affects diffusion is the lung disease emphysema. As lung tissue breaks down and is destroyed, the surface area available for diffusion of oxygen decreases. Consequently, less oxygen can move into the body. In severe cases, the oxygen that reaches the cells is not enough to sustain any muscular activity and the patient is confined to bed.
3. *The rate of diffusion across a membrane is inversely proportional to the thickness of the membrane.* The thicker the membrane, the slower the rate at which diffusion takes place. For most biological membranes, thickness is essentially constant. However, diffusion distance comes into play in certain lung conditions in which the exchange epithelium of the lung is thickened with scar tissue. This slows diffusion so that the oxygen entering the body is not adequate to meet metabolic needs.

The rules for simple diffusion across membranes are summarized in Table 5-1. They can be combined mathematically into an equation known as **Fick's law of diffusion**, a relationship that involves the three factors just mentioned for membrane diffusion plus the factor of concentration gradient from our earlier general discussion of diffusion. In an abbreviated form, Fick's law says that:

$$\text{rate of diffusion} \propto \frac{\text{surface area} \times \text{concentration gradient} \times \text{membrane permeability}}{\text{membrane thickness}}$$

Figure 5-6 ● illustrates the principles of Fick's law.

Membrane permeability is the most complex of the four terms in Fick's law because several factors influence it: (1) the size of the diffusing molecule, (2) the lipid-solubility of the molecule, and (3) the composition of the lipid bilayer across which it is diffusing. As molecular size increases, membrane permeability decreases. As lipid solubility of the diffusing molecule increases, membrane permeability to the molecule increases. Alterations in lipid composition of the membrane change how easily diffusing molecules can slip between the individual phospholipids. For example, cholesterol molecules in membranes pack themselves into the spaces between the fatty acids tails and retard passage of molecules through those spaces [Fig. 3-4, p. 58], making the membrane less permeable.

In most physiological situations, membrane thickness is a constant. In that case, we can remove membrane thickness from our Fick's law equation and rearrange the equation to read:

$$\frac{\text{diffusion rate}}{\text{surface area}} = \text{concentration gradient} \times \text{membrane permeability}$$

This equation now describes the flux of a molecule across the membrane, because **flux** is defined as the diffusion rate per unit surface area of membrane:

$$\text{flux} = \text{concentration gradient} \times \text{membrane permeability}$$

In other words, the flux of a molecule across a membrane depends on the concentration gradient and the membrane's permeability to the molecule.

One point to remember is that the principles of diffusion apply to all biological membranes, not just to the cell membrane. Diffusion of materials in and out of organelles follows the same rules.

CONCEPT CHECK

7. Where does the energy for diffusion come from?
8. Which is more likely to cross a cell membrane by simple diffusion: a fatty acid molecule or a glucose molecule?
9. What happens to the rate of diffusion in each of the following cases?
   (a) membrane thickness increases
   (b) concentration gradient increases
   (c) surface area decreases
10. Two compartments are separated by a membrane that is permeable only to water and to yellow dye molecules. Compartment A is filled with an aqueous solution of yellow dye, and compartment B is filled with an aqueous solution of an equal concentration of blue dye. If the system is left undisturbed for a long time, what color will compartment A be: yellow, blue, or green? (Remember, yellow plus blue makes green.) What color will compartment B be?
11. What keeps atmospheric oxygen from diffusing into our bodies across the skin? (*Hint:* What kind of epithelium is skin?)

Answers: p. 176

PROTEIN-MEDIATED TRANSPORT

In the body, simple diffusion across membranes is limited to lipophilic molecules. The majority of molecules in the body are either lipophobic or electrically charged and therefore cannot cross membranes by simple diffusion. Instead, the vast majority of solutes cross membranes with the help of membrane proteins, a process we call **mediated transport**.

If mediated transport is passive and moves molecules down their concentration gradient, and if net transport stops when concentrations are equal on both sides of the membrane, the process is known as **facilitated diffusion**. If protein-mediated transport requires energy from ATP or another outside source and moves a substance against its concentration gradient, the process is known as **active transport**.

Membrane Proteins Function as Structural Proteins, Enzymes, Receptors, and Transporters

Protein-mediated transport across a membrane is carried out by membrane-spanning proteins known as *transporters*. For physiologists, classifying membrane proteins by their function is more useful than classifying them by their structure. Our functional classification scheme recognizes four broad categories of membrane proteins: (1) structural proteins, (2) enzymes, (3) receptors, and (4) transporters. These groupings are not completely distinct, and as you will learn, some membrane proteins have more than one function, such as receptor-channels and receptor-enzymes. Figure 5-7 ● is a map comparing the structural and functional classifications of membrane proteins.

Structural Proteins The **structural proteins** have three major roles. The first is to connect the membrane to the cytoskeleton to maintain the shape of the cell [Fig. 3-6, p. 60]. The microvilli of transporting epithelia are one example of membrane shaping by the cytoskeleton [Fig. 3-14, p. 66]. The second role is to create cell junctions that hold tissues together, such as tight junctions and gap junctions [Fig. 3-21, p. 73]. Finally, the third role is to attach cells to the extracellular matrix by linking cytoskeleton fibers to extracellular collagen and other protein fibers [p. 80].

Enzymes **Membrane enzymes** catalyze chemical reactions that take place either on the cell's external surface or just inside the cell. For example, enzymes on the external surface of cells lining the small intestine are responsible for digesting peptides and carbohydrates. Enzymes attached to the intracellular surface of many cell membranes play an important role in transferring signals from the extracellular environment to the cytoplasm, as you will learn in Chapter 6.

Receptors **Membrane receptor proteins** are part of the body's chemical signaling system. The binding of a receptor with its ligand usually triggers another event at the membrane, such as activation of an enzyme (Fig. 5-8 ●). Membrane receptors play an important role in some forms of vesicular transport.

Transporters The fourth group of membrane proteins—**transporters**—moves molecules across membranes. We can further subdivide transport proteins into two categories: channels and carriers. **Channel proteins** create water-filled passageways that directly link the intracellular and extracellular compartments (Fig. 5-9 ●). **Carrier proteins** bind to the substrates that they carry but never form a direct connection between the intracellular fluid and extracellular fluid. As Figure 5-9 shows, carriers are open to one side of the membrane

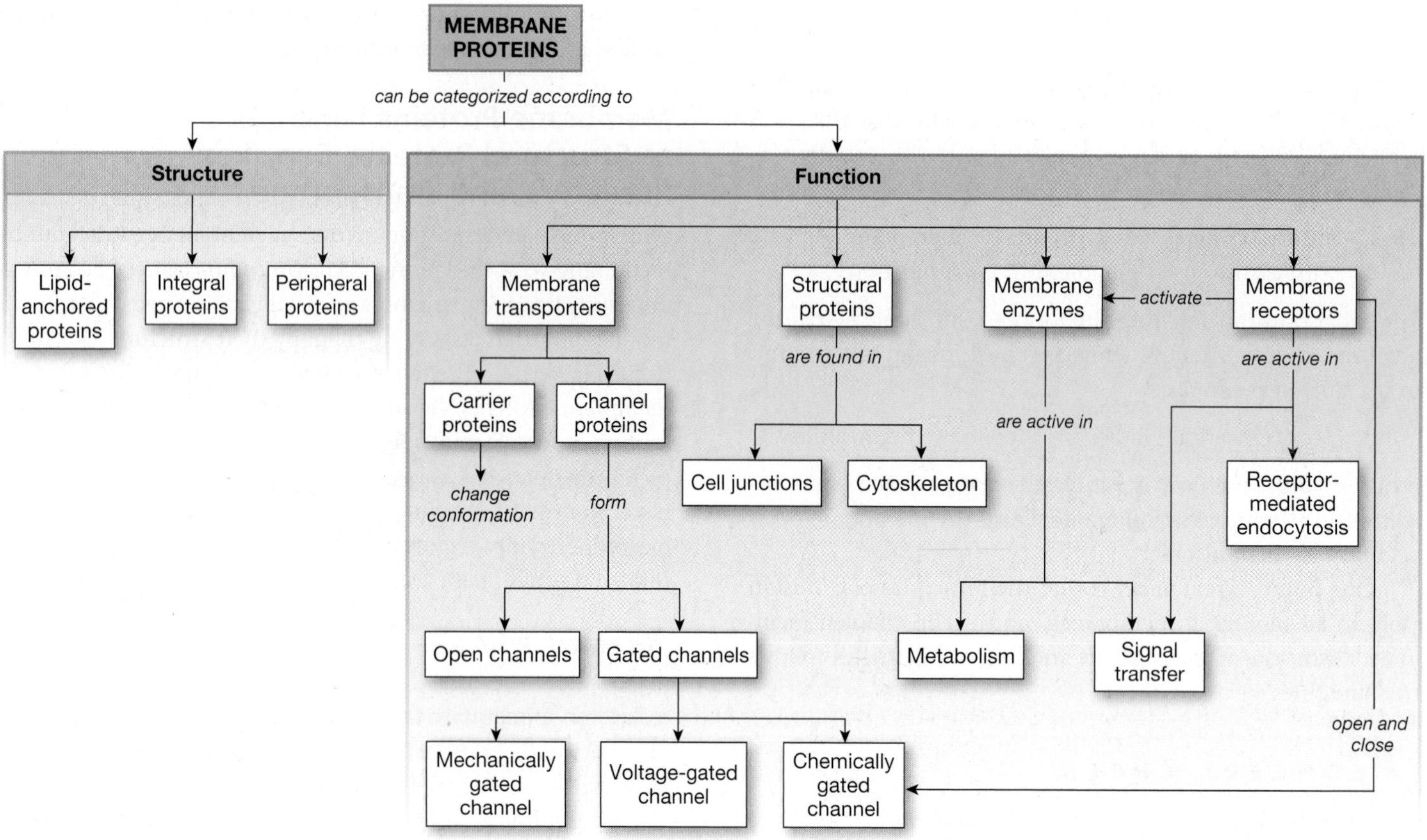

● **FIGURE 5-7** ***Map of membrane proteins.*** Functional categories of membrane proteins include transporters, structural proteins, enzymes, and receptors.

or the other, but not to both at once the way channel proteins are.

Why do cells need both channels and carriers? The answer lies in the different properties of the two transporters. Channel proteins allow more rapid transport across the membrane but generally are limited to moving small ions and water. Carriers, while slower, can move larger molecules than channels can.

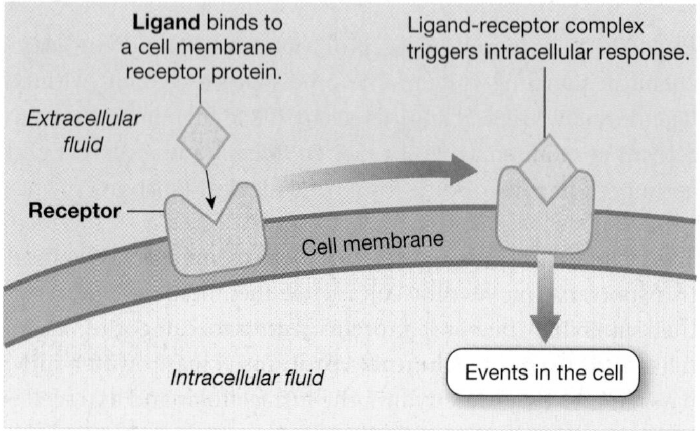

● **FIGURE 5-8** ***Membrane receptor proteins bind ligands to initiate a cellular response.***

EMERGING CONCEPTS

TRANSPORTER GENE FAMILIES

One outcome of the Human Genome project has been the recognition that many proteins are closely related to each other, both within and across species. As a result, scientists have discovered that most membrane transporters for organic solutes belong to one of two gene "super-families": the ATP-binding cassette (ABC) superfamily or the solute carrier (SLC) superfamily. The ABC family transporters use ATP's energy to transport small organic molecules across membranes. Interestingly, the CFTR chloride channel is also a member of the ABC family and is the only known ion channel in that superfamily. The 43 families of the SLC superfamily family include most facilitated diffusion carriers, such as the GLUTs, as well as the secondary active transporters shown in Table 5-3.

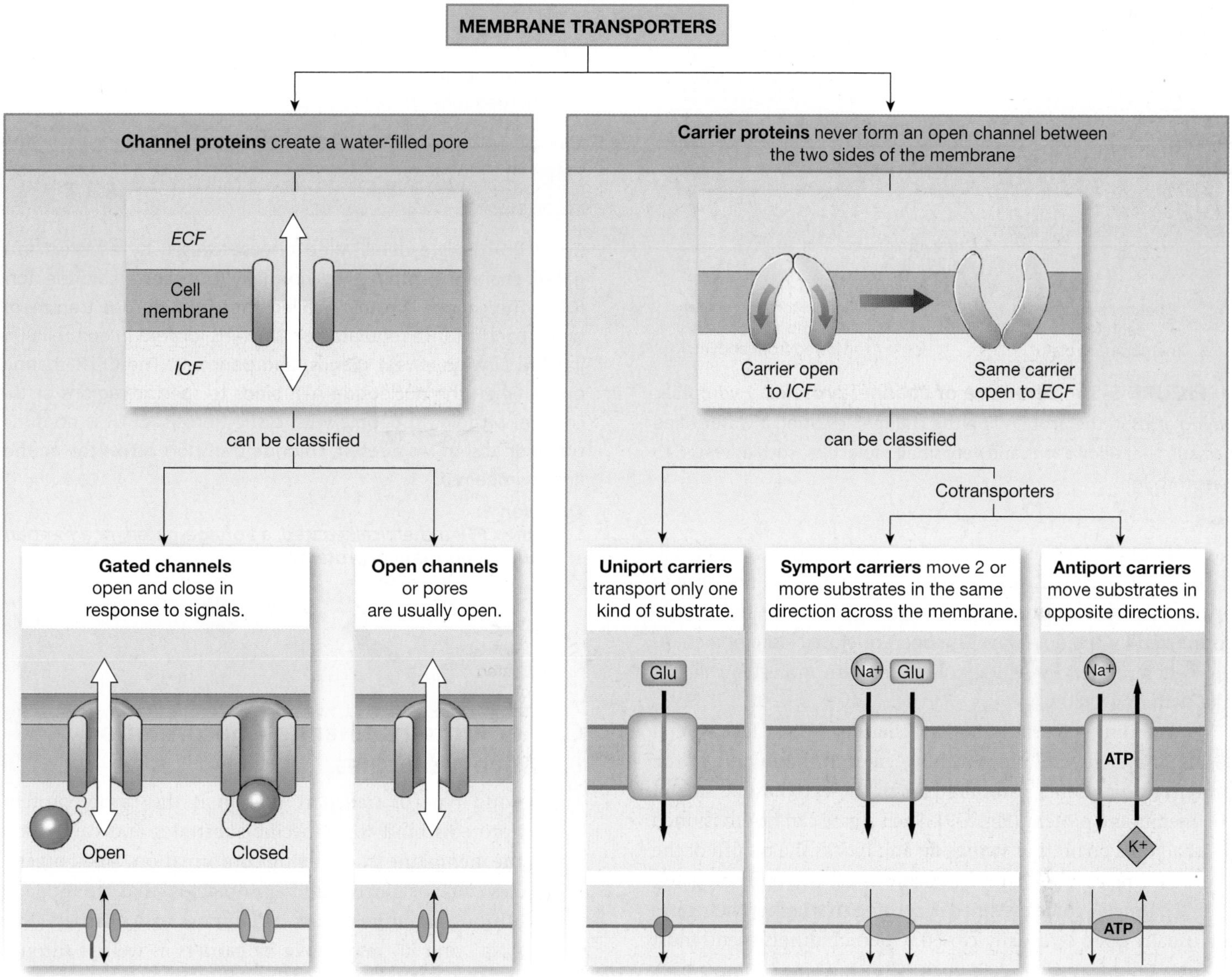

● **FIGURE 5-9** ***Summary of membrane transport proteins.*** Membrane transporters in this book are drawn in close-up views (top two rows) and distant views (bottom row). Primary active transport is indicated by *ATP* on the protein.

Channel Proteins Form Open, Water-Filled Passageways

Channel proteins are made of membrane-spanning protein subunits that create a cluster of cylinders with a tunnel or *pore* through the center. Nuclear pore complexes [p. 71] and gap junctions [Fig. 3-21c, p. 73] can be considered very large forms of channels. In this book we restrict use of the term "channel" to smaller channels whose centers are narrow, water-filled pores (Fig. 5-10 ●). Movement through these smaller channels is mostly restricted to water and ions. When water-filled ion channels are open, tens of millions of ions per second can whisk through them unimpeded.

Channel proteins are named according to the substance(s) they allow to pass. Most cells have **water channels** made from a protein called *aquaporin*. In addition, more than 100 types of **ion channels** have been identified. Ion channels may be specific for one ion or may allow ions of similar size and charge to pass. For example, there are Na^+ channels, K^+ channels, and nonspecific *monovalent* ("one charge") cation channels that transport Na^+, K^+, and lithium ions (Li^+). Other ion channels you will encounter frequently in this text are Ca^{2+} channels and Cl^- channels.

The selectivity of a channel is determined by the diameter of its central pore and by the electrical charge of the amino acids that line the channel. If the channel amino acids are positively charged, positive ions are repelled and negative ions can pass through the channel. On the other hand, a cation channel must have a negative charge that attracts cations but prevents the passage of Cl^- or other anions.

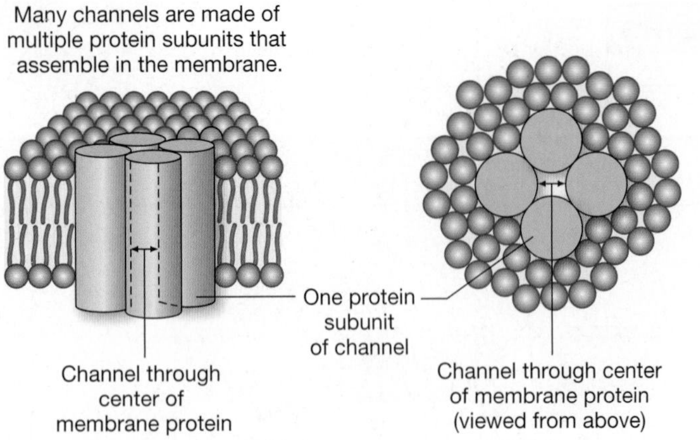
Many channels are made of multiple protein subunits that assemble in the membrane.
One protein subunit of channel
Channel through center of membrane protein
Channel through center of membrane protein (viewed from above)

● **FIGURE 5-10** ***Structure of channel proteins.*** Hydrophilic amino acids in the protein line the channel, creating a water-filled passage that allows ions and very small molecules, such as water, to pass through.

Channel proteins are like narrow doorways into the cell. If the door is closed, nothing can go through. If the door is open, there is a continuous passage between the two rooms connected by the doorway. The open or closed state of a channel is determined by regions of the protein molecule that act like swinging "gates."

According to current models, channel "gates" take several forms. Some channel proteins have gates in the middle of the protein's pore. Other gates are part of the cytoplasmic side of the membrane protein (Fig. 5-9). Such a gate can be envisioned as a ball on a chain that swings up and blocks the mouth of the channel. One type of channel in neurons has two different gates.

Channels can be classified according to whether their gates are usually open or usually closed. **Open channels** spend most of their time with their gate open, allowing ions to move back and forth across the membrane without regulation. These gates may occasionally flicker closed, but for the most part these channels behave as if they have no gates. Open channels are sometimes called either *leak channels* or pores, as in *water pores*.

Gated channels spend most of their time in a closed state, which allows these channels to regulate the movement of ions through them. When a gated channel opens, ions move through the channel just as they move through open channels. When a gated channel is closed, which it may be much of the time, it allows no ion movement between the intracellular and extracellular fluid.

What controls the opening and closing of gated channels? For **chemically gated channels** the gating is controlled by intracellular messenger molecules or extracellular ligands that bind to the channel protein. **Voltage-gated channels** open and close when the electrical state of the cell changes. Finally, **mechanically gated channels** respond to physical forces, such as increased temperature or pressure that puts tension on the membrane and pops the channel gate open. You will encounter many variations of these channel types as you study physiology.

CONCEPT CHECK

12. Positively charged ions are called ________, and negatively charged ions are called ________.

Answers: p. 176

RUNNING PROBLEM

Cystic fibrosis is a debilitating disease caused by a defect in a gated channel protein that normally transports chloride ions (Cl^-). The channel protein—called the cystic fibrosis transmembrane conductance regulator, or CFTR—is located in epithelia lining the airways, sweat glands, and pancreas. The CFTR channel opens when the nucleotide ATP binds to specific regions of the channel protein. In people with cystic fibrosis, CFTR is nonfunctional or absent. As a result, chloride transport across the epithelium is impaired.

Question 1:

Is the CFTR a chemically gated, a voltage-gated, or a mechanically gated channel protein?

133 144 156 161 165 171

Carrier Proteins Change Conformation to Move Molecules

The second type of transport protein is the carrier protein. Carrier proteins bind with specific substrates and carry them across the membrane by changing conformation. Small organic molecules (such as glucose and amino acids) that are too large to pass through channels cross membranes using carriers. Ions such as Na^+ and K^+ may move by carriers as well as through channels. Carrier proteins move solutes and ions into and out of cells as well as into and out of intracellular organelles, such as the mitochondria.

Some carrier proteins move only one kind of molecule and are known as **uniport carriers** (Fig. 5-9). However, it is common to find carriers that move two or even three kinds of molecules. A carrier that moves more than one kind of molecule at one time is called a **cotransporter**. If the molecules being transported are moving in the same direction, whether into or out of the cell, the carrier proteins are **symport carriers** [*sym-*, together + *portare,* to carry]. If the molecules are being carried in opposite directions, the carrier proteins are **antiport carriers** [*anti,* opposite + *portare,* to carry]. Symport and antiport carriers are shown in Figure 5-9.

Carriers are large, complex proteins with multiple subunits. The conformation change required of a carrier protein makes this mode of transmembrane transport much slower than movement through channel proteins. A carrier protein can only move 1000 to 1,000,000 molecules per second, in contrast to tens of millions of ions per second that move through a channel protein.

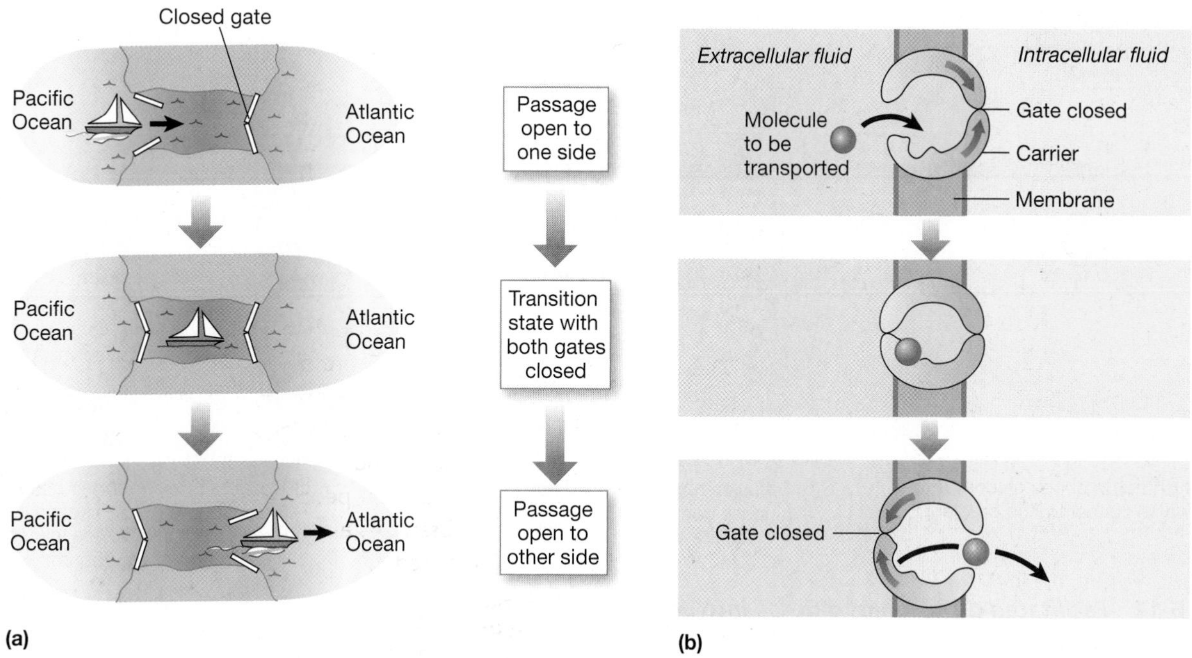

● **FIGURE 5-11** ***Facilitated diffusion by means of a carrier protein.*** Carrier proteins, like the canal illustrated, never form a continuous passageway between the extracellular and intracellular fluids.

Carrier proteins differ from channel proteins in another way: carriers never create a continuous passage between the inside and outside of the cell. If channels are like doorways, then carriers are like revolving doors that allow movement between inside and outside without ever creating an open hole. Carrier proteins can transport molecules across a membrane in both directions, like a revolving door at a hotel, or they can restrict their transport to one direction, like the turnstile at an amusement park that allows you out of the park but not back in.

One side of the carrier protein always creates a barrier that prevents free exchange across the membrane. In this respect, carrier proteins function like the Panama Canal (Fig. 5-11a ●). Picture the canal with only two gates, one on the Atlantic side and one on the Pacific side. Only one gate at a time is open. When the Atlantic gate is closed, the canal opens into the Pacific. A ship enters the canal from the Pacific, and the gate closes behind it. Now the canal is isolated from both oceans with the ship trapped in the middle. Then the Atlantic gate opens, making the canal continuous with the Atlantic Ocean. The ship sails out of the gate and off into the Atlantic, having crossed the barrier of the land without the canal ever forming a continuous connection between the two oceans.

Movement across the membrane through a carrier protein is similar (Fig. 5-11b). The molecule to be transported binds to the carrier on one side of the membrane (the extracellular side in our example). This binding changes the conformation of the carrier so that the opening closes. After a brief transition in which both sides are closed, the opposite side of the carrier opens to the other side of the membrane. The carrier then releases the molecule being transported into the opposite compartment, having brought it through the membrane without creating a continuous connection between the extracellular and intracellular compartments.

CONCEPT CHECK

13. Name four functions of membrane proteins.
14. Which kinds of particles pass through open channels?
15. Name two ways channels differ from carriers.
16. If a channel is lined with amino acids that have a net positive charge, which of the following ions is/are likely to move freely through the channel? Na^+, Cl^-, K^+, Ca^{2+}
17. Why doesn't glucose cross the cell membrane through open channels?

Answers: p. 176

Facilitated Diffusion Uses Carrier Proteins

As noted earlier, facilitated diffusion is protein-mediated transport in which no outside source of energy is needed to move molecules across the cell membrane. Active transport is protein-mediated transport that requires an outside energy source. Let us look first at facilitated diffusion.

Some polar molecules appear to move into and out of cells by diffusion, even though we know from their chemical properties that they are unable to pass easily through the lipid core of the cell membrane. The solution to this seeming contradiction is that these polar molecules cross the cell membrane by facilitated diffusion, with the aid of specific carriers. Sugars and amino acids are examples of molecules that enter or leave cells using facilitated diffusion. For example, the family of carrier

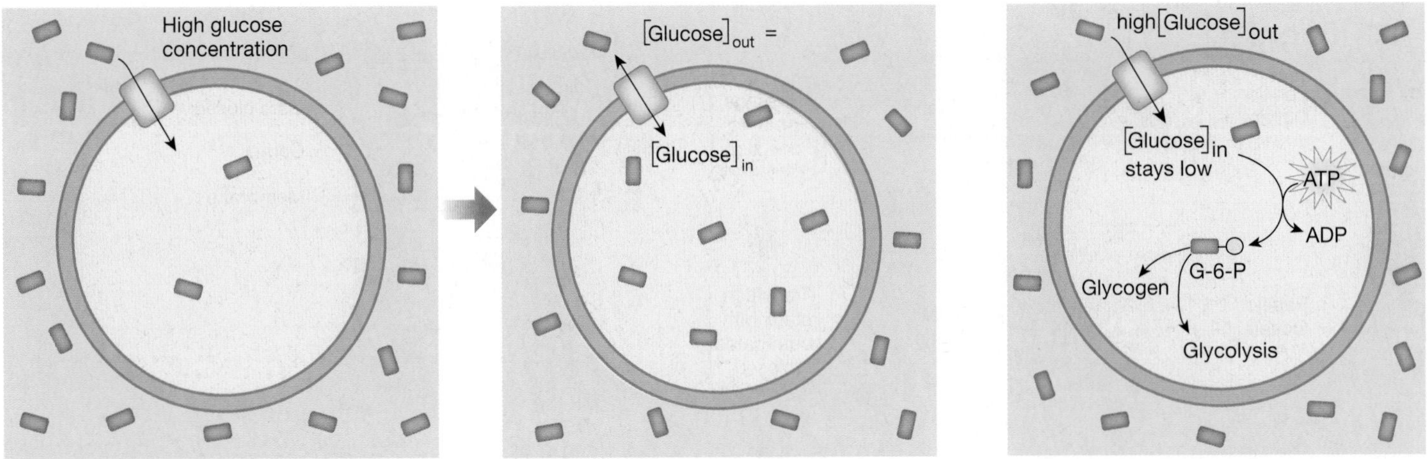

(a) Facilitated diffusion brings glucose into the cell down its concentration gradient.

(b) Diffusion reaches equilibrium when the glucose concentrations inside and outside the cell are equal.

(c) Conversion of imported glucose into glucose-6-phosphate (G-6-P) keeps intracellular glucose concentrations low so that diffusion never reaches equilibrium.

● **FIGURE 5-12** ***Facilitated diffusion of glucose into cells.*** This figure shows glucose transport using a GLUT carrier protein.

proteins known as **GLUT transporters** move glucose and related hexose sugars across membranes.

Facilitated diffusion has the same properties as simple diffusion (Table 5-1). The transported molecules move down their concentration gradient, the process requires no input of energy, and net movement stops at equilibrium, when the concentration inside the cell equals the concentration outside the cell (Fig. 5-12 ●):

$$[\text{glucose}]_{ECF} = [\text{glucose}]_{ICF}$$

Note that in this book the presence of brackets around a solute's name indicates concentration.

Cells in which facilitated diffusion takes place can avoid reaching equilibrium by keeping the concentration of substrate in the cell low. With glucose, for example, this is accomplished by phosphorylation (Fig. 5-12c). As soon as a glucose molecule enters the cell, it is phosphorylated to glucose 6-phosphate, the first step of glycolysis [p. 107]. Addition of the phosphate group prevents build-up of glucose inside the cell and also prevents glucose from leaving the cell.

CONCEPT CHECK

18. Liver cells are able to convert glycogen to glucose, thereby making the intracellular glucose concentration higher than the extracellular glucose concentration. What do you think happens to facilitated diffusion of glucose when this occurs?

Answers: p. 176

Active Transport Moves Substances Against Their Concentration Gradients

Active transport is a process that moves molecules *against* their concentration gradient—that is, from areas of lower concentration to areas of higher concentration. Rather than creating an equilibrium state, where the concentration of the molecule is equal throughout the system, active transport creates a state of *dis*equilibrium by making concentration differences more pronounced. Moving molecules against their concentration gradient requires the input of outside energy, just as pushing a ball up a hill requires energy [Fig. 4-2, p. 96]. The energy for active transport comes either directly or indirectly from the high-energy phosphate bond of ATP.

Active transport can be divided into two types. In **primary (direct) active transport**, the energy to push molecules against their concentration gradient comes directly from the high-energy phosphate bond of ATP. **Secondary (indirect) active transport** uses potential energy [p. 96] stored in the concentration gradient of one molecule to push other molecules against their concentration gradient. All secondary active transport ultimately depends on primary active transport because the concentration gradients that drive secondary transport are created using energy from ATP.

The mechanism for both types of active transport appears to be similar to that for facilitated diffusion. A substrate to be transported binds to a membrane carrier and the carrier then changes conformation, releasing the substrate into the opposite compartment. Active transport differs from facilitated diffusion because the conformation change in the carrier protein requires energy input.

Primary Active Transport Because primary active transport uses ATP as its energy source, many primary active transporters are known as **ATPases**. You may recall from Chapter 4 that the suffix *-ase* signifies an enzyme, and the stem (ATP) is the substrate upon which the enzyme is acting [p. 104]. These enzymes hydrolyze ATP to ADP and inorganic phosphate (P_i), releasing usable energy in the process. Most of the ATPases

TABLE 5-2 Primary Active Transporters

NAMES	TYPE OF TRANSPORT
Na^+-K^+-ATPase or sodium-potassium pump	Antiport
Ca^{2+}-ATPase	Uniport
H^+-ATPase or proton pump	Uniport
H^+-K^+-ATPase	Antiport

you will encounter in your study of physiology are listed in Table 5-2 ●. ATPases are sometimes called *pumps*, as in the sodium-potassium pump, Na^+-K^+-ATPase, mentioned earlier in this chapter.

The sodium-potassium pump is probably the single most important transport protein in animal cells because it maintains the concentration gradients of Na^+ and K^+ across the cell membrane (Fig. 5-13 ●). The transporter is arranged in the cell membrane so that it pumps 3 Na^+ out of the cell and 2 K^+ into the cell for each ATP consumed. In some cells, the energy needed to move these ions uses 30% of all the ATP produced by the cell. The current model of how the Na^+-K^+-ATPase works is illustrated in Figure 5-14 ●.

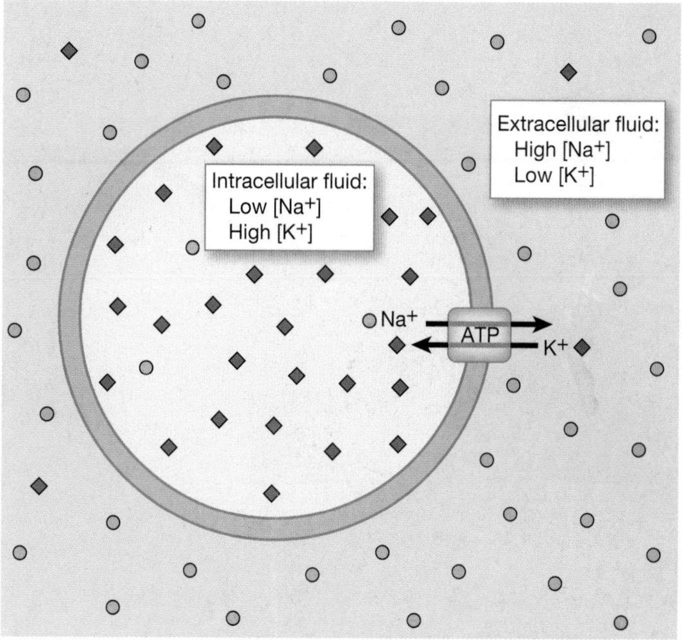

The Na^+-K^+-ATPase uses energy from ATP to pump Na^+ out of the cell and K^+ into the cell.

● **FIGURE 5-13** ***The sodium-potassium pump, Na^+-K^+-ATPase.*** In this book, carrier proteins that hydrolyze ATP have the letters *ATP* written on the membrane protein.

Secondary Active Transport The sodium concentration gradient, with Na^+ concentration high in the extracellular fluid and low inside the cell, is a source of potential energy that the cell can harness for other functions. For example, nerve cells use the sodium gradient to transmit electrical signals, and epithelial cells use it to drive the uptake of nutrients, ions, and water. Membrane transporters that use potential energy stored in concentration gradients to move molecules are called *secondary active transporters*.

Secondary active transport uses the kinetic energy of one molecule moving down its concentration gradient to push other molecules against their concentration gradient. The cotransported molecules may go in the same direction across the membrane (symport) or in opposite directions (antiport). The most common secondary active transport systems are driven by the sodium concentration gradient.

As a Na^+ moves into the cell, it either brings one or more molecules with it or trades places with molecules exiting the cell. The major Na^+-dependent transporters are listed in Table 5-3 ●. Notice that the cotransported substances may be either other ions or uncharged molecules, such as glucose.

The mechanism of the **Na^+-glucose secondary active transporter** (SGLT) is illustrated in Figure 5-15 ●. Both Na^+ and glucose bind to the SGLT protein on the extracellular fluid side. Sodium binds first and causes a conformational change in the protein that creates a high-affinity binding site for glucose. When glucose binds to SGLT, the protein changes conformation again and opens its channel to the intracellular fluid side. Sodium is released as it moves down its concentration gradient. The loss of Na^+ from the protein changes the binding site for glucose back to a low-affinity site, so glucose is released and follows Na^+ into the cytoplasm. The net result is the entry of glucose into the cell against its concentration gradient, coupled to the movement of Na^+ into the cell down its concentration gradient. The SGLT transporter can move glucose only into cells because glucose must follow the Na^+ gradient.

In contrast, GLUT transporters are reversible and can move glucose into or out of cells depending on the concentration gradient. For example, when blood glucose levels are high, GLUT transporters on liver cells bring glucose into those cells. During times of fasting, when blood glucose levels fall, liver cells convert their glycogen stores to glucose. When the glucose concentration inside the liver cells builds up and exceeds the glucose concentration in the plasma, glucose leaves the cells on the reversible GLUT transporters. GLUT transporters are found on all cells of the body.

Then why does the body need the SGLT Na^+-glucose symporter? The simple answer is that both SGLT and GLUT are needed to move glucose from one side of an epithelium to the other. Consequently, SGLT transporters are found on certain epithelial cells, such as intestinal and kidney cells, that bring glucose into the body from the external environment. We discuss the process of transepithelial transport of glucose later in this chapter.

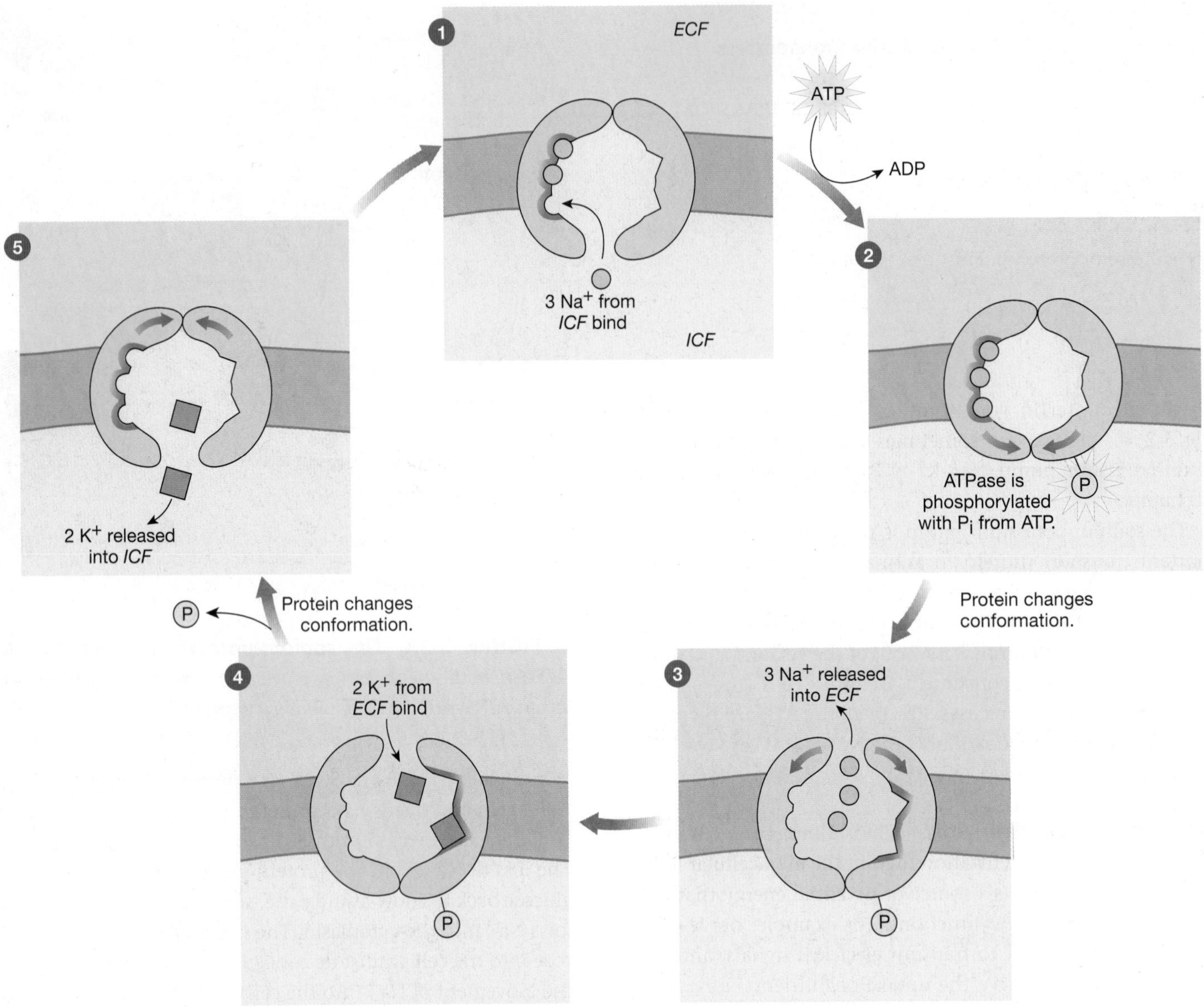

● **FIGURE 5-14** ***Mechanism of the*** Na^+***-***K^+***-ATPase.*** This figure presents one model of how the Na^+-K^+-ATPase uses energy and inorganic phosphate (P_i) from ATP to move ions across a membrane.

The use of energy to drive active transport is summarized in Figure 5-16 ●. The organism imports energy from the environment in the chemical bonds of nutrients such as glucose. This energy is transferred to the high-energy bonds of ATP through oxidative phosphorylation in the mitochondria [p. 112]. The energy in ATP is then used either to fuel primary active transport or to create ion concentration gradients for secondary active transport. For example, the Na^+-K^+-ATPase pushes sodium out of the cell and potassium into it. As this happens, the energy from ATP is transformed into potential energy stored in the ion concentration gradients. This potential energy can be harnessed by various sodium-dependent cotransporters, such as the *Na^+-K^+-$2Cl^-$ transporter* (NKCC). The kinetic energy of Na^+ moving into the cell down its concentration gradient is linked to the uphill movement of K^+ and Cl^- into the cell. As you study the different systems of the body, you will find these secondary active transporters taking part in many physiological processes.

CONCEPT CHECK

19. Name two ways active transport by the Na^+-K^+-ATPase (Fig. 5-14) differs from secondary transport by the SGLT (Fig. 5-15). Answers: p. 176

Carrier-Mediated Transport Exhibits Specificity, Competition, and Saturation

Both passive and active forms of carrier-mediated transport demonstrate three properties: specificity, competition, and saturation. These concepts were introduced in the discussion on

TABLE 5-3 Examples of Secondary Active Transporters

SYMPORT CARRIERS	ANTIPORT CARRIERS
Sodium-dependent transporters	
Na^+-K^+-2 Cl^- (NKCC)	Na^+-H^+ (NHE)
Na^+-glucose (SGLT)	Na^+-Ca^{2+}
Na^+-amino acids (several types)	
Na^+-bile salts (small intestine)	
Na^+-choline uptake (nerve cells)	
Na^+-neurotransmitter uptake (nerve cells)	
Nonsodium-dependent transporters	
	HCO_3^--Cl^-

protein interactions [p. 40] and reflect the binding of a substrate to the protein.

Specificity As noted in Chapter 2, specificity refers to the ability of a carrier to move only one molecule or only a group of closely related molecules. One example of specificity is found in the GLUT family of transporters, which move 6-carbon sugars (*hexoses*), such as glucose, mannose, galactose, and fructose [p. 28], across cell membranes. GLUT transporters have binding sites that recognize and transport hexoses, but they will not transport the disaccharide maltose or any form of glucose that is not normally found in nature. For this reason we can say that GLUT transporters are specific for naturally occurring 6-carbon monosaccharides.

For many years, scientists assumed that there must be different isoforms of the glucose facilitated diffusion carrier because they had observed that glucose transport was regulated by hormones in some cells but not in others. However, it was not until the 1980s that the first glucose transporter was isolated. To date, about 12 GLUT genes have been identified. The important GLUT proteins you will encounter in this book include GLUT1, found in most cells of the body; GLUT2, found in liver and kidney and intestinal epithelium; GLUT3, found in neurons; GLUT4, the insulin-regulated transporter of skeletal muscle; and GLUT5, the intestinal fructose transporter. The restriction of different GLUT transporters to different tissues is an important feature in the metabolism and homeostasis of glucose.

Competition The property of competition is closely related to specificity. A transporter may move several members of a related group of substrates, but those substrates will compete with one another for the binding sites on the transporter. For example, GLUT transporters move the family of hexose sugars, but each different GLUT transporter has a "preference" for one or more hexoses, based on its binding affinity.

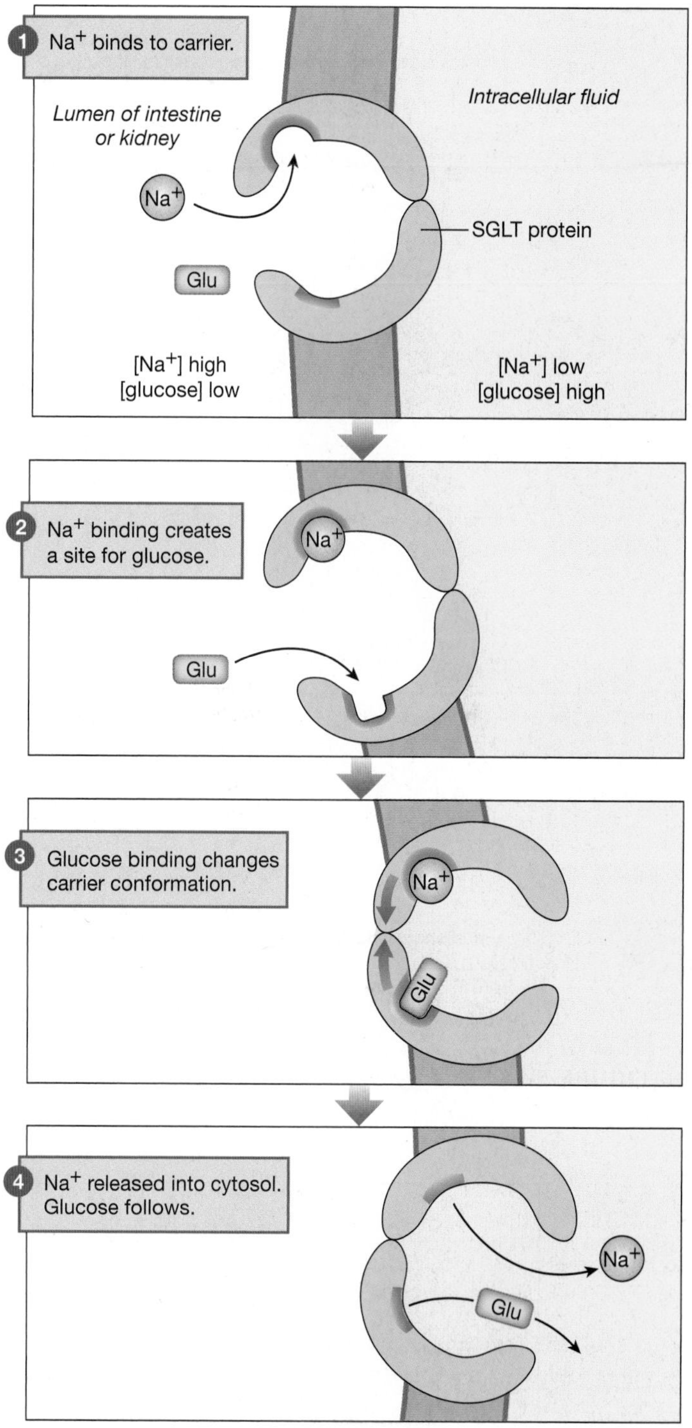

1 Na+ binds to carrier.
Lumen of intestine or kidney
Intracellular fluid
Na+
SGLT protein
Glu
[Na+] high [glucose] low
[Na+] low [glucose] high
2 Na+ binding creates a site for glucose.
Na+
Glu
3 Glucose binding changes carrier conformation.
Na+
Glu
4 Na+ released into cytosol. Glucose follows.
Na+
Glu

● **FIGURE 5-15** ***Mechanism of the SGLT transporter.*** This transporter uses the potential energy stored in the Na^+ concentration gradient to move glucose against its concentration gradient.

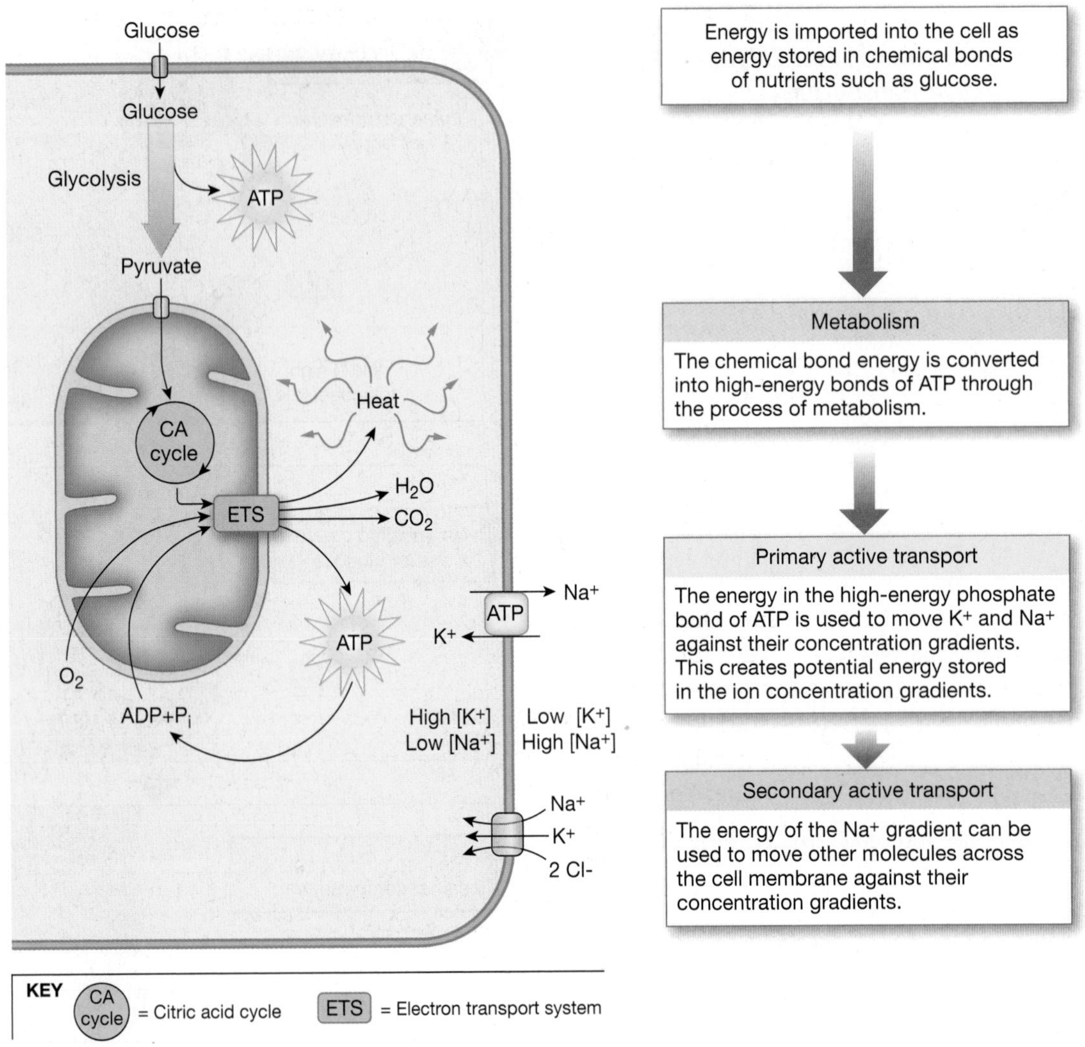

● **FIGURE 5-16** ***Energy transfer in living cells***

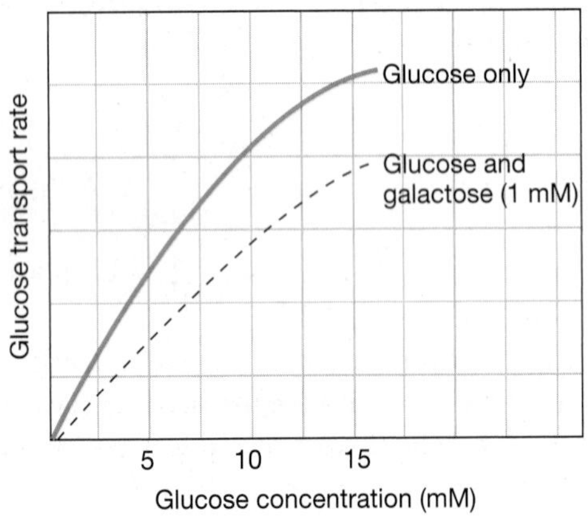

● **FIGURE 5-17** ***Graph of transport competition.*** This graph shows glucose transport rate as a function of glucose concentration. In one experiment, only glucose was present. In the second experiment a constant concentration of galactose was also present.

The results of an experiment demonstrating competition are shown in Figure 5-17 ●. The graph shows glucose transport rate as a function of glucose concentration. The top line shows transport when only glucose is present. The bottom line shows how glucose transport decreases if galactose is also present. Galactose competes for binding sites on the GLUT transporters and displaces some glucose molecules. With fewer glucose able to bind to the GLUT protein, the rate of glucose transport into the cell decreases.

Sometimes the competing molecule is not transported but merely blocks the transport of another substrate. In this case, the competing molecule is a *competitive inhibitor* [p. 42]. In the glucose transport system, the disaccharide maltose is a competitive inhibitor (Fig. 5-18 ●). It competes with glucose for the binding site but once bound is too large to be moved across the membrane.

Competition between transported substrates has been put to good use in medicine. An example involves gout, a disease

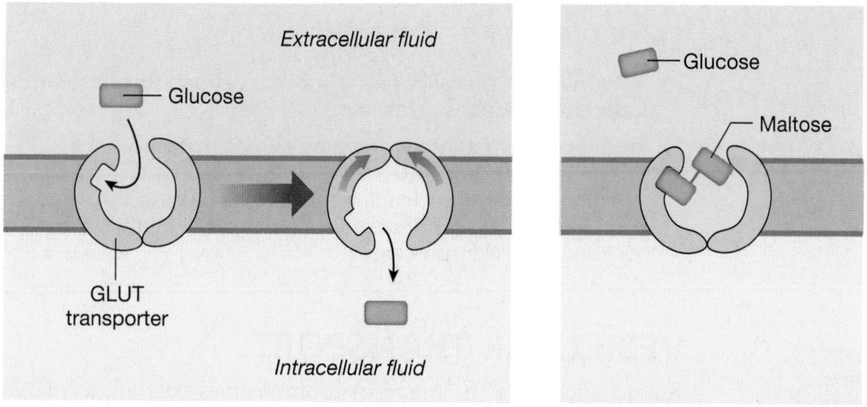

(a) The **GLUT transporter** brings glucose across cell membranes.

(b) Maltose is a competitive inhibitor that binds to the GLUT transporter but is not itself carried across the membrane.

● **FIGURE 5-18** ***Competitive inhibition of glucose transport.*** The inhibitor in this case is the disaccharide maltose, a molecule much larger than glucose.

caused by elevated levels of uric acid in the plasma. One method of decreasing plasma uric acid is to enhance its excretion in the urine. Normally, the kidney's *organic anion transporter* (OAT) reclaims uric acid from the urine and returns the acid to the plasma. However, if an organic acid called probenecid is administered to the patient, OAT binds to probenecid instead of to uric acid, preventing the reabsorption of uric acid. As a result, more uric acid leaves the body in the urine, lowering the uric acid concentration in the plasma.

Saturation The rate of substrate transport depends on both the substrate concentration and the number of carrier molecules, a property that is shared by enzymes [p. 45]. For a fixed number of carriers, however, as substrate concentration increases, the transport rate increases up to a maximum, the point at which all carrier binding sites are filled with substrate. At this point, the carriers are said to have reached saturation. At saturation, the carriers are working at their maximum rate, and a further increase in substrate concentration has no effect. Figure 5-19 ● shows saturation represented graphically.

For an analogy, think of the carriers as doors into a concert hall. Each door has a maximum number of people that it can allow to enter the hall in a given period of time. Suppose all the doors together can allow a maximum of 100 people per minute to enter the hall. This is the maximum transport rate, also called the **transport maximum**. When the concert hall is empty, three maintenance people enter the doors every hour. The transport rate is 3 people/60 minutes, or 0.05 people/minute, well under the maximum. For a local dance recital, about 50 people per minute go through the doors, still well under the maximum. When the most popular rock group of the day appears in concert, however, thousands of people gather outside. When the doors open, thousands of people are clamoring to get in, but the doors will allow only 100 people/minute into the hall. The doors are working at the maximum rate, so it does not matter whether there are 1000 or 3000 people trying to get in. The transport rate is saturated at 100 people/minute.

GRAPH QUESTION

On the *x*-axis, mark the substrate concentration at which the carriers first become saturated.

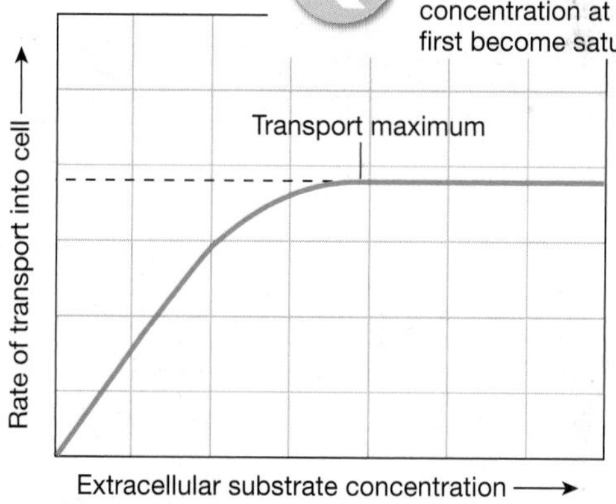

Transport rate is proportional to substrate concentration until the carriers are saturated.

● **FIGURE 5-19** ***Graph showing saturation of carrier-mediated transport***

How can cells increase their transport capacity and avoid saturation? One way is to increase the number of carriers in the membrane. This would be like opening more doors into the concert hall. Under some circumstances, cells are able to insert additional carriers into their membranes. Under other circumstances, a cell may withdraw carriers to decrease movement of a molecule into or out of the cell.

All forms of carrier-mediated transport show specificity, competition, and saturation, but as you learned earlier in the

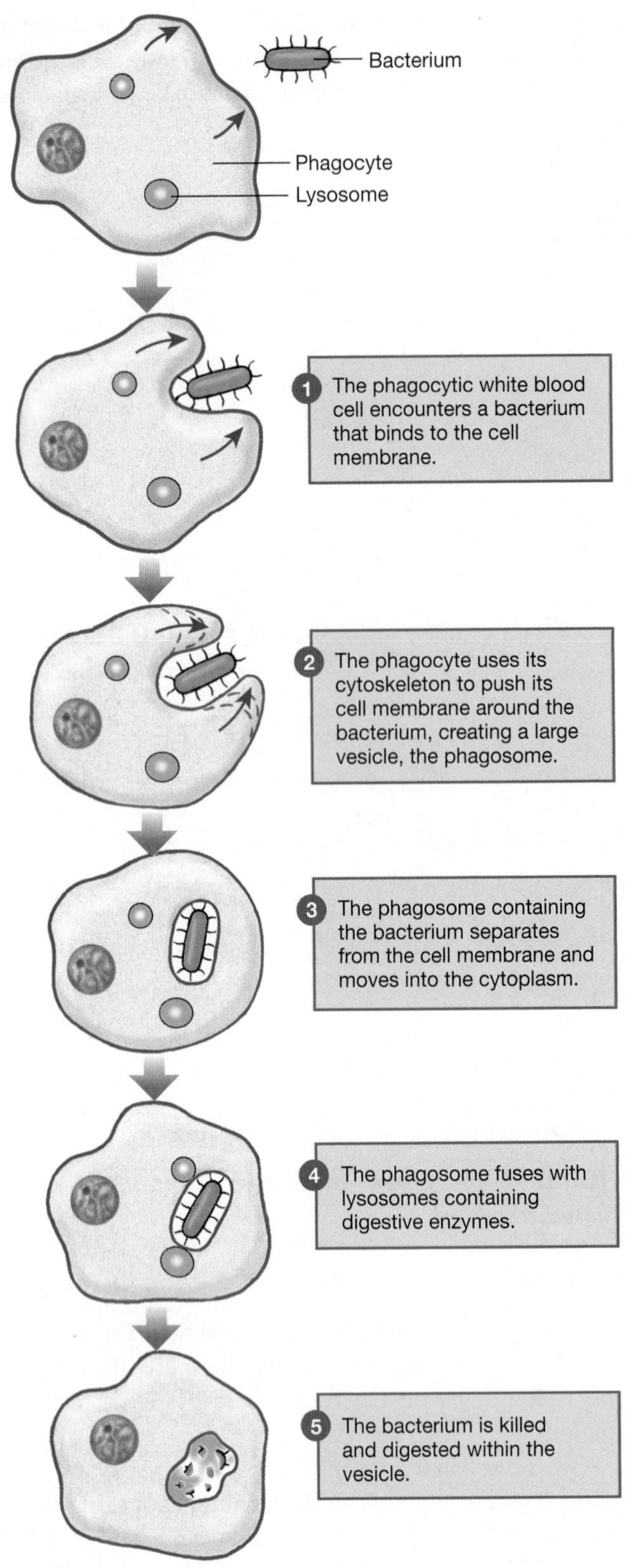
Bacterium
Phagocyte
Lysosome
1 The phagocytic white blood cell encounters a bacterium that binds to the cell membrane.
2 The phagocyte uses its cytoskeleton to push its cell membrane around the bacterium, creating a large vesicle, the phagosome.
3 The phagosome containing the bacterium separates from the cell membrane and moves into the cytoplasm.
4 The phagosome fuses with lysosomes containing digestive enzymes.
5 The bacterium is killed and digested within the vesicle.

● **FIGURE 5-20** ***Phagocytosis***

chapter, they also differ in one important way: passive mediated transport—better known as facilitated diffusion—requires no input of energy from an outside source. Active transport requires energy input from ATP, either directly or indirectly.

CONCEPT CHECK

20. What would you call a carrier that moves two substrates in opposite directions across a membrane?
21. In the concert-hall door analogy, we described how the maximum transport rate might be increased by increasing the number of doors leading into the hall. Using the same analogy, can you think of another way a cell might increase its maximum transport rate?

Answers: p. 176

VESICULAR TRANSPORT

What happens to the many macromolecules that are too large to enter or leave cells through protein channels or carriers? They move in and out of the cell with the aid of bubble-like *vesicles* [p. 68] created from the cell membrane. Cells use two basic processes to import large molecules and particles: phagocytosis and endocytosis. Phagocytosis once was considered a type of endocytosis, but as scientists learned more about the mechanisms behind the two processes, they decided that phagocytosis was fundamentally different. Material leaves cells by the process known as exocytosis, a process that is similar to endocytosis run in reverse.

Phagocytosis Creates Vesicles Using the Cytoskeleton

If you studied *Amoeba* in your biology laboratory, you may have watched these one-cell creatures ingest their food by surrounding it and enclosing it within a vesicle that is brought into the cytoplasm. **Phagocytosis** [*phagein,* to eat + *cyte,* cell + *-sis,* process] is the actin-mediated process by which a cell engulfs a bacterium or other particle into a large membrane-bound vesicle called a **phagosome** [*soma,* body]. The phagosome pinches off from the cell membrane and moves to the interior of the cell, where it fuses with a lysosome [p. 69], whose digestive enzymes destroy the bacterium. Phagocytosis requires energy from ATP for the movement of the cytoskeleton and for the intracellular transport of the vesicles. In humans, phagocytosis occurs only in certain types of white blood cells called *phagocytes,* which specialize in "eating" bacteria and other foreign particles (Fig. 5-20 ●).

Endocytosis Creates Smaller Vesicles

Endocytosis, the second process by which large molecules or particles move into cells, differs from phagocytosis in two important ways. First, in endocytosis the membrane surface indents rather than pushes out. Second, the vesicles formed from endocytosis are much smaller. In addition, some endocytosis is *constitutive;* that is, it is an essential function that is always taking place. In contrast, phagocytosis must be triggered by the presence of a substance to be ingested.

Endocytosis is an active process that requires energy from ATP. It can be nonselective, allowing extracellular fluid to enter the cell—a process called **pinocytosis** [*pino-,* drink]—or it can

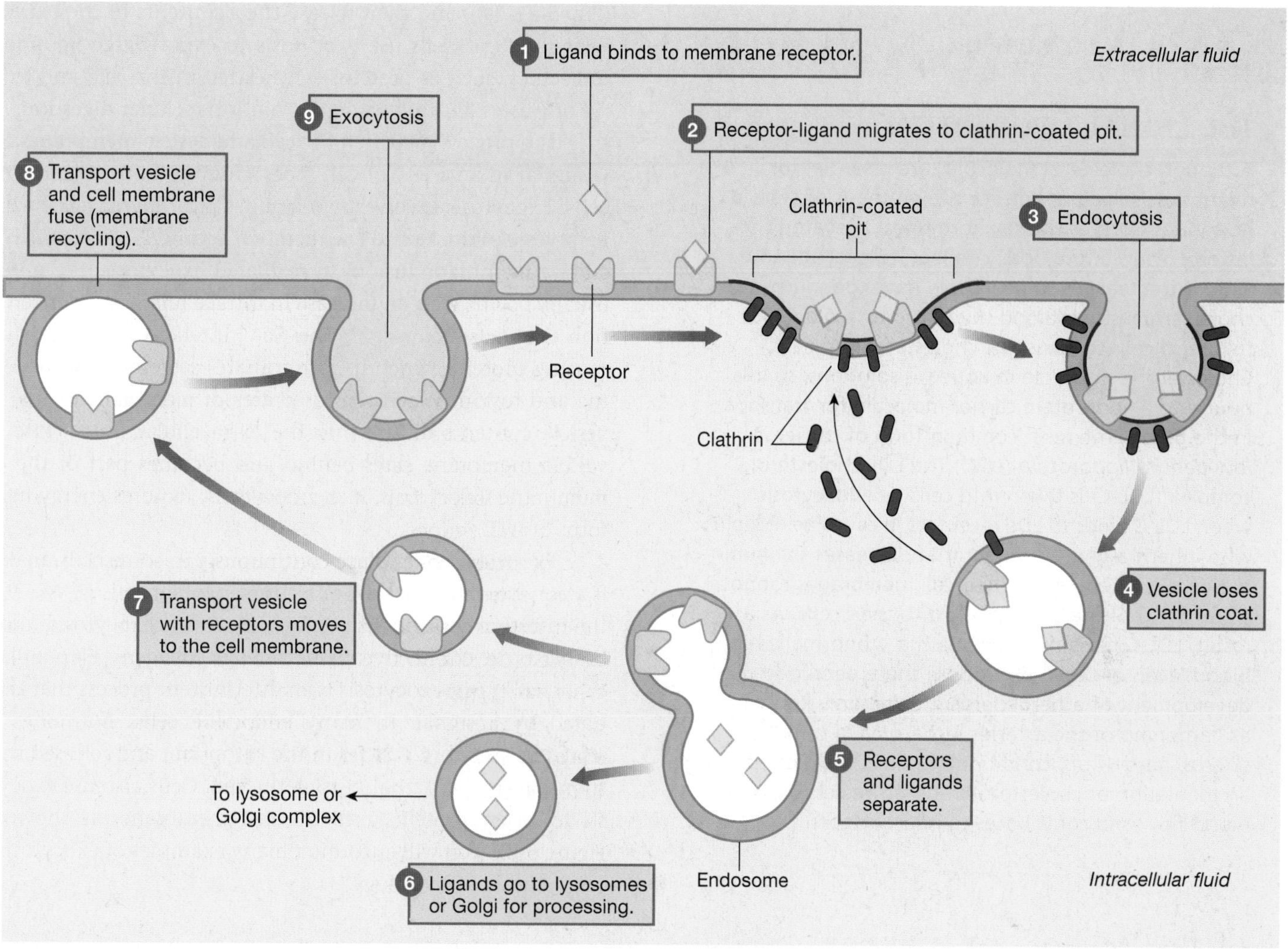

● **FIGURE 5-21** ***Receptor-mediated endocytosis and exocytosis.*** Steps 1–4 illustrate endocytosis and steps 7–9 show exocytosis. Segments of cell membrane are withdrawn as vesicles and reinserted during exocytosis in the process known as membrane recycling.

be highly selective, allowing only specific molecules to enter the cell. Two types of endocytosis require a ligand to bind to a membrane receptor protein: receptor-mediated endocytosis and potocytosis.

Receptor-Mediated Endocytosis **Receptor-mediated endocytosis** takes place in regions of the cell membrane known as **coated pits**, indentations where the cytoplasmic side of the membrane has high concentrations of protein. The most common protein found in coated pits is *clathrin* (Fig. 5-21 ●). In the first step of the process, extracellular ligands that will be brought into the cell bind to their membrane receptors (①, Fig. 5-21). The receptor-ligand complex migrates along the cell surface until it encounters a coated pit ②. Once the receptor-ligand complex is in the coated pit, the membrane draws inward, or *invaginates* ③, then pinches off from the cell membrane and becomes a cytoplasmic vesicle. The clathrin molecules are released and recycle back to the membrane ④. In the vesicle, the receptor and ligand separate, leaving the ligand inside an *endosome* ⑤. The endosome moves to a lysosome if the ligand is to be destroyed, or to the Golgi complex if the ligand is to be processed ⑥.

Meanwhile, the ligand's receptors may be reused in a process known as **membrane recycling**. The vesicle with the receptors moves to the cell membrane ⑦ and fuses with it ⑧. The vesicle membrane then is incorporated back into the cell membrane by exocytosis ⑨. Notice in Figure 5-21 that the cytoplasmic face of the membrane remains the same throughout endocytosis and recycling. The extracellular surface of the cell membrane becomes the inside face of the vesicle membrane.

Receptor-mediated endocytosis transports a variety of substances into the cell, including protein hormones, growth factors, antibodies, and plasma proteins that serve as carriers for iron and cholesterol. Abnormalities in receptor-mediated removal of cholesterol from the blood are associated with elevated plasma cholesterol levels and cardiovascular disease.

CLINICAL FOCUS

THE LETHAL LIPOPROTEIN

Although cholesterol molecules are essential for membrane structure and for the synthesis of steroid hormones (such as the sex hormones), elevated cholesterol levels in the body can lead to heart disease. One of the reasons some people have too much cholesterol in their blood (*hypercholesterolemia*) is failure of cells to transport cholesterol into cells. Cholesterol is insoluble in aqueous solutions, so it is bound to a lipoprotein carrier molecule for transport in the blood. The most common form of carrier is *low-density lipoprotein (LDL)*. The LDL-cholesterol complex (LDL-C) is taken into cells by endocytosis when LDL-C binds to LDL receptors in caveolae. People who inherit a genetic defect that decreases the number of LDL receptors on their cell membranes cannot transport cholesterol normally into their cells. As a result, LDL-C remains in the plasma. Abnormally high blood levels of LDL-C predispose these people to the development of **atherosclerosis,** commonly known as hardening of the arteries [*atheroma,* a tumor + *skleros,* hard + *-sis,* condition]. In this condition, the accumulation of cholesterol in blood vessels blocks blood flow and contributes to heart attacks.

Potocytosis and Caveolae The form of endocytosis known as **potocytosis** is distinguished from receptor-mediated endocytosis by the fact that potocytosis uses **caveolae** ("little caves") rather than clathrin-coated pits to concentrate and bring receptor-bound molecules into the cell. Caveolae are membrane regions with lipid rafts [p. 60], membrane receptor proteins, and a coat of membrane proteins named *caveolins*. The receptors in caveolae are lipid-anchored proteins [p. 59]. In many cells, caveolae appear as small indented pockets on the cell membrane, which is how they acquired their name.

Caveolae have several functions: to concentrate and internalize small molecules, to help in the transfer of macromolecules across the capillary endothelium (see Fig. 5-24), and to participate in cell signaling. Caveolae appear to be involved in some disease processes, including viral and parasitic infections. Two forms of the disease *muscular dystrophy* are associated with abnormalities in the protein caveolin. Scientists are currently trying to discover more details about the role of caveolae in normal physiology and pathophysiology.

Exocytosis Releases Molecules Too Large for Transport Proteins

Exocytosis is the opposite of endocytosis. In exocytosis, intracellular vesicles move to the cell membrane, fuse with it (Fig. 5-21, ⑧), and then release their contents to the extracellular fluid ⑨. Cells use exocytosis to export large lipophobic molecules, such as proteins synthesized in the cell, and to get rid of wastes left in lysosomes from intracellular digestion.

The process by which the cell and vesicle membranes fuse is similar in a variety of cell types, from neurons to endocrine cells. Exocytosis involves two families of proteins: *Rabs,* which help vesicles dock onto the membrane, and *SNAREs,* which facilitate membrane fusion. In regulated exocytosis, the process usually begins with an increase in intracellular Ca^{2+} concentration that acts as a signal. The Ca^{2+} interacts with a calcium-sensing protein, which in turn initiates secretory vesicle docking and fusion. When the fused area of membrane opens, the vesicle contents diffuse into the extracellular fluid while the vesicle membrane stays behind and becomes part of the cell membrane. Exocytosis, like endocytosis, requires energy in the form of ATP.

Exocytosis takes place continuously in some cells, making it a constitutive process. For example, goblet cells [p. 79] in the intestine continuously release mucus by exocytosis, and fibroblasts in connective tissue release collagen [p. 80]. In other cell types, exocytosis is an intermittent process that is initiated by a signal. In many endocrine cells, hormones are stored in secretory vesicles in the cytoplasm and released in response to a signal from outside the cell. Cells also use exocytosis to insert proteins into the cell membrane, as shown in Figure 5-21. You will encounter many examples of exocytosis in your study of physiology.

CONCEPT CHECK

22. How does phagocytosis differ from endocytosis?
23. Name the two membrane protein families associated with endocytosis.
24. How do cells move large proteins into the cell? Out of the cell?

Answers: p. 176

EPITHELIAL TRANSPORT

All the transport processes described in the previous sections deal with the movement of molecules across a single membrane, that of the cell. However, molecules entering and leaving the body or moving between certain compartments within the body must cross a layer of epithelial cells [p. 74] that are connected to one another by adhesive junctions and tight junctions [p. 75].

The tight junctions of epithelia separate the cell membrane into two regions, or poles. The surface of the epithelial cell that faces the lumen of an organ is called the *apical* [*apex,* the highest point] membrane (Fig. 5-22 ●). It is often folded into microvilli that increase its surface area. Below the tight junctions the three surfaces of the cell that face the extracellular fluid are collectively called the *basolateral* membrane [*basal,*

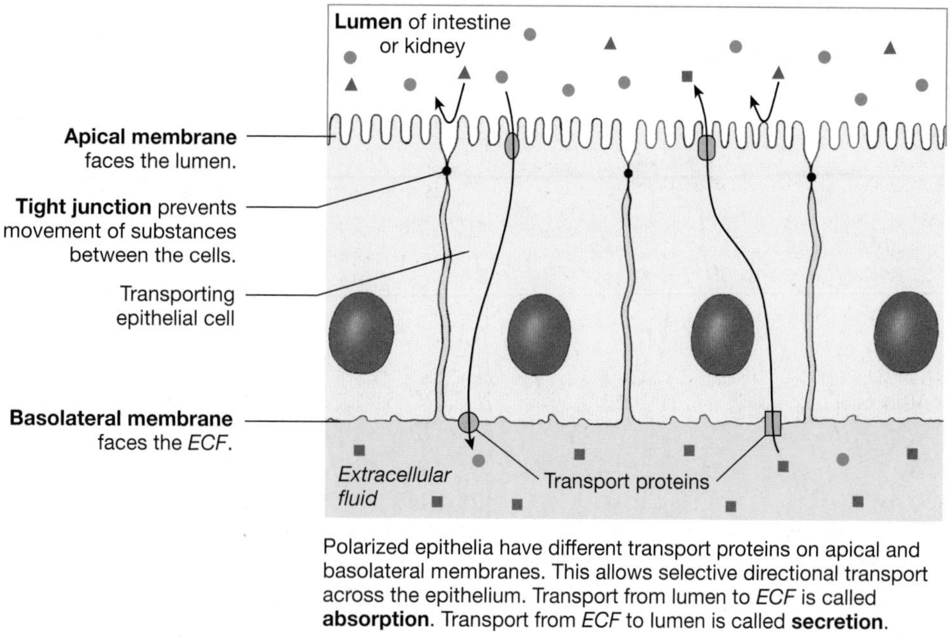
Lumen of intestine or kidney
Apical membrane faces the lumen.
Tight junction prevents movement of substances between the cells.
Transporting epithelial cell
Basolateral membrane faces the ECF.
Extracellular fluid
Transport proteins
Polarized epithelia have different transport proteins on apical and basolateral membranes. This allows selective directional transport across the epithelium. Transport from lumen to ECF is called absorption. Transport from ECF to lumen is called secretion.

● **FIGURE 5-22** ***Polarized cells of transporting epithelia.*** The apical membrane and the basolateral membrane are the two poles of the cell.

base + *latus,* side]. The apical membrane is also called the *mucosal* membrane. The corresponding term for the basolateral membrane is *serosal* membrane.

Transporting epithelial cells are said to be *polarized* because their apical and basolateral membranes have very different properties. Certain transport proteins, such as the Na^+-K^+-ATPase, are almost always found only on the basolateral membrane. Others, like the Na^+-glucose symporter SGLT, are localized to the apical membrane. This polarized distribution of transporters allows the one-way movement of certain molecules across the epithelium.

Transport of material from the lumen of an organ to the extracellular fluid is called **absorption**. When material is moved from the ECF to the lumen, the process is called *secretion.* Note that the term *secretion* is also used more broadly to mean the release of a substance from a cell.

Epithelial Transport May Be Paracellular or Transcellular

Movement across an epithelium, or **epithelial transport**, may take place either through the junctions between adjacent cells (**paracellular transport** [*para-*, beside]) or through the epithelial cells themselves (**transcellular transport**). In "tight" epithelia the cell-cell junctions act as barriers to minimize the unregulated diffusion of material between the cells, so there is very little paracellular transport. In recent years, however, scientists have learned that some epithelia have the ability to change the "tightness" of their junctions. It appears that some junctional proteins such as *claudins* can form large holes or pores that allow water, ions, and a few small uncharged solutes to move by the paracellular pathway. In certain pathological states increased movement through the paracellular route is a hallmark of the disease.

In contrast, substances moving by the transcellular route must cross two cell membranes. Molecules cross the first membrane when they move into the epithelial cell from one compartment, and cross the second membrane when they leave the epithelial cell to enter the second compartment. Transcellular transport uses a combination of active and passive transport mechanisms.

Protein-mediated transcellular transport is usually a two-step process, with one "uphill" step that requires energy and one "downhill" step in which the molecule moves passively down its gradient. You will see these steps in the example of glucose transport that follows. Molecules that are too large to be moved by membrane proteins can be transported across the cell in vesicles.

The cells of transporting epithelia can alter their permeability by selectively inserting or withdrawing membrane proteins. Transporters pulled out of the membrane may be destroyed in lysosomes, or they may be stored in vesicles inside the cell, ready to be reinserted into the membrane in response to a signal (another example of membrane recycling). Most epithelial transport you will study in this book involves the transporting epithelia of intestine and kidney, which are specialized to selectively transport molecules into and out of the body.

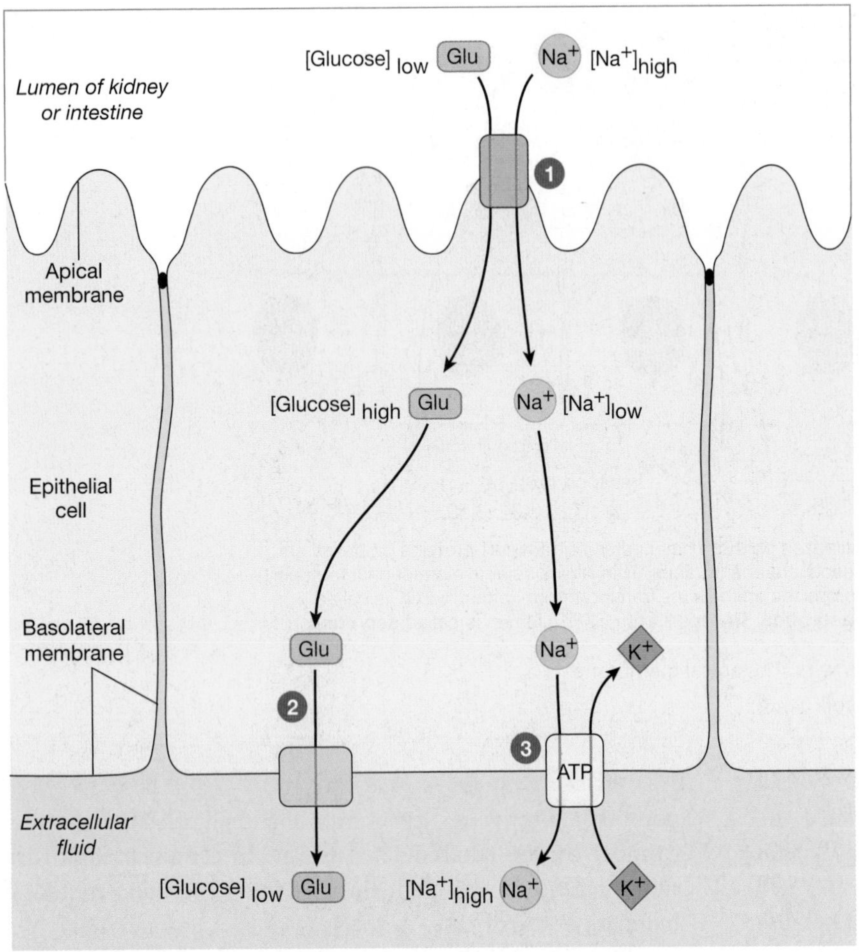
Lumen of kidney or intestine
[Glucose] low
Glu
Na+
[Na+]high
Apical membrane
1
[Glucose] high
Glu
Na+
[Na+]low
Epithelial cell
Basolateral membrane
Glu
2
Na+
K+
3
ATP
Extracellular fluid
[Glucose] low
Glu
[Na+]high
Na+
K+
1 Na+- glucose symporter brings glucose into cell against its gradient using energy stored in the Na+ concentration gradient.
2 GLUT transporter transfers glucose to ECF by facilitated diffusion.
3 Na+-K+- ATPase pumps Na+ out of the cell, keeping ICF Na+ concentration low.

FIGURE QUESTIONS

- Match each transporter to its location.
  1. GLUT — a) apical membrane
  2. Na^+-glucose symporter — b) basolateral membrane
  3. Na^+-K^+-ATPase
- Is glucose movement across the basolateral membrane active or passive? Explain.
- Why doesn't Na^+ movement at the apical membrane require ATP?

● **FIGURE 5-23** ***Transepithelial transport of glucose.*** This process involves indirect (secondary) active transport of glucose across the apical membrane and glucose diffusion across the basolateral membrane.

RUNNING PROBLEM

The sweat test that Daniel will undergo analyzes levels of the salt NaCl in sweat. Sweat—a mixture of ions and water—is secreted into sweat ducts by the epithelial cells of sweat glands. As sweat moves toward the skin's surface through the sweat ducts, CFTR and Na^+ channels move Cl^- and Na^+ out of the sweat and back into the body. This portion of the sweat gland epithelium is not permeable to water, and so normal reabsorption of NaCl creates sweat with a low salt content. However, in the absence of CFTR in the epithelium, salt is not reabsorbed. "Normally, sweat contains about 120 millimoles of salt per liter," says Beryl Rosenstein, M.D., of the Cystic Fibrosis Center at the Johns Hopkins Medical Institutions. "In cystic fibrosis, salt concentrations in the sweat can be four times the normal amount."

Question 2:

Based on the information given, is CFTR protein on the apical or basolateral surface of the sweat gland epithelium?

133 144 156 161 165 171

Transcellular Transport of Glucose Uses Membrane Proteins

The movement of glucose from the lumen of the kidney tubule or intestine to the extracellular fluid is an important example of directional movement across a transporting epithelium. Transepithelial movement of glucose involves three transport systems: the SGLT-mediated secondary active transport of glucose with Na^+ from the lumen into the epithelial cell at the apical membrane, followed by the movement of both Na^+ and glucose out of the cell and into the extracellular fluid on the basolateral side of the cell. Sodium moves out by primary active transport via a Na^+-K^+-ATPase, and glucose leaves the cell by facilitated diffusion on GLUT carriers.

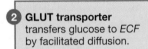

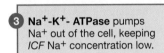

Figure 5-23 ● shows the process in detail. The glucose concentration in the transporting epithelial cell is higher than the glucose concentration in either the extracellular fluid or the lumen of the kidney or intestine. For this reason moving glucose from the lumen into the cell requires the input of energy—in this case, energy stored in the Na^+ concentration gradient. Sodium ions in the lumen bind to the SGLT carrier, as previ-

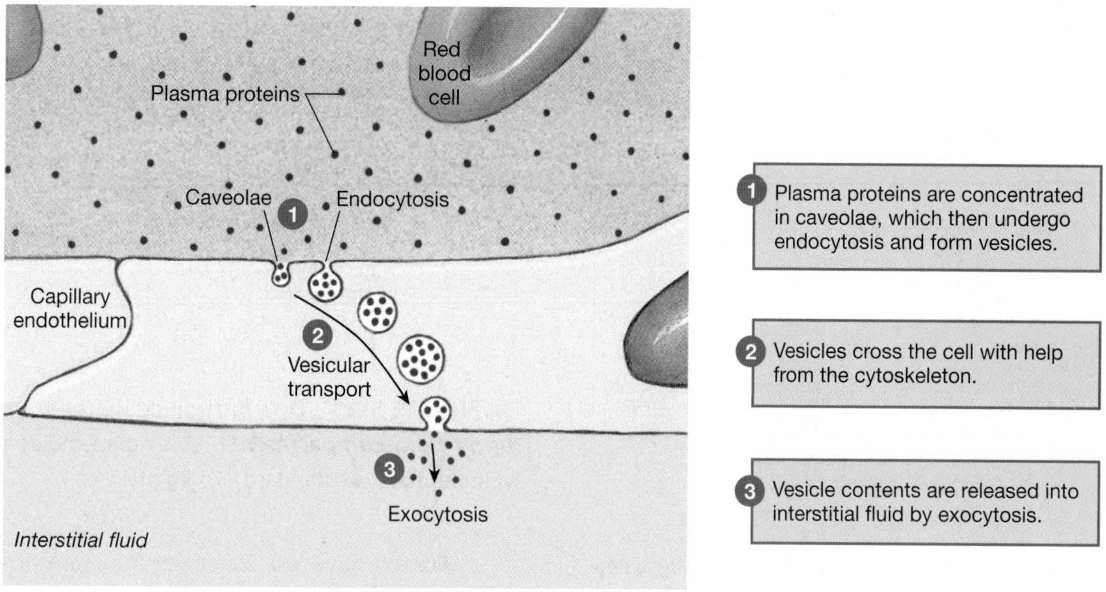

● **FIGURE 5-24** ***Transcytosis across the capillary endothelium***

ously described (see Fig. 5-15), and bring glucose with them into the cell. The energy needed to move glucose against its concentration gradient comes from the kinetic energy of Na^+ moving down its concentration gradient (① Fig. 5-23).

Once glucose is in the epithelial cell, it leaves by moving down its concentration gradient on the facilitated diffusion GLUT transporter in the basolateral membrane (② Fig. 5-23). The Na^+ is pumped out of the cell on the basolateral side using the Na^+-K^+-ATPase ③. Sodium is more concentrated in the extracellular fluid than in the cell; therefore, this step requires energy provided by ATP.

The removal of Na^+ from the cell is essential if glucose is to continue to be absorbed from the lumen. The energy to run the SGLT symporter comes from the sodium concentration gradient, which depends on low intracellular concentrations of Na^+. If the basolateral Na^+-K^+-ATPase is poisoned with *ouabain* (pronounced wah-bane—a compound related to the heart drug digitalis), Na^+ that enters the cell cannot be pumped out. The Na^+ concentration inside the cell gradually increases until it is equal to that in the lumen. Without a sodium gradient, there is no energy source to run the SGLT symporter, and the movement of glucose across the epithelium stops.

Transepithelial transport can use ion movement through channels in addition to carrier-mediated transport. For example, the apical membrane of a transporting epithelium may use the Na^+-K^+-2 Cl^- (NKCC) symporter to bring K^+ into the cell against its concentration gradient, using energy from the Na^+ gradient. Because the K^+ concentration inside the cell is higher than in the extracellular fluid, the K^+ can move out of the cell on the basolateral side through open K^+ leak channels. The Na^+ must be pumped out by the Na^+-K^+-ATPase. By this simple mechanism the body can absorb Na^+ and K^+ at the same time from the lumen of the intestine or the kidney.

CONCEPT CHECK

25. Why does Na^+ movement from the cytoplasm to the extracellular fluid require energy?
26. Ouabain, an inhibitor of the Na^+-K^+-ATPase, cannot pass through cell membranes. What would happen to the transepithelial glucose transport shown in Figure 5-23 if ouabain were applied to the apical side of the epithelium? To the basolateral side of the epithelium?
27. Which GLUT transporter is illustrated in Figure 5-23?

Answers: p. 176

Transcytosis Uses Vesicles to Cross an Epithelium

Some molecules, such as proteins, are too large to cross epithelia on membrane transporters. Instead they are moved across epithelia by **transcytosis**, which is a combination of endocytosis, vesicular transport across the cell, and exocytosis (Fig. 5-24 ●). In this process, the molecule is brought into the epithelial cell via receptor-mediated endocytosis or potocytosis. The resulting vesicle attaches to microtubules in the cell's cytoskeleton and is transported across the cell by a process known as **vesicular transport**. At the opposite side of the epithelium, the contents of the vesicle are expelled into the interstitial fluid by exocytosis.

Transcytosis makes it possible for large proteins to move across an epithelium and remain intact. It is the means by which infants absorb maternal antibodies in breast milk. The antibodies are absorbed on the apical surface of the infant's intestinal epithelium and then released into the extracellular fluid.

CONCEPT CHECK

28. If a poison that disassembles microtubules is applied to a capillary endothelial cell, what happens to transcytosis?

Answers: p. 176

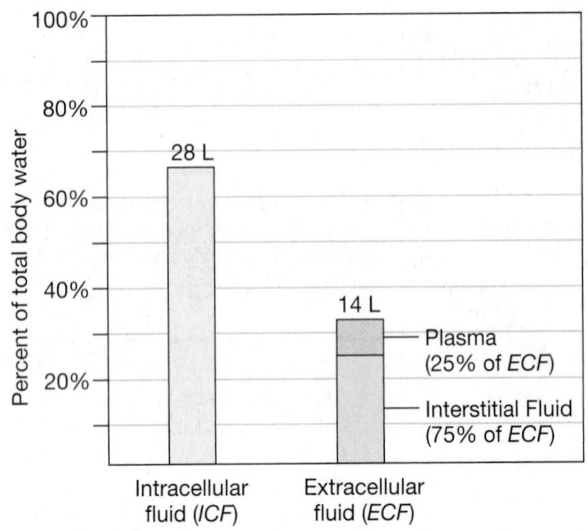

GRAPH QUESTIONS

- Using the ECF volume shown, calculate the volumes of the plasma and interstitial fluid.
- What is this person's total body water volume?
- Use your answers from the two questions above to calculate the percentage of total body water in the plasma and interstitial fluid.

● **FIGURE 5-25** ***Distribution of water volume in the three body fluid compartments.*** This figure shows the compartment volumes for the "standard" 70-kg man.

Now that we have considered how solutes move between the body's compartments, we will examine the movement of water.

OSMOSIS AND TONICITY

The distribution of solutes in the body depends on whether a substance can cross cell membranes, either by simple diffusion, protein-mediated transport, or vesicular transport. Water, on the other hand, is able to move freely in and out of nearly every cell in the body by traversing water-filled ion channels and special water channels created by the protein *aquaporin.* In this section we examine the relationship between solute movement and water movement across cell membranes. A sound understanding of this topic provides the foundation for the clinical use of intravenous (IV) fluid therapy.

The Body Is Mostly Water

Water is the most important molecule in the human body because it is the solvent for all living matter. As we look for life in distant parts of the solar system, one of the first questions scientists ask about a planet is, "Does it have water?" Without water, life as we know it cannot exist.

How much water is in the human body? Because one individual differs from the next, there is no single answer. However, in human physiology we often speak of standard values for physiological functions, based on "the 70-kg man." These standard values are derived from data obtained by studying young white males whose average weight was 70 kg. So when you hear someone speak of standard or average values in physiology, remember that these numbers need to be adjusted for an individual's age, sex, weight, and ethnic origin.

The "standard" 70-kilogram (154-pound) male has 60% of his total body weight, or 42 kg (92.4 lb), in the form of water. Each kilogram of water has a volume of 1 liter, so his **total body water** is 42 liters. This is the equivalent of 21 two-liter soft drink bottles!

Women have less water per kilogram of body mass than men because women have more adipose tissue. Look back at Figure 3-31 [p. 83] and note how the large fat droplets in adipose tissue occupy most of the cell, displacing the more aqueous cytoplasm. Age also influences body water content. Infants have relatively more water than adults, and water content decreases as people grow older than 60.

Table 5-4 ● shows water content as a percentage of total body weight in people of various ages and both sexes. In clinical practice, it is necessary to allow for the variability of body water content when prescribing drugs. Because women and older people have less body water, they will have a higher concentration of a drug in the plasma than will young men if all are given an equal dose per kilogram of body mass.

The distribution of water among body compartments is less variable. When we look at the relative volumes of the body compartments, the intracellular compartment contains about two-thirds (67%) of the body's water (Fig. 5-25 ●). The

TABLE 5-4 Water Content as Percentage of Total Body Weight by Age and Sex

AGE	MALE	FEMALE
Infant	65%	65%
1–9	62%	62%
10–16	59%	57%
17–39	61%	51%
40–59	55%	47%
60+	52%	46%

Adapted from Edelman and Leibman, *American Journal of Medicine 27;* 256–277, 1959.

CLINICAL FOCUS

ESTIMATING BODY WATER

Clinicians estimate a person's fluid loss in dehydration by equating weight loss to water loss. Because 1 liter of pure water weighs 1 kilogram, a decrease in body weight of 1 kilogram (or 2.2 lb) is considered equivalent to the loss of 1 liter of body fluid. A baby with diarrhea can easily be weighed to estimate its fluid loss. A decrease of 1.1 pounds (0.5 kg) of body weight is assumed to mean the loss of 500 mL of fluid. This calculation provides a quick estimate of how much fluid needs to be replaced.

remaining third (33%) is split between the interstitial fluid (which contains about 75% of the extracellular water) and the plasma (which contains about 25% of the extracellular water).

The Body Is in Osmotic Equilibrium

Water is able to move freely between cells and the extracellular fluid, and distributes itself until water concentrations are equal throughout the body—in other words, until the body is in a state of osmotic equilibrium. The movement of water across a membrane in response to a solute concentration gradient is called **osmosis**. In osmosis, water moves to dilute the more concentrated solution. Once concentrations are equal, net movement of water stops.

Look at the example shown in Figure 5-26 ●, in which two compartments of equal volume are separated by a selectively permeable membrane that is permeable to water but that does not allow glucose to cross. In ①, compartments A and B contain equal volumes of glucose solution. Compartment B has more solute (glucose) per volume of solution and therefore is the more concentrated solution. A concentration gradient across the membrane exists for glucose, but the membrane is not permeable to glucose, so glucose cannot diffuse to equalize its distribution.

Water, by contrast, can cross the membrane freely. It will move by osmosis from compartment A, which contains the dilute glucose solution, to compartment B, which contains the more concentrated glucose solution. Thus, water moves to dilute the more concentrated solution (Fig. 5-26, ②).

How can we make quantitative measurements of osmosis? One method is shown in Figure 5-26, ③. Place a piston into compartment B, which has a higher solute concentration than compartment A. By pushing down on the piston, you can keep water from flowing from A to B. The pressure that must be applied to the piston to exactly oppose the osmotic movement of water into compartment B is known as the **osmotic pressure** of

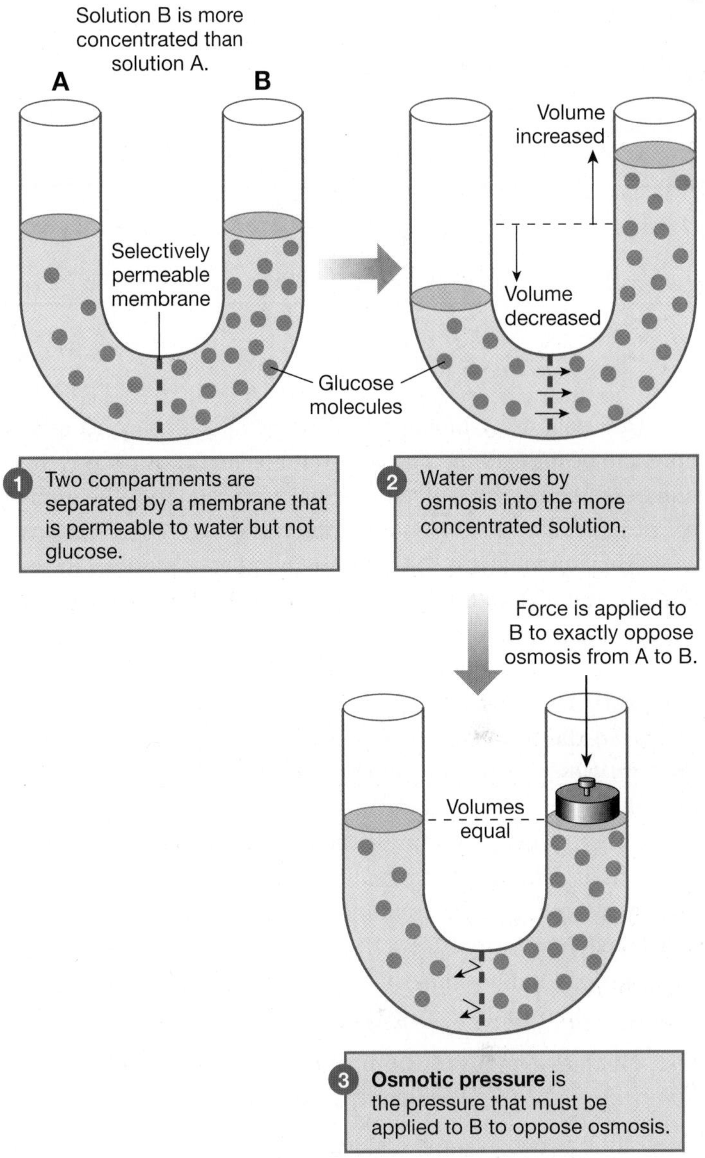

● **FIGURE 5-26** *Osmosis and osmotic pressure*

solution B. The units for osmotic pressure, just as with other pressures in physiology, are *atmospheres* (atm) or *millimeters of mercury* (mm Hg). A pressure of 1 mm Hg is equivalent to the hydrostatic pressure exerted on a 1-cm^2 area by a 1-mm-high column of mercury.

Osmolarity Describes the Number of Particles in Solution

Another way to predict the osmotic movement of water quantitatively is to know the concentrations of the solutions with which we are dealing. In chemistry, concentrations are usually expressed as *molarity* (*M*), which is defined as number of moles of dissolved solute per liter of solution (mol/L). Recall from Chapter 2 that one *mole* is 6.02×10^{23} molecules [p. 37].

TABLE 5-5 Comparing Osmolarities

SOLUTION A = 1 OsM GLUCOSE	SOLUTION B = 2 OsM GLUCOSE	SOLUTION C = 1 OsM NACL
A is hyposmotic to B	B is hyperosmotic to A	C is isosmotic to A
A is isosmotic to C	B is hyperosmotic to C	C is hyposmotic to B

However, using molarity to describe biological concentrations can be misleading. The important factor for osmosis is the number of *particles* in a given volume of solution, not the number of molecules. Because some molecules dissociate into ions when they dissolve in a solution, the number of particles in solution is not always the same as the number of molecules.

For example, one glucose molecule dissolved in water yields one particle, but one NaCl dissolved in water yields two ions (particles): Na^+ and Cl^-. Water moves by osmosis in response to the total concentration of *particles* in the solution. The particles may be ions, uncharged molecules, or a mixture of both.

Consequently, we express the concentration of biological solutions as **osmolarity**, the number of particles (ions or intact molecules) per liter of solution. Osmolarity is expressed in *osmoles* per liter (osmol/L or OsM) or, for very dilute physiological solutions, milliosmoles/liter (mOsM). To convert between molarity and osmolarity, use the following equation:

$$\text{molarity (mol/L)} \times \text{number of particles/molecule} = \text{osmolarity (osmol/L)}$$

Let us look at two examples, glucose and sodium chloride, and compare their molarity with their osmolarity.

One mole of glucose molecules dissolved in enough water to create 1 liter of solution yields a 1 molar solution (1 M). Because glucose does not dissociate in solution, the solution has only one mole of osmotically active particles:

$$1 \text{ M glucose} \times 1 \text{ particle per glucose molecule} = 1 \text{ OsM glucose}$$

Unlike glucose, sodium chloride dissociates into two ions when placed in solution.* Thus, one mole of NaCl dissociates in solution to yield two moles of particles: one mole of Na^+ and one mole of Cl^-. The result is a 2 OsM solution:

$$1 \text{ M NaCl} \times 2 \text{ ions per NaCl} = 2 \text{ OsM NaCl}$$

Osmolarity describes only the number of particles in the solution. It says nothing about the composition of the particles. A 1 OsM solution could be composed of pure glucose or pure Na^+ and Cl^- or a mixture of the three.

The normal osmolarity of the human body ranges from 280 to 296 milliosmoles per liter (mOsM). In this book, to simplify calculations we will round that number up slightly to 300 mOsM.

A term related to osmolarity that you may hear used is osmolality. **Osmolality** is concentration expressed as osmoles of solute per kilogram of water. Because biological solutions are dilute and little of their weight comes from solute, physiologists sometimes use the terms *osmolarity* and *osmolality* interchangeably. Osmolality is usually used in clinical situations because it is easy to estimate people's body water content by weighing them.

CONCEPT CHECK

29. A mother brings her baby to the emergency room because he has lost fluid through diarrhea and vomiting for two days. The staff weighs the baby and finds that he has lost 2 pounds. If you assume that the reduction in weight is due to water loss, what volume of water has the baby lost (2.2 pounds = 1 kilogram)? Answers: p. 176

Comparing Osmolarities of Two Solutions Osmolarity is a property of every solution. You can compare the osmolarities of different solutions as long as the concentrations are expressed in the same units—for example, as milliosmoles per liter. If two solutions contain the same number of solute particles per unit volume, we say that the solutions are **isosmotic** [*iso-*, equal]. If solution A has a higher osmolarity (contains more particles per unit volume, is more concentrated) than solution B, we say that solution A is **hyperosmotic** to solution B. In the same example, solution B, with fewer osmoles per unit volume, is **hyposmotic** to solution A. Table 5-5 ● shows some examples of comparative osmolarities.

Osmolarity is a *colligative* property of solutions, meaning it depends strictly on the *number* of particles per liter of solution. Osmolarity says nothing about what the particles are or how they behave. Before we can predict whether osmosis will take place between any two solutions divided by a membrane, we must know the properties of the membrane and of the solutes on each side of it.

If the membrane is permeable only to water and not to any solutes, water will move by osmosis from a less concentrated (hyposmotic) solution into a more concentrated (hyperosmotic) solution, as illustrated in Figure 5-26. Most biological systems are not this simple, however. Biological membranes are selectively permeable and allow some solutes to cross in addition to water. To predict the movement of water into and out of cells, you must know the *tonicity* of the solution, explained in the next section.

*For the purposes of this discussion, we assume that all solutes that can dissociate do so completly (complete dissociation). The actual dissociation constant for NaCl is about 1.8.

RUNNING PROBLEM

Daniel's medical history tells a frightening story of almost constant medical problems since birth: recurring bouts of respiratory infections, digestive ailments, and, for the past six months, a history of weight loss. Then, last week, when Daniel began having trouble breathing, his mother rushed him to the hospital. A culture taken from Daniel's lungs raised a red flag for cystic fibrosis: the mucus from his airways was unusually thick and dehydrated. In cystic fibrosis, this thick mucus causes life-threatening respiratory congestion and provides a perfect breeding ground for infection-causing bacteria. The thickened mucus is a direct result of faulty CFTR. Normally these proteins in the lungs transport chloride ions out of the epithelial cells and into the airways.

Question 3:

Why would failure to transport Cl^- into the lumen of the airways cause the secreted mucus to be thick? (Hint: Remember that water moves to dilute more concentrated regions.)

133
144
156
161
165
171

Tonicity of a Solution Describes the Volume Change of a Cell Placed in That Solution

Tonicity [*tonikos,* pertaining to stretching] is a physiological term used to describe a solution and how that solution affects cell volume. If a cell placed in the solution gains water and swells, we say that the solution is **hypotonic** to the cell. If the cell loses water and shrinks when placed in the solution, the solution is said to be **hypertonic**. If the cell does not change size in the solution, the solution is **isotonic** (Tbl. 5-6 ●). By convention, we always describe the tonicity of the solution relative to the cell. Tonicity describes the cell volume once the cell has come to equilibrium with the solution.

How, then, does tonicity differ from osmolarity?

1. Osmolarity describes the number of solute particles dissolved in a volume of solution. It has units, such as osmoles/liter. The osmolarity of a solution can be measured by a machine called an *osmometer*. Tonicity has no units; it is only a comparative term.
2. Osmolarity can be used to compare any two solutions, and the relationship is reciprocal (solution A is hyperosmotic to solution B; therefore, solution B is hyposmotic to solution A). Tonicity always compares a solution and a cell, and by convention, tonicity is used to describe only the solution—for example, "Solution A is hypotonic to red blood cells."
3. Osmolarity alone does not tell you what happens to a cell placed in a solution. Tonicity by definition tells you what happens to cell volume when the cell is placed in the solution.

This third point is the one that is most confusing to students. Why can't osmolarity be used to predict tonicity? The reason is that the tonicity of a solution depends not only on its concentration (osmolarity) but also on the *nature* of the solutes in the solution. By nature of the solutes, we mean whether the solute particles can cross the cell membrane. If the solute particles (ions or molecules) can enter the cell, we call them **penetrating solutes.** We call particles that cannot cross the cell membrane **nonpenetrating solutes.** Tonicity depends on the concentration of nonpenetrating solutes only. Let's see why this is true.

First, some preliminary information. The most important nonpenetrating solute in physiology is NaCl. If a cell is placed in a solution of NaCl, the Na^+ and Cl^- will not cross the membrane into the cell. (In reality, a few Na^+ ions may leak across, but they are immediately transported back to the extracellular fluid by the Na^+-K^+-ATPase. For this reason NaCl is considered a *functionally* nonpenetrating solute.) By convention, we assume that cells are filled with other types of nonpenetrating solutes. In other words, the solutes inside the cell are unable to leave so long as the cell membrane remains intact.

Now we are ready to see why osmolarity alone cannot be used to predict tonicity. Suppose you know the composition and osmolarity of a solution. How can you figure out the tonicity of the solution without actually putting a cell in it? The key lies in knowing *the relative concentrations of nonpenetrating solutes in the cell and in the solution.*

Here are the rules for predicting tonicity:

1. *If the cell has a higher concentration of nonpenetrating solutes than the solution,* there will be net movement of water into the cell. The cell swells, and the solution is *hypotonic.*
2. *If the cell has a lower concentration of nonpenetrating solutes than the solution,* there will be net movement of water out of the cell. The cell shrinks, and the solution is *hypertonic.*
3. *If the concentrations of nonpenetrating solutes are the same in the cell and the solution,* there will be no net movement of water at equilibrium. The solution is *isotonic* to the cell.

Let's look at three examples of how this works. The first two examples are simple because they use only nonpenetrating solutes or penetrating solutes. The third example shows how combining penetrating and nonpenetrating solutes can complicate the situation.

TABLE 5-6 Tonicity of Solutions

SOLUTION	CELL BEHAVIOR WHEN PLACED IN THE SOLUTION	DESCRIPTION OF THE SOLUTION RELATIVE TO THE CELL
A	Cell swells	Solution A is hypotonic
B	Cell doesn't change size	Solution B is isotonic
C	Cell shrinks	Solution C is hypertonic

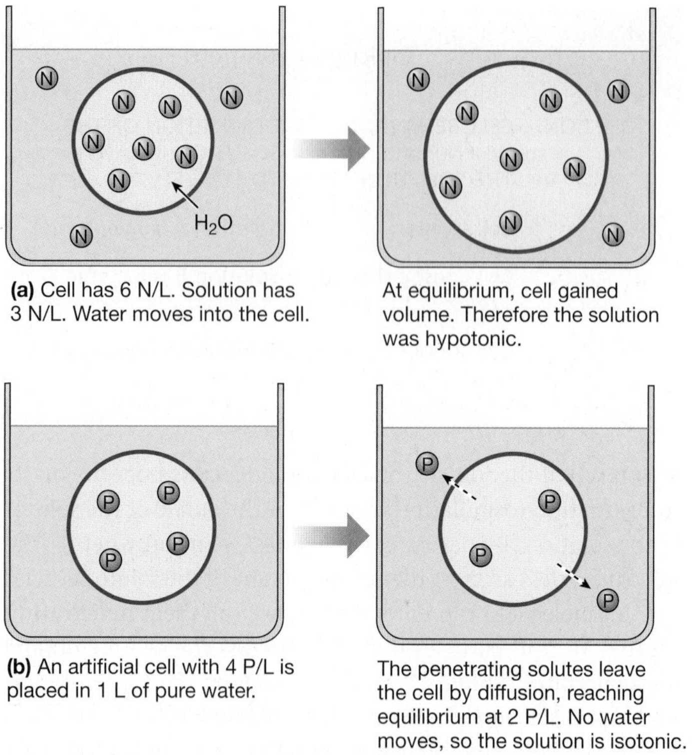
N
P
H_2O
(a) Cell has 6 N/L. Solution has 3 N/L. Water moves into the cell.
At equilibrium, cell gained volume. Therefore the solution was hypotonic.
(b) An artificial cell with 4 P/L is placed in 1 L of pure water.
The penetrating solutes leave the cell by diffusion, reaching equilibrium at 2 P/L. No water moves, so the solution is isotonic.

● **FIGURE 5-27** ***Tonicity depends on the relative concentrations of nonpenetrating solutes.*** Water and penetrating solutes (P) can cross the cell membrane and come to equilibrium, but nonpenetrating solutes (N) cannot cross. The "cell" and the solution are each 1 liter in the top figures.

The artificial cell at the left of Figure 5-27a ● contains six particles of nonpenetrating solute in 1 liter of cell volume. The 1 liter of solution contains three particles of nonpenetrating solute per liter. As in the example shown in Figure 5-26, there is a concentration gradient for the solute, but the solute cannot cross the cell membrane to equilibrate. There is also an osmotic gradient, however, and because water *can* cross the membrane, water moves into the cell until the solute concentrations have equilibrated (right of Fig. 5-27a). The cell gains volume at equilibrium, which means the solution was hypotonic to the cell. We could have predicted this by using rule 1: if the cell has a higher concentration of nonpenetrating solutes than the solution, there will be net movement of water into the cell and the solution is hypotonic.

Now let's consider a situation in which an artificial cell with a volume of 1 liter has four particles of penetrating solute and is placed in 1 liter of pure water (left of Fig. 5-27b). Based on osmolarity alone, you might think that water would move into the cell because the cell is more concentrated. However, there is a concentration gradient for the solute, and the solute is able to cross the cell membrane. Solute therefore moves out of the cell by diffusion until solute concentrations in the cell and the solution reach equilibrium (right of Fig. 5-27b). Once the penetrating solute is at equilibrium, the cell and solution have equal osmolarities (two particles/liter), and the net movement of water is zero. The solution in this instance is isotonic. You could have predicted this from rule 3 above: if the concentrations of nonpenetrating solutes are the same in the cell and the solution, there will be no net movement of water at equilibrium and the solution is isotonic. In this example, the concentrations of nonpenetrating solute in cell and solution are both zero. Remember, however, that we assume that real cells always contain only nonpenetrating solutes.

Now let's look at a complex example that mixes penetrating and nonpenetrating solutes. In Figure 5-28a ●, the artificial cell contains six particles of nonpenetrating solute in a 1 liter volume. The 1 liter of solution also contains six particles of solute: three nonpenetrating and three penetrating. Because cell and solution have the same concentrations (six particles per liter), they are isosmotic, and no water moves initially when the two are placed together (Fig. 5-28b).

Using the tonicity rules above, let us compare the concentrations of nonpenetrating solutes in the solution and cell. The nonpenetrating solutes are more concentrated in the cell than in the solution (six versus three). We therefore predict that water will move from the solution into the cell, increasing cell volume. However, the solution is isosmotic to the cell, and so what will cause osmosis?

You have learned that penetrating solutes move freely into and out of cells. In this example, there is a concentration gradient for the penetrating solute: 3/L in the solution versus 0/L in the cell. The penetrating solute therefore diffuses down its concentration gradient and moves into the cell. As soon as one particle moves in, we have a total of five solutes outside the cell but seven inside. This solute imbalance disturbs the osmotic balance and creates an osmotic gradient (Fig. 5-28c). Once this osmotic gradient exists, water moves into the cell and cell volume increases (solute movement has no significant effect on cell volume). Water movement continues until the concentrations of *nonpenetrating* solutes are equal, as in Figure 5-28d. Thus, in this example, an isosmotic solution is hypotonic because cell volume increased (rule 1).

If accepting the rules makes you uneasy, let's look at this example mathematically. We began with 1 L of solution in the cell and 1 L outside, a total of 2 L, and a total of 12 particles, giving a concentration of 6 particles/L. The system does not gain or lose solute or water, so the overall concentration remains 6 particles/L. When the cell is placed in the solution, the two penetrating solutes move into the cell, disturbing the osmotic balance. Water has to enter the cell so that the concentration remains at 6 particles/L:

$$8 \text{ particles/? liters} = 6 \text{ particles/L}$$

The cell volume at equilibrium is 1.33 liters: 8 particles/1.33 L = 6 particles/L. The solution has lost 0.33 liter of water that moved into the cell:

$$4 \text{ particles/}(1 - 0.33) \text{ L} = 6 \text{ particles/L}$$

At equilibrium, the concentrations of the cell and the solution are always the same.

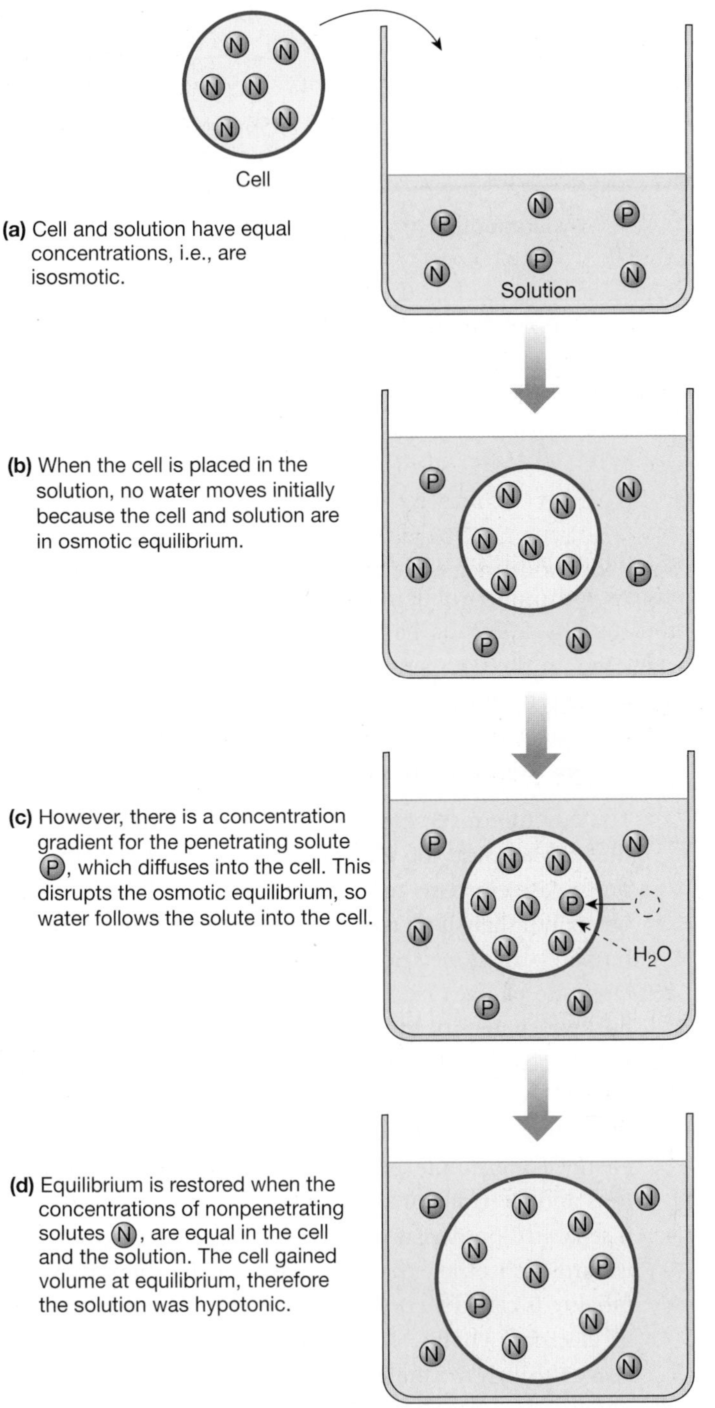
Cell
(a) Cell and solution have equal concentrations, i.e., are isosmotic.
Solution
(b) When the cell is placed in the solution, no water moves initially because the cell and solution are in osmotic equilibrium.
(c) However, there is a concentration gradient for the penetrating solute (P), which diffuses into the cell. This disrupts the osmotic equilibrium, so water follows the solute into the cell.
H2O
(d) Equilibrium is restored when the concentrations of nonpenetrating solutes (N), are equal in the cell and the solution. The cell gained volume at equilibrium, therefore the solution was hypotonic.

FIGURE QUESTION

Using the same cell, give the relative osmolarity and the tonicity of the following solutions, if the solution has
(a) 6 nonpenetrating particles,
(b) 6 nonpenetrating and 3 penetrating particles, or
(c) 3 nonpenetrating and 6 penetrating particles.

● **FIGURE 5-28** ***In a solution of mixed solutes, only the concentration of nonpenetrating solutes contributes to the tonicity of the solution.***

TABLE 5-7 Rules for Osmolarity and Tonicity

1. Assume that all intracellular solutes are nonpenetrating.
2. Compare osmolarities before the cell and solution are put together. (At equilibrium, the cell and solution are always isosmotic.)
3. Tonicity of a solution describes the volume change of a cell at equilibrium (Tbl. 5-6).
4. Determine tonicity by comparing nonpenetrating solute concentrations in the cell and the solution. Net water movement will be into the compartment with the higher concentration of nonpenetrating solutes.
5. Hyposmotic solutions are always hypotonic.

Learning the rules rather than depending on mathematical calculations is important for clinical situations, when you will not know exact volumes for the person needing fluids. Table 5-7 ● lists some rules to help you distinguish between osmolarity and tonicity.

Understanding the difference between the two properties is critical to making good clinical decisions about intravenous (IV) fluid therapy. The choice of IV fluid depends on how the clinician wants the solutes and water to distribute between the extracellular and intracellular fluid compartments. If the problem is dehydrated cells, the cells need fluid and the appropriate IV solution is hypotonic. If the situation requires fluid that remains in the extracellular fluid to replace blood loss, an isotonic IV solution is used. In medicine, the tonicity of a solution is usually the important consideration. Table 5-8 ● lists the most common IV solutions and their approximate osmolarity and tonicity relative to the normal human cell.

CONCEPT CHECK

30. Which of the following solutions has/have the most water per unit volume: 1 M glucose, 1 M NaCl, or 1 OsM NaCl?
31. Two compartments are separated by a membrane that is permeable to water and urea but not to NaCl. Which way will water move when the following solutions are placed in the two compartments?

Compartment A	Membrane	Compartment B
(a) 1 M NaCl	|	1 OsM NaCl
(b) 1 M urea	|	2 M urea
(c) 1 OsM NaCl	|	1 OsM urea

32. You have a patient who lost 1 liter of blood, and you need to restore volume quickly while waiting for a blood transfusion to arrive from the blood bank.
    (a) Which would be better to administer: 5% dextrose (another name for glucose) in water or 0.9% NaCl in water? (*Hint*: Think about how these solutes distribute in the body.) Defend your choice.
    (b) How much of your solution of choice would you have to administer to return blood volume to normal?

Answers: p. 176

TABLE 5-8 Intravenous Solutions

SOLUTION	ALSO KNOWN AS	OSMOLARITY	TONICITY
0.9% saline*	Normal saline	Isosmotic	Isotonic
5% dextrose† in 0.9% saline	D5–normal saline	Hyperosmotic	Isotonic
5% dextrose in water	D5W	Isosmotic	Hypotonic
0.45% saline	Half-normal saline	Hyposmotic	Hypotonic
5% dextrose in 0.45% saline	D5–half-normal saline	Hyperosmotic	Hypotonic

*Saline = NaCl.
†Dextrose = glucose.

THE RESTING MEMBRANE POTENTIAL

Many of the body's solutes, including organic compounds such as pyruvate and lactate, are ions and therefore carry a net electrical charge. Potassium (K^+) is the major cation within cells, and sodium (Na^+) dominates the extracellular fluid (see Fig. 5-3, p. 135). On the anion side, chloride ions (Cl^-) mostly remain with Na^+ in the extracellular fluid. Phosphate ions and negatively charged proteins are the major anions of the intracellular fluid.

However, the intracellular compartment is not electrically neutral: there are some protein anions inside cells that do not have matching cations, giving the cells a net negative charge. At the same time, the extracellular compartment has a net positive charge: some cations in the extracellular fluid do not have matching anions. One consequence of this uneven distribution of ions is that the intracellular and extracellular compartments are not in electrical equilibrium. Instead, the two compartments exist in a state of electrical disequilibrium [p. 135].

The concept of electrical disequilibrium has traditionally been taught in chapters on nerve and muscle function because those tissues generate electrical signals known as action potentials. Yet one of the most exciting recent discoveries in physiology is the realization that other kinds of cells also use electrical signals for communication. In fact, all living organisms, including plants, use electrical signals! This section reviews the basic principles of electricity and discusses what creates electrical disequilibrium in the body. The chapter ends with a look at how beta cells of the pancreas use changes in the distribution of ions across cell membranes to trigger insulin secretion.

Electricity Review

Atoms are electrically neutral [p. 21]. They are composed of positively charged protons, negatively charged electrons, and uncharged neutrons, but in balanced proportions, so that an atom is neither positive nor negative. The removal or addition of electrons to an atom creates the charged particles we know as ions. We have discussed several ions that are important in the human body, such as Na^+, K^+, and H^+. For each of these positive ions, somewhere in the body there is a matching electron, usually found as part of a negative ion. For example, when Na^+ in the body enters in the form of NaCl, the "missing" electron from Na^+ can be found on the Cl^-.

Remember the following important principles when you deal with electricity in physiological systems:

1. The **law of conservation of electrical charge** states that the net amount of electrical charge produced in any process is zero. This means that for every positive charge on an ion, there is an electron on another ion. Overall, the human body is electrically neutral.
2. Opposite charges (+ and −) are attracted to each other, but two charges of the same type (+ and +, or − and −) repel each other. The protons and electrons in an atom exhibit this attraction.
3. Separating positive charges from negative charges requires energy. For example, energy is needed to separate the protons and electrons of an atom.
4. If separated positive and negative charges can move freely toward each other, the material through which they are moving is called a **conductor.** Water is a good conductor of electrical charge. If separated charges are unable to move through the material that separates them, the material is known as an **insulator.** The phospholipid bilayer of the cell membrane is a good insulator, as is the plastic coating on electrical wires.

The word *electricity* comes from the Greek word *elektron,* meaning "amber," the fossilized resin of trees. The Greeks discovered that if they rubbed a rod of amber with cloth, the amber acquired the ability to attract hair and dust. This attraction (called static electricity) arises from the separation of electrical charge that occurs when electrons move from the amber atoms to the cloth. To separate these charged particles, energy (work) must be put into the system. In the case of the amber, work was done by rubbing the rod. In the case of biological systems, the work is usually done by energy stored in ATP and other chemical bonds.

RUNNING PROBLEM

Three days after Daniel's sweat test, the lab returns the grim results: salt levels in his sweat are more than twice the normal concentration. Daniel is diagnosed with cystic fibrosis. Now, along with antibiotics to prevent lung infections and therapy to loosen the mucus in his airways, Daniel must begin a regimen of pancreatic enzymes to be taken whenever he eats, for the rest of his life. In cystic fibrosis, thick mucus in the pancreatic ducts blocks the secretion of digestive enzymes into the intestine. Without artificial enzymes, he would starve.

Question 4:

Why will Daniel starve if he does not take artificial pancreatic enzymes?

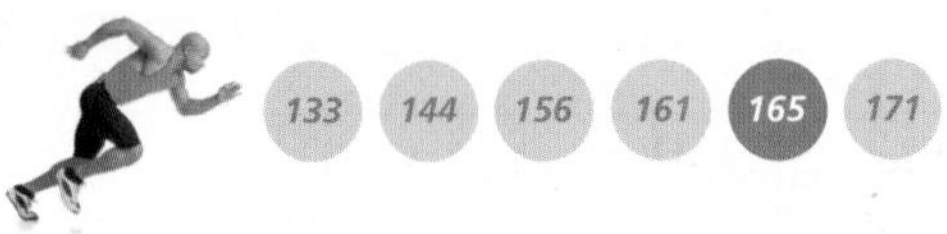

The Cell Membrane Enables Separation of Electrical Charge in the Body

In the body, separation of electrical charge takes place across the cell membrane. This process is shown in Figure 5-29 ●. The diagram shows an artificial cell filled with molecules that dissociate into positive and negative ions, represented by the plus and minus signs. Because the molecules were electrically neutral to begin with, there are equal numbers of positive and negative ions inside the cell. The cell is placed in an aqueous solution, also electrically neutral, that contains the same types of cations and anions. The phospholipid bilayer of the artificial cell, like the bilayer of a real cell, is not permeable to ions. Water can freely cross this cell membrane, making the extracellular and intracellular ion concentrations equal. In Figure 5-29a, the system is at osmotic, chemical, and electrical equilibrium.

In Figure 5-29b, an active transport carrier protein is inserted into the membrane. This carrier uses energy to move positive ions out of the cell against their concentration gradient. The negative ions in the cell attempt to follow the positive ions because of the attraction of positive and negative charges. Because the membrane is impermeable to negative ions, however, they remain trapped in the cell. Positive ions outside the cell might try to move into the cell, attracted by the net negative charge of the intracellular fluid, but the membrane does not allow these cations to leak across it.

As soon as the first positive ion leaves the cell, the electrical equilibrium between the extracellular fluid and intracellular fluid is disrupted: the cell's interior has a net charge of -1 while the cell's exterior has a net charge of $+1$. The input of energy to transport ions across the membrane has created an **electrical gradient**—that is, a difference in the net charge between two regions. In this example, the inside of the cell became negative relative to the outside.

(a) Cell and solution are electrically and chemically at equilibrium.

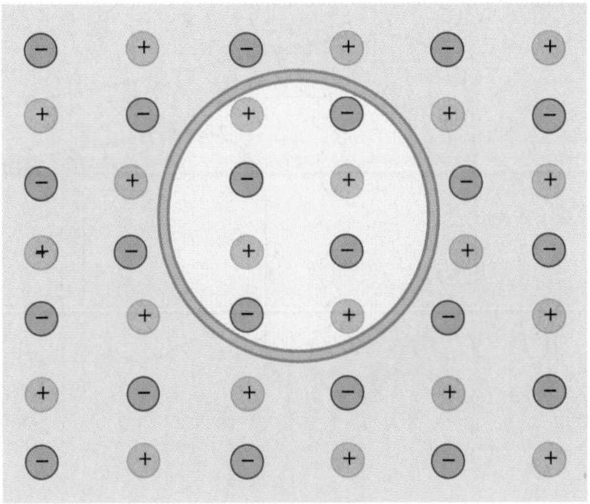

(b) Cell and solution in chemical and electrical disequilbrium. Energy is used to pump one cation out of the cell, leaving a net charge of -1 in the cell and +1 outside the cell.

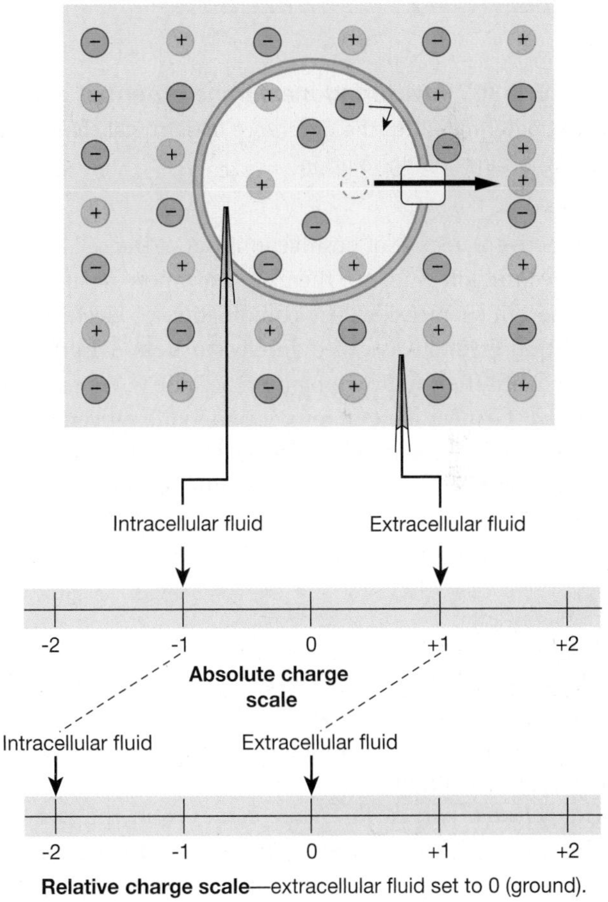

(c) On an absolute charge scale, the extracellular fluid *(ECF)* would be at +1 and the intracellular fluid *(ICF)* at -1. Physiological measurements, however, are always on a relative scale, on which the extracellular fluid is assigned a value of zero. This shifts the scale to the left and gives the inside of the cell a relative charge of -2.

● **FIGURE 5-29** ***Separation of electrical charge.*** The cell membrane acts as an insulator to prevent free movement of ions between the intracellular and extracellular compartments.

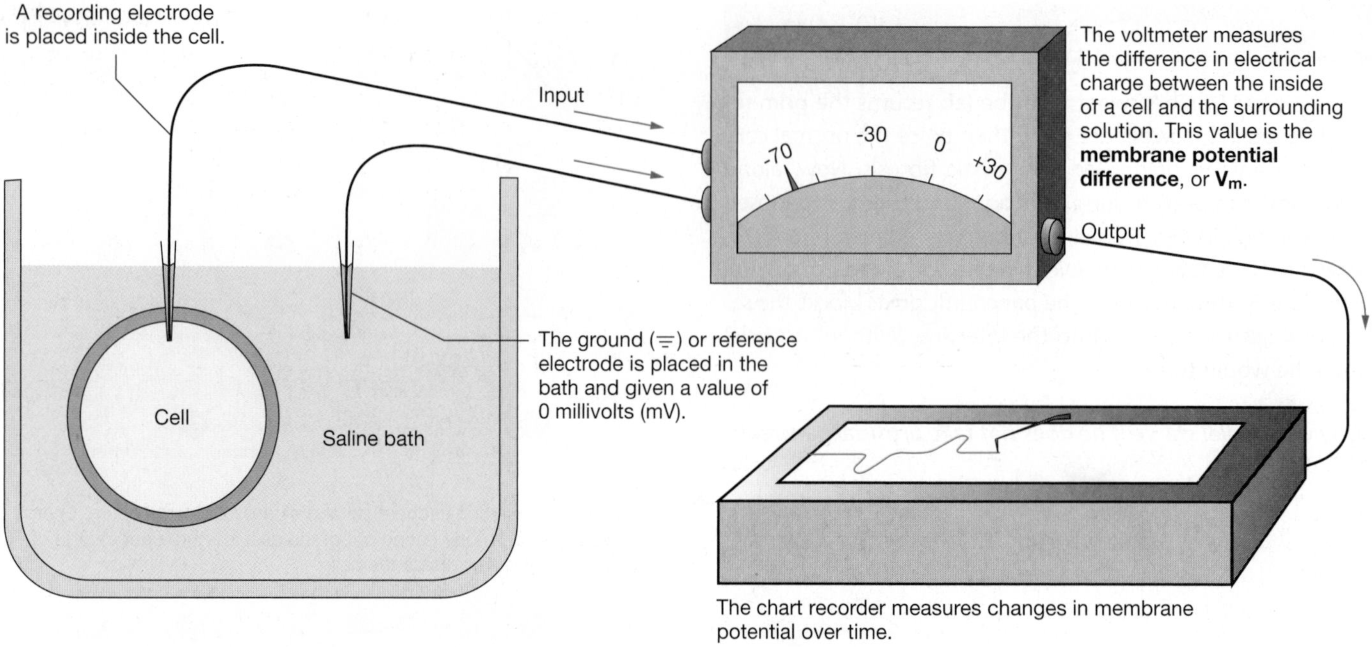
A recording electrode is placed inside the cell.
Input
-70
-30
0
+30
The voltmeter measures the difference in electrical charge between the inside of a cell and the surrounding solution. This value is the **membrane potential difference**, or V_m.
Output
The ground (⏚) or reference electrode is placed in the bath and given a value of 0 millivolts (mV).
Cell
Saline bath
The chart recorder measures changes in membrane potential over time.

● **FIGURE 5-30** ***Measuring membrane potential difference.*** In the laboratory, a voltmeter measures the difference in electrical charge between the inside of a cell and the surrounding solution.

The active transport of positive ions out of the cell also creates a concentration gradient: there are now more positive ions outside the cell than inside. The combination of electrical and concentration gradients is called an **electrochemical gradient.** The cell remains in osmotic equilibrium because water can move freely across the membrane in response to solute movement.

An electrical gradient between the extracellular fluid and the intracellular fluid is known as the **resting membrane potential difference**, or **membrane potential** for short. Although the name sounds intimidating, we can break it apart to see what it means.

1. The *resting* part of the name comes from the fact that this electrical gradient is seen in all living cells, even those that appear to be without electrical activity. In these "resting" cells, the membrane potential has reached a steady state and is not changing.
2. The *potential* part of the name comes from the fact that the electrical gradient created by active transport of ions across the cell membrane is a form of stored, or potential, energy, just as concentration gradients are a form of potential energy. When oppositely charged molecules come back together, they release energy that can be used to do work, in the same way that molecules moving down their concentration gradient can do work. The work done by electrical energy includes opening voltage-gated membrane channels and sending electrical signals.
3. The *difference* part of the name is to remind you that the membrane potential represents a difference in the amount of electrical charge inside and outside the cell. The word *difference* is usually dropped from the name, as noted earlier.

In living systems, we measure electrical gradients on a relative scale rather than an absolute scale. Figure 5-29c compares the two scales. On the absolute scale, the extracellular fluid in our simple example has a net charge of +1 from the positive ion it gained, and the intracellular fluid has a net charge of −1 from the now-unbalanced negative ion that was left behind.

However, in real life we cannot measure electrical charge as numbers of electrons gained or lost. Instead we use a device that measures the *difference* in electrical charge between two points. This device artificially sets the net electrical charge of one side of the membrane at zero and measures the net charge of the second side relative to the first. In our example, resetting the extracellular fluid net charge to zero gives the intracellular fluid a net charge of −2, and we call this value the cell's resting membrane potential.

The equipment for measuring a cell's membrane potential is depicted in Figure 5-30 ●. *Electrodes* are created from hollow glass tubes drawn to very fine points. These *micropipettes* are filled with a liquid that conducts electricity and then connected to a *voltmeter,* which measures the electrical difference between two points in units of either volts (V) or millivolts (mV). A *recording electrode* is inserted through the cell membrane into the cytoplasm of the cell. A *reference electrode* is placed in the external bath, which represents the extracellular fluid.

In living systems, by convention, the extracellular fluid is designated as the *ground* and assigned a charge of 0 mV

(a) An artificial cell whose membrane is impermeable to ions is filled with K^+ and large protein anions. It is placed in a solution of Na^+ and Cl^-. Both cell and solution are electrically neutral.

(b) A K^+ leak channel is inserted into the membrane. K^+ leaks out of the cell because there is a K^+ concentration gradient.

(c) The negative membrane potential attracts K^+ back into the cell. When the electrical gradient exactly opposes the K^+ concentration gradient, the resting membrane potential is the **equilibrium potential** for K^+.

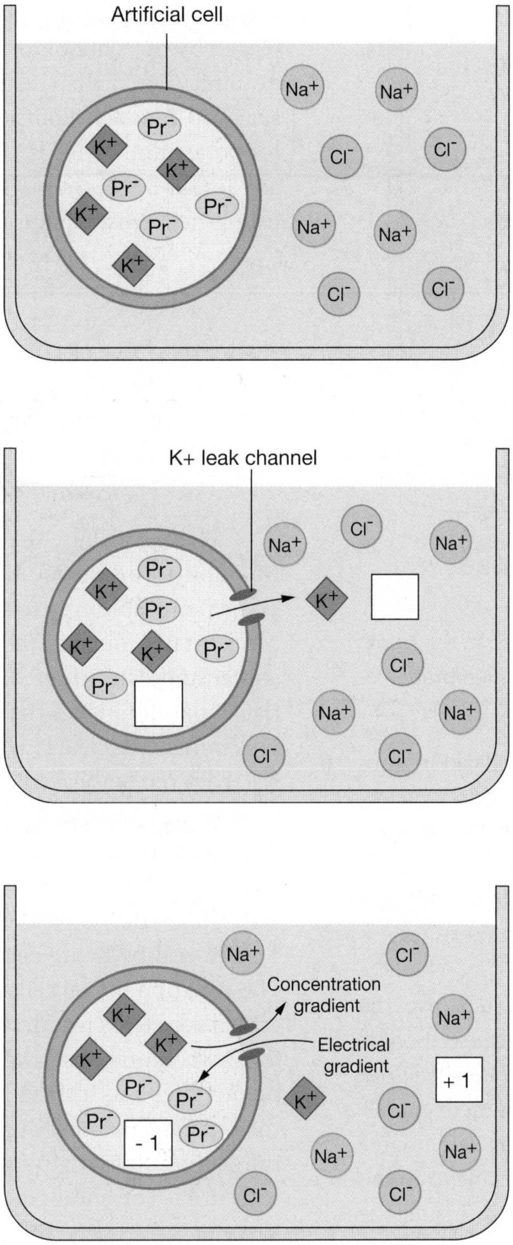

● **FIGURE 5-31** ***Potassium equilibrium potential.*** The potassium equilibrium potential, or E_K, is the membrane potential at which the chemical and electrical gradients are equal in magnitude and opposite in direction, resulting in no net movement of K^+.

FIGURE QUESTION

In the white boxes write the net electrical charge of the intracellular and extracellular compartments as shown.

FIGURE QUESTION

Why don't Na^+, Cl^-, and the proteins (Pr^-) cross the membrane?

(Fig. 5-29c). When the recording electrode is placed inside a living cell, the voltmeter measures the membrane potential—in other words, the electrical difference between the intracellular fluid and the extracellular fluid. A chart recorder connected to the voltmeter can make a recording of the membrane potential versus time.

For nerve and muscle cells, the voltmeter will record a resting membrane potential between -40 and -90 mV, indicating that the intracellular fluid is negative relative to the extracellular fluid (0 mV). (Throughout this discussion, remember that the extracellular fluid is not really neutral because it has excess positive charges that exactly balance the excess negative charges inside the cell, as shown in Figure 5-29c. The total body remains electrically neutral at all times.)

The Resting Membrane Potential Is Due Mostly to Potassium

Which ions create the resting membrane potential in animal cells? The artificial cell shown in Figure 5-29b used an active transport protein to move an unspecified positive ion across a membrane that was otherwise impermeable to ions. But what processes go on in living cells to create an electrical gradient?

Real cells are not completely impermeable to all ions. They have open channels and protein transporters that allow ions to move between the cytoplasm and the extracellular fluid. We can use a different artificial cell to show how the resting membrane potential arises in a typical living cell.

The artificial cell in Figure 5-31a ● has a membrane that is impermeable to ions. The cell contains K^+ and large negatively

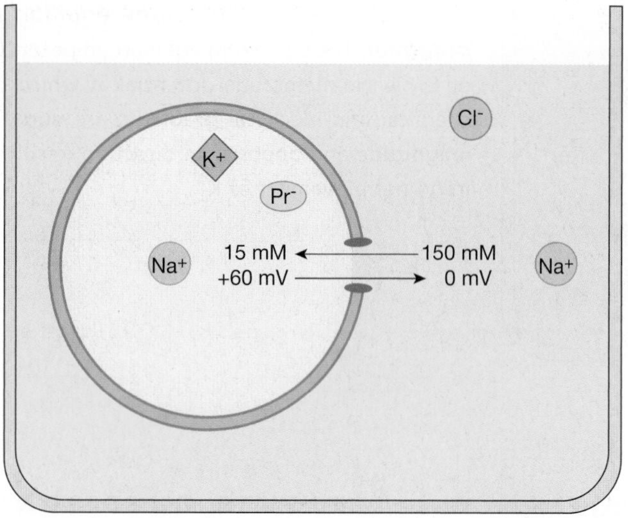

The Na^+ concentration gradient shown is exactly opposed by a membrane potential of +60 mV. Therefore +60 mV is the E_{Na} or Na^+ equilibrium potential.

● **FIGURE 5-32** ***Sodium equilibrium potential.*** In this book, ion channels are represented by open pores on the membrane.

charged proteins, represented by Pr^-. The cell is placed in a solution of Na^+ and Cl^-. Both the cell and the solution are electrically neutral, and the system is in electrical equilibrium. However, it is not in chemical equilibrium. There are concentration gradients for all four types of ions in the system, and they would all diffuse down their respective concentration gradients if they could cross the cell membrane.

In Figure 5-31b, a K^+ leak channel is inserted into the membrane, making it permeable only to K^+. Because there is no K^+ in the extracellular fluid initially, some K^+ ions leak out of the cell, moving down their concentration gradient. As K^+ leaves the cell, the negatively charged proteins, Pr^-, are unable to follow because the cell membrane is not permeable to them. The proteins gradually build up a negative charge inside the cell as more and more K^+ diffuses out of the cell.

If the only force acting on K^+ were the concentration gradient, K^+ would leak out of the cell until the K^+ concentration inside the cell equaled the K^+ concentration outside. The loss of positive ions from the cell creates an electrical gradient, however. Because opposite charges attract each other, the negative proteins inside the cell try to pull K^+ back into the cell. At some point in this process, the electrical force attracting K^+ into the cell becomes equal in magnitude to the chemical concentration gradient driving K^+ out of the cell. At that point, net movement of K^+ across the membrane stops (Fig. 5-31c). The rate at which K^+ ions move out of the cell down the concentration gradient is exactly equal to the rate at which K^+ ions move into the cell down the electrical gradient.

In a cell that is permeable to only one ion, such as the artificial cell just described, the membrane potential that exactly opposes the concentration gradient of the ion is known as the **equilibrium potential,** or $\mathbf{E_{ion}}$ (where the subscript *ion* is replaced by the symbol for whichever ion we are looking at). For example, when the concentration gradient is 150 mM K^+ inside and 5 mM K^+ outside the cell, the equilibrium potential for potassium, or E_K, is −90 mV. The equilibrium potential for any ion at 37° C (human body temperature) can be calculated using the Nernst equation:

$$E_{ion} = \frac{61}{z} \log \frac{[\text{ion}]_{out}}{[\text{ion}]_{in}}$$

where 61 is 2.303 RT/F at 37° C*

z is the electrical charge on the ion (+1 for K^+),

$[\text{ion}]_{out}$ and $[\text{ion}]_{in}$ are the ion concentrations outside and inside the cell, and

E_{ion} is measured in mV.

Now we will use the same artificial cell (K^+ and Pr^- inside, Na^+ and Cl^- outside), but this time we will make the membrane permeable only to Na^+ (Fig. 5-32 ●). Because Na^+ is more concentrated outside the cell, some Na^+ moves into the cell and accumulates there. Meanwhile, Cl^- left behind in the extracellular fluid gives that compartment a net negative charge. This imbalance creates an electrical gradient that tends to drive Na^+ back out of the cell. When the Na^+ concentration is 150 mM outside and 15 mM inside, the equilibrium potential for Na^+ (E_{Na}) is +60 mV. In other words, the concentration gradient moving Na^+ into the cell (150 mM outside, 15 mM inside) is exactly opposed by a positive membrane potential of +60 mV.

In reality, living cells are not permeable to only one ion. The situation in real cells is similar to a combination of the two artificial systems just described. If a cell is permeable to several ions, we cannot use the Nernst equation to calculate membrane potential. Instead we must use a related equation called the *Goldman equation* that considers concentration gradients of the permeable ions and the relative permeability of the cell to each ion. For more detail on the Goldman equation, see Chapter 8.

The cell illustrated in Figure 5-33 ● has a resting membrane potential of −70 mV. Most cells are about 40 times more permeable to K^+ than to Na^+, and as a result a cell's resting membrane potential is closer to the E_K of −90 mV than to the E_{Na} of +60 mV. A small amount of Na^+ leaks into the cell, making the inside of the cell less negative than it would be if Na^+ were totally excluded. Additional Na^+ that leaks in is promptly pumped out by the Na^+-K^+-ATPase, as described earlier. At the same time, K^+ ions that leak out of the cell are pumped back in. The pump contributes to the membrane potential by pumping 3 Na^+ out for every 2 K^+ pumped in. Because the Na^+-K^+-ATPase helps maintain the electrical gradient, it is called an *electrogenic* pump.

Not all ion transport creates an electrical gradient. Many transporters, like the Na^+-K^+-$2Cl^-$ (NKCC) symporter, are elec-

*R is the ideal gas constant, T is absolute temperature, and F is the Faraday constant. For additional information, see Appendix B.

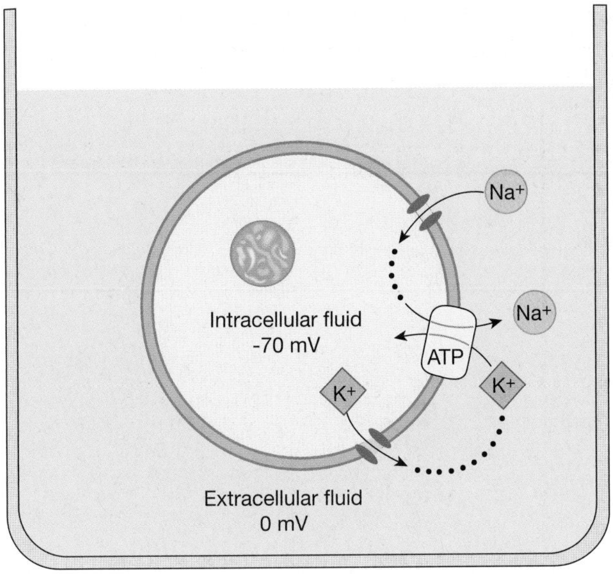

FIGURE QUESTIONS

- What force(s) promote(s) Na^+ leak into the cell?
- What force(s) promote(s) K^+ leak out of the cell?

● **FIGURE 5-33** ***Resting membrane potential in an actual cell.*** Most cells in the human body are about 40 times more permeable to K^+ than to Na^+, and the resting membrane potential is about −70 mV.

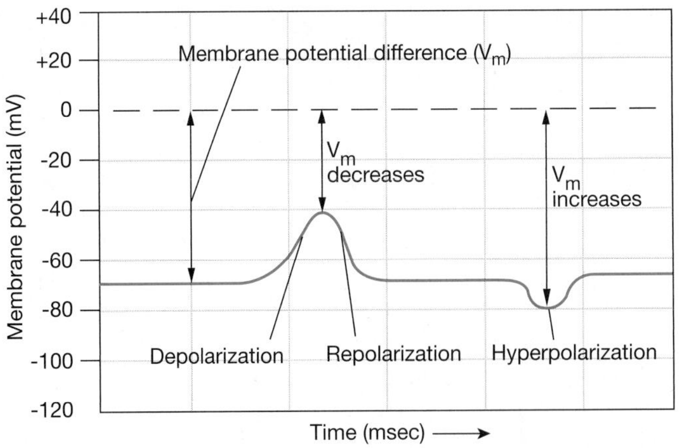

● **FIGURE 5-34** ***Terminology associated with changes in membrane potential.*** If the membrane potential becomes less negative, the cell depolarizes. If the membrane potential becomes more negative than the resting potential, the cell hyperpolarizes.

trically neutral. Some make an even exchange: for each charge that enters the cell, the same charge leaves. An example is the HCO_3^--Cl^- antiporter of red blood cells, which transports these ions in a one-for-one, electrically neutral exchange. Electrically neutral transporters have little effect on the resting membrane potential of the cell.

CONCEPT CHECK

33. Add a Cl^- leak channel to the artificial cell shown in Figure 5-31a, and then figure out which way Cl^- will move along the concentration and electrical gradients. Will the Cl^- equilibrium potential be positive or negative?
34. What would happen to the resting membrane potential of a cell poisoned with ouabain (an inhibitor of the Na^+-K^+-ATPase)?

Answers: p. 176

Changes in Ion Permeability Change the Membrane Potential

As you have just learned, two factors influence a cell's membrane potential: (1) the concentration gradients of different ions across the membrane and (2) the permeability of the membrane to those ions. If the cell's permeability to an ion changes, the cell's membrane potential changes. We monitor changes in membrane potential using the same recording electrodes that we use to record resting membrane potential (Fig. 5-30).

Figure 5-34 ● shows a recording of membrane potential plotted against time. The extracellular electrode is set at 0 mV, and the intracellular electrode records the membrane potential difference. The membrane potential (V_m) begins at a steady resting value of −70 mV. When the trace moves upward (becomes less negative), the potential difference between the inside of the cell and the outside (0 mV) decreases, and the cell is said to have *depolarized.* A return to the resting membrane potential is termed *repolarization.* If the resting potential moves away from 0 mV, the membrane potential becomes more negative, the potential difference has increased, and the cell has *hyperpolarized.*

A major point of confusion when we talk about changes in membrane potential is the use of the phrases "the membrane potential decreased" or "the membrane potential increased." Normally, we associate "increase" with becoming more positive and "decrease" with becoming more negative—the opposite of what is happening in our cell discussion. One way to avoid confusion is to add the word *difference* after *membrane potential.* If the membrane potential *difference* is *increasing,* the value of V_m must be moving away from the ground value of zero and becoming *more negative.* If the membrane potential *difference* is *decreasing,* the value of V_m is moving closer to the ground value of 0 mV and is becoming *less negative.*

What causes changes in membrane potential? In most cases, membrane potential changes in response to movement of one of four ions: Na^+, Ca^{2+}, Cl^-, and K^+. The first three are more concentrated in the extracellular fluid than in the cytosol, and the resting cell is minimally permeable to them. If a cell suddenly becomes more permeable to any one of these ions, then those ions will move across the membrane into the cell. Entry of Ca^{2+} or Na^+ depolarizes the cell (makes the membrane potential more positive). Entry of Cl^- hyperpolarizes the cell (makes the membrane potential more negative).

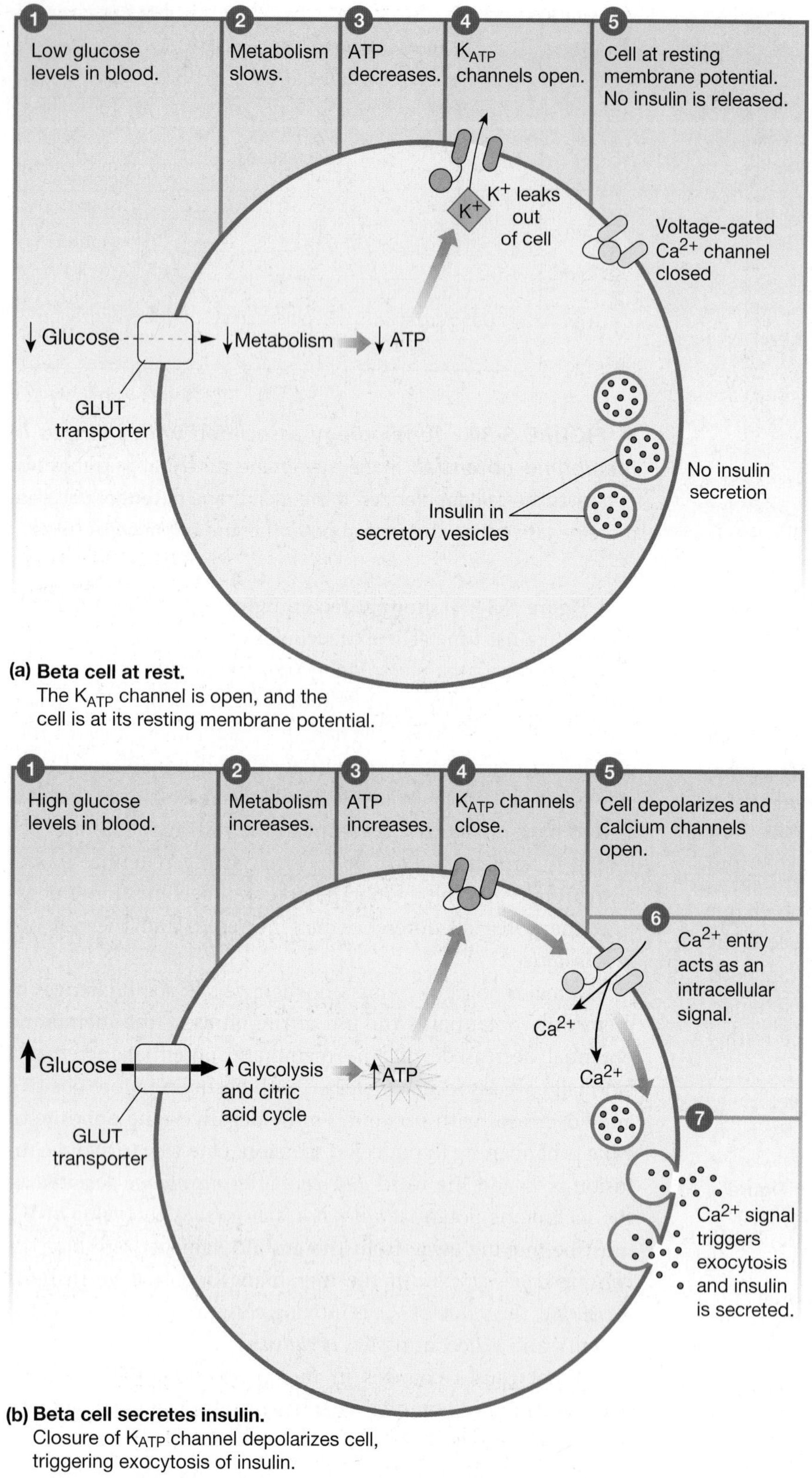

● **FIGURE 5-35** ***Insulin secretion and membrane transport processes***

Most resting cells are fairly permeable to K^+, but making them more permeable allows even more K^+ to leak out. The cell hyperpolarizes until it approaches the equilibrium potential for K^+. Making the cell *less* permeable to K^+ allows fewer K^+ to leak out of the cell. When the cell retains K^+, it becomes more positive and depolarizes. You will encounter instances of all these permeability changes as you study physiology.

It is important to learn that a significant change in membrane potential requires the movement of very few ions. *The concentration gradient does not have to reverse to change the membrane potential.* For example, to change the membrane potential by 100 mV, only one of every 100,000 K^+ must enter or leave the cell. This is such a tiny fraction of the total number of K^+ ions in the cell that the concentration gradient for K^+ remains essentially unchanged.

INTEGRATED MEMBRANE PROCESSES: INSULIN SECRETION

The movement of Na^+ and K^+ across cell membranes has been known to play a role in generating electrical signals in excitable tissues for many years. You will study these processes in detail in the chapters on the nervous and muscular systems. Recently, however, we have come to understand that small changes in membrane potential act as signals in nonexcitable tissues, such as endocrine cells. One of the best-studied examples of this process involves the beta cell of the pancreas. Release of the hormone insulin by beta cells demonstrates how membrane processes—such as facilitated diffusion, exocytosis, and the opening and closing of ion channels by ligands and membrane potential—work together to regulate cell function.

The beta cells of the pancreas synthesize the protein hormone insulin and store it in cytoplasmic secretory vesicles [p. 68]. When blood glucose levels increase, such as after a meal, the beta cells release insulin by exocytosis. Insulin then directs other cells of the body to take up and use glucose, bringing blood concentrations down to pre-meal levels.

A key question about the process that went unanswered until recently was, "How does a beta cell 'know' that glucose levels have gone up and that it needs to release insulin?" The answer, we have now learned, links the beta cell's metabolism to its electrical activity.

Figure 5-35a ● shows a beta cell at rest. Recall from earlier sections in this chapter that the gates of membrane channels can be opened or closed by chemical or electrical signals. The beta cell has two such channels that help control insulin release. One is a **voltage-gated Ca^{2+} channel.** This channel is closed at the cell's resting membrane potential (⑤ in Fig. 5-35a). The other is a K^+ leak channel (that is, the channel is usually open) that closes when ATP binds to it. It is called an **ATP-gated K^+ channel**, or **K_{ATP} channel.** In the resting cell, when glucose concentrations are low, the cell makes less ATP ①-③. There is little ATP to bind to the K_{ATP} channel, and the channel remains open, allowing K^+ to leak out of the cell ④. At the resting membrane potential, the voltage-gated Ca^{2+} channels are closed, and there is no insulin secretion ⑤.

Figure 5-35b shows a beta cell secreting insulin. Following a meal, plasma glucose levels increase as glucose is absorbed from the intestine ①. Glucose reaching the beta cell diffuses into the cell with the aid of a GLUT transporter. Increased glucose in the cell stimulates the metabolic pathways of glycolysis and the citric acid cycle [p. 107], and ATP production increases ②, ③. When ATP binds to the K_{ATP} channel, the gate to the channel closes, preventing K^+ from leaking out of the cell ④. Retention of K^+ depolarizes the cell ⑤, which then causes the voltage-sensitive Ca^{2+} channels to open ⑥. Calcium ions enter the cell from the extracellular fluid, moving down their electrochemical gradient. The Ca^{2+} binds to proteins that initiate exocytosis of the insulin-containing vesicles, and insulin is released into the extracellular space ⑦.

The discovery that cells other than nerve and muscle cells use changes in membrane potential as signals for physiological responses changes our traditional thinking about the role of the resting membrane potential. In the next chapter, we describe some other types of signals that the body uses for communication and coordination.

RUNNING PROBLEM CONCLUSION

Cystic Fibrosis

In this running problem, you learned about cystic fibrosis, one of the most common inherited diseases in the United States. Although there is no cure for this disease, treatments have become better and better so that the life span of CF patients continues to improve. Today the median survival age is around 37.

Cystic fibrosis is caused by a defect in the CFTR channel protein, which regulates the transport of Cl^- into and out of epithelial cells. Because CFTR channels are found in the epithelial cell membranes of several organs—the sweat glands, lungs, and pancreas—cystic fibrosis may affect many different body processes. Some of the most interesting animal research on cystic fibrosis uses genetically altered mice. These model animals can be bred to have either totally nonfunctional CFTR or CFTR channels with altered functions corresponding to the mutations of the CFTR gene in humans. An excellent review paper, "The CF mouse: An important tool for studying cystic fibrosis," can be found in the online journal *Expert Reviews in Molecular Medicine* at *http://www-ermm.cbcu.cam.ac.uk/01002551h.htm* (12 March 2001).

To learn more about current research in this disease, go to the Cystic Fibrosis Foundation web site (*www.cff.org*) and click on the link to Research Overview. To check your understanding of the running problem, compare your answers with the information in the following table.

▶

RUNNING PROBLEM CONCLUSION *(continued)*

	QUESTION	FACTS	INTEGRATION AND ANALYSIS
1	Is the CFTR a chemically gated, a voltage-gated, or a mechanically gated channel protein?	Chemically gated channels open when a ligand binds to them. Voltage-gated channels open with a change in the cell's membrane potential. Mechanically gated channels open when a physical force opens the channel. CFTRs open when ATP binds to the channel protein.	ATP is a chemical ligand, which means CFTRs are chemically gated channel proteins.
2	Based on the information given, is the CFTR protein on the apical or basolateral surface of the sweat gland epithelium?	In normal people, the CFTR channels move Cl^- from sweat into epithelial cells.	The epithelial surface that faces the lumen of the sweat gland, which contains sweat, is the apical membrane. Therefore, the CFTR proteins are on the apical surface.
3	Why would failure to transport Cl^- into the lumen of the airways cause the secreted mucus to be thick? (*Hint*: Remember that water moves to dilute more concentrated regions.)	If Cl^- (followed by Na^+) is secreted into the lumen of the airways, the solute concentration of the airway fluid increases. Water follows in response to concentration gradients.	Normally, the movement of Cl^- and Na^+ creates an osmotic gradient so that water also enters the airway lumen, creating a saline solution that thins the thick mucus. If Cl^- cannot be secreted into the airways, there will be no fluid movement to thin the mucus.
4	Why will Daniel starve if he does not take artificial pancreatic enzymes?	The pancreas secretes mucus and digestive enzymes into ducts that empty into the small intestine. In cystic fibrosis, mucus in the ducts is thick because of lack of Cl^- and fluid secretion. This thick mucus blocks the ducts and prevents digestive enzymes from reaching the small intestine.	Without digestive enzymes, Daniel cannot digest the food he eats. His weight loss over the past six months suggests that this has already become a problem. Taking artificial enzymes will enable him to digest his food.

133 144 156 161 165 171

CHAPTER SUMMARY

In this chapter several key themes come together. You learned how the cell membrane acts as a barrier to create distinct intracellular and extracellular compartments, repeating the theme of *compartmentation* that was introduced in Chapters 3 and 4. Although the contents of the intracellular and extracellular compartments differ, *homeostasis* keeps them in a dynamic steady state. Movement of materials between and within compartments is necessary for *communication* and is accomplished by *mass flow* and *biological transport*. Mass flow across cell membranes occurs in response to osmotic, chemical (concentration), or electrical gradients. The selectively permeable cell membrane creates resistance to mass flow that can be overcome by changing the composition of the membrane lipids or by inserting membrane proteins that act as channels or transporters. Biological transport in the body requires *energy* from different sources: molecular motion, concentration gradients, or chemical bonds. Finally, the binding of substrates to transporters exemplifies the theme of *protein interactions*.

Mass Balance and Homeostasis

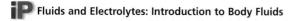

iP Fluids and Electrolytes: Introduction to Body Fluids

1. The **law of mass balance** says that if the amount of a substance in the body is to remain constant, any input must be offset by an equal loss. (p. 133; Fig. 5-1)
2. Input of a substance into the body comes from metabolism or from the outside environment. Output occurs through metabolism or **excretion**. (p. 133; Fig. 5-2)
3. **Clearance** is the rate at which a material is removed from the blood by excretion, metabolism, or both. The liver, kidneys, lungs, and skin all clear substances from the blood. (p. 133)
4. The rate of intake, production, or output of a substance x is expressed as **mass flow**, where mass flow = concentration × volume flow. (p. 134)
5. Cells and the extracellular fluid both maintain homeostasis, but without being in equilibrium with each other. Most solutes are concentrated in either one compartment or the other, creating a state of **chemical disequilibrium.** (p. 134; Fig. 5-3)

6. Cations and anions are not distributed equally between the body compartments, creating a state of **electrical disequilibrium.** (p. 135)
7. Water moves freely between the cells and extracellular fluid, resulting in a state of **osmotic equilibrium.** (p. 135)
8. In **bulk flow** a pressure gradient moves a fluid along with its dissolved and suspended materials. (p. 136)

Diffusion

9. The cell membrane is a selectively permeable barrier that restricts free exchange between the cell and the interstitial fluid. The movement of a substance across the membrane depends on the **permeability** of the membrane to that substance. (p. 136)
10. Movement of molecules across membranes can be classified either by energy requirements or by the physical means the molecule uses to cross the membrane. (p. 136; Fig. 5-4)
11. Lipid-soluble substances can diffuse through the phospholipid bilayer. Less lipid-soluble molecules require the assistance of a membrane protein to cross the membrane. (p. 136)
12. **Passive transport** does not require the input of energy. (p. 136)
13. **Diffusion** is the passive movement of molecules down a chemical (concentration) gradient from an area of higher concentration to an area of lower concentration. Net movement stops when the system reaches **equilibrium,** although molecular movement continues. (p. 137; Fig. 5-5)
14. Diffusion rate depends on the magnitude of the concentration gradient. Diffusion is slow over long distances, is directly related to temperature, and is inversely related to molecular size. (p. 138)
15. **Simple diffusion** across a membrane is directly proportional to membrane surface area, concentration gradient, and membrane permeability, and inversely proportional to membrane thickness. (p. 139; Fig. 5-6)

Protein-Mediated Transport

16. Most molecules cross membranes with the aid of membrane proteins. (p. 141)
17. Membrane proteins have four functional roles: **structural proteins** maintain cell shape and form cell junctions; **membrane-associated enzymes** catalyze chemical reactions and help transfer signals across the membrane; **receptor proteins** are part of the body's signaling system; and **transport proteins** move many molecules into or out of the cell. (pp. 141–142; Fig. 5-7)
18. **Channel proteins** form water-filled channels that link the intracellular and extracellular compartments. **Gated channels** regulate movement of substances through them by opening and closing. Gated channels are regulated by ligands, by the electrical state of the cell, or by physical changes such as pressure. (pp. 141–144; Fig. 5-9)
19. **Carrier proteins** never form a continuous connection between the intracellular and extracellular fluid. They bind to substrates, then change conformation. (p. 144; Fig. 5-11)
20. Protein-mediated diffusion is called **facilitated diffusion.** It has the same properties as simple diffusion. (p. 145; Tbl. 5-1; Fig. 5-12)
21. **Active transport** moves molecules against their concentration gradient and requires an outside source of energy. In **primary (direct) active transport**, the energy comes directly from ATP. **Secondary (indirect) active transport** uses the potential energy stored in a concentration gradient and is indirectly driven by energy from ATP. (pp. 146–148)
22. The most important primary active transporter is the **sodium-potassium ATPase** (Na^+-K^+-ATPase), which pumps Na^+ out of the cell and K^+ into the cell. (p. 147; Fig. 5-13)
23. Most secondary active transport systems are driven by the sodium concentration gradient. (p. 147; Tbl. 5-3; Fig. 5-15)
24. All carrier-mediated transport demonstrates **specificity, competition,** and **saturation.** Specificity refers to the ability of a transporter to move only one molecule or a group of closely related molecules. Related molecules may compete for a single transporter. Saturation occurs when a group of membrane transporters are working at their maximum rate. (pp. 148–151; Figs. 5-17, 5-19)

Vesicular Transport

25. Large macromolecules and particles are brought into cells by **phagocytosis** and **endocytosis.** Material leaves cells by **exocytosis.** When vesicles that come into the cytoplasm by endocytosis are returned to the cell membrane, the process is called **membrane recycling.** (p. 152; Figs. 5-20, 5-21)
26. In **receptor-mediated endocytosis,** ligands bind to membrane receptors that concentrate in **coated pits,** the site of endocytosis. In **potocytosis,** receptors are located in **caveolae** that have a caveolin protein coating. (pp. 153–154; Fig. 5-21)
27. In exocytosis, the vesicle membrane fuses with the cell membrane before releasing its contents into the extracellular space. Exocytosis requires ATP. (p. 154)

Epithelial Transport

28. Transporting epithelia have different membrane proteins on their **apical** and **basolateral** surfaces. This polarization allows one-way movement of molecules across the epithelium. (pp. 154–155; Figs. 5-22, 5-23)
29. Molecules cross epithelia by moving between the cells (the **paracellular** route) or through the cells (**transcellular** route). (p. 155)
30. Larger molecules cross epithelia by **transcytosis,** which includes **vesicular transport.** (p. 157; Fig. 5-24)

Osmosis and Tonicity

31. The movement of water across a membrane in response to a concentration gradient is called **osmosis.** (p. 159; Fig. 5-26)
32. To compare solution concentrations, we express the concentration in terms of **osmolarity,** the number of particles (ions or intact molecules) per liter of solution, expressed as milliosmoles per liter (mOsM). (p. 160)
33. **Tonicity** of a solution describes the cell volume change that occurs if the cell is placed in that solution. Cells swell in **hypotonic solutions** and shrink in **hypertonic solutions.** If the cell does not change size at equilibrium, the solution is **isotonic.** (p. 161)
34. The osmolarity of a solution cannot be used to determine the tonicity of the solution. The relative concentrations of **nonpenetrating solutes** in the cell and in the solution determine tonicity. **Penetrating solutes** contribute to the osmolarity of a solution but not to its tonicity. (p. 162; Figs. 5-27, 5-28)

The Resting Membrane Potential

iP Nervous I: The Membrane Potential

35. Although the total body is electrically neutral, diffusion and active transport of ions across the cell membrane create an **electrical gradient,** with the inside of cells negative relative to the extracellular fluid. (p. 165; Fig. 5-30)
36. The electrical gradient between the extracellular fluid and the intracellular fluid is known as the **resting membrane potential difference.** (p. 166)

37. The movement of an ion across the cell membrane is influenced by the **electrochemical gradient** for that ion. (p. 166)
38. The membrane potential that exactly opposes the concentration gradient of an ion is known as the **equilibrium potential** (E_{ion}). The equilibrium potential for any ion can be calculated using the Nernst equation. (p. 168; Fig. 5-31)
39. In most living cells, K^+ is the primary ion that determines the resting membrane potential. (p. 168)
40. Changes in membrane permeability to ions such as K^+, Na^+, Ca^{2+}, or Cl^- alter membrane potential and create electrical signals. (p. 169)

Integrated Membrane Processes: Insulin Secretion

41. The use of electrical signals to initiate a cellular response is a universal property of living cells. Pancreatic beta cells release insulin in response to a change in membrane potential. (p. 171; Fig. 5-35)

QUESTIONS

(Answers to the Review Questions begin on page A1.)

THE PHYSIOLOGY PLACE

Access more review material online at **The Physiology Place** web site. There you'll find review questions, problem-solving activities, case studies, flashcards, and direct links to both *Interactive Physiology®* and *PhysioEx™*. To access the site, go to *www.physiologyplace.com* and select *Human Physiology*, Fifth Edition.

LEVEL ONE REVIEWING FACTS AND TERMS

1. List the four functions of membrane proteins, and give an example of each.
2. Distinguish between active transport and passive transport.
3. Which of the following processes are examples of active transport, and which are examples of passive transport? Simple diffusion, phagocytosis, facilitated diffusion, exocytosis, osmosis, endocytosis, potocytosis.
4. List four factors that increase the rate of diffusion in air.
5. Match the membrane channels with the appropriate description(s). Answers may be used once, more than once, or not at all.

(a) chemically gated channel	1. channel that spends most of its time in the open state
(b) open pore	2. channel that opens in response to a signal
(c) voltage-gated channel	3. channel that opens when resting membrane potential changes
(d) mechanically gated channel	4. channel that opens when a ligand binds to it
	5. channel that opens in response to membrane stretch
	6. channel through which water can pass

6. List the three physical methods by which materials enter cells.
7. A cotransporter is a protein that moves more than one molecule at a time. If the molecules are moved in the same direction, the cotransporters are called ________ carriers; if the molecules are transported in opposite directions, the cotransporters are called ________ carriers. A transport protein that moves only one substrate is called a(n) ________ carrier.
8. The two types of active transport are ________, which derives energy directly from ATP, and ________, which couples the kinetic energy of one molecule moving down its concentration gradient to the movement of another molecule against its concentration gradient.
9. A molecule that moves freely between the intracellular and extracellular compartments is said to be a(n) ________ solute. A molecule that is not able to enter cells is called a(n) ________ solute.
10. Rank the following individuals in order of how much body water they contain, from highest to lowest: (a) a 25-year-old, 70-kg male; (b) a 25-year-old, 50-kg female; (c) a 65-year-old, 50-kg female; and (d) a 1-year-old male toddler.
11. What determines the osmolarity of a solution? In what units is body osmolarity usually expressed?
12. What does it mean if we say that a solution is hypotonic to a cell? Hypertonic to the same cell? What determines the tonicity of a solution relative to a cell?
13. In your own words, state the four principles of electricity important in physiology.
14. Match each of the following items with its primary role in cellular activity.

(a) Na^+-K^+-ATPase	1. ion channel
(b) protein	2. extracellular cation
(c) unit of measurement for membrane potential	3. source of energy
(d) K^+	4. intracellular anion
(e) Cl^-	5. intracellular cation
(f) ATP	6. millivolts
(g) Na^+	7. electrogenic pump
	8. extracellular anion
	9. milliosmoles

15. The membrane potential at which the electrical gradient exactly opposes the concentration gradient for an ion is known as the ________.
16. A material that allows free movement of electrical charges is called a(n) ________, whereas one that prevents this movement is called a(n) ________.

LEVEL TWO REVIEWING CONCEPTS

17. Create a map of transport across cell membranes using the following terms. You may add additional terms if you wish.

active transport	glucose
carrier	GLUT transporter
caveolae	ion
channel	large polar molecule
clathrin-coated pit	ligand
concentration gradient	Na^+-K^+-ATPase
electrochemical gradient	osmosis
exocytosis	passive transport
facilitated diffusion	phospholipid bilayer

potocytosis	transcytosis
receptor-mediated endocytosis	vesicle
secondary active transport	vesicular transport
simple diffusion	water
small polar molecule	

18. Draw a large rectangle to represent the total body volume. Using the information in Figure 5-25, divide the box proportionately into compartments to represent the different body compartments. Use the information in Figure 5-3 and add solutes to the compartments. Use large letters for solutes with higher concentrations, and small letters for solutes with low concentrations. Label the cell membranes and the endothelial membrane.
19. What factors influence the rate of diffusion across a membrane? Briefly explain each one.
20. Define the following terms and explain how they differ from one another: specificity, competition, saturation. Apply these terms in a short explanation of facilitated diffusion of glucose.
21. Red blood cells are suspended in a solution of NaCl. The cells have an osmolarity of 300 mOsM, and the solution has an osmolarity of 250 mOsM. (a) The solution is (hypertonic, isotonic, or hypotonic) to the cells. (b) Water would move (into the cells, out of the cells, or not at all).
22. Two compartments are separated by a membrane that is permeable to glucose. Each compartment is filled with 1 M glucose. After 6 hours, compartment A contains 1.5 M glucose and compartment B contains 0.5 M glucose. What kind of transport occurred?
23. A 2 M NaCl solution is placed in compartment A and a 2 M glucose solution is placed in compartment B. The compartments are separated by a membrane that is permeable to water but not to NaCl or glucose. Complete the following statements. Defend your answers.
    (a) The salt solution is ________ osmotic to the glucose solution.
    (b) True or false? Water will move from one compartment to another. If water moves, it will move from compartment ________ to compartment ________.
24. Explain the differences between a chemical gradient, an electrical gradient, and an electrochemical gradient.

LEVEL THREE PROBLEM SOLVING

25. Sweat glands secrete into their lumen a fluid that is identical to interstitial fluid. As the fluid moves through the lumen on its way to the surface of the skin, the cells of the sweat gland's epithelium make the fluid hypotonic by removing Na^+ and leaving water behind. Design an epithelial cell that will reabsorb Na^+ but not water. You may place water pores, Na^+ leak channels, K^+ leak channels, and the Na^+-K^+-ATPase in the apical membrane, basolateral membrane, or both.
26. Insulin is a hormone that promotes the movement of glucose into many types of cells, thereby lowering blood glucose concentration. Propose a mechanism that explains how this occurs, using your knowledge of cell membrane transport.
27. The following terms have been applied to membrane carriers: specificity, competition, saturation. These terms can also be applied to enzymes. How does the application of these terms change in the two situations? What chemical characteristics do enzymes and carriers share that allow these terms to be applied to both?
28. NaCl is a nonpenetrating solute and urea is a penetrating solute for cells. Red blood cells are placed in each of the solutions below. The intracellular concentration of nonpenetrating solute is 300 mOsM. What will happen to the cell volume in each solution? Label each solution with all the terms that apply: hypertonic, isotonic, hypotonic, hyperosmotic, hyposmotic, isosmotic. Watch units!
    (a) 150 mM NaCl plus 150 mM urea
    (b) 100 mM NaCl plus 50 mM urea
    (c) 100 mM NaCl plus 100 mM urea
    (d) 150 mM NaCl plus 100 mM urea
    (e) 100 mM NaCl plus 150 mM urea
29. Integral membrane glycoproteins have sugars added as the proteins pass through the lumen of the endoplasmic reticulum and Golgi complex [p. 124]. Based on this information, where would you predict finding the sugar "tails" of the proteins: on the cytoplasmic side of the membrane, the extracellular side, or both? Explain your reasoning.

LEVEL FOUR QUANTITATIVE PROBLEMS

30. The addition of dissolved solutes to water lowers the freezing point of water. A 1 OsM solution depresses the freezing point of water 1.86° C. If a patient's plasma shows a freezing-point depression of 0.550° C, what is her plasma osmolarity? (Assume that 1 kg water = 1 L.)
31. The patient in the previous question is found to have total body water volume of 42 L, ECF volume of 12.5 L, and plasma volume of 2.7 L.
    (a) What is her intracellular fluid (ICF) volume? Her interstitial fluid volume?
    (b) How much solute (osmoles) exists in her whole body? ECF? ICF? plasma? (*Hint*: concentration = solute amount/volume of solution)
32. What is the osmolarity of half-normal saline (= 0.45% NaCl)? [p. 37] Assume that all NaCl molecules dissociate into two ions.
33. If you give 1 L of half-normal saline (see question 32) to the patient in question 31, what happens to each of the following at equilibrium? (*Hint:* NaCl is a nonpenetrating solute.)
    (a) her total body volume
    (b) her total body osmolarity
    (c) her ECF and ICF volumes
    (d) her ECF and ICF osmolarities
34. The following graph shows the results of an experiment in which a cell was placed in a solution of glucose. The cell had no glucose in it at the beginning, and its membrane can transport glucose. Which of the following processes is/are illustrated by this experiment?
    (a) simple diffusion
    (b) saturation
    (c) competition
    (d) active transport

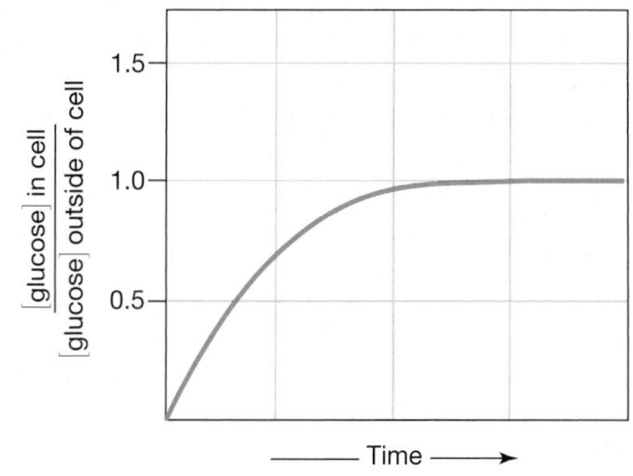

ANSWERS

Answers to Concept Check Questions

Page 134

1. The remaining 1 milligram of salt remains in the body.
2. Glucose metabolism adds CO_2 and water to the body, disturbing the mass balance of these two substances. To maintain mass balance, both metabolites must be either excreted or further metabolized.

Page 136

3. Plasma is part of the ECF, so knowing the plasma concentration of (a) Na^+ and (b) K^+ tells you the ECF concentration of these ions. The ICF ion concentrations are different from the ECF, so plasma concentration will not tell you the ICF values. (c) The body is in osmotic equilibrium, so water concentration is the same in all compartments. (d) Proteins are in the plasma but not in the interstitial fluid, so plasma protein concentration will not tell you ECF or ICF protein concentrations.

Page 136

4. The stem preceding the suffix *–ase* is the name of the substrate on which the enzyme acts; therefore ATP is a substrate for this enzyme.
5. Intracellular fluid has a high K^+ concentration and low Na^+, Cl^-, and Ca^{2+} concentrations.

Page 139

6. If distance triples, diffusion takes nine times as long.

Page 141

7. Energy for diffusion comes from molecular motion.
8. Because it is lipophilic, the fatty acid is more likely to cross by simple diffusion.
9. The diffusion rate (a) decreases, (b) increases, (c) decreases.
10. Compartment A remains yellow, and compartment B turns green.
11. The skin's thick extracellular matrix is generally impermeable to oxygen. Also, oxygen needs a moist surface to effectively diffuse across a membrane.

Page 144

12. Positive ions are cations, and negative ions are anions.

Page 145

13. Membrane proteins serve as structural proteins, receptors, enzymes, and transporters.
14. Ions and water molecules move through open channels.
15. Channel proteins form continuous connections between the two sides of a membrane and transport molecules more quickly.
16. A channel lined with positive charges attracts anions, which in this instance means Cl^-.
17. Glucose is too large to pass through a channel.

Page 146

18. The direction of facilitated diffusion of glucose reverses, and glucose leaves the cell.

Page 148

19. The ATPase is an antiporter, but the SGLT is a symporter. The ATPase requires energy from ATP to change conformation, whereas the SGLT uses energy stored in the Na^+ concentration gradient.

Page 152

20. An antiporter moves substrates in opposite directions.
21. Larger doors could move more people. This would be analogous to a cell's synthesizing a new isoform of the transporter that would let the transporter move more substrate per second.

Page 154

22. In phagocytosis, the cytoskeleton pushes the membrane out to engulf a particle in a large vesicle. In endocytosis, the membrane surface indents and the vesicle is much smaller.
23. The proteins associated with endocytosis are clathrin and caveolin.
24. Proteins move into cells by endocytosis and out of cells by exocytosis.

Page 157

25. Sodium movement out of the cell requires energy because the direction of ion flow is against the concentration gradient.
26. Ouabain applied to the apical side would have no effect because there are no Na^+-K^+-ATPase molecules on that side. Ouabain applied to the basolateral side would stop the pump. Glucose transport would continue for a time until the Na^+ gradient between the cell and the lumen disappears because Na^+ has entered the cell.
27. The GLUT2 transporter is illustrated.

Page 157

28. Transcytosis will stop because vesicular transport by the cytoskeleton depends on functioning microtubules.

Page 160

29. The baby has lost 0.91 kg of water, which is 0.91 liter.

Page 163

30. 1 M NaCl = 2 OsM NaCl. The 1 M (= 1 OsM) glucose and 1 OsM NaCl have the most water.
31. (a) Water moves into A because A is 2 OsM; (b) no net movement occurs because urea will diffuse across the membrane until it reaches equilibrium; (c) water moves into A, because A has a higher concentration of nonpenetrating solutes.
32. (a) The NaCl solution is better, even though both solutions are isosmotic to the body (Tbl. 5-8). Because blood is lost from the extracellular compartment, the best replacement solution would remain in the ECF. For this reason glucose is not as good a choice because it slowly enters cells, taking water with it. (b) If 1 L has been lost, you should replace at least 1 L.

Page 169

33. Cl^- will move into the cell down its concentration gradient, which would make the inside of the cell negative. The positive charges left outside would attract Cl^- back outside. The equilibrium potential would be negative.
34. Over time, Na^+ would leak into the cell, and the resting membrane potential would become more positive.

Answers to Figure and Graph Questions

Page 135

Fig. 5-3: 1. Plasma contains proteins and large anions not present in interstitial fluid. 2. The extracellular compartment contains more Na^+, Cl^-, and bicarbonate than the intracellular compartment, and fewer K^+.

Page 151

Fig. 5-19: You should mark the *x*-axis at the point where the curve levels off to a horizontal line.

Page 156

Fig. 5-23: (a) 1 = b; 2 = a; 3 = b. (b) Basolateral glucose transport is passive because the glucose moves down its concentration gradient. (c) Na^+ movement across the apical membrane does not require ATP because Na^+ is moving down its concentration gradient.

Page 158

Fig. 5-25: (1) 25% of 14 L = 3.5 L plasma. 75% = 10.5 L interstitial fluid. (2) Total body water = 42 L. (3) 3.5 L/42 L = 8.3% plasma; 10.5 L/42 L = 25% interstitial volume.

Page 163

Fig. 5-28: (a) isosmotic and isotonic; (b) hyperosmotic and isotonic; (c) hyperosmotic and hypotonic.

Page 167

Fig. 5-31: ICF = −1 and ECF = +1. The cell membrane is not permeable to Na^+, Cl^-, and proteins.

Page 169

Fig. 5-33: (1) Na^+ leak, into the cell is promoted by concentration and electrical gradients. (2) K^+ leaks out of the cell are promoted by the concentration gradient.

6 Communication, Integration, and Homeostasis

BACKGROUND BASICS

Homeostasis: **4** Nucleotides: **34** Cell junctions: **72** Extracellular matrix: **80** Endocrine glands: **79** Membrane structure: **56** Membrane proteins: **58, 141** Diffusion: **136** Exocytosis: **154**

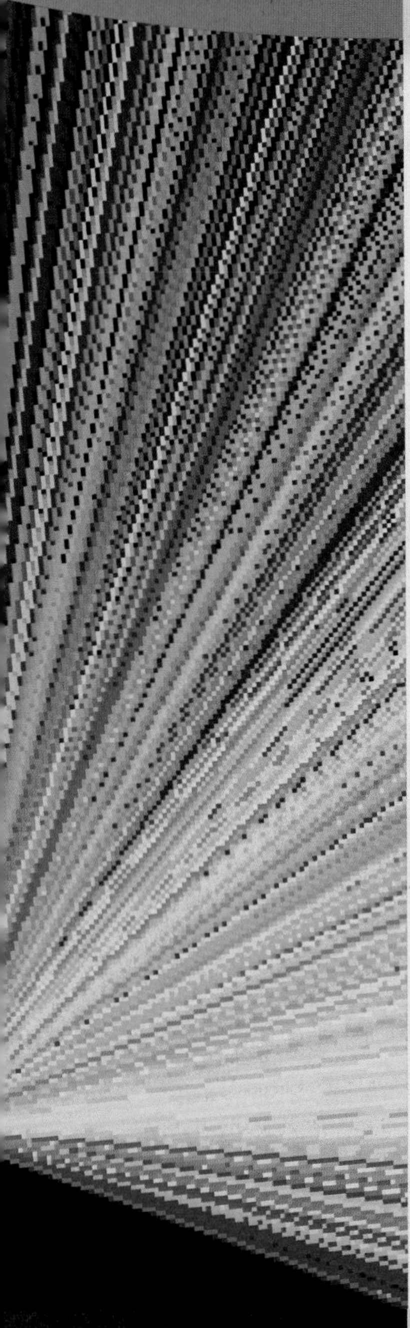

Computer analysis of microarray data showing gene expression.

Future progress in medicine will require a quantitative understanding of the many interconnected networks of molecules that comprise our cells and tissues, their interactions, and their regulation.

—Overview of the NIH Roadmap, 2003

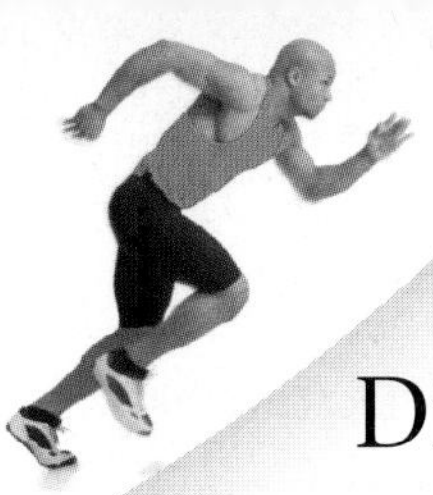

RUNNING PROBLEM

Diabetes Mellitus

It is 8:00 A.M., and Marvin Garcia, age 20, is hungry. He came to his family physician's office before breakfast to have a fasting blood glucose test as part of a routine physical examination. In this test, blood is drawn after an overnight fast, and the glucose concentration in the blood is measured. Because he knows he is in good condition, Marvin isn't worried about the results. He is surprised, then, when the nurse practitioner in the doctor's office calls two days later. "Your fasting blood sugar is a bit elevated, Marvin. It is 150 milligrams per deciliter, and normal is 110 or less. Does anyone in your family have diabetes?" "Well, yeah—my dad has it. What exactly is diabetes?"

179 182 195 198 201 205 210

In 2003 the United States National Institutes of Health embarked on an ambitious project to promote translation of basic research into new medical treatments and strategies for disease prevention. Contributors to the NIH Roadmap (*http://nihroadmap.nih.gov*) are compiling information on biological pathways in an effort to understand how cells communicate with one another and maintain the body in a healthy state. In this chapter we examine the basic patterns of cell-to-cell communication and see how the coordination of function resides in chemical and electrical signals. Each cell in the body can communicate with most other cells to maintain homeostasis by using a combination of simple diffusion across small distances, widespread distribution of molecules through the circulatory system, and rapid, specific delivery of messages by the nervous system.

CELL-TO-CELL COMMUNICATION

In recent years the amount of information available about cell-to-cell communication has mushroomed as a result of advances in research technology. Signal pathways that once seemed fairly simple and direct are now known to be incredibly complex networks and webs of information transfer. In the sections that follow, we distill what is known about cell-to-cell communication into some basic patterns that you can learn and recognize when you encounter them again in your study of physiology.

By most estimates the human body is composed of about 75 *trillion* cells. Those cells face a daunting task—to communicate with one another in a manner that is rapid and yet conveys a tremendous amount of information. Surprisingly, there are only two basic types of physiological signals: electrical and chemical. **Electrical signals** are changes in a cell's membrane potential [p. 164]. **Chemical signals** are molecules secreted by cells into the extracellular fluid. Chemical signals are responsible for most communication within the body. The cells that receive electrical or chemical signals are called **target cells**, or **targets** for short.

Our bodies use four basic methods of cell-to-cell communication: (1) **gap junctions**, which allow direct cytoplasmic transfer of electrical and chemical signals between adjacent cells; (2) **contact-dependent signals**, which occur when surface molecules on one cell membrane bind to surface molecules on another cell's membrane; (3) **local communication** by chemicals that diffuse through the extracellular fluid; and (4) **long-distance communication** through a combination of electrical signals carried by nerve cells and chemical signals transported in the blood. A given molecule can function as a signal by more than one method. For example, a molecule can act close to the cell that released it (local communication) as well as in distant parts of the body (long-distance communication).

Gap Junctions Create Cytoplasmic Bridges

The simplest form of cell-to-cell communication is the direct transfer of electrical and chemical signals through *gap junctions*, protein channels that create cytoplasmic bridges between adjacent cells (Fig. 6-1a ●) [p. 72]. A gap junction forms from the union of membrane-spanning proteins, called *connexins*, on two adjacent cells. The united connexins create a protein channel, or *connexon*, that can open and close. When the channel is open, the connected cells function like a single cell that contains multiple nuclei (a *syncytium*).

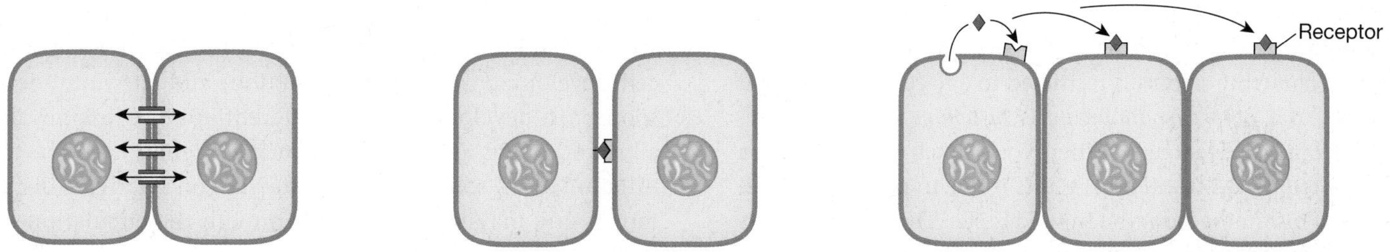

(a) Gap junctions form direct cytoplasmic connections between adjacent cells.

(b) Contact-dependent signals require interaction between membrane molecules on two cells.

(c) Autocrine signals act on the same cell that secreted them. **Paracrine signals** are secreted by one cell and diffuse to adjacent cells.

● **FIGURE 6-1** *Direct contact and local cell-to-cell communication*

When gap junctions are open, ions and small molecules such as amino acids, ATP, and cyclic AMP diffuse directly from the cytoplasm of one cell to the cytoplasm of the next. As with other membrane channels, larger molecules cannot pass through gap junctions. In addition, gap junctions are the only means by which electrical signals can pass *directly* from cell to cell. Movement of molecules through gap junctions can be modulated or shut off completely.

Gap junctions are not all alike. Scientists have discovered more than 20 different isoforms of connexins that may mix or match to form gap junctions. The variety of connexin isoforms allows gap junction selectivity to vary from tissue to tissue. In mammals, gap junctions are found in almost every cell type, including heart muscle, some types of smooth muscle, lung, liver, and neurons of the brain.

Contact-Dependent Signals Require Cell-to-Cell Contact

Some cell-to-cell communication requires that surface molecules on one cell membrane bind to a membrane protein of another cell (Fig. 6-1b). Such *contact-dependent signaling* occurs in the immune system and during growth and development, such as when nerve cells send out long extensions that must grow from the central axis of the body to the *distal* (distant) ends of the limbs. **CAMs,** cell adhesion molecules first known for their role in cell-to-cell adhesion [p. 72], have now been shown to act as receptors in cell-to-cell signaling. CAMs are linked to the cytoskeleton and to intracellular enzymes. Through these linkages, CAMs transfer signals in both directions across cell membranes.

Paracrine and Autocrine Signals Carry Out Local Communication

Local communication is accomplished by paracrine and autocrine signaling. A **paracrine signal** [*para-,* beside + *krinen,* to secrete] is a chemical that acts on cells in the immediate vicinity of the cell that secreted the signal. If a chemical signal acts on the cell that secreted it, it is called an **autocrine signal** [*auto-,* self]. In some cases a molecule may act as both an autocrine signal and a paracrine signal.

Paracrine and autocrine signal molecules reach their target cells by diffusing through the interstitial fluid (Fig. 6-1c). Because distance is a limiting factor for diffusion, the effective range of paracrine signals is restricted to adjacent cells. A good example of a paracrine molecule is *histamine,* a chemical released from damaged cells. When you scratch yourself with a pin, the red, raised *wheal* that results is due in part to the local release of histamine from the injured tissue. The histamine acts as a paracrine signal, diffusing to capillaries in the immediate area of the injury and making them more permeable to white blood cells and antibodies in the plasma. Fluid also leaves the blood vessels and collects in the interstitial space, causing swelling around the area of injury.

Several important classes of molecules act as local signals. *Cytokines* are regulatory peptides, and *eicosanoids* [p. 31] are lipid-derived paracrine and autocrine signal molecules. We discuss cytokines and eicosanoids in more detail below.

Long-Distance Communication May Be Electrical or Chemical

All cells in the body can release paracrine signals, but most long-distance communication between cells is the responsibility of the nervous and endocrine systems. The endocrine system communicates by using **hormones** [*hormon,* to excite], chemical signals that are secreted into the blood and distributed all over the body by the circulation. Hormones come in contact with most cells of the body, but only those cells with receptors for the hormone are target cells (Fig. 6-2a ●).

The nervous system uses a combination of chemical signals and electrical signals to communicate over long distances. An electrical signal travels along a nerve cell (*neuron*) until it reaches the very end of the cell, where it is translated into a chemical signal secreted by the neuron. Such a chemical signal is called a **neurocrine.**

If a neurocrine molecule diffuses from the neuron across a narrow extracellular space to a target cell and has a rapid effect, it is called a **neurotransmitter** (Fig. 6-2b). If a neurocrine acts more slowly as an autocrine or paracrine signal, it is called a **neuromodulator**. If a neurocrine released by a neuron diffuses into the blood for distribution, it is called a **neurohormone** (Fig. 6-2c). The similarities between neurohormones and classic hormones secreted by the endocrine system blur the distinction between the nervous and endocrine systems, making them a continuum rather than two distinct systems (see Fig. 6-31, p. 207).

Cytokines May Act as Both Local and Long-Distance Signals

Cytokines are among the most recently identified communication molecules. Initially the term *cytokine* referred only to proteins that modulate immune responses, but in recent years the definition has been broadened to include a variety of regulatory peptides. All nucleated cells synthesize and secrete cytokines in response to stimuli. Cytokines control cell development, cell differentiation, and the immune response. In development and differentiation, cytokines usually function as autocrine or paracrine signals. In stress and inflammation, some cytokines may act on relatively distant targets and may be transported through the circulation just as hormones are.

How do cytokines differ from hormones? In general, cytokines act on a broader spectrum of target cells. In addition,

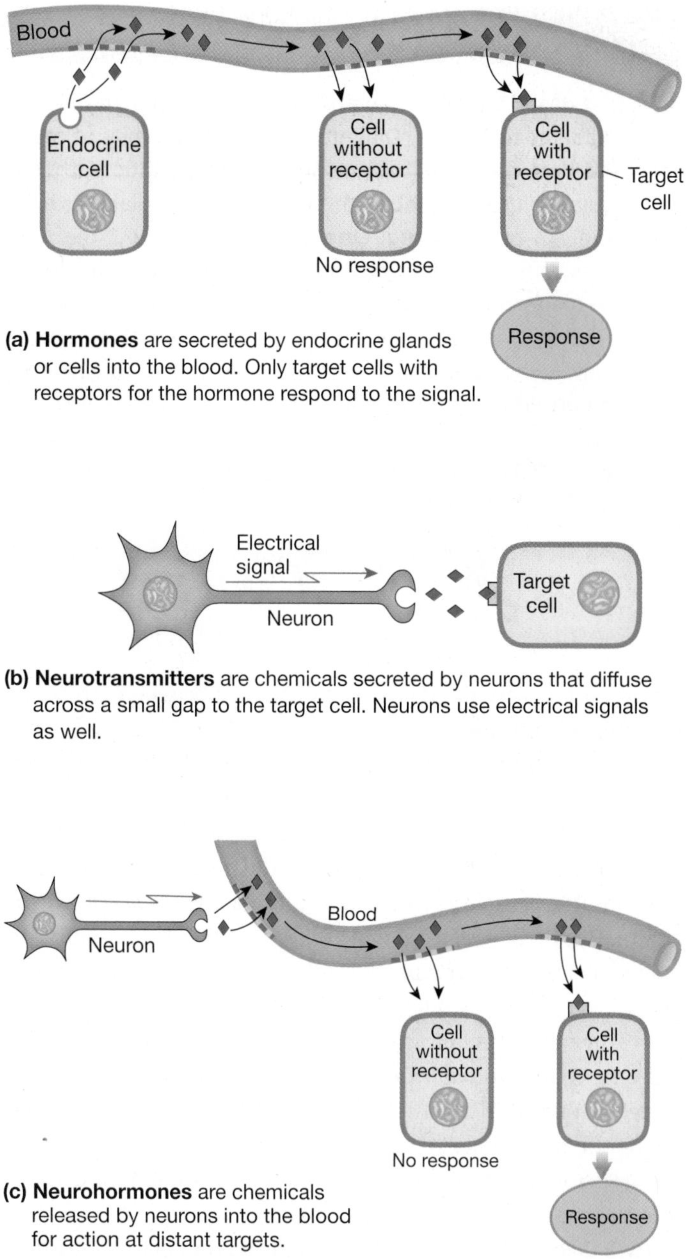

(a) Hormones are secreted by endocrine glands or cells into the blood. Only target cells with receptors for the hormone respond to the signal.

(b) Neurotransmitters are chemicals secreted by neurons that diffuse across a small gap to the target cell. Neurons use electrical signals as well.

(c) Neurohormones are chemicals released by neurons into the blood for action at distant targets.

● **FIGURE 6-2** ***Long distance cell-to-cell communication may be chemical or electrical.***

cytokines are not produced by specialized cells the way hormones are, and they are made on demand. In contrast, most protein or peptide hormones are made in advance and stored in the endocrine cell until needed. Also, the signal pathways for cytokines are usually different from those for hormones. However, the distinction between cytokines and hormones is sometimes blurry. For example, erythropoietin, the molecule that controls synthesis of red blood cells, is by tradition considered a hormone but functionally fits the definition of a cytokine.

CONCEPT CHECK

1. Match the communication method on the left with its property on the right.

	Communication occurs by:
(a) autocrine	1. electrical signals
(b) cytokine	2. chemical signals
(c) gap junction	3. both electrical and chemical signals
(d) hormone	
(e) neurohormone	
(f) neurotransmitter	
(g) paracrine	

2. Which signal molecules listed in the previous question are transported through the circulatory system? Which are released by neurons?
3. A cat sees a mouse and pounces on it. Do you think the internal signal to pounce could have been transmitted by a paracrine signal? Give two reasons to explain why or why not.

Answers: p. 213

SIGNAL PATHWAYS

Chemical signals in the form of paracrine and autocrine molecules and hormones are released from cells into the extracellular compartment. This is not a very specific way for these signals to find their targets because substances that travel through the blood reach nearly every cell in the body. Yet cells do not respond to every signal that reaches them. Why do some cells respond to a chemical signal while other cells ignore it? The answer lies in the target-cell **receptor proteins** to which chemical signals bind [p. 141]. *A cell cannot respond to a chemical signal if the cell lacks the appropriate receptor proteins for that signal* (Fig. 6-2a).

If a target cell has a receptor for a signal molecule, binding of the signal to the receptor protein will initiate a response. All signal pathways share the following common features (Fig. 6-3 ●):

1. The signal molecule is a *ligand* that binds to a receptor. The ligand is also known as a *first messenger* because it brings information to its target cell.
2. Ligand-receptor binding activates the receptor.
3. The receptor in turn activates one or more intracellular signal molecules.
4. The last signal molecule in the pathway initiates synthesis of target proteins or modifies existing target proteins to create a response.

In the following sections, we describe some basic signal pathways. They may seem complex at first, but they follow patterns that you will encounter over and over as you study the systems of the body. Most physiological processes, from the beating of your heart to learning and memory, use some variation of these pathways. One of the wonders of physiology is the fundamental importance of these signal pathways and the way they have been conserved in animals ranging from worms to humans.

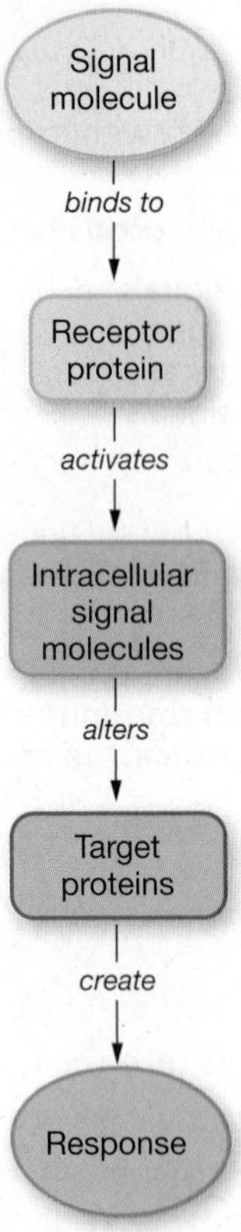

NAVIGATOR

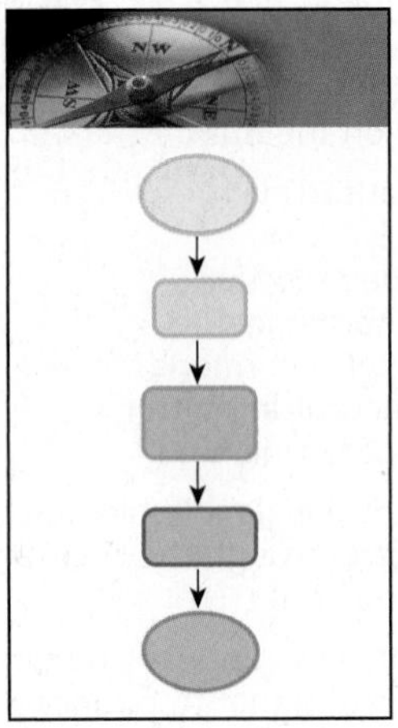

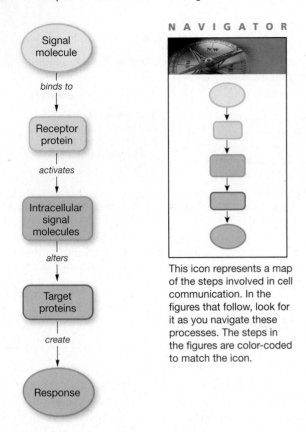

This icon represents a map of the steps involved in cell communication. In the figures that follow, look for it as you navigate these processes. The steps in the figures are color-coded to match the icon.

● **FIGURE 6-3** ***The general pattern of a signal pathway***

Receptor Proteins Are Located Inside the Cell or on the Cell Membrane

Chemical signals fall into two broad categories based on their lipid solubility: lipophilic or lipophobic. Target-cell receptors may be found in the nucleus, in the cytosol, or on the cell membrane as integral proteins. Where a chemical signal binds to its receptor largely depends on whether the signal molecule can enter the cell (Fig. 6-4 ●).

Lipophilic signal molecules can diffuse through the phospholipid bilayer of the cell membrane [p. 136] and bind to *cytosolic receptors* or *nuclear receptors*. In these cases, receptor activation often turns on a gene and directs the nucleus to make new mRNA (transcription, [p. 120]). The mRNA then provides a template for synthesis of new proteins (translation, [p. 123]). This process is relatively slow and the cell's response may not be noticeable for an hour or longer. In some instances the activated receptor can also turn off, or repress, gene activity. Many lipophilic signal molecules that follow this pattern are hormones, so we will defer further discussion of their action to the next chapter.

Lipophobic signal molecules are unable to diffuse through the phospholipid bilayer of the cell membrane. Instead, these signal molecules remain in the extracellular fluid and bind to receptor proteins on the cell membrane. (Some lipophilic signal molecules also bind to cell membrane receptors.) In general, the response time for pathways linked to membrane receptor proteins is very rapid, and responses can be seen within milliseconds to minutes.

Protein receptors for signal molecules play an important role in physiology and medicine. About half of all drugs currently in use act on receptor proteins. We can group membrane receptors into four major categories, illustrated in Figure 6-5 ●. The simplest receptors are chemically gated (*ligand-gated*) ion channels called *receptor-channels* [p. 141]. Ligand binding opens or closes the channel and alters ion flow across the membrane.

Three other receptor types are shown in Figure 6-5: *receptor-enzymes, G protein-coupled receptors,* and *integrin receptors*. For all three, information from the signal molecule must be passed across the membrane to initiate an intracellular response. This transmission of information from one side of a membrane to the other using membrane proteins is known as *signal transduction*. We will take a closer look at signal transduction before returning to the four receptor types that participate in it.

RUNNING PROBLEM

Later that day in the physician's office, the nurse practitioner explains diabetes to Marvin. Diabetes mellitus is a family of metabolic disorders caused by defects in the homeostatic pathways that regulate glucose metabolism. Several forms of diabetes exist, and some can be inherited. One form, called type 1 diabetes mellitus, is caused by deficient production of insulin, a protein hormone made in the pancreas. In another form, called type 2 diabetes mellitus, insulin may be present in normal or above-normal levels, but the insulin-sensitive cells of the body do not respond normally to the hormone.

Question 1:
In which type of diabetes is the signal pathway for insulin more likely to be defective?

CONCEPT CHECK

4. List four components of signal pathways.
5. Name three cellular locations of receptors.

Answers: p. 213

Membrane Proteins Facilitate Signal Transduction

Signal transduction is the process by which an extracellular signal molecule activates a membrane receptor that in turn alters intracellular molecules to create a response. The extracellular signal molecule is the first messenger, and the intracellular molecules form a *second messenger system*. The term *signal transduction* comes from the verb *to transduce,* meaning "to lead across" [*trans,* across + *ducere,* to lead].

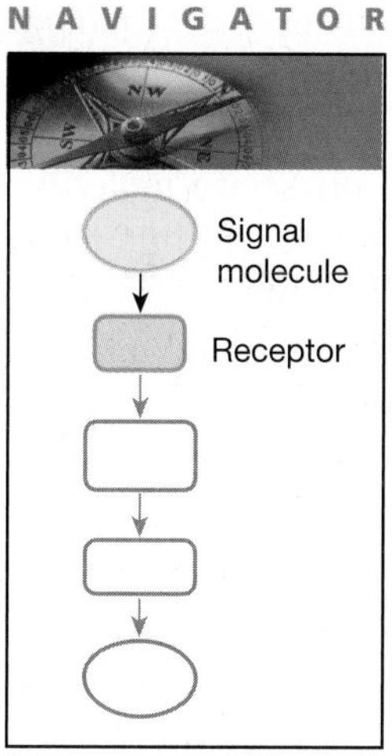

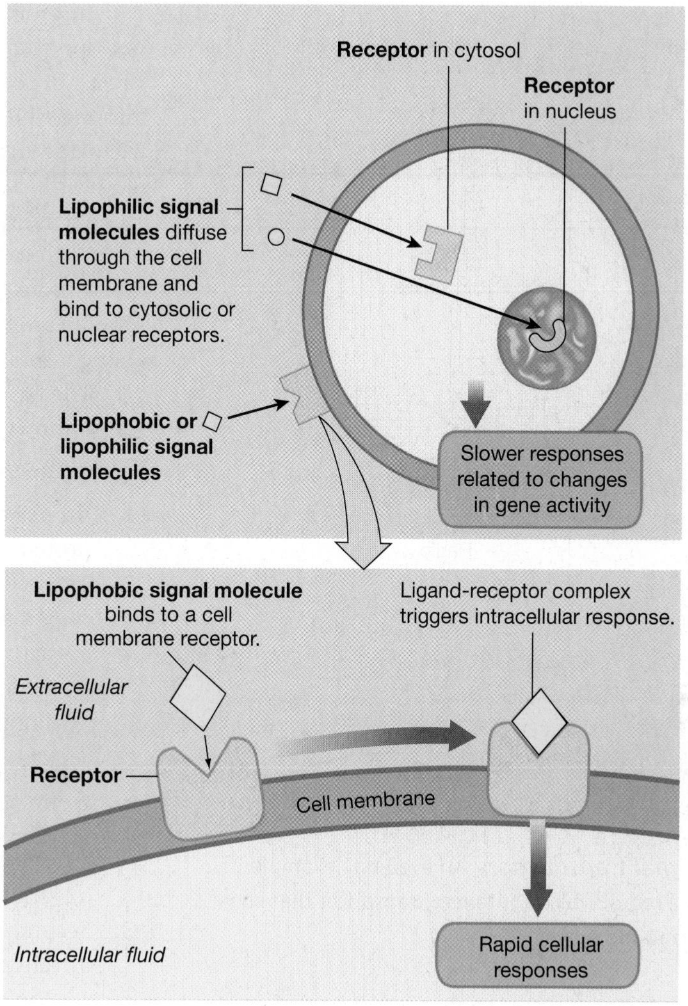

● **FIGURE 6-4** *Target cell receptors may be located in the cell membrane or inside the cell.*

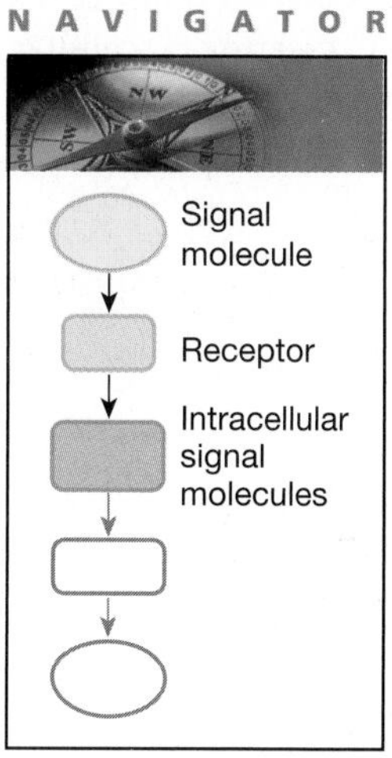

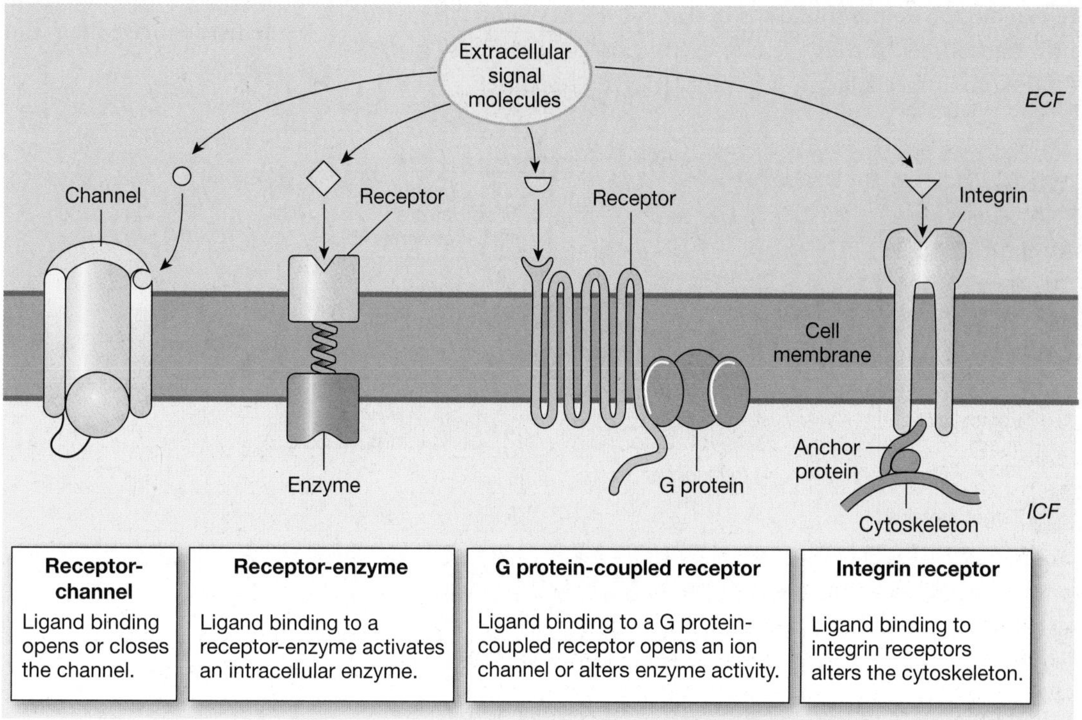

● **FIGURE 6-5** *Four categories of membrane receptors*

Signal transduction converts one form of signal into a different form.

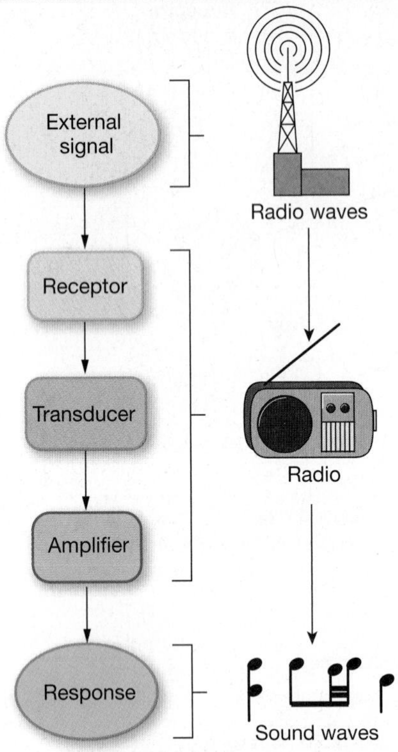
External signal
Radio waves
Receptor
Transducer
Radio
Amplifier
Response
Sound waves

● **FIGURE 6-6** ***Signal transduction.*** An everyday example of signal transduction is a radio, which contains a transducer that converts radio waves into sound waves.

A **transducer** is a device that converts a signal from one form into a different form. For example, the transducer in a radio converts radio waves into sound waves (Fig. 6-6 ●). In biological systems, transducers convert the message of extracellular signal molecules into intracellular messages that trigger a response.

In biological systems, as in a radio, the original signal is not only transformed but also amplified [*amplificare,* to make larger]. In cells, **signal amplification** turns one signal molecule into multiple second messenger molecules. The process begins when the ligand combines with its receptor (Fig. 6-7 ●). The receptor-ligand complex then turns on an **amplifier enzyme**, an enzyme that activates several more molecules. By the end of the process, the effects of the ligand have been amplified much more than if there were a 1:1 ratio between each step. Amplification gives the body "more bang for the buck" by enabling a small amount of ligand to create a large effect.

The basic pattern of a biological signal transduction pathway is shown in Figure 6-8 ● and can be broken down into the following events.

1. An extracellular signal molecule binds to and activates a protein or glycoprotein membrane receptor.
2. The activated membrane receptor turns on its associated proteins. These proteins then may:
    a. activate **protein kinases**, which are enzymes that transfer a phosphate group from ATP to a protein [p. 104]. Phosphorylation is an important biochemical method of regulating cellular processes.
    b. activate amplifier enzymes that create intracellular **second messengers**. The most common amplifier enzymes and second messengers are listed in Tables 6-1 ● and 6-2 ●.
3. Second messenger molecules in turn
    a. alter the gating of ion channels. Opening or closing ion channels creates electrical signals by altering the cell's membrane potential [p. 166].
    b. increase intracellular calcium. Calcium binding to proteins changes their function, creating a cellular response.

NAVIGATOR

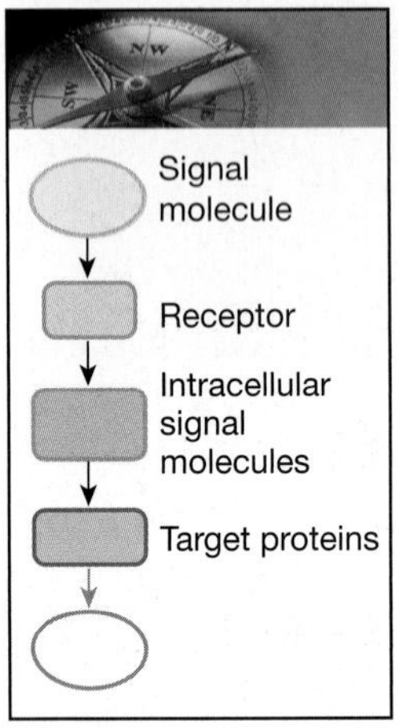
Signal molecule
Receptor
Intracellular signal molecules
Target proteins

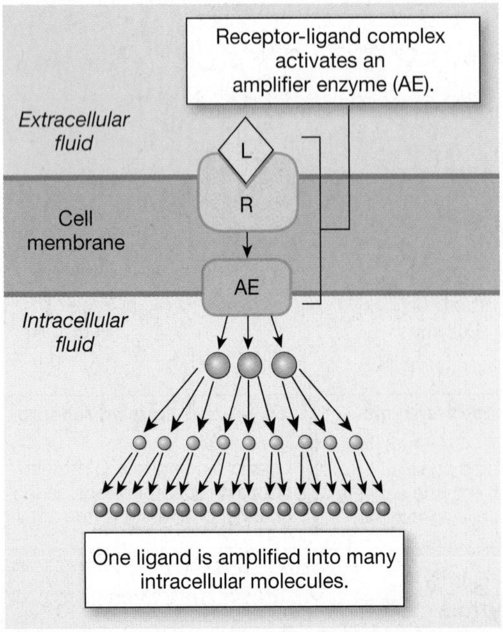
Receptor-ligand complex activates an amplifier enzyme (AE).
Extracellular fluid
L
R
Cell membrane
AE
Intracellular fluid
One ligand is amplified into many intracellular molecules.

● **FIGURE 6-7** ***Signal amplification***

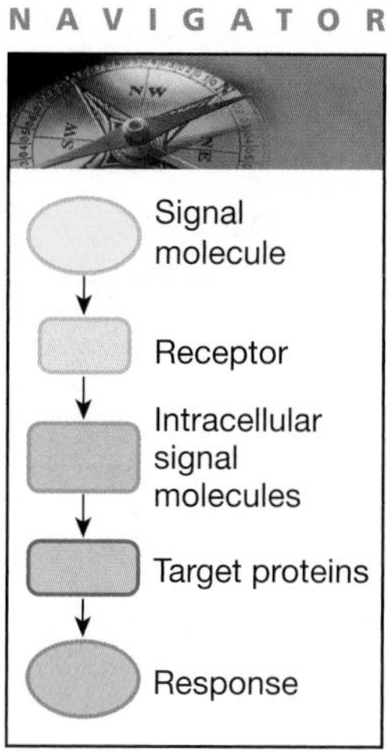

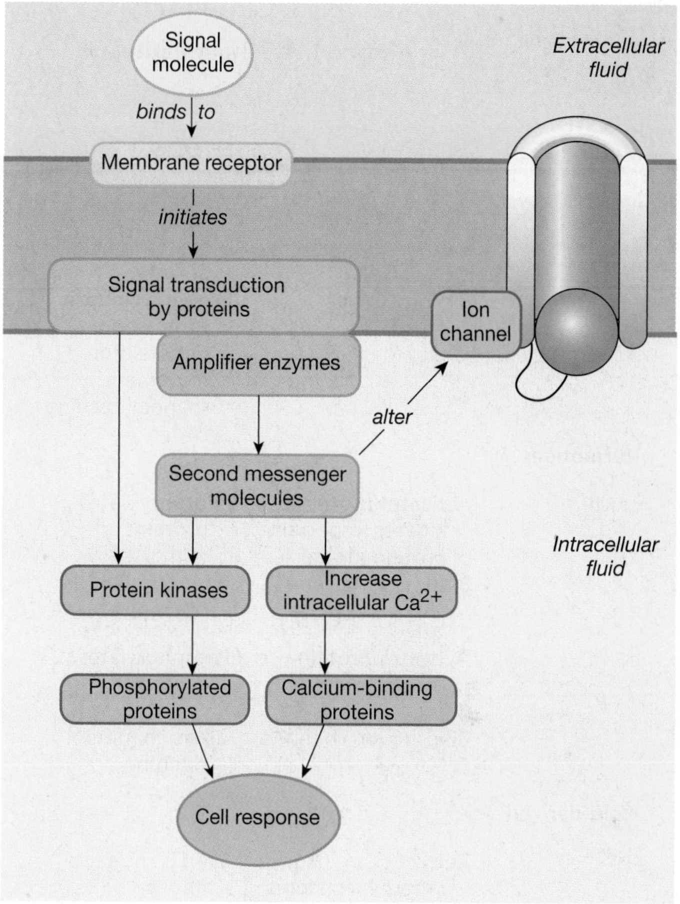

● **FIGURE 6-8** ***Biological signal transduction converts chemical signals into cellular responses.***

TABLE 6-1 Amplifier Enzymes

AMPLIFIER ENZYME	CELLULAR LOCATION	ACTIVATED BY	CONVERTS	TO
Adenylyl cyclase	Membrane	G protein-coupled receptor	ATP	cAMP
Guanylyl cyclase	Membrane Cytosol	Receptor-enzyme Nitric oxide (NO)	GTP	cGMP
Phospholipase C	Membrane	G protein-coupled receptor	Membrane phospholipids	IP_3 and DAG*

*IP_3 = Inositol trisphosphate; DAG = diacylglycerol

c. change enzyme activity, especially of protein kinases or **protein phosphatases**, enzymes that remove a phosphate group. The phosphorylation or *dephosphorylation* of a protein can change its configuration and create a response. Examples of changes that occur with phosphorylation include increased or decreased enzyme activity and opening or closing gated ion channels.

4. The proteins modified by calcium binding and phosphorylation control one or more of the following:
   a. metabolic enzymes,
   b. motor proteins for muscle contraction and cytoskeletal movement,
   c. proteins that regulate gene activity and protein synthesis, and
   d. membrane transport and receptor proteins.

If you think this list includes almost everything a cell does, you're right!

You can see from this basic pattern that the steps of a signal transduction pathway form a **cascade** (Fig. 6-9 ●). A signaling cascade starts when a stimulus (the signal molecule) converts inactive molecule A (the receptor) to an active form. Active A then converts inactive molecule B into active B, active molecule B in turn converts inactive molecule C into active C, and so

TABLE 6-2 Second Messenger Pathways

SECOND MESSENGER	ACTION	EFFECTS
Ions		
Ca^{2+}	Binds to calmodulin	Alters enzyme activity
	Binds to other proteins	Exocytosis, muscle contraction, cytoskeleton movement, channel opening
Nucleotides		
cAMP	Activates protein kinases, especially protein kinase A	Phosphorylates proteins
	Binds to ion channels	Alters channel opening
cGMP	Activates protein kinases, especially protein kinase G	Phosphorylates proteins
	Binds to ion channels	Alters channel opening
Lipid-derived		
IP_3	Releases Ca^{2+} from intracellular stores	See Ca^{2+} effects above
DAG	Activates protein kinase C	Phosphorylates proteins

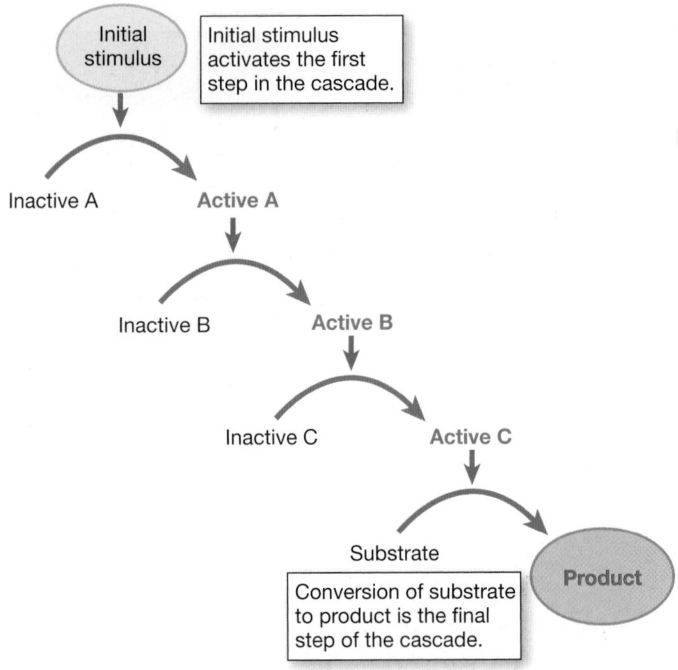

FIGURE QUESTION

Using Tables 6-1 and 6-2, create a cascade that includes ATP, cAMP, adenylyl cyclase, a phosphorylated protein, and protein kinase A. Match these molecules to the steps shown in the figure above.

● **FIGURE 6-9** ***Steps of a cascade***

on, until at the final step a substrate is converted into a product. Many intracellular signal pathways are cascades. Blood clotting is an important example of an extracellular cascade.

In the sections that follow, we will examine in more detail the four major types of membrane receptors (see Fig. 6-5). Keep in mind that these receptors may be responding to any of the different kinds of signal molecules—hormones, neurohormones, neurotransmitters, cytokines, paracrines, or autocrines.

CONCEPT CHECK

6. What are the four steps of signal transduction?
7. What happens during amplification?
8. Why do steroid hormones not require signal transduction and second messengers to exert their action? (*Hint:* Are steroids lipophobic or lipophilic? [p. 25])

Answers: p. 213

Receptor-enzymes Have Protein Kinase or Guanylyl Cyclase Activity

Receptor-enzymes have two regions: a receptor region on the extracellular side of the cell membrane, and an enzyme region on the cytoplasmic side (see Fig. 6-5). In some instances, the receptor region and enzyme region are parts of the same protein molecule. In other cases, the enzyme region is a separate protein. Ligand binding to the receptor activates the enzyme. The enzymes of receptor-enzymes are either protein kinases, such as *tyrosine kinase* (Fig. 6-10 ●), or *guanylyl cyclase,* the amplifier enzyme that converts GTP to **cyclic GMP (cGMP)** [p. 34].

Ligands for receptor-enzymes include the hormone insulin as well as many growth factors and cytokines. The insulin receptor protein has intrinsic tyrosine kinase activity. In contrast, most cytokine receptor proteins do not have intrinsic enzyme activity. Instead, cytokine binding activates a cytosolic enzyme called *Janus family tyrosine kinase,* usually abbreviated as *JAK kinase.*

Most Signal Transduction Uses G Proteins

The **G protein-coupled receptors (GPCR)** are a large and complex family of membrane-spanning proteins that cross the phospholipid bilayer seven times (see Fig. 6-5). The cytoplasmic tail of the receptor protein is linked to a three-part membrane transducer molecule known as a **G protein**. Hundreds of G protein-coupled receptors have been identified, and the list continues to grow. The types of ligands that bind to G protein-coupled receptors include hormones, growth factors, olfactory molecules, visual pigments, and neurotransmitters. In 1994 Alfred G. Gilman and Martin Rodbell received a Nobel prize for the discovery of G proteins and their role in cell signaling.

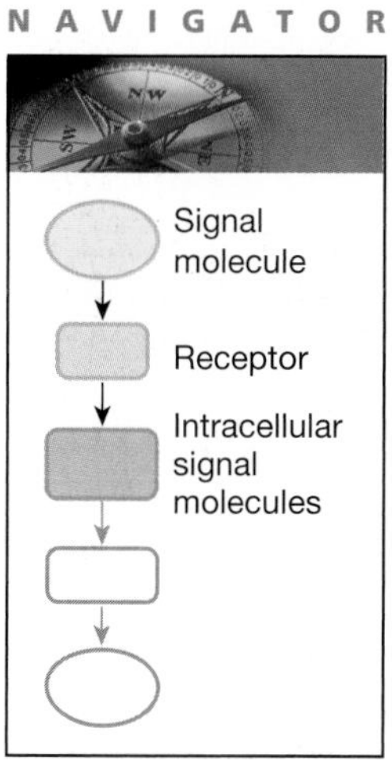

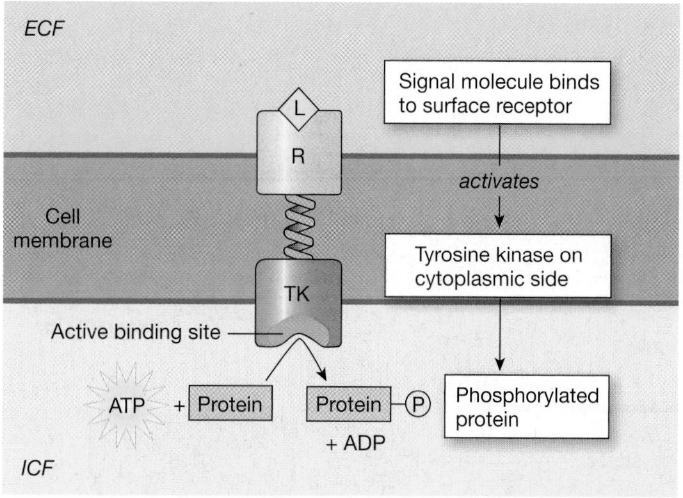

● **FIGURE 6-10** ***The tyrosine kinase receptor is an example of a receptor-enzyme.*** Tyrosine kinase (TK) transfers a phosphate group from ATP to a tyrosine (an amino acid) of a protein.

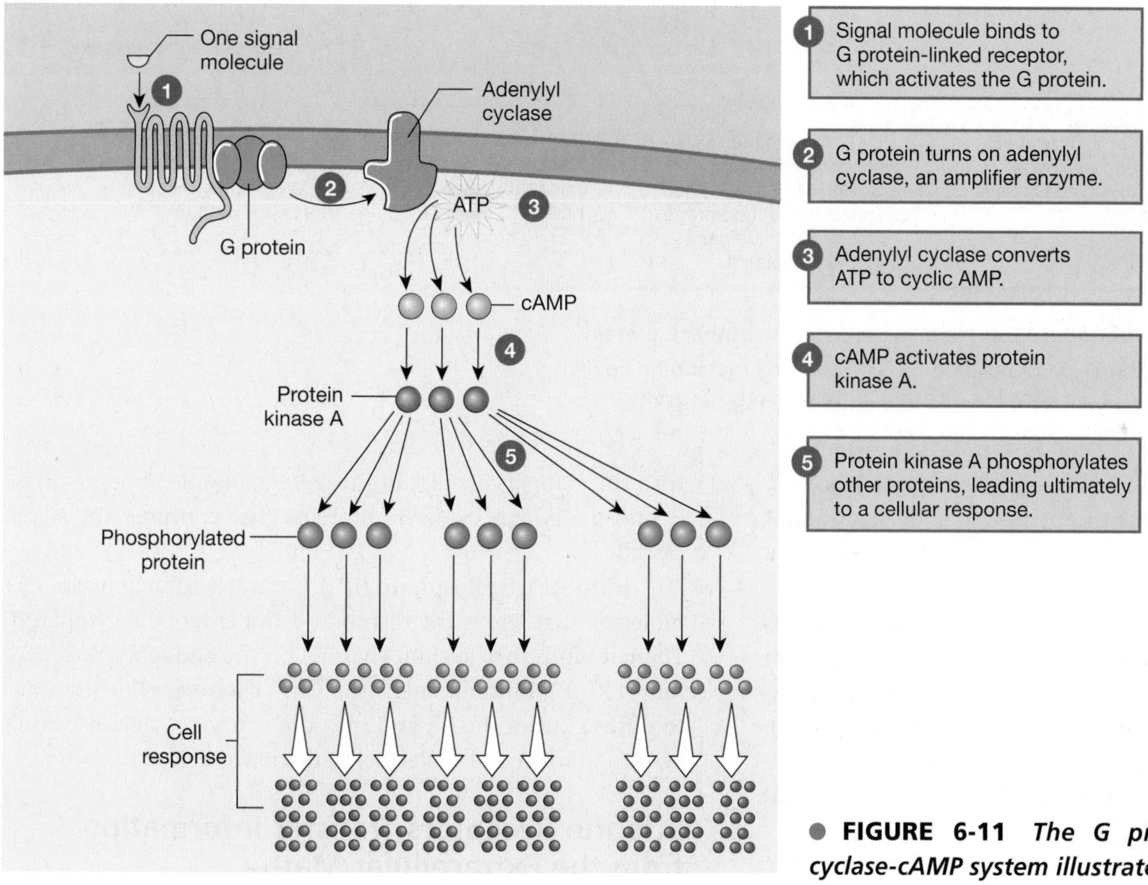

● **FIGURE 6-11** ***The G protein-coupled adenylyl cyclase-cAMP system illustrates a signal cascade.***

G proteins get their name from the fact that they bind guanosine nucleotides [p. 34]. Inactive G proteins are bound to guanosine diphosphate (GDP). Exchanging the GDP for guanosine triphosphate (GTP) activates the G protein. When G proteins are activated, they either (1) open an ion channel in the membrane or (2) alter enzyme activity on the cytoplasmic side of the membrane.

G proteins linked to amplifier enzymes make up the bulk of all known signal transduction mechanisms. The two most common amplifier enzymes for G protein-coupled receptors are adenylyl cyclase and phospholipase C. The pathways for these amplifier enzymes are described next.

Many Lipophobic Hormones Use GPCR-cAMP Pathways

The **G protein-coupled adenylyl cyclase-cAMP system** was the first identified signal transduction pathway (Fig. 6-11 ●). It was discovered in the 1950s by Earl Sutherland when he was

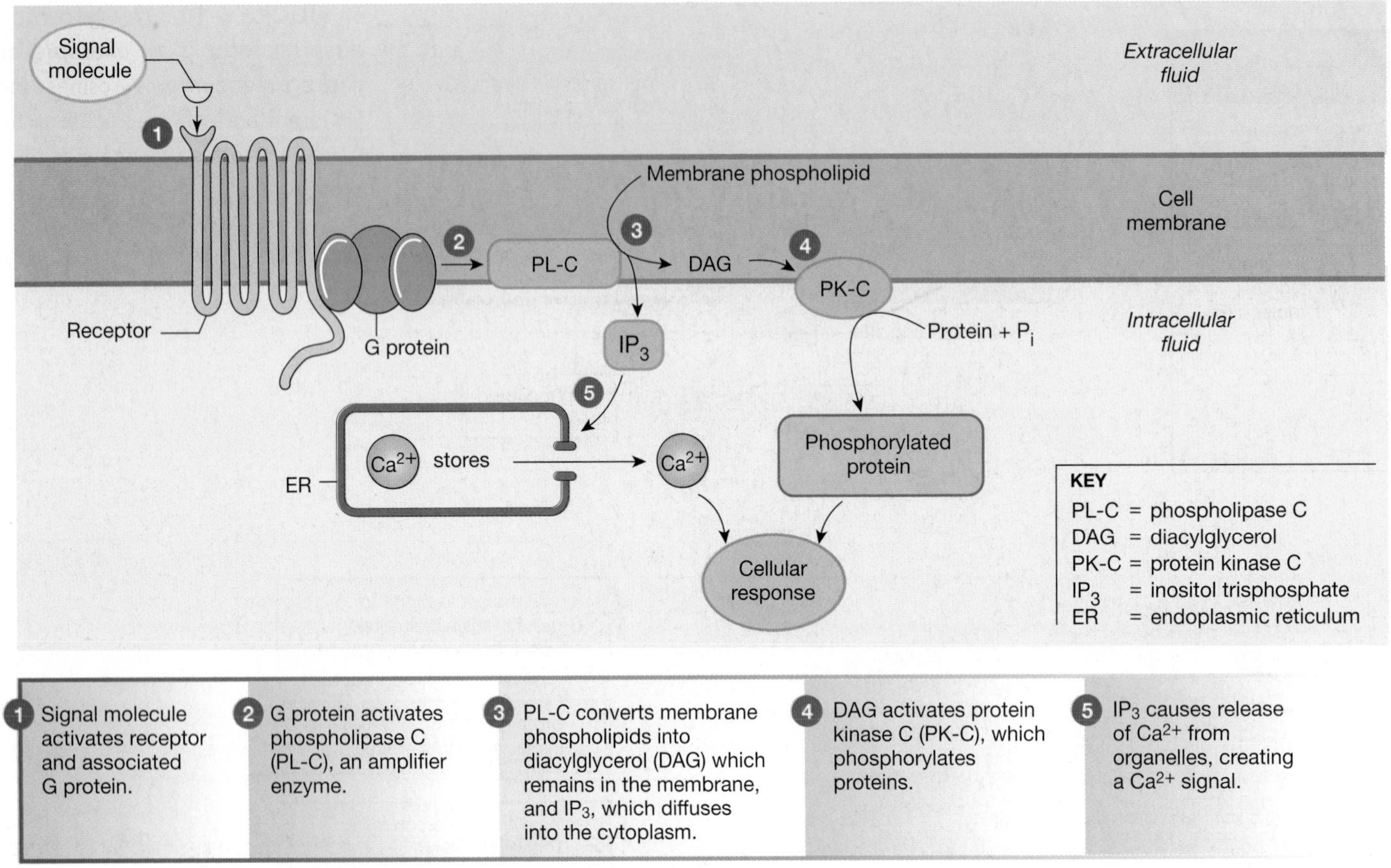

● **FIGURE 6-12** ***The phospholipase C system.*** In this system—another G protein-coupled second messenger system—phospholipase C (PL-C) converts membrane lipids into two second messengers: diacylglycerol (DAG) and inositol trisphosphate (IP_3).

studying the effects of hormones on carbohydrate metabolism. This discovery proved so significant to our understanding of signal transduction that in 1971 Sutherland was awarded a Nobel prize for his work.

The G protein-coupled adenylyl cyclase-cAMP system is the signal transduction system for many protein hormones. In this system, *adenylyl cyclase* is the amplifier enzyme that converts ATP to the second messenger molecule *cyclic AMP* (cAMP). Cyclic AMP then activates *protein kinase A* (PK-A), which in turn phosphorylates other intracellular proteins as part of the signal cascade.

G Protein-Coupled Receptors Also Use Lipid-Derived Second Messengers

Some G protein-coupled receptors are linked to a different amplifier enzyme: phospholipase C (Fig. 6-12 ●). When a signal molecule activates this G protein-coupled pathway, **phospholipase C (PL-C)** converts a membrane phospholipid (*phosphatidylinositol bisphosphate*) into two lipid-derived second messenger molecules: diacylglycerol and inositol trisphosphate.

Diacylglycerol (DAG) is a nonpolar diglyceride that remains in the lipid portion of the membrane and interacts with **protein kinase C** (PK-C), a Ca^{2+}-activated enzyme associated with the cytoplasmic face of the cell membrane. Protein kinase C phosphorylates cytosolic proteins that continue the signal cascade.

Inositol trisphosphate (IP_3) is a water-soluble messenger molecule that leaves the membrane and enters the cytoplasm. There it binds to a calcium channel on the endoplasmic reticulum (ER). IP_3 binding opens the Ca^{2+} channel, allowing Ca^{2+} to diffuse out of the ER and into the cytosol. Calcium is itself an important signal molecule, as discussed below.

Integrin Receptors Transfer Information from the Extracellular Matrix

The membrane-spanning proteins called *integrins* [p. 74] mediate blood clotting, wound repair, cell adhesion and recognition in the immune response, and cell movement during development. On the extracellular side of the membrane, integrin receptors bind either to proteins of the extracellular matrix [p. 80] or to ligands such as antibodies and molecules involved in blood clotting. Inside the cell, integrins attach to the cytoskeleton via *anchor proteins* (Fig. 6-5). Ligand binding to the receptor causes integrins to activate intracellular enzymes or alter the organization of the cytoskeleton.

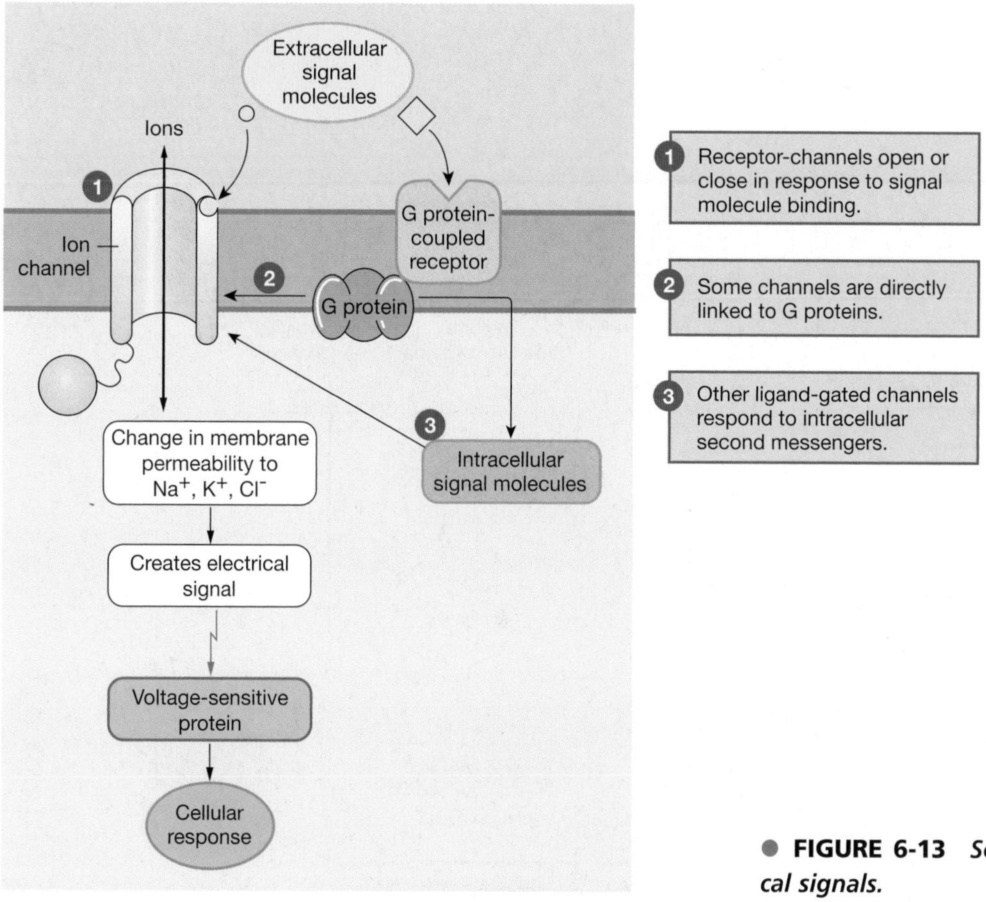

● **FIGURE 6-13** ***Some second messengers create electrical signals.***

The importance of integrin receptors is illustrated by inherited conditions in which the receptor is absent. In one condition, platelets—cell fragments that play a key role in blood clotting—lack an integrin receptor. As a result, blood clotting is defective in these individuals.

The Most Rapid Signal Pathways Change Ion Flow Through Channels

The simplest receptors are ligand-gated ion channels, and most of them are neurotransmitter receptors found in nerve and muscle. The activation of **receptor-channels** initiates the most rapid intracellular responses of all receptors. When an extracellular ligand binds to the receptor-channel protein, a channel gate opens or closes, altering the cell's permeability to an ion. Increasing or decreasing ion permeability rapidly changes the cell's membrane potential [p. 169], creating an electrical signal that alters voltage-sensitive proteins (Fig. 6-13 ●).

One example of a receptor-channel is the acetylcholine-gated cation channel of skeletal muscle. The neurotransmitter *acetylcholine* released from an adjacent neuron binds to the acetylcholine receptor and opens the channel, allowing Na^+ to enter the cell along its electrochemical gradient. Net entry of positive charge depolarizes the cell. In skeletal muscle, this cascade of intracellular events results in muscle contraction.

Note that not all ligand-gated ion channels are receptor-channels directly activated by extracellular signal molecules. Some ligand-gated ion channels are controlled by intracellular second messengers, such as cAMP or ATP. The ATP-gated K^+ channels of the pancreatic beta cell are an example [Fig. 5-35, p. 170]. Other ion channels open or close in response to extracellular signals, but the signal ligand does not bind to the channel protein. Instead it binds to a G protein-coupled receptor that is indirectly linked to the ion channel.

Figure 6-14 ● is a summary map of basic signal transduction, showing the general relationships among first messengers, membrane receptors, second messengers, and cell responses.

CONCEPT CHECK

9. Name the four categories of membrane receptors.
10. What is the difference between a first messenger and a second messenger?
11. Place the following terms in the correct order for a signal transduction pathway:
    (a) cell response, receptor, second messenger, ligand
    (b) amplifier enzyme, cell response, phosphorylated protein, protein kinase, second messenger
12. In each of the following situations, will a cell depolarize or hyperpolarize?
    (a) Cl^- channel opens
    (b) K^+ channel opens
    (c) Na^+ channel opens

Answers: p. 213

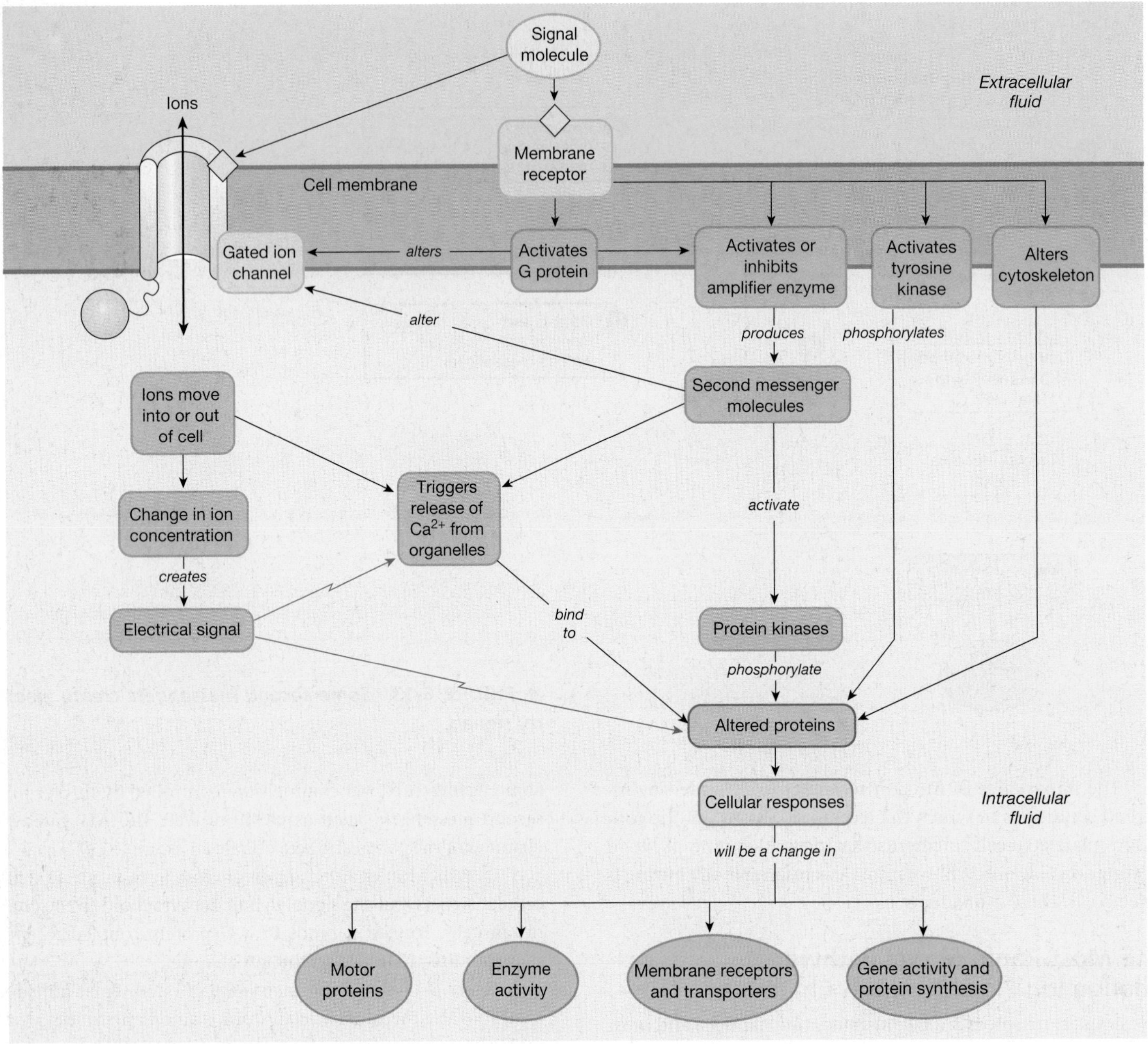

● **FIGURE 6-14** ***Summary map of signal transduction systems***

NOVEL SIGNAL MOLECULES

In Chapters 7 and 8, you will learn more about hormones and neurotransmitters and their signal pathways. The following sections introduce you to some unusual signal molecules that are important in physiology and medicine. They include an ion (Ca^{2+}), three gases, and a family of lipid-derived messengers. The processes controlled by these signal molecules have been known for years, but the control signals themselves were discovered only relatively recently.

Calcium Is an Important Intracellular Signal

Calcium ions are the most versatile ionic messengers (Fig. 6-15 ●). Calcium enters the cell either through voltage-gated Ca^{2+} channels or through ligand-gated or mechanically gated channels. Calcium can also be released from intracellular compartments by second messengers, such as IP_3. Most intracellular Ca^{2+} is stored in the endoplasmic reticulum [p. 68], where it is concentrated by active transport.

Release of Ca^{2+} into the cytosol (from any of the sources just mentioned) creates a Ca^{2+} signal, or Ca^{2+} "spark," that can

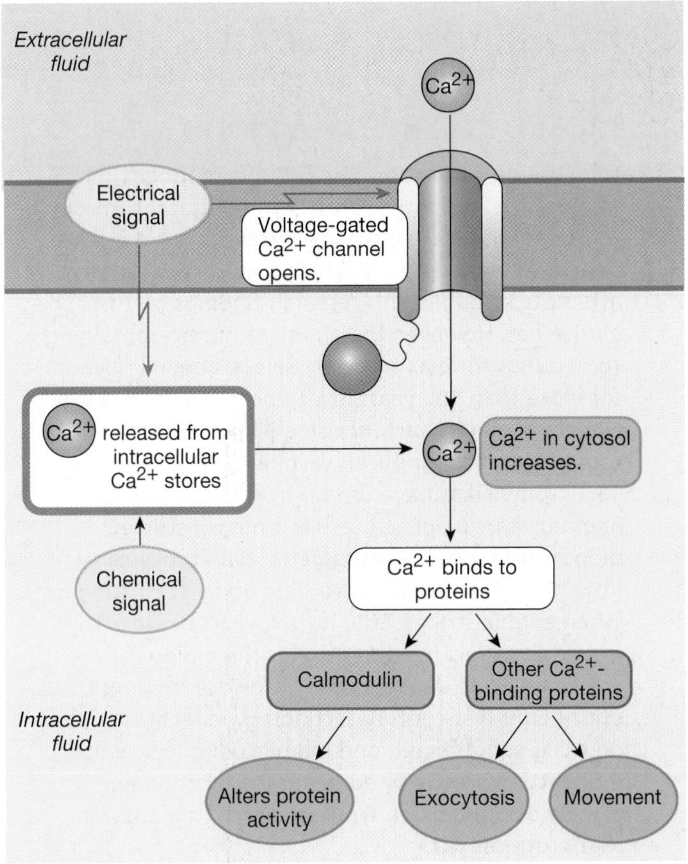

● **FIGURE 6-15** ***Calcium as an intracellular messenger.*** Calcium signals occur in the cytosol when Ca^{2+} enters the cell or is released from intracellular stores.

be recorded using special Ca^{2+}-imaging techniques (see Biotechnology box: Measuring Calcium Signals). The calcium ions combine with cytoplasmic calcium-binding proteins to exert various effects. Several types of calcium-dependent events occur in the cell:

1. Ca^{2+} binds to the protein **calmodulin**, found in all cells, and alters enzyme or transporter activity or the gating of ion channels.
2. Calcium binds to other regulatory proteins and alters movement of contractile or cytoskeletal proteins such as microtubules. For example, Ca^{2+} binding to the regulatory protein *troponin* initiates muscle contraction in a skeletal muscle cell.
3. Ca^{2+} binds to regulatory proteins to trigger exocytosis of secretory vesicles [p. 171]. This was illustrated in Chapter 5 in the description of pancreatic beta cell release of insulin.
4. Ca^{2+} binds directly to ion channels to alter their gating state. An example of this target is a Ca^{2+}-activated K^+ channel found in nerve cells.
5. Ca^{2+} entry into a fertilized egg initiates development of the embryo.

BIOTECHNOLOGY

MEASURING CALCIUM SIGNALS

If you've ever run your hand through a tropical ocean at night and seen the glow of bioluminescent jellyfish, you've seen a calcium signal. Aequorin, a protein complex isolated from jellyfish, is one of the molecules that scientists use to monitor the presence of calcium ions during a cellular response. When aequorin combines with calcium, it releases light that can be measured by electronic detection systems. Since the first use of aequorin in 1967, researchers have been designing better and better indicators that allow them to follow calcium signals in cells. With the help of molecules called fura, Oregon green, BAPTA, and chameleons, we can now watch calcium ions diffuse through gap junctions and flow out of intracellular organelles.

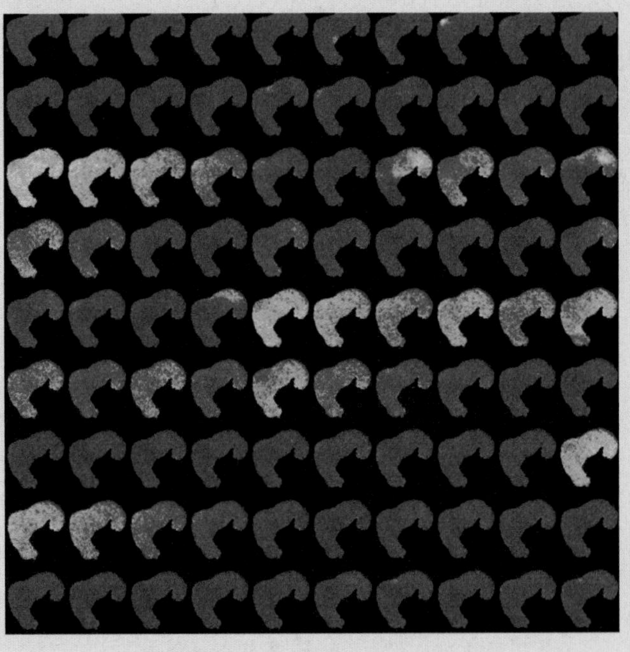

CONCEPT CHECK

13. The concentration of extracellular Ca^{2+} averages 2.5 mmol/L. Free cytosolic Ca^{2+} concentration is about 0.001 mmol/L. If a cell is going to move calcium ions from its cytosol to the extracellular fluid, will it use passive or active transport? Explain.

Answers: p. 213

Gases Are Ephemeral Signal Molecules

Soluble gases are short-acting paracrine/autocrine signal molecules that act close to where they are produced. The best-known gaseous signal molecule is **nitric oxide** (NO), but carbon monoxide and hydrogen sulfide, two gases better known for their noxious effects, can also act as local signals.

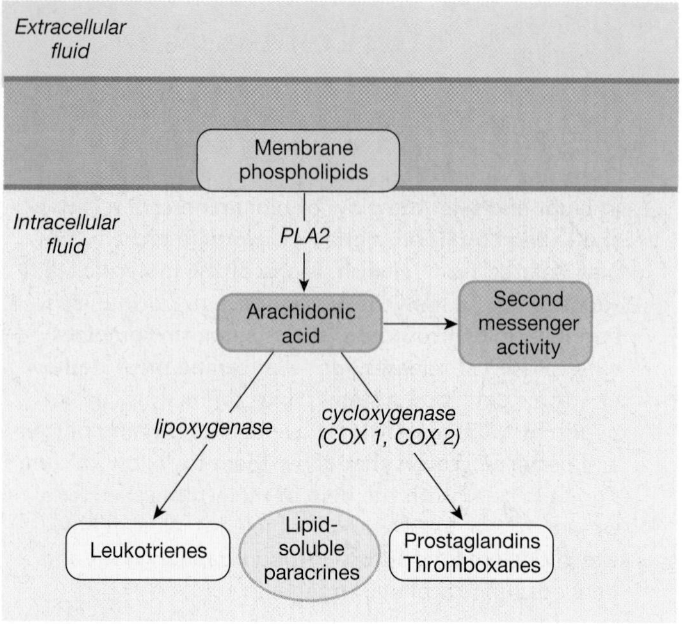

● **FIGURE 6-16** ***The arachidonic acid cascade produces lipid messengers.***

For years researchers knew of a short-lived signal molecule produced by the endothelial cells lining blood vessels. This molecule, initially named *endothelial-derived relaxing factor* (EDRF), diffuses from the endothelium into adjacent smooth muscle cells, causing the muscle to relax and dilate the blood vessel. Scientists took years to identify EDRF as nitric oxide because it is rapidly broken down, with a half-life of only 2 to 30 seconds. (*Half-life* is the time required for the signal to lose half of its activity.) As a result of this difficult work on NO in the cardiovascular system, Robert Furchgott, Louis Ignarro, and Ferid Murad received the 1998 Nobel prize for physiology and medicine.

In tissues, NO is synthesized by the action of the enzyme *nitric oxide synthase* (NOS) on the amino acid arginine:

$$\text{Arginine} + O_2 \xrightarrow{\textit{nitric oxide synthase}} \text{NO} + \text{citrulline (an amino acid)}$$

The NO produced in this reaction diffuses into target cells, where it binds to a receptor that activates the cytosolic form of guanylyl cyclase and causes formation of the second messenger cGMP. In addition to relaxing blood vessels, NO in the brain acts as a neurotransmitter and a neuromodulator.

Carbon monoxide (CO), a gas known mostly for its toxic effects, is also a signal molecule produced in minute amounts by certain cells. Like NO, CO activates guanylyl cyclase and cGMP, but it may also work independently to exert its effects. Carbon monoxide targets smooth muscle and neural tissue.

The newest gaseous signal molecule to be described is **hydrogen sulfide** (H_2S). Hydrogen sulfide also acts in the cardiovascular system to relax blood vessels. Garlic is a major dietary source of the sulfur-containing precursors, which may explain studies suggesting that eating garlic has protective effects on the heart.

CLINICAL FOCUS

FROM DYNAMITE TO VASODILATION

Who would have thought that a component of smog and a derivative of dynamite would turn out to be a biological messenger? Certainly not the peer reviewers who initially rejected Louis Ignarro's attempts to publish his research findings on the elusive gas. However, the ability of nitrate-containing compounds to relax blood vessels has been known for more than 100 years, ever since workers in Alfred Nobel's dynamite factory complained of headaches caused by nitrate-induced vasodilation. Since the 1860s, physicians have used nitroglycerin to relieve *angina*, heart pain that results from constricted blood vessels, and heart patients even today carry little nitroglycerin tablets to slide under their tongues when angina strikes. Still, it took years of work to isolate the short-lived gas that is the biologically active molecule derived from nitroglycerin. Despite all our twenty-first-century technology, direct research on NO is still difficult, and many studies look at its influence indirectly by studying the location and activity of nitric oxide synthase (NOS), the enzyme that produces NO.

Some Lipids Are Important Paracrine Signals

One of the interesting developments from sequencing the human genome and using genes to find proteins has been the identification of *orphan receptors,* receptors that have no known ligand. Scientists are trying to work backward through signal pathways to find the ligands that bind to these orphan receptors. As a result of this type of research, investigators recognized the importance and universality of *eicosanoids,* lipid-derived paracrine signals that play important roles in many physiological processes.

All eicosanoid signal molecules are derived from arachidonic acid, a 20-carbon fatty acid. The synthesis process is a network called the *arachidonic acid cascade* (Fig. 6-16 ●). For simplicity, we will break the cascade into steps.

Arachidonic acid is produced from membrane phospholipids by the action of an enzyme, **phospholipase** $\mathbf{A_2}$ (PLA2). The activity of phospholipase A_2 is controlled by hormones and other signals. Arachidonic acid itself may act directly as a second messenger, altering ion channel activity and intracellular enzymes. It may also be converted into one of several classes of eicosanoid paracrines. These lipid-soluble molecules can diffuse out of the cell and combine with receptors on neighboring cells to exert their action.

There are two major groups of arachidonic acid-derived paracrines to be aware of:

1. **Leukotrienes** are molecules produced by the action of the enzyme *lipoxygenase* on arachidonic acid [*leuko-*, white + *triene*, a molecule with three double bonds between carbon atoms]. Leukotrienes are secreted by certain types of white blood cells. They play a significant role in asthma, a lung condition in which the smooth muscle of the airways constricts, making it difficult to breathe, and in the severe allergic reaction known as *anaphylaxis*. For this reason, pharmaceutical companies have been actively developing drugs to block leukotriene synthesis or action.
2. **Prostanoids** are molecules produced when the enzyme **cyclooxygenase (COX)** acts on arachidonic acid. Prostanoids include **prostaglandins** and **thromboxanes.** These eicosanoids act on many tissues of the body, including smooth muscle in various organs, platelets, kidney, and bone. In addition, prostaglandins are involved in sleep, inflammation, pain, and fever.

The nonsteroidal anti-inflammatory drugs (NSAIDs), such as aspirin and ibuprofen, help prevent inflammation by inhibiting COX enzymes and decreasing prostaglandin synthesis. However, NSAIDs are not specific and may have serious unwanted side effects, such as bleeding in the stomach. The discovery of two COX isozymes, COX1 and COX2, enabled the design of drugs that target a specific COX isozyme. By inhibiting only COX2, the enzyme that produces inflammatory prostaglandins, physicians hoped to treat inflammation with fewer side effects. However, studies have shown that some patients who take COX2 inhibitors and other NSAIDs have increased risk of heart attacks and strokes, so these drugs are not recommended for long-term use.

Eicosanoids are not the only known lipid signal molecules. Lipids called *sphingolipids* also act as extracellular signals to help regulate inflammation, cell adhesion and migration, and cell growth and death. Like the eicosanoids, sphingolipids combine with G protein-coupled receptors in the membranes of their target cells.

CONCEPT CHECK

14. Based on what you have learned about signal molecules, where might a drug that blocks leukotriene action act? How might a drug that blocks leukotriene synthesis act? Answers: p. 213

MODULATION OF SIGNAL PATHWAYS

As you have just learned, signal pathways in the cell can be very complex. To complicate matters, different cells may respond differently to a given signal molecule. How can one molecule trigger response A in tissue 1 and response B in tissue 2? *For most signal molecules, the target cell response is determined by the receptor or its associated intracellular pathways, not by the ligand.*

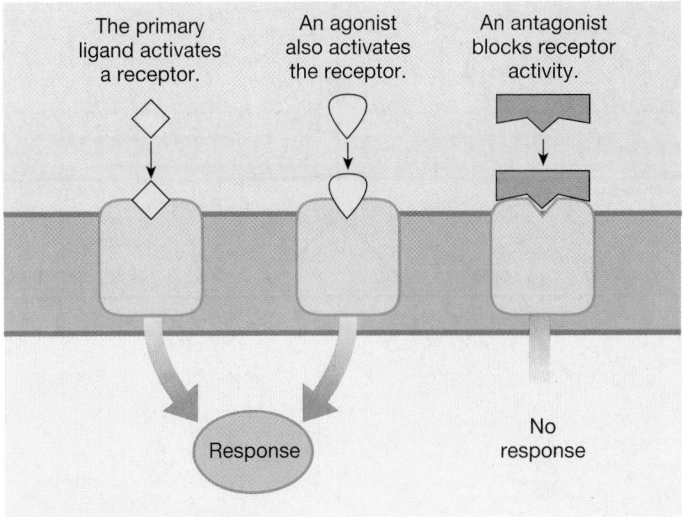

● **FIGURE 6-17** ***Agonists and antagonists***

Because of the importance of signal pathways, cells use receptors to maintain flexibility in their responses.

Receptors Exhibit Saturation, Specificity, and Competition

Receptors are proteins, which means that receptor-ligand binding exhibits the protein-binding characteristics of specificity, competition, and saturation discussed in Chapter 2 [p. 40]. You learned about similar protein-binding properties in enzymes, discussed in Chapter 4 [p. 100], and transporters, discussed in Chapter 5 [p. 148].

Specificity and Competition: Multiple Ligands for One Receptor Receptors have binding sites for their ligands, just as enzymes and transporters do. As a result, different molecules with similar structures may be able to bind to the same receptor. A classic example of this principle involves two neurocrines responsible for the fight-or-flight response: the neurotransmitter *norepinephrine* and its cousin the neurohormone *epinephrine* (also called *adrenaline*). Both molecules bind to a class of receptors called *adrenergic receptors*. (*Adrenergic* is the adjective relating to adrenaline.) The ability of adrenergic receptors to bind these neurocrines, but not others, demonstrates specificity of the receptors.

Epinephrine and norepinephrine also compete for a single receptor type. Both neurocrines bind to subtypes of adrenergic receptors designated alpha (α) and beta (β). However, α-receptors have a higher binding affinity for norepinephrine, while the β_2-receptor subtype has a higher affinity for epinephrine.

Agonists and Antagonists When a ligand combines with a receptor, one of two events follows. Either the ligand activates the receptor and elicits a response, or the ligand occupies the binding site and prevents the receptor from responding (Fig. 6-17 ●). Ligands that turn receptors on are known as *agonists*, and ligands that block receptor activity are called *antagonists*.

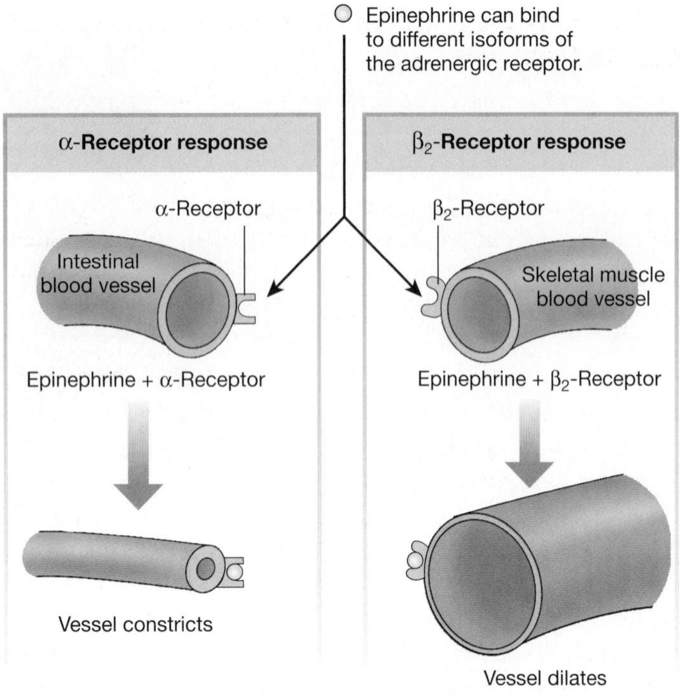
Epinephrine can bind to different isoforms of the adrenergic receptor.
α-Receptor response
β2-Receptor response
α-Receptor
Intestinal blood vessel
Epinephrine + α-Receptor
Vessel constricts
β2-Receptor
Skeletal muscle blood vessel
Epinephrine + β2-Receptor
Vessel dilates

● **FIGURE 6-18** ***Target response depends on the target receptor.*** In this example, epinephrine will either dilate or constrict blood vessels depending on the receptor found on the blood vessel.

Pharmacologists use the principle of competing agonists [p. 40] to design drugs that are longer-acting and more resistant to enzymatic degradation than the *endogenous* ligand produced by the body [*endo-*, within + *-genous*, developing]. One example is the family of modified estrogens (female sex hormones) in birth control pills. These drugs are agonists of naturally occurring estrogens but have chemical groups added to protect them from breakdown and extend their active life.

Multiple Receptors for One Ligand For many years physiologists were unable to explain the observation that a single signal molecule could have different effects in different tissues. For example, epinephrine, the neurohormone previously described, dilates blood vessels in skeletal muscle but constricts blood vessels in the intestine. How can one chemical have opposite effects? The answer became clear when scientists discovered that receptors, like other proteins, may come as families of related isoforms [p. 41].

The cellular response that follows binding of a signal molecule to a receptor depends on which isoform of the receptor is involved. For example, the α- and β_2-adrenergic receptors for epinephrine described earlier are isoforms of each other. When epinephrine binds to α-receptors on smooth muscle in intestinal blood vessels, signal pathways begin that cause the vessels to constrict (Fig. 6-18 ●). When epinephrine binds to β_2-receptors on certain skeletal muscle blood vessels, the associated signal transduction pathways cause the vessels to dilate. In other words, the response of the blood vessel to epinephrine depends on the receptor isoform and its signal transduction pathway, not on the ligand that activates the receptor. Many drugs now are designed so that they are specific for only one receptor isoform.

CONCEPT CHECK

15. What do receptors, enzymes, and transporters have in common that explains why they all exhibit saturation, specificity, and competition?
16. Insulin increases the number of glucose transporters on a skeletal muscle cell but not on the membrane of a liver cell. List two possible mechanisms that could explain how this one hormone can have these two different effects. Answers: p. 213

Up- and Down-Regulation Enable Cells to Modulate Responses

Saturation of proteins refers to the fact that protein activity reaches a maximum rate because cells contain limited numbers of protein molecules [p. 151]. This phenomenon can be observed with enzymes, transporters, and receptors. A cell's ability to respond to a chemical signal therefore can be limited by the finite number of receptors for that signal.

A single cell contains between 500 and 100,000 receptors on the surface of its cell membrane, with additional receptors in the cytosol and nucleus. In any given cell, the number of receptors may change over time. Old receptors are withdrawn from the membrane by endocytosis and are broken down in lysosomes. New receptors are inserted into the membrane by exocytosis. Intracellular receptors are also made and broken down. This flexibility permits a cell to vary its responses to chemical signals depending on the extracellular conditions and the internal needs of the cell.

What happens when a signal molecule is present in the body in abnormally high concentrations for a sustained period of time? Initially the increased signal level creates an enhanced response. As this enhanced response continues, the target cells may attempt to bring their response back to normal by either down-regulation or desensitization of the receptors for the signal [p. 44].

Down-regulation is a decrease in receptor number. The cell can physically remove receptors from the membrane through endocytosis [Fig. 5-21, p. 153]. A quicker and more easily reversible way to decrease cell response is *desensitization,* which can be achieved by binding a chemical modulator to the receptor protein. For example, the β-adrenergic receptors described in the previous section can be desensitized by phosphorylation of the receptor. The result of decreased receptor number or desensitization is a diminished response of the target cell even though the concentration of the signal molecule remains high. Down-regulation and desensitization are one explanation for the development of *drug tolerance,* a condition in which the response to a given dose decreases despite continuous exposure to the drug.

In the opposite situation, when the concentration of a ligand decreases, the target cell may use *up-regulation* to insert

RUNNING PROBLEM

"My dad takes insulin shots for his diabetes," Marvin says. "What does insulin do?" The nurse practitioner replies that normally insulin helps many cells take up and utilize glucose. In both types of diabetes, however, fasting blood glucose concentrations are elevated because the cells are not taking up and using glucose normally. If people with type 1 diabetes are given shots of insulin, their blood glucose levels decline. If people with type 2 diabetes are given insulin, blood glucose levels may change very little.

Question 2:
In which form of diabetes are the insulin receptors more likely to be up-regulated?

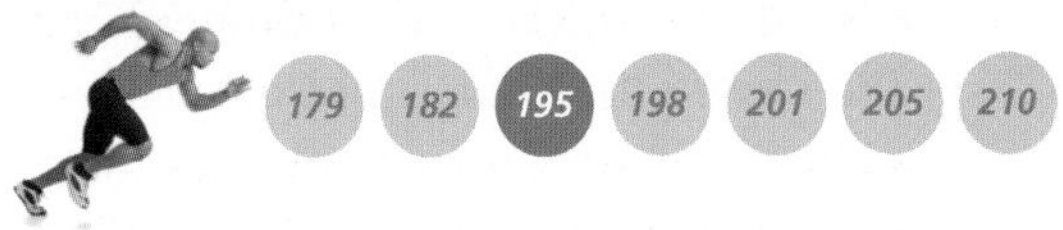
179
182
195
198
201
205
210

more receptors into the cell membrane in an attempt to keep its response at a normal level. For example, if a neuron is damaged and unable to release normal amounts of neurotransmitter, the target cell may up-regulate its receptors. This up-regulation makes the target cell more responsive to whatever neurotransmitters are present. Up-regulation is also programmed during development as a mechanism that allows cells to vary their responsiveness to growth factors and other signal molecules.

CONCEPT CHECK

17. To decrease a receptor's binding affinity, a cell might (select all that apply):
    (a) synthesize a new isoform of the receptor
    (b) withdraw receptors from the membrane
    (c) insert new receptors into the membrane
    (d) use a covalent modulator (*Hint:* p. 42)

Answers: p. 213

Cells Must Be Able to Terminate Signal Pathways

In the body, signals turn on and off, so cells must be able to tell when a signal is over. This requires that signaling processes have built-in termination mechanisms. For example, to stop the response to a calcium signal, a cell removes Ca^{2+} from the cytosol by pumping it either back into the endoplasmic reticulum or out into the extracellular fluid.

Receptor activity can be stopped in a variety of ways. The extracellular ligand can be degraded by enzymes in the extracellular space. An example is the breakdown of the neurotransmitter acetylcholine. Other chemical messengers, particularly neurotransmitters, can be removed from the extracellular fluid by being transported into neighboring cells. A widely used class of antidepressant drugs called *selective serotonin reuptake inhibitors,* or SSRIs, extends the active life of the neurotransmitter serotonin by slowing its removal from the extracellular fluid.

Once a ligand is bound to its receptor, activity can also be terminated by endocytosis of the receptor-ligand complex. This process was illustrated in Figure 5-21 [p. 153]. After the vesicle is in the cell, the ligand is removed, and the receptors can be returned to the membrane by exocytosis.

Many Diseases and Drugs Target the Proteins of Signal Transduction

As researchers learn more about cell signaling, they are realizing how many diseases are linked to problems with signal pathways. Diseases can be caused by alterations in receptors or by problems with G proteins or second messenger pathways (see Tbl. 6-3 ● for some examples). A single change in the amino acid sequence of a receptor protein can alter the shape of the

TABLE 6-3 Some Diseases or Conditions Linked to Abnormal Signaling Mechanisms

Genetically inherited abnormal receptors		
RECEPTOR	PHYSIOLOGICAL ALTERATION	DISEASE OR CONDITION THAT RESULTS
Vasopressin receptor (X-linked defect)	Shortens half-life of the receptor	Congenital diabetes insipidus
Calcium sensor in parathyroid gland	Fails to respond to increase in plasma Ca^{2+}	Familial hypercalcemia
Rhodopsin receptor in retina of eye	Improper protein folding	Retinitis pigmentosa
Toxins affecting signal pathways		
TOXIN	PHYSIOLOGICAL EFFECT	CONDITION THAT RESULTS
Bordetella pertussis toxin	Blocks inhibition of adenylate cyclase (i.e., keeps it active)	Whooping cough
Cholera toxin	Blocks enzyme activity of G proteins; cell keeps making cAMP	Ions secreted into lumen of intestine, causing massive diarrhea

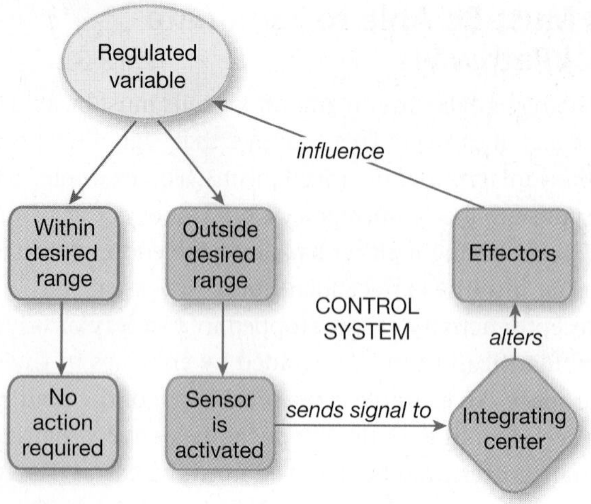

● **FIGURE 6-19** ***Physiological control systems keep regulated variables within a desired range during homeostasis.***

receptor's binding site, thereby either destroying or modifying its activity.

Pharmacologists are using information about signaling mechanisms to design drugs to treat disease. Some of the alphabet soup of drugs in widespread use are ARBs (angiotensin receptor blockers), β-adrenergic receptor blockers, and calcium-channel blockers for treating high blood pressure; SERMs (selective estrogen receptor modulators) for treating estrogen-dependent cancers; and H_2 (histamine type 2) receptor antagonists for decreasing acid secretion in the stomach. We will encounter many of these drugs again when we study the systems in which they are effective.

CONTROL PATHWAYS: RESPONSE AND FEEDBACK LOOPS

In Chapter 1 you learned that homeostasis is the ability of the body to maintain a relatively stable internal environment [p. 4]. Homeostasis is a continuous process that uses a **physiological control system** to monitor key functions, which are often called **regulated variables.**

In its simplest form, any control system has three basic parts: (1) an input signal; (2) a controller, which is programmed to respond to certain input signals; and (3) an output signal [Fig. 1-5, p. 7]. Physiological control systems are a little more complex. The input signal consists of the regulated variable and a specialized **sensor.** If the variable moves out of its desirable range, the sensor is activated and sends a signal to the controller (Fig. 6-19 ●). The controller acts as an **integrating center** [*integrare,* to restore] that evaluates information coming from the sensor and initiates a response that is designed to bring the regulated variable back into the desired range. The integrating center is often a neuron or an endocrine cell. The muscles and other tissues controlled by integrating centers are known as **effectors** [*effectus,* the carrying out of a task] because they effect a change.

Cannon's Postulates Describe Regulated Variables and Control Systems

Walter Cannon, the father of American physiology, described a number of properties of homeostatic control systems in the 1920s based on his observations of the body in health and disease states.* You will encounter these properties repeatedly as you study the various organ systems of the body. Cannon's four postulates are:

1. **The nervous system has a role in preserving the "fitness" of the internal environment.** *Fitness* in this instance means conditions that are compatible with normal function. The nervous system coordinates and integrates blood volume, blood osmolarity, blood pressure, and body temperature, among other regulated variables. (In physiology, a regulated variable is also known as a **parameter** [*para-*, beside + *meter*, measure]).
2. **Some systems of the body are under tonic control [*tonos,* tone].** To quote Cannon, "An agent may exist which has a moderate activity which can be varied up and down." Tonic control is like the volume control on a radio, where by turning a single knob you can make the sound level louder or softer. A physiological example of a tonically controlled system is the neural regulation of diameter in certain blood vessels, in which increased input from the nervous system decreases diameter, and decreased input from the nervous system increases diameter (Fig. 6-20 ●). *Tonic control* is one of the more difficult concepts in physiology because we have a tendency to think of responses stopping and starting when a controller turns off or on rather than as responses increasing and decreasing.
3. **Some systems of the body are under antagonistic control.** Cannon wrote, "When a factor is known which can shift a homeostatic state in one direction, it is reasonable to look for a factor or factors having an opposing effect." Systems that are not under tonic control are usually under *antagonistic control,* either by hormones or the nervous system. For example, insulin and glucagon are antagonistic hormones. Insulin decreases the concentration of glucose in the blood and glucagon increases it. In pathways controlled by the nervous system, the sympathetic and parasympathetic divisions often have opposing effects. For example, chemical signals from a sympathetic neuron increase heart rate, but chemical signals from a parasympathetic neuron decrease it (Fig. 6-21 ●).

* "Organization for Physiological Homeostasis," *Physiological Reviews* 9: 399–443, 1929.

FIGURE 6-20 *Tonic control of blood vessel diameter*

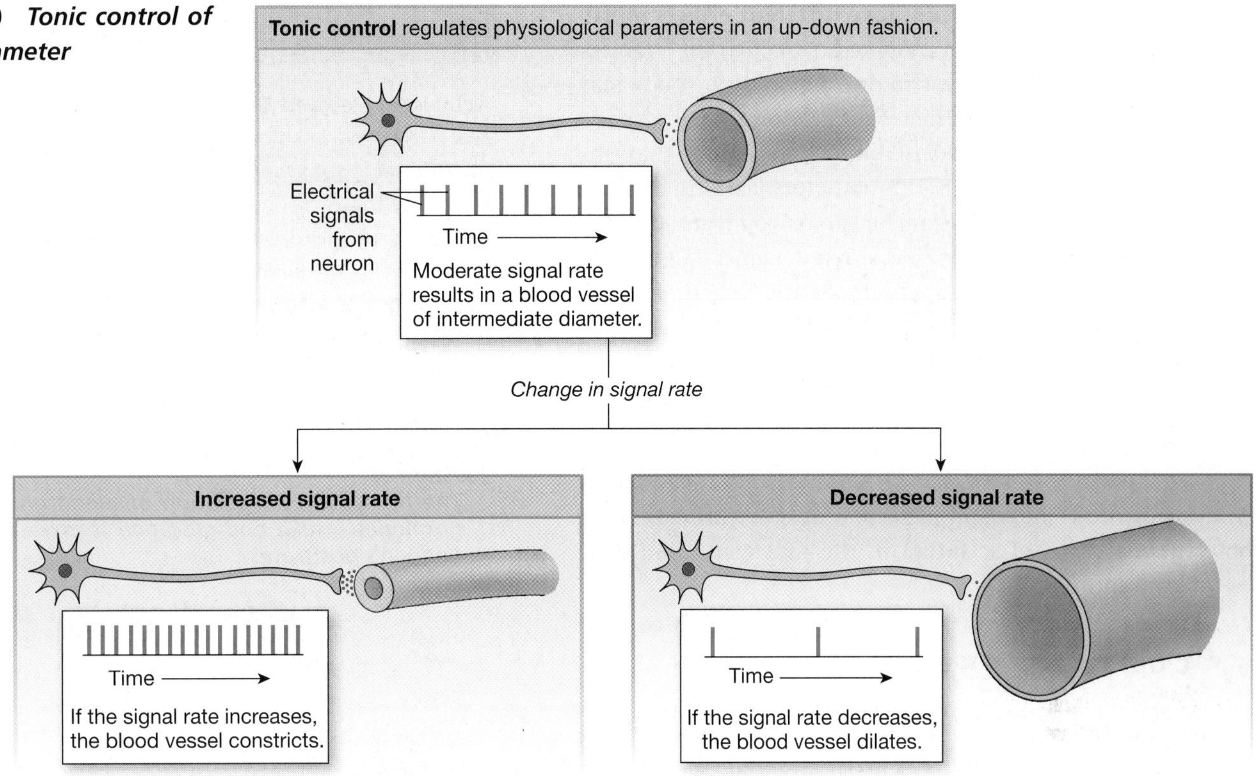
Tonic control regulates physiological parameters in an up-down fashion.
Electrical signals from neuron
Time
Moderate signal rate results in a blood vessel of intermediate diameter.
Change in signal rate
Increased signal rate
Time
If the signal rate increases, the blood vessel constricts.
Decreased signal rate
Time
If the signal rate decreases, the blood vessel dilates.

FIGURE 6-21 *Antagonistic control of heart rate*

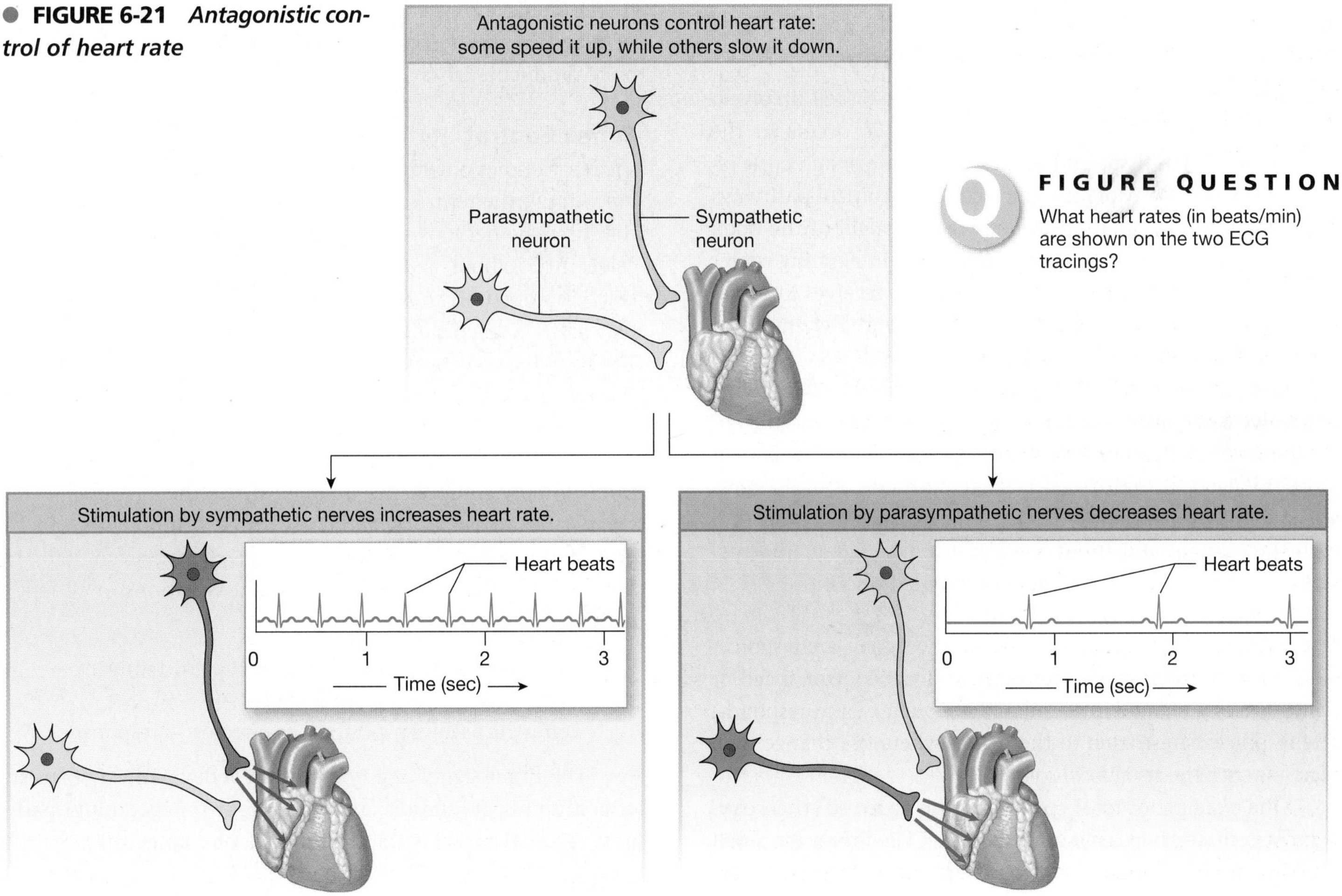
Antagonistic neurons control heart rate: some speed it up, while others slow it down.
Parasympathetic neuron
Sympathetic neuron
Stimulation by sympathetic nerves increases heart rate.
Heart beats
0
1
2
3
Time (sec)
Stimulation by parasympathetic nerves decreases heart rate.
Heart beats
0
1
2
3
Time (sec)

FIGURE QUESTION

What heart rates (in beats/min) are shown on the two ECG tracings?

4. **One chemical signal can have different effects in different tissues.** Cannon observed correctly that "homeostatic agents antagonistic in one region of the body may be cooperative in another region." However, it was not until scientists learned about cell receptors that the basis for the seemingly contradictory actions of some hormones or nerves became clear. As you learned in the first part of this chapter, a single chemical signal can have different effects depending on the receptor and signal pathway of the target cell. For example, epinephrine constricts or dilates blood vessels, depending on whether the vessel has α- or β-adrenergic receptors (see Fig. 6-18).

The remarkable accuracy of Cannon's postulates, now confirmed with cellular and molecular data, is a tribute to the observational skills of scientists in the nineteenth and early twentieth centuries.

CONCEPT CHECK

18. What is the difference between tonic control and antagonistic control?
19. How can one chemical signal have opposite effects in two different tissues?

Answers: p. 214

Homeostasis May Be Maintained by Local or Long-Distance Pathways

The simplest control takes place at the tissue or cell involved. In **local control**, a relatively isolated change occurs in the vicinity of a cell or tissue and evokes a paracrine or autocrine response (Fig. 6-22 ●). More complicated **reflex control pathways** respond to changes that are widespread throughout the body or *systemic* in nature. In a reflex pathway, an integrating center located away from the affected cell or tissue receives information, evaluates it, and decides whether to send a chemical or electrical signal to initiate a response.

Long-distance reflex pathways are traditionally considered to involve two control systems: the nervous system and the endocrine system. However, cytokines [p. 180] are now known to be involved in some long-distance pathways. During stress and systemic inflammatory responses, cytokines work together with the nervous and endocrine systems to integrate information from all over the body into coordinated responses.

Local Control Paracrine and autocrine signals are responsible for the simplest control systems. In local control, a cell or tissue senses a change in its immediate vicinity and responds. The response is restricted to the region where the change took place—hence the term *local control.*

One example of local control can be observed when oxygen concentration in a tissue decreases. Cells lining the small blood vessels that bring blood to the area sense the fall in oxygen concentration and respond by secreting a paracrine signal.

RUNNING PROBLEM

"Why is an elevated blood glucose concentration bad?" Marvin asks. "The elevated blood glucose itself is not bad," says the nurse practitioner, "but when it is high after an overnight fast, it suggests that there is something wrong with the way your body is regulating its glucose metabolism." When a normal person absorbs a meal containing carbohydrates, blood glucose levels increase and stimulate insulin release. When cells have taken up the glucose from the meal and blood glucose levels fall, secretion of another pancreatic hormone, glucagon, increases. Glucagon raises blood glucose and helps keep the level within the homeostatic range.

Question 3:

The homeostatic regulation of blood glucose levels by the hormones insulin and glucagon is an example of which of Cannon's postulates?

The paracrine molecule relaxes muscles in the blood vessel wall, dilating the blood vessel and bringing more blood and therefore more oxygen to the area. Paracrine signal molecules involved in this response include carbon dioxide and metabolic products such as lactic acid.

Reflex Control In a reflex control pathway, coordination of the reaction lies outside the organ that carries out the response. We will use the term *reflex* to mean any long-distance pathway that uses the nervous system, endocrine system, or both to receive input about a change, integrate the information, and react appropriately. A reflex pathway can be broken down into two parts: a response loop and a feedback loop (Fig. 6-23 ●). The response loop begins with a stimulus and ends with the response of the target cell. We will discuss response loops first and then consider how they interact with feedback loops.

As with any other control system, a **response loop** has three primary components: an *input signal,* the *integration of the signal,* and an *output signal.* These three components can be broken down into the following sequence of seven steps to form a pattern that is found with slight variations in all reflex pathways:

Stimulus → sensor or receptor → afferent pathway →
integrating center →
efferent pathway → target or effector → response

The input signal of a homeostatic reflex pathway consists of a stimulus, its sensor, and an afferent (or incoming) pathway. (1) A **stimulus** is the disturbance or change that sets the pathway in motion. The stimulus may be a change in temperature, oxygen content, blood pressure, or any one of a myriad

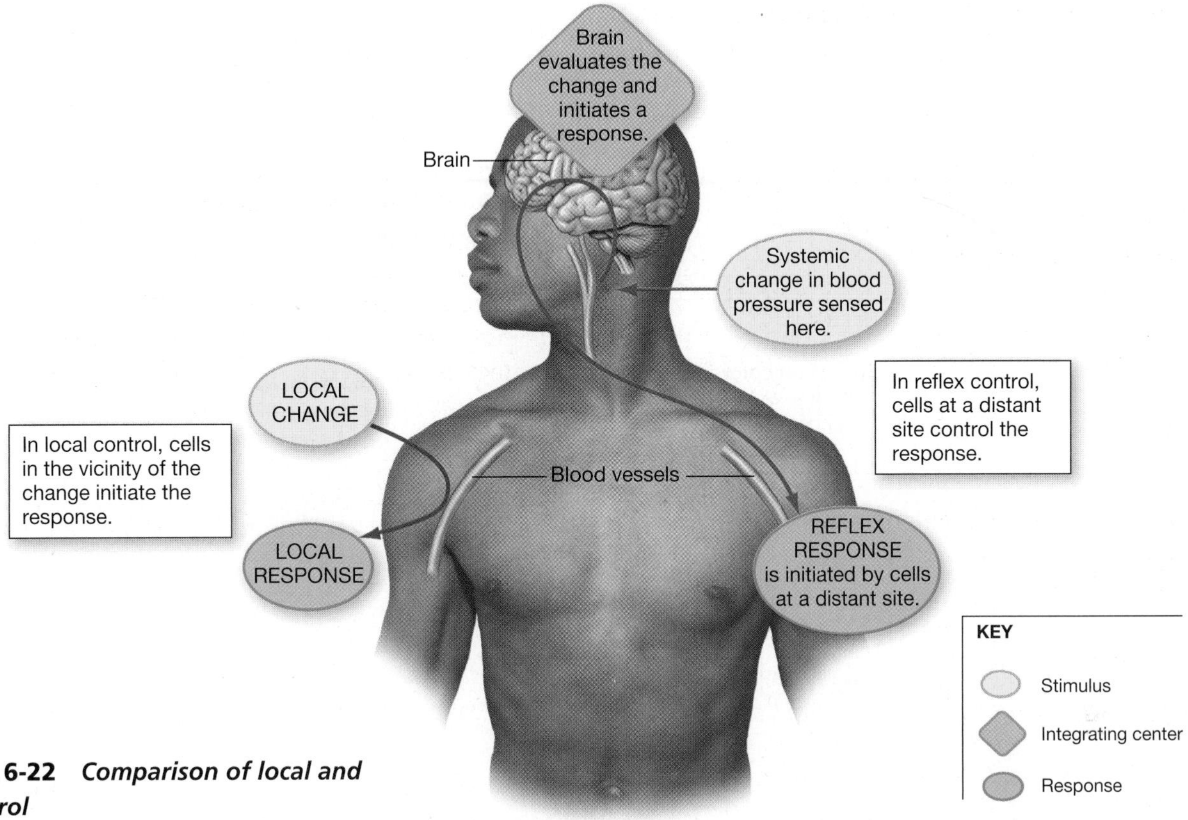

● **FIGURE 6-22** ***Comparison of local and reflex control***

of other variables. The stimulus is sensed by (2) a **sensor** or sensory receptor that is continuously monitoring its environment. When alerted to a change, the sensory receptor sends (3) a signal, or **afferent** (incoming) **pathway**, that links the receptor to (4) an integrating center. The integrating center then evaluates the incoming signal, compares it with the **setpoint**, or desired value, and decides on an appropriate response. The integrating center then initiates (5) the output signal, or **efferent** (outgoing) **pathway.** This is an electrical and/or chemical signal that travels to (6) the effector. The effector, or target, is the cell or tissue that carries out (7) the appropriate response to bring the situation back to within normal limits.

Receptor The first step in a physiological response loop is activation of a sensor or receptor by the stimulus. NOTICE! This is a new and different application of the word *receptor*. Like many other terms in physiology, *receptor* can have different meanings (Fig. 6-24 ●). The sensory receptors of a neural reflex are not protein receptors that bind to signal molecules, like those involved in signal transduction. Rather, sensory receptors are specialized cells, parts of cells, or complex multicellular receptors such as the eye that respond to changes in the environment around them.

There are many sensory receptors in the body, each located where it is in the best position to monitor the variable it detects. The eyes, ears, and nose are receptors that sense light, sound and motion, and odors, respectively. Your skin is covered with less complex receptors that sense touch, temperature, vibration,

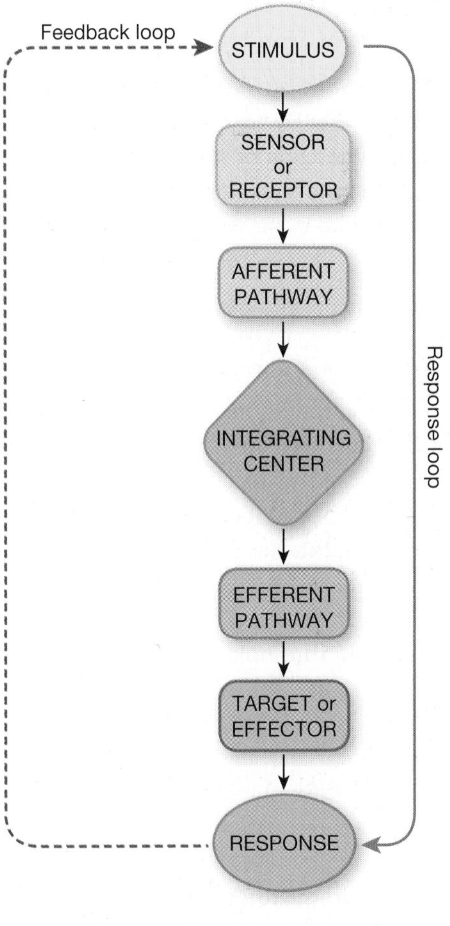

● **FIGURE 6-23** ***Steps in the response loop of a reflex control pathway***

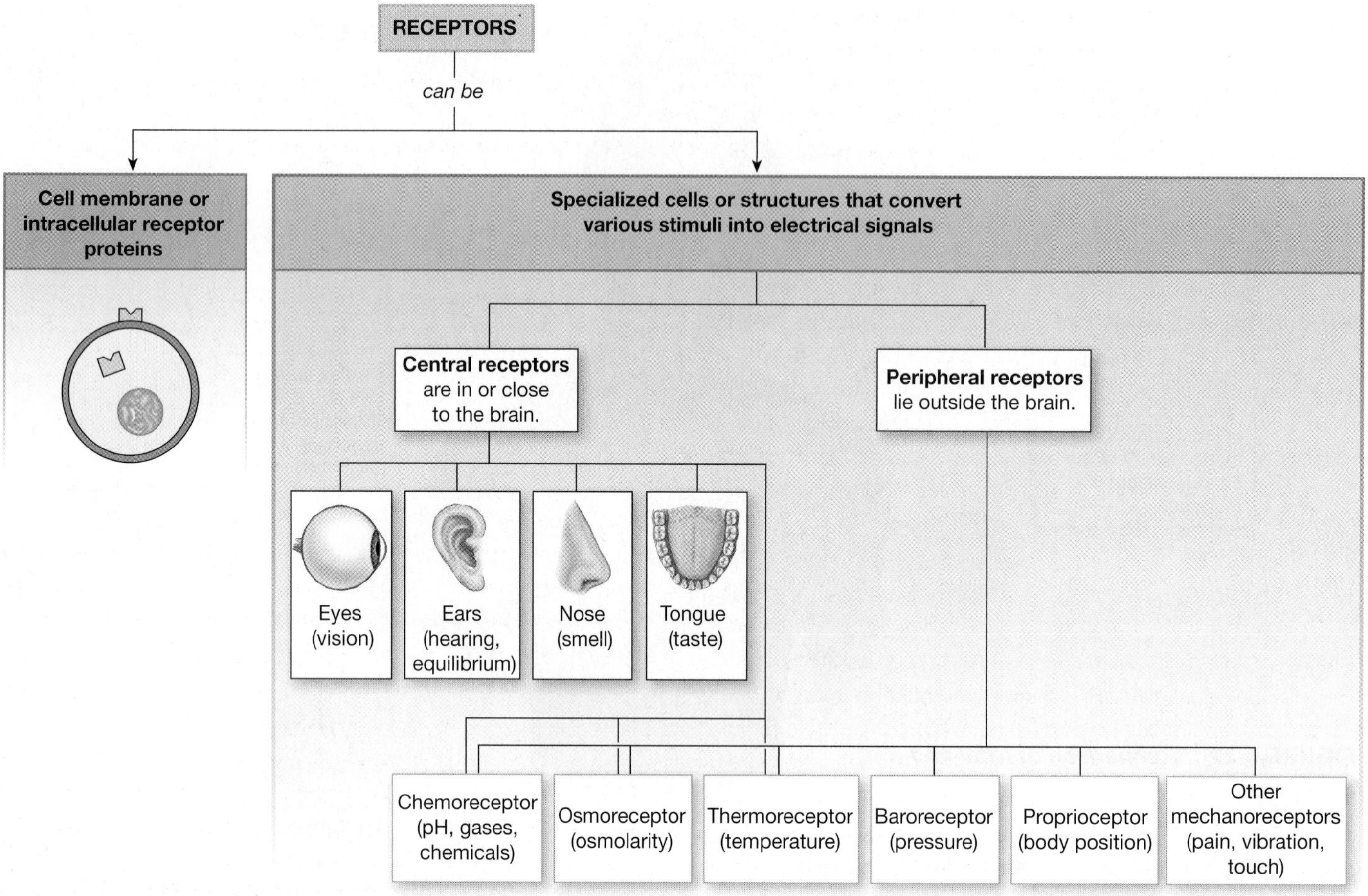

● **FIGURE 6-24** ***Multiple meanings of the word* receptor.** The word *receptor* may mean a protein that binds to a ligand. Receptor can also mean a specialized cell or structure for transduction of stimuli into electrical signals (a *sensory receptor* or *sensor*). Sensory receptors are classified as central or peripheral, depending on whether they are found in the brain or outside the brain.

and pain. Other sensory receptors are internal: receptors in the joints of the skeleton that send information to the brain about body position, or blood pressure and oxygen receptors in blood vessels that monitor conditions in the circulatory system. The sensory receptors involved in neural reflexes are divided into *central receptors,* located in or closely linked to the brain, and *peripheral receptors,* which reside elsewhere in the body.

All sensory receptors have a **threshold**, a minimum stimulus that must be achieved to set the reflex response in motion. If a stimulus is below the threshold, no response loop is initiated. You can demonstrate threshold easily by touching the back of your hand with a sharp, pointed object, such as a pin. If you touch the point to your skin lightly enough, you can see the contact between the point and your skin even though you do not feel anything. In this case, the stimulus (pressure from the point of the pin) is below threshold, and the pressure receptors of the skin are not responding. As you press harder, the stimulus reaches threshold, and the receptors respond by sending a signal through the afferent pathway, causing you to feel the pin.

Endocrine reflexes that are not associated with the nervous system do not use sensory receptors to initiate their pathways. Instead, endocrine cells act both as sensor and integrating center for the reflex. You were introduced to an example of this in Chapter 5, when we discussed how the pancreatic beta cells sense and respond to changes in blood glucose concentrations [p. 171].

Afferent Pathway The afferent pathway in a reflex varies depending on the type of reflex. In a neural reflex, such as the pin touch above, the afferent pathway is the electrical and chemical signals carried by a sensory neuron. In an endocrine reflex, there is no afferent pathway because the stimulus comes directly into the endocrine cell, which serves as both sensor and integrating center.

Integrating Center The integrating center in a reflex pathway is the cell that receives information about the change and is programmed to initiate an appropriate response. In endocrine reflexes, the integrating center is the endocrine cell. In neural reflexes, the integrating center usually lies within the central nervous system, which is composed of the brain and the spinal cord.

If information is coming from a single stimulus, it is a relatively simple task for an integrating center to compare that information with the setpoint and initiate a response (if necessary). Integrating centers really "earn their pay," however, when two or more conflicting signals come in from different sources. The center must evaluate each signal on the basis of its strength and importance and must come up with an appropriate response that integrates information from all contributing receptors. This is similar to the kind of decision-making you must do when on one evening your parents want to take you to dinner, your friends are having a party, there is a television program you want to watch, and you have a major physiology test in three days. It is up to you to rank those items in order of importance and decide how you will act on them.

Efferent Pathway Efferent pathways are relatively simple. In the nervous system, the efferent pathway is always the electrical and chemical signals transmitted by an efferent neuron. Because all electrical signals traveling through the nervous system are identical, the distinguishing characteristic of the signal is the anatomical route taken by the neuron through which the signal goes. For example, the vagus nerve carries a neural signal to the heart, and the phrenic nerve carries one to the diaphragm. Because the nature of the electrical message is always the same and because there are relatively few types of neurotransmitters, nervous system efferent pathways are named using the anatomical description of the nerve that carries the signal.

In the endocrine system, the anatomical routing of the efferent pathway is always the same because all hormones travel in the blood to get to their target. Hormonal efferent pathways are distinguished by the chemical nature of the signal and are therefore named for the hormone that carries the message. For example, the efferent pathway for a reflex integrated through the pancreas will be either the hormone insulin or the hormone glucagon, depending on the stimulus and the appropriate response.

Effectors The effectors of reflex control pathways are the target cells or tissues that carry out the response. The targets of neural pathways are muscles, glands, and some adipose tissue. The targets of endocrine pathways are any cells that have the proper receptor for the hormone.

Responses There are two levels of response for any reflex control pathway. One is the very specific *cellular response* that takes place in the target cell. The more general *systemic response* describes what those specific cellular events mean either to the tissue or to the organism as a whole. For example, when the hormone epinephrine combines with β_2-adrenergic receptors on the walls of certain blood vessels, the cellular response is relaxation of the smooth muscle. The systemic response to relaxation of the blood vessel wall is increased blood flow through the vessel.

CONCEPT CHECK

20. What is the difference between local control and reflex control?
21. Name the seven steps in a reflex control pathway in their correct order.

Answers: p. 214

Response Loops Begin with a Stimulus and End with a Response

To illustrate response loops, we will now apply the concept to nonbiological and biological examples. A simple nonbiological analogy to a homeostatic reflex pathway is an aquarium whose heater is programmed to maintain the water temperature at 30° C in a room whose temperature is 25° C (Fig. 6-25 ●). The desired water temperature (30° C) is the *setpoint* for the regulated variable.

Assume that initially the aquarium water is at room temperature, 25° C. When you turn the control box on, you set the response loop in motion. The thermometer (sensor) registers a temperature of 25° C. It sends this information via a wire (afferent path) to the control box (integrating center). The control box is programmed to evaluate the incoming temperature signal, compare it with the setpoint for the system (30° C), and "decide" whether a response is needed to bring the water temperature up to the setpoint. The control box sends a signal via another wire (efferent path) to the heater (effector), which turns on and starts heating the water (response). This sequence—from stimulus to response—is the response loop.

This aquarium example involves a variable (temperature) that is under *tonic control* (see p. 196) by a single control system (the heater). We can also describe a nonbiological analogy that illustrates Cannon's postulate of *antagonistic control*. For example, think of a house that has both heating and air conditioning. The owner would like the house to remain at 70° F (about 21° C). On chilly autumn mornings, the heater turns on to warm the house. Then, as the day warms up, the heater is no

RUNNING PROBLEM

Marvin is fascinated by the ability of the body to keep track of glucose. "How does the pancreas know which hormone to secrete?" he wonders. Special cells in the pancreas called beta cells sense an increase in blood glucose concentrations after a meal, and they release insulin in response. Insulin then acts on many tissues of the body so that they take up and utilize glucose.

Question 4:

In the insulin reflex pathway that regulates blood glucose levels, what are the stimulus, the sensor, the integrating center, the efferent pathway, the effector(s), and the response(s)?

179 182 195 198 201 205 210

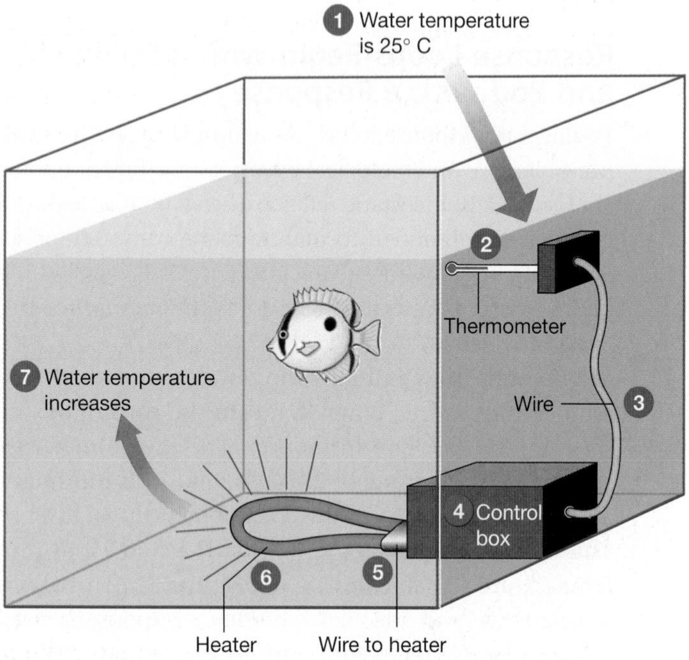
1 Water temperature is 25° C
2
Thermometer
Wire
3
4 Control box
5
6
Heater
Wire to heater
7 Water temperature increases

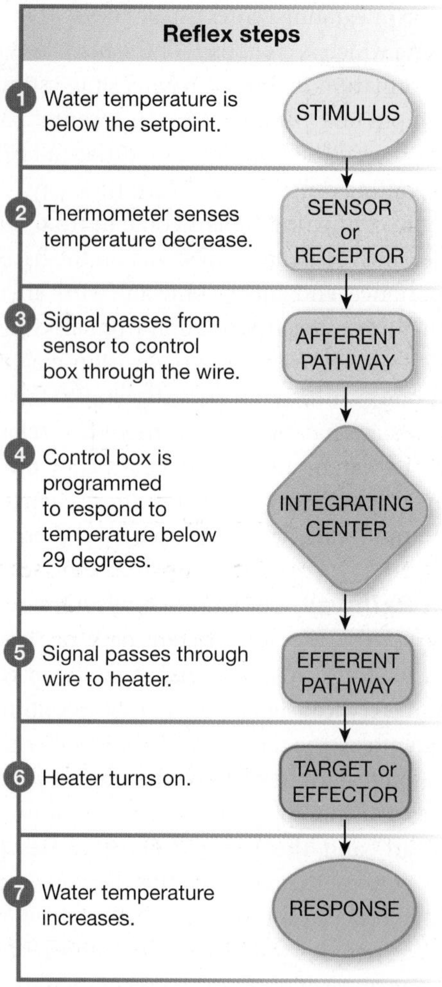
Reflex steps
1 Water temperature is below the setpoint.
STIMULUS
2 Thermometer senses temperature decrease.
SENSOR or RECEPTOR
3 Signal passes from sensor to control box through the wire.
AFFERENT PATHWAY
4 Control box is programmed to respond to temperature below 29 degrees.
INTEGRATING CENTER
5 Signal passes through wire to heater.
EFFERENT PATHWAY
6 Heater turns on.
TARGET or EFFECTOR
7 Water temperature increases.
RESPONSE

● **FIGURE 6-25** ***In this example of a nonbiological response loop, the control box is set to maintain a water temperature of 30° ± 1° C.***

longer needed. When the sun heats the house above the setpoint, the air conditioner turns on to cool the house back to 70° F. The heater and air conditioner have antagonistic control over house temperature. A similar physiological example would be the hormones insulin and glucagon, which exert antagonistic control over glucose metabolism, as noted earlier.

CONCEPT CHECK

22. What is the drawback of having only a single control system (a heater) for maintaining aquarium water temperature in some desired range?

Answers: p. 214

Setpoints Can Be Varied

In physiological systems, the setpoint for any given regulated variable can vary from person to person, or even for the same individual over a period of time. Factors that influence an individual's setpoint for a given variable include inheritance and the conditions to which the person has become accustomed. The adaptation of physiological processes to a given set of environmental conditions is known as **acclimatization** if it occurs naturally, and as **acclimation** if the process is induced artificially in a laboratory setting. Each winter, northerners go south in February, hoping to escape the bitter subzero temperatures and snows of the northern climate. As the northerners walk around in 40° F weather in short-sleeve shirts, the southerners, all bundled up in coats and gloves, think they are crazy: the weather is cold! The difference in behavior is due to different temperature acclimatization, a difference in the setpoint for body temperature regulation that is a result of prior conditioning.

Physiological setpoints also vary within individuals in response to external cues, such as the daily light-dark cycles and the seasons. These changing setpoints cause certain variables to vary in predictable ways over a period of time, forming patterns of change known as biorhythms, which we discuss later in this chapter.

Feedback Loops Modulate the Response Loop

The response loop is only part of a reflex. For example, in the aquarium just described, the sensor sends temperature information to the control box, which recognizes that the water is too cold. The control box responds by turning on the heater to warm the water. Once the response starts, though,

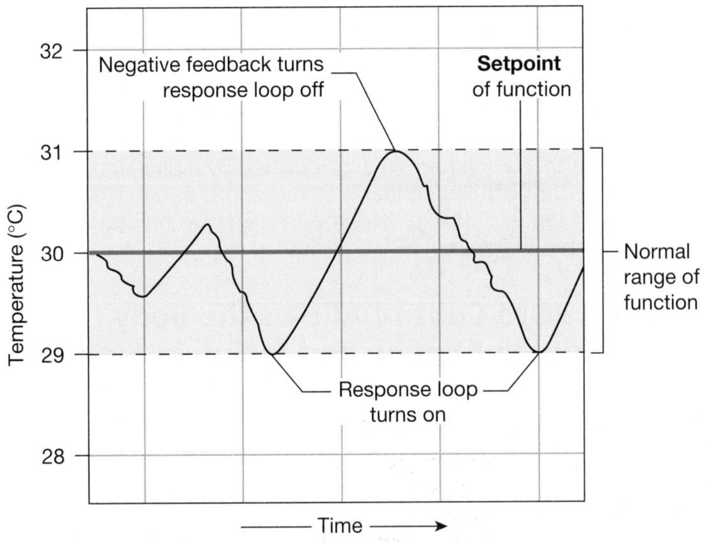

● **FIGURE 6-26** ***Oscillation around the setpoint.*** Most functions that are controlled homeostatically have a setpoint, or normal value. The response loop that controls the function is activated when the function moves outside a predetermined normal range.

what keeps the heater from sending the temperature up to, say, 50° C?

The answer is a **feedback loop**, where the response "feeds back" to influence the input portion of the pathway. In the aquarium example, turning on the heater increases the temperature of the water. The sensor continuously monitors the temperature and sends that information to the control box. When the temperature warms up to the maximum acceptable value, the control box shuts off the heater, thus ending the reflex response.

Negative Feedback Loops Are Homeostatic For most reflexes, feedback loops are homeostatic—that is, designed to keep the system at or near a setpoint so that the variable being regulated is relatively stable. How well an integrating center succeeds in maintaining stability depends on the *sensitivity* of the system. In the case of our aquarium, the control box is programmed to have a sensitivity of ±1° C. If the water temperature drops from 30° C to 29.5° C, it is still within the acceptable range, and no response is triggered. If the water temperature drops below 29° C (30° − 1°), the control box turns the heater on (Fig. 6-26 ●). As the water heats up, the control box constantly receives information about the water temperature from the sensor. When the water reaches 31° C (30° ± 1°), the upper limit for the acceptable range, the feedback loop causes the control box to turn the heater off. The water then gradually cools off until the cycle starts all over again. The end result is a regulated variable that *oscillates* [*oscillare,* to swing] around the setpoint.

In physiological systems, some sensors are more sensitive than others. For example, the sensors for osmolarity trigger reflexes to conserve water when blood osmolarity increases only 3% above normal, but the sensors for low oxygen in the blood will not respond until oxygen has decreased by 40%.

A pathway in which the response opposes or removes the signal is known as **negative feedback** (Fig. 6-27a ●). Negative feedback loops *stabilize* the variable being regulated and thus aid the system in maintaining homeostasis. In the aquarium example, the heater warms the water (the response) and removes the stimulus (low water temperature). With loss of the stimulus for the pathway, the response loop shuts off. All homeostatic reflexes are controlled by negative feedback so that the variable being regulated stays within a normal range. *Negative feedback loops can restore the normal state but cannot prevent the initial disturbance.*

Positive Feedback Loops Are Not Homeostatic A few reflex pathways are not homeostatic. In a **positive feedback loop**, the response *reinforces* the stimulus rather than decreasing

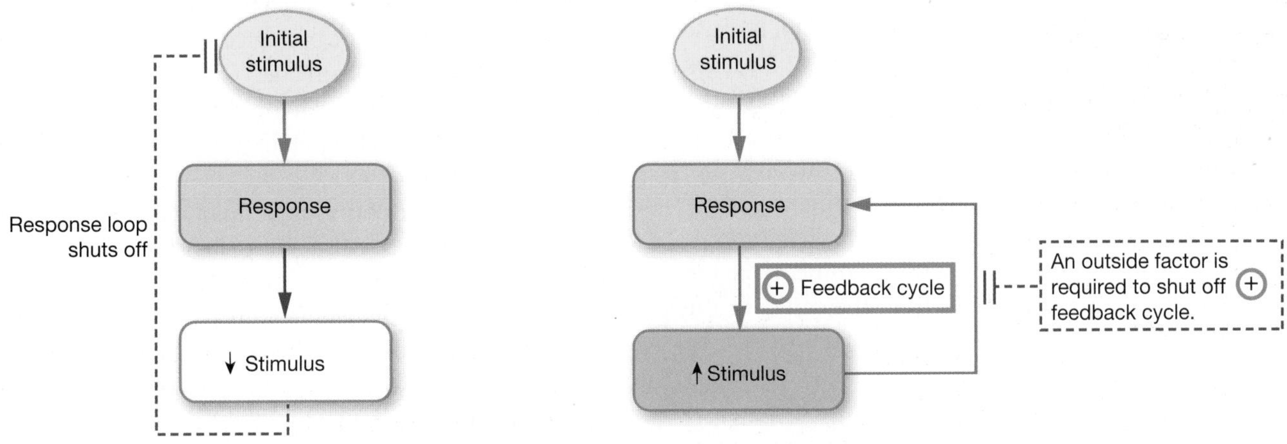

(a) Negative feedback: the response counteracts the stimulus, shutting off the response loop.

(b) Positive feedback: the response reinforces the stimulus, sending the variable farther from the setpoint.

● **FIGURE 6-27** ***Negative and positive feedback***

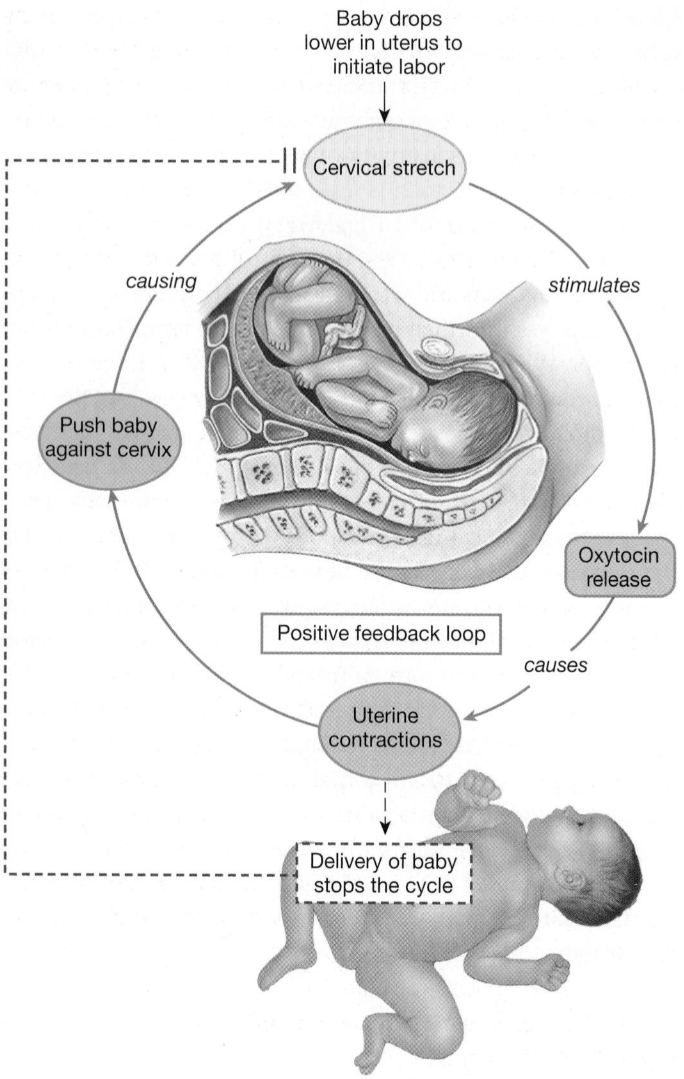

● **FIGURE 6-28** ***A positive feedback loop***

or removing it. In positive feedback, the response sends the variable being regulated even farther from its normal value, triggering a vicious cycle of ever-increasing response and sending the system temporarily out of control (Fig. 6-27b). Because positive feedback escalates the response, this type of feedback requires some intervention or event outside the loop to stop the response.

One example of a positive feedback loop involves the hormonal control of uterine contractions during childbirth (Fig. 6-28 ●). When the baby is ready to be delivered, it drops lower in the uterus and begins to put pressure on the *cervix,* the opening of the uterus. Sensory signals from the cervix to the brain cause release of the hormone *oxytocin,* which causes the uterus to contract and push the baby's head even harder against the cervix, further stretching it. The increased stretch causes more oxytocin release, which causes more contractions that push the baby harder against the cervix. This cycle continues until finally the baby is delivered, releasing the stretch on the cervix and stopping the positive feedback loop.

CONCEPT CHECK

23. Does the aquarium heating system in Figure 6-25 function using positive feedback or negative feedback? Draw in the appropriate feedback loop on the reflex steps in the figure, using either a solid arrow accompanied by a plus sign inside a circle for positive feedback, or two short, parallel "stop" lines at the end of a dashed line for negative feedback, as illustrated in Figure 6-27. Answers: p. 214

Feedforward Control Allows the Body to Anticipate Change and Maintain Stability

Negative feedback loops can stabilize a function and maintain it within a normal range but are unable to prevent the change that triggered the reflex in the first place. A few reflexes have evolved that enable the body to predict that a change is about to occur and start the response loop in anticipation of the change. These anticipatory responses are called **feedforward control.**

An easily understood physiological example of feedforward control is the salivation reflex. The sight, smell, or even the thought of food is enough to start our mouths watering in expectation of the food to eat. This reflex extends even further, because the same stimuli can start the secretion of hydrochloric acid as the stomach anticipates food on the way. One of the most complex feedforward reflexes appears to be the body's response to exercise, discussed in Chapter 25.

Biological Rhythms Result from Changes in a Setpoint

Many reflex pathways are activated in response to an obvious stimulus. In the aquarium example, a change in temperature is the stimulus that turns on the heater to ensure that temperature is maintained within the desired range. But not all physiological pathways have such obvious stimuli to initiate them. Many hormones, for example, are secreted continuously, with levels that rise and fall throughout the day. Physiological functions that change over time in a predictable manner are examples of biological rhythms, and the timing of the rhythm often coincides with a predictable environmental change, such as light-dark cycles or the seasons. Biological rhythms reflect changes in the setpoint of the regulated variable.

All animals exhibit some form of daily biological rhythm, called a **circadian rhythm** [*circa,* about + *dies,* day]. Humans have circadian rhythms for many body functions, including blood pressure, body temperature, and metabolic processes. Body temperature peaks in the late afternoon and declines dramatically in the early hours of the morning (Fig. 6-29a ●). Have you ever been studying late at night and noticed that you feel cold? This is not because of a drop in environmental temperature but because your thermoregulatory reflex has turned down your internal thermostat.

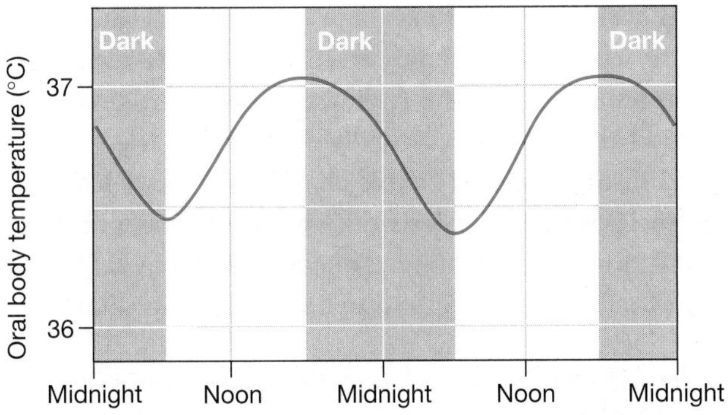

(a) Body temperature is lowest in the early morning and peaks in the late afternoon and early evening.

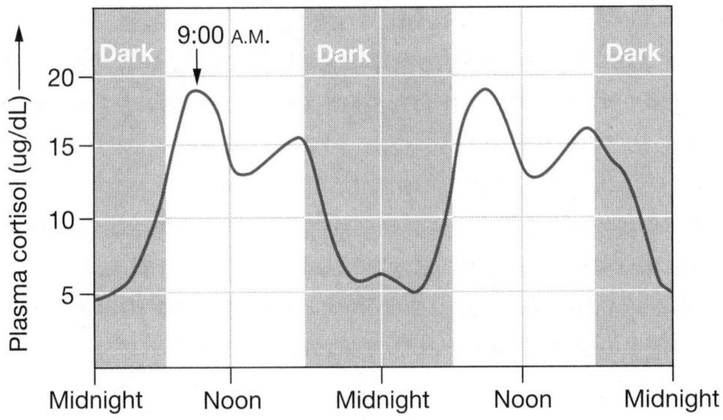

(b) Plasma cortisol is lowest during sleep and peaks shortly after awakening.

● **FIGURE 6-29** ***Circadian rhythms in humans.*** Data in part (a) from W. E. Scales et al., *J. Appl. Physiol.* 65(4): 1840–1846, 1988. Data in part (b) from L. Weibel et al., *Am. J. Physiol. Endocrinol. Metab.* 270: E608–E613, 1996.

Many hormones in humans are secreted so that their concentration in the blood fluctuates predictably through a 24-hour cycle as their setpoints change. Cortisol, growth hormone, and the sex hormones are among the most noted examples. If an abnormality in hormone secretion is suspected, it is important to know at what time of day the body fluid used for testing was taken from the patient. A cortisol value in a 9:00 A.M. sample might be nearly twice as high as one taken in the early afternoon (Fig. 6-29b). One strategy for avoiding this type of error uses a 24-hour collection period that results in an average value for the hormone over the course of a day. For example, cortisol secretion is monitored indirectly by measuring all urinary cortisol metabolites excreted in 24 hours.

What is the adaptive significance of functions that vary with a circadian rhythm? Our best answer is that biological rhythms create an anticipatory response to a predictable environmental variable. There are seasonal rhythms of reproduction in many mammalian and non-mammalian vertebrates and invertebrates, rhythms timed so that the offspring have food and other favorable conditions to maximize survival. Circadian rhythms cued by the light-dark cycle may correspond to our rest-activity cycles. These rhythms allow our bodies to anticipate behavior and coordinate body processes accordingly. You may hear someone who is accustomed to eating dinner at 6:00 P.M. say that he cannot digest his food if he waits until 10:00 P.M. to eat because his digestive system has "shut down" in anticipation of going to bed.

One of the interesting correlations between circadian rhythms and behavior involves body temperature. Researchers found that self-described "morning people" have temperature rhythms that cause body temperature to climb before they awaken in the morning, so that they get out of bed prepared to face the world. On the other hand, "night people" may be forced by school and work schedules to get out of bed while their body temperature is still at its lowest point, before their bodies are prepared for activity. These night people are still going strong and working productively in the early hours of the morning when the morning peoples' body temperatures are dropping and they are fast asleep.

Circadian rhythms arise from special groups of cells in the brain and are reinforced by information about the light-dark cycle that comes in through the eyes. Research in simpler animals such as flies is beginning to explain the molecular basis for biological rhythms. We discuss the cellular and molecular basis for circadian rhythms in Chapter 9.

Now that you have been introduced to response loops and feedback loops, we can turn to an analysis of the different control systems.

Control Systems Vary in Their Speed and Specificity

Physiological reflex control pathways are mediated by the nervous system, the endocrine system, or a combination of the two (Fig. 6-30 ●). A reflex mediated solely by the nervous system or solely by the endocrine system is relatively simple, but

RUNNING PROBLEM

"OK, just one more question," says Marvin. "You said that people with diabetes have high blood glucose levels. If glucose is so high, why can't it just leak into the cells?"

Question 5:
Why can't glucose always diffuse into cells when the blood glucose concentration is higher than the intracellular glucose concentration?

Question 6:
What do you think happens to the rate of insulin secretion when blood glucose levels fall? What kind of feedback loop is operating?

179 182 195 198 201 205 210

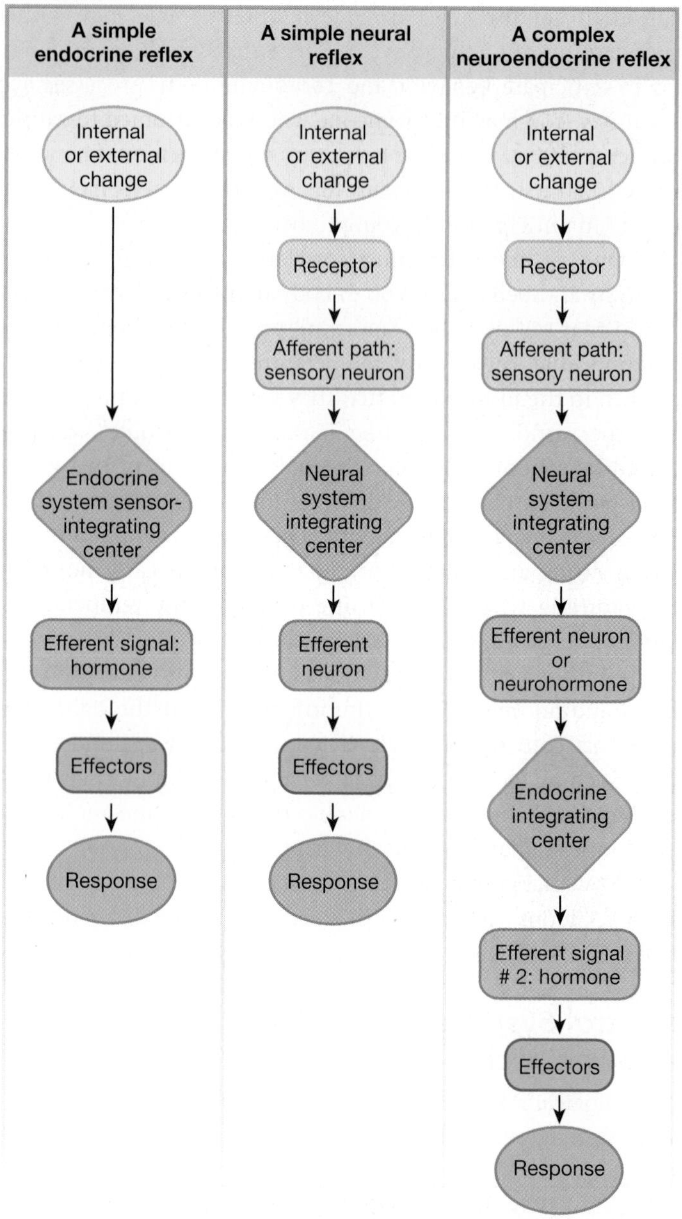

● **FIGURE 6-30** ***Endocrine, neural, and neuroendocrine control pathways***

combination reflex pathways can be quite complex. In the most complex pathways, signals pass through three different integrating centers before finally reaching the target tissue. With so much overlap between pathways controlled by the nervous and endocrine systems, it makes sense to consider these systems as parts of a continuum rather than as two discrete systems.

Why does the body need different types of control systems? To answer that question, let us compare endocrine control with neural control to see what the differences are. Five major differences are summarized in Table 6-4 ● and discussed next.

Specificity Neural control is very specific because each neuron has a specific target cell or cells to which it sends its message. Anatomically, we can isolate a neuron and trace it from its origin to where it terminates on its target. Endocrine control is more general because the chemical messenger is released into the blood and can reach virtually every cell in the body. As you learned in the first half of this chapter, the body's response to a specific hormone depends on which cells have receptors for that hormone and which receptor type they have. Multiple tissues in the body can respond to a hormone simultaneously.

Nature of the Signal The nervous system uses both electrical and chemical signals to send information throughout the body. Electrical signals travel long distances through neurons, releasing chemical signals (neurotransmitters) that diffuse across the small gap between the neuron and its target (Fig. 6-31 ●, ①). In a limited number of instances, electrical signals pass directly from cell to cell through gap junctions.

The endocrine system uses only chemical signals: hormones secreted by endocrine glands or cells into the blood (Fig. 6-31, ⑥). The neurohormone pathway shown in Fig. 6-31, ② represents a hybrid of the neural and endocrine reflexes. In a neurohormone pathway, a neuron creates an electrical signal, but the chemical the cell releases is a neurohormone that goes into the blood for general distribution.

CONCEPT CHECK

24. (a) In the simple neural reflex shown in Figure 6-30, which box or boxes represent(s) the brain and spinal cord? (b) Which box or boxes represent(s) the central and peripheral sense organs? (c) In the simple neural reflex, add a dashed line connecting boxes to show how a negative feedback loop would shut off the reflex.

Answers: p. 214

Speed Neural reflexes are much faster than endocrine reflexes. The electrical signals of the nervous system cover great distances very rapidly, with speeds of up to 120 m/sec. Neurotransmitters also create very rapid responses, on the order of milliseconds.

Hormones are much slower than neural reflexes. Their distribution through the circulatory system and diffusion from capillary to receptors take considerably longer than signals through neurons. In addition, hormones have a slower onset of action. In target tissues, the response may take minutes to hours before it can be measured.

Why do we need the speedy reflexes of the nervous system? Consider this example. A mouse ventures out of his hole and sees a cat ready to pounce on him and eat him. A signal must go from the mouse's eyes and brain down to his feet, telling him to run back into the hole. If his brain and feet were only 5 micrometers (5 μm = 1/200 millimeter) apart, it would take a chemical signal 20 milliseconds (msec) to diffuse across the space and the mouse could escape. If the brain and feet were 50 μm (1/20 millimeter) apart, diffusion would take 2 seconds and the mouse might get caught. But because the head and tail of a mouse are *centimeters* apart, it would take a chemical

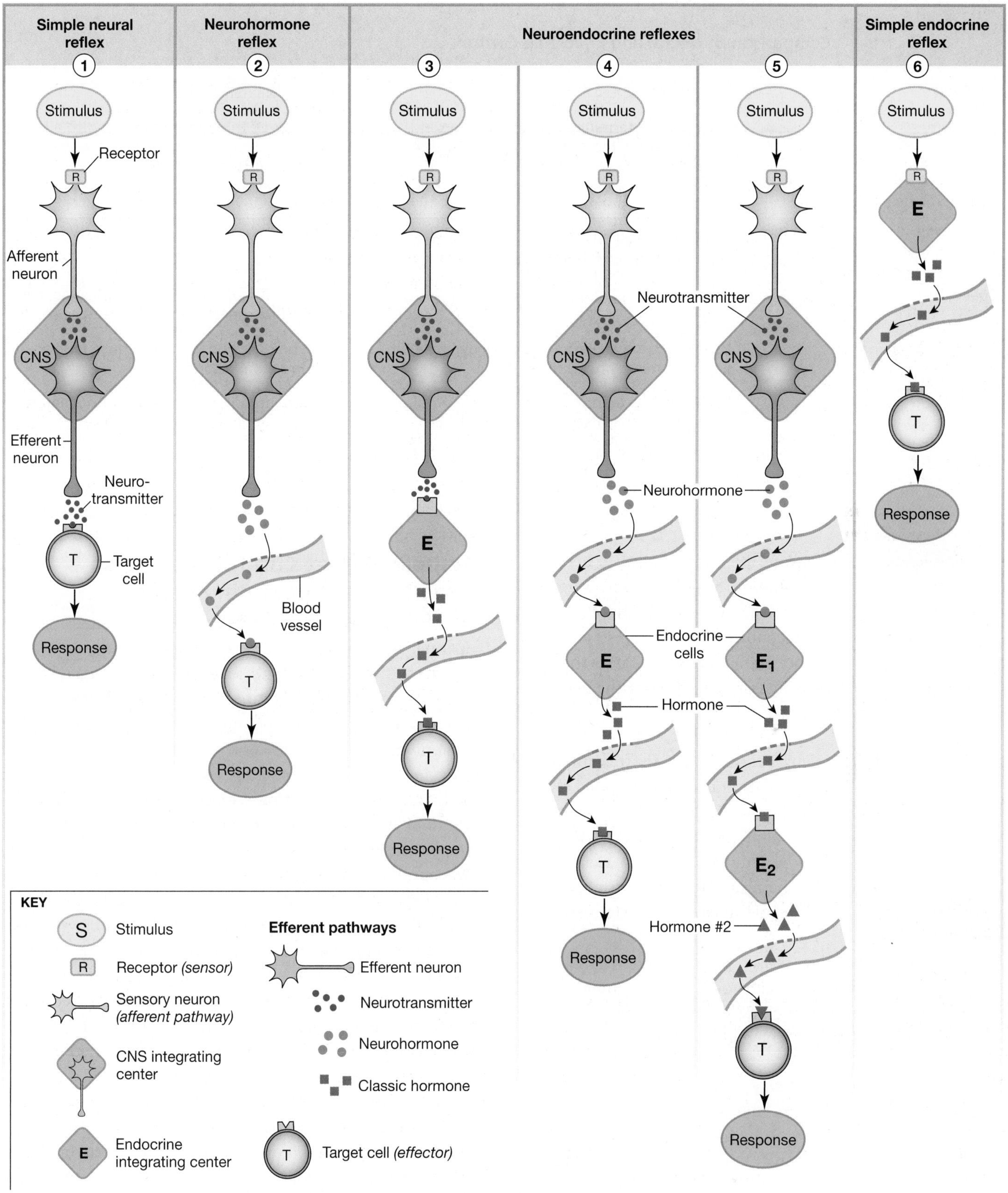

FIGURE 6-31 ***Simple and complex control pathways.*** An example of pathway ① is the knee jerk reflex. An example of ② is secretion of oxytocin in response to suckling. An example of ③ is the secretion of insulin in response to a signal from the brain. Insulin release in response to an increase in blood glucose is an example of pathway ⑥.

TABLE 6-4 Comparison of Neural and Endocrine Control

PROPERTY	NEURAL REFLEX	ENDOCRINE REFLEX
Specificity	Each neuron terminates on a single target cell or on a limited number of adjacent target cells.	Most cells of the body are exposed to a hormone. The response depends on which cells have receptors for the hormone.
Nature of the signal	Electrical signal passes through neuron, then chemical neurotransmitters pass the signal from cell to cell. In a few cases, signals pass cell-to-cell through gap junctions.	Chemical signals are secreted in the blood for distribution throughout the body.
Speed	Very rapid.	Distribution of the signal and onset of action are much slower than in neural responses.
Duration of action	Usually very short. Responses of longer duration are mediated by neuromodulators.	Duration of action is usually much longer than in neural responses.
Coding for stimulus intensity	Each signal is identical in strength. Stimulus intensity is correlated with increased frequency of signaling.	Stimulus intensity is correlated with amount of hormone secreted.

signal *three weeks* to diffuse from the mouse's head to his feet. Poor mouse! Even if the distribution of the chemical were accelerated by help from the circulatory system, the chemical message would still take 10 seconds to get to the feet, and the mouse would become cat food. The moral of this tale is that reflexes requiring a speedy response are mediated by the nervous system because they are so much more rapid.

Duration of Action Neural control is of shorter duration than endocrine control. The neurotransmitter released by a neuron combines with a receptor on the target cell and initiates a response. The response is usually very brief, however, because the neurotransmitter is rapidly removed from the vicinity of the receptor by various mechanisms. To get a sustained response, multiple repeating signals must be sent through the neuron.

Endocrine reflexes are slower to start, but they are of longer duration. This means that most of the ongoing, long-term functions of the body, such as metabolism and reproduction, fall under the control of the endocrine system.

Coding for Stimulus Intensity As a stimulus increases in intensity, control systems must have a mechanism for conveying this information to the integrating center. The signal strength from any one neuron is constant in magnitude and therefore cannot reflect stimulus intensity. Instead, the frequency of signaling through the afferent neuron increases. In the endocrine system, stimulus intensity is reflected by the amount of hormone released: the stronger the stimulus, the greater the amount of hormone released.

Complex Reflex Control Pathways Have Several Integrating Centers

Figure 6-31 summarizes variations in the neural, neuroendocrine, and endocrine reflex control pathways.

In a simple endocrine reflex pathway (Fig. 6-30 [left]; Fig. 6-31, ⑥), the endocrine cell monitors the regulated variable and acts as both sensor and integrating center; there is no afferent pathway. The efferent pathway is the hormone, and the target is any cell having the appropriate receptor protein.

An example of a simple endocrine reflex is secretion of the hormone insulin in response to changes in blood glucose level. The endocrine cells that secrete insulin monitor blood glucose concentrations by using ATP production in the cell as an indicator [Fig. 5-35, p. 170]. When blood glucose increases, intracellular ATP production exceeds the threshold level, and the endocrine cells respond by secreting insulin into the blood. Any target cell in the body that has insulin receptors responds to the hormone and initiates processes that take glucose out of the blood. The removal of the stimulus acts in a negative feedback manner, and the response loop shuts off when blood glucose levels fall below a certain concentration.

In a simple neural reflex, all the steps of the pathway are present, from receptor to target (Fig. 6-30 [middle], Fig. 6-31, ①). The neural reflex is represented in its simplest form by the knee jerk (or patellar tendon) reflex (see Fig. 13-7). A blow to the knee (the stimulus) activates a stretch receptor. An electrical and chemical signal travels through an afferent neuron to the spinal cord (the integrating center). If the blow is strong enough (exceeds threshold), a signal travels from the spinal cord through an efferent neuron to the muscles of the thigh

TABLE 6-5 Comparison of Neural, Neuroendocrine, and Endocrine Reflexes

	NEURAL	NEUROENDOCRINE	ENDOCRINE
Sensor or receptor	Special and somatic sensory receptors	Special and somatic sensory receptors	Endocrine cell
Afferent pathway	Afferent sensory neuron	Afferent sensory neuron	None
Integrating center	Brain or spinal cord	Brain or spinal cord	Endocrine cell
Efferent pathway	Efferent neuron (electrical signal and neurotransmitter)	Efferent neuron (electrical signal and neurohormone)	Hormone
Effector(s)	Muscles and glands, some adipose tissue	Most cells of the body	Most cells of the body
Response	Contraction and secretion primarily; may have some metabolic effects.	Change in enzymatic reactions, membrane transport, or cell proteins	Change in enzymatic reactions or membrane transport or cell proteins

(the target or effector). In response, the muscles contract, causing the lower leg to kick outward (the knee jerk).

CONCEPT CHECK

25. Match the following terms for parts of the knee jerk reflex to the parts of the simple neural reflex shown in Figure 6-30 (middle): blow to knee, leg muscles, neuron to leg muscles, sensory neuron, brain and spinal cord, stretch receptor, muscle contraction. Answers: p. 214

The neurohormone reflex, shown in Figure 6-31, ②, is identical to the neural reflex except that the neurohormone released by the neuron travels in the blood to its target, just like a hormone. A simple neurohormone reflex is the release of breast milk in response to a baby's suckling. The baby's mouth on the nipple stimulates sensory signals that travel through sensory neurons to the brain (integrating center). An electrical signal in the efferent neuron triggers the release of the neurohormone oxytocin from the brain into the circulation. Oxytocin is carried to the breast, where it causes contraction of smooth muscles in the breast (effectors), with the resultant ejection of milk.

In complex pathways, there may be more than one integrating center. Figure 6-31 shows three examples of complex neuroendocrine pathways. The simplest of these, Figure 6-31, ③, combines a neural reflex with a classic endocrine reflex. The target of the neural reflex is an endocrine cell that releases a hormone. An example of this pattern can be found in the control of insulin release by the nervous system, in which both excitatory and inhibitory neurons terminate on the endocrine cells of the pancreas. The endocrine cells must integrate information from three sources: the two antagonistic inputs from the nervous system and direct detection of blood glucose levels.

CONCEPT CHECK

26. Match the following terms with the appropriate parts of the simple neuroendocrine reflex in Figure 6-31, ③ (terms may be used more than once): food in stomach following a meal, brain and spinal cord, endocrine cells of pancreas, stretch receptors, efferent neuron to pancreas, insulin, adipose cell, blood, sensory neuron. Answers: p. 214

Another complex reflex (Fig. 6-31, ④) uses a neurohormone to control the release of a classic hormone. The secretion of growth hormone is an example of this pathway. The most complex neuroendocrine pathways, shown as Figure 6-31, ⑤, include a neurohormone and two classic hormones. This pattern is typical of some hormones released by the anterior pituitary, an endocrine gland located just below the brain (see Chapter 7 for details).

In describing complex neuroendocrine reflex pathways, we identify only one receptor and afferent pathway, as indicated in Figure 6-31. In the three complex pathways shown, the brain is the first integrating center and the neurohormone is the first efferent pathway. In Figure 6-31, ⑤, the endocrine target (E_1) of the neurohormone is the second integrating center, and its hormone is the second efferent pathway. The second endocrine gland in the pathway (E_2) is the third integrating center, and its hormone is the third efferent pathway. The target of the last signal in the sequence is the effector.

Table 6-5 ● compares the various steps in neural, neuroendocrine, and endocrine reflexes. In the remainder of the text, we use the general patterns shown in Figure 6-31 as a tool for classifying complex reflex pathways. In the next chapter we look in detail at some pathways of the endocrine system and the roles these pathways play in homeostasis.

RUNNING PROBLEM CONCLUSION

Diabetes Mellitus

Marvin underwent further tests and was diagnosed with early type 2 diabetes. With careful attention to his diet and with a regular exercise program, he has managed to keep his blood glucose levels under control. Diabetes is becoming a major health issue in the United States. To learn more about diabetes, see the American Diabetes Association website (www.diabetes.org) or the Centers for Disease Control and Prevention (www.cdc.gov).

In this running problem, you learned about glucose homeostasis and how it is maintained by insulin and glucagon. The disease diabetes mellitus is an indication that glucose homeostasis has been disrupted. Check your understanding of this running problem by comparing your answers to the information in the summary table.

	QUESTION	FACTS	INTEGRATION AND ANALYSIS
1	In which type of diabetes is the signal pathway for insulin more likely to be defective?	Insulin is a peptide hormone that uses membrane receptors linked to second messengers to transmit its signal to cells [p. 184]. People with type 1 diabetes lack insulin; people with type 2 diabetes have normal-to-elevated insulin levels.	Normal or high insulin levels suggest that the problem is not with amount of insulin but with the action of the insulin at the cell. The problem in type 2 diabetes could be a defective signal transduction mechanism.
2	In which form of diabetes are the insulin receptors more likely to be up-regulated?	Up-regulation of receptors usually occurs if a signal molecule is present in unusually low concentrations [p. 194]. In type1 diabetes, insulin is not secreted by the pancreas.	In type 1 diabetes, insulin levels are low. Therefore, type 1 is more likely to cause up-regulation of the insulin receptors.
3	The homeostatic regulation of blood glucose levels by the hormones insulin and glucagon is an example of which of Cannon's postulates?	Cannon's postulates describe the role of the nervous system in maintaining homeostasis, and the concepts of tonic activity, antagonistic control, and different effects of signals in different tissues.	Insulin decreases blood glucose levels, and glucagon increases them. Therefore, the two hormones are an example of an antagonistic control.
4	In the insulin pathway that regulates blood glucose levels, what are the stimulus, the sensor, the integrating center, the efferent pathway, the effector(s), and the response(s)?	See the steps of reflex pathways [p. 198].	*Stimulus:* increase in blood glucose levels; *sensor:* beta cells of the pancreas that sense the change; *integrating center:* beta cells; *efferent pathway* (the signal): insulin; *effectors:* any tissues of the body that respond to insulin; *responses:* cellular uptake and use of glucose.
5	Why can't glucose always diffuse into cells when the blood glucose concentration is higher than the intracellular glucose concentration?	Glucose is lipophobic. Simple diffusion goes across the phospholipid bilayer. Facilitated diffusion uses protein carriers [p. 145].	Because glucose is lipophobic, it must cross the membrane by facilitated diffusion. If a cell lacks the necessary protein carriers, facilitated diffusion cannot take place.
6	What do you think happens to the rate of insulin secretion when blood glucose levels fall? What kind of feedback loop is operating?	The stimulus for insulin release is an increase in blood glucose levels. In negative feedback, the response offsets the stimulus. In positive feedback, the response enhances the stimulus.	An increase in blood glucose concentration stimulates insulin release; therefore, a decrease in blood glucose should decrease insulin release. In this example, the response (lower blood glucose) offsets the stimulus (increased blood glucose), so a negative feedback loop is operating.

179 182 195 198 201 205 210

CHAPTER SUMMARY

This chapter focuses on two of the major themes in physiology: *homeostasis and control systems,* and *communication*. The sensors, integrating centers, and effectors of physiological control systems are described in the context of reflex control pathways, which vary from simple to complex. Functional control systems require efficient communication that uses various combinations of chemical and electrical signals. Those signals that cannot cross cell membranes must use membrane receptor proteins and signal transduction to transfer their information into the cell. The interaction of signal molecules with protein receptors illustrates another fundamental theme of physiology, *molecular interactions*.

Cell-to-Cell Communication

1. There are two basic types of physiological signals: chemical and electrical. Chemical signals are the basis for most communication within the body. (p. 179)
2. There are four methods of cell-to-cell communication: (1) direct cytoplasmic transfer through gap junctions, (2) contact-dependent signaling, (3) local chemical communication, and (4) long-distance communication. (p. 179; Figs. 6-1 and 6-2)
3. **Gap junctions** are protein channels that connect two adjacent cells. When they are open, chemical and electrical signals pass directly from one cell to the next. (p. 179)
4. **Contact-dependent signals** require direct contact between surface molecules of two cells. (p. 180)
5. Local communication is accomplished by **paracrine signals**, chemicals that act on cells in the immediate vicinity of the cell that secreted the paracrine. A chemical that acts on the cell that secreted it is called an **autocrine signal**. The activity of paracrine and autocrine signal molecules is limited by diffusion distance. (p. 180)
6. Long-distance communication is accomplished by **neurocrine molecules** and electrical signals in the nervous system, and by **hormones** in the endocrine system. Only cells that possess receptors for a hormone will be **target cells.** (p. 180)
7. **Cytokines** are regulatory peptides that control cell development, differentiation, and the immune response. They function as both local and long-distance signals. (p. 180)

Signal Pathways

8. Chemical signals bind to **receptors** and change intracellular signal molecules that direct the response. (p. 181; Fig. 6-3)
9. Lipophilic signal molecules enter the cell and combine with cytoplasmic or nuclear receptors. Lipophobic signal molecules and some lipophilic molecules combine with membrane receptors. (p. 182; Fig. 6-4)
10. **Signal transduction** pathways use membrane receptor proteins and intracellular second messenger molecules to translate signal information into an intracellular response. (p. 182)
11. Some signal transduction pathways activate **protein kinases**. Others activate **amplifier enzymes** that create **second messenger** molecules. (p. 184)
12. Signal pathways create intracellular **cascades** that amplify the original signal. (p. 185; Figs. 6-7 and 6-9)
13. **Receptor-enzymes** activate protein kinases, such as **tyrosine kinase** (Fig. 6-10), or the amplifier enzyme **guanylyl cyclase**, which produces the second messenger **cGMP**. (p. 186)
14. **G proteins** linked to amplifier enzymes are the most prevalent signal transduction system. **G protein-coupled receptors** also alter ion channels. (p. 186)
15. The **G protein-coupled adenylyl cyclase-cAMP-protein kinase A** pathway is the most common pathway for protein and peptide hormones. (p. 184; Fig. 6-11)
16. The amplifier enzyme **phospholipase C** creates two second messengers: **IP_3** and **diacylglycerol** (DAG). IP_3 causes Ca^{2+} release from intracellular stores. Diacylglycerol activates **protein kinase C**. (p. 188; Fig. 6-12)
17. **Integrin** receptors link the extracellular matrix to the cytoskeleton. (p. 188; Fig. 6-5)
18. **Ligand-gated ion channels** open or close to create electrical signals. (p. 189; Fig. 6-13)

Novel Signal Molecules

19. Calcium is an important signal molecule that binds to **calmodulin** to alter enzyme activity. It also binds to other cell proteins to alter movement and initiate exocytosis. (p. 191; Fig. 6-15)
20. **Nitric oxide (NO)**, **carbon monoxide (CO)**, and hydrogen sulfide (H_2S) are short-lived gaseous signal molecules. NO activates guanylyl cyclase directly. (p. 192)
21. The arachidonic acid cascade creates lipid signal molecules, such as **leukotrienes**, **prostaglandins**, and **thromboxanes**. (p. 193; Fig. 6-16)

Modulation of Signal Pathways

22. The response of a cell to a signal molecule is determined by the cell's receptor for the signal. (p. 193)
23. Receptor proteins exhibit specificity, competition, and saturation. (p. 193)
24. A receptor may have multiple ligands. **Agonists** mimic the action of a signal molecule. **Antagonists** block the signal pathway. (p. 193; Fig. 6-17)
25. Receptors come in related forms called **isoforms**. One ligand may have different effects when binding to different isoforms. (p. 194; Fig. 6-18)
26. Cells exposed to abnormally high concentrations of a signal for a sustained period of time attempt to bring their response back to normal by decreasing the number of receptors (**down-regulation**) or decreasing the binding affinity of the receptors (*desensitization*). **Up-regulation** is the opposite of down-regulation. (p. 194)
27. Cells have mechanisms for terminating signal pathways, such as removing the signal molecule or breaking down the receptor-ligand complex. (p. 195)
28. Many diseases have been linked to defects with various aspects of signal pathways, such as missing or defective receptors. (p. 195)

Control Pathways: Response and Feedback Loops

29. Walter Cannon first described four basic postulates of homeostasis: (1) The nervous system plays an important role in maintaining homeostasis. (2) Some parameters are under **tonic control**, which allows the parameter to be increased or decreased by a single signal (Fig. 6-20). (3) Other parameters are under **antagonistic control**, in which one hormone or neuron increases the parameter while another

decreases it (Fig. 6-21). (4) Chemical signals can have different effects in different tissues of the body, depending on the type of receptor present at the target cell. (p. 196)

30. The simplest homeostatic control takes place at the tissue or cell level and is known as **local control**. (p. 198)
31. In **reflex** control pathways, the decision that a response is needed is made away from the cell or tissue. A chemical or electrical signal to the cell or tissue then initiates the response. Long-distance reflex pathways involve the nervous and endocrine systems and cytokines. (p. 198; Fig. 6-22)
32. Reflex pathways can be broken down into **response loops** and **feedback loops**. A response loop begins when a **stimulus** is sensed by a sensor or **sensory receptor**. The sensor is linked by an **afferent pathway** to an **integrating center** that decides on an appropriate response. An **efferent pathway** travels from the integrating center to an **effector** that carries out the appropriate **response**. (p. 199; Fig. 6-23)
33. In **negative feedback**, a homeostatic response is turned off when the response of the system opposes or removes the original stimulus. (p. 203; Fig. 6-27a)
34. In **positive feedback** loops, the response reinforces the stimulus rather than decreasing or removing it. This destabilizes the system until some intervention or event outside the loop stops the response. (p. 203; Fig. 6-27b)
35. **Feedforward control** allows the body to predict that a change is about to occur and start the response loop in anticipation of the change. (p. 204)
36. Apparently spontaneous reflexes that occur in a predictable manner are called biological rhythms. Those that coincide with light-dark cycles are called **circadian rhythms**. (p. 204)
37. Neural control is faster and more specific than endocrine control but is usually of shorter duration. Endocrine control is less specific and slower to start but is longer lasting and is usually amplified. (p. 206; Tbl. 6-4)
38. Many reflex pathways are combinations of neural and endocrine control mechanisms. (p. 208; Fig. 6-31)

QUESTIONS

(Answers to the Review Questions begin on page A1.)

THE PHYSIOLOGY PLACE

Access more review material online at **The Physiology Place** web site. There you'll find review questions, problem-solving activities, case studies, flashcards, and direct links to both *Interactive Physiology®* and *PhysioEx™*. To access the site, go to *www.physiologyplace.com* and select *Human Physiology*, Fifth Edition.

LEVEL ONE REVIEWING FACTS AND TERMS

1. What are the two routes for long-distance signal delivery in the body?
2. Which two body systems are charged with maintaining homeostasis by responding to changes in the environment?
3. What two types of physiological signals are used to send messages through the body? Of these two types, which is available to all cells?
4. The process of maintaining a relatively stable internal environment is called ________.
5. List at least three parameters maintained by homeostasis.
6. Distinguish between the "target" and the "receptor" in physiological systems.
7. In a signal pathway, the signal ligand, also called a(n) ________ ________, binds to a(n) ________, which activates and changes intracellular ________.
8. The three main amplifier enzymes are (a) ________, which forms cAMP; (b) ________, which forms cGMP; and (c) ________, which converts a phospholipid from the cell's membrane into two different second messenger molecules.
9. An enzyme known as protein kinase adds the functional group ________ to its substrate, by transferring it from a(n) ________ molecule.
10. Put the following parts of a reflex in the correct order for a physiological response loop: efferent pathway, afferent pathway, effector, stimulus, response, receptor, integrating center.
11. Distinguish between central and peripheral receptors.
12. Match each of the following terms with its description:

(a) threshold	1. the desired target value for a parameter
(b) setpoint	2. the parameter value at which a response stops
(c) effector	3. the minimum stimulus to trigger a response
(d) oscillation	4. the organ or gland that performs the change
	5. movement of a parameter within the desired range

13. Receptors for signal pathways may be found in the ________, ________, or ________ of the cell.
14. The name for the daily fluctuations of body functions, including blood pressure, temperature, and metabolic processes, is ________ ________. These cycles arise in special cells in the ________.
15. Down-regulation results in a(n) ________ (increased or decreased?) number of receptors in response to a prolonged signal.
16. List two ways a cell may decrease its response to a signal.
17. In a negative feedback loop, the effector moves the system in the ________ (same/opposite) direction as the stimulus.

LEVEL TWO REVIEWING CONCEPTS

18. Explain the relationships of the terms in each of the following sets. Give a physiological example or location if applicable.
    (a) gap junctions, connexins, syncytium, connexon
    (b) autocrine, paracrine, cytokine, neurocrine, hormone
    (c) agonist, antagonist
    (d) transduction, amplification, cascade
19. List and compare the four classes of membrane receptors for signal pathways. Give an example of each.

20. Who was Walter Cannon? Restate his four postulates in your own words.
21. Briefly define the following terms and give an anatomical example when applicable: efferent pathway, afferent pathway, effector, stimulus, response, integrating center.
22. Explain the differences among positive feedback, negative feedback, and feedforward mechanisms. Under what circumstances would each be advantageous?
23. Compare and contrast the advantages and disadvantages of neural versus endocrine control mechanisms.
24. Label each of the following systems as positive or negative feedback.
    (a) glucagon secretion in response to declining blood glucose
    (b) increasing milk letdown and secretion in response to more suckling
    (c) urgency in emptying one's urinary bladder
    (d) sweating in response to rising body temperature
25. Identify the effector organ for each example in question 24.
26. Now identify the integrating center for examples (a), (c), and (d) in question 24.

LEVEL THREE PROBLEM SOLVING

27. In each of the following situations, identify the components of the reflex.
    (a) You are sitting quietly at your desk, studying, when you become aware of the bitterly cold winds blowing outside at 30 mph, and you begin to feel a little chilly. You start to turn up the thermostat, remember last month's bill, and reach for an afghan to pull around you instead. Pretty soon you are toasty warm again.
    (b) While you are strolling through the shopping district, the aroma of cinnamon sticky buns reaches you. You inhale appreciatively, but remind yourself that you're not hungry, because you just had lunch an hour ago. You go about your business, but 20 minutes later you're back at the bakery, sticky bun in hand, ravenously devouring its sweetness, saliva moistening your mouth.
28. A researcher is studying the smooth muscle of the respiratory system airways. When she exposes the airways to the neurotransmitter acetylcholine, the smooth muscle contracts. When she exposes the airways to the neurohormone epinephrine, the airways relax.
    (a) The phenomenon just described is an example of ________ control.
    (b) What distinguishes a neurotransmitter from a neurohormone?
    (c) Which chemical messenger is secreted in higher concentrations: acetylcholine or epinephrine? Defend your answer.

LEVEL FOUR QUANTITATIVE PROBLEMS

29. In a signal cascade for rhodopsin, a photoreceptor molecule, one rhodopsin activates 1000 molecules of transducin, the next molecule in the signal cascade. Each transducin activates one phosphodiesterase, and each phosphodiesterase converts 4000 cGMP to GMP.
    (a) What is the name of the phenomenon described in this paragraph?
    (b) Activation of one rhodopsin will result in the production of how many GMP molecules?

ANSWERS

Answers to Concept Check Questions

Page 181

1. All the communication methods listed are chemical signals except for (c) gap junctions, which transfer both chemical and electrical signals. Neurohormones (e) and neurotransmitters (f) are associated with electrical signaling in neurons but are themselves chemicals.
2. Cytokines, hormones, and neurohormones travel through the blood. Cytokines, neurohormones, and neurotransmitters are released by neurons.
3. The signal to pounce could not have been a paracrine signal because the eyes are too far away from the legs and because the response was too rapid for it to have taken place by diffusion.

Page 182

4. The components of signal pathways are signal molecule, receptor, intracellular signal molecule(s), and target proteins.
5. The cellular locations of receptors are cell membrane, cytosol, and nucleus.

Page 186

6. The steps of signal transduction are (1) signal molecule binds to receptor that (2) activates a protein that (3) creates second messengers that (4) create a response.
7. Amplification turns one signal molecule (first messenger) into multiple second messenger molecules.
8. Steroids are lipophilic, so they can enter cells and bind to intracellular receptors.

Page 189

9. Receptors are either ligand-gated ion channels, receptor-enzymes, G protein-coupled receptors, or integrins.
10. First messengers are extracellular; second messengers are intracellular.
11. (a) ligand, receptor, second messenger, cell response; (b) amplifier enzyme, second messenger, protein kinase, phosphorylated protein, cell response
12. (a) Cl^- channel opens: cell hyperpolarizes; (b) K^+ channel opens: cell hyperpolarizes; (c) Na^+ channel opens: cell depolarizes.

Page 191

13. The cell must use active transport to move Ca^{2+} against its concentration gradient.

Page 193

14. A drug that blocks leukotriene action could act at the receptor or at any step downstream. A drug that blocks leukotriene synthesis might inhibit lipoxygenase.

Page 194

15. Receptors, enzymes, and transporters are all proteins.
16. Insulin could be using different second messenger systems or binding to different receptor isoforms.

Page 195

17. Choices (a) and (d) could decrease binding affinity. Changing receptor number would not affect binding affinity.

Page 198

18. Tonic control usually involves one control system, but antagonistic control uses two.
19. A signal can have opposite effects by using different receptors or different signal pathways.

Page 201

20. Local control takes place in or very close to the target cell. Reflex control is mediated by a distant integrating center.
21. Stimulus, sensor or sensory receptor, afferent pathway, integrating center, efferent pathway, target or effector, response (tissue and systemic)

Page 202

22. If the aquarium water became overheated, there is no control mechanism for bringing it back into the desired range.

Page 204

23. Negative feedback shuts off the heater. This feedback loop is shown as a dashed line going from the response back to the stimulus, with parallel "stop" lines at the stimulus end.

Page 206

24. (a) The "neural system integrating center" is the brain and spinal cord. (b) "Receptor" represents the sense organs. (c) The dashed line indicating negative feedback runs from "Response" back to "Internal or external change."

Page 209

25. blow to knee = internal or external change; leg muscles = effectors; neuron to leg muscles = efferent neuron; sensory neuron = afferent pathway; brain and spinal cord = integrating center; stretch receptor = receptor; muscle contraction = response.

Page 209

26. food in stomach = stimulus; brain and spinal cord = CNS integrating center; endocrine cells of pancreas = E (integrating center); stretch receptors = receptor; efferent neuron to pancreas = efferent neuron; insulin = classic hormone; adipose cell = target cell; sensory neuron = afferent neuron. Blood is the anatomical route that hormones use to reach their target but is not part of the reflex pathway.

Answers to Figure Questions

Page 186

Fig. 6-9: See Figure 6-11. A (inactive and active) = adenylyl cyclase; inactive B = ATP; active B = cAMP; C (inactive and active) = protein kinase A; product = phosphorylated protein.

Page 197

Fig. 6-21: 180 beats/min for the left ECG and 60 beats/min for the right ECG.

7

Introduction to the Endocrine System

BACKGROUND BASICS

Receptors: **181** Peptides and proteins: **31** Comparison of endocrine and nervous systems: **206**
Signal transduction: **182** Steroids: **28** Specificity: **40**

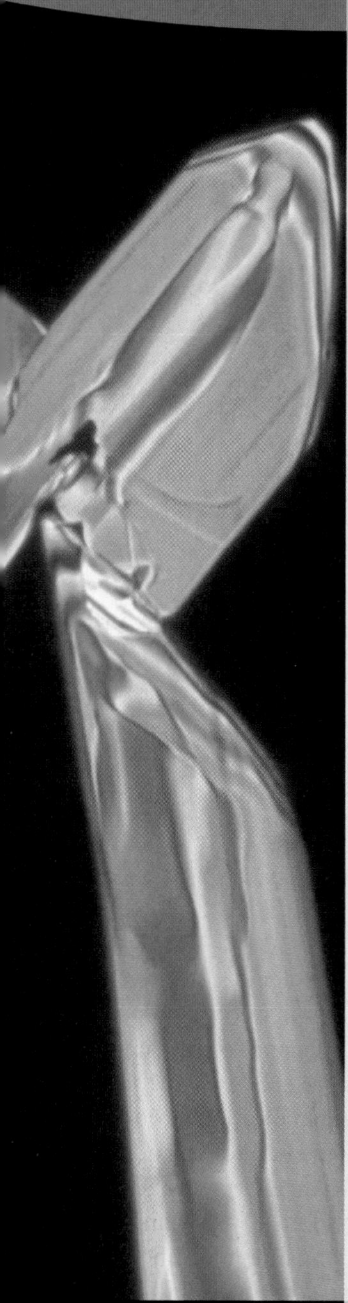

Thyroxine crystals

The separation of the endocrine system into isolated subsystems must be recognized as an artificial one, convenient from a pedagogical point of view but not accurately reflecting the interrelated nature of all these systems.

—Howard Rasmussen, *in* Williams' Textbook of Endocrinology, 1974

RUNNING PROBLEM

Graves' Disease

The ball slid by the hole and trickled off the green: another bogey. Ben Crenshaw's golf game was falling apart. The 33-year-old professional had won the Masters Tournament only a year ago, but now something was not right. He was tired and weak, had been losing weight, and felt hot all the time. He attributed his symptoms to stress, but his family thought otherwise. At their urging, he finally saw a physician. The diagnosis? Graves' disease, which results in an overactive thyroid gland.

216 226 231 234 238 240 240

David was seven years old when the symptoms first appeared. His appetite at meals increased, and he always seemed to be in the kitchen looking for food. Despite eating more, however, he was losing weight. When he started asking for water instead of soft drinks, David's mother became concerned, and when he wet the bed three nights in a row, she knew something was wrong. The doctor confirmed the suspected diagnosis after running tests to determine the concentration of glucose in David's blood and urine. David had diabetes mellitus. In his case, the disease was due to lack of insulin, a hormone produced by the pancreas. David was placed on insulin injections, a treatment he would continue for the rest of his life.

One hundred years ago, David would have died not long after the onset of symptoms. The field of **endocrinology**, the study of hormones, was then in its infancy. Most hormones had not been discovered, and the functions of known hormones were not well understood. There was no treatment for diabetes, no birth control pill for contraception. Babies born with inadequate secretion of thyroid hormone did not grow or develop normally.

Today, all that has changed. We have identified a long and growing list of hormones. The endocrine diseases that once killed or maimed can now be controlled by synthetic hormones and sophisticated medical procedures. Although physicians do not hesitate to use these treatments, we are still learning exactly how hormones act on their target cells. This chapter provides an introduction to the basic principles of hormone structure and function. You will learn more about individual hormones as you encounter them in your study of the various systems.

HORMONES

As you learned in Chapter 6, hormones are chemical messengers secreted into the blood by specialized cells. Hormones are responsible for many functions that we think of as long-term, ongoing functions of the body. Processes that fall mostly under hormonal control include growth and development, metabolism, regulation of the internal environment (temperature, water balance, ions), and reproduction. Hormones act on their target cells in one of three basic ways: (1) by controlling the rates of enzymatic reactions, (2) by controlling the transport of ions or molecules across cell membranes, or (3) by controlling gene expression and the synthesis of proteins.

● **FIGURE 7-1** ***An endocrine disorder in ancient art.*** This pre-Colombian stone carving of a woman shows a mass at her neck. This mass is an enlarged thyroid gland, a condition known as goiter. It was considered a sign of beauty among the people who lived high in the Andes mountains.

Hormones Have Been Known Since Ancient Times

Although the scientific field of endocrinology is relatively young, diseases of the endocrine system have been documented for more than a thousand years. Evidence of endocrine abnormalities can even be seen in ancient art. For example, one pre-Colombian statue of a woman shows a mass on the front of her neck (Fig. 7-1 ●). The mass is an enlarged thyroid gland, or *goiter,* a common condition high in the Andes, where the dietary iodine needed to make thyroid hormones was lacking.

The first association of endocrine structure and function was probably the link between the testes and male sexuality. Castration of animals and men was a common practice in both Eastern and Western cultures because it was known to decrease the sex drive and render males infertile.

In 1849, A. A. Berthold performed the first classic experiment in endocrinology. He removed the testes from roosters and observed that the castrated birds had smaller combs, less aggressiveness, and less sex drive than uncastrated roosters. If the testes were surgically placed back into the donor cock or into another castrated bird, normal male behavior and comb development resumed. Because the reimplanted testes were not connected to nerves, Berthold concluded that the glands must be secreting something into the blood that affected the entire body.

Experimental endocrinology did not receive much attention, however, until 1889, when the 72-year-old French physician Charles Brown-Séquard made a dramatic announcement of his sexual rejuvenation after injecting himself with extracts made from bull testes ground up in water. An international uproar followed, and physicians on both sides of the Atlantic began to inject their patients with extracts of many different endocrine organs, a practice known as *organotherapy*.

We now know that the increased virility Brown-Séquard reported was most likely a placebo effect because testosterone is a hydrophobic steroid that cannot be extracted by an aqueous preparation. His research opened the door to hormone therapy, however, and in 1891 organotherapy had its first true success: a woman was treated for low thyroid hormone levels with glycerin extracts of sheep thyroid glands.

As the study of "internal secretions" grew, Berthold's experiments became a template for endocrine research. Once a gland or structure was suspected of secreting hormones, the classic steps for identifying an endocrine gland became:

1. Remove the suspected gland and monitor the animal for anatomical, behavioral, or physiological abnormalities. This is equivalent to inducing a state of *hormone deficiency*.
2. Either place the gland back in the animal or administer an extract of the gland and see if the abnormalities disappear. Such *replacement therapy* should eliminate the symptoms of hormone deficiency.
3. Either implant the gland in a normal animal or administer an extract from the gland to a normal animal, and see if symptoms characteristic of *hormone excess* appear.
4. Once a gland is identified as a potential source of hormones, purify extracts of the gland to isolate the active substance. The test for hormone activity is usually a biological assay in which an animal is injected with the purified extract and monitored for a response.

Hormones identified by this technique are sometimes called *classic hormones*. They include hormones of the pancreas, thyroid, adrenal glands, pituitary, and gonads, all discrete endocrine glands that could be easily identified and surgically removed. Not all hormones come from identifiable glands, however, and we have been slower to discover them.

The Anatomy Summary in Figure 7-2 ● lists the major hormones of the body and the glands or cells that secrete them, along with the major properties of each hormone.

CLINICAL FOCUS

DIABETES

THE DISCOVERY OF INSULIN

Diabetes mellitus, the metabolic condition associated with pathologies of insulin function, has been known since ancient times. Detailed clinical descriptions of insulin-deficient diabetes were available to physicians, but they had no means of treating the disease, and patients invariably died. However, in a series of classic experiments in endocrine physiology, Oscar Minkowski at the University of Strasbourg (Germany) pinpointed the relationship between diabetes and the pancreas. In 1889, Minkowski surgically removed the pancreas from dogs (*pancreatectomy*) and noticed that they developed symptoms that mimicked diabetes. He also found that implanting pieces of pancreas under the dogs' skin would prevent development of diabetes. Subsequently, in 1921 Fredrick G. Banting and Charles H. Best (Toronto, Canada) identified an antidiabetic substance in pancreas extracts. Banting and Best and others injected pancreatic extracts into diabetic animals and found that the extracts reversed the elevated blood glucose levels of diabetes. From there, it was a relatively short process until, in 1922, purified insulin was used in the first clinical trials.

What Makes a Chemical a Hormone?

In 1905, the term *hormone* was coined from the Greek verb meaning "to excite or arouse." The traditional definition of a **hormone** is a chemical secreted by a cell or group of cells into the blood for transport to a distant target, where it exerts its effect at very low concentrations. However, as scientists learn more about chemical communication in the body, this definition is continually being challenged.

Hormones Are Secreted by a Cell or Group of Cells

Traditionally, the field of endocrinology has focused on chemical messengers secreted by endocrine *glands*, the discrete and readily identifiable tissues derived from epithelial tissue [p. 79]. However, we now know that molecules that act as hormones are secreted not only by classic endocrine glands but also by isolated endocrine cells (hormones of the *diffuse endocrine system*), by neurons (*neurohormones*), and by cells of the immune system (*cytokines*).

Hormones Are Secreted into the Blood **Secretion**, first presented in Chapter 3 [p. 56], is the movement of a substance from the intracellular compartment either to the extracellular compartment or to the external environment. According to the traditional definition, hormones are secreted into the blood. However, the term *ectohormone* [*ektos,* outside]

ANATOMY SUMMARY

HORMONES

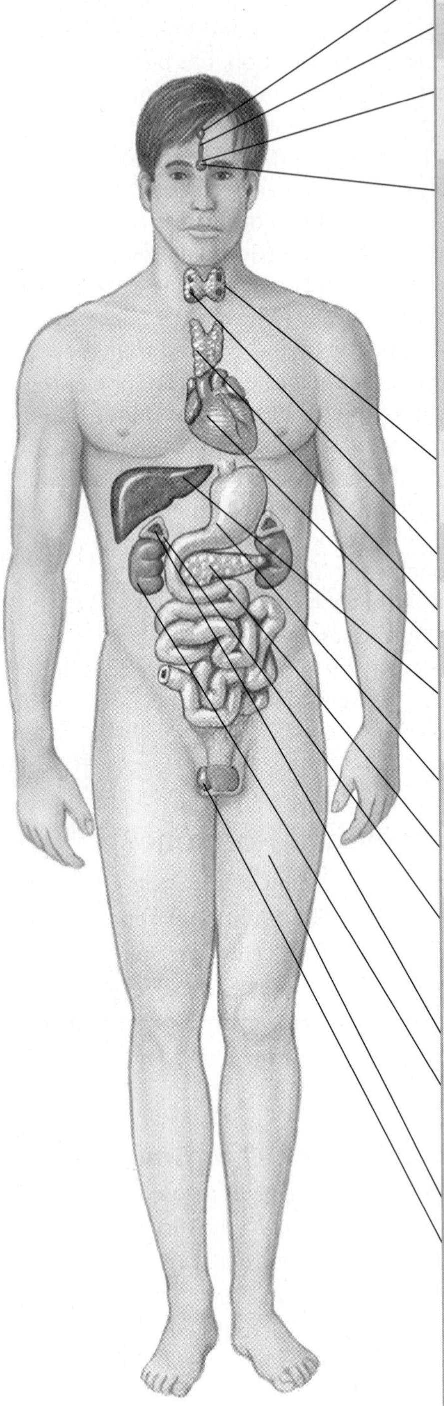

Location	Hormone	Primary Target(s)
Pineal gland	Melatonin [A]	Brain, other tissues
Hypothalamus (N)	Trophic hormones [P] (see Fig. 7-13)	Anterior pituitary
Posterior pituitary (N)	Oxytocin [P]	Breast and uterus
	Vasopressin (ADH) [P]	Kidney
Anterior pituitary (G)	Prolactin [P]	Breast
	Growth hormone (somatotropin) [P]	Liver Many tissues
	Corticotropin (ACTH) [P]	Adrenal cortex
	Thyrotropin (TSH) [P]	Thyroid gland
	Follicle-stimulating hormone [P]	Gonads
	Luteinizing hormone [P]	Gonads
Thyroid gland	Triiodothyronine and thyroxine [A]	Many tissues
	Calcitonin [P]	Bone
Parathyroid gland	Parathyroid hormone [P]	Bone, kidney
Thymus gland	Thymosin, thymopoietin [P]	Lymphocytes
Heart (C)	Atrial natriuretic peptide [P]	Kidneys
Liver (C)	Angiotensinogen [P]	Adrenal cortex, blood vessels
	Insulin-like growth factors [P]	Many tissues
Stomach and small intestine (C)	Gastrin, cholecystokinin, secretin, and others [P]	GI tract and pancreas
Pancreas (G)	Insulin, glucagon, somatostatin, pancreatic polypeptide [P]	Many tissues
Adrenal cortex (G)	Aldosterone [S]	Kidney
	Cortisol [S]	Many tissues
	Androgens [S]	Many tissues
Adrenal medulla (N)	Epinephrine, norepinephrine [A]	Many tissues
Kidney (C)	Erythropoietin [P]	Bone marrow
	1,25 Dihydroxy-vitamin D_3 (calciferol) [S]	Intestine
Skin (C)	Vitamin D_3 [S]	Intermediate form of hormone
Testes (male) (G)	Androgens [S]	Many tissues
	Inhibin [P]	Anterior pituitary
Ovaries (female) (G)	Estrogen, progesterone [S]	Many tissues
	Inhibin [P]	Anterior pituitary
	Relaxin (pregnancy) [P]	Uterine muscle
Adipose tissue (C)	Leptin, adiponectin, resistin	Hypothalamus, other tissues
Placenta (pregnant females only) (C)	Estrogen, progesterone [S]	Many tissues
	Chorionic somatomammotropin [P]	Many tissues
	Chorionic gonadotropin [P]	Corpus luteum

KEY

G = gland
C = endocrine cells
N = neurons

P = peptide
S = steroid
A = amino acid–derived

● **FIGURE 7-2**

Main Effect(s)
Circadian rhythms; immune function; antioxidant
Release or inhibit pituitary hormones
Milk ejection; labor and delivery; behavior
Water reabsorption
Milk production
Growth factor secretion
Growth and metabolism
Cortisol release
Thyroid hormone synthesis
Egg or sperm production; sex hormone production
Sex hormone production; egg or sperm production
Metabolism, growth, and development
Plasma calcium levels (minimal effect in humans)
Regulate plasma Ca^{2+} and phosphate levels
Lymphocyte development
Increases Na^+ excretion
Aldosterone secretion; increases blood pressure
Growth
Assist digestion and absorption of nutrients
Metabolism of glucose and other nutrients
Na^+ and K^+ homeostasis
Stress response
Sex drive in females
Fight-or-flight response
Red blood cell production
Increase calcium absorption
Precursor of 1,25 dihydroxy-vitamin D_3
Sperm production, secondary sex characteristics
Inhibits FSH secretion
Egg production, secondary sex characteristics
Inhibits FSH secretion
Relaxes muscle
Food intake, metabolism, reproduction
Fetal, maternal development
Metabolism
Hormone secretion

has been given to signal molecules secreted into the external environment.

Pheromones [*pherein,* to bring] are specialized ectohormones that act on other organisms of the same species to elicit a physiological or behavioral response. For example, sea anemones secrete alarm pheromones when danger threatens, and ants release trail pheromones to attract fellow workers to food sources. Pheromones are also used to attract members of the opposite sex for mating purposes. Sex pheromones can be found throughout the animal kingdom, in animals from fruit flies to dogs.

But do humans have pheromones? This question is still a matter of debate. Some studies have shown that human *axillary* (armpit) sweat glands secrete volatile steroids related to sex hormones that may serve as human sex pheromones. In one study, when female students were asked to rate the odors of T-shirts worn by male students, each woman preferred the odor of men who were genetically dissimilar from her. In another study, female axillary secretions rubbed on the upper lip of young women altered the timing of their menstrual cycles. The selling of putative human pheromones as perfume is becoming the latest fad in the mating game, as you will see if you do a Google search for *human pheromone*. How humans might sense pheromones is discussed in Chapter 10.

Hormones Are Transported to a Distant Target By the traditional definition, a hormone must be transported by the blood to a distant target cell. Experimentally, this property is sometimes difficult to demonstrate. Molecules that are suspected of being hormones but not fully accepted as such are called *candidate hormones*. They are usually identified by the word *factor*. For example, in the early 1970s, the hypothalamic regulating hormones were known as "releasing factors" and "inhibiting factors" rather than releasing and inhibiting hormones.

Currently, **growth factors**, a large group of substances that influence cell growth and division, are being studied to determine if they meet all the criteria for hormones. Although many growth factors have been shown to act locally as *autocrines* or *paracrines* [p. 180], most do not seem to be distributed widely in the circulation. A similar situation exists with the lipid-derived signal molecules called *eicosanoids* [p. 31].

Complicating the classification of signal molecules is the fact that a molecule may act as a hormone when secreted from one location but as a paracrine or autocrine signal when secreted from a different location. For example, in the 1920s scientists discovered that *cholecystokinin* (CCK) in extracts of intestine caused contraction of the gall bladder. For many years thereafter, CCK was known only as an intestinal hormone. Then in the mid-1970s, CCK was found in neurons of the brain, where it acts as a neurotransmitter or neuromodulator. In recent years, CCK has become famous for its possible role in controlling hunger.

TABLE 7-1 Comparison of Peptide, Steroid, and Amino Acid–Derived Hormones

			TYROSINE DERIVATIVES	
	PEPTIDE HORMONES	STEROID HORMONES	Catecholamines	Thyroid Hormones
Synthesis and storage	Made in advance; stored in secretory vesicles	Synthesized on demand from precursors	Made in advance; stored in secretory vesicles	Made in advance; precursor stored in secretory vesicles
Release from parent cell	Exocytosis	Simple diffusion	Exocytosis	Simple diffusion
Transport in blood	Dissolved in plasma	Bound to carrier proteins	Dissolved in plasma	Bound to carrier proteins
Half-life	Short	Long	Short	Long
Location of receptor	Cell membrane	Cytoplasm or nucleus; some have membrane receptors also	Cell membrane	Nucleus
Response to receptor-ligand binding	Activation of second messenger systems; may activate genes	Activation of genes for transcription and translation; may have nongenomic actions	Activation of second messenger systems	Activation of genes for transcription and translation
General target response	Modification of existing proteins and induction of new protein synthesis	Induction of new protein synthesis	Modification of existing proteins	Induction of new protein synthesis
Examples	Insulin, parathyroid hormone	Estrogen, androgens, cortisol	Epinephrine, norepinephrine	Thyroxine (T_4)

Hormones Exert Their Effect at Very Low Concentrations

One hallmark of a hormone is its ability to act at concentrations in the nanomolar (10^{-9} M) to picomolar (10^{-12} M) range. Some chemical signals transported in the blood to distant targets are not considered hormones because they must be present in relatively high concentrations before an effect is noticed. For example, histamine released during severe allergic reactions may act on cells throughout the body, but its concentration exceeds the accepted range for a hormone.

As researchers discover new signal molecules and new receptors, the boundary between hormones and nonhormonal signal molecules continues to be challenged, just as the distinction between the nervous and endocrine systems has blurred. Many *cytokines* [p. 180] seem to meet the previously stated definition of a hormone. However, experts in cytokine research do not consider cytokines to be hormones because peptide cytokines are synthesized and released on demand, in contrast to classic peptide hormones, which are made in advance and stored in the parent endocrine cell. A few cytokines—for example, *erythropoietin,* the molecule that controls red blood cell production—were classified as hormones before the term *cytokine* was coined, contributing to the overlap between the two groups of signal molecules.

Hormones Act by Binding to Receptors

All hormones bind to target cell receptors and initiate biochemical responses. These responses are known as the **cellular mechanism of action** of the hormone. As you can see in Figure 7-2, one hormone may act on multiple tissues. To complicate matters, the effects may vary in different tissues or at different stages of development. Or a hormone may have no effect at all in a particular cell. Insulin is an example of a hormone with varied effects. In muscle and adipose tissues, it alters glucose transport proteins and enzymes for glucose metabolism. In the liver, it modulates enzyme activity but has no direct effect on glucose transport proteins. In the brain and certain other tissues, glucose metabolism is totally independent of insulin.

CONCEPT CHECK

1. Name the membrane transport process by which glucose moves from the extracellular fluid into cells. Answers: p. 245

The variable responsiveness of a cell to a hormone depends primarily on the cell's receptor and signal transduction pathways [p. 182]. If there are no hormone receptors in a tissue, its cells cannot respond. If tissues have different receptors and receptor-linked pathways for the same hormone, they will respond differently.

Hormone Action Must Be Terminated

Signal activity by hormones and other chemical signals must be of limited duration if the body is to respond to changes in its internal state. For example, insulin is secreted when blood glucose concentrations increase following a meal. As long as insulin is present, glucose leaves the blood and enters cells. However, if insulin activity continues too long, blood glucose levels could fall so low that the nervous system becomes unable to function properly—a potentially fatal situation. Normally the body avoids this situation in several ways: by limiting insulin secretion, by removing or inactivating insulin circulating in the blood, and by terminating insulin activity in target cells.

In general, hormones in the bloodstream are *degraded* (broken down) into inactive metabolites by enzymes found primarily in the liver and kidneys. The metabolites are then excreted in either the bile or the urine. The rate of hormone breakdown is indicated by a hormone's **half-life** in the circulation, the amount of time required to reduce the concentration of hormone by one-half. Half-life is one indicator of how long a hormone is active in the body.

Hormones bound to target membrane receptors have their activity terminated in several ways. Enzymes that are always present in the plasma can degrade peptide hormones bound to cell membrane receptors. In some cases, the receptor-hormone complex is brought into the cell by endocytosis, and the hormone is then digested in lysosomes [Fig. 5-21, p. 153]. Intracellular enzymes metabolize hormones that enter cells.

CONCEPT CHECK

2. What is the suffix in a chemical name that tells you a molecule is an enzyme? [*Hint:* p. 103] Use that suffix to name an enzyme that digests peptides.

Answers: p. 245

THE CLASSIFICATION OF HORMONES

Hormones can be classified according to different schemes. The scheme used in Figure 7-2 groups them according to their source. A different scheme divides hormones into those whose release is controlled by the brain and those whose release in not controlled by the brain. Another scheme groups hormones according to whether they bind to G protein–coupled receptors, tyrosine kinase-linked receptors, or intracellular receptors, and so on.

A final scheme divides hormones into three main chemical classes: peptide/protein hormones, steroid hormones, and amino–acid derived hormones (Table 7-1 ●). The peptide/protein hormones are composed of linked amino acids. The steroid hormones are all derived from cholesterol [p. 30]. The amino–acid derived hormones are modifications of single amino acids, either tryptophan or tyrosine.

CONCEPT CHECK

3. What is the classic definition of a hormone?
4. Based on what you know about the organelles involved in protein and steroid synthesis [p. 68], what would be the major differences between the organelle composition of a steroid-producing cell and that of a protein-producing cell?

Answers: p. 245

Most Hormones Are Peptides or Proteins

The peptide/protein hormones range from small peptides of only three amino acids to larger proteins and glycoproteins. Despite the size variability among hormones in this group, they are usually called peptide hormones for the sake of simplicity. You can remember which hormones fall into this category by exclusion: if a hormone is not a steroid hormone and not an amino acid derivative, then it must be a peptide or protein.

Peptide Hormone Synthesis, Storage, and Release The synthesis and packaging of peptide hormones into membrane-bound secretory vesicles is similar to that of other proteins. The initial peptide that comes off the ribosome is a large inactive protein known as a preprohormone (Fig. 7-3 ●). **Preprohormones** contain one or more copies of a peptide hormone, a *signal sequence* that directs the protein into the lumen of the rough endoplasmic reticulum, and other peptide sequences that may or may not have biological activity.

As an inactive preprohormone moves through the endoplasmic reticulum and Golgi complex, the signal sequence is removed, creating a smaller, still-inactive molecule called a **prohormone** (Fig. 7-3). In the Golgi complex, the prohormone is packaged into secretory vesicles along with *proteolytic* [*proteo-*, protein + *lysis,* rupture] enzymes that chop the prohormone into active hormone and other fragments. This process is called *post-translational modification* [p. 124].

The secretory vesicles containing peptides are stored in the cytoplasm of the endocrine cell until the cell receives a signal for secretion. At that time, the vesicles move to the cell membrane and release their contents by calcium-dependent exocytosis [p. 154]. All of the peptide fragments created from the prohormone are released together into the extracellular fluid, in a process known as *co-secretion*.

Post-Translational Modification of Prohormones Studies of prohormone processing have led to some interesting discoveries. Some prohormones, such as that for *thyrotropin-releasing hormone* (TRH), contain multiple copies of the hormone (Fig. 7-4a ●). Another interesting prohormone is called *pro-opiomelanocortin* (Fig. 7-4b). This prohormone splits into three active peptides plus an inactive fragment. In some instances, even the fragments are clinically useful. For example, proinsulin is cleaved into active insulin and an inactive fragment known as *C-peptide* (Fig. 7-4c). Clinicians measure the levels of C-peptide in the blood of diabetics to monitor how much insulin the patient's pancreas is producing.

Transport in the Blood and Half-Life of Peptide Hormones Peptide hormones are water soluble and therefore generally dissolve easily in the extracellular fluid for transport throughout the body. The half-life for peptide hormones is

7

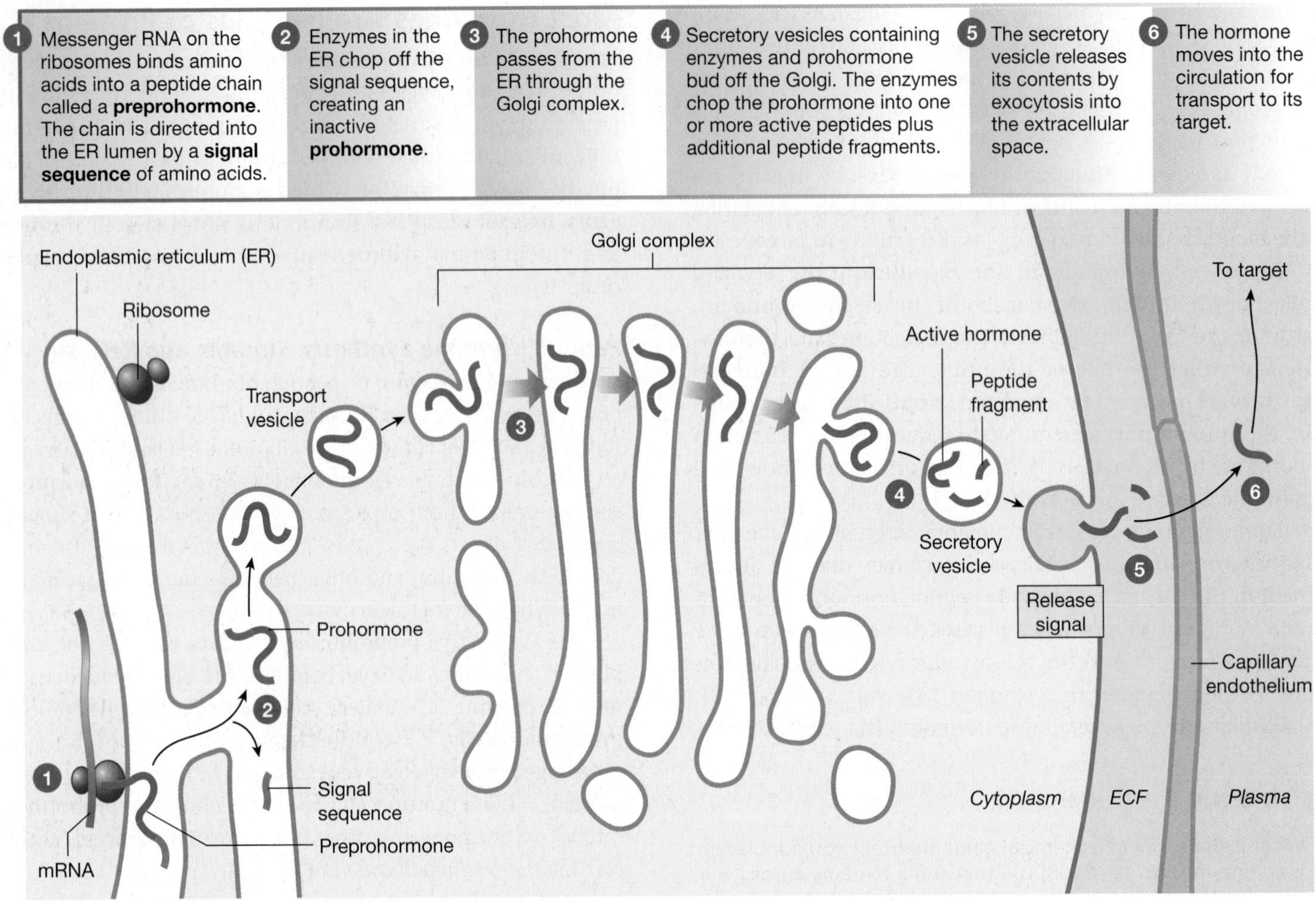

1 Messenger RNA on the ribosomes binds amino acids into a peptide chain called a preprohormone. The chain is directed into the ER lumen by a signal sequence of amino acids.
2 Enzymes in the ER chop off the signal sequence, creating an inactive prohormone.
3 The prohormone passes from the ER through the Golgi complex.
4 Secretory vesicles containing enzymes and prohormone bud off the Golgi. The enzymes chop the prohormone into one or more active peptides plus additional peptide fragments.
5 The secretory vesicle releases its contents by exocytosis into the extracellular space.
6 The hormone moves into the circulation for transport to its target.
Endoplasmic reticulum (ER)
Ribosome
Transport vesicle
Golgi complex
Active hormone
Peptide fragment
To target
Secretory vesicle
Release signal
Prohormone
Capillary endothelium
Signal sequence
Preprohormone
mRNA
Cytoplasm
ECF
Plasma

FIGURE 7-3 ***Peptide hormone synthesis, packaging, and release***

usually quite short, in the range of several minutes. If the response to a peptide hormone must be sustained for an extended period of time, the hormone must be secreted continually.

Cellular Mechanism of Action of Peptide Hormones

Because peptide hormones are lipophobic, they are usually unable to enter the target cell. Instead, they bind to surface membrane receptors. The hormone-receptor complex initiates the cellular response by means of a *signal transduction* system (Fig. 7-5 ●). Many peptide hormones work through cAMP second messenger systems [p. 186]. A few peptide hormone receptors, such as that of insulin, have tyrosine kinase activity [p. 186] or work through other signal transduction pathways.

The response of cells to peptide hormones is usually rapid because second messenger systems modify existing proteins. The changes triggered by peptide hormones include opening or closing membrane channels and modulating metabolic enzymes or transport proteins. Researchers have recently discovered that some peptide hormones also have longer-lasting effects when their second messenger systems activate genes and direct the synthesis of new proteins.

Steroid Hormones Are Derived from Cholesterol

Steroid hormones have a similar chemical structure because they are all derived from cholesterol (Fig. 7-6 ●). Unlike peptide hormones, which are made in tissues all over the body, steroid hormones are made in only a few organs. Three types of steroid hormones are made in the adrenal cortex, the outer portion of the adrenal glands [*cortex*, bark]. One adrenal gland sits atop each kidney [*ad-*, upon + *renal*, kidney]. The gonads produce the sex steroids (estrogens, progesterone, and androgens). In pregnant women, the placenta is also a source of steroid hormones.

Steroid Hormone Synthesis and Release Cells that secrete steroid hormones have unusually large amounts of smooth endoplasmic reticulum, the organelle in which steroids are synthesized. Steroids are lipophilic and diffuse easily across membranes, both out of their parent cell and into their target cell. This property also means that steroid-secreting cells cannot store hormones in secretory vesicles. Instead, they synthesize their hormone as it is needed. When a stimulus activates the endocrine cell, precursors in the cytoplasm are rapidly converted to

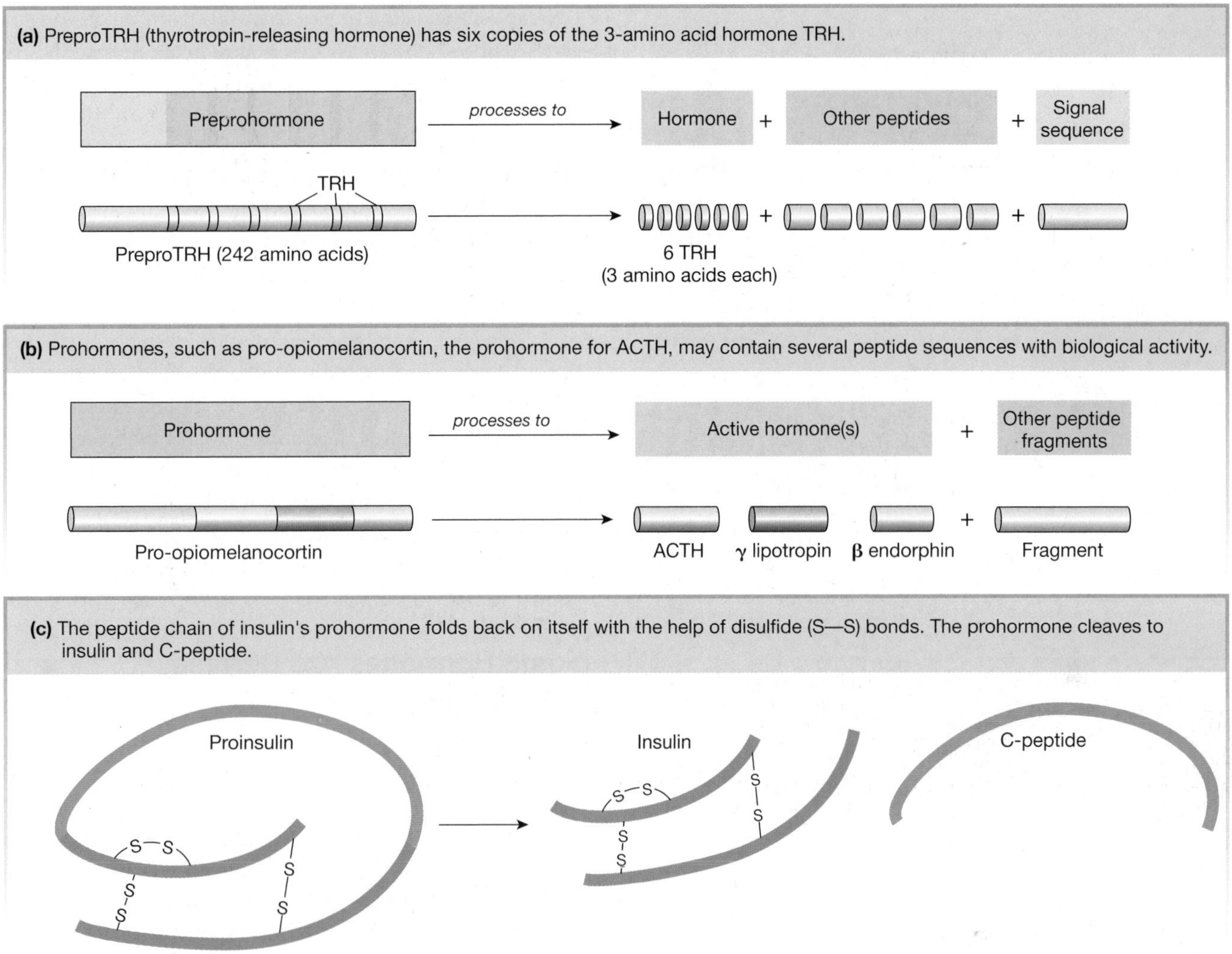
(a) PreproTRH (thyrotropin-releasing hormone) has six copies of the 3-amino acid hormone TRH.
Preprohormone
processes to
Hormone
+
Other peptides
+
Signal sequence
TRH
PreproTRH (242 amino acids)
6 TRH
(3 amino acids each)
(b) Prohormones, such as pro-opiomelanocortin, the prohormone for ACTH, may contain several peptide sequences with biological activity.
Prohormone
processes to
Active hormone(s)
+
Other peptide fragments
Pro-opiomelanocortin
ACTH
γ lipotropin
β endorphin
Fragment
(c) The peptide chain of insulin's prohormone folds back on itself with the help of disulfide (S—S) bonds. The prohormone cleaves to insulin and C-peptide.
Proinsulin
Insulin
C-peptide
S—S
S
S

● **FIGURE 7-4** ***Peptide hormone processing.*** Peptide hormones are made as large, inactive preprohormones that include a signal sequence, one or more copies of the hormone, and additional peptide fragments.

active hormone. The hormone concentration in the cytoplasm rises, and the hormones move out of the cell by simple diffusion.

Transport in the Blood and Half-Life of Steroid Hormones Like their parent cholesterol, steroid hormones are not very soluble in plasma and other body fluids. For this reason, most of the steroid hormone molecules found in the blood are bound to protein carrier molecules. Some hormones have specific carriers, such as *corticosteroid-binding globulin.* Others simply bind to general plasma proteins, such as *albumin.*

The binding of a steroid hormone to a carrier protein protects the hormone from enzymatic degradation and results in an extended half-life. For example, **cortisol,** a hormone produced by the adrenal cortex, has a half-life of 60–90 minutes. (Compare this with epinephrine, an amino acid–based hormone whose half-life is measured in seconds.)

Although binding steroid hormones to protein carriers extends their half-life, it also blocks their entry into target cells. The carrier-steroid complex remains outside the cell because the carrier proteins are lipophobic and cannot diffuse through the membrane. Only unbound hormone molecule can diffuse into the target cell (Fig. 7-7 ●). As unbound hormone leaves the plasma, the carriers obey the law of mass action and release hormone so that the ratio of unbound to bound hormone in the plasma remains constant [the K_d; p. 40].

Fortunately, hormones are active in minute concentrations, and only a tiny amount of unbound steroid is enough to produce a response. As unbound hormone leaves the blood and enters cells, additional carriers release their bound steroid so that some unbound hormone is always in the blood and ready to enter a cell.

Cellular Mechanism of Action of Steroid Hormones

The best-studied steroid hormone receptors are found within cells, either in the cytoplasm or in the nucleus. The ultimate destination of steroid receptor-hormone complexes is the nucleus, where the complex acts as a *transcription factor,* binding to

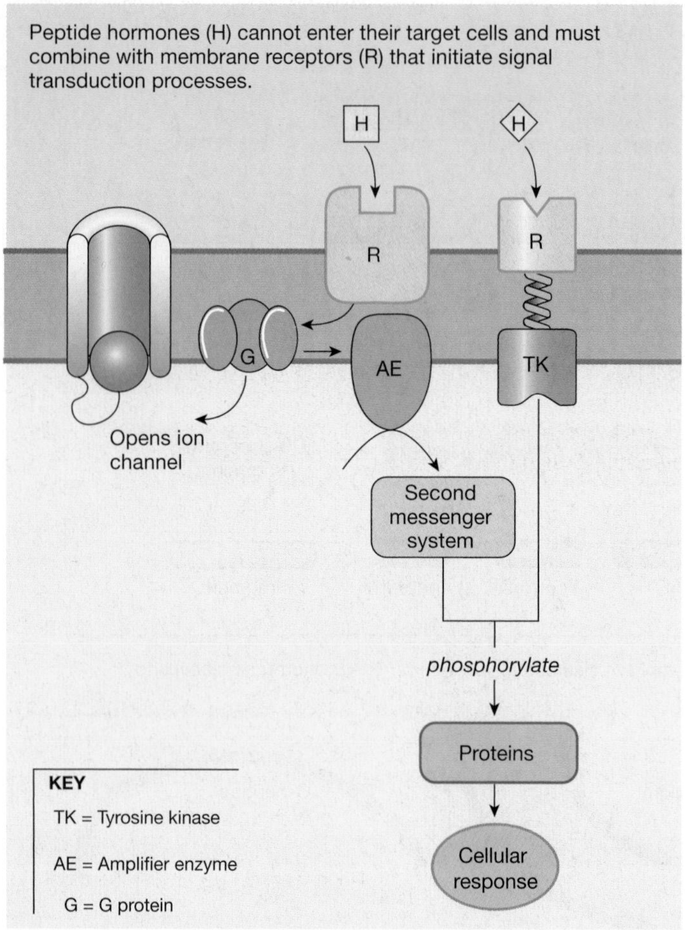

● **FIGURE 7-5** ***Membrane receptors and signal transduction for peptide hormones***

DNA and either activating or *repressing* (turning off) one or more genes (Fig. 7-7, ③). Activated genes create new mRNA that directs the synthesis of new proteins. Any hormone that alters gene activity is said to have a *genomic effect* on the target cell.

When steroid hormones activate genes to direct the production of new proteins, there is usually a lag time between hormone-receptor binding and the first measurable biological effects. This lag can be as much as 90 minutes. Consequently, steroid hormones do not mediate reflex pathways that require rapid responses.

In recent years researchers have discovered that several steroid hormones, including estrogens and aldosterone, have cell membrane receptors linked to signal transduction pathways, just as peptide hormones do. These receptors enable those steroid hormones to initiate rapid **nongenomic responses** in addition to their slower genomic effects. With the discovery of nongenomic effects of steroid hormones, the functional differences between steroid and peptide hormones seem almost to have disappeared.

Some Hormones Are Derived from Single Amino Acids

The amino acid–derived hormones are small molecules created from either tryptophan or tyrosine, both notable for the carbon ring structures in their R-groups [p. 30]. The pineal gland hormone **melatonin** is derived from tryptophan (see *Focus on the Pineal Gland,* Fig. 7-22) but all of the other amino acid–based hormones—the catecholamines and thyroid hormones—are derived from tyrosine (Fig. 7-8 ●). Catecholamines

● **FIGURE 7-6** ***Examples of steroid hormones derived from cholesterol***

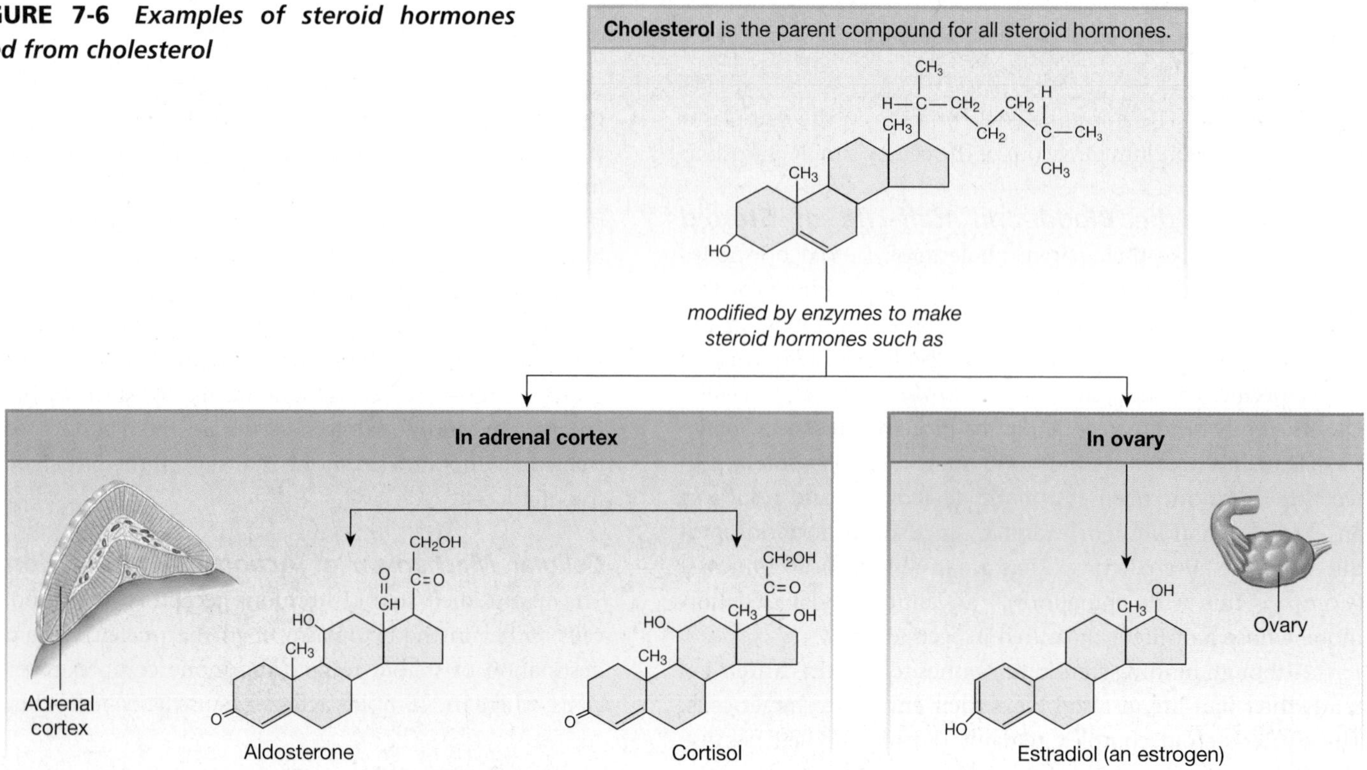

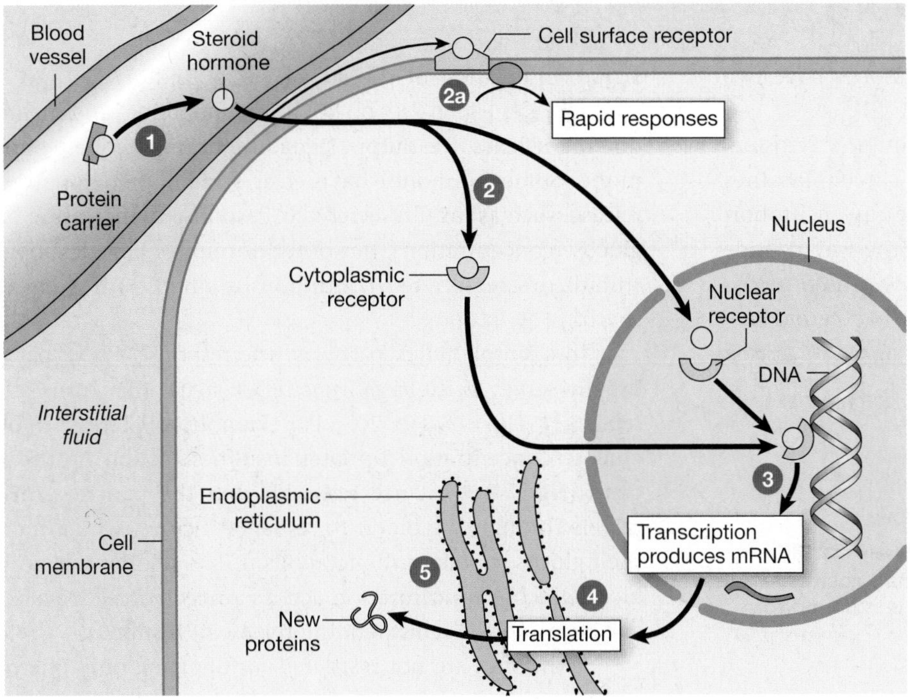

1. Most hydrophobic steroids are bound to plasma protein carriers. Only unbound hormones can diffuse into the target cell.
2. Steroid hormone receptors are in the cytoplasm or nucleus.

2a. Some steroid hormones also bind to membrane receptors that use second messenger systems to create rapid cellular responses.

3. The receptor-hormone complex binds to DNA and activates or represses one or more genes.
4. Activated genes create new mRNA that moves back to the cytoplasm.
5. Translation produces new proteins for cell processes.

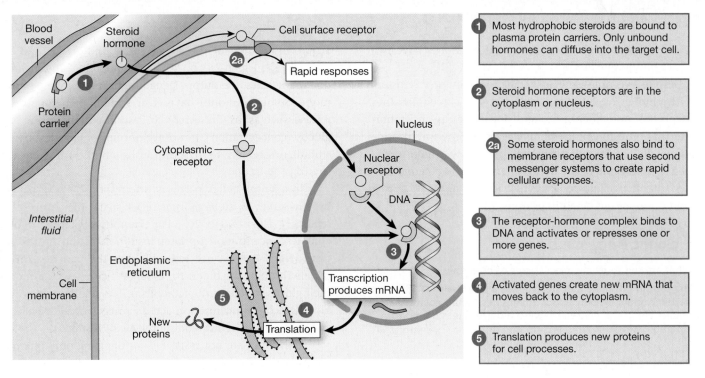

FIGURE 7-7 ***Steroid hormone action***

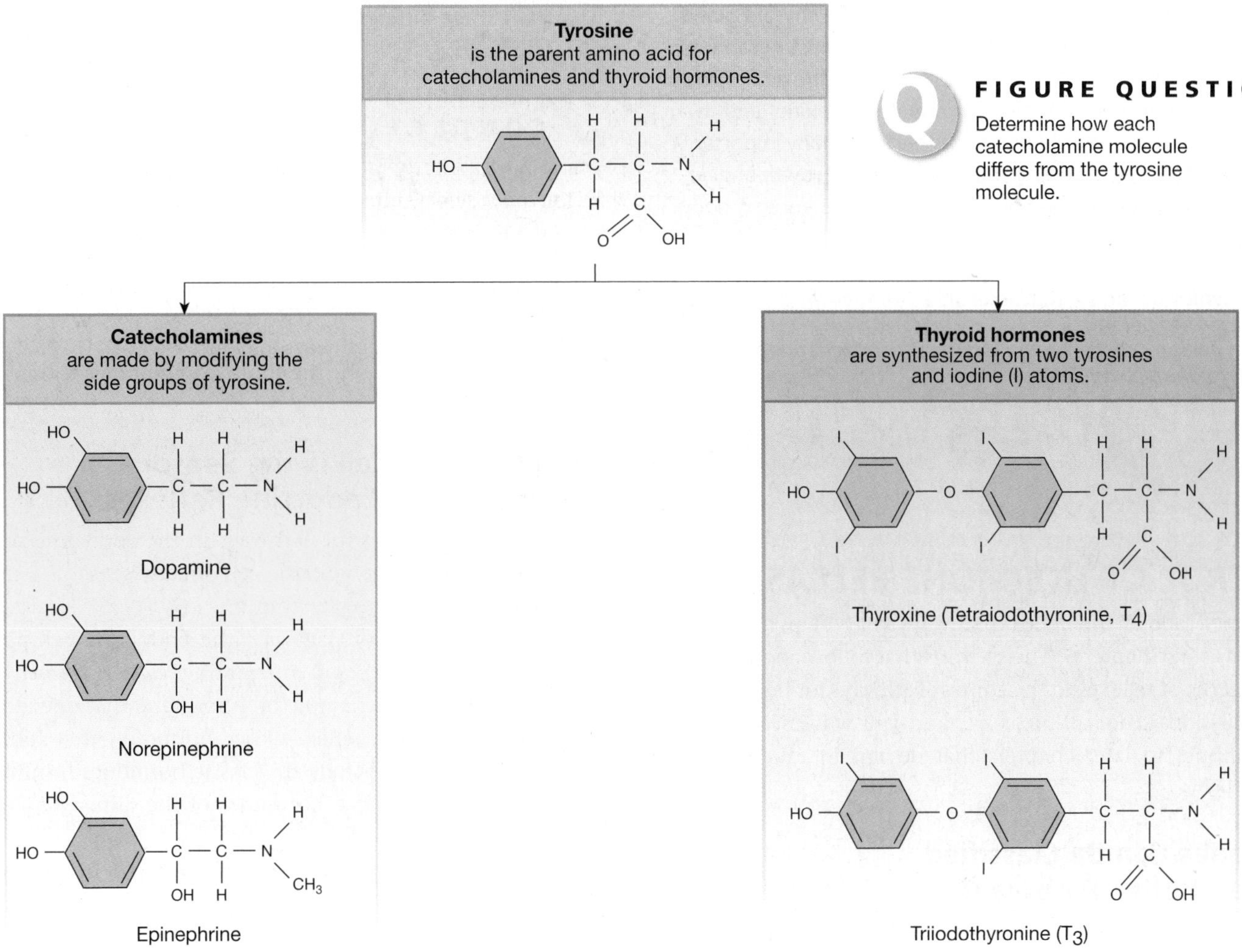

FIGURE QUESTION

Determine how each catecholamine molecule differs from the tyrosine molecule.

FIGURE 7-8 ***Tyrosine-derived hormones***

have one tyrosine molecule; the thyroid hormones have two tyrosines plus iodine atoms.

Despite a common precursor, the two groups of tyrosine-based hormones have little in common. The **catecholamines** (epinephrine, norepinephrine, and dopamine) are neurohormones that bind to cell membrane receptors the way peptide hormones do. The **thyroid hormones**, produced by the butterfly-shaped thyroid gland in the neck, behave more like steroid hormones, with intracellular receptors that activate genes. We discuss thyroid hormones in detail in Chapter 23.

CONCEPT CHECK

5. What are the three chemical classes of hormones?
6. The steroid hormone aldosterone has a short half-life for a steroid hormone—only about 20 minutes. What would you predict about the degree to which aldosterone is bound to blood proteins?

Answers: p. 245

RUNNING PROBLEM

Shaped like a butterfly, the thyroid gland straddles the trachea just below the Adam's apple. Responding to hormonal signals from the hypothalamus and anterior pituitary, the thyroid gland concentrates iodine, an element found in food (most notably as an ingredient added to salt), and combines it with the amino acid tyrosine to make two thyroid hormones, thyroxine and triiodothyronine. These thyroid hormones perform many important functions in the body, including the regulation of growth and development, oxygen consumption, and the maintenance of body temperature.

Question 1:

a. To which of the three classes of hormones do the thyroid hormones belong?

b. If a person's diet is low in iodine, predict what happens to thyroxine production.

216
226
231
234
238
240
240

CONTROL OF HORMONE RELEASE

You learned about the reflex pathways that help maintain homeostasis in Chapter 6. The sections that follow apply those basic patterns of reflexes to the control pathways for hormones. This discussion is not all-inclusive, and you will encounter a few hormones in later chapters that do not fit exactly into these patterns.

Hormones Can Be Classified by Their Reflex Pathways

Reflex pathways are a convenient way to classify hormones and simplify learning the pathways that regulate their secretion. All reflex pathways have similar components: a stimulus, an input signal, integration of the signal, an output signal, and a response [Fig. 6-25, p. 202]. In endocrine and neuroendocrine reflexes, the output signal is a hormone or a neurohormone. Some hormones have clear stimuli that initiate their release, such as insulin secreted in response to increasing blood glucose concentrations, but other hormones have less obvious stimuli or are secreted continuously, often with a circadian rhythm [p. 204].

In a simple reflex pathway, the response of the pathway usually serves as the *negative feedback* signal that turns off the reflex [Fig. 6-27a, p. 203]. For example, an increase in blood glucose concentration initiates insulin secretion by the pancreas (Fig. 7-9 ●). Once released from the pancreas, insulin travels through the blood to its target tissues, which increase their glucose uptake and metabolism. The resultant decrease in blood glucose concentration acts as a negative feedback signal and turns off the reflex, ending release of insulin.

Hormones are not restricted to following only one reflex pathway pattern, however. For example, insulin secretion can also be triggered by input signals from the nervous system (Fig. 7-9) or by a hormone secreted from the digestive tract as a meal is eaten (not shown). The pancreatic endocrine cells—the integrating center for this reflex—therefore must evaluate input signals from three different sources when "deciding" whether to secrete insulin.

CONCEPT CHECK

7. In Figure 6-23 [p. 199], which reflex step(s) represent(s) the input signal? Integration of the signal? The output signal?
8. In the blood glucose example, the increase in blood glucose corresponds to which step of a reflex pathway? Insulin secretion and the decrease in blood glucose correspond to which steps?
9. Which three reflex pathways in Figure 6-31 [p. 207] match insulin release by the three different mechanisms just described?

Answers: p. 245

The Endocrine Cell Is the Sensor in the Simplest Endocrine Reflexes

The simplest reflex control pathways in the endocrine system are those in which an endocrine cell directly senses a stimulus and responds by secreting its hormone [Fig. 6-31, pattern 6, p. 207]. In this type of pathway, the endocrine cell acts as both sensor (receptor) and integrating center. **Parathyroid hormone** (PTH) is an example of a hormone that operates via this simple endocrine reflex. Other hormones that follow a simple reflex pattern include the classic hormones insulin and glucagon, as well as some hormones of the diffuse endocrine system.

Parathyroid endocrine cells are clustered in four small glands that lie behind the thyroid gland. They monitor plasma Ca^{2+} concentration with the aid of G protein-coupled Ca^{2+} receptors on their cell membrane. When a certain number of

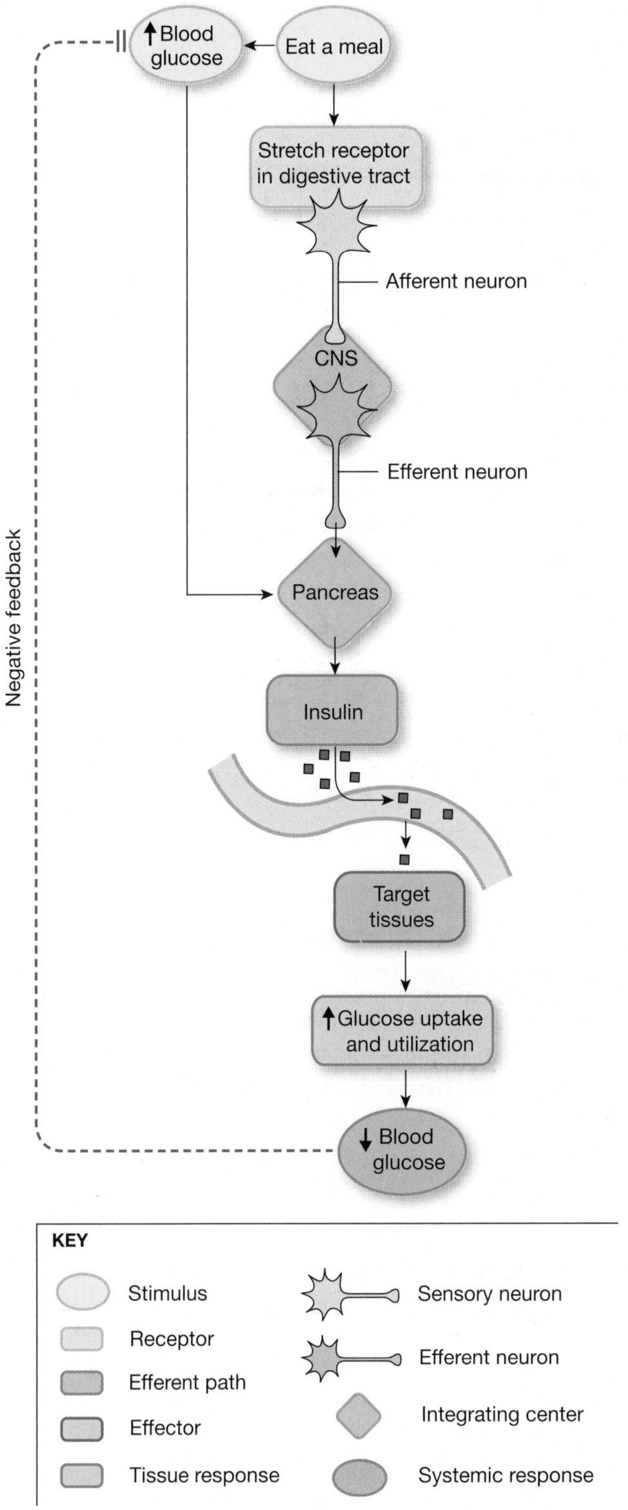

FIGURE QUESTION

What shuts off the pathway that begins with the stimulus of "eat a meal?"

● **FIGURE 7-9** ***Insulin can be released by increased blood glucose or through neural stimulation resulting from ingestion of a meal.***

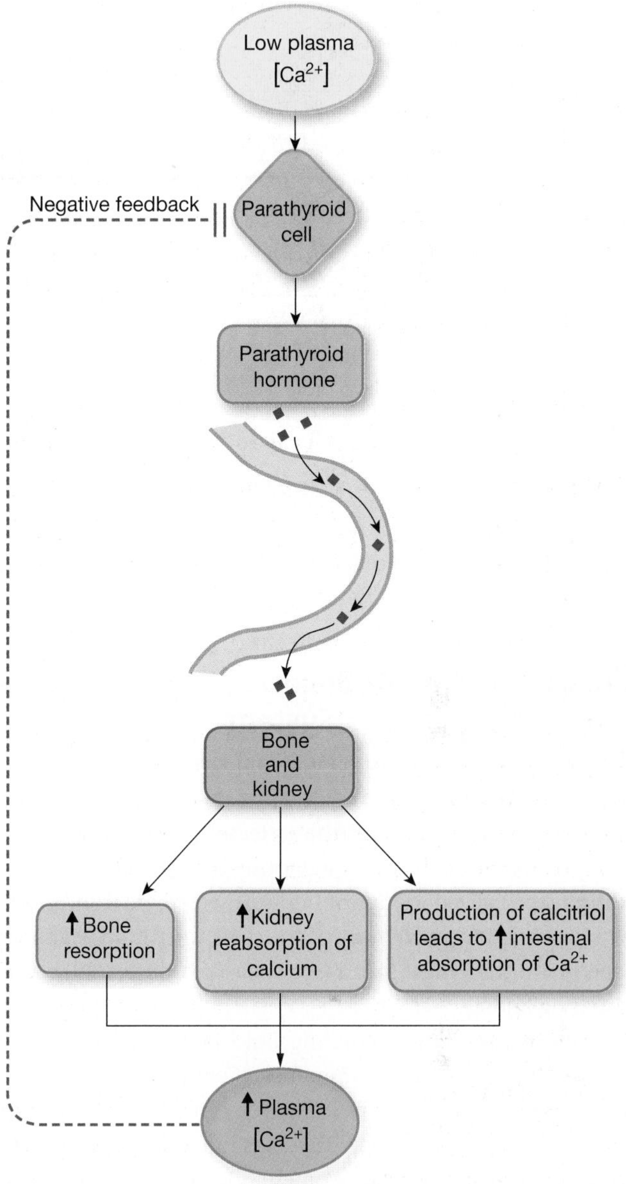

● **FIGURE 7-10** ***A simple endocrine reflex: parathyroid hormone***

receptors are bound to Ca^{2+}, PTH secretion is inhibited. If the plasma Ca^{2+} concentration falls below a certain level and fewer receptors are bound, inhibition ceases and the parathyroid cells secrete PTH (Fig. 7-10 ●). Parathyroid hormone travels through the blood to act on bone, kidney, and intestine, initiating responses that increase the concentration of Ca^{2+} in the plasma. The increase in plasma Ca^{2+} is a negative feedback signal that turns off the reflex, ending the release of parathyroid hormone.

CONCEPT CHECK

10. Glucagon is released from the endocrine pancreas when blood glucose levels decrease and it acts on multiple target tissues to increase blood glucose. Draw a reflex pathway to match this description.

Answers: p. 245

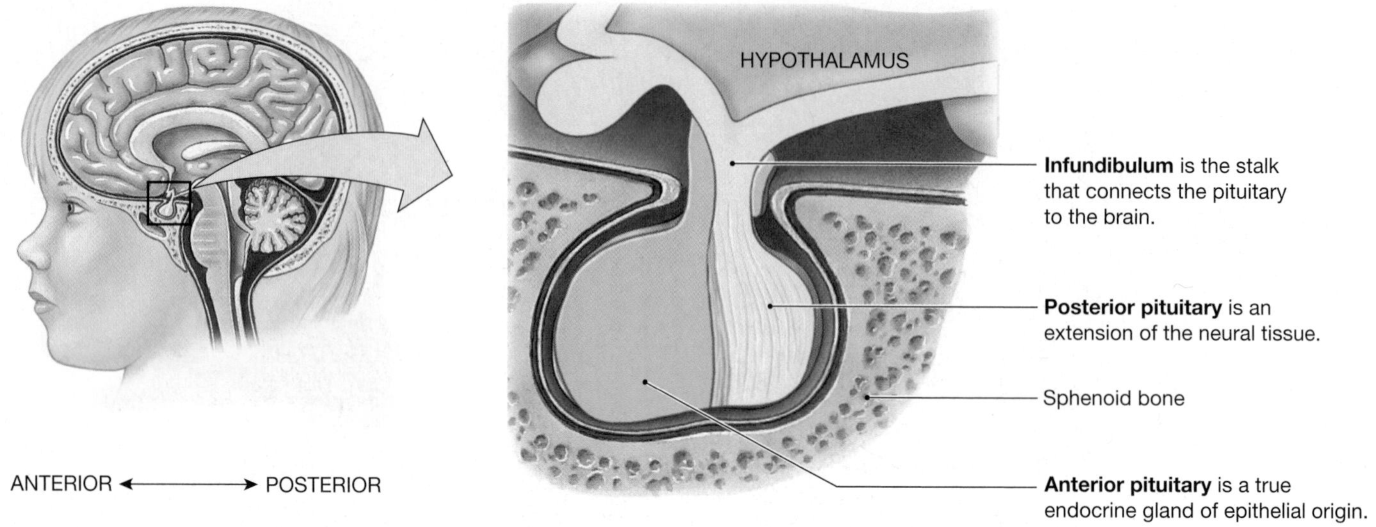

● **FIGURE 7-11** ***The pituitary gland sits in a protected pocket of bone, connected to the brain by a thin stalk.***

Many Endocrine Reflexes Involve the Nervous System

The nervous system and the endocrine system overlap in both structure and function. Stimuli that are integrated by the central nervous system influence the release of many hormones through efferent neurons, as previously described for insulin. In addition, specialized groups of neurons secrete neurohormones, and two endocrine structures are incorporated in the anatomy of the brain: the pineal gland (see Focus box on p. 239) and the pituitary gland.

One of the most fascinating links between the brain and the endocrine system is the influence of emotions over hormone secretion and function. Physicians for centuries have recorded instances in which emotional state has influenced health or normal physiological processes. Women today know that the timing of their menstrual periods may be altered by stressors such as travel or final exams. The condition known as "failure to thrive" in infants can often be linked to environmental or emotional stress that increases secretion of some pituitary hormones and decreases production of others. The interactions among stress, the endocrine system, and the immune system are receiving intense study, and we discuss them further in Chapter 24.

Neurohormones Are Secreted into the Blood by Neurons

As noted in Chapter 6, neurohormones are chemical signals released into the blood by a neuron [Fig. 6-31, reflex 2]. The human nervous system produces three major groups of neurohormones: (1) catecholamines, made by modified neurons in the adrenal medulla, (2) hypothalamic neurohormones secreted from the posterior pituitary, and (3) hypothalamic neurohormones that control hormone release from the anterior pituitary. Because the latter two groups of neurohormones are associated with the pituitary gland, we describe that important endocrine structure first.

CONCEPT CHECK

11. Catecholamines belong to which chemical class of hormone?

Answers: p. 245

The Pituitary Gland Is Actually Two Fused Glands

The **pituitary gland** is a lima bean–sized structure that extends downward from the brain, connected to it by a thin stalk and cradled in a protective pocket of bone (Fig. 7-11 ●). The first accurate description of the function of the pituitary gland came from Richard Lower (1631–1691), an experimental physiologist at Oxford University. Using observations and some experiments, he theorized that substances produced in the brain passed down the stalk into the gland and from there into the blood.

Lower did not realize that the pituitary gland is actually two different tissue types that merged during embryonic development. The **anterior pituitary** is a true endocrine gland of epithelial origin, derived from embryonic tissue that formed the roof of the mouth [Fig. 3-28, p. 79]. It is also called the *adenohypophysis* [*adeno-*, gland + *hypo-*, beneath + *phyein*, to grow], and its hormones are *adenohypophyseal* secretions. The **posterior pituitary**, or *neurohypophysis*, is an extension of the neural tissue of the brain. It secretes neurohormones made in the hypothalamus.

The Posterior Pituitary Stores and Releases Two Neurohormones

The posterior pituitary is the storage and release site for two neurohormones: oxytocin and vasopressin. These small peptide hormones are synthesized in the cell bodies of neurons in the hypothalamus, a region of the brain that controls many homeostatic functions (Fig. 7-12 ●). Each hormone is made in a separate cell type.

Hypothalamic neurohormones follow the standard pattern for peptide synthesis, storage, and release described earlier in this chapter. However, secretory vesicles containing hormone are transported down long extensions of the neurons into the posterior pituitary, where they are stored in the cell terminals. When a stimulus reaches the hypothalamus, an electrical signal passes from the neuron cell body to the distal (distant) end of the cell in the posterior pituitary, and the vesicle contents are released into the circulation.

The two posterior pituitary neurohormones are composed of nine amino acids each. **Vasopressin**, also known as antidiuretic hormone or ADH, regulates water balance in the body. In women, **oxytocin** released from the posterior pituitary controls the ejection of milk during breast-feeding and contractions of the uterus during labor and delivery.

A few neurons release oxytocin as a neurotransmitter or neuromodulator onto neurons in other parts of the brain. A number of animal experiments plus a few human experiments suggest that oxytocin plays an important role in social, sexual, and maternal behaviors. Some investigators postulate that *autism,* a developmental disorder in which patients are unable to form normal social relationships, may be related to defects in the normal oxytocin-modulated pathways of the brain.

CONCEPT CHECK

12. What intracellular structure is used for transport of secretory vesicles within the cytoplasm?
13. Name the membrane process by which the contents of secretory vesicles are released into the extracellular fluid.

Answers: p. 245

The Anterior Pituitary Secretes Six Hormones

As late as 1889, it was being said in reviews of physiological function that the pituitary was of little or no use to higher vertebrates! By the early 1900s, however, researchers had discovered that animals with their anterior pituitary glands surgically removed were unable to survive more than a day or two. This observation, combined with the clinical signs associated with pituitary tumors, made scientists realize that the anterior pituitary is a major endocrine gland that secretes not one but six physiologically significant hormones: prolactin (PRL), thyrotropin (TSH), adrenocorticotropin (ACTH), growth hormone (GH), follicle-stimulating hormone (FSH), and luteinizing hormone (LH). Secretion of all the anterior pituitary hormones is controlled by hypothalamic neurohormones.

The anterior pituitary hormones, their associated hypothalamic neurohormones, and their targets are illustrated in Figure 7-13 ●. Notice that all but one of the anterior pituitary

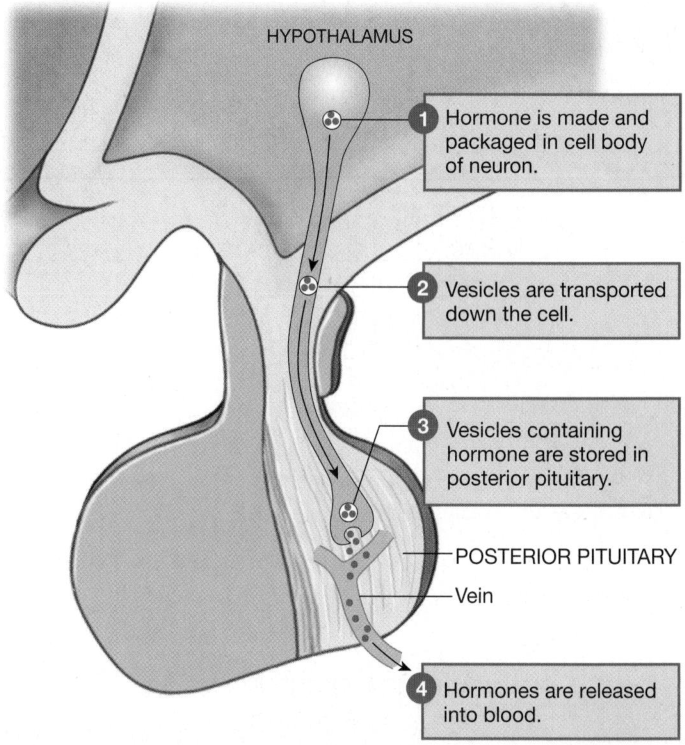

● **FIGURE 7-12** ***Synthesis, storage, and release of posterior pituitary hormones***

hormones have another endocrine gland or cell as one of their targets. A hormone that controls the secretion of another hormone is known as a **trophic hormone.**

The adjective *trophic* comes from the Greek word *trophikós,* which means "pertaining to food or nourishment" and refers to the manner in which the trophic hormone "nourishes" the target cell. Trophic hormones often have names that end with the suffix *-tropin,* as in *gonadotropin.** The root word to which the suffix is attached is the target tissue: the gonadotropins are hormones that are trophic to the gonads. The hypothalamic neurohormones that control release of the anterior pituitary hormones are also trophic hormones, but for historical reasons they are described as either *releasing hormones* (e.g., thyrotropin-releasing hormone) or *inhibiting hormones* (e.g., growth hormone–inhibiting hormone).

One complication you should be aware of is that many of the hypothalamic and anterior pituitary hormones have multiple names as well as standardized abbreviations. For example, **somatostatin** (SS) is also called *growth hormone–inhibiting hormone* (GHIH) and *somatotropin release-inhibiting hormone* (SRIH). The hypothalamic and anterior pituitary abbreviations and alternate names are listed in the caption of Figure 7-13.

*A few hormones whose names end in *-tropin* do not have endocrine cells as their targets. For example, melanotropin acts on pigment-containing cells in many animals.

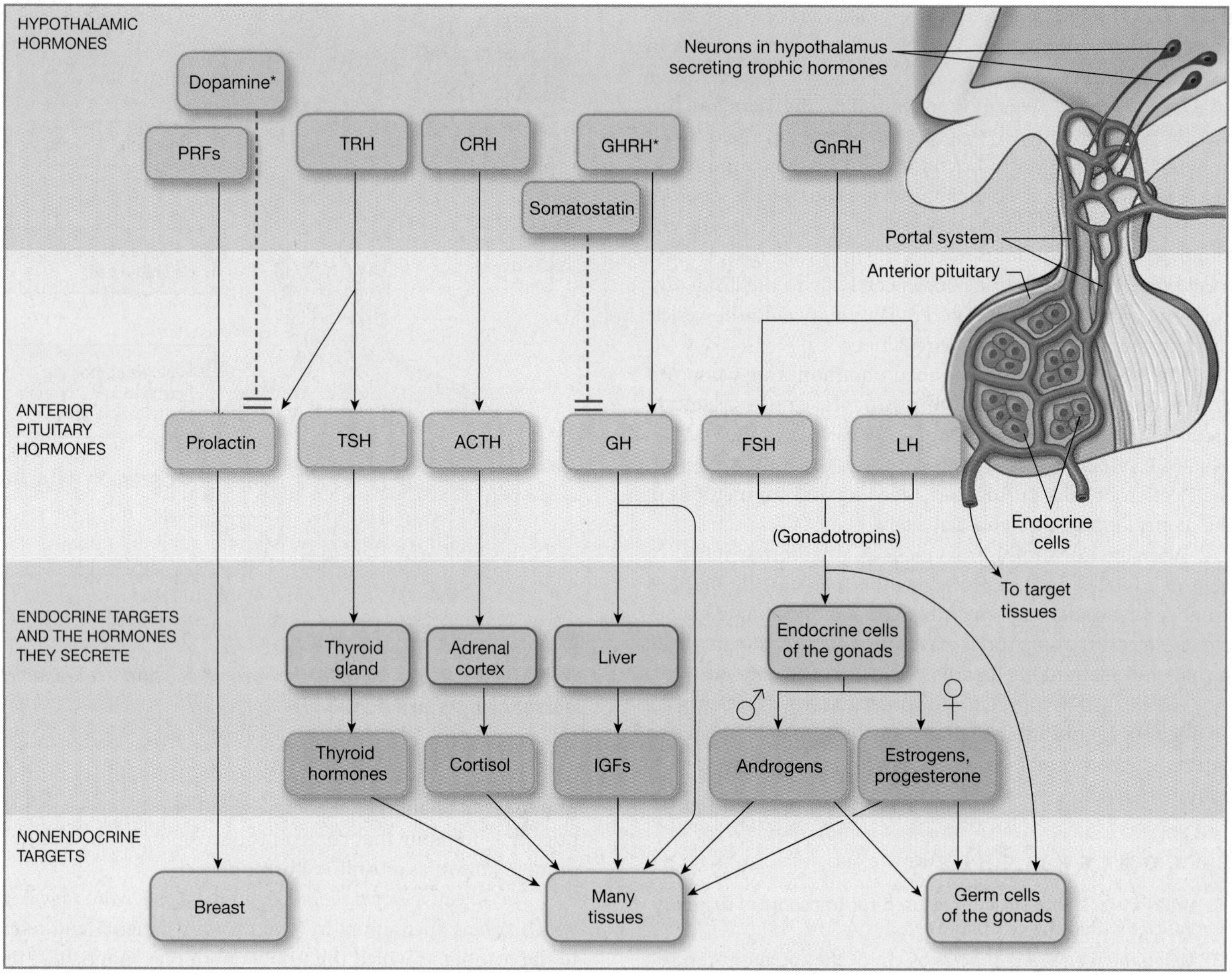

● **FIGURE 7-13** ***Hormones of the hypothalamic-anterior pituitary pathway.*** The hypothalamus secretes releasing hormones (-RH) and inhibiting hormones (-IH) that act on endocrine cells of the anterior pituitary to influence secretion of their hormones. Where there is antagonistic control by two or more hormones, the dominant control is indicated by*. Anterior pituitary hormones then act either on additional endocrine glands or directly on target cells. ACTH = adrenocorticotropic hormone (corticotropin); CRH = corticotropin-releasing hormone; FSH = follicle-stimulating hormone; GH = growth hormone; somatostatin (SS; also called growth hormone–inhibiting hormone, GHIH or somatotropin release-inhibiting hormone, SRIH); GHRH = growth hormone–releasing hormone; GnRH = gonadotropin-releasing hormone; IGFs = insulin-like growth factors; LH = luteinizing hormone; dopamine = DA, also called prolactin-inhibiting hormone or PIH; PRFs = multiple prolactin-releasing factors; prolactin = PRL; TRH = thyrotropin-releasing hormone; TSH = thyroid-stimulating hormone (thyrotropin).

Feedback Loops Are Different in the Hypothalamic-Pituitary Pathway

The pathways in which anterior pituitary hormones act as trophic hormones are among the most complex endocrine reflexes because they involve three integrating centers: the hypothalamus, the anterior pituitary, and the endocrine target of the pituitary hormone (Fig. 7-14 ●). Feedback in these complex pathways follows a pattern that is different from the pattern described previously. Instead of the response acting as the negative feedback signal, the hormones themselves are the feedback signal. Each hormone in the pathway feeds back to suppress hormone secretion by integrating centers earlier in the reflex pathway.

When secretion of one hormone in a complex pathway increases or decreases, the secretion of other hormones also changes because of feedback loops that link the hormones. In pathways with two or three hormones in sequence, the "downstream" hormone usually feeds back to suppress the hormone(s) that controlled its secretion. (A major exception to this is feedback by ovarian hormones, as you will learn in Chapter 26.)

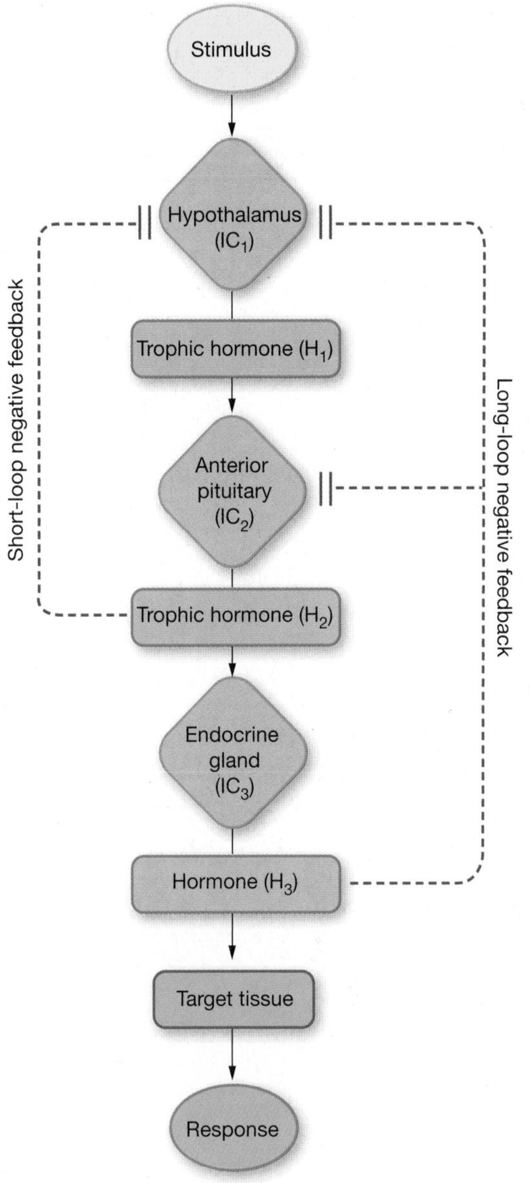

● **FIGURE 7-14** ***Negative feedback loops in the hypothalamic-anterior pituitary pathway.*** In complex endocrine pathways, the hormones of the pathway serve as negative feedback signals.

For example, cortisol secreted from the adrenal cortex feeds back to suppress secretion of the trophic hormones corticotropin-releasing hormone (CRH) and adrenocorticotropin (ACTH) (Fig. 7-15 ●). This relationship is called **long-loop negative feedback**.

In **short-loop negative feedback**, pituitary hormones feed back to decrease hormone secretion by the hypothalamus. We see this type of feedback in cortisol secretion in Figure 7-15, where ACTH exerts short-loop negative feedback on the secretion of CRH. With this system of negative feedback, the hormones normally stay within the range needed for an appropriate response. Feedback patterns are important in the diagnosis of endocrine pathologies, to be discussed later in the chapter.

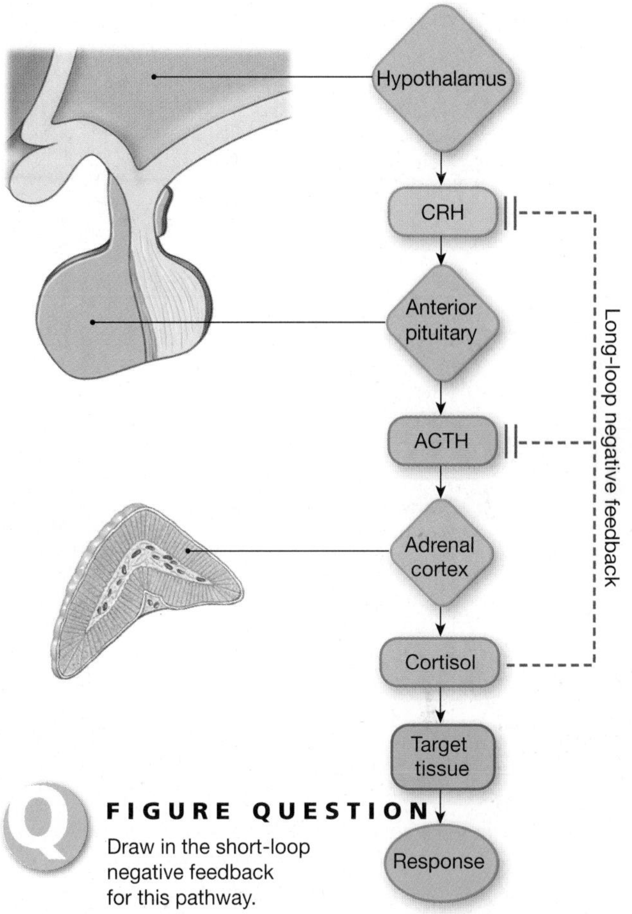

● **FIGURE 7-15** ***Control pathway for cortisol secretion.*** Cortisol is a steroid hormone secreted by the adrenal cortex. ACTH = corticotropin or adrenocorticotropic hormone; CRH = corticotropin-releasing hormone.

CONCEPT CHECK

14. Which pathway in Figure 6-31 [p. 207] fits the pituitary hormone pattern just described, in which there are three integrating centers?

Answers: p. 245

RUNNING PROBLEM

Thyroid hormone production is regulated by thyroid-stimulating hormone (TSH), a hormone secreted by the anterior pituitary. The production of TSH is in turn regulated by the neurohormone thyrotropin-releasing hormone (TRH) from the hypothalamus.

Question 2:

a. ***In a normal person, when thyroid hormone levels in the blood increase, will negative feedback increase or decrease the secretion of TSH?***
b. ***In a person with a hyperactive gland that is producing too much thyroid hormone, would you expect the level of TSH to be higher or lower than in a normal person?***

216 226 231 234 238 240 240

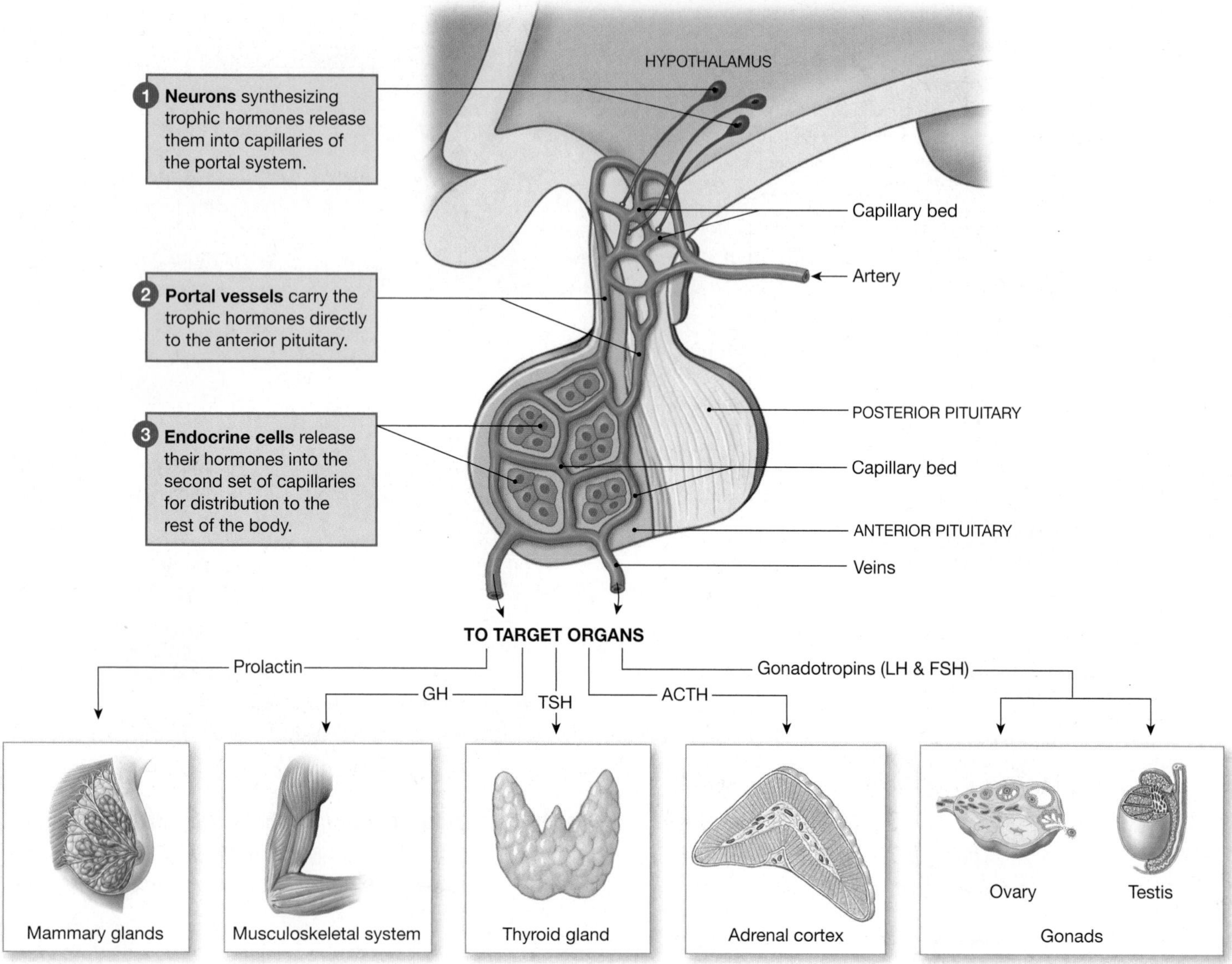
HYPOTHALAMUS
1 Neurons synthesizing trophic hormones release them into capillaries of the portal system.
2 Portal vessels carry the trophic hormones directly to the anterior pituitary.
3 Endocrine cells release their hormones into the second set of capillaries for distribution to the rest of the body.
Capillary bed
Artery
POSTERIOR PITUITARY
Capillary bed
ANTERIOR PITUITARY
Veins
TO TARGET ORGANS
Prolactin
GH
TSH
ACTH
Gonadotropins (LH & FSH)
Mammary glands
Musculoskeletal system
Thyroid gland
Adrenal cortex
Ovary
Testis
Gonads

● **FIGURE 7-16** *The hypothalamic-hypophyseal portal system*

A Portal System Delivers Hormones from Hypothalamus to Anterior Pituitary

The hypothalamic trophic hormones that regulate secretion of anterior pituitary hormones are transported directly to the pituitary through a special set of blood vessels known as the **hypothalamic-hypophyseal portal system** (Fig. 7-16 ●). A **portal system** is a specialized region of the circulation consisting of two sets of capillaries directly connected by a set of larger blood vessels. There are three portal systems in the body: one in the kidneys, one in the digestive system, and this one in the brain.

Hormones secreted into a portal system have a distinct advantage over hormones secreted into the general circulation because with a portal system, a much smaller amount of hormone can be secreted to elicit a given level of response. A dose of hormone secreted into the general circulation is rapidly diluted by the total blood volume, which is typically more than 5 L. The same dose secreted into the tiny volume of blood flowing through the portal system remains concentrated while it is taken directly to its target. In this way a small number of neurosecretory neurons in the hypothalamus can effectively control the anterior pituitary.

The minute amounts of hormone secreted into the hypothalamic-hypophyseal portal system posed a great challenge to the researchers who first isolated these hormones. Because such tiny quantities of hypothalamic-releasing hormones are secreted, Roger Guillemin and Andrew Shalley had to work with huge amounts of tissue to obtain enough hormone to analyze. Guillemin and his colleagues processed more than 50 tons of sheep hypothalami, and a major meat packer donated more than 1 million pig hypothalami to Shalley and his associates. For the final analysis, they needed 25,000 hypothalami to isolate and identify the amino acid sequence of just 1 mg of thyrotropin-releasing hormone, a tiny peptide made of three amino acids (see Fig. 7-4a). For their discovery, Guillemin and Shalley shared a Nobel prize in 1977.

Anterior Pituitary Hormones Control Growth, Metabolism, and Reproduction

The hormones of the anterior pituitary control so many vital functions that the pituitary is often called the master gland of the body. In general, we can say that the anterior pituitary hormones control metabolism, growth, and reproduction, all very complex processes.

One anterior pituitary hormone, **prolactin** (PRL), controls milk production in the female breast, along with other effects. In both sexes, prolactin appears to play a role in regulation of the immune system. **Growth hormone** (GH; also called *somatotropin*) affects metabolism of many tissues in addition to stimulating hormone production by the liver (Fig. 7-17 ●). Prolactin and growth hormone are the only two anterior pituitary hormones whose secretion is controlled by both releasing hormones and inhibiting hormones, as you can see in Figure 7-13 on page 230. We discuss these hormones in detail in Chapters 26 and 23, respectively.

CONCEPT CHECK

15. Which pathway(s) in Figure 6-31 (p. 207) fit(s):
    (a) the hypothalamic trophic hormone-prolactin-breast pattern just described?
    (b) the growth hormone pathway shown in Figure 7-17?

Answers: p. 245

The remaining four anterior pituitary hormones all have another endocrine gland as their primary target. **Follicle-stimulating hormone** (FSH) and **luteinizing hormone** (LH), known collectively as the **gonadotropins**, were originally named for their effects on the ovaries, but both hormones are trophic on testes as well. **Thyroid-stimulating hormone** (TSH, or *thyrotropin*) controls hormone synthesis and secretion in the thyroid gland. **Adrenocorticotrophic hormone** (ACTH, or *corticotropin*) acts on certain cells of the adrenal cortex to control synthesis and release of the steroid hormone cortisol.

We discuss the hormones of the anterior and posterior pituitary in more detail in later chapters.

CONCEPT CHECK

16. What is the target tissue of a hypothalamic hormone secreted into the hypothalamic-hypophyseal portal system?
17. Look at the pathway in Figure 7-9 for insulin release as the result of eating a meal. What event serves as the negative feedback signal to shut off insulin release?

Answers: p. 245

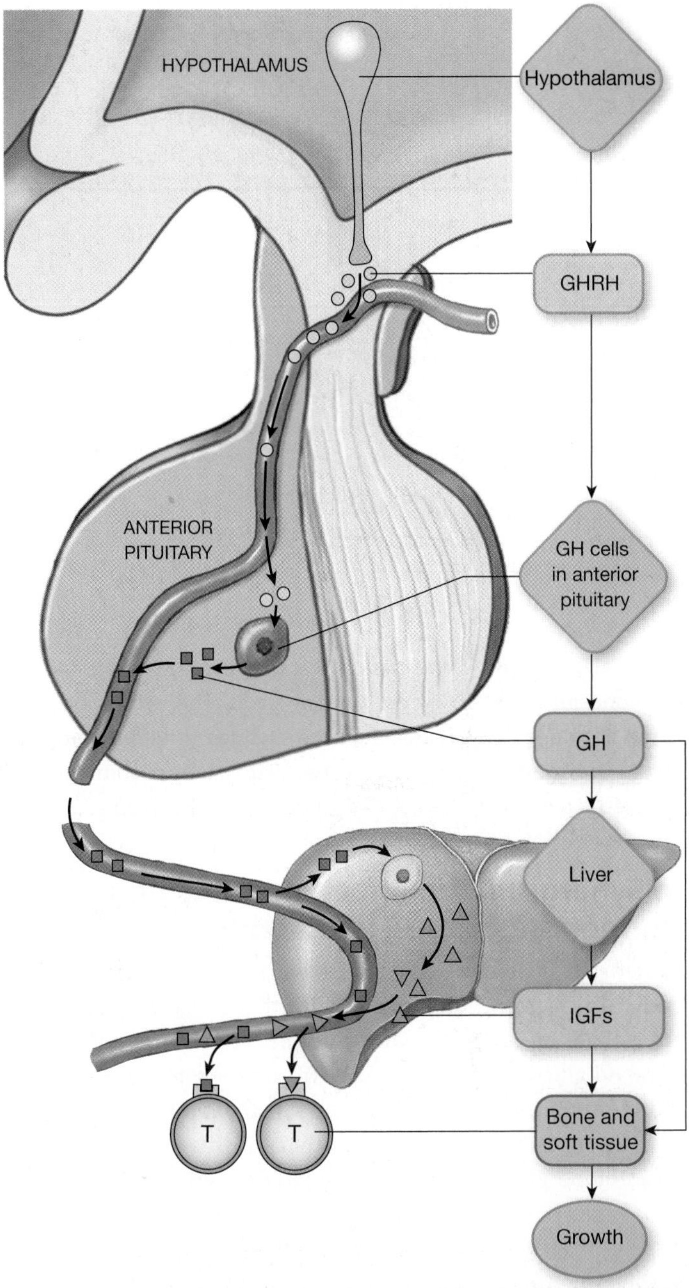

● **FIGURE 7-17** ***Growth hormone is an example of a complex endocrine pathway.*** Growth hormone acts directly on many body tissues but also influences liver production of insulin-like growth factors (IGFs or *somatomedins*), another group of hormones that regulate growth.

HORMONE INTERACTIONS

One of the most complicated and confusing aspects of endocrinology is the way hormones interact at their target cells. It would be simple if each endocrine reflex were a separate entity and if each cell were under the influence of only a single hormone. In many instances, however, cells and tissues are controlled by multiple hormones that may be present at the same time. Complicating the picture is the fact that multiple hormones acting on a single cell can interact in ways that cannot be predicted by knowing the individual effects of the hormone. In this section, we examine three types of hormone interaction: synergism, permissiveness, and antagonism.

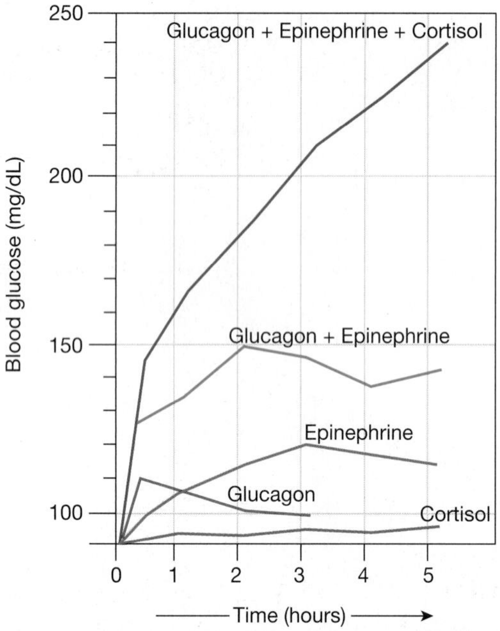

● **FIGURE 7-18** ***Synergism.*** This graph shows the effect of hormone infusions on blood glucose levels. The effects of combined hormones are greater than the summed effects of the individual hormones, indicating synergistic relationships. (Data adapted from Eigler *et al.*, *J. Clin. Invest.* 63: 114, 1979.)

In Synergism, the Effect of Interacting Hormones Is More Than Additive

Sometimes different hormones have the same effect on the body, although they may accomplish that effect through different cellular mechanisms. One example is the hormonal control of blood glucose levels. Glucagon from the pancreas is the hormone primarily responsible for elevating blood glucose levels, but it is not the only hormone that has that effect. Cortisol raises blood glucose concentration, as does epinephrine.

What happens if two of these hormones are present in a target cell at the same time, or if all three hormones are secreted at the same time? You might expect their effects to be additive. In other words, if a given amount of epinephrine elevates blood glucose 5 mg/100 mL blood, and glucagon elevates blood glucose 10 mg/100 mL blood, you might expect both hormones acting at the same time to elevate blood glucose 15 mg/100 mL blood (5 + 10).

Frequently, however, two (or more) hormones interact at their targets so that the combination yields a result that is greater than additive. This type of interaction is called **synergism**. For our epinephrine/glucagon example, a synergistic reaction would be:

epinephrine	elevates blood glucose	5 mg/100 mL blood
glucagon	elevates blood glucose	10 mg/100 mL blood
epinephrine + glucagon	elevate blood glucose	22 mg/100 mL blood

In other words, the combined effect of the two hormones is greater than the sum of the effects of the two hormones individually. Synergism is sometimes known as *potentiation,* as in "Epinephrine potentiates glucagon's effect on blood glucose."

An example of synergism involving epinephrine, glucagon, and cortisol is shown in Figure 7-18 ●. The cellular mechanisms that underlie synergistic effects are not always clear, but with peptide hormones, synergism is often linked to overlapping effects on second messenger systems.

Synergism is not limited to hormones. It can occur with any two (or more) chemicals in the body. Pharmacologists have developed drugs with synergistic components. For example, the effectiveness of the antibiotic penicillin is enhanced by the presence of clavulanic acid in the same pill.

A Permissive Hormone Allows Another Hormone to Exert Its Full Effect

In **permissiveness**, one hormone cannot fully exert its effects unless a second hormone is present. For example, maturation of the reproductive system is controlled by gonadotropin-releasing hormone from the hypothalamus, gonadotropins from the anterior pituitary, and steroid hormones from the gonads. However, if thyroid hormone is not present in sufficient amounts, maturation of the reproductive system is delayed. Because thyroid hormone by itself cannot stimulate maturation of the reproductive system, thyroid hormone is considered to have a permissive effect on sexual maturation.

The results of this interaction can be summarized as follows:

thyroid hormone alone	no development of reproductive system
reproductive hormones alone	delayed development of reproductive system
reproductive hormones with adequate thyroid hormone	normal development of reproductive system

RUNNING PROBLEM

Ben Crenshaw was diagnosed with Graves' disease, one form of hyperthyroidism. The goal of treatment is to reduce thyroid hormone activity, and Ben's physician offered him several alternatives. One treatment involves drugs that prevent the thyroid gland from using iodine. Another treatment is a single dose of radioactive iodine that destroys the thyroid tissue. A third treatment is surgical removal of all or part of the thyroid gland. Ben elected initially to use the thyroid-blocking drug. Several months later he was given radioactive iodine.

Question 3:

Why is radioactive iodine (rather than some other radioactive element, such as cobalt) used to destroy thyroid tissue?

The molecular mechanisms responsible for permissiveness are not well understood in most instances.

Antagonistic Hormones Have Opposing Effects

In some situations, two molecules work against each other, one diminishing the effectiveness of the other. This tendency of one substance to oppose the action of another is called *antagonism*. Recall from Chapter 6 that antagonism may result when two molecules compete for the same receptor [p. 42]. When one molecule binds to the receptor but does not activate it, that molecule acts as a *competitive inhibitor*, or antagonist, to the other molecule. This type of receptor antagonism has been put to use in the development of pharmaceutical compounds, such as the estrogen receptor antagonist *tamoxifen*, which is used to treat breast cancers that are stimulated by estrogen.

In endocrinology, two hormones are considered *functional antagonists* if they have opposing physiological actions. For example, both glucagon and growth hormone raise the concentration of glucose in the blood, and both are antagonistic to insulin, which lowers the concentration of glucose in the blood. Hormones with antagonistic actions do not necessarily compete for the same receptor. Instead, they may act through different metabolic pathways, or one hormone may decrease the number of receptors for the opposing hormone. For example, evidence suggests that growth hormone decreases the number of insulin receptors, providing part of its functional antagonistic effects on blood glucose concentration.

The synergistic, permissive, and antagonistic interactions of hormones make the study of endocrinology both challenging and intriguing. With this brief survey of hormone interactions, you have built a solid foundation for learning more about hormone interactions in later chapters.

ENDOCRINE PATHOLOGIES

As one endocrinologist said, "There are no good or bad hormones. A balance of hormones is important for a healthy life. . . . Unbalance leads to diseases."* We can learn much about the normal functions of a hormone by studying the diseases caused by hormone imbalances. There are three basic patterns of endocrine pathology: hormone excess, hormone deficiency, and abnormal responsiveness of target tissues to a hormone.

To illustrate endocrine pathologies, we will use a single example, that of cortisol production by the adrenal cortex (see Fig. 7-15). This is a complex reflex pathway that starts with the secretion of corticotropin-releasing hormone (CRH) from the hypothalamus. CRH stimulates release of adrenocorticotropin (ACTH) from the anterior pituitary. ACTH in turn controls the synthesis and release of cortisol from the adrenal cortex. As in all other homeostatic reflex pathways, negative feedback shuts off the pathway. As cortisol increases, it acts as a negative feedback signal, causing the pituitary and hypothalamus to decrease their output of ACTH and CRH, respectively.

*W. König, preface to *Peptide and Protein Hormones* (New York: VCH Publishers, 1993).

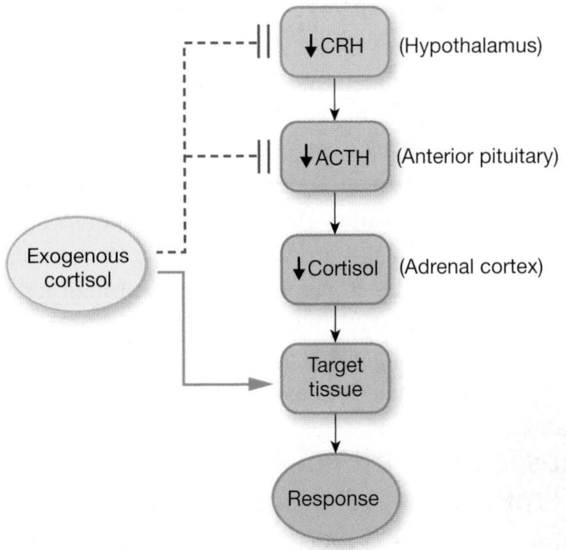

● **FIGURE 7-19** ***Negative feedback by exogenous cortisol.*** Hormone administered to a person for medical reasons has the same negative feedback effect as the endogenous hormone.

Hypersecretion Exaggerates a Hormone's Effects

If a hormone is present in excessive amounts, the normal effects of the hormone are exaggerated. Most instances of hormone excess are due to **hypersecretion**. There are numerous causes of hypersecretion, including benign tumors (*adenomas*) and cancerous tumors of the endocrine glands. Occasionally, nonendocrine tumors secrete hormones.

Any substance coming from outside the body is referred to as *exogenous* [*exo-*, outside], and sometimes a patient may exhibit signs of hypersecretion as the result of medical treatment with an exogenous hormone or agonist. In this case, the condition is said to be *iatrogenic*, or physician-caused [*iatros*, healer + *-gen*, to be born]. It seems simple enough to correct the hormone imbalance by stopping treatment with the exogenous hormone, but this is not always the case.

In our example, exogenous cortisol in the body acts as a negative feedback signal, just as cortisol produced within the body would, shutting off the production of CRH and ACTH (Fig. 7-19 ●). Without the trophic "nourishing" influence of ACTH, the body's own cortisol production shuts down. If the pituitary remains suppressed and the adrenal cortex is deprived of ACTH long enough, the cells of both glands shrink and lose their ability to manufacture ACTH and cortisol. The loss of cell mass is known as **atrophy** [*a-*, without + *trophikós*, nourishment].

If the cells of an endocrine gland atrophy because of exogenous hormone administration, they may be very slow or totally unable to regain normal function when the treatment with exogenous hormone is stopped. As you may know, steroid hormones can be used to treat poison ivy and severe allergies. However, when treatment is complete, the dosage must be tapered off gradually to allow the pituitary and adrenal gland to work back up to normal hormone production. As a result, packages of steroid pills direct patients ending treatment to take six pills one day, five the day after that, and so on. Low-dose, over-the-counter steroid creams usually do not pose a risk of feedback suppression when used as directed.

Hyposecretion Diminishes or Eliminates a Hormone's Effects

Symptoms of hormone deficiency occur when too little hormone is secreted (**hyposecretion**). Hyposecretion may occur anywhere along the endocrine control pathway, in the hypothalamus, pituitary, or other endocrine glands. For example, hyposecretion of thyroid hormone may occur if there is insufficient dietary iodine for the thyroid gland to manufacture the iodinated hormone. The most common cause of hyposecretion pathologies is atrophy of the gland due to some disease process.

Negative feedback pathways are affected in hyposecretion, but in the opposite direction from hypersecretion. The absence of negative feedback causes trophic hormone levels to rise as the trophic hormones attempt to make the defective gland increase its hormone output. For example, if the adrenal cortex atrophies as a result of tuberculosis, cortisol production diminishes. The hypothalamus and anterior pituitary sense that cortisol levels are below normal, so they increase secretion of CRH and ACTH, respectively, in an attempt to stimulate the adrenal gland into making more cortisol.

CONCEPT CHECK

18. Draw a reflex pathway similar to the one in Figure 7-19 to illustrate what happens to hormone levels and feedback when the adrenal cortex atrophies and cortisol secretion is below normal.

Answers: p. 245

Receptor or Second Messenger Problems Cause Abnormal Tissue Responsiveness

Endocrine diseases do not always arise from problems with endocrine glands. They may also be triggered by changes in the responsiveness of target tissues to the hormones. In these situations, the target tissues show abnormal responses even though the hormone levels may be within the normal range. Changes in the target tissue response are usually caused by abnormal interactions between the hormone and its receptor or by alterations in signal transduction pathways. We covered these concepts for signal molecules in general in Chapter 6 [p. 193], so we restrict this discussion to some typical examples of abnormal tissue responsiveness in the endocrine system.

Down-Regulation If hormone secretion is abnormally high for an extended period of time, target cells may *down-regulate* (decrease the number of) their receptors in an effort to diminish their responsiveness to excess hormone. **Hyperinsulinemia** [*hyper-*, elevated + insulin + *-emia,* in the blood] is a classic example of down-regulation in the endocrine system. In this disorder, sustained high levels of insulin in the blood cause target cells to remove insulin receptors from the cell membrane. Patients suffering from hyperinsulinemia may show signs of diabetes despite their high blood insulin levels.

Receptor and Signal Transduction Abnormalities Many forms of inherited endocrine pathologies can be traced to problems with hormone action in the target cell. Endocrinologists once believed that these problems were rare, but they are being recognized more frequently as scientists increase their understanding of receptors and signal transduction mechanisms.

Some pathologies are due to problems with the hormone receptor. If a mutation alters the protein sequence of the receptor, the cellular response to receptor-hormone binding may be altered. In other mutations the receptors may be absent or completely nonfunctional. For example, in *testicular feminizing syndrome,* androgen receptors are nonfunctional in the male fetus because of a genetic mutation. As a result, androgens produced by the developing fetus are unable to influence development of the genitalia. The result is a child who appears to be female but lacks a uterus and ovaries.

Genetic alterations in signal transduction pathways can lead to symptoms of hormone excess or deficiency. In the disease called *pseudohypoparathyroidism* [*pseudo-,* false + *hypo-,* decreased + parathyroid + *-ism,* condition or state of being], patients show signs of low parathyroid hormone even though blood levels of the hormone are normal or elevated. These patients have inherited a defect in the G protein that links the hormone receptor to the cAMP amplifier enzyme, adenylyl cyclase. Because the signal transduction pathway does not function, target cells are unable to respond to parathyroid hormone, and signs of hormone deficiency appear.

Diagnosis of Endocrine Pathologies Depends on the Complexity of the Reflex

Diagnosis of endocrine pathologies may be simple or complicated, depending on the complexity of the reflex. In the simplest endocrine reflex, such as that for parathyroid hormone, if there is too much or too little hormone, there is only one location where the problem can arise: the parathyroid glands (see Fig. 7-10). However, with complex hypothalamic-pituitary-endocrine gland reflexes, the diagnosis can be much more difficult.

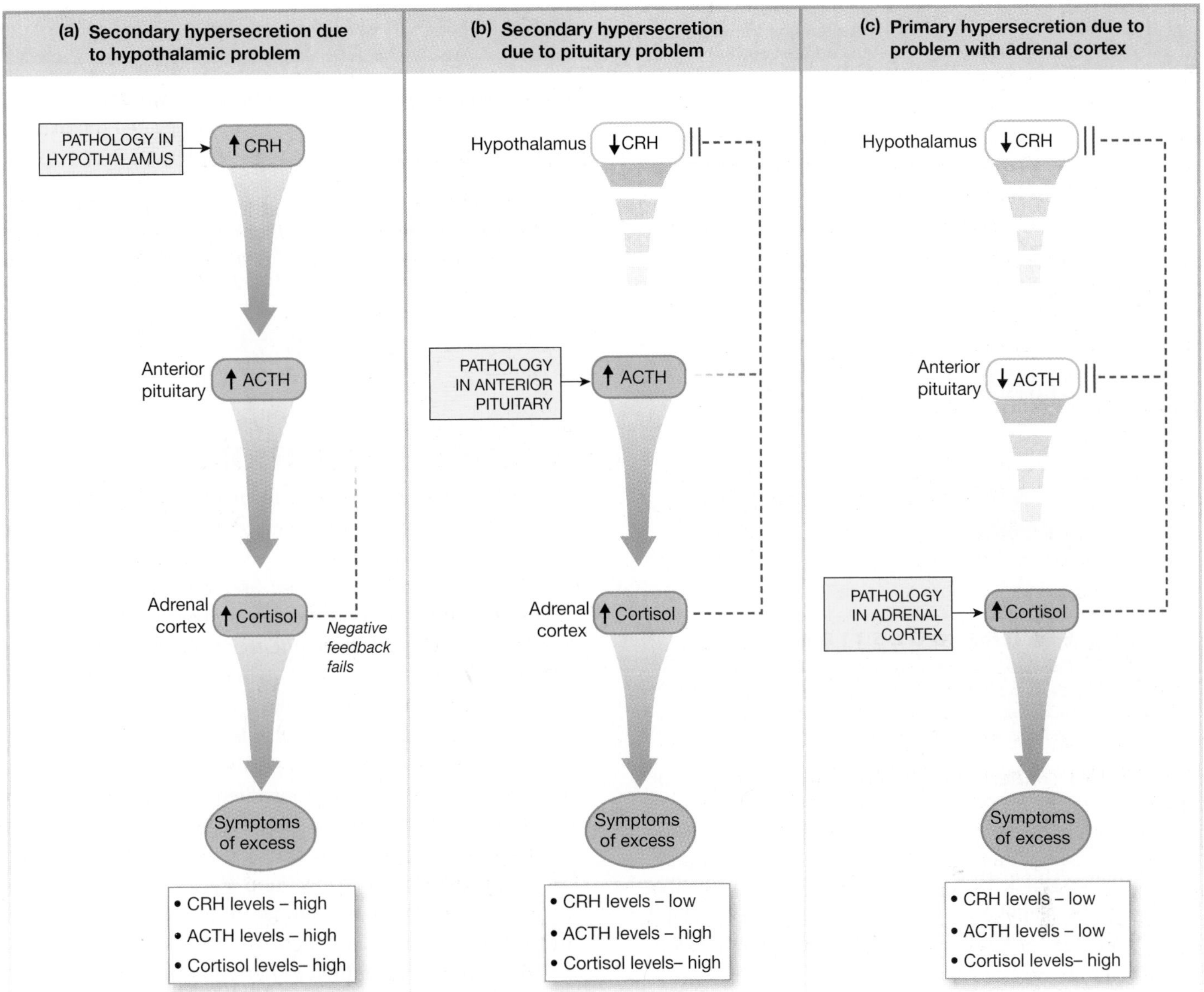
(a) Secondary hypersecretion due to hypothalamic problem
PATHOLOGY IN HYPOTHALAMUS
↑ CRH
Anterior pituitary
↑ ACTH
Adrenal cortex
↑ Cortisol
Negative feedback fails
Symptoms of excess
• CRH levels – high
• ACTH levels – high
• Cortisol levels– high
(b) Secondary hypersecretion due to pituitary problem
Hypothalamus
↓CRH
PATHOLOGY IN ANTERIOR PITUITARY
↑ ACTH
Adrenal cortex
↑ Cortisol
Symptoms of excess
• CRH levels – low
• ACTH levels – high
• Cortisol levels– high
(c) Primary hypersecretion due to problem with adrenal cortex
Hypothalamus
↓ CRH
Anterior pituitary
↓ ACTH
PATHOLOGY IN ADRENAL CORTEX
↑ Cortisol
Symptoms of excess
• CRH levels – low
• ACTH levels – low
• Cortisol levels– high

● **FIGURE 7-20** ***Primary and secondary hypersecretion of cortisol.*** When there is a pathology in an endocrine gland, negative feedback fails.

If a pathology (deficiency or excess) arises in the last endocrine gland in a reflex, the problem is considered to be a **primary pathology.** For example, if a tumor in the adrenal cortex begins to produce excessive amounts of cortisol, the resulting condition is called *primary hypersecretion*. If dysfunction occurs in one of the tissues producing trophic hormones, the problem is a **secondary pathology.** For example, if the pituitary is damaged because of head trauma and ACTH secretion diminishes, the resulting cortisol deficiency is considered to be *secondary hyposecretion* of cortisol.

The diagnosis of pathologies in complex endocrine pathways depends on understanding negative feedback in the control pathway. Figure 7-20 ● shows three possible causes of excess cortisol secretion. To determine which is the correct *etiology* (cause) of the disease in a particular patient, the clinician must assess the levels of the three hormones in the control pathway. If the problem is overproduction of CRH by the hypothalamus (Fig. 7-20a) CRH levels are higher than normal. High CRH in turn causes high ACTH, which in turn causes high cortisol. This is therefore secondary hypersecretion arising from a problem in the hypothalamus. In clinical practice, hypothalamic pathologies are rare.

Figure 7-20b shows a secondary hypersecretion of cortisol due to an ACTH-secreting tumor of the pituitary. Once again, the high levels of ACTH cause high cortisol production, but in this example the high cortisol level has a negative feedback effect on the hypothalamus, decreasing production of CRH. The combination of low CRH and high ACTH isolates the problem

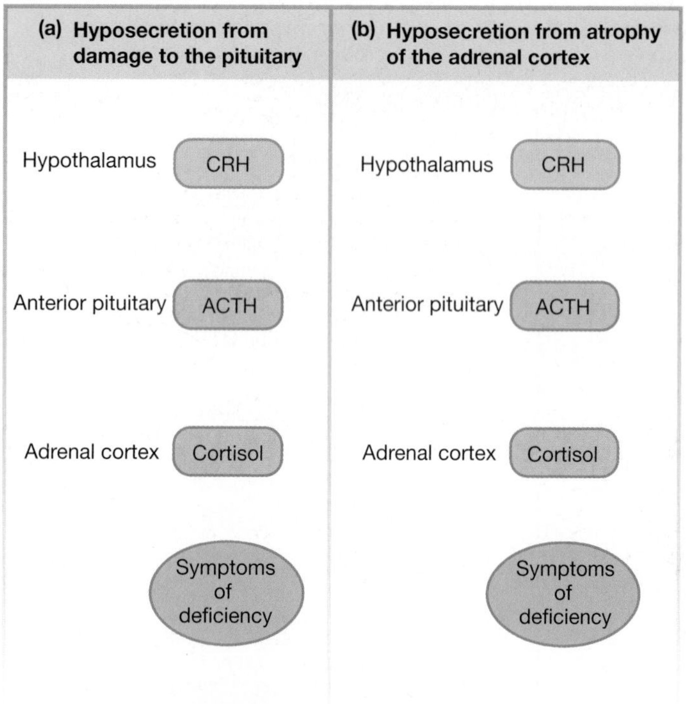

FIGURE QUESTION

For each condition, use arrows to indicate whether levels of the three hormones in the pathway will be increased, decreased, or unchanged. Draw in negative feedback loops where functional.

● **FIGURE 7-21** ***Patterns of hormone secretion in hypocortisolism***

to the pituitary. This pathology is responsible for about two-thirds of cortisol hypersecretion *syndromes* [*syn-*, together + *-drome,* running; a combination of symptoms characteristic of a particular pathology].

If cortisol levels are high but levels of both trophic hormones are low, the problem must be a primary disorder (Fig. 7-20c). There are two possible explanations: endogenous cortisol hypersecretion or the exogenous administration of cortisol for therapeutic reasons (see Fig. 7-19). In either case, high levels of cortisol act as a negative feedback signal that shuts off production of CRH and ACTH. The pattern of high cortisol with low trophic hormone levels points to a primary disorder.

When the problem is an adrenal tumor that is secreting cortisol in an unregulated fashion, the normal control pathways are totally ineffective. Although negative feedback shuts off production of the trophic hormones, the tumor is not dependent on them for cortisol production, so cortisol secretion continues in their absence. The tumor must be removed or suppressed before cortisol secretion can be controlled.

Figure 7-21 ● shows two possible etiologies for hyposecretion of cortisol. You can apply your understanding of negative feedback in the hypothalamic-pituitary control pathway to predict whether the levels of CRH, ACTH, and cortisol will be high or low in each case.

RUNNING PROBLEM

Graves' disease is one form of thyroid gland hyperactivity. For this reason, people with Graves' disease have elevated thyroxine levels in the blood. Their TSH levels are very low.

Question 4:

If levels of TSH are low and thyroxine levels are high, is Graves' disease a primary disorder or a secondary disorder (one that arises as a result of a problem with the anterior pituitary or the hypothalamus)? Explain your answer.

HORMONE EVOLUTION

Chemical signaling is an ancient method for communication and the maintenance of homeostasis. As scientists sequence the genomes of diverse species, they are discovering that in many cases hormone structure and function have changed amazingly little from the most primitive vertebrates through the mammals. In fact, hormone signaling pathways that were once considered exclusive to vertebrates, such as those for thyroid hormones and insulin, have now been shown to play physiological or developmental roles in invertebrates such as echinoderms and insects. This *evolutionary conservation* of hormone function is also demonstrated by the fact that some hormones from other organisms have biological activity when administered to humans. By studying which portions of a hormone molecule do not change from species to species, scientists have acquired important clues to aid in the design of agonist and antagonist drugs.

The ability of nonhuman hormones to work in humans was a critical factor in the birth of endocrinology. When Best and Banting discovered insulin in 1921 and the first diabetic patients were treated with the hormone, the insulin was extracted from cow, pig, or sheep pancreases. Before the mid-1980s slaughterhouses were the major source of insulin for the medical profession. Now, with genetic engineering, the human gene for insulin has been inserted into bacteria, which then synthesize the hormone, providing us with a plentiful source of human insulin.

Although many hormones have the same function in most vertebrates, a few hormones that play a significant role in the physiology of lower vertebrates seem to be evolutionarily "on their way out" in humans. Calcitonin is a good example of such a hormone. Although it plays a major role in calcium metabolism in fish, calcitonin apparently has no significant influence on daily calcium balance in adult humans. Neither calcitonin deficiency nor calcitonin excess is associated with any pathological condition or symptom.

Although calcitonin is not a significant hormone in humans, the calcitonin gene does code for a biologically active protein. In the brain, cells process mRNA from the calcitonin

FOCUS ON . . . THE PINEAL GLAND

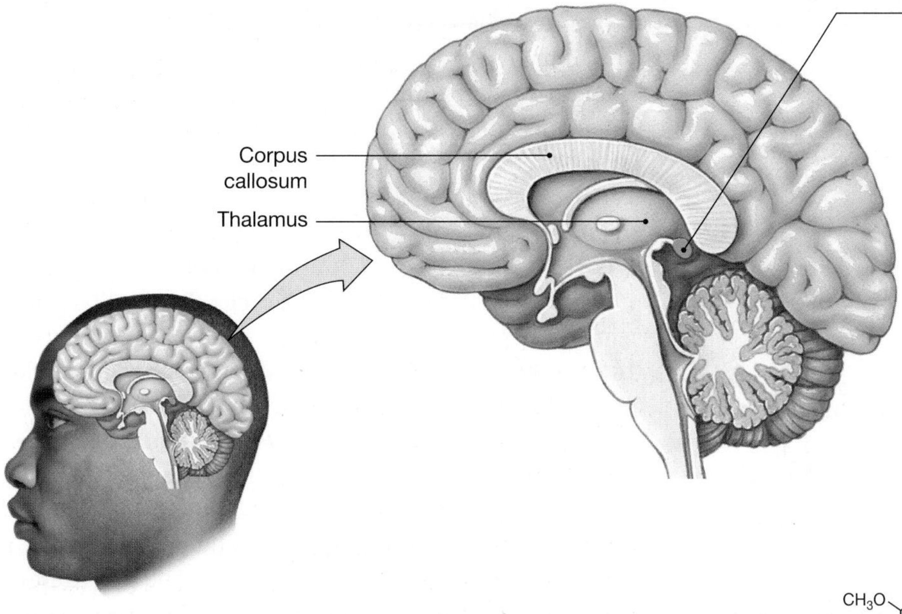

The **pineal gland** is a pea-sized structure buried deep in the brain of humans. Nearly 2000 years ago, this "seat of the soul" was thought to act as a valve that regulated the flow of vital spirits and knowledge into the brain. By 1950, however, scientists had decided that it was a vestigial structure with no known function.

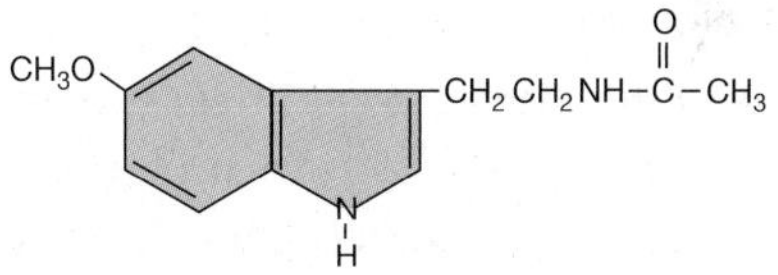

Melatonin is an amino acid–derived hormone made from tryptophan.

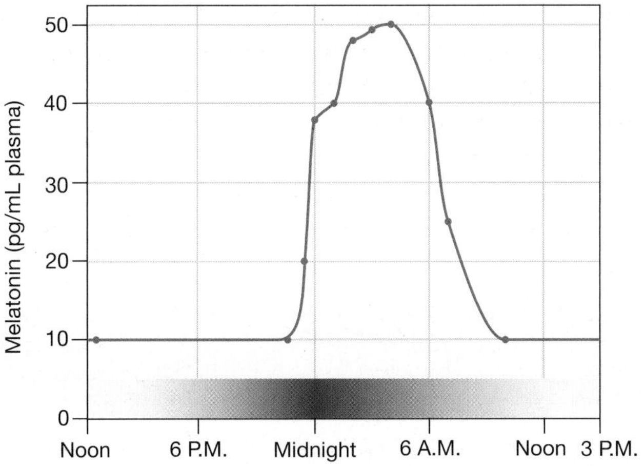

Melatonin is the "darkness hormone," secreted at night as we sleep. It is the chemical messenger that transmits information about light-dark cycles to the brain center that governs the body's biological clock.

(Adapted from J. Arendt, *Clin. Endocrinol.* 29:205-229, 1988.)

About 1957 one of the wonderful coincidences of scientific research occurred. An investigator heard about a factor in beef pineal glands that could lighten the skin of amphibians. Using the classical methodology of endocrinology, he obtained pineal glands from a slaughterhouse and started making extracts. His biological assay consisted of dropping pineal extracts into bowls of live tadpoles to see if their skin color blanched. Several years and hundreds of thousands of pineal glands later, he had isolated a small amount of melatonin.

Fifty years later, we are still learning about the functions of melatonin in humans. In addition to its role in sleep-wake cycles and the body's internal clock, scientists have evidence that melatonin is a powerful antioxidant [p. 24]. Some studies using mouse models of Alzheimer's disease suggest that melatonin may help slow the progression of the disease. The hormone is also known to enhance immune function, and studies are underway to see if it can slow the growth of cancerous tumors. Melatonin has also been linked to sexual function, the onset of puberty, and seasonal affective disorder (SADD) in the darker winter months. For a review, see "Melatonin: Lowering the high price of free radicals," *News in Physiological Sciences* 15: 246–250, Oct. 2000 (*http://nips.physiology.org*).

● **FIGURE 7-22** ***The pineal gland and melatonin***

RUNNING PROBLEM

Researchers have learned that Graves' disease is an autoimmune disorder in which the body fails to recognize its own tissue. In this condition, the body produces antibodies that mimic TSH and bind to the TSH receptor, turning it on. This false signal "fools" the thyroid gland into overproducing thyroid hormone. More women than men are diagnosed with Graves' disease, perhaps because of the influence of female hormones on thyroid function. Stress and other environmental factors have also been implicated in hyperthyroidism.

Question 5:
Antibodies are proteins that bind to the TSH receptor. From that information, what can you conclude about the cellular location of the TSH receptor?

Question 6:
In Graves' disease, why doesn't negative feedback shut off thyroid hormone production before it becomes excessive?

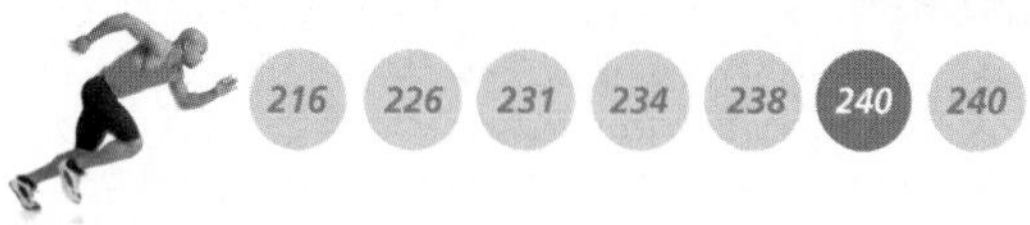

gene to make a peptide known as *calcitonin gene-related peptide* (CGRP), which apparently acts as a neurotransmitter. CGRP can act as a powerful dilator of blood vessels, and one recent study found that a CGRP receptor antagonist effectively treated migraine headaches, which occur when cerebral blood vessels dilate (vasodilation). The ability of one gene to produce multiple peptides is one reason research is shifting from genomics to physiology and proteomics (the study of the role of proteins in physiological function) [p. 6].

Some endocrine structures that are important in lower vertebrates are *vestigial* [*vestigium,* trace] in humans, meaning that in humans these structures are present as minimally functional glands. For example, *melanocyte-stimulating hormone* (MSH) from the intermediate lobe of the pituitary controls pigmentation in reptiles and amphibians. However, adult humans have only a vestigial intermediate lobe and normally do not have measurable levels of MSH in their blood.

In the research arena, *comparative endocrinology*—the study of endocrinology in nonhuman organisms—has made significant contributions to our quest to understand the human body. Many of our models of human physiology are based on research carried out in fish or frogs or rats, to name a few. For example, the pineal gland hormone *melatonin* (Fig. 7-22 ●) was discovered through research using tadpoles. Many small nonhuman vertebrates have short life cycles that facilitate studying aging or reproductive physiology. Genetically altered mice (transgenic or knockout mice) have provided researchers valuable information about proteomics.

Opponents of animal research argue that scientists should not experiment with animals at all and should use only cell cultures and computer models. Cell cultures and models are valuable tools and can be helpful in the initial stages of medical research, but at some point new drugs and procedures must be tested on intact organisms prior to clinical trials in humans. Responsible scientists follow guidelines for appropriate animal use and limit the number of animals killed to the minimum needed to provide valid data.

In this chapter we have examined how the endocrine system with its hormones helps regulate the slower processes in the body. In the next chapter, you will learn how the nervous system can take care of the more rapid responses needed to maintain homeostasis.

RUNNING PROBLEM CONCLUSION

Graves' Disease

In this running problem, you learned that in Graves' disease, thyroid hormone levels are high because an immune-system protein mimics TSH. You also learned that the thyroid gland concentrates iodine for synthesis of thyroid hormones and that radioactive iodine can concentrate in the gland and destroy the thyroid cells.

Graves' disease is the most common form of hyperthyroidism. Other famous people who have suffered from it include former U.S. President George H. W. Bush and First Lady Barbara Bush. To learn more about Graves' disease and other thyroid conditions, check out the Endocrine Society's Hormone Foundation web site at *www.hormone.org* or the American Thyroid Association at *www.thyroid.org*. Check your answers to the problem questions by comparing them to the information in the summary table below.

	QUESTION	FACTS	INTEGRATION AND ANALYSIS
1a	To which of the three classes of hormones do thyroid hormones belong?	The three classes of hormones are peptides, steroids, and amino acid derivatives.	Thyroid hormones are made from the amino acid tyrosine; therefore, they are amino acid derivatives.

(continued)

	QUESTION	FACTS	INTEGRATION AND ANALYSIS
1b	If a person's diet is low in iodine, predict what happens to thyroxine production.	The thyroid gland concentrates iodine and combines it with the amino acid tyrosine to make thyroid hormones.	If iodine is lacking in the diet, a person is unable to make thyroid hormones.
2a	In a normal person, when thyroid hormone levels in the blood increase, will negative feedback increase or decrease the secretion of TSH?	Negative feedback shuts off response loops.	Normally negative feedback decreases TSH secretion.
2b	In a person with a hyperactive gland that is producing too much thyroid hormone, would you expect the level of TSH to be higher or lower than in a normal person?		If thyroid hormone is high, you would expect strong negative feedback and even lower levels of TSH.
3	Why is radioactive iodine (rather than some other radioactive element, such as cobalt) used to destroy thyroid tissue?	The thyroid gland concentrates iodine to make thyroid hormones.	Radioactive iodine is concentrated in the thyroid gland and therefore selectively destroys that tissue. Other radioactive elements would distribute more widely throughout the body and might harm normal tissues.
4	If levels of TSH are low and thyroxine levels are high, is Graves' disease a primary disorder or a secondary disorder (one that arises as a result of a problem with the anterior pituitary or the hypothalamus)? Explain your answer.	In secondary hypersecretion disorders, you would expect the levels of the hypothalamic and/or anterior pituitary trophic hormones to be elevated.	In Graves' disease, TSH from the anterior pituitary is very low. Therefore, the oversecretion of thyroid hormones is not the result of elevated TSH. This means that Graves' disease is a primary disorder that is caused by a problem in the thyroid gland itself.
5	Antibodies are proteins that bind to the TSH receptor. From that information, what can you conclude about the cellular location of the TSH receptor?	Receptors may be membrane receptors or intracellular receptors. Proteins cannot cross the cell membrane.	The TSH receptor is a membrane receptor. It uses the cAMP second messenger pathway for signal transduction.
6	In Graves' disease, why doesn't negative feedback shut off thyroid hormone production before it becomes excessive?	In normal negative feedback, increasing levels of thyroid hormone shut off TSH secretion. Without TSH stimulation, the thyroid stops producing thyroid hormone.	In Graves' disease, high levels of thyroid hormone have shut off endogenous TSH production. However, the thyroid gland still produces hormone in response to the binding of antibody to the TSH receptor. In this situation, negative feedback fails to correct the problem.

216 226 231 234 238 240 240

CHAPTER SUMMARY

This chapter introduced you to the endocrine system and the role it plays in *communication* and *control* of physiological processes. As you've seen before, the *compartmentalization of the body* into intracellular and extracellular compartments means that special mechanisms are required to enable signals to pass from one compartment to the other.

The chapter also presented basic patterns that you will encounter again as you study various organ systems: differences among the three chemical classes of hormones, reflex pathways for hormones, types of hormone interactions, and endocrine pathologies.

Hormones

iP Endocrine System: Endocrine System Review

1. The specificity of a hormone depends on its receptors and their associated signal transduction pathways. (p. 216)
2. A **hormone** is a chemical secreted by a cell or group of cells into the blood for transport to a distant target, where it is effective at very low concentrations. (p. 217)
3. **Pheromones** are chemical signals secreted into the external environment. (p. 219)
4. Hormones bind to receptors to initiate responses known as the **cellular mechanism of action.** (p. 220)
5. Hormone activity is limited by terminating secretion, removing hormone from the blood, or terminating activity at the target cell. (p. 220)
6. The rate of hormone breakdown is indicated by a hormone's **half-life.** (p. 221)

The Classification of Hormones

iP Endocrine System: Biochemistry, Secretion and Transport of Hormones, and the Actions of Hormones on Target Cells

7. There are three types of hormones: **peptide/protein hormones,** composed of three or more amino acids; **steroid hormones,** derived from cholesterol; and **amino acid-derived hormones,** derived from either tyrosine (e.g., catecholamines and thyroid hormones) or tryptophan (e.g., melatonin). (p. 221)
8. Peptide hormones are made as inactive **preprohormones** and processed to **prohormones.** Prohormones are chopped into active hormone and peptide fragments that are co-secreted. (p. 221; Figs. 7-3, 7-4)
9. Peptide hormones dissolve in the plasma and have a short half-life. They bind to surface receptors on their target cells and initiate rapid cellular responses through signal transduction. In some instances, peptide hormones also initiate synthesis of new proteins. (p. 221; Fig. 7-5)
10. Steroid hormones are synthesized as they are needed. They are hydrophobic, and most steroid hormones in the blood are bound to protein carriers. Steroids have an extended half-life. (p. 222)
11. Traditional steroid receptors are inside the target cell, where they turn genes on or off and direct the synthesis of new proteins. Cell response is slower than with peptide hormones. Steroid hormones may bind to membrane receptors and have nongenomic effects. (p. 223; Fig. 7-7)
12. Amine hormones may behave like typical peptide hormones or like a combination of a steroid hormone and a peptide hormone. (p. 225; Fig. 7-8)

Control of Hormone Release

iP Endocrine System: The Hypothalamic-Pituitary Axis

13. Classic endocrine cells act as both sensor and integrating center in the simple reflex pathway. (p. 226; Fig. 7-10)
14. Many endocrine reflexes involve the nervous system, either through **neurohormones** or through neurons that influence hormone release. (p. 228)
15. The pituitary gland is composed of the anterior pituitary (a true endocrine gland) and the posterior pituitary (an extension of the brain). (p. 228; Fig. 7-11)
16. The posterior pituitary releases two neurohormones, oxytocin and vasopressin, that are made in the hypothalamus. (p. 228; Fig. 7-12)
17. **Trophic hormones** control the secretion of other hormones. (p. 229)
18. Anterior pituitary hormones are controlled by releasing hormones and inhibiting hormones from the hypothalamus. (p. 229; Fig. 7-13)
19. In complex endocrine reflexes, hormones of the pathway act as negative feedback signals. (p. 230; Fig. 7-14)
20. The hypothalamic trophic hormones reach the pituitary through the **hypothalamic-hypophyseal portal system.** (p. 232; Fig. 7-16)
21. There are six anterior pituitary hormones: prolactin, growth hormone, follicle-stimulating hormone, luteinizing hormone, thyroid-stimulating hormone, and adrenocorticotrophic hormone. (p. 233; Fig. 7-13)

Hormone Interactions

22. If the combination of two or more hormones yields a result that is greater than additive, the interaction is **synergism.** (p. 234; Fig. 7-18)
23. If one hormone cannot exert its effects fully unless a second hormone is present, the second hormone is said to be **permissive** to the first. (p. 234)
24. If one hormone opposes the action of another, the two are **antagonistic** to each other. (p. 235)

Endocrine Pathologies

25. Diseases of hormone excess are usually due to **hypersecretion**. Symptoms of hormone deficiency occur when too little hormone is secreted (**hyposecretion**). **Abnormal tissue responsiveness** may result from problems with hormone receptors or signal transduction pathways. (pp. 235–236)
26. **Primary pathologies** arise in the last endocrine gland in a reflex. A **secondary pathology** is a problem with one of the tissues producing trophic hormones. (p. 237; Fig. 7-20)

Hormone Evolution

27. Many human hormones are similar to hormones found in other vertebrate animals. (p. 238)

QUESTIONS

(Answers to the Review Questions begin on page A1.)

THE PHYSIOLOGY PLACE

Access more review material online at **The Physiology Place** web site. There you'll find review questions, problem-solving activities, case studies, flashcards, and direct links to both *Interactive Physiology®* and *PhysioEx™*. To access the site, go to *www.physiologyplace.com* and select *Human Physiology,* Fifth Edition.

LEVEL ONE REVIEWING FACTS AND TERMS

1. The study of hormones is called ________.
2. List the three basic ways hormones act on their target cells.
3. List five endocrine glands, and name one hormone secreted by each. Give one effect of each hormone you listed.
4. Match the following researchers with their experiments:

(a) Lower	1. isolated trophic hormones from the hypothalami of pigs and sheep
(b) Berthold	2. claimed sexual rejuvenation after injections of testicular extracts
(c) Guillemin and Shalley	3. isolated insulin
(d) Brown-Séquard	4. accurately described the function of the pituitary gland
(e) Banting and Best	5. studied comb development in castrated roosters

5. Put the following steps for identifying an endocrine gland in order:
   (a) Purify the extracts and separate the active substances.
   (b) Perform replacement therapy with the gland or its extracts and see if the abnormalities disappear.
   (c) Implant the gland or administer the extract from the gland to a normal animal and see if symptoms characteristic of hormone excess appear.
   (d) Put the subject into a state of hormone deficiency by removing the suspected gland, and monitor the development of abnormalities.
6. For a chemical to be defined as a hormone, it must be secreted into the ________ for transport to a(n) ________ and take effect at ________ concentrations.
7. What is meant by the term *half-life* in connection with the activity of hormone molecules?
8. Metabolites are inactivated hormone molecules, broken down by enzymes found primarily in the ________ and ________, to be excreted in the ________ and ________, respectively.
9. Candidate hormones often have the word ________ as part of their name.
10. List and define the three chemical classes of hormones. Name one hormone in each class.
11. Decide if each of the following characteristics applies best to peptide hormones, steroid hormones, both classes, or neither class.
    (a) are lipophobic and must use a signal transduction system
    (b) have a short half-life, measured in minutes
    (c) often have a lag time of 90 minutes before effects are noticeable
    (d) are water-soluble, and thus easily dissolve in the extracellular fluid for transport
    (e) most hormones belong to this class
    (f) are all derived from cholesterol
    (g) consist of three or more amino acids linked together
    (h) are released into the blood to travel to a distant target organ
    (i) are transported in the blood bound to protein carrier molecules
    (j) are all lipophilic, so diffuse easily across membranes
12. Why do steroid hormones usually take so much longer to act than peptide hormones?
13. When steroid hormones act on a cell nucleus, the hormone-receptor complex acts as a(n) ________ factor, binds to DNA, and activates one or more ________, which create mRNA to direct the synthesis of new ________.
14. Researchers have discovered that some cells have additional steroid hormone receptors on their________, enabling a faster response.
15. Melatonin is made from the amino acid ________, and the catecholamines and thyroid hormones are made from the amino acid ________.
16. A hormone that controls the secretion of another hormone is known as a(n) ________ hormone.
17. In reflex control pathways involving trophic hormones and multiple integrating centers, the hormones themselves act as ________ ________ signals, suppressing trophic hormone secretion earlier in the reflex.
18. What characteristic defines neurohormones?
19. List the two hormones secreted by the posterior pituitary gland. To what chemical class do they belong?
20. What is the hypothalamic-hypophyseal portal system? Why is it important?
21. List the six hormones of the anterior pituitary gland; give an action of each. Which ones are trophic hormones?
22. How do long-loop negative feedback and short-loop negative feedback differ? Give an example of each type in the body's endocrine system.
23. When two hormones work together to create a result that is greater than additive, that interaction is called ________. When two hormones must both be present to achieve full expression of an effect, that interaction is called ________. When hormone activities oppose each other, that effect is called ________.

LEVEL TWO REVIEWING CONCEPTS

24. Compare and contrast the terms in each of the following sets:
    (a) paracrine, hormone, cytokine
    (b) primary and secondary endocrine pathologies
    (c) hypersecretion and hyposecretion
    (d) anterior and posterior pituitary
25. Compare and contrast the three chemical classes of hormones.

26. Map the following groups of terms. Add additional terms if you like.

List 1	List 2
co-secretion	ACTH
endoplasmic reticulum	anterior pituitary
exocytosis	blood
Golgi complex	endocrine cell
hormone receptor	gonadotropins
peptide hormone	growth hormone
preprohormone	hypothalamus
prohormone	inhibiting hormone
secretory vesicle	neurohormone
signal sequence	neuron
synthesis	oxytocin
target cell response	peptide/protein
	peripheral endocrine gland
	portal system
	posterior pituitary
	prolactin
	releasing hormone
	trophic hormone
	TSH
	vasopressin

LEVEL THREE PROBLEM SOLVING

27. You encountered the terms *specificity, receptors,* and *down-regulation* in other chapters in this text. Do their meanings change when applied to the endocrine system? What chemical and physical characteristics do hormones, enzymes, transport proteins, and receptors have in common that makes specificity important?

28. Dexamethasone is a drug used to suppress the secretion of adrenocorticotrophic hormone (ACTH) from the anterior pituitary. Two patients with hypersecretion of cortisol are given dexamethasone. Patient A's cortisol secretion falls to normal as a result, but patient B's cortisol secretion remains elevated. Draw maps of the reflex pathways for these two patients (see Fig. 7-15 for a template) and use the maps to determine which patient has primary hypercortisolism. Explain your reasoning.

29. Some early experiments for male birth control pills used drugs that suppressed gonadotropin (FSH and LH) release. However, men given these drugs stopped taking them because the drugs decreased testosterone secretion, which decreased the men's sex drive and caused impotence.
    (a) Use the information given in Figure 7-13 to draw the GnRH-FSH/LH-testosterone reflex pathway. Use the pathway to show how suppressing gonadotropins decreases sperm production and testosterone secretion.
    (b) Researchers subsequently suggested that a better treatment would be to give men extra testosterone. Draw another copy of the reflex pathway to show how testosterone could suppress sperm production without the side effect of impotence.

LEVEL FOUR QUANTITATIVE PROBLEMS

30. The following graph represents the disappearance of a drug from the blood as the drug is metabolized and excreted. Based on the graph, what is the half-life of the drug?

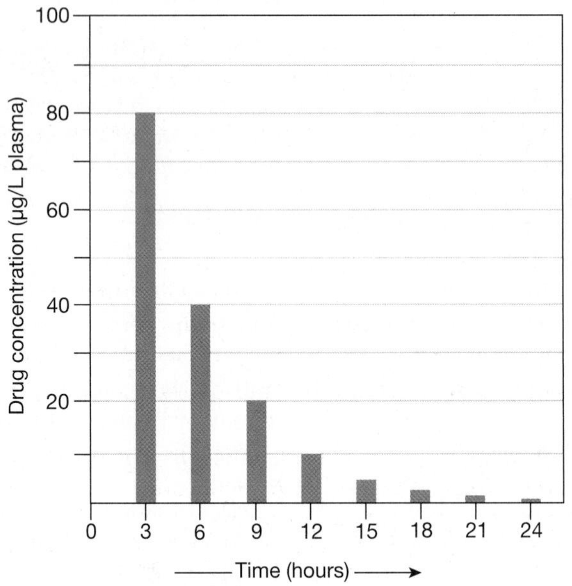

31. The following graph shows plasma TSH concentration in three groups of subjects. Which pattern would be consistent with the following pathologies? Explain your reasoning.
    (a) primary hypothyroidism
    (b) primary hyperthyroidism
    (c) secondary hyperthyroidism

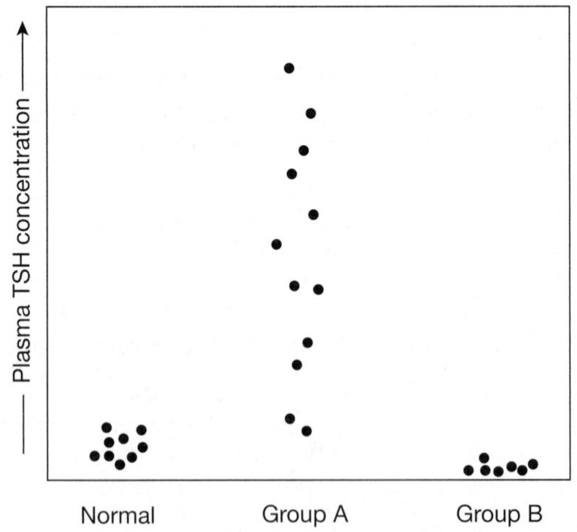

32. Based on what you have learned about the pathway for insulin secretion, draw and label a graph showing the effect of plasma glucose concentration on insulin secretion.

ANSWERS

Answers to Concept Check Questions

Page 220

1. Glucose enters cells by facilitated diffusion (GLUT transporters).

Page 221

2. The suffix *-ase* indicates an enzyme. A *peptidase* digests peptides.

Page 221

3. A hormone is a chemical that is secreted into the blood and acts on a distant target in very low concentrations.
4. A steroid-producing cell would have extensive smooth endoplasmic reticulum; a protein-producing cell would have lots of rough endoplasmic reticulum and secretory vesicles.

Page 226

5. The three chemical classes of hormones are peptide, steroid, and amino acid–derived.
6. The short half-life suggests that aldosterone is not bound to plasma proteins as much as other steroid hormones are.

Page 226

7. The input signal is the stimulus, receptor, and afferent pathway. Integration of the signal takes place in the integrating center. The output signal is the efferent pathway.
8. Increased blood glucose is the stimulus. Insulin secretion is the efferent pathway; decrease in blood glucose is the response.
9. Insulin release by blood glucose is reflex 6. Insulin release triggered by a neural signal following a meal is reflex 3. Insulin release in response to a digestive hormone is closest to reflex 4, although the question does not indicate whether the hormone is neurosecretory. If it is not, there is no matching pathway in Figure 6-31.

Page 227

10. Stimulus: decreased blood glucose; sensor/integrating center: pancreatic endocrine cells; efferent path: glucagon; effector: multiple target tissues; response: increased blood glucose.

Page 228

11. Catecholamines are amino acid–derived hormones.

Page 229

12. Microtubules of the cytoskeleton move secretory vesicles.
13. Contents of secretory vesicles are released by exocytosis.

Page 231

14. Pathway 5 in Figure 6-31 fits the complex pattern described.

Page 233

15. (a) Pathway 4; (b) pathway 4 for GH acting directly on targets, and pathway 5 for GH acting on the liver.

Page 233

16. The target is endocrine cells of the anterior pituitary.
17. The pathway shuts off when food is no longer present in the intestine to create stretch. A decrease in blood glucose can also serve as a negative feedback signal.

Page 236

18. Cortisol level is low; low negative feedback makes CRH and ACTH levels high.

Answers to Figure Questions

Page 225

Fig. 7-8: The conversion of tyrosine to dopamine adds a hydroxyl (−OH) group to the 6-carbon ring and changes the carboxyl (−COOH) group to a hydrogen. Norepinephrine is made from dopamine by changing one hydrogen to a hydroxyl group. Epinephrine is made from norepinephrine by changing one hydrogen attached to the nitrogen to a methyl ($-CH_3$) group.

Page 227

Fig. 7-9: The pathway begun by eating a meal shuts off when the stretch stimulus disappears as the meal is digested and absorbed from the digestive tract.

Page 231

Fig. 7-15: In short-loop negative feedback, ACTH feeds back to inhibit CRH.

Page 238

Fig. 7-21: (a) CRH high, ACTH low, cortisol low. No negative feedback loops are functioning. (b) CRH normal/high, ACTH high, cortisol low. Absence of negative feedback by cortisol increases trophic hormones. Short-loop negative feedback from ACTH may keep CRH within the normal range.

8

Neurons: Cellular and Network Properties

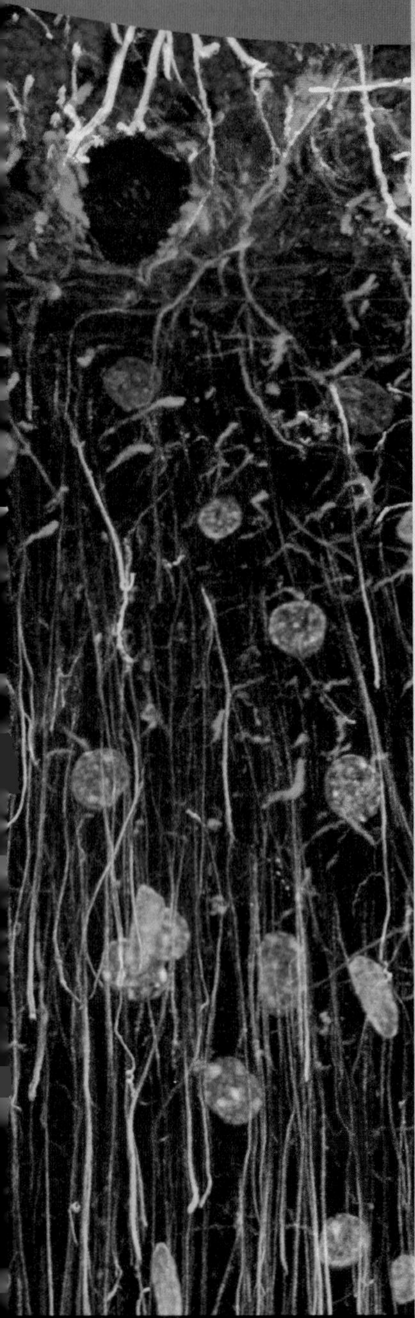

Purkinje cells (red) and glial cells (green) in the cerebellum

BACKGROUND BASICS

Reflex pathways: **198** Organelles: **63** Neurohormones: **180** Gated channels: **144** Matrix: **80** Gap junctions: **179** Positive feedback: **203** Phagocytosis: **152** Antagonistic control: **196** Neurocrine secretions: **180** Resting membrane potential: **166** Exocytosis: **154** Equilibrium potential: **168** Biolelectricity: **164**

The future of clinical neurology and psychiatry is intimately tied to that of molecular neural science.

—Eric R. Kandel, James H. Schwartz, and Thomas M. Jessell, ***in the preface to their book,*** Principles of Neural Science, 2000

RUNNING PROBLEM

Mysterious Paralysis

"Like a polio ward from the 1950s" is how Guy McKhann, M.D., a neurology specialist at the Johns Hopkins School of Medicine, describes a ward of Beijing Hospital that he visited on a trip to China in 1986. Dozens of paralyzed children—some attached to respirators to assist their breathing—filled the ward to overflowing. The Chinese doctors thought the children had Guillain-Barré syndrome (GBS), a rare paralytic condition, but Dr. McKhann wasn't convinced. There were simply too many stricken children for the illness to be the rare Guillain-Barré syndrome. Was it polio—as some of the Beijing staff feared? Or was it another illness, perhaps one that had not yet been discovered?

In an eerie scene from a science fiction movie, white-coated technicians move quietly through a room filled with bubbling cylindrical fish tanks. As the camera zooms in on one tank, no fish are seen darting through aquatic plants. The lone occupant of the tank is a gray mass with a convoluted surface like a walnut and a long tail that appears to be edged with beads. Floating off the beads are hundreds of fine fibers, waving softly as the oxygen bubbles weave through them. This is no sea creature. . . . It is a brain and spinal cord, removed from its original owner and awaiting transplantation into another body. Can this be real? Is this scenario possible? Or is it just the creation of an imaginative movie screenwriter?

The brain is regarded as the seat of the soul, the mysterious source of those traits that we think of as setting humans apart from animals. The brain and spinal cord are also integrating centers for homeostasis, movement, and many other body functions. They are the control center of the **nervous system**, a network of billions or trillions of nerve cells linked together in a highly organized manner to form the rapid control system of the body.

Nerve cells, or **neurons**, carry electrical signals rapidly and, in some cases, over long distances. They are uniquely shaped cells, and most have long, thin extensions, or **processes**, that can extend up to a meter in length. In most pathways, neurons release chemical signals, called **neurotransmitters**, into the extracellular fluid. In a few pathways, neurons are linked by *gap junctions* [p. 179], allowing electrical signals to pass directly from cell to cell.

Using electrical signals to release chemicals from a cell is not unique to neurons, as you learned in Chapter 5 [p. 164]. Single-celled protozoa and plants also employ electrical signaling mechanisms, in many cases using the same types of ion channels as vertebrates do. Scientists sequencing ion channel proteins have found that many of these proteins have been highly conserved during evolution, indicating their fundamental importance.

TABLE 8-1 Synonyms in Neuroscience

TERM USED IN THIS BOOK	SYNONYM(S)
Action potential	AP, spike, nerve impulse, conduction signal
Autonomic nervous system	Visceral nervous system
Axon	Nerve fiber
Axonal transport	Axoplasmic flow
Axon terminal	Synaptic knob, synaptic bouton, presynaptic terminal
Axoplasm	Cytoplasm of an axon
Cell body	Cell soma, nerve cell body
Cell membrane of an axon	Axolemma
Glial cells	Neuroglia, glia
Interneuron	Association neuron
Rough endoplasmic reticulum	Nissl substance, Nissl body
Sensory neuron	Afferent neuron, afferent

Although electrical signaling is universal, sophisticated neural networks are unique to animal nervous systems. Reflex pathways in the nervous system do not necessarily follow a straight line from one neuron to the next. One neuron may influence multiple neurons, or many neurons may affect the function of a single neuron. The intricacy of neural networks underlies the **emergent properties** of the nervous system: complex processes, such as consciousness, intelligence, and emotion, that cannot be predicted from what we know about the properties of individual nerve cells. The search to explain emergent properties makes neuroscience one of the most active research areas in physiology today.

Neuroscience, like many other areas of science, has its own specialized language. In many instances, multiple terms describe a single structure or function, which potentially can lead to confusion. Table 8-1 ● lists some neuroscience terms used in this book, along with their common synonyms.

ORGANIZATION OF THE NERVOUS SYSTEM

The nervous system can be divided into two parts. The **central nervous system (CNS)** consists of the **brain** and the **spinal cord**. The **peripheral nervous system (PNS)** consists of

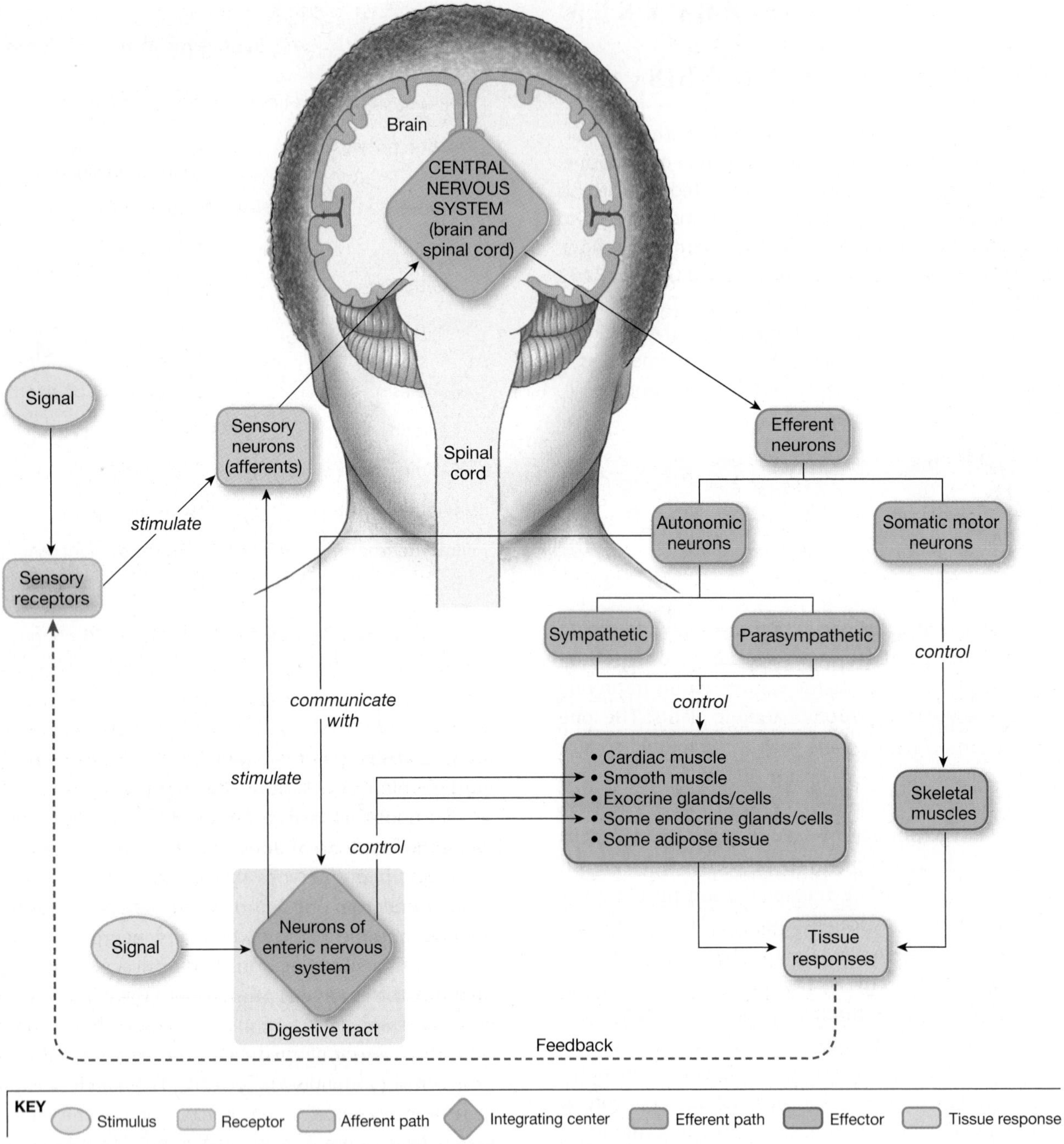

● **FIGURE 8-1** ***Organization of the nervous system.*** The peripheral nervous system (PNS) sends information to the central nervous system (CNS) through afferent (sensory) neurons and takes information from the CNS to target cells via efferent neurons. The enteric nervous system can act autonomously or can be controlled by the CNS through the autonomic division of the PNS.

afferent (or **sensory**) **neurons** and **efferent neurons**. Information flow through the nervous system follows the basic reflex pattern described in Chapter 6 [p. 198].

Sensory receptors throughout the body continuously monitor conditions in both the internal and external environments (Fig. 8-1 ●). These receptors send information along afferent neurons to the central nervous system. We discuss afferent pathways and their associated sensory receptors in Chapter 10.

The CNS is the integrating center for neural reflexes. CNS neurons integrate information that arrives from the afferent branch of the PNS and determine whether a response is needed. Chapter 9 examines the complex structure and functions of the CNS.

The CNS then sends output signals directing an appropriate response (if any) that travel through efferent neurons to their targets, which are mostly muscles and glands. Efferent neurons are subdivided into the **somatic motor division**, which controls skeletal muscles, and the **autonomic division**, which controls smooth and cardiac muscles, exocrine glands, some endocrine glands, and some types of adipose tissue. Terminology used to describe efferent neurons can be confusing. The expression *motor neuron* is sometimes used to refer to all efferent neurons. However, clinically, the term *motor neuron* (or *motoneuron*) is often used to describe somatic motor neurons that control skeletal muscles.

The autonomic division of the PNS is also called the *visceral nervous system* because it controls contraction and secretion in the various internal organs [*viscera,* internal organs]. Autonomic neurons are further divided into **sympathetic** and **parasympathetic branches**, which can be distinguished by their anatomical organization and by the chemicals they use to communicate with their target cells. Many internal organs receive innervation from both types of autonomic neurons, and it is a common pattern to find that the two divisions exert *antagonistic control* over a single target [p. 396]. We discuss the PNS in Chapter 11.

In recent years, a third division of the nervous system has received considerable attention. The **enteric nervous system** is a network of neurons in the walls of the digestive tract. It is frequently controlled by the autonomic division of the nervous system, but it is also able to function autonomously as its own integrating center. We discuss the enteric nervous system further in Chapter 21 on the digestive system.

Although most of this book focuses on the role of neural reflexes in communication, coordination, and homeostasis in the body, it is important to note that significant processes in the central nervous system can take place without input or output from the peripheral nervous system. The CNS has the ability to initiate activity without sensory input, and it need not create any measurable output. Two examples are thinking and dreaming, complex higher-brain functions that can take place totally within the CNS.

CONCEPT CHECK

1. Organize the following terms describing functional types of neurons into a map or outline: afferent, autonomic, brain, central, efferent, enteric, parasympathetic, peripheral, sensory, somatic motor, spinal, sympathetic. Answers: p. 294

RUNNING PROBLEM

Guillain-Barré syndrome is a relatively rare paralytic condition that strikes after a viral infection or an immunization. There is no cure, but usually the paralysis slowly disappears, and lost sensation slowly returns. In classic Guillain-Barré, patients can neither feel sensations nor move their muscles.

Question 1:

Which division(s) of the nervous system may be involved in Guillain-Barré syndrome (GBS)?

247
249
252
273
275
279
287
290

CELLS OF THE NERVOUS SYSTEM

The nervous system is composed primarily of two cell types: neurons—the basic signaling units of the nervous system—and support cells known as *glial cells* (or glia or neuroglia).

Neurons Carry Electrical Signals

The neuron is the functional unit of the nervous system. (A *functional unit* is the smallest structure that can carry out the functions of a system.) Neurons are uniquely shaped cells with long processes that extend outward from the cell body. These processes are usually classified as either **dendrites** (which receive incoming signals) or **axons** (which carry outgoing information). The shape, number, and length of axons and dendrites vary from one neuron to the next, but these structures are an essential feature that allows neurons to communicate with one another and with other cells.

Traditionally we use efferent neurons similar to the model neurons shown in Figure 8-2 ● and Figure 8-3e ● to teach how a neuron functions. In other neuron types, the processes shown in the model may be missing or modified. However, if you understand these model neurons, you will understand how most neurons work.

Neurons may be classified either structurally or functionally. Structurally, neurons are classified by the number of processes that originate from the cell body. They may be described as *pseudounipolar* (axon and dendrites fuse during development to create one long process; Fig. 8-3a), *bipolar* (single axon and single dendrite; Fig. 8-3b), *multipolar* (many dendrites and branched axons; Fig. 8-3d), or *anaxonic* (lacking an identifiable axon; Fig. 8-3c). Because physiology is concerned chiefly with function, however, we will classify neurons not structurally but rather according to function: sensory (afferent) neurons, interneurons, and efferent (somatic motor and autonomic) neurons, as shown at the top of Figure 8-3.

Sensory neurons carry information about temperature, pressure, light, and other stimuli from sensory receptors to the CNS.

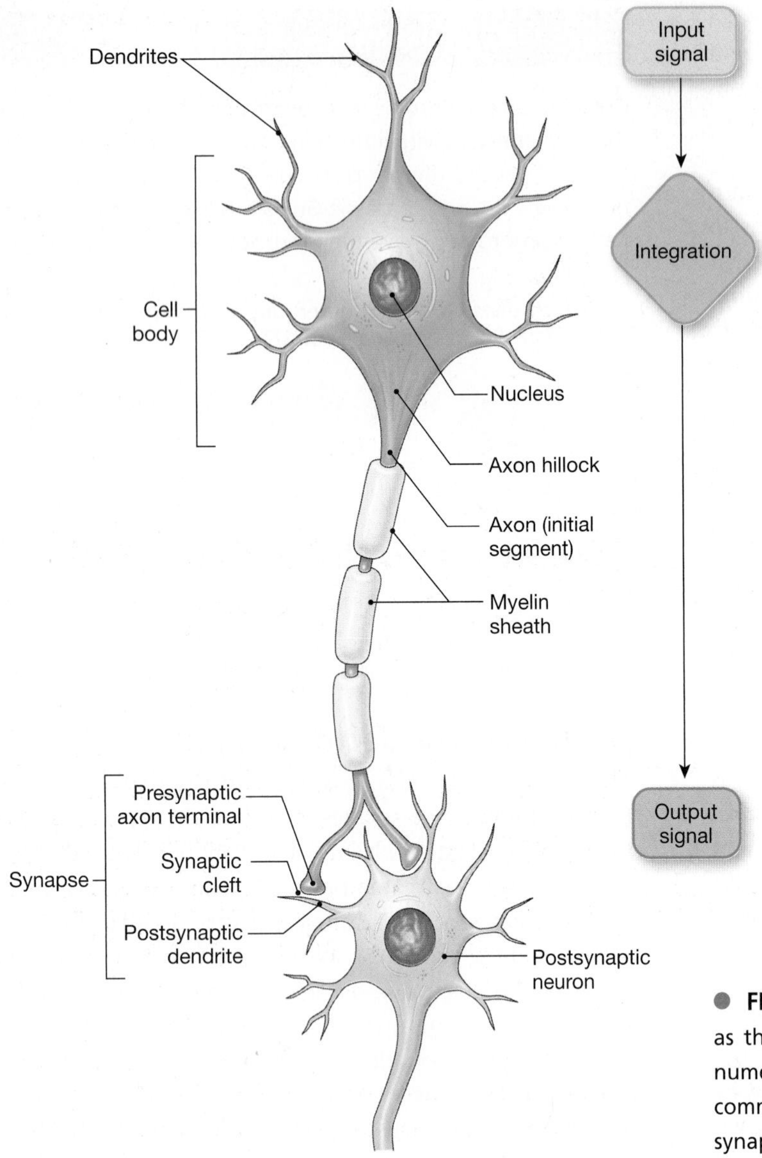

NAVIGATOR

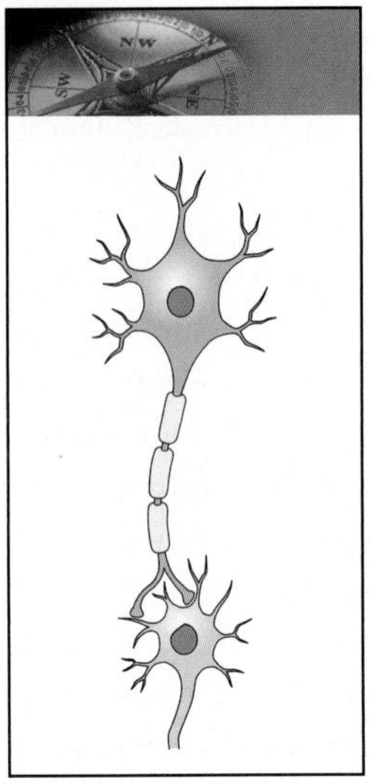

This icon represents the different components of typical neurons. Look for it in the figures that follow to help you navigate your way through the structure and function of the nervous system.

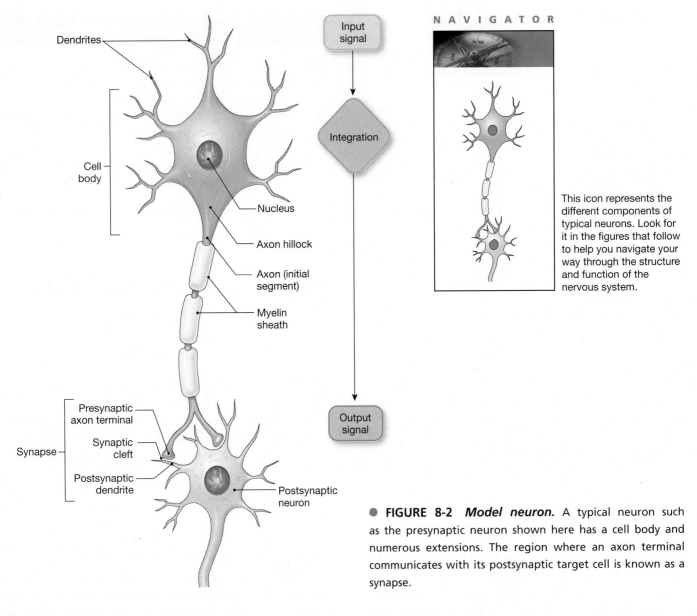

● **FIGURE 8-2** ***Model neuron.*** A typical neuron such as the presynaptic neuron shown here has a cell body and numerous extensions. The region where an axon terminal communicates with its postsynaptic target cell is known as a synapse.

They vary from the model neuron in the length and organization of their processes. For example, peripheral sensory neurons have cell bodies that are found close to the CNS, with very long processes that extend to receptors in the limbs and internal organs. In these neurons, the cell body is out of the direct path of signals passing along the axon (Fig. 8-3a). In contrast, sensory neurons for smell and vision, with receptors located very close to the CNS, have two long processes so that signals that begin at the dendrites travel through the cell body to the axon (Fig. 8-3b).

Neurons that lie entirely within the CNS are known as **interneurons** (short for *interconnecting neurons*). They come in a variety of forms but often have quite complex branching processes that allow them to communicate with many other neurons (Fig. 8-3c, d). Some interneurons are quite small compared to the model neuron.

Efferent neurons, both somatic motor and autonomic, are generally very similar to the model neuron in Figure 8-2. In the autonomic division, some neurons have enlarged regions along the axon called **varicosities** (see Fig. 11-8). The varicosities store and release neurotransmitter. The long axons of both afferent and efferent peripheral neurons are bundled together with connective tissue into cordlike fibers called **nerves** that extend from the CNS to the targets of the component neurons. Nerves may carry afferent signals only (**sensory nerves**), efferent signals only (**motor nerves**), or signals in both directions (**mixed nerves**). Many nerves are large enough to be seen with the naked eye and have been given anatomical names. For example, the *phrenic nerve* runs from the spinal cord to the muscles of the diaphragm.

The Cell Body Is the Control Center of the Neuron

The **cell body** *(cell soma)* of a neuron resembles the typical cell described in Chapter 3, with a nucleus and all organelles needed to direct cellular activity [p. 63]. An extensive cytoskeleton extends outward into the axon and dendrites. The position of the cell body varies in different types of neurons,

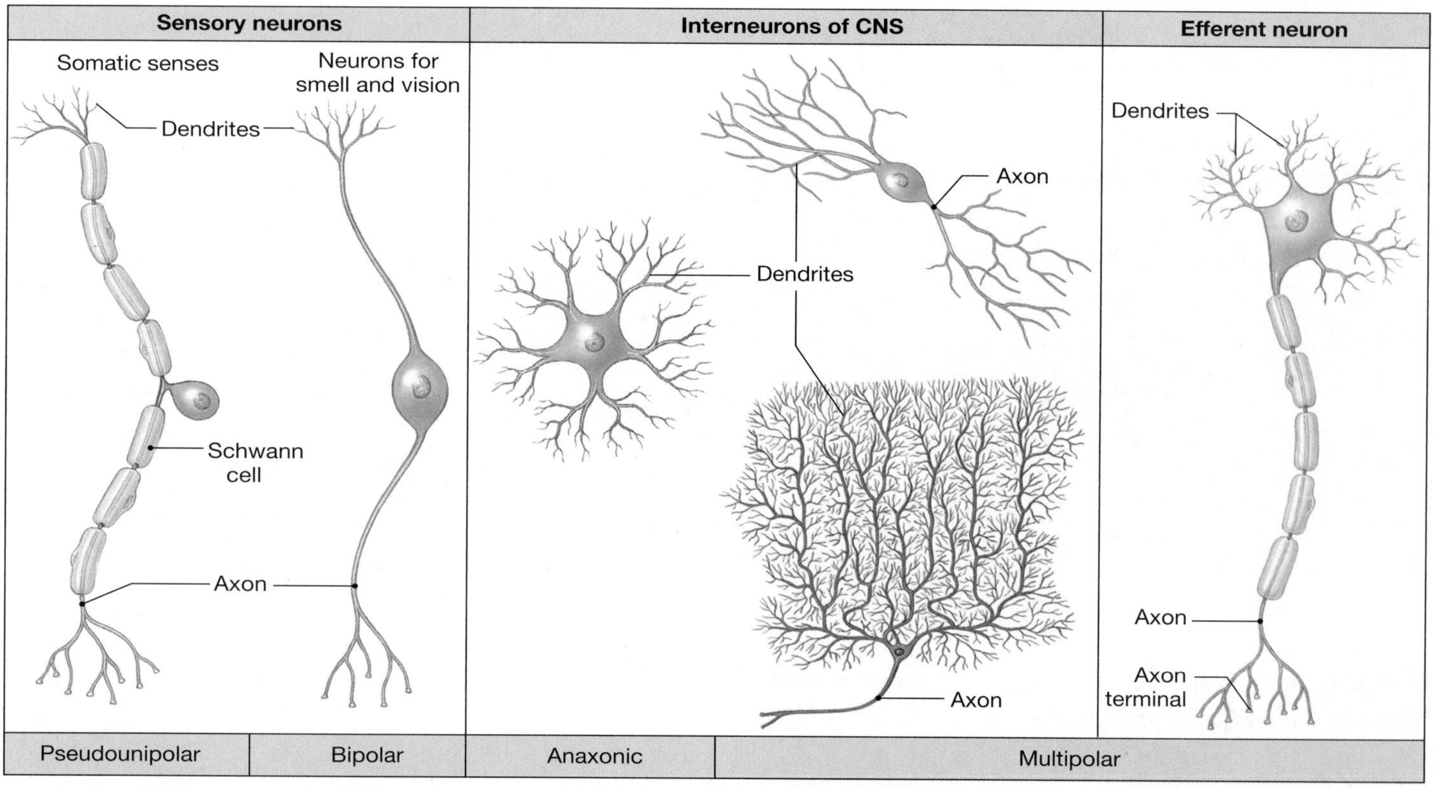

(a) Pseudounipolar neurons have a single process called the axon. During development, the dendrite fused with the axon.

(b) Bipolar neurons have two relatively equal fibers extending off the central cell body.

(c) Anaxonic CNS interneurons have no apparent axon.

(d) Multipolar CNS interneurons are highly branched but lack long extensions.

(e) A typical multipolar efferent neuron has five to seven dendrites, each branching four to six times. A single long axon may branch several times and end at enlarged axon terminals.

● **FIGURE 8-3** ***Anatomic and functional categories of neurons***

but in most neurons the cell body is small, generally making up one-tenth or less of the total cell volume.

Despite its small size, the cell body with its nucleus is essential to the well-being of the cell. If a neuron is cut apart, any sections separated from the cell body are likely to degenerate slowly and die because they lack the cellular machinery to make essential proteins. In an injured somatic motor neuron whose axon has been severed, degeneration of the distal (distant) portions of the neuron results in permanent paralysis of the muscles *innervated* by the neuron. (The term *innervated* means "controlled by a neuron.") If the damaged neuron is a sensory neuron, the person may experience loss of sensation (numbness or tingling) in the region previously innervated by the neuron. Scientists are trying to understand the cellular events that occur when neurons are damaged so that they can develop procedures to repair the functional loss that accompanies spinal cord and other neurological injuries.

Dendrites Receive Incoming Signals Dendrites [*dendron,* tree] are thin, branched processes that receive incoming information from neighboring cells. Dendrites increase the surface area of a neuron, allowing it to communicate with multiple other neurons. The simplest neurons have only a single dendrite. At the other extreme, neurons in the brain may have multiple dendrites with incredibly complex branching (Fig. 8-3d). A dendrite's surface area can be expanded even more by the presence of **dendritic spines** that vary from thin spikes to mushroom-shaped knobs (see Fig. 8-30, p. 285).

The primary function of dendrites in the peripheral nervous system is to receive incoming information and transfer it to an integrating region within the neuron. Within the CNS, dendrite function is more complex. Dendritic spines can function as independent compartments, sending signals back and forth with other neurons in the brain. Many dendritic spines contain polyribosomes and can make their own proteins.

Dendritic spines can change their size and shape in response to input from neighboring cells. Changes in spine morphology are associated with learning and memory as well as with various pathologies, including genetic disorders that cause mental retardation and degenerative diseases such as Alzheimer's disease. Because of these associations, dendritic spines are a hot topic in neuroscience research.

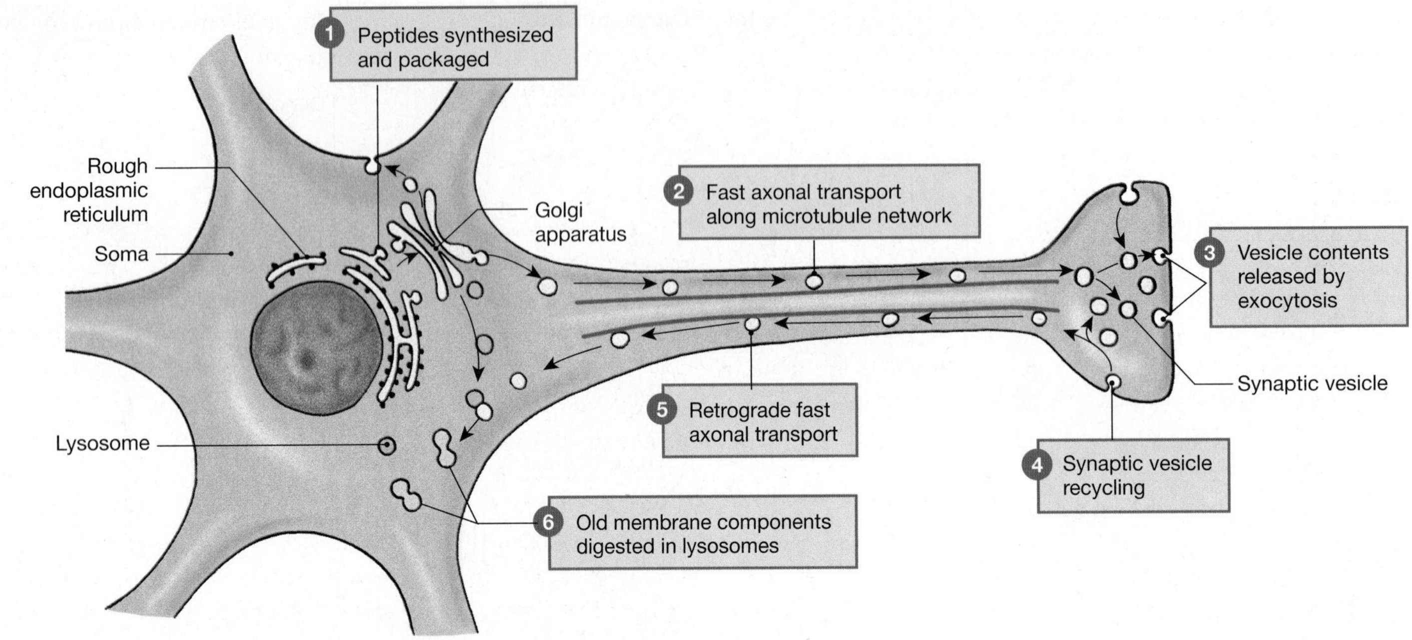
1 Peptides synthesized and packaged
Rough endoplasmic reticulum
Soma
Golgi apparatus
2 Fast axonal transport along microtubule network
3 Vesicle contents released by exocytosis
Synaptic vesicle
Lysosome
5 Retrograde fast axonal transport
4 Synaptic vesicle recycling
6 Old membrane components digested in lysosomes

● **FIGURE 8-4** ***Fast axonal transport moves membranous organelles between cell body and axon terminals.***

Axons Carry Outgoing Signals to the Target Most peripheral neurons have a single axon that originates from a specialized region of the cell body called the **axon hillock** (Fig. 8-2). Axons vary in length from more than a meter to only a few micrometers. They often branch sparsely along their length, forming **collaterals** [*col-*, with + *lateral*, something on the side]. In our model neuron, each collateral ends in a swelling called an **axon terminal**. The axon terminal contains mitochondria and membrane-bound vesicles filled with *neurocrine* molecules [p. 180].

The primary function of an axon is to transmit outgoing electrical signals from the integrating center of the neuron to the end of the axon. At the distal end of the axon, the electrical signal is usually translated into a chemical message by secretion of a neurotransmitter, neuromodulator, or neurohormone. Neurons that secrete neurotransmitters and neuromodulators terminate near their target cells, which are usually other neurons, muscles, or glands.

The region where an axon terminal meets its target cell is called a **synapse** [*syn-*, together + *hapsis*, to join]. The neuron that delivers the signal to the synapse is known as the **presynaptic cell**, and the cell that receives the signal is called the **postsynaptic cell**. The narrow space between the two cells is called the **synaptic cleft**.

RUNNING PROBLEM

In classic Guillain-Barré syndrome, the disease affects both sensory and somatic motor neurons. Dr. McKhann observed that although the Beijing children could not move their muscles, they could feel a pin prick.

Question 2:

Do you think the paralysis found in the Chinese children affected both sensory (afferent) and somatic motor neurons? Why or why not?

247 249 252 273 275 279 287 290

CONCEPT CHECK

2. Where do neurons that secrete neurohormones terminate?
3. Draw a chain of three neurons that synapse on one another in sequence. Label the presynaptic and postsynaptic ends of each neuron, the cell bodies, dendrites, axons, and axon terminals.

Answers: p. 294

Axons are specialized to convey chemical and electrical signals. Their cytoplasm is filled with many types of fibers and filaments but lacks ribosomes and endoplasmic reticulum. For this reason, any proteins destined for the axon or the axon terminal must be synthesized on the rough endoplasmic reticulum in the cell body. The proteins are then moved down the axon by a process known as **axonal transport**.

Slow axonal transport moves material by **axoplasmic** (cytoplasmic) **flow** from the cell body to the axon terminal. Material moves at a rate of only 0.2–2.5 mm/day, which means that slow transport can only be used for components that are not consumed rapidly by the cell, such as enzymes and cytoskeleton proteins.

Fast axonal transport moves organelles at rates of up to 400 mm (about 15.75 in.) per day (Fig. 8-4 ●). The neuron uses stationary microtubules as tracks along which transported vesicles and mitochondria "walk" with the aid of attached footlike motor proteins. These motor proteins alternately bind and unbind to the microtubules with the help of ATP, stepping their organelles along the axon in a stop-and-go fashion. The role of motor proteins in axonal transport is similar to their role in muscle contraction and in the movement of chromosomes during cell division.

Fast axonal transport goes in two directions. Forward (or *anterograde*) transport moves synaptic and secretory vesicles and mitochondria from the cell body to the axon terminal. Backward (or *retrograde*) transport returns old cellular components from the axon terminal to the cell body for recycling. There is evidence that nerve growth factors and some viruses also reach the cell body by fast retrograde transport.

Glial Cells Provide Support for Neurons

Glial cells [*glia,* glue] are the unsung heroes of the nervous system, outnumbering neurons by 10–50 to 1. For many years scientists thought that glial cells' primary function was physical support and that they had little influence on information processing. That view has changed. Although glial cells do not participate directly in the transmission of electrical signals over long distances, they do communicate with and provide important biochemical support to neurons. The peripheral nervous system has two types of glial cells—Schwann cells and satellite cells—and the CNS has four types: oligodendrocytes, microglia, astrocytes, and ependymal cells (Fig. 8-5 ●).

Neural tissue secretes very little extracellular matrix [p. 80], and glial cells provide structural stability to neurons by wrapping around them. **Schwann cells** in the PNS and **oligodendrocytes** in the CNS support and insulate axons by forming **myelin**, a substance composed of multiple concentric layers of phospholipid membrane (Fig. 8-6 ●). In addition to providing support, the myelin acts as insulation around axons and speeds up their signal transmission.

Myelin forms when these glial cells wrap around an axon, squeezing out the glial cytoplasm so that each wrap becomes two membrane layers (Fig. 8-6a). As an analogy, think of wrapping a deflated balloon tightly around a pencil. Some neurons have as many as 150 wraps (300 membrane layers) in the myelin sheath that surrounds their axons. Gap junctions connect the membrane layers and allow flow of nutrients and information from layer to layer.

One difference between oligodendrocytes and Schwann cells is the number of axons each cell wraps around. In the CNS, one oligodendrocyte forms myelin around portions of several axons (Fig. 8-5a). In the peripheral nervous system, one Schwann cell associates with one axon, and a single axon may have as many as 500 different Schwann cells along its length. Each Schwann cell wraps around a 1–1.5 mm segment of the axon, leaving tiny gaps, called the **nodes of Ranvier**, between the myelin-insulated areas (Fig. 8-6b). At each node a tiny section of axon membrane remains in direct contact with the extracellular fluid, so the nodes play an important role in the transmission of electrical signals along the axon.

The second type of PNS glial cell, the **satellite cell**, is a nonmyelinating Schwann cell. Satellite cells form supportive capsules around nerve cell bodies located in ganglia. A **ganglion** [cluster or knot] is a cluster of nerve cell bodies found outside the CNS. Ganglia appear as knots or swellings along a nerve. A cluster of nerve cells bodies inside the CNS is the equivalent of a peripheral ganglion, but is known as a **nucleus** [plural, *nuclei*].

All glial cells communicate with neurons and with one another primarily through chemical signals. Glial-derived growth and *trophic* (nourishing) factors help maintain neurons and guide them during repair and development. Glial cells in turn respond to neurotransmitters and neuromodulators secreted by neurons. Glial cell function is an active area of neuroscience research, and scientists are still exploring the roles these important cells play in the nervous system.

Astrocytes [*astron,* a star] are highly branched glial cells that by some estimates make up about half of all cells in the brain. They come in several subtypes and they form a functional network by communicating with one another through gap junctions. Astrocytes have multiple roles. The terminals of some astrocyte processes are closely associated with synapses, where they take up and release chemicals. Astrocytes also provide neurons with substrates for ATP production, and they help maintain homeostasis in the CNS extracellular fluid by taking up K^+ and water. Finally, the terminals of some astrocyte processes surround blood vessels and become part of the so-called *blood-brain barrier* that regulates the movement of materials between blood and extracellular fluid.

The glial cells known as **microglia** are specialized immune cells that reside permanently in the CNS. When activated, they remove damaged cells and foreign invaders. However, it now appears that microglia are not always helpful. Activated microglia sometimes release damaging *reactive oxygen species (ROS)* that form free radicals [p. 23]. The *oxidative stress* caused by ROS is believed to contribute to neurodegenerative diseases such as *amyotrophic lateral sclerosis* (*ALS,* also known as Lou Gehrig's disease).

Adults Have Neural Stem Cells

The final class of glial cells is the **ependymal cells,** specialized cells that create a selectively permeable epithelial layer, the *ependyma,* that separates the fluid compartments of the CNS (Fig. 8-5a). The ependyma is one source of **neural stem cells** [p. 85], immature cells that can differentiate into neurons and glial cells.

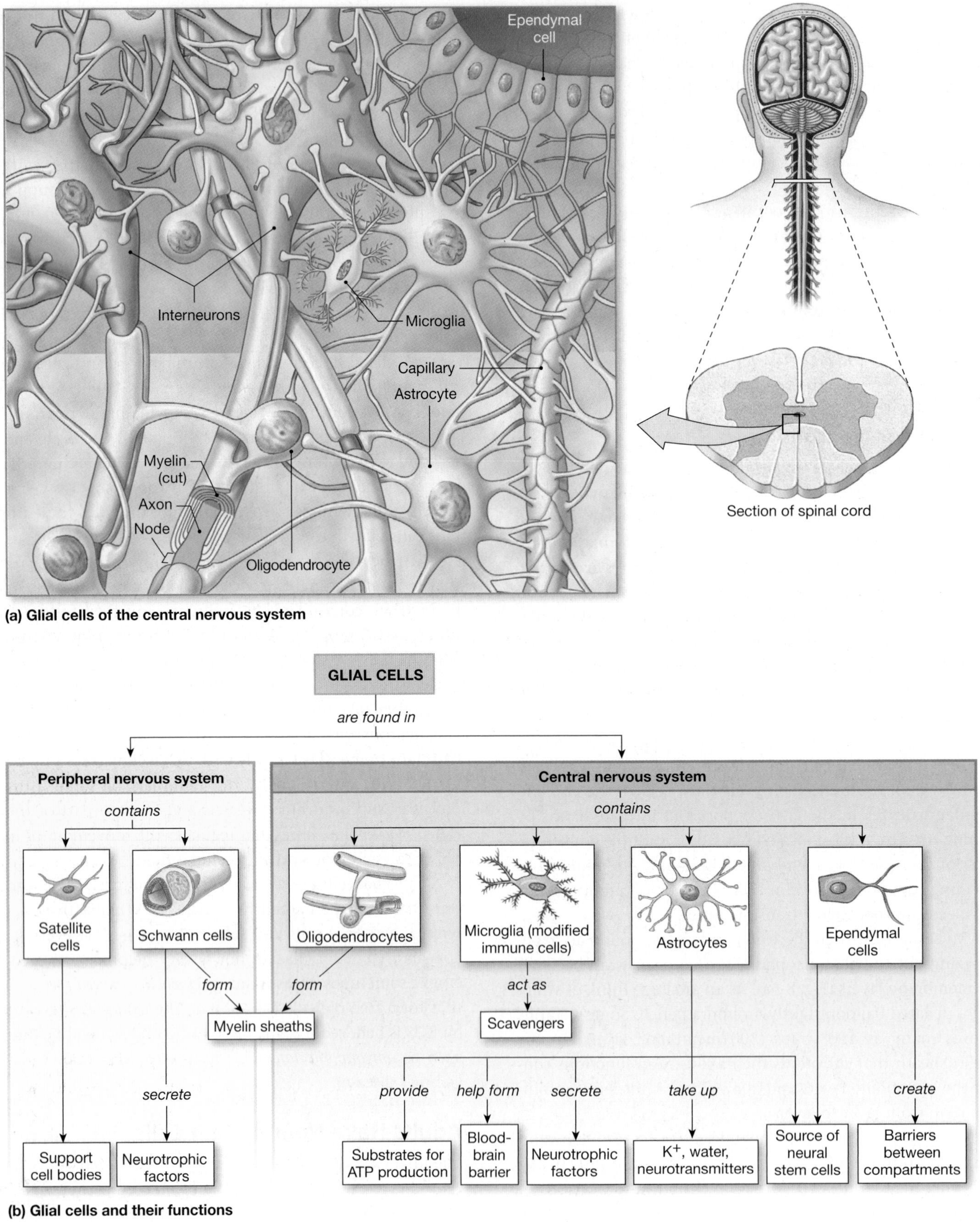

(a) Glial cells of the central nervous system

(b) Glial cells and their functions

● **FIGURE 8-5** ***Glial cells provide physical and biochemical support for neurons.***

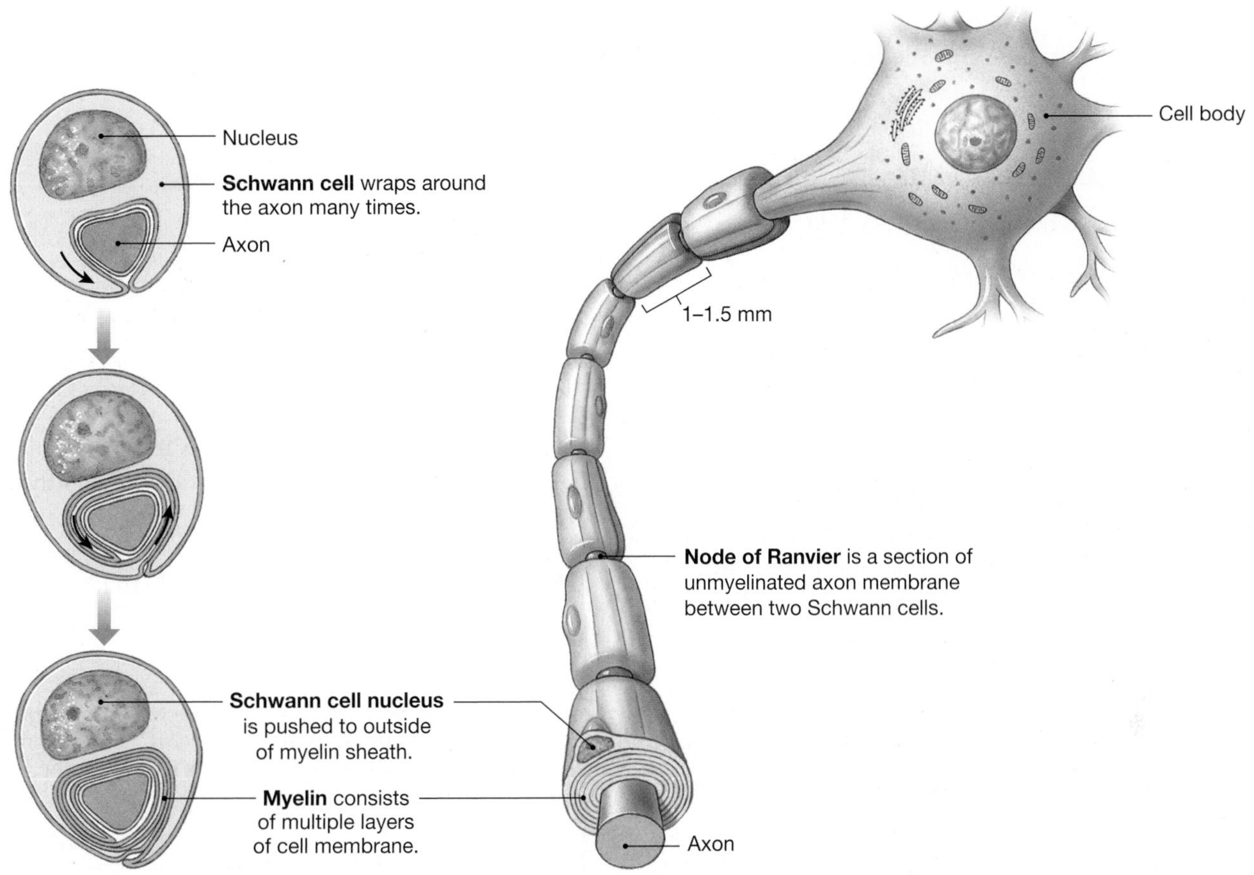
Nucleus
Schwann cell wraps around the axon many times.
Axon
Schwann cell nucleus is pushed to outside of myelin sheath.
Myelin consists of multiple layers of cell membrane.
Cell body
1–1.5 mm
Node of Ranvier is a section of unmyelinated axon membrane between two Schwann cells.
Axon

(a) Myelin formation in the peripheral nervous system

(b) Each Schwann cell forms myelin around a small segment of one axon.

FIGURE 8-6 ***Schwann cells form myelin around peripheral neurons.***

Scientists once believed that if a neuron died, it could never be replaced. The discovery of neural stem cells changed that view. During early development, an undifferentiated cell layer called *neuroepithelium* lines the lumen of the neural tube, a structure that will later become the brain and spinal cord. As development proceeds, some cells migrate out of the neuroepithelium and differentiate into neurons. Other cells bordering the lumen of the neural tube specialize into the epithelium of the ependyma. However, among the ependymal cells and in the subependymal layer, some neural stem cells remain unspecialized, waiting until they are called upon to replace damaged cells. Neural stem cells have also been found in other parts of the body, including the *hippocampus* of the brain and the enteric nervous system of the gut.

When neural stem cells receive the correct signals, they transform into neurons and glial cells. Scientists are working intensely to learn how to control this transformation, in the hope that stem cell transplants can reverse the loss of function that comes with degenerative neurological diseases. Most of these studies are being done with mice and rats, but in late 2006, the first stem cell transplant into a human brain took place. The patient was a child suffering from Batten disease, a fatal lysosomal enzyme disorder similar to Tay-Sachs [p. 94], and physicians hoped the transplanted neural stem cells would produce the missing enzymes. Within the year, another five patients with Batten disease also received transplants. It is still too early to know whether the stem cells will mature and treat the disease.

CONCEPT CHECK

4. What is the primary function of each of the following: myelin, microglia, ependymal cells?
5. Name the two glial cell types that form myelin. How do they differ from each other?

Answers: p. 294

ELECTRICAL SIGNALS IN NEURONS

The property of nerve and muscle cells that characterizes them as *excitable tissues* is their ability to propagate electrical signals rapidly in response to a stimulus. We now know that many other cell types generate electrical signals to initiate intracellular processes (see insulin secretion, p. 171), but the ability of nerve and muscle cells to send a constant electrical signal over long distance is characteristic of electrical signaling in these tissues.

TABLE 8-2 Ion Concentrations and Equilibrium Potentials

ION	EXTRACELLULAR FLUID (mM)	INTRACELLULAR FLUID (mM)	E_{ion} AT 37° C
K^+	5 mM (normal range: 3.5–5)	150 mM	−90 mV
Na^+	145 mM (normal range: 135–145)	15 mM	+60 mV
Cl^-	108 mM (normal range: 100–108)	10 mM (range: 5–15)	−63 mV
Ca^{2+}	1 mM	0.0001 mM	see Concept Check question 6

The Nernst Equation Predicts Membrane Potential for a Single Ion

Recall from Chapter 5 that all living cells have a resting membrane potential (V_m) [p. 166] that results from the uneven distribution of ions across the cell membrane. Two factors influence the membrane potential:

1. *Concentration gradients of ions* across the membrane. Normally, sodium (Na^+), chloride (Cl^-), and calcium (Ca^{2+}) are more concentrated in the extracellular fluid than in the cytosol. Potassium (K^+) is more concentrated in the cytosol than in the extracellular fluid.
2. *Membrane permeability to those ions.* The resting cell membrane is much more permeable to K^+ than to Na^+ or Ca^{2+}. This makes K^+ the major ion contributing to the resting membrane potential.

Chapter 5 introduced the *Nernst equation,* which describes the membrane potential that a single ion would produce if the membrane were permeable to only that one ion [p. 168]. For any one ion, this membrane potential is called the *equilibrium potential* of the ion (E_{ion}):

$$E_{ion}\ (\text{in mV}) = \frac{61}{z}\log\frac{[\text{ion}]_{out}}{[\text{ion}]_{in}}$$

where:

61 is 2.303 *RT/F* at 37° C,

z is the electrical charge on the ion (+1 for K^+), and

$[\text{ion}]_{out}$ and $[\text{ion}]_{in}$ are the ion concentrations outside and inside the cell.

(*R* is the ideal gas constant, *T* is absolute temperature, and *F* is the Faraday constant. For additional information on these values, see Appendix B.)

When we use the estimated intracellular and extracellular concentrations for K^+ (Tbl. 8-2 ●) in the Nernst equation, the equation predicts a potassium equilibrium potential, or E_K, of −90 mV. However, an average value for the resting membrane potential of neurons is −70 mV (inside the cell relative to outside), more positive than predicted by the potassium equilibrium potential. This means that other ions must be contributing to the membrane potential. Neurons at rest are slightly permeable to Na^+, and the leak of positive Na^+ into the cell makes the resting membrane potential slightly more positive than it would be if the cell were permeable only to K^+.

CONCEPT CHECK

6. Given the values in Table 8-2, use the Nernst equation to calculate the equilibrium potential for Ca^{2+}. Use the information about logarithms given in Appendix B, and try the calculations without a calculator. Answers: p. 294

The GHK Equation Predicts Membrane Potential Using Multiple Ions

The **Goldman-Hodgkin-Katz (GHK) equation** is used to calculate the resting membrane potential that results from the contribution of all ions that can cross the membrane. The GHK equation includes membrane permeability values because the permeability of an ion influences its contribution to the membrane potential. If the membrane is not permeable to an ion, that ion does not affect the membrane potential.

For mammalian cells, we assume that Na^+, K^+, and Cl^- are the three ions that influence membrane potential in resting cells. Each ion's contribution to the membrane potential is proportional to its ability to cross the membrane. The GHK equation for cells that are permeable to Na^+, K^+, and Cl^- is

$$V_m = 61\log\frac{P_K[K^+]_{out} + P_{Na}[Na^+]_{out} + P_{Cl}[Cl^-]_{in}}{P_K[K^+]_{in} + P_{Na}[Na^+]_{in} + P_{Cl}[Cl^-]_{out}}$$

where:

V_m is the resting membrane potential in mV at 37° C,

61 is 2.303 *RT/F* at 37° C,

P is the relative permeability of the membrane to the ion shown in the subscript, and

$[\text{ion}]_{out}$ and $[\text{ion}]_{in}$ are the ion concentrations outside and inside the cell.

Although this equation looks quite intimidating, it can be simplified into words to say: Resting membrane potential is determined by the combined contributions of the (concentration gradient × membrane permeability) for each ion.

If the membrane is not permeable to an ion, the permeability value for that ion is zero, and the ion drops out of the equation. For example, cells at rest normally are not permeable to Ca^{2+}, and therefore Ca^{2+} is not part of the GHK equation.

The GHK equation predicts resting membrane potentials based on given ion concentrations and membrane permeabilities, and it explains how the cell's slight permeability to Na^+ makes the resting membrane potential more positive than the E_K determined with the Nernst equation. The GHK equation can also be used to predict what happens to the membrane potential when ion concentrations or membrane permeabilities change.

Ion Movement Creates Electrical Signals

The resting membrane potential of living cells is determined primarily by the K^+ concentration gradient and the cell's resting permeability to K^+, Na^+, and Cl^-. A change in either the K^+ concentration gradient or ion permeabilities changes the membrane potential. For example, at rest, the cell membrane of a neuron is only slightly permeable to Na^+. However, if the membrane suddenly increases its Na^+ permeability, Na^+ enters the cell, moving down its electrochemical gradient [p. 166]. The addition of positive Na^+ to the intracellular fluid *depolarizes* the cell membrane and creates an electrical signal [Fig. 5-34, p. 169].

The movement of ions across the membrane can also *hyperpolarize* a cell. If the cell membrane suddenly becomes more permeable to K^+, positive charge is lost from inside the cell and the cell becomes more negative (hyperpolarizes). A cell may also hyperpolarize if negatively charged ions, such as Cl^-, enter the cell from the extracellular fluid.

CONCEPT CHECK

7. Would a cell with a resting membrane potential of −70 mV depolarize or hyperpolarize in the following cases? (You must consider both the concentration gradient and the electrical gradient of the ion to determine net ion movement.)
   (a) Cell becomes more permeable to Ca^{2+}.
   (b) Cell becomes less permeable to K^+.
8. Would the cell membrane depolarize or hyperpolarize if a small amount of Na^+ leaked into the cell? Answers: p. 294

It is important to understand that a change in membrane potential from −70 mV to a positive value, such as +30 mV, *does not mean that the ion concentration gradients have reversed!* A significant change in membrane potential occurs with the movement of very few ions. For example, to change the membrane potential by 100 mV, only 1 of every 100,000 K^+ must enter or leave the cell. This is such a tiny fraction of the total number of K^+ in the cell that the intracellular concentration of K^+ remains essentially unchanged even though the membrane potential has changed by 100 mV.

An analogous situation is moving one grain of sand from a beach into your eye. There are so many grains of sand on the beach that the loss of one grain is not significant, just as the movement of one K^+ across the cell membrane does not significantly alter the concentration of K^+. However, the electrical signal created by moving a few K^+ across the membrane has a significant effect on the cell's membrane potential, just as getting that one grain of sand in your eye creates significant discomfort.

Gated Channels Control the Ion Permeability of the Neuron

How does a cell change its ion permeability? The simplest way is to open or close existing channels in the membrane. Neurons contain a variety of gated ion channels that alternate between open and closed states, depending on the intracellular and extracellular conditions [p. 144]. A slower method for changing membrane permeability is for the cell to insert new channels into the membrane or remove some existing channels.

Ion channels are usually named according to the primary ion(s) they allow to pass through them. There are four major types of selective ion channels in the neuron: (1) Na^+ channels, (2) K^+ channels, (3) Ca^{2+} channels, and (4) Cl^- channels. Other channels are less selective, such as the monovalent cation channels that allow both Na^+ and K^+ to pass.

The ease with which ions flow through a channel is called the channel's **conductance** [*conductus,* escort]. Channel conductance varies with the gating state of the channel and with the channel protein isoform. As described in Chapter 5, some ion channels, such as the *K^+ leak channels* that are the major determinant of resting membrane potential, spend most of their time in an open state. Other channels have gates that open or close in response to particular stimuli:

1. **Mechanically gated ion channels** are found in sensory neurons and open in response to physical forces such as pressure or stretch.
2. **Chemically gated ion channels** in most neurons respond to a variety of ligands, such as extracellular neurotransmitters and neuromodulators or intracellular signal molecules.
3. **Voltage-gated ion channels** respond to changes in the cell's membrane potential. These channels play an important role in the initiation and conduction of electrical signals.

Not all channels behave in exactly the same way. The **threshold voltage**, or minimum stimulus [p. 200], for channel opening varies from one channel type to another. For example, some channels we think of as leak channels are actually voltage-gated channels that remain open in the voltage range of the resting membrane potential.

CLINICAL FOCUS

CHANNELOPATHIES

Ion channels are proteins, and like other proteins they may lose or change function if their amino acid sequence is altered. **Channelopathies** [*pathos,* suffering] are inherited diseases caused by mutations in ion channel proteins. Because ion channels are so intimately linked to the electrical activity of cells, many channelopathies manifest themselves as disorders of the excitable tissues (nerve and muscle). One significant contribution of molecular biology to medicine was the discovery that what the medical community considers to be one disease can actually be a family of related diseases with different causes but similar symptoms. For example, the condition known as *long Q-T syndrome* (LQTS; named for changes in the electrocardiogram test) is a cardiac problem characterized by an irregular heart beat (*arrhythmia; a–,* without), fainting, and sometimes sudden death. Scientists have identified eight different gene mutations in K^+, Na^+, or Ca^{2+} channels that result in various subtypes of LQTS. Other well-known channelopathies include some forms of epilepsy and malignant hyperthermia. The most common channelopathy is cystic fibrosis, which results from defects in chloride channel function (see Chapter 5 Running Problem).

The speed with which a gated channel opens and closes also differs among different types of channels. Channel opening to allow ion flow is called channel *activation*. For example, Na^+ channels and K^+ channels of axons are both activated by cell depolarization. The Na^+ channels open very rapidly, but the K^+ channels are slower to open. The result is an initial flow of Na^+ across the membrane, followed later by a flow of K^+.

Many channels that open in response to depolarization close only when the cell repolarizes. The gating portion of the channel protein has an electrical charge that moves the gate between open and closed positions as membrane potential changes. This is like a spring-loaded door that opens when you push on it, then closes when you release it.

But some channels that open with a stimulus close even though the activating stimulus continues, a process known as *inactivation*. This is similar to doors with an automatic open-close mechanism. The door opens when you hit the button, then after a certain period of time, it closes itself, whether you are still standing in the doorway or not. An inactivated channel returns to its normal closed state shortly after the membrane repolarizes. The specific mechanisms underlying channel inactivation vary with different channel types.

Each major channel type has several to many subtypes with varying properties, and the list of subtypes gets longer each year. Within each subtype there may be multiple isoforms that express different opening and closing *kinetics* [*kinetikos,* moving] and associated proteins that modify channel properties. In addition, channel activity can be modulated by chemical factors that bind to the channel protein, such as phosphate groups.

Changes in Channel Permeability Create Electrical Signals

When ion channels open, ions may move into or out of the cell. The flow of electrical charge carried by an ion is called the ion's **current**, abbreviated $\mathbf{I_{ion}}$. The direction of ion movement depends on the *electrochemical* (combined concentration and electrical) gradient of the ion. Potassium ions usually move out of the cell. Na^+, Cl^-, and Ca^{2+} usually flow into the cell. The net flow of ions across the membrane depolarizes or hyperpolarizes the cell, creating an electrical signal.

Electrical signals can be classified into two basic types: graded potentials and action potentials (Table 8-3 ●). **Graded potentials** are variable-strength signals that travel over short distances and lose strength as they travel through the cell. They are used for short-distance communication. If a depolarizing graded potential is strong enough when it reaches an integrating region within a neuron, the graded potential initiates an action potential. **Action potentials** are very brief, large depolarizations that travel for long distances through a neuron without losing strength. Their function is rapid signaling over long distances.

Graded Potentials Reflect Stimulus Strength

Graded potentials in neurons are depolarizations or hyperpolarizations that occur in the dendrites and cell body or, less frequently, near the axon terminals. These changes in membrane potential are called "graded" because their size, or *amplitude* [*amplitudo,* large], is directly proportional to the strength of the triggering event. A large stimulus causes a strong graded potential, and a small stimulus results in a weak graded potential.

In neurons of the CNS and the efferent division, graded potentials occur when chemical signals from other neurons open chemically gated ion channels, allowing ions to enter or leave the neuron. Mechanical stimuli (such as stretch) open ion channels in some sensory neurons. Graded potentials may also occur when an open channel closes, decreasing the movement of ions through the cell membrane. For example, if K^+ channels close, fewer K^+ leave the cell, and the retention of K^+ depolarizes the cell.

TABLE 8-3 Comparison of Graded Potential and Action Potential in Neurons

	GRADED POTENTIAL	ACTION POTENTIAL
Type of signal	Input signal	Regenerating conduction signal
Occurs where?	Usually dendrites and cell body	Trigger zone through axon
Types of gated ion channels involved	Mechanically, chemically, or voltage-gated channels	Voltage-gated channels
Ions involved	Usually Na^+, Cl^-, Ca^{2+}	Na^+ and K^+
Type of signal	Depolarizing (e.g., Na^+) or hyperpolarizing (e.g., Cl^-)	Depolarizing
Strength of signal	Depends on initial stimulus; can be summed	All-or-none phenomenon; cannot be summed
What initiates the signal?	Entry of ions through channels	Above-threshold graded potential at the trigger zone
Unique characteristics	No minimum level required to initiate	Threshold stimulus required to initiate
	Two signals coming close together in time will sum	Refractory period: two signals too close together in time cannot sum
	Initial stimulus strength is indicated by frequency of a series of action potentials	

CONCEPT CHECK

9. Match each ion's movement with the type of graded potential it creates.

(a) Na^+ entry 1. depolarizing
(b) Cl^- entry 2. hyperpolarizing
(c) K^+ exit
(d) Ca^{2+} entry

Answers: p. 294

Figure 8-7 ● shows a graded potential that begins when a stimulus opens monovalent cation channels on the cell body of a neuron. Sodium ions move into the neuron, bringing in electrical energy. The positive charge carried in by the Na^+ spreads as a wave of depolarization through the cytoplasm, just as a stone thrown into water creates ripples or waves that spread outward from the point of entry. The wave of depolarization that moves through the cell is known as **local current flow**. By convention, current in biological systems is the net movement of *positive* electrical charge.

The strength of the initial depolarization in a graded potential is determined by how much charge enters the cell, just as the size of waves caused by a stone tossed in water is determined by the size of the stone. If more Na^+ channels open, more Na^+ enters, and the graded potential has a higher initial amplitude. The stronger the initial amplitude, the farther the graded potential can spread through the neuron before dying out.

Why do graded potentials lose strength as they move through the cytoplasm? There are two reasons:

1. *Current leak*. Some of the positive ions leak back across the membrane as the depolarization wave moves through the cell. The membrane in the neuron cell body is not a good insulator and has open leak channels that allow positive charge to flow out into the extracellular fluid.
2. *Cytoplasmic resistance*. The cytoplasm itself provides resistance to the flow of electricity, just as water creates resistance that diminishes the waves from the stone. The combination of current leak and cytoplasmic resistance means that the strength of the signal inside the cell decreases over distance.

Graded potentials that are strong enough eventually reach the region of the neuron known as the **trigger zone**. In efferent neurons and interneurons, the trigger zone is the axon hillock and the very first part of the axon, a region known as the **initial segment** (see Fig. 8-2). In sensory neurons, the trigger zone is immediately adjacent to the receptor, where the dendrites join the axon.

CONCEPT CHECK

10. Identify the trigger zones of the neurons illustrated in Figure 8-3, if possible.

Answers: p. 294

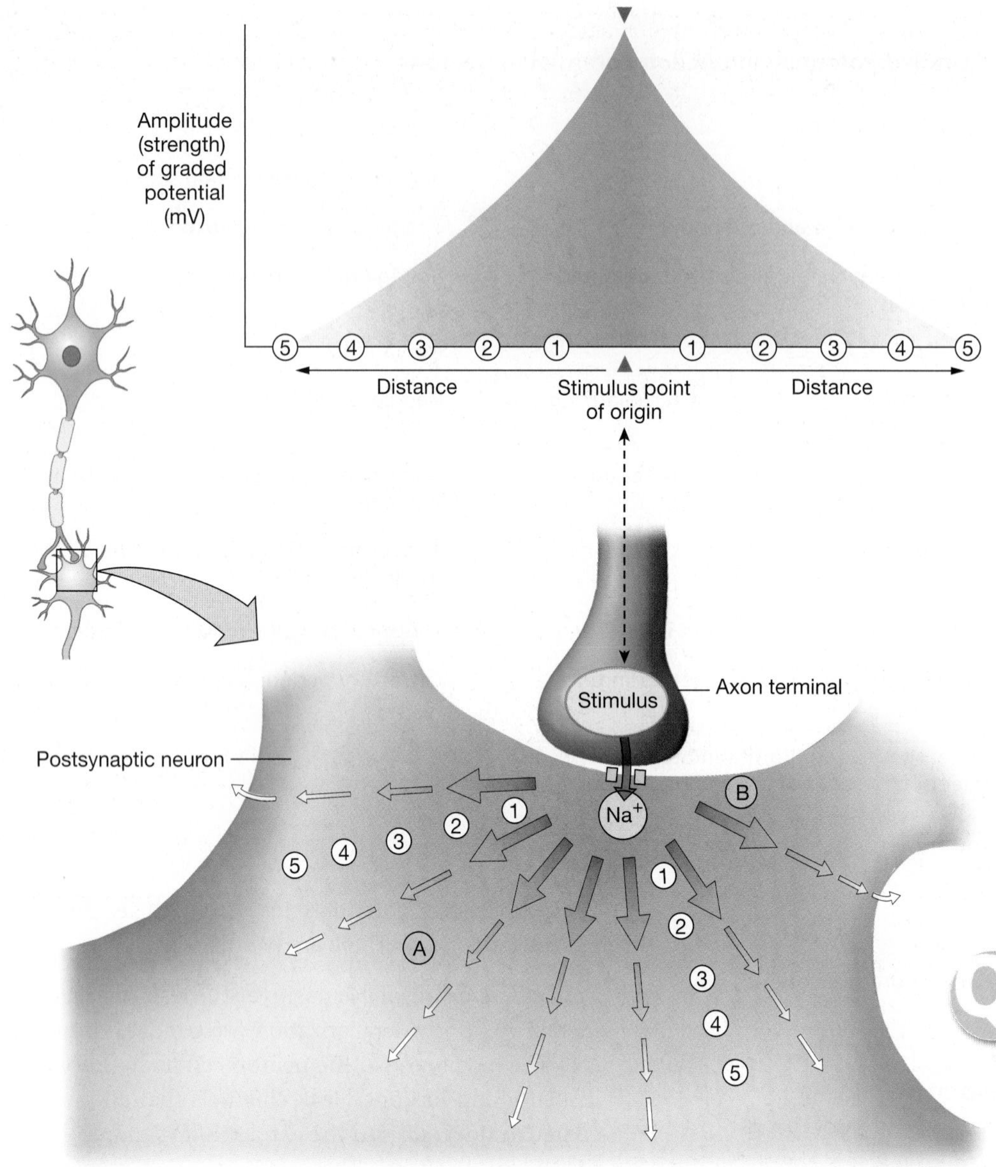

FIGURE QUESTION

At which point of the neuron will the graded potential be stronger, A or B? On the curve of the graph, mark and label the approximate locations of A and B.

● **FIGURE 8-7** ***Graded potentials decrease in strength as they spread out from the point of origin.***

The trigger zone is the integrating center of the neuron and contains a high concentration of voltage-gated Na^+ channels in its membrane. If graded potentials reaching the trigger zone depolarize the membrane to the threshold voltage, voltage-gated Na^+ channels open, and an action potential is initiated. If the depolarization does not reach threshold, the graded potential simply dies out as it moves into the axon.

Because depolarization makes a neuron more likely to fire an action potential, depolarizing graded potentials are considered to be *excitatory*. A hyperpolarizing graded potential moves the membrane potential farther from the threshold value and makes the neuron less likely to fire an action potential. Consequently, hyperpolarizing graded potentials are considered to be *inhibitory*.

Figure 8-8 ● shows a neuron with three recording electrodes placed at intervals along the cell body and trigger zone. In Figure 8-8a, a single stimulus triggers a *subthreshold* graded potential, one that is below threshold by the time it reaches the trigger zone. Although the cell is depolarized to −40 mV at the site where the graded potential begins, the current decreases as it travels through the cell body. As a result, the graded potential is below threshold by the time it reaches the trigger zone. (For the typical mammalian neuron, threshold is about −55 mV.) The stimulus is not strong enough to depolarize the cell to threshold at the trigger zone, and the graded potential dies out without triggering an action potential.

Figure 8-8b shows a stronger initial stimulus that initiates a stronger depolarization and ultimately causes an action potential. Although this graded potential also diminishes with

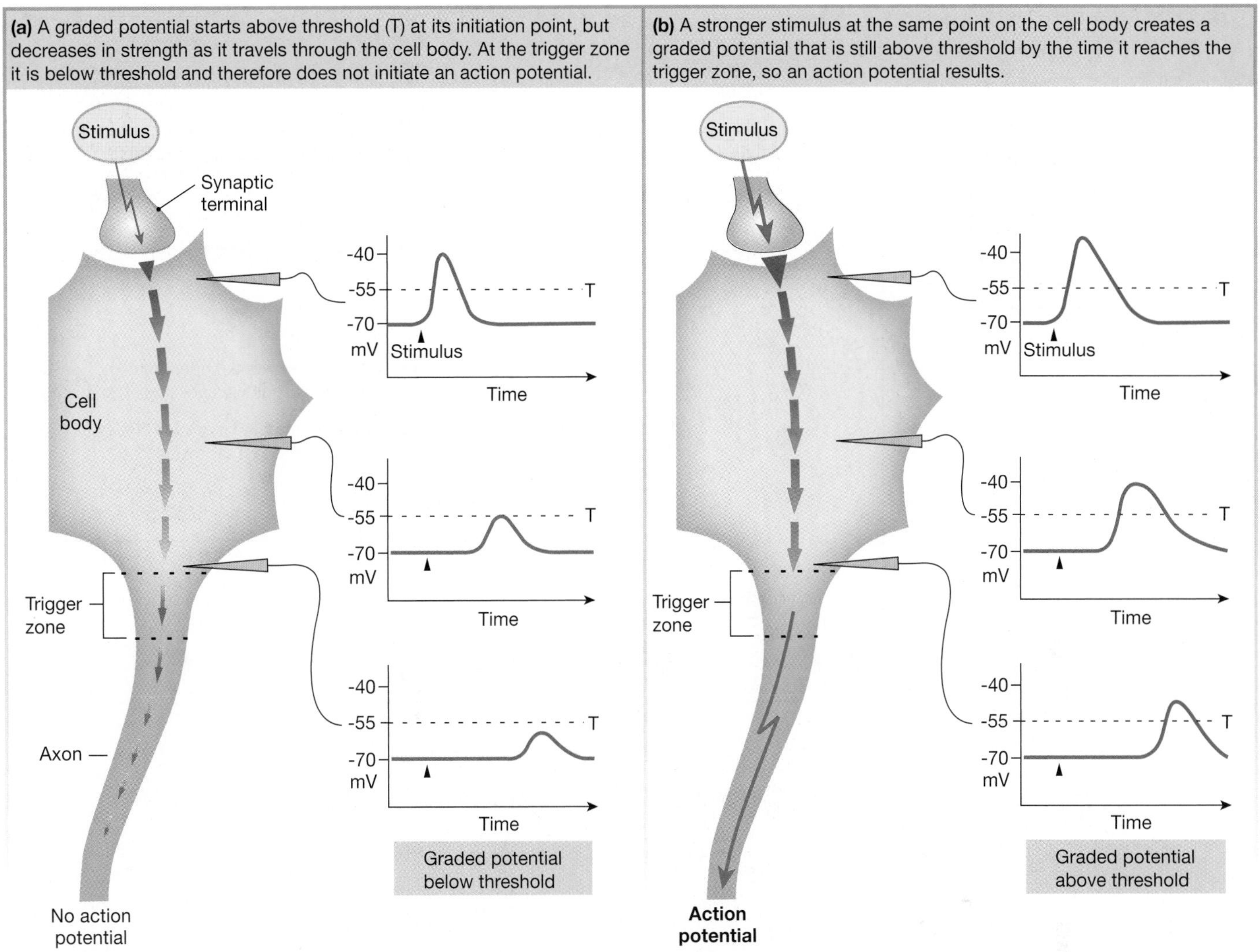
(a) A graded potential starts above threshold (T) at its initiation point, but decreases in strength as it travels through the cell body. At the trigger zone it is below threshold and therefore does not initiate an action potential.
(b) A stronger stimulus at the same point on the cell body creates a graded potential that is still above threshold by the time it reaches the trigger zone, so an action potential results.
Stimulus
Synaptic terminal
Cell body
Trigger zone
Axon
-40
-55
-70
mV
T
Stimulus
Time
Graded potential below threshold
No action potential
Graded potential above threshold
Action potential

● **FIGURE 8-8** ***Subthreshold and suprathreshold graded potentials in a neuron.*** In (a), the graded potential is below the threshold value (T) of −55 mV as it reaches the trigger zone. In (b), the graded potential is above the threshold value when it reaches the trigger zone.

distance through the neuron, its higher initial strength ensures that it is above threshold at the trigger zone. In this example, an action potential is triggered.

Action Potentials Travel Long Distances

Action potentials, also known as *spikes,* differ from graded potentials in that they do not diminish in strength as they travel through the neuron. The ability of a neuron to respond rapidly to a stimulus and fire an action potential is called the cell's **excitability**.

Recordings of neuronal action potentials show them to be depolarizations of about 100 mV amplitude. The strength of the graded potential that initiates an action potential has no influence on the amplitude of the action potential. Action potentials are sometimes called **all-or-none** phenomena because they either occur as a maximal depolarization (if the stimulus reaches threshold) or do not occur at all (if the stimulus is below threshold). An action potential measured at the distal end of an axon is identical to the action potential that started at the trigger zone. This property is essential for the transmission of signals over long distances, such as from a fingertip to the spinal cord.

The explanation of action potential firing that follows is typical of what goes on in PNS neurons. In this simple but elegant mechanism, for whose description A. L. Hodgkin and A. F. Huxley won a 1963 Nobel prize, a *suprathreshold* (above-threshold) stimulus causes an action potential, as you saw in Figure 8-8b. These action potentials require only two types of gated ion channels: a voltage-gated Na^+ channel and a voltage-gated K^+ channel, plus some leak channels that help set the resting membrane potential.

The process of electrical signaling in the CNS can be much more complex, however. Brain neurons show different electrical

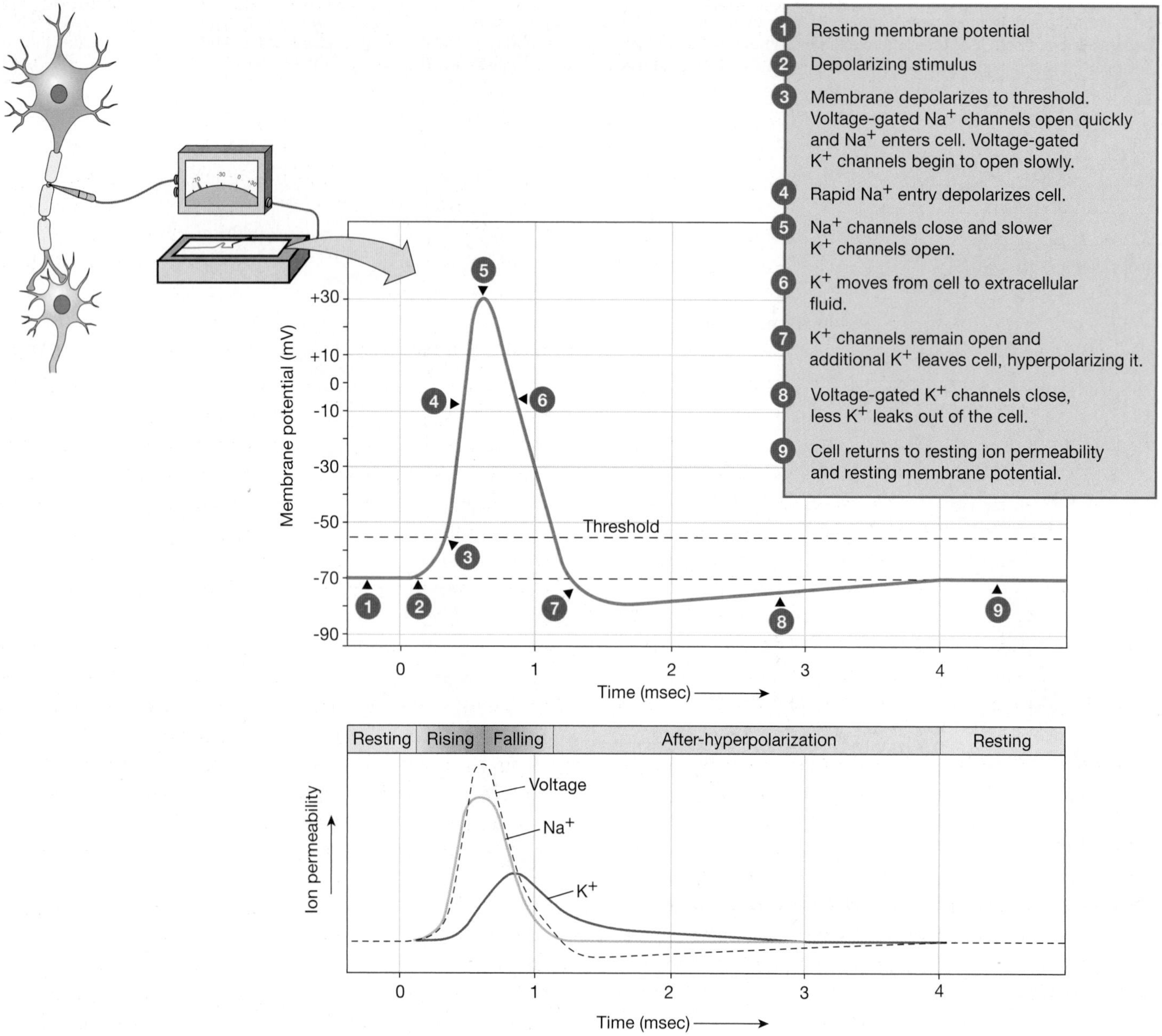
1 Resting membrane potential
2 Depolarizing stimulus
3 Membrane depolarizes to threshold. Voltage-gated Na+ channels open quickly and Na+ enters cell. Voltage-gated K+ channels begin to open slowly.
4 Rapid Na+ entry depolarizes cell.
5 Na+ channels close and slower K+ channels open.
6 K+ moves from cell to extracellular fluid.
7 K+ channels remain open and additional K+ leaves cell, hyperpolarizing it.
8 Voltage-gated K+ channels close, less K+ leaks out of the cell.
9 Cell returns to resting ion permeability and resting membrane potential.
Membrane potential (mV)
+30
+10
0
-10
-30
-50
-70
-90
Threshold
Time (msec)
Resting
Rising
Falling
After-hyperpolarization
Resting
Voltage
Na+
K+
Ion permeability
Time (msec)

● **FIGURE 8-9** ***Voltage and ion permeability changes during the action potential.***

personalities by firing action potentials in a variety of patterns, and sometimes without requiring an external stimulus to bring them to threshold. For example, neurons can be *tonically active* [p. 196], firing regular trains of action potentials (beating pacemakers), or they can exhibit *bursting,* bursts of action potentials rhythmically alternating with intervals of quiet (rhythmic pacemakers).

These different firing patterns are created by ion channel variants that differ in their activation and inactivation voltages, opening and closing speeds, and sensitivity to neuromodulators. This variability makes brain neurons more dynamic and complicated than the simple somatic motor neuron we will use as our model in the discussion that follows.

Na^+ and K^+ Move Across the Membrane During Action Potentials

Action potentials occur when voltage-gated ion channels open, altering membrane permeability to Na^+ and K^+. Figure 8-9 ● shows the voltage and ion permeability changes that take place in one section of membrane during an action potential. The graph can be divided into three phases: the rising phase of the action potential, the falling phase, and the after-hyperpolarization phase. Before and after the action potential, at ① and ⑨, the neuron is at its resting membrane potential of −70 mV.

Rising Phase of the Action Potential The rising phase is due to a sudden temporary increase in the cell's permeability to Na^+. An action potential begins when a graded potential reaching the trigger zone ② depolarizes the membrane to threshold (−55 mV) ③. As the cell depolarizes, voltage-gated Na^+ channels open, making the membrane much more permeable to Na^+. Because Na^+ is more concentrated outside the cell and because the negative membrane potential inside the cell attracts these positively charged ions, Na^+ flows into the cell.

The addition of positive charge to the intracellular fluid depolarizes the cell membrane, making it progressively more positive (shown by the steep rising phase on the graph ④). In the top third of the rising phase, the inside of the cell has become more positive than the outside and the membrane potential has reversed polarity. This reversal is represented on the graph by the *overshoot,* that portion of the action potential above 0 mV.

As soon as the cell membrane potential becomes positive, the electrical driving force moving Na^+ into the cell disappears. However, the Na^+ concentration gradient remains, so Na^+ continues to move into the cell. As long as Na^+ permeability remains high, the membrane potential moves toward the Na^+ *equilibrium potential* (E_{Na}) of +60 mV. (Recall from Chapter 5 that E_{Na} is the membrane potential at which the movement of Na^+ into the cell down its concentration gradient is exactly opposed by the positive membrane potential [p. 168].) However, before the E_{Na} is reached, the Na^+ channels in the axon close. Sodium permeability decreases dramatically, and the action potential peaks at +30 mV ⑤.

Falling Phase of the Action Potential The falling phase corresponds to an increase in K^+ permeability. Voltage-gated K^+ channels, like Na^+ channels, start to open in response to depolarization. The K^+ channel gates are much slower to open, however, and peak K^+ permeability occurs later than peak Na^+ permeability (Fig. 8-9, lower graph). By the time the K^+ channels are open, the membrane potential of the cell has reached +30 mV because of Na^+ influx through faster-opening Na^+ channels.

When the Na^+ channels close at the peak of the action potential, the K^+ channels have just finished opening, making the membrane very permeable to K^+. At a positive membrane potential, the concentration and electrical gradients for K^+ favor movement of K^+ out of the cell. As K^+ moves out of the cell, the membrane potential rapidly becomes more negative, creating the falling phase of the action potential ⑥ and sending the cell toward its resting potential.

When the falling membrane potential reaches −70 mV, the voltage-gated K^+ channels have not yet closed. Potassium continues to leave the cell through both voltage-gated and K^+ leak channels, and the membrane hyperpolarizes, approaching the E_K of −90 mV. This after-hyperpolarization ⑦ is also called the *undershoot*. Once the slow voltage-gated K^+ channels finally close, some of the outward K^+ leak stops ⑧. Retention of K^+ and Na^+ leak inward bring the membrane potential back to −70 mV ⑨, the value that reflects the cell's resting permeability to K^+, Cl^-, and Na^+.

To summarize, the action potential is a change in membrane potential that occurs when voltage-gated ion channels in the membrane open, increasing the cell's permeability first to Na^+ and then to K^+. The *influx* (movement into the cell) of Na^+ depolarizes the cell. This depolarization is followed by K^+ *efflux* (movement out of the cell), which restores the cell to the resting membrane potential.

Na^+ Channels in the Axon Have Two Gates

One question that puzzled scientists for many years was how the voltage-gated Na^+ channels could close when the cell was depolarized. Why should these channels *close* when depolarization was the stimulus for Na^+ channel *opening*? After many years of study, they found the answer. These voltage-gated Na^+ channels have two gates to regulate ion movement rather than a single gate. The two gates, known as **activation** and **inactivation gates**, flip-flop back and forth to open and shut the Na^+ channel.

When a neuron is at its resting membrane potential, the activation gate of the Na^+ channel is closed and no Na^+ moves through the channel (Fig. 8-10a ●). The inactivation gate, apparently an amino acid sequence resembling a ball and chain on the cytoplasmic side of the channel, is open. When the cell membrane near the channel depolarizes, the activation gate swings open (Fig. 8-10b). This opens the channel pore and allows Na^+ to move into the cell down its electrochemical gradient (Fig. 8-10c).

The addition of positive charge further depolarizes the inside of the cell and starts a positive feedback loop [p. 203] (Fig. 8-11 ●). More Na^+ channels open, and more Na^+ enters, further depolarizing the cell. As long as the cell remains depolarized, activation gates in Na^+ channels remain open.

As happens in all positive feedback loops, outside intervention is needed to stop the escalating depolarization of the cell. This outside intervention is the role of the inactivation gates in the Na^+ channels. Both activation and inactivation gates move in response to depolarization, but the inactivation gate delays its movement for 0.5 msec. During that delay the Na^+ channel is open, allowing enough Na^+ influx to create the rising phase of the action potential. When the slower inactivation gate finally closes, Na^+ influx stops, and the action potential peaks (Fig. 8-10d).

While the neuron repolarizes during K^+ efflux, the Na^+ channel gates reset to their original positions so they can respond to the next depolarization (Fig. 8-10e). The double-gated mechanism that axonal voltage-gated Na^+ channels use for opening and closing allows electrical signals to be conducted in only one direction, as you will see in the next section.

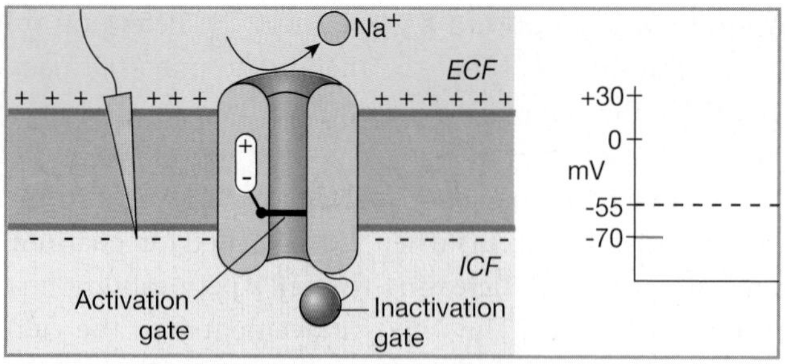

(a) At the resting membrane potential, the activation gate closes the channel.

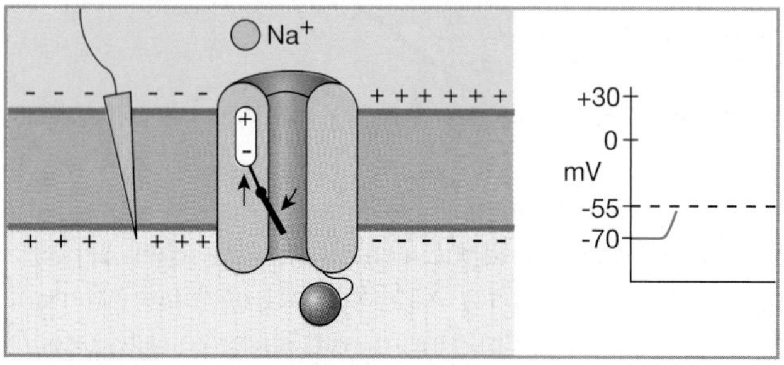

(b) Depolarizing stimulus arrives at the channel. Activation gate opens.

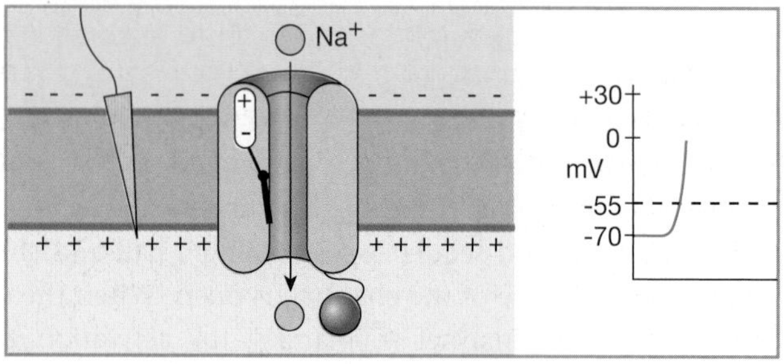

(c) With activation gate open, Na^+ enters the cell.

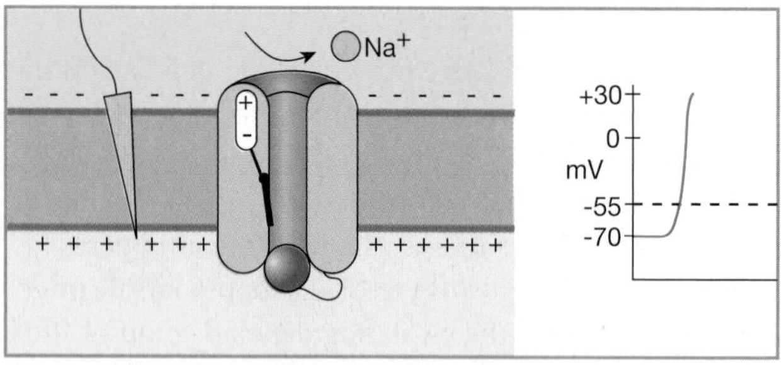

(d) Inactivation gate closes and Na^+ entry stops.

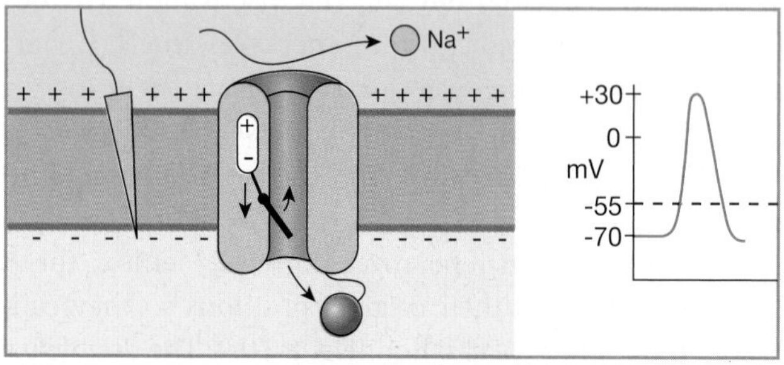

(e) During repolarization caused by K^+ leaving the cell, the two gates reset to their original positions.

● **FIGURE 8-10** ***Model of voltage-gated Na^+ channel function.*** The distinguishing feature of this channel is the presence of two gates: an activation gate that opens rapidly and an inactivation gate whose closure is delayed.

CONCEPT CHECK

11. The pyrethrin insecticides, derived from chrysanthemums, disable inactivation gates of Na^+ channels so that the channels remain open. In neurons poisoned with pyrethrins, what would you predict would happen to the membrane potential? Explain your answer.
12. When Na^+ channel gates are resetting, is the activation gate opening or closing? Is the inactivation gate opening or closing?

Answers: p. 294

Action Potentials Will Not Fire During the Absolute Refractory Period

The double gating of Na^+ channels plays a major role in the phenomenon known as the **refractory period**. The adjective *refractory* comes from a Latin word meaning "stubborn." The "stubbornness" of the neuron refers to the fact that once an action potential has begun, a second action potential cannot be triggered for about 2 msec, no matter how large the stimulus. This 2 msec represents the time required for the Na^+ channel gates to reset to their resting positions and is called the **absolute refractory period** (Fig. 8-12 ●). Because of the absolute refractory period, a second action potential cannot occur before the first has finished. Consequently, *action potentials moving from trigger zone to axon terminal cannot overlap and cannot travel backward.*

A **relative refractory period** follows the absolute refractory period. During the relative refractory period, some but not all Na^+ channel gates have reset to their original positions. Those Na^+ channels that have not quite returned to their resting position can be opened by a higher-than-normal graded potential, which has the effect of moving the threshold value closer to zero. This means that a stronger-than-normal depolarizing graded potential is needed to bring the cell up to threshold.

In addition, during the relative refractory period, K^+ channels are still open. Although Na^+ can enter through newly reopened Na^+ channels, depolarization due to Na^+ entry will be offset by K^+ loss. As a result, any action potentials that fire have a smaller amplitude than normal.

The refractory period is a key characteristic that distinguishes action potentials from graded potentials. If two stimuli reach the dendrites of a neuron within a short time, the successive graded potentials created by those stimuli can be added to one another. If, however, two suprathreshold graded potentials reach the action potential trigger zone within the absolute refractory period, the second graded potential has no effect because the Na^+ channels are inactivated and cannot open again so soon.

Refractory periods limit the rate at which signals can be transmitted down a neuron. The absolute refractory period also ensures one-way travel of an action potential from cell body to

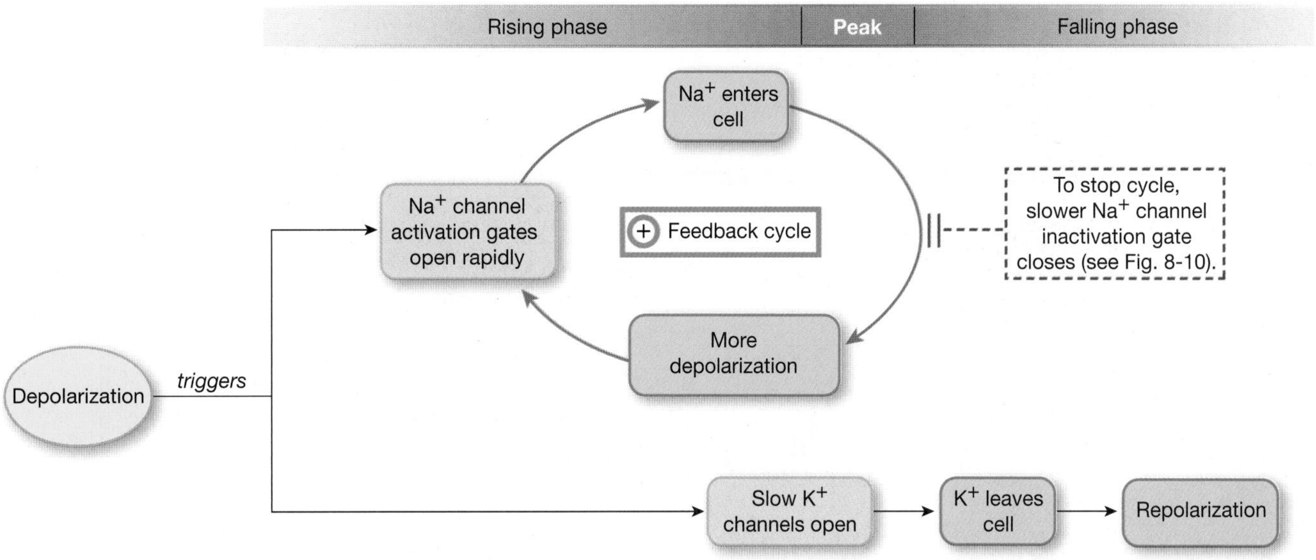

● **FIGURE 8-11** ***Na^+ entry during an action potential creates a positive feedback loop.*** The positive feedback loop stops when the Na^+ channel inactivation gates close.

axon terminal by preventing the action potential from traveling backward.

Stimulus Intensity Is Coded by the Frequency of Action Potentials

One distinguishing characteristic of action potentials is that every action potential in a given neuron is identical to every other action potential in that neuron. If all action potentials are the same, how does the neuron transmit information about the strength and duration of the stimulus that started the action potential? The answer lies not in the amplitude of the action potential but in the frequency of action potentials (number of action potentials per second).

A graded potential reaching the trigger zone does not usually trigger a single action potential. Instead, even a small graded potential that is above threshold triggers a burst of action potentials (Fig. 8-13a ●). As graded potentials increase in strength (amplitude), they trigger more frequent action potentials (Fig. 8-13b).

The amount of neurotransmitter released at the axon terminal is directly related to the total number of action potentials that arrive at the terminal per unit time. Often a burst of action potentials arriving at the terminal results in increased neurotransmitter release, as shown in Figure 8-13. However, in some cases of sustained activity, neurotransmitter release may decrease because the axon cannot replenish its neurotransmitter supply rapidly enough.

One Action Potential Does Not Alter Ion Concentration Gradients

As you just learned, an action potential results from ion movements across the neuron membrane. First Na^+ moves into the cell, and then K^+ moves out. However, it is important to understand that very few ions move across the membrane in a single action potential, so that *the relative Na^+ and K^+ concentrations inside and outside the cell remain essentially unchanged.* For example, only 1 in every 100,000 K^+ must leave the cell to shift the membrane potential from +30 to −70 mV, equivalent to the falling phase of the action potential. The tiny number of ions that cross the membrane during an action potential does not disrupt the Na^+ and K^+ concentration gradients.

Normally, the ions that do move into or out of the cell during action potentials are rapidly restored to their original compartments by the Na^+-K^+-ATPase (also known as the Na^+-K^+ pump). The pump uses energy from ATP to exchange Na^+ that enters the cell for K^+ that leaked out of it [p. 147]. *This exchange does not need to happen before the next action potential fires, however, because the ion concentration gradient was not significantly altered by one action potential!* A neuron without a functional Na^+-K^+ pump may fire a thousand or more action potentials before a significant change in the ion gradients occurs.

CONCEPT CHECK

13. If you put ouabain, an inhibitor of the Na^+-K^+ pump, on a neuron and then stimulate the neuron repeatedly, what do you expect to happen to action potentials generated by that neuron?
    (a) They cease immediately.
    (b) There is no immediate effect, but they diminish over time and eventually disappear.
    (c) They get smaller immediately, then stabilize with smaller amplitude.
    (d) Ouabain has no effect on action potentials.

Answers: p. 294

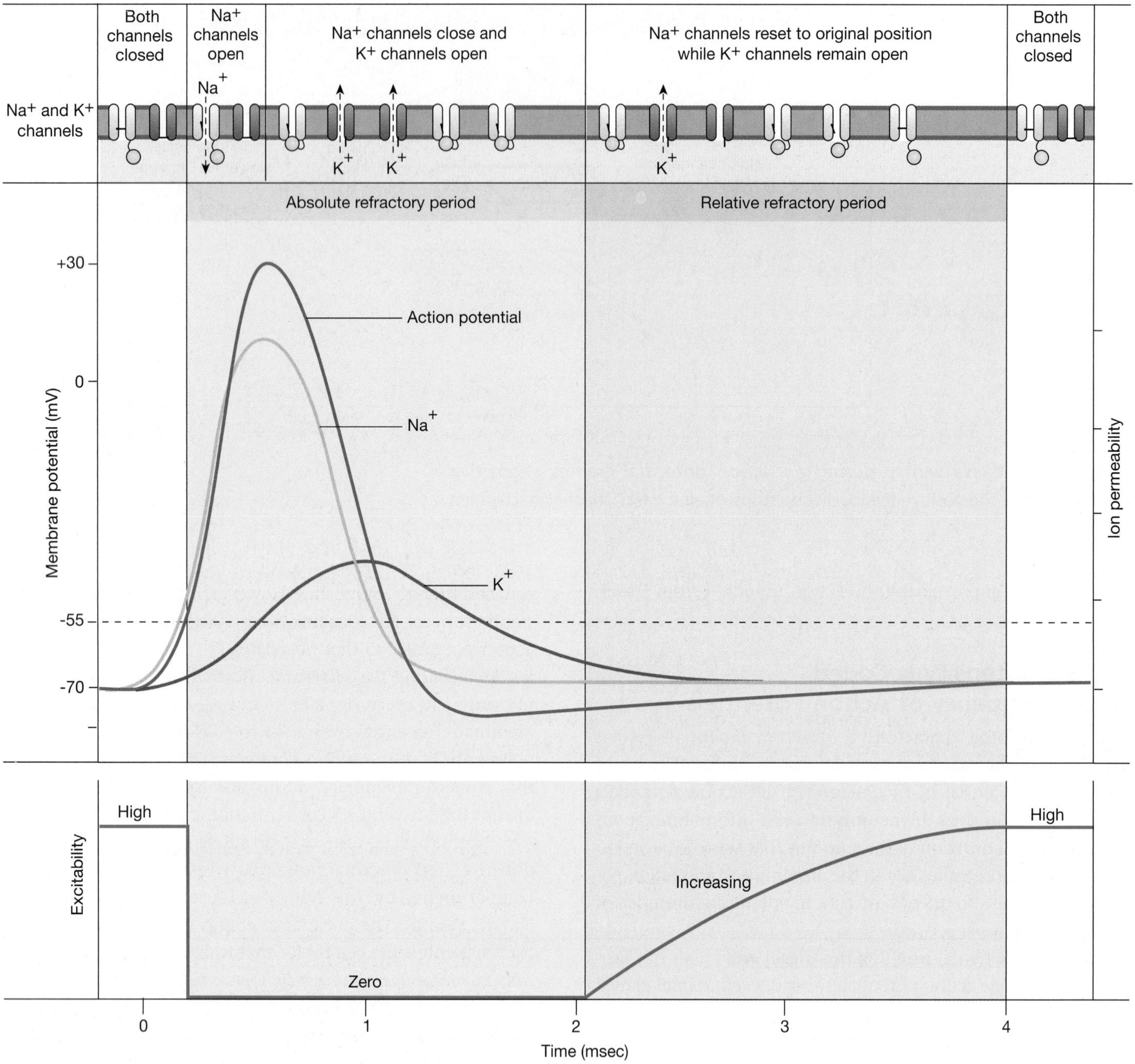

● **FIGURE 8-12** ***Refractory periods following an action potential.*** During the absolute refractory period, no stimulus can trigger another action potential. During the relative refractory period, only a larger-than-normal stimulus can initiate a new action potential. A single channel shown during a phase means that the majority of channels are in this state. Where more than one channel of a particular type is shown, the population is split between the states.

Action Potentials Are Conducted

The high-speed movement of an action potential along the axon is called **conduction** of the action potential. In action potentials, the flow of electrical energy is a process that constantly replenishes lost energy, which is why an action potential does not lose strength over distance, as a graded potential does. The action potential that reaches the end of the axon is identical to the action potential that started at the trigger zone. To see how this happens, we must examine conduction at the cellular level.

The depolarization of a section of axon causes positive current to spread through the cytoplasm in all directions by

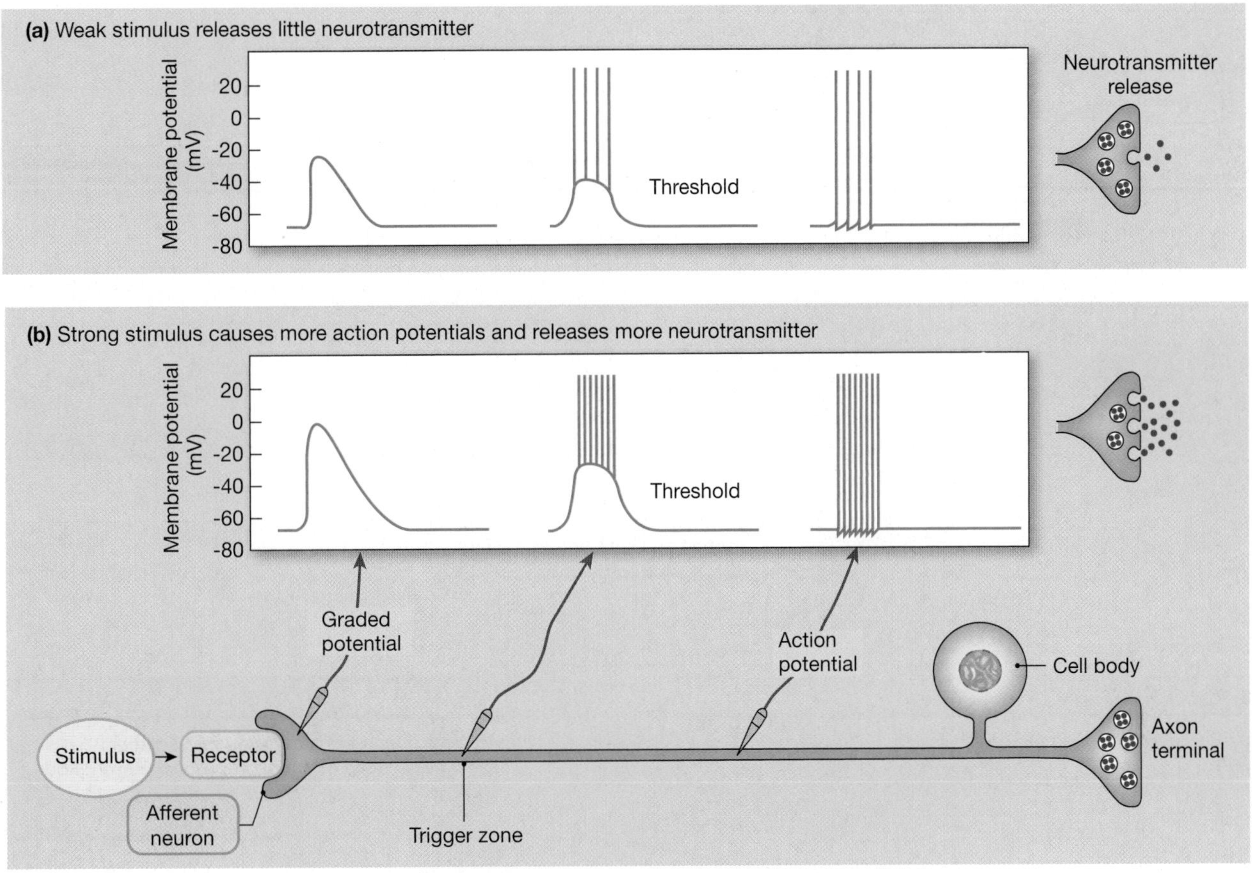
(a) Weak stimulus releases little neurotransmitter
Membrane potential (mV)
20
0
-20
-40
-60
-80
Threshold
Neurotransmitter release
(b) Strong stimulus causes more action potentials and releases more neurotransmitter
Membrane potential (mV)
20
0
-20
-40
-60
-80
Threshold
Graded potential
Action potential
Cell body
Axon terminal
Stimulus
Receptor
Afferent neuron
Trigger zone

● **FIGURE 8-13** ***The frequency of action potential firing indicates the strength of a stimulus.*** Stronger stimuli release more neurotransmitter into the synapse.

local current flow (Fig. 8-14 ●). Simultaneously, on the outside of the axon membrane, current flows back toward the depolarized section. The local current flow in the cytoplasm diminishes over distance as energy dissipates, and would eventually die out were it not for voltage-gated channels.

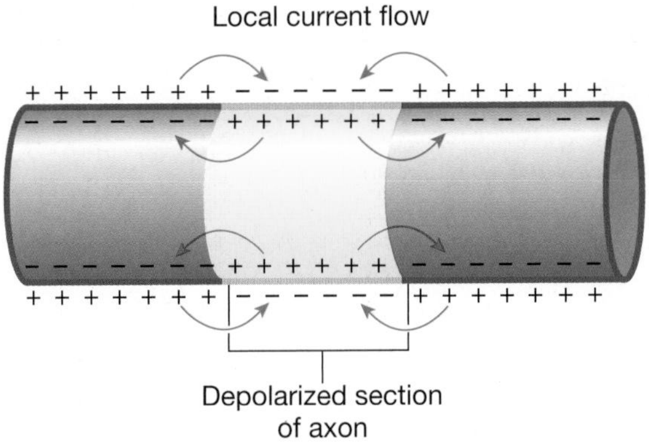
Local current flow
Depolarized section of axon

● **FIGURE 8-14** ***Local current flow.*** When a section of axon depolarizes, positive charges move by local current flow into adjacent sections of the cytoplasm. On the extracellular surface, current flows toward the depolarized region.

The axon is well supplied with voltage-gated Na^+ channels. Whenever the depolarization reaches those channels, they open, allowing more Na^+ to enter the cell and reinforcing the depolarization. This mechanism initiates the positive feedback loop shown in Figure 8-11. Let's see how this works when an action potential begins at the axon's trigger zone.

The stimulus is a graded potential above threshold that enters the trigger zone (Fig. 8-15, ① ●). The depolarization opens voltage-gated Na^+ channels, Na^+ enters the axon, and the initial segment of axon depolarizes ②. Positive charge from the depolarized trigger zone spreads to adjacent sections of membrane ③, repelled by the Na^+ that entered the cytoplasm and attracted by the negative charge of the resting membrane potential.

The flow of local current toward the axon terminal (to the right in Figure 8-15) begins conduction of the action potential. When the membrane distal to the trigger zone depolarizes, its Na^+ channels open, allowing Na^+ into the cell ④. This starts the positive feedback loop: depolarization opens Na^+ channels, Na^+ enters, causing more depolarization and opening more Na^+ channels in the adjacent membrane. The continuous entry of Na^+ down the axon toward the axon terminal means that the strength

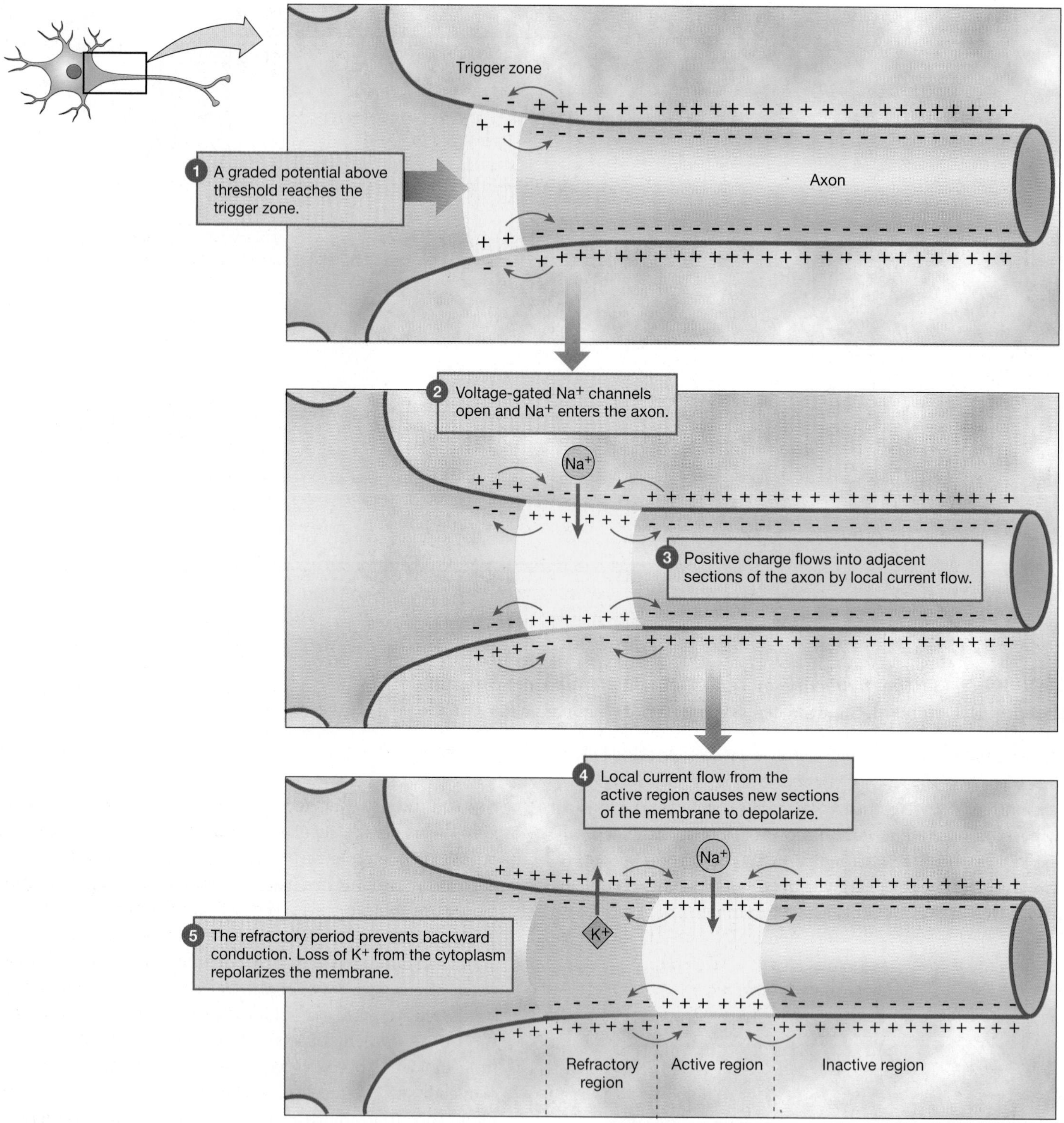
Trigger zone
Axon
1 A graded potential above threshold reaches the trigger zone.
2 Voltage-gated Na+ channels open and Na+ enters the axon.
Na+
3 Positive charge flows into adjacent sections of the axon by local current flow.
4 Local current flow from the active region causes new sections of the membrane to depolarize.
Na+
K+
5 The refractory period prevents backward conduction. Loss of K+ from the cytoplasm repolarizes the membrane.
Refractory region
Active region
Inactive region

FIGURE QUESTION

Match the segments of the neuron in the bottom frame with the corresponding phrase(s):

a) proximal axon (blue)
b) absolute refractory period (pink)
c) active region (yellow)
d) relative refractory period (purple)
e) distal inactive region (blue)

1. rising phase of action potential
2. falling phase of action potential
3. after-hyperpolarization
4. resting potential

FIGURE 8-15 ***Conduction of action potentials***

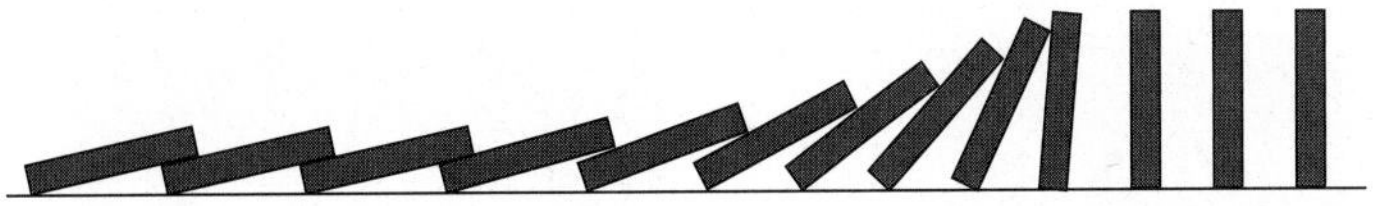

(a) The transmission of action potentials can be compared to a "snapshot" of dominos falling, where each domino is in a different position.

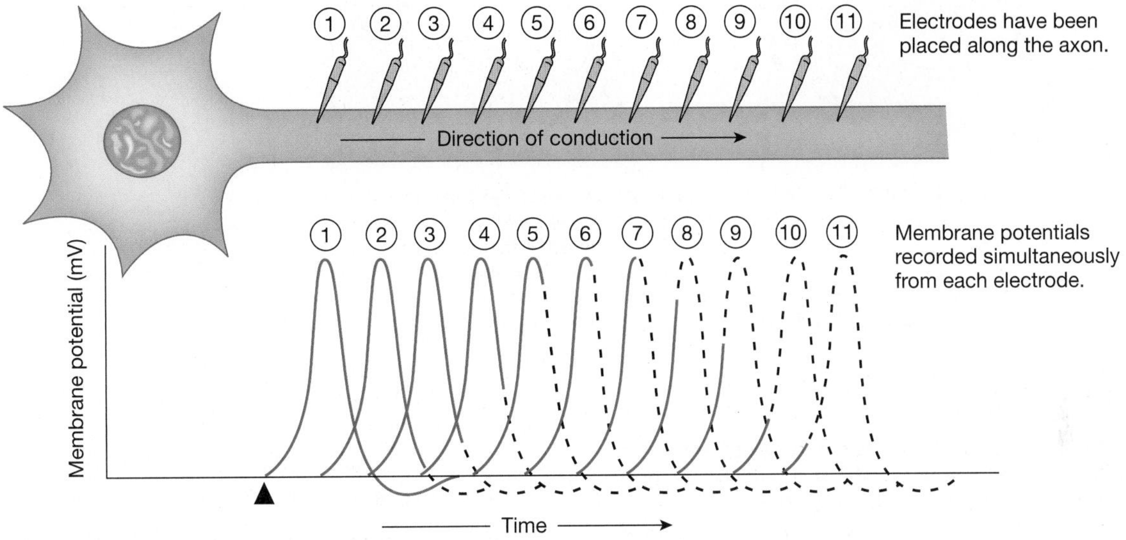

(b) Simultaneous recordings show that each section of axon is experiencing a different phase of the action potential.

● **FIGURE 8-16** ***Action potentials along an axon***

of the signal does not diminish as the action potential propagates itself. (Contrast this with graded potentials in Figure 8-7, in which Na^+ enters only at the point of stimulus, resulting in a membrane potential change that loses strength over distance.)

As each segment of axon reaches the peak of the action potential, its Na^+ channels inactivate. During the action potential's falling phase, K^+ channels are open, allowing K^+ to leave the cytoplasm. Finally, the K^+ channels close and the membrane in that segment of axon returns to its resting potential.

Although positive charge from a depolarized segment of membrane may flow backward toward the trigger zone ⑤, depolarization in that direction has no effect on the axon. The section of axon that has just completed an action potential is in its absolute refractory period, with its Na^+ channels inactivated. For this reason, the action potential cannot move backward.

What happens to current flow backward from the trigger zone into the cell body? Scientists used to believe that there were few voltage-gated ion channels in the cell body, so that retrograde current flow could be ignored. However, they now know that the cell body and dendrites do have voltage-gated ion channels and may respond to local current flow from the trigger zone. These retrograde signals are able to influence and modify the next signal that reaches the cell.

When we talk about action potentials, it is important to realize that there is no single action potential that moves through the cell. The action potential that occurs at the trigger zone is like the movement in the first domino of a series of dominos standing on end. As the first domino falls, it strikes the next, passing on its kinetic energy. As the second domino falls, it passes kinetic energy to the third domino, and so on. If you could take a snapshot of the line of falling dominos, you would see that as the first domino is coming to rest in the fallen position, the next one is almost down, the third one most of the way down, and so forth, until you reach the domino that has just been hit and is starting to fall (Fig. 8-16a ●).

In the same way, a wave of action potentials moves down the axon. An action potential is simply a representation of the membrane potential in a given segment of cell membrane at any given moment. As the electrical energy of the action potential passes from one part of the axon to the next, the energy state is reflected in the membrane potential of that region. If we were to insert a series of recording electrodes along the length of an axon and start an electrical signal at the trigger zone, we would see a series of overlapping action potentials at different parts of the waveform, just like the dominos that are frozen in different positions (Fig. 8-16b).

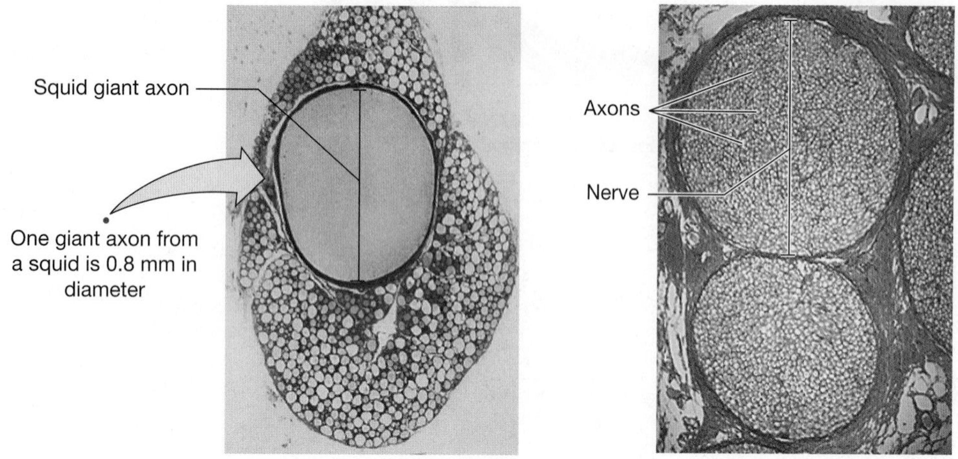
Squid giant axon
One giant axon from a squid is 0.8 mm in diameter
Axons
Nerve

(a) Large axons offer less resistance to current flow, but occupy space.

(b) Small myelinated axons conduct action potentials as rapidly as large unmyelinated axons. Two hundred of these axons would fit into the area occupied by the one giant axon in (a).

FIGURE 8-17 ***Larger axons conduct action potentials more rapidly.***

FIGURE QUESTION

A squid giant axon is 0.8 mm in diameter. A typical myelinated mammalian axon is 0.002 mm in diameter. What would be the diameter of a mammalian nerve if it contained 100 axons that were each the size of a squid giant axon? (Hint: The area of a circle is π x radius^2, and π = 3.1459.)

CONCEPT CHECK

14. If you place an electrode in the middle of an axon and artificially depolarize the cell above threshold, in which direction will an action potential travel: to the axon terminal, to the cell body, or to both? Explain your answer. Answers: p. 294

Larger Neurons Conduct Action Potentials Faster

Two key physical parameters influence the speed of action potential conduction in a mammalian neuron: (1) the diameter of the axon and (2) the resistance of the axon membrane to ion leakage out of the cell. The larger the diameter of the axon or the more leak-resistant the membrane, the faster an action potential will move.

To understand the relationship between diameter and conduction, think of a water pipe with water flowing through it. The water that touches the walls of the pipe encounters resistance due to friction between the flowing water molecules and the stationary walls. The water in the center of the pipe meets no direct resistance from the walls and therefore flows faster. In a large-diameter pipe, a smaller fraction of the water flowing through the pipe is in contact with the walls, making the total resistance lower. In the same way, charges flowing inside an axon meet resistance from the membrane. Thus, the larger the diameter of the axon, the lower its resistance to ion flow.

The connection between axon diameter and speed of conduction is especially evident in the giant axons that certain organisms, such as squid, earthworms, and fish, use for rapid escape responses. These giant axons may be up to 1 mm in diameter and their large diameter means they can easily be punctured with electrodes (Fig. 8-17a ●). As a result, these species have been very important in research on electrical signaling.

If you compare a cross section of a squid giant axon with a cross section of a mammalian nerve, you will find that the mammalian nerve contains about 200 axons in the same cross-sectional area (Fig. 8-17b). Complex nervous systems pack more axons into a small nerve by using smaller-diameter axons wrapped in insulating membranes of myelin instead of large-diameter unmyelinated axons.

Conduction Is Faster in Myelinated Axons

The conduction of action potentials down an axon is faster in high-resistance axons, in which current leak out of the cell is minimized. The unmyelinated axon depicted in Figure 8-15 has low resistance to current leak because the entire axon membrane is in contact with the extracellular fluid and has ion channels through which current can leak.

In contrast, myelinated axons limit the amount of membrane in contact with the extracellular fluid. In these axons, small sections of bare membrane—the nodes of Ranvier—alternate with longer segments wrapped in multiple layers of membrane (the myelin sheath). The myelin sheath creates a high-resistance wall that prevents ion flow out of the cytoplasm. The myelin membranes are analogous to heavy coats of plastic surrounding electrical wires, as they increase the effective thickness of the axon membrane by as much as 100-fold.

As an action potential passes down the axon from trigger zone to axon terminal, it passes through alternating regions of myelinated axon and nodes of Ranvier (Fig. 8-18a ●). The conduction process is similar to that described previously for the unmyelinated axon, except that it occurs only at the nodes in myelinated axons. Each node has a high concentration of voltage-gated Na^+ channels, which open with depolarization and allow Na^+ into the axon. Sodium ions entering at a node

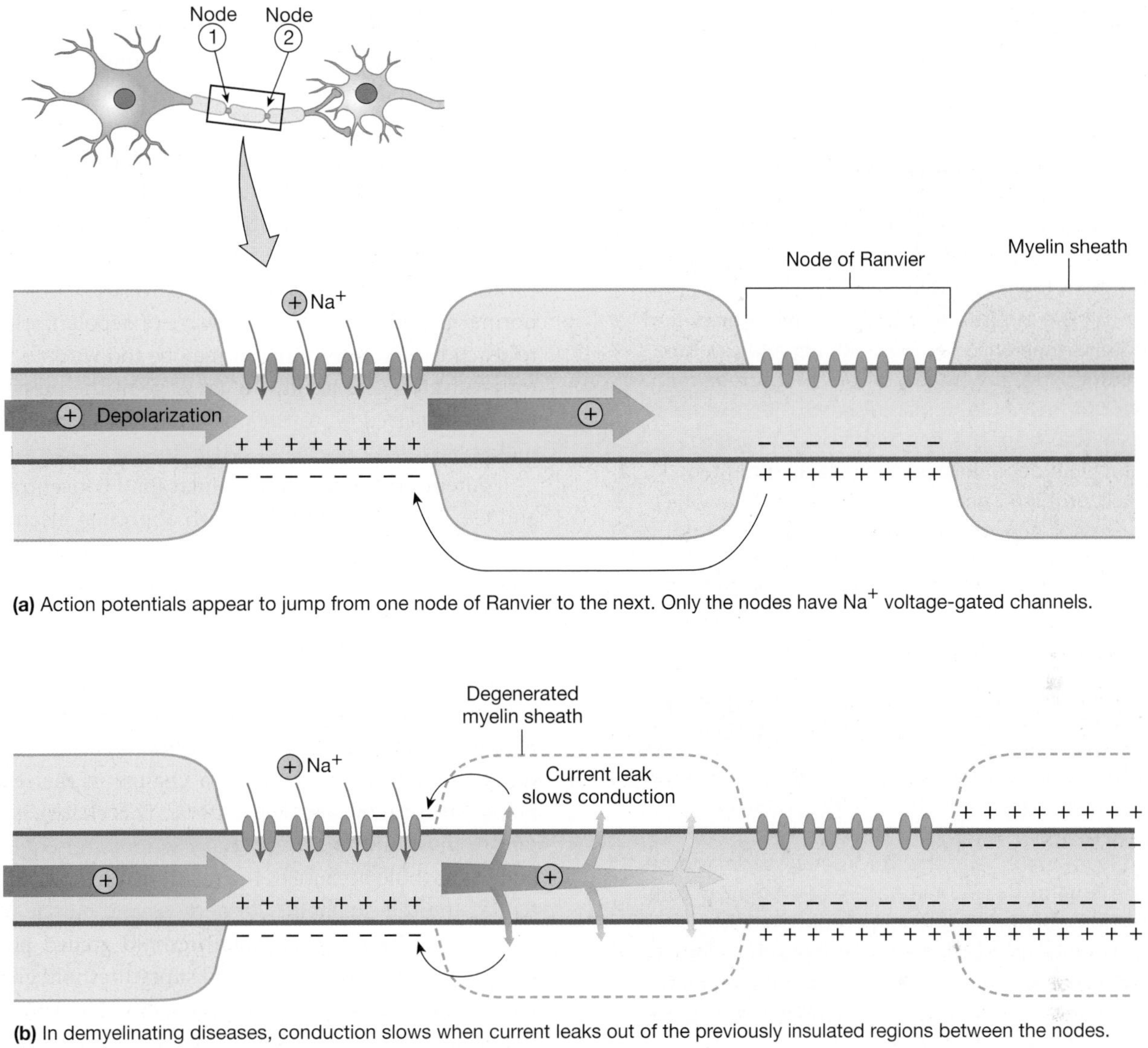
Node
1
Node
2
Node of Ranvier
Myelin sheath
Na+
Depolarization
(a) Action potentials appear to jump from one node of Ranvier to the next. Only the nodes have Na+ voltage-gated channels.
Degenerated
myelin sheath
Na+
Current leak
slows conduction
(b) In demyelinating diseases, conduction slows when current leaks out of the previously insulated regions between the nodes.

● **FIGURE 8-18** ***Saltatory conduction***

reinforce the depolarization and keep the amplitude of the action potential constant as it passes from node to node. The apparent jump of the action potential from node to node is called **saltatory conduction**, from the Latin word *saltare,* meaning "to leap."

What makes conduction more rapid in myelinated axons? The answer is that channel opening slows conduction slightly. In unmyelinated axons, channels must open sequentially all the way down the axon membrane to maintain the amplitude of the action potential. One clever student compared this process to moving across a computer screen by repeatedly pressing the space bar.

In myelinated axons, however, only the nodes need Na^+ channels because of the insulating properties of the myelin membrane. As the action potential passes along myelinated segments, conduction is not slowed by channel opening. In the student's analogy, this is like zipping across the screen by using the TAB key.

Saltatory conduction thus is an effective alternative to large-diameter axons and allows rapid action potentials through small axons. A myelinated frog axon 10 μm in diameter conducts action potentials at the same speed as an unmyelinated 500-μm squid axon. A myelinated 8.6 μm mammalian neuron conducts action potentials at 120 m/sec (432 km/hr or 268 miles per hour) while action potentials in a smaller unmyelinated 1.5 μm pain fiber only travel 2 m/s (7.2 km/hr or 4.5 mph). In summary, action potentials travel through different axons at different rates, depending on the two parameters of axon diameter and myelination.

CONCEPT CHECK

15. Place the following neurons in order of their speed of conduction, from fastest to slowest:
 (a) myelinated axon, diameter 20 μm
 (b) unmyelinated axon, diameter 20 μm
 (c) unmyelinated axon, diameter 200 μm

Answers: p. 294

BIOTECHNOLOGY

MUTANT MOUSE MODELS

The use of animal models to study human diseases has become a valuable part of biomedical research. The mouse genome sequencing effort tells us that 99% of the approximately 30,000 mouse genes have direct human *homologs* (equivalents). This means that we can use the mouse to understand what genes, and the proteins they encode, do in healthy and sick humans. Sometimes, natural mutations produce animal diseases that resemble human diseases. Two examples of such mutants are the twitcher mouse, in which normal myelin degenerates owing to an inherited metabolic problem, and the wobbler mouse, in which somatic motor neurons controlling the limbs die. In other cases, scientists have used biotechnology techniques to create mice that lack specific genes (**knockout mice**) or to breed mice that contain extra genes that were inserted artificially (**transgenic mice**). The mouse is the ideal organism for conducting these experiments. It is small, relatively inexpensive, and has a short lifespan. Additionally, its biological processes are similar to those of humans, and the mouse genome can be easily manipulated by genetic engineering technologies.

To learn more, read the articles in a special Mouse Genome issue of the journal *Nature* (*www.nature.com/nature/mousegenome*). You can obtain additional information about the different knockout and transgenic mice being used for research from the Mouse Genome Informatics databases at The Jackson Laboratory (*www.informatics.jax.org*).

In *demyelinating diseases,* the loss of myelin from vertebrate neurons can have devastating effects on neural signaling. In the central and peripheral nervous systems, the loss of myelin slows the conduction of action potentials. In addition, when ions leak out of the now-uninsulated regions of membrane between the channel-rich nodes of Ranvier, the depolarization that reaches a node may not be above threshold and conduction may fail (Fig. 8-18b).

Multiple sclerosis is the most common and best-known demyelinating disease. It is characterized by a variety of neurological complaints, including fatigue, muscle weakness, difficulty walking, and loss of vision. Guillain-Barré syndrome, described in this chapter's Running Problem, is also characterized by the destruction of myelin. At this time, we can treat some of the symptoms but not the causes of demyelinating diseases, which are mostly either inherited or autoimmune disorders. Currently, researchers are using recombinant DNA technology to study demyelinating disorders in mice.

Chemical Factors Alter Electrical Activity

A large variety of chemicals alter the conduction of action potentials by binding to Na^+, K^+, or Ca^{2+} channels in the neuron membrane. For example, some *neurotoxins* bind to and block Na^+ channels. Local anesthetics such as procaine, which block sensation, function the same way. If Na^+ channels are not functional, Na^+ cannot enter the axon. A depolarization that begins at the trigger zone then cannot be replenished as it travels and loses strength as it moves down the axon, much like a normal graded potential. If the wave of depolarization manages to reach the axon terminal, it may be too weak to release neurotransmitter. As a result, the message of the presynaptic neuron is not passed on to the postsynaptic cell and electrical signaling fails.

Alterations in the extracellular fluid concentrations of K^+ and Ca^{2+} are also associated with abnormal electrical activity in the nervous system. The relationship between extracellular fluid K^+ levels and the conduction of action potentials is the most straightforward and easiest to understand, as well as being one of the most clinically significant.

The concentration of K^+ in the blood and interstitial fluid is the major determinant of the resting potential of all cells. If K^+ concentration in the blood moves out of the normal range of 3.5–5 mmol/L, the result is a change in the resting membrane potential of cells (Fig. 8-19 ●). This change is not important to most cells, but it can have serious consequences to the body as a whole because of the relationship between resting potential and the excitability of nervous and muscle tissue.

At normal K^+ levels, subthreshold graded potentials do not trigger action potentials, and suprathreshold graded potentials do (Fig. 8-19a, b). An increase in blood K^+ concentration—**hyperkalemia** [*hyper-,* above + *kalium,* potassium + *-emia,* in the blood]—shifts the resting membrane potential of a neuron closer to threshold and cause the cells to fire action potentials in response to smaller graded potentials (Fig. 8-19c).

If blood K^+ concentration falls too low (**hypokalemia**), the resting membrane potential of the cells hyperpolarizes, moving farther from threshold. In this case, a stimulus strong enough to trigger an action potential when the resting potential is the normal −70 mV does not reach the threshold value (Fig. 8-19d). This condition shows up as muscle weakness because the neurons that control skeletal muscles are not firing normally.

Hypokalemia and its resultant muscle weakness are one reason that sport drinks supplemented with Na^+ and K^+, such as Gatorade™, were developed. When people sweat excessively, they lose both salts and water. If they replace this fluid loss with pure water, the K^+ remaining in the blood is diluted, causing hypokalemia. By replacing sweat loss with a dilute salt solution, a person can prevent potentially dangerous drops in blood K^+ levels. Because of the importance of K^+ to normal

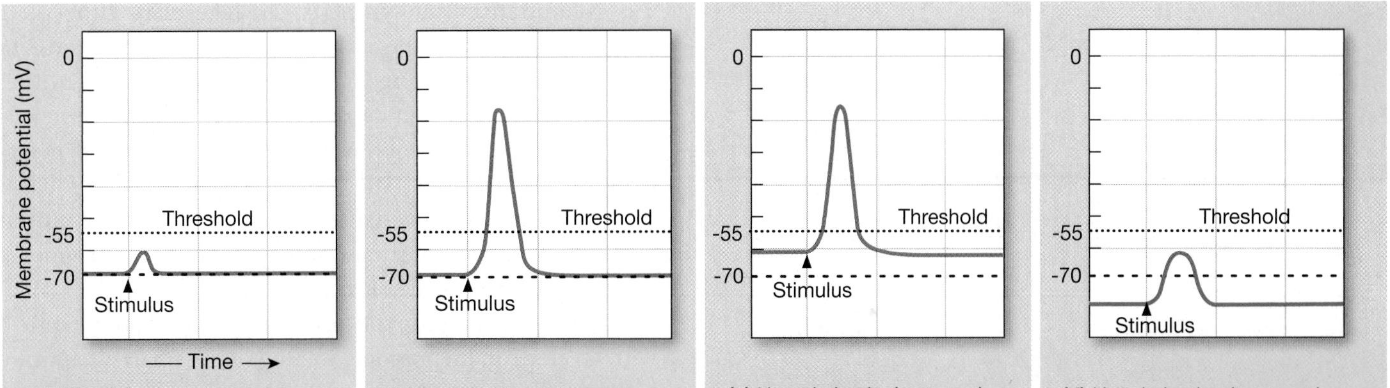

(a) When blood K^+ is in the normal range (normokalemia), a subthreshold graded potential does not fire an action potential.

(b) In normokalemia, a suprathreshold (above-threshold) stimulus will fire an action potential.

(c) Hyperkalemia, increased blood K^+ concentration, brings the membrane closer to the threshold. Now a stimulus that would normally be subthreshold can trigger an action potential.

(d) Hypokalemia, decreased blood K^+ concentration, hyperpolarizes the membrane and makes the neuron less likely to fire an action potential in response to a stimulus that would normally be above the threshold.

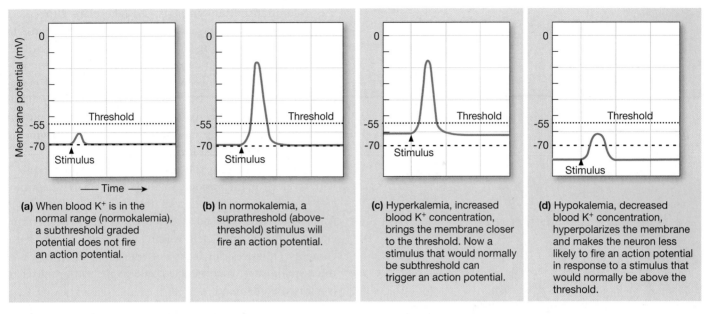

● **FIGURE 8-19** ***Effect of extracellular potassium concentration on the excitability of neurons.*** In hyperkalemia (c), the membrane depolarizes and the cell becomes more excitable. With hypokalemia (d), the membrane hyperpolarizes and the cell becomes less excitable.

function of the nervous system, the body regulates blood K^+ levels within a narrow range. We discuss the important role of the kidneys in maintaining ion balance in Chapter 19.

CELL-TO-CELL COMMUNICATION IN THE NERVOUS SYSTEM

Information flow through the nervous system using electrical and chemical signals is one of the most active areas of neuroscience research today because so many devastating diseases affect this process. The specificity of neural communication depends on several factors: the signal molecules secreted by neurons, the target cell receptors for these chemicals, and the anatomical connections between neurons and their targets, which occur in regions known as synapses.

RUNNING PROBLEM

The classic form of Guillain-Barré syndrome found in Europe and North America is an illness in which the myelin that insulates axons is destroyed. One way that GBS, multiple sclerosis, and other demyelinating illnesses are diagnosed is through the use of a nerve conduction test. This test measures the combined strength of action potentials from many neurons and the rate at which these action potentials are conducted as they travel down axons.

Question 3:

In GBS, what would you expect the results of a nerve conduction test to be?

247 249 252 273 275 279 287 290

Neurons Communicate at Synapses

Each synapse has two parts: (1) the axon terminal of the *presynaptic cell* and (2) the membrane of the *postsynaptic cell* (Fig. 8-20 ●). In a neural reflex, information moves from presynaptic cell to postsynaptic cell. The postsynaptic cells may be neurons or non-neuronal cells. In most neuron-to-neuron synapses, the presynaptic axon terminals are next to either the dendrites or the cell body of the postsynaptic neuron.

In general, postsynaptic neurons with many dendrites also have many synapses. A moderate number of synapses is 10,000, but some cells in the brain are estimated to have 150,000 or more synapses on their dendrites! Synapses can also occur on the axon and even at the axon terminal of the postsynaptic cell. Synapses are classified as electrical or chemical depending on the type of signal that passes from the presynaptic cell to the postsynaptic one.

Electrical Synapses **Electrical synapses** pass an electrical signal, or current, directly from the cytoplasm of one cell to another through gap junctions. Information can flow in both directions through most gap junctions but in some, current can flow in only one direction (a *rectifying synapse*).

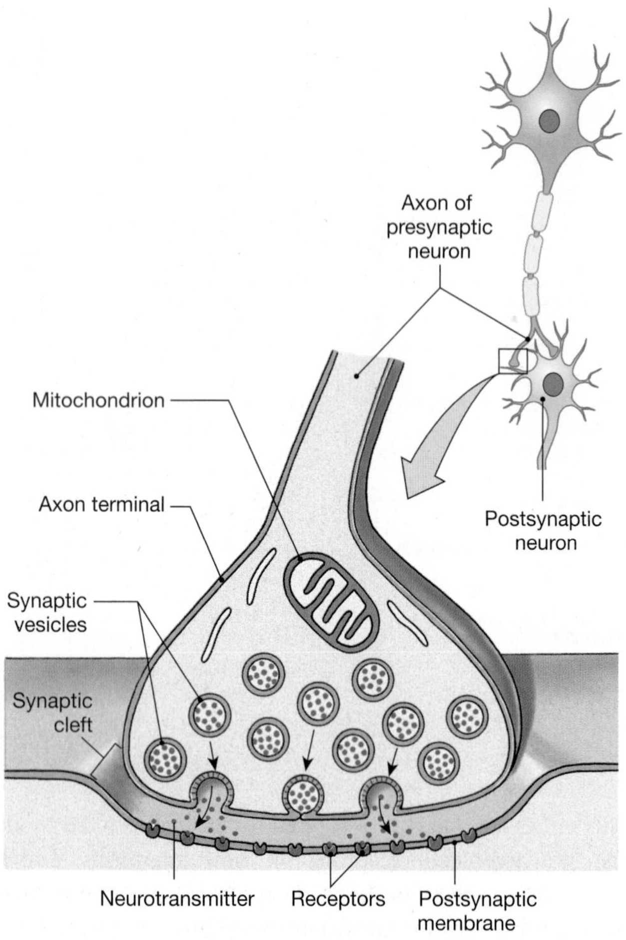

● **FIGURE 8-20** ***Neurotransmitters are the message at a chemical synapse.*** The axon terminal contains mitochondria and synaptic vesicles filled with neurotransmitter. The postsynaptic membrane has receptors for neurotransmitter that diffuses across the synaptic cleft.

Electrical synapses occur mainly in neurons of the CNS. They are also found in glial cells, in cardiac and smooth muscle, and in nonexcitable cells that use electrical signals, such as the pancreatic beta cell. The primary advantage of electrical synapses is rapid conduction of signals from cell to cell that synchronizes activity within a network of cells. Gap junctions also allow chemical signal molecules to diffuse between adjacent cells.

Chemical Synapses The vast majority of synapses in the nervous system are **chemical synapses**, which use neurotransmitters to carry information from one cell to the next. At chemical synapses, the electrical signal of the presynaptic cell is converted into a chemical signal that crosses the synaptic cleft between the presynaptic neuron and its target (Fig. 8-20). Neurotransmitter binding with its receptor on the postsynaptic cell either initiates an electrical response (a very rapid response) or activates a second messenger pathway (a slower response) [p. 184].

Neurotransmitter synthesis can take place either in the nerve cell body or in the axon terminal. However, axon terminals do not have the organelles needed for protein synthesis. Consequently, polypeptide neurotransmitters and protein enzymes needed for metabolism in the axon terminal must be made in the cell body. The dissolved enzymes are brought to axon terminals by slow axonal transport, but the neurotransmitters, which are consumed more rapidly than enzymes, are moved in vesicles by fast axonal transport.

When we examine the axon terminal of a presynaptic cell with an electron microscope, we find many small synaptic vesicles and large mitochondria in the cytoplasm (Fig. 8-21 ●). Some vesicles are "docked" at active zones along the membrane closest to the synaptic cleft, waiting for a signal to release their contents. Other vesicles act as a reserve pool, clustering close to the docking sites. Each vesicle contains neurotransmitter that is released on demand.

CONCEPT CHECK

16. Which organelles are needed to synthesize proteins and package them into vesicles?
17. What is the function of mitochondria in a cell?
18. How do mitochondria get to the axon terminals?

Answers: p. 294

Calcium Is the Signal for Neurotransmitter Release at the Synapse

The release of neurotransmitters into the synaptic cleft takes place by exocytosis. From what we can tell, exocytosis in neurons is similar to exocytosis in other types of cells, such as the pancreatic beta cell described in Chapter 5 [p. 171]. Neurotoxins that block neurotransmitter release, including tetanus and botulinum toxins, exert their action by inhibiting specific proteins of the cell's exocytotic apparatus.

Figure 8-21 shows how neurotransmitters are released by exocytosis. When the depolarization of an action potential reaches the axon terminal, the change in membrane potential sets off a sequence of events ①. The axon terminal membrane has voltage-gated Ca^{2+} channels that open in response to depolarization ②. Calcium ions are more concentrated in the extracellular fluid than in the cytosol, and so they move into the cell. The Ca^{2+} binds to regulatory proteins and initiates exocytosis ③. The membrane of the synaptic vesicle fuses with the cell membrane, aided by multiple membrane proteins. The fused area opens and neurotransmitter inside the synaptic vesicle moves into the synaptic cleft ④. The neurotransmitter molecules diffuse across the gap to bind with membrane receptors on the postsynaptic cell. When neurotransmitters bind to their receptors, a response is initiated in the postsynaptic cell ⑤.

In the classic model of exocytosis, the membrane of the vesicle becomes part of the axon terminal membrane [Fig. 5-21, p. 153]. This increase in membrane surface area is countered by endocytotic recycling of the vesicles at regions away

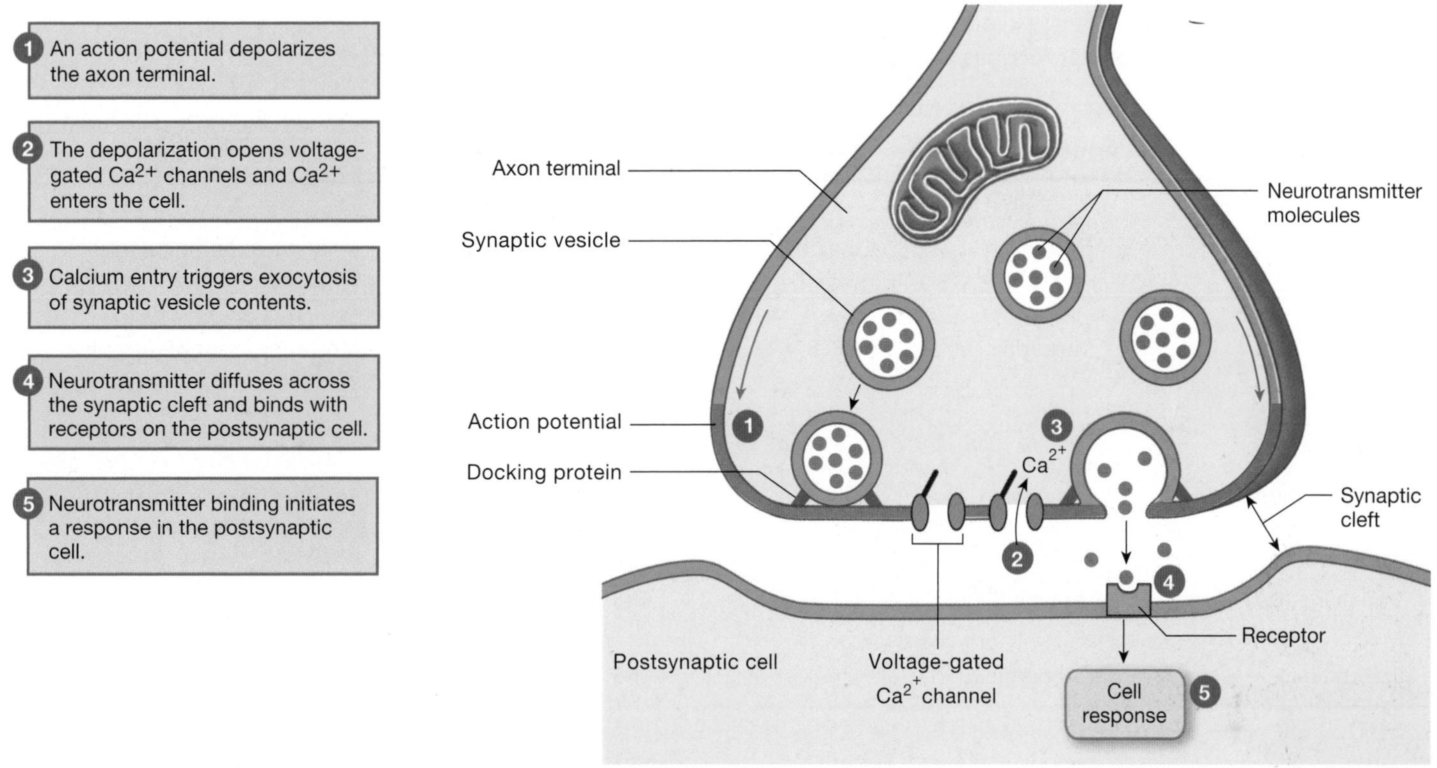
1 An action potential depolarizes the axon terminal.
2 The depolarization opens voltage-gated Ca2+ channels and Ca2+ enters the cell.
3 Calcium entry triggers exocytosis of synaptic vesicle contents.
4 Neurotransmitter diffuses across the synaptic cleft and binds with receptors on the postsynaptic cell.
5 Neurotransmitter binding initiates a response in the postsynaptic cell.
Axon terminal
Synaptic vesicle
Neurotransmitter molecules
Action potential
Docking protein
Ca2+
Synaptic cleft
Receptor
Postsynaptic cell
Voltage-gated Ca2+ channel
Cell response

● **FIGURE 8-21** ***Information transfer at the synapse***

from the active sites (see Fig. 8-4, p. 252). However, a second model of secretion is emerging. In this model, called the **kiss-and-run pathway**, synaptic vesicles fuse to the presynaptic membrane at a complex called the **fusion pore**. This fusion opens a small channel that is just large enough for neurotransmitter to pass through. Then, instead of opening the fused area wider and incorporating the vesicle membrane into the cell membrane, the vesicle pulls back from the fusion pore and returns to the pool of vesicles in the cytoplasm.

CONCEPT CHECK

19. In an experiment on synaptic transmission, a synapse was bathed in a Ca^{2+}-free medium that was otherwise equivalent to extracellular fluid. An action potential was triggered in the presynaptic neuron. Although the action potential reached the axon terminal at the synapse, the usual response of the postsynaptic cell did not occur. What conclusion did the researchers make on the basis of these results? Answers: p. 295

Neurons Secrete Chemical Signals

What are the neurocrine signal molecules that neurons release? Their chemical composition is varied, and they may function as neurotransmitters, neuromodulators, or neurohormones [page 252]. Neurotransmitters and neuromodulators act as *paracrine signals,* with target cells located close to the neuron that secretes them. Neurohormones, in contrast, are secreted into the blood and distributed throughout the body [p. 180].

Generally, neurotransmitters act at a synapse and elicit a rapid response. Neuromodulators act at both synaptic and non-synaptic sites and are slower acting. Some neuromodulators and neurotransmitters also act on the cell that secretes them, making them *autocrine* signals as well as paracrines. The number of molecules identified as neurotransmitters and neuromodulators is large and growing daily.

The Nervous System Secretes Neurocrines

The array of neurocrines in the body is truly staggering (Tbl. 8-4 ●). They can be informally grouped into seven classes according to their structure: (1) acetylcholine, (2) amines,

RUNNING PROBLEM

Dr. McKhann decided to perform nerve conduction tests on some of the paralyzed children in Beijing Hospital. He found that although the rate of conduction along the children's nerves was normal, the strength of the summed action potentials traveling down the nerve was greatly diminished.

Question 4:

Is the paralytic illness that affected the Chinese children a demyelinating condition? Why or why not?

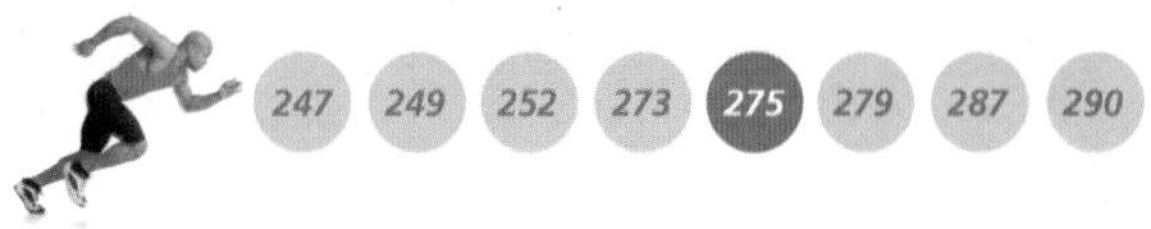
247 249 252 273 275 279 287 290

TABLE 8-4 Major Neurocrines*

CHEMICAL	RECEPTOR	TYPE	RECEPTOR LOCATION	KEY AGONISTS, ANTAGONISTS, AND POTENTIATORS†
Acetylcholine (ACh)	Cholinergic			
	Nicotinic	ICR‡ (Na^+, K^+)	Skeletal muscles, autonomic neurons, CNS	Nicotine: agonist; curare, α-bungarotoxin: antagonists
	Muscarinic	GPCR	Smooth and cardiac muscle, endocrine and exocrine glands, CNS	Muscarine: agonist; atropine: antagonist
Amines				
Norepinephrine (NE)	Adrenergic (α, β)	GPCR	Smooth and cardiac muscle, endocrine and exocrine glands, CNS	Ergotamine, phentolamine: α-antagonists; propranolol: β-antagonist
Dopamine (DA)	Dopamine (D)	GPCR	CNS	Antipsychotic drugs: antagonists; bromocriptine: agonist
Serotonin (5-hydroxytryptamine, 5-HT)	Serotonergic (5-HT)	ICR (Na^+, K^+)	CNS	Sumatriptan: agonist LSD: antagonist
Histamine	Histamine (H)	GPCR	CNS	Ranitidine (Zantac®) and cimetidine (Tagamet®): antagonists
Amino acids				
Glutamate	Glutaminergic ionotropic (iGluR)			
	AMPA	ICR (Na^+, K^+)	CNS	
	NMDA	ICR (Na^+, K^+, Ca^{2+})	CNS	
	Glutaminergic metabotropic (mGluR)	GPCR	CNS	Glycine: potentiator; quisqualate: agonist
GABA (γ-aminobutyric acid)	GABA	ICR (Cl^-)	CNS	Picrotoxin: antagonist; alcohol, barbiturates: potentiators
Glycine	Glycine	ICR (Cl^-)	CNS	Strychnine: antagonist
Purines				
Adenosine	Purine (P)	GPCR	CNS	
Gases				
Nitric oxide (NO)	None	N/A	N/A	

*This table does not include the numerous peptides that can act as neurocrines.

†This list does not include many chemicals that are used as agonists and antagonists in physiological research. To review potentiation, see p. 234.

‡ICR = ion channel-receptor; GPCR = G protein–coupled receptor; AMPA = α-amino-3-hydroxy-5-methyl-4 isoxazole proprionic acid; NMDA = N-methyl-D-aspartate; LSD = lysergic acid diethylamine; N/A = not applicable.

(3) amino acids, (4) purines, (5) gases, (6) peptides, and (7) lipids. CNS neurons release many different neurocrines, including some polypeptides known mostly for their hormonal activity. In contrast, the PNS secretes only three major neurocrines: the neurotransmitters acetylcholine and norepinephrine, and the neurohormone epinephrine.

Acetylcholine Acetylcholine (ACh), in a chemical class by itself, is synthesized from choline and acetyl coenzyme A (acetyl CoA). Choline is a small molecule also found in membrane phospholipids. Acetyl CoA is the metabolic intermediate that links glycolysis to the citric acid cycle [p. 110]. The synthesis of ACh from these two precursors is a simple enzymatic reaction that takes place in the axon terminal (Fig. 8-22 ●). Neurons that secrete ACh and receptors that bind ACh are described as **cholinergic**.

Amines Amine neurotransmitters, like the amine hormones [p. 224], are derived from single amino acids. The amino acid tyrosine is converted to **dopamine**, **norepinephrine**, and **epinephrine**. All three of these neurocrines also function as neurohormones when secreted by the adrenal medulla [Fig. 11-10, p. 394].

Neurons that secrete norepinephrine are called **adrenergic neurons**, or, more properly, **noradrenergic neurons**. The adjective *adrenergic* does not have the same obvious link to its neurotransmitter as *cholinergic* does to *acetylcholine*. Instead, the adjective derives from the British name for epinephrine, *adrenaline*. In the early part of the twentieth century, British researchers thought that sympathetic neurons secreted adrenaline (epinephrine), hence the modifier *adrenergic*. Although our understanding has changed, the name persists. Whenever you see reference to "adrenergic control" of a function, you must make the connection to a neuron secreting norepinephrine.

Other amine neurotransmitters include **serotonin** (also called *5-hydroxytryptamine* or **5-HT**), made from the amino acid tryptophan, and histamine, made from histadine. The amine neurotransmitters are all active in the CNS. In addition, norepinephrine is the major neurotransmitter of the peripheral autonomic sympathetic division.

Amino Acids At least four amino acids function as neurotransmitters in the CNS. **Glutamate** is the primary excitatory neurotransmitter of the CNS, and **aspartate** serves the same function in selected regions of the brain. The main inhibitory neurotransmitter in the brain is **gamma-aminobutyric acid (GABA)**. The amino acid **glycine** is the primary inhibitory neurotransmitter of the spinal cord. It also potentiates the excitatory effects of glutamate at one type of glutamate receptor [p. 234, potentiation].

Peptides The nervous system secretes a variety of peptides that act as neurotransmitters and neuromodulators in addition to functioning as neurohormones. These peptides include **substance P**, involved in some pain pathways, and the **opioid peptides** (**enkephalins** and **endorphins**) that mediate pain relief, or *analgesia* [*an-*, without + *algos*, pain]. Peptides that function as both neurohormones and neurotransmitters include *cholecystokinin (CCK), vasopressin,* and *atrial natriuretic peptide*. Many peptide neurotransmitters are cosecreted with other neurotransmitters.

Purines *Adenosine, adenosine monophosphate* (AMP), and *adenosine triphosphate* (ATP) can all act as neurotransmitters. These molecules, known collectively as *purines* [p. 34], bind to *purinergic* receptors in the CNS and on other excitable tissues such as the heart.

Gases One of the most interesting neurotransmitters is *nitric oxide* (NO), an unstable gas synthesized from oxygen and the amino acid arginine. Nitric oxide acting as a neurotransmitter diffuses freely into a target cell rather than binding to a membrane receptor [p. 191]. Once inside the target cell, nitric oxide binds to proteins. With a half-life of only 2–30 seconds, nitric oxide is elusive and difficult to study. It is also released from cells other than neurons and often acts as a paracrine.

BIOTECHNOLOGY

OF SNAKES, SNAILS, SPIDERS, AND SUSHI

What do snakes, marine snails, and spiders have to do with neurophysiology? They all provide neuroscientists with compounds for studying synaptic transmission, extracted from the neurotoxic venoms these creatures use to kill their prey. The Asian snake *Bungarus multicinctus* provides us with α-bungarotoxin, a long-lasting poison that binds tightly to nicotinic acetylcholine receptors. The fish-hunting cone snail, *Conus geographus*, and the funnel web spider, *Agelenopsis aperta*, use toxins that block different types of voltage-gated Ca^{2+} channels. One of the most potent poisons known, however, comes from the Japanese puffer fish, a highly prized delicacy whose flesh is consumed as sushi. The puffer has tetrodotoxin (TTX) in its gonads. This neurotoxin blocks Na^{+} channels on axons and prevents the transmission of action potentials, so ingestion of only a tiny amount can be fatal. The chefs who prepare the puffer fish, or *fugu*, for consumption are carefully trained to avoid contaminating the fish's flesh as they remove the toxic gonads. There's always some risk involved in eating *fugu,* though—one reason that the youngest person at the table is the first to sample the dish.

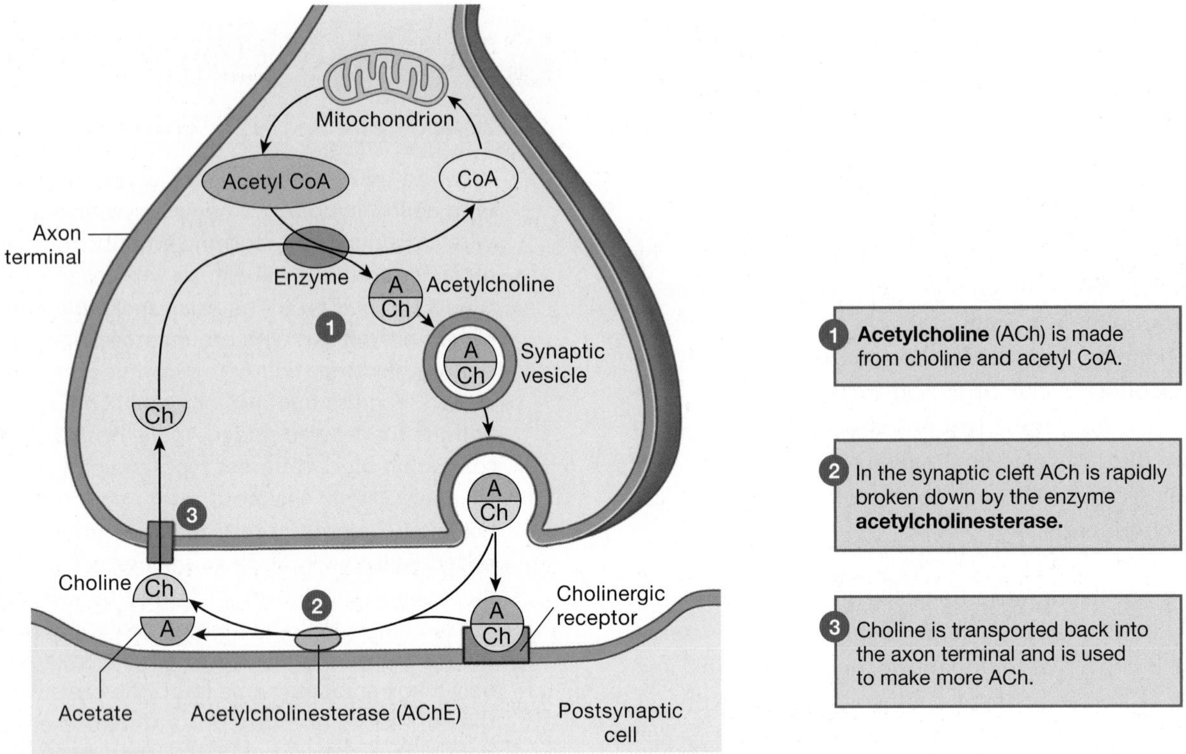
Mitochondrion
Acetyl CoA
CoA
Axon terminal
Enzyme
Acetylcholine
A
Ch
1
Synaptic vesicle
Ch
3
Choline
2
Cholinergic receptor
Acetate
Acetylcholinesterase (AChE)
Postsynaptic cell
1 Acetylcholine (ACh) is made from choline and acetyl CoA.
2 In the synaptic cleft ACh is rapidly broken down by the enzyme acetylcholinesterase.
3 Choline is transported back into the axon terminal and is used to make more ACh.

● **FIGURE 8-22** ***Synthesis and recycling of acetylcholine at a synapse***

CLINICAL FOCUS

MYASTHENIA GRAVIS

What would you think was wrong if suddenly your eyelids started drooping, you had difficulty watching moving objects, and it became difficult to chew, swallow, and talk? What disease attacks these skeletal muscles but leaves the larger muscles of the arms and legs alone? The answer is **myasthenia gravis** [*myo-*, muscle + *asthenes,* weak + *gravis,* severe], an autoimmune disease in which the body fails to recognize the acetylcholine (ACh) receptors on skeletal muscle as part of "self." The immune system then produces antibodies to attack the receptors. The antibodies bind to the ACh receptor protein and change it in some way that causes the muscle cell to withdraw the receptors from the membrane and destroy them. This destruction leaves the muscle with fewer ACh receptors in the membrane. Even though neurotransmitter release is normal, the muscle target has a diminished response that is exhibited as muscle weakness. Currently medical science does not have a cure for myasthenia gravis, although various drugs can help control its symptoms. To learn more about this disease, visit the web site for the Myasthenia Gravis Foundation of America at *www.myasthenia.org*.

Recent work suggests that *carbon monoxide* (CO) and hydrogen sulfide (H_2S), both known as toxic gases, are produced by the body in tiny amounts to serve as neurotransmitters.

Lipids Lipid neurocrines include several eicosanoids [p. 31] that are the endogenous ligands for *cannabinoid receptors*. The CB_1 cannabinoid receptor is found in the brain, and the CB_2 receptor is found on immune cells. The receptors were named for one of their exogenous ligands, Δ^9-tetrahydrocannabinoid (THC), which comes from the plant *Cannabis sativa,* more commonly known as marijuana.

Multiple Receptor Types Amplify the Effects of Neurotransmitters

All neurotransmitters except nitric oxide bind to one or more receptor types. Each receptor type may have multiple subtypes, allowing one neurotransmitter to have different effects in different tissues. Receptor subtypes are distinguished by combinations of letter and number subscripts. For example, serotonin (5-HT) has at least 20 receptor subtypes that have been identified, including 5-HT_{1A} and 5-HT_4.

Neurotransmitter receptors fall into two of the membrane receptor categories that we discussed in Chapter 6 [p. 182]: ligand-gated ion channels and G protein–coupled receptors (GPCR). Receptors that alter ion channel function are called *ionotropic* receptors. Receptors that work through second messenger systems are called *metabotropic* receptors. Some metabotropic GPCRs regulate the opening or closing of ion channels.

The study of neurotransmitters and their receptors has been greatly simplified by two advances in molecular biology. The genes for many receptor subtypes have been cloned, allowing researchers to create mutant receptors and study their properties. In addition, researchers have discovered or synthesized a variety of agonists and antagonist molecules that mimic or inhibit neurotransmitter activity by binding to the receptors [p. 41].

Table 8-4 includes descriptions of receptor types and some of their agonists or antagonists.

Cholinergic Receptors **Cholinergic receptors** come in two main subtypes: **nicotinic**, named because *nicotine* is an agonist, and **muscarinic**, for which *muscarine*, a compound found in some fungi, is an agonist. Cholinergic nicotinic receptors are found on skeletal muscle, in the autonomic division of the PNS, and in the CNS. Nicotinic receptors are monovalent cation channels through which both Na^+ and K^+ can pass. Sodium entry into cells exceeds K^+ exit because the electrochemical gradient for Na^+ is stronger. As a result, net Na^+ entry depolarizes the postsynaptic cell and makes it more likely to fire an action potential.

Cholinergic muscarinic receptors come in five related subtypes. They are all coupled to G proteins and are linked to second messenger systems. The tissue response to activation of a muscarinic receptor varies with the receptor subtype. These receptors occur in the CNS and in the autonomic parasympathetic division of the PNS.

Adrenergic Receptors **Adrenergic receptors** are divided into two classes: α (alpha) and β (beta), with multiple subtypes of each. Like cholinergic muscarinic receptors, adrenergic receptors are linked to G proteins and initiate second messenger cascades. The action of epinephrine on β-receptors in dog liver led E. W. Sutherland to the discovery of cyclic AMP and the concept of second messenger systems as transducers of extracellular messengers [p. 187]. The two classes of adrenergic receptors work through different second messenger pathways.

CONCEPT CHECK

20. When pharmaceutical companies design drugs, they try to make a given drug as specific as possible for the particular receptor subtype they are targeting. For example, a drug might target adrenergic β_1- receptors rather than all adrenergic α- and β-receptors. What would be the advantage to this?

Answers: p. 295

Glutaminergic Receptors **Glutamate** is the main excitatory neurotransmitter in the CNS and also acts as a neuromodulator. The action of glutamate at a particular synapse depends on which of its receptor types occurs on the target cell.

RUNNING PROBLEM

Dr. McKhann then asked to see autopsy reports on some of the children who had died of their paralysis at Beijing Hospital. In the reports, pathologists noted that the patients had normal myelin but damaged axons. In some cases, the axon had been completely destroyed, leaving only a hollow shell of myelin.

Question 5:

Do the results of Dr. McKhann's investigation suggest that the Chinese children had classic Guillain-Barré syndrome? Why or why not?

247 249 252 273 275 279 287 290

Metabotropic glutaminergic receptors act through GPCRs. Two ionotropic glutamate receptors are receptor-channels. NMDA receptors are named for the glutamate agonist *N-methyl-D-aspartate,* and AMPA receptors are named for their agonist *α-amino-3-hydroxy-5-methylisoxazole-4-proprionic acid.*

AMPA receptors are ligand-gated monovalent cation channels similar to nicotinic acetylcholine channels. Glutamate binding opens the channel, and the cell depolarizes because of net Na^+ influx.

NMDA receptors are unusual for several reasons. First, they are cation channels that allow Na^+, K^+, and Ca^{2+} to pass through the channel. Second, channel opening requires both glutamate binding and a change in membrane potential. The NMDA receptor channel is blocked by a magnesium ion (Mg^{2+}) at resting membrane potentials. Glutamate binding opens the ligand-activated gate, but ions cannot flow past the Mg^{2+}. However, if the cell depolarizes, the Mg^{2+} blocking the channel is expelled, and then ions flow through the pore (see Fig. 8-32).

Some Postsynaptic Responses Are Slow

A neurotransmitter combining with its receptor sets in motion a series of responses in the postsynaptic cell (Fig. 8-23 ●). In the simplest response, the neurotransmitter binds to and opens a receptor-channel on the postsynaptic cell, leading to ion movement between the postsynaptic cell and the extracellular fluid. The resulting change in membrane potential is called a **fast synaptic potential** because it begins quickly and lasts only a few milliseconds.

If the synaptic potential is depolarizing, it is called an **excitatory postsynaptic potential (EPSP)** because it makes the cell more likely to fire an action potential. If the synaptic potential is hyperpolarizing, it is called an **inhibitory postsynaptic potential (IPSP)** because hyperpolarization moves the membrane potential farther from threshold and makes the cell less likely to fire an action potential.

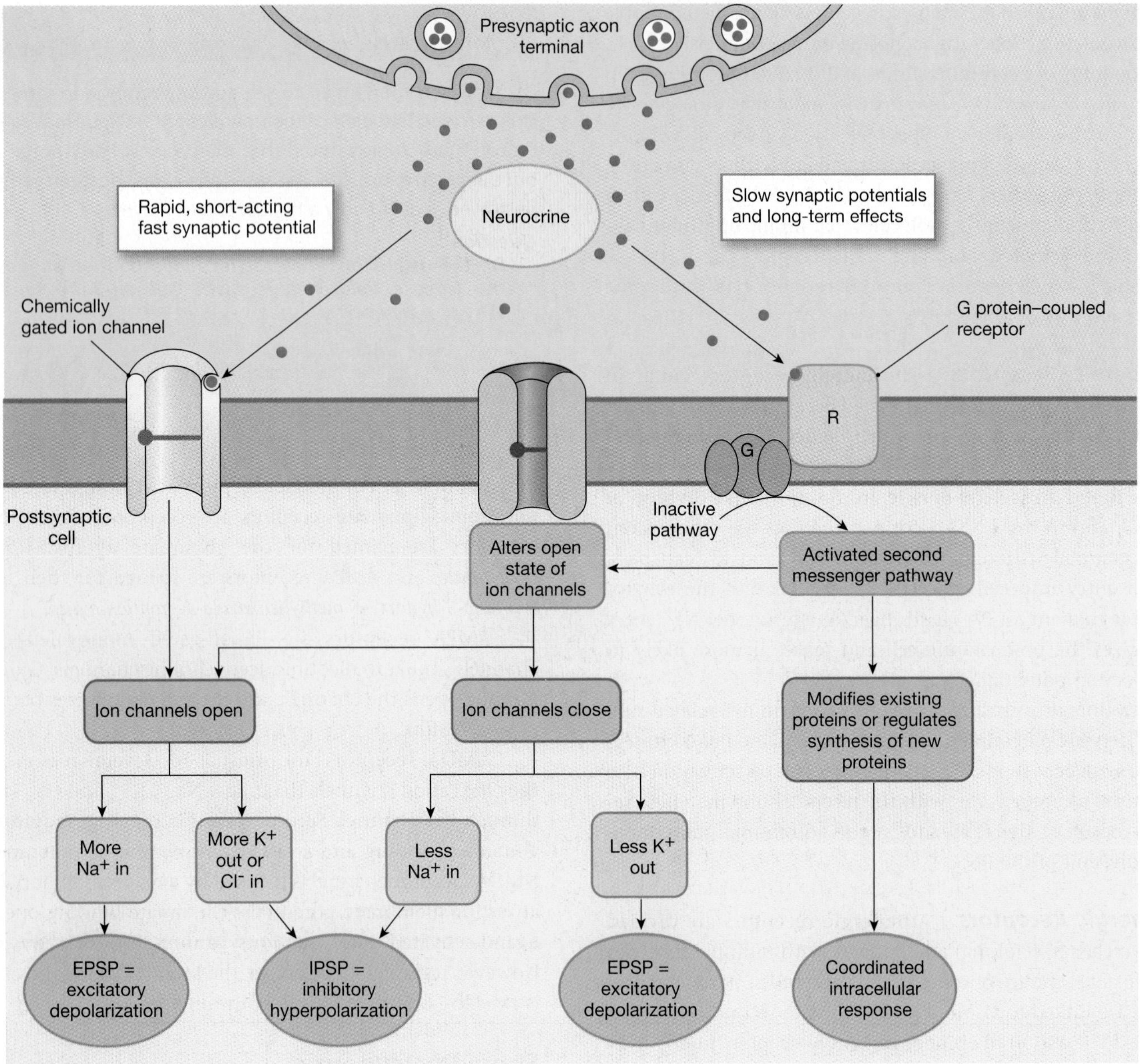

● **FIGURE 8-23** ***Fast and slow responses in postsynaptic cells.*** Neurotransmitters create rapid, short-acting responses by directly opening ion channels. When they bind to different receptors, neurotransmitters can create slower, longer-lasting responses by activating second messenger systems.

In slow postsynaptic responses, neurotransmitters bind to G protein–coupled receptors linked to second messenger systems. The second messengers may act from the cytoplasmic side of the cell membrane to open or close ion channels. (Fast synaptic potentials always open ion channels.) Membrane potentials resulting from this process are called **slow synaptic potentials** because the second messenger method takes longer to create a response. In addition, the response itself lasts longer, usually seconds to minutes.

Slow postsynaptic responses are not limited to altering the open state of ion channels. Neurotransmitter activation of second messenger systems may also modify existing cell proteins or regulate the production of new cell proteins. This type of slow response has been linked to the growth and development of neurons and to the mechanisms underlying long-term memory.

Neurotransmitter Activity Is Rapidly Terminated

A key feature of neural signaling is its short duration, which is achieved by the rapid removal or inactivation of neurotransmitter in the synaptic cleft. Recall from Chapter 2 that ligand binding to a protein is reversible and goes to a state of equilibrium,

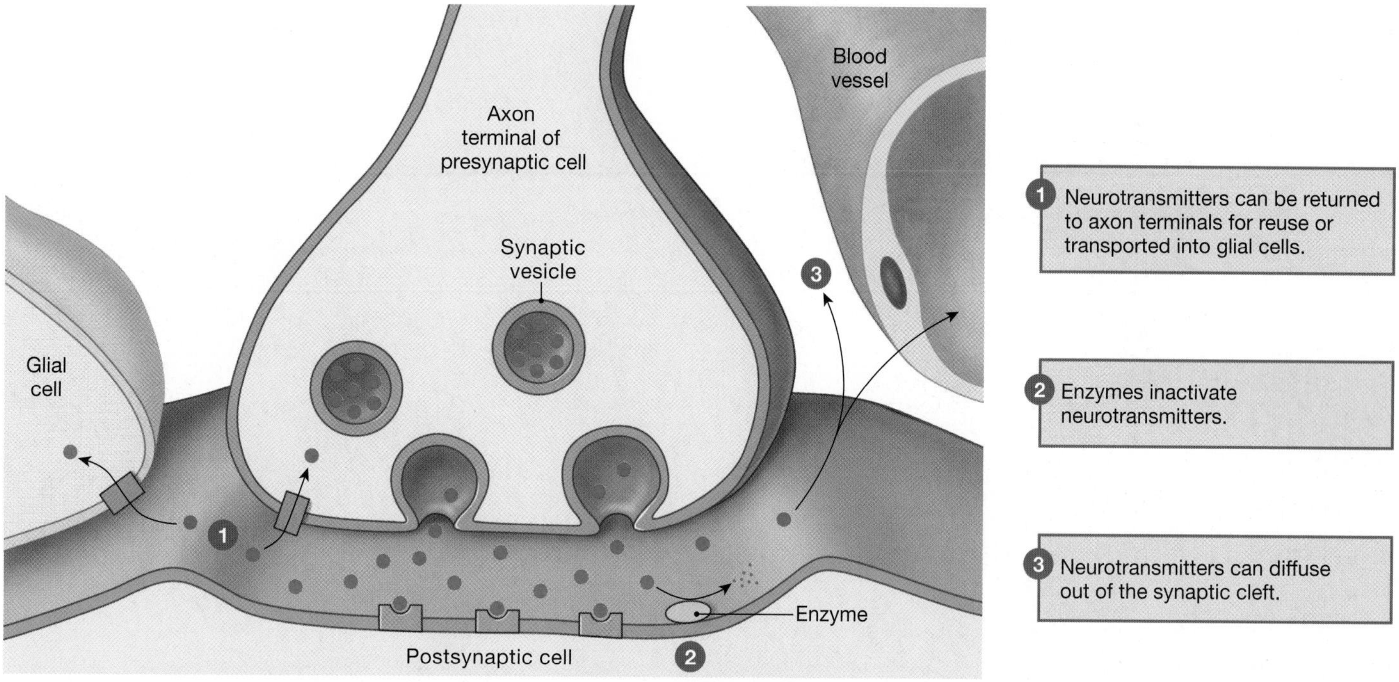

● **FIGURE 8-24** ***Neurotransmitter action terminates when the chemicals are broken down, are taken up into cells, or diffuse away from the synapse.***

with a constant ratio of unbound:bound ligand [p. 40]. If unbound neurotransmitter is removed from the synapse, the receptors release bound neurotransmitter, terminating its activity, to keep the ratio of unbound:bound transmitter constant.

Removal of unbound neurotransmitter from the synaptic cleft can be accomplished in various ways (Fig. 8-24 ●). Some neurotransmitter molecules simply diffuse away from the synapse, distancing them from their receptors. Other neurotransmitters are inactivated by enzymes in the synaptic cleft. Many neurotransmitters are removed from the extracellular fluid by transport either back into the presynaptic cell or into adjacent neurons or glial cells.

For example, acetylcholine (ACh) in the extracellular fluid is rapidly broken down by the enzyme **acetylcholinesterase** (AChE) in the extracellular matrix and in the membrane of the postsynaptic cell (see Fig. 8-22). Choline from degraded ACh is actively transported back into the presynaptic axon terminal and used to make new acetylcholine to refill recycled synaptic vesicles.

In contrast, norepinephrine action at the target tissue is terminated when the intact neurotransmitter is actively transported back into the presynaptic axon terminal. Once back in the axon terminal, norepinephrine is either repackaged into vesicles or broken down by intracellular enzymes such as *monoamine oxidase (MAO),* found in mitochondria.

CONCEPT CHECK

21. One class of antidepressant drugs is called selective serotonin reuptake inhibitors (SSRIs). What do these drugs do to serotonin activity at the synapse? Answers: p. 295

INTEGRATION OF NEURAL INFORMATION TRANSFER

Communication between neurons is not always a one-to-one event. Frequently a single presynaptic neuron branches, and its collaterals synapse on multiple target neurons. This pattern is known as **divergence** (Fig. 8-25a ●). On the other hand, when a group of presynaptic neurons provide input to a smaller number of postsynaptic neurons, the pattern is known as **convergence** (Fig. 8-25b).

Combination of convergence and divergence in the CNS may result in one postsynaptic neuron with synapses from as many as 10,000 presynaptic neurons (Fig. 8-26 ●). For example, the Purkinje neurons of the CNS have highly branched dendrites so that they can receive information from many neurons (Fig. 8-27 ●).

In addition, we now know that the traditional view of chemical synapses as sites of one-way communication, with all messages moving from presynaptic cell to postsynaptic cell, is not always correct. In the brain, there are some synapses where cells on both sides of the synaptic cleft release neurotransmitters that act on the opposite cell. Perhaps more important, we have learned that many postsynaptic cells "talk back" to their presynaptic neurons by sending neuromodulators that bind to presynaptic receptors. Variations in synaptic activity play a major role in determining how communication takes place in the nervous system.

Modulation of activity at synapses is called **synaptic plasticity** [*plasticus*, that which may be molded]. Modulation may enhance activity at the synapse (facilitation or potentiation

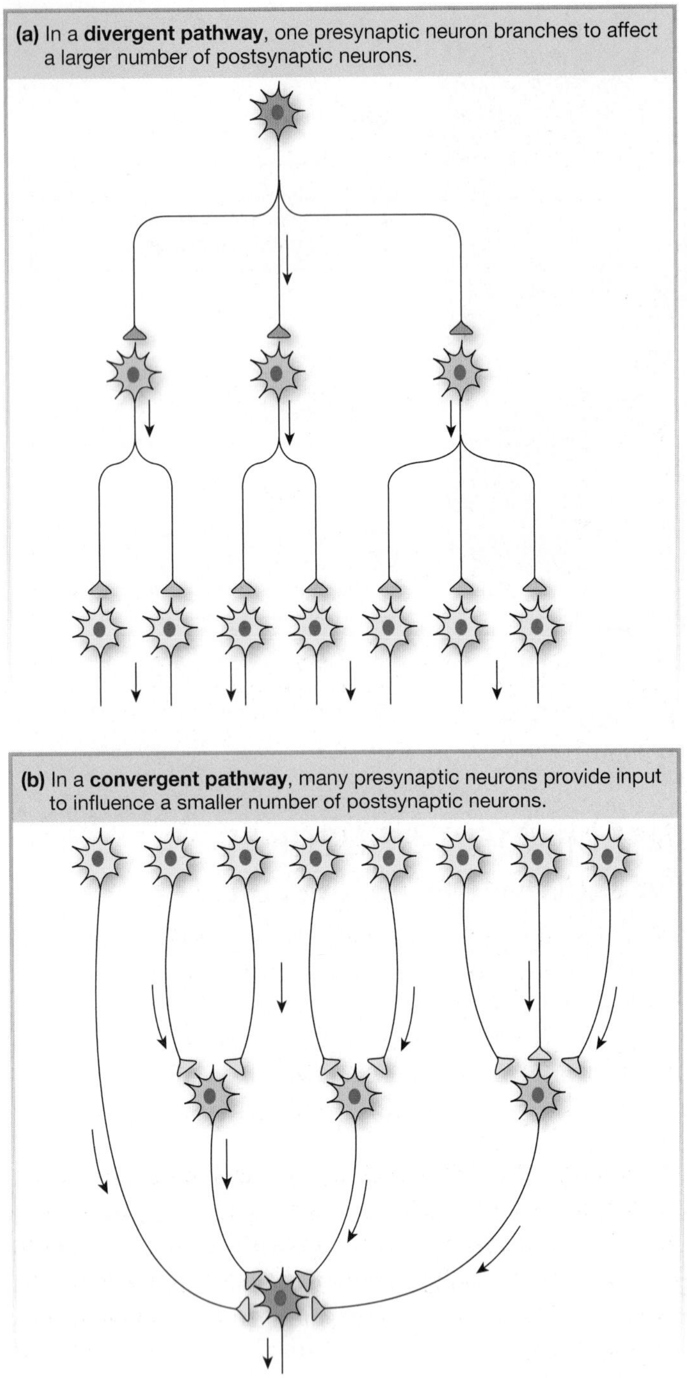
(a) In a divergent pathway, one presynaptic neuron branches to affect a larger number of postsynaptic neurons.
(b) In a convergent pathway, many presynaptic neurons provide input to influence a smaller number of postsynaptic neurons.

FIGURE QUESTION

The pattern of divergence in (a) is similar to _______________ in a second messenger system.

● **FIGURE 8-25** ***Divergence and convergence***

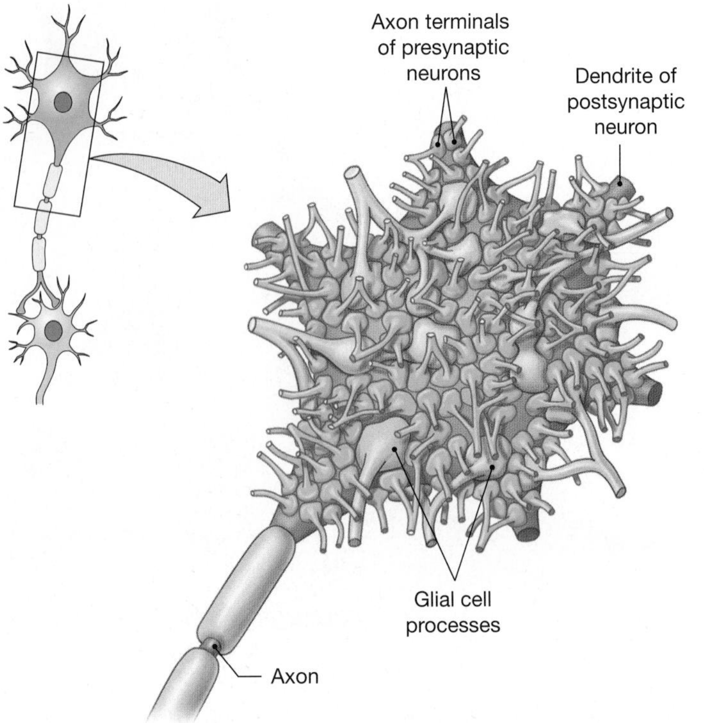
Axon terminals of presynaptic neurons
Dendrite of postsynaptic neuron
Glial cell processes
Axon

● **FIGURE 8-26** ***The cell body and dendrites of a somatic motor neuron are nearly covered with synapses providing input from other neurons.***

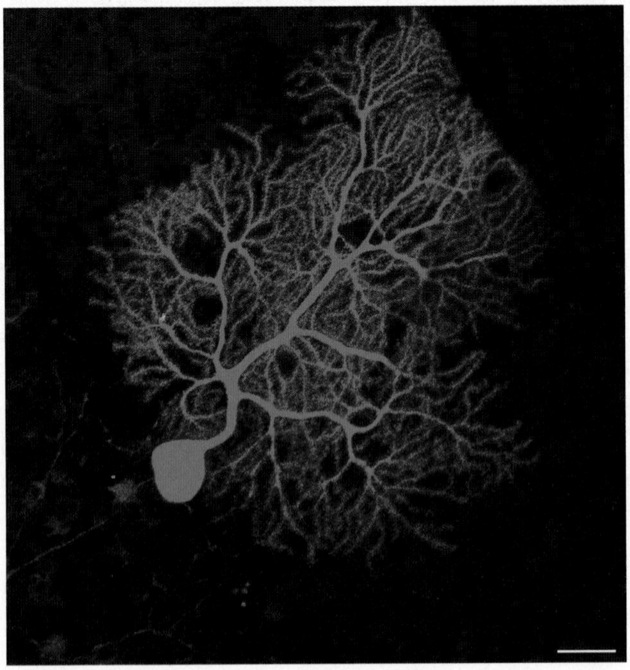

● **FIGURE 8-27** ***The highly branched dendrites of a Purkinje cell (neuron) demonstrate convergence of signals from many synapses onto the cell body.***

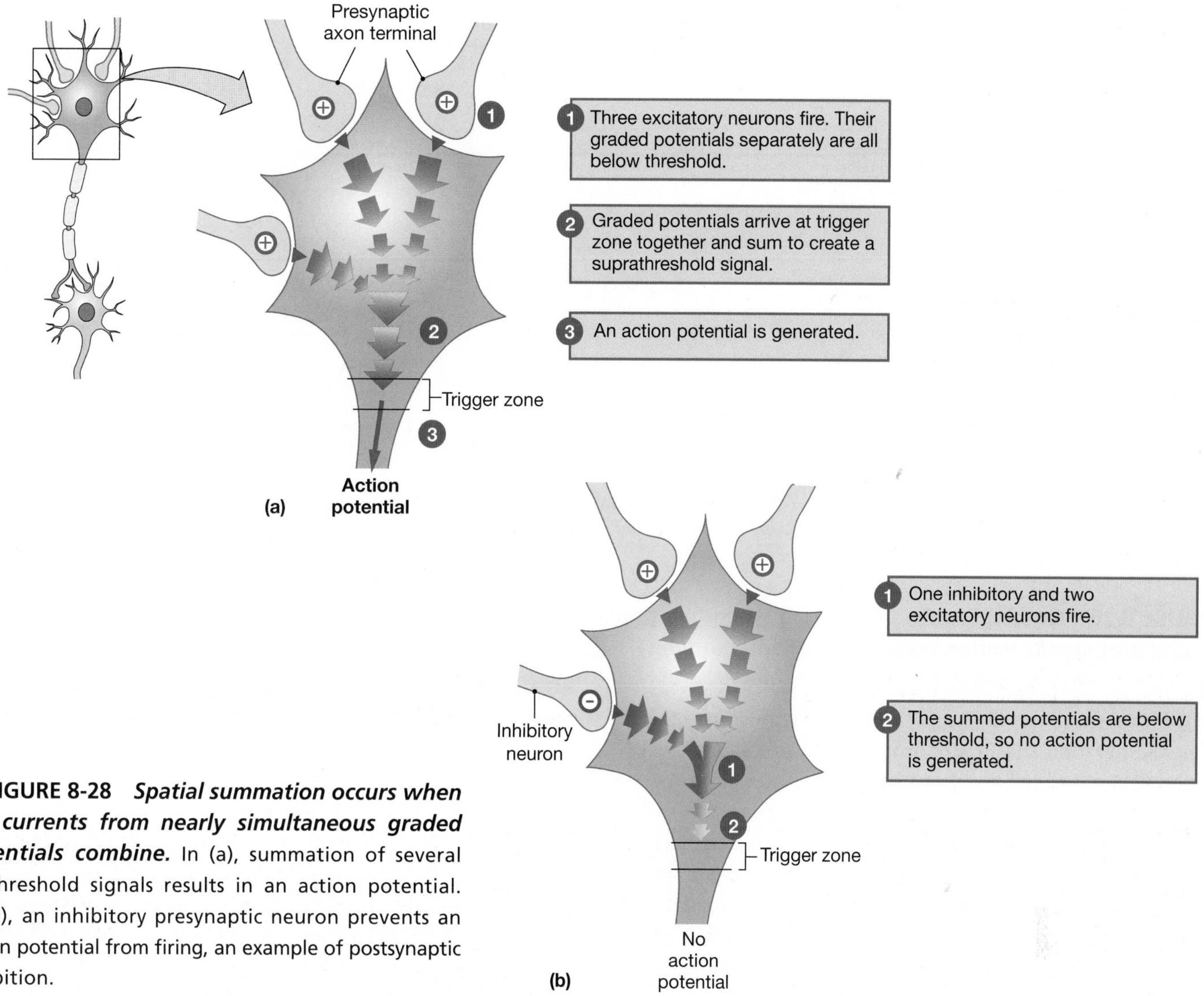

● **FIGURE 8-28** ***Spatial summation occurs when the currents from nearly simultaneous graded potentials combine.*** In (a), summation of several subthreshold signals results in an action potential. In (b), an inhibitory presynaptic neuron prevents an action potential from firing, an example of postsynaptic inhibition.

[p. 234]) or it may decrease activity (inhibition or depression). Sometimes the changes are short-lived (short term) but in other instances changes at the synapse persist for significant periods of time (long term). In this section we examine some of the ways that communication at synapses can be modified.

Neural Pathways May Involve Many Neurons

When two or more presynaptic neurons converge on the dendrites or cell body of a single postsynaptic cell, the response of the postsynaptic cell is determined by the summed input from the presynaptic neurons. If the stimuli all create subthreshold excitatory postsynaptic potentials (EPSPs), those EPSPs can add together to create a suprathreshold potential at the trigger zone.

The initiation of an action potential from several nearly simultaneous graded potentials is an example of **spatial summation**. The word *spatial* [*spatium,* space] refers to the fact that the graded potentials originate at different locations (spaces) on the neuron.

Figure 8-28a ● illustrates spatial summation when three presynaptic neurons releasing excitatory neurotransmitters ("excitatory neurons") converge on one postsynaptic neuron. Each neuron's EPSP is too weak to trigger an action potential by itself, but if the three presynaptic neurons fire simultaneously, the sum of the three EPSPs is suprathreshold and creates an action potential.

Postsynaptic inhibition may occur when a presynaptic neuron releases an inhibitory neurotransmitter onto a postsynaptic cell and alters its response. Figure 8-28b shows three neurons, two excitatory and one inhibitory, converging on a postsynaptic cell. The neurons fire, creating one inhibitory postsynaptic potential (IPSP) and two excitatory graded potentials that sum as they reach the trigger zone. The IPSP counteracts the two EPSPs, creating an integrated signal that is below threshold. As a result, no action potential leaves the trigger zone.

Summation of graded potentials does not always require input from more than one presynaptic neuron. Two subthreshold graded potentials from the same presynaptic neuron can be

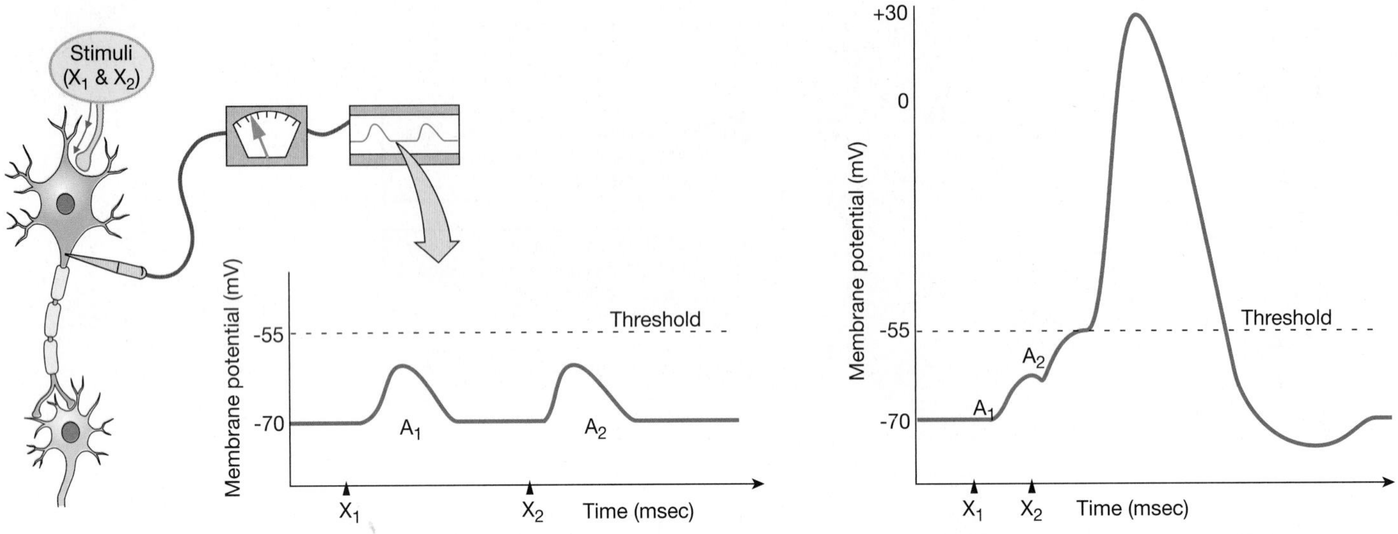

(a) No summation. Two subthreshold graded potentials will not initiate an action potential if they are far apart in time.

(b) Summation causing action potential. If two subthreshold potentials arrive at the trigger zone within a short period of time, they may sum and initiate an action potential.

● **FIGURE 8-29** ***Temporal summation occurs when two graded potentials from one presynaptic neuron occur close together in time.***

summed if they arrive at the trigger zone close enough together in time. Summation that occurs from graded potentials overlapping in time is called **temporal summation** [*tempus,* time]. Let's see how this can happen.

Figure 8-29a ● shows recordings from an electrode placed in the trigger zone of a neuron. A stimulus (X_1) starts a subthreshold graded potential on the cell body at the time marked on the *x*-axis. The graded potential reaches the trigger zone and depolarizes it, as shown on the graph (A_1), but not enough to trigger an action potential. A second stimulus (X_2) occurs later, and its subthreshold graded potential (A_2) reaches the trigger zone some time after the first. The interval between the two stimuli is so long that the two graded potentials do not overlap. Neither potential by itself is above threshold, so no action potential is triggered.

In Figure 8-29b, the two stimuli are given closer together in time. As a result, the two subthreshold graded potentials arrive at the trigger zone at almost the same time. The second graded potential adds its depolarization to that of the first, causing the trigger zone to depolarize to threshold.

In many situations, graded potentials in a neuron incorporate both temporal and spatial summation. The summation of graded potentials demonstrates a key property of neurons: *postsynaptic integration.* When multiple signals reach a neuron, postsynaptic integration creates a signal based on the relative strengths and durations of the signals. If the integrated signal is above threshold, the neuron fires an action potential. If the integrated signal is below threshold, the neuron does not fire. Figure 8-30 ● shows the distribution of excitatory and inhibitory synapses on a three-dimensional reconstruction of dendritic spines of various shapes and sizes. The summed input from these synapses determines the activity of the postsynaptic neuron.

CONCEPT CHECK

22. In Figure 8-28b, assume the postsynaptic neuron has a resting membrane potential of −70 mV and a threshold of −55 mV. If the inhibitory presynaptic neuron creates an IPSP of −5 mV and the two excitatory presynaptic neurons have EPSPs of 10 and 12 mV, will the postsynaptic neuron fire an action potential?
23. In the graphs of Figure 8-29, why doesn't the membrane potential change at the same time as the stimulus?

Answers: p. 295

Synaptic Activity Can Be Modulated

The examples of modulation we have just discussed all took place on the postsynaptic side of a synapse, but the activity of presynaptic cells can also be altered. When a modulatory neuron (inhibitory or excitatory) terminates on or close to an axon terminal of a presynaptic cell, its EPSP or IPSP can alter the action potential reaching the terminal and create *presynaptic modulation.*

If activity in the modulatory neuron decreases neurotransmitter release, the modulation is called *presynaptic inhibition* (Fig. 8-31a ●). Presynaptic inhibition allows selective modulation of collaterals and their targets. One collateral can be inhibited while others remain unaffected. In *presynaptic facilitation,* modulatory input increases neurotransmitter release by the presynaptic cell.

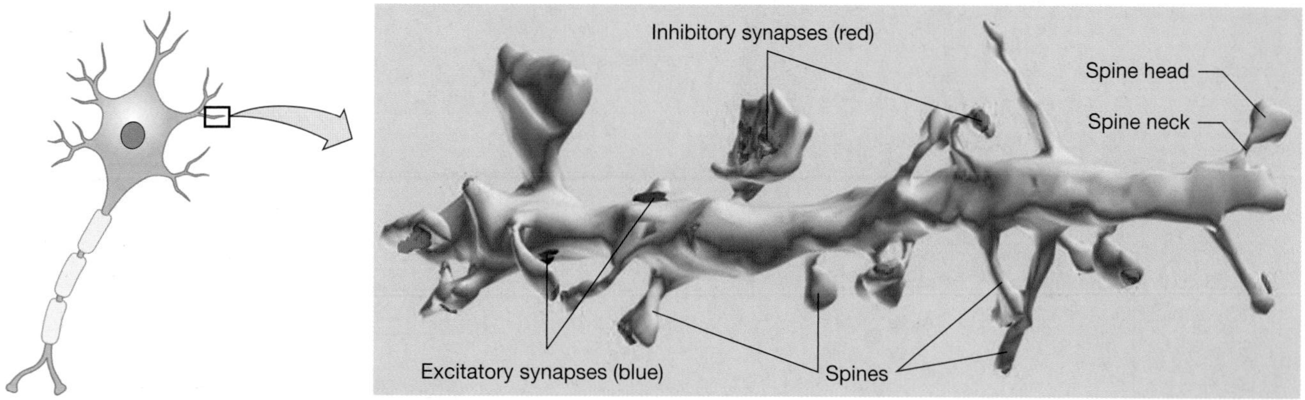
Inhibitory synapses (red)
Spine head
Spine neck
Excitatory synapses (blue)
Spines

● **FIGURE 8-30** ***A three-dimensional reconstruction of dendritic spines and their synapses***

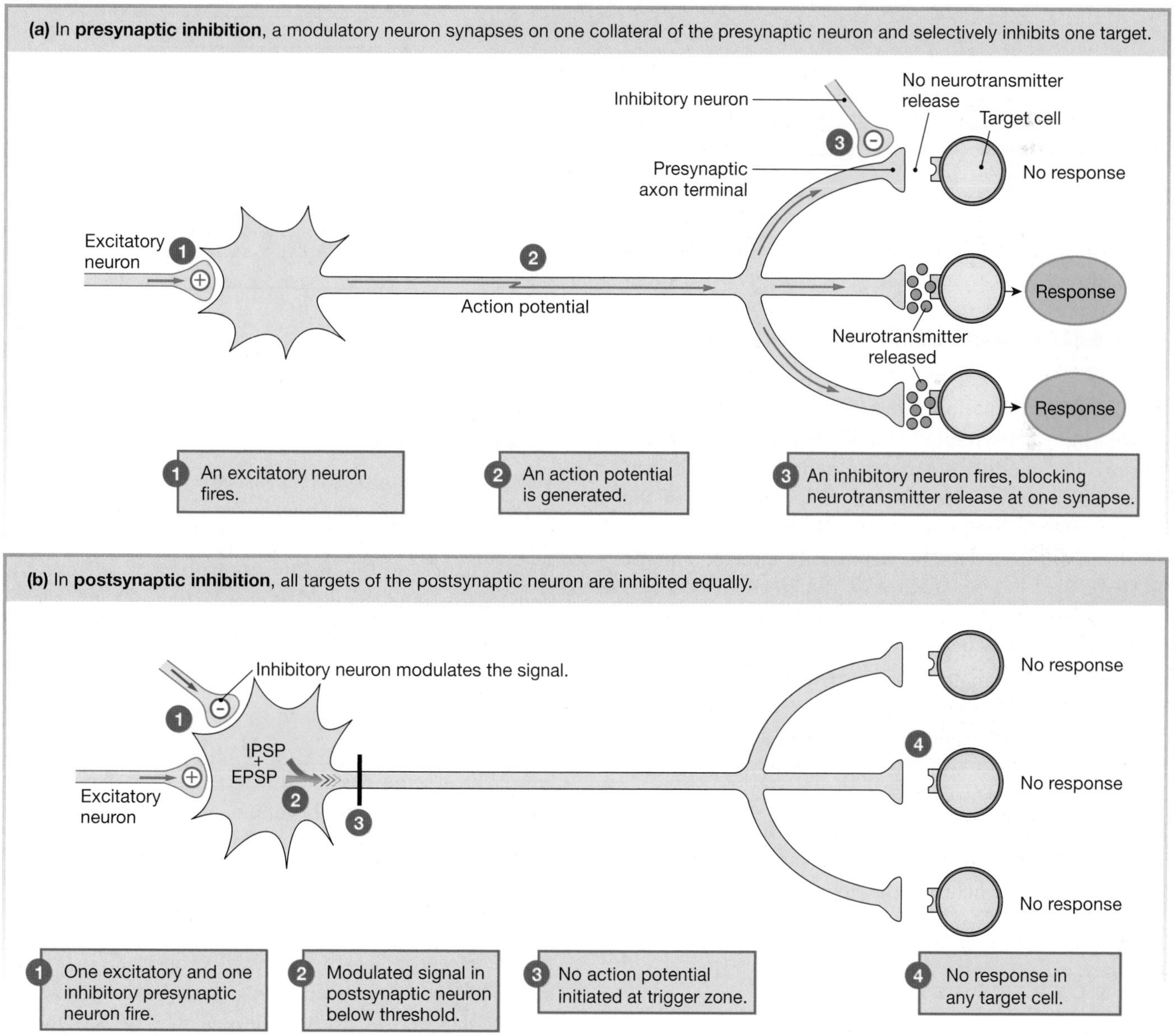
(a) In **presynaptic inhibition**, a modulatory neuron synapses on one collateral of the presynaptic neuron and selectively inhibits one target.
Inhibitory neuron
No neurotransmitter release
Target cell
3
Presynaptic axon terminal
No response
Excitatory neuron
1
2
Action potential
Response
Neurotransmitter released
Response
1 An excitatory neuron fires.
2 An action potential is generated.
3 An inhibitory neuron fires, blocking neurotransmitter release at one synapse.
(b) In **postsynaptic inhibition**, all targets of the postsynaptic neuron are inhibited equally.
Inhibitory neuron modulates the signal.
No response
1
IPSP + EPSP
4
No response
Excitatory neuron
2
3
No response
1 One excitatory and one inhibitory presynaptic neuron fire.
2 Modulated signal in postsynaptic neuron below threshold.
3 No action potential initiated at trigger zone.
4 No response in any target cell.

● **FIGURE 8-31** ***Presynaptic and postsynaptic inhibition***

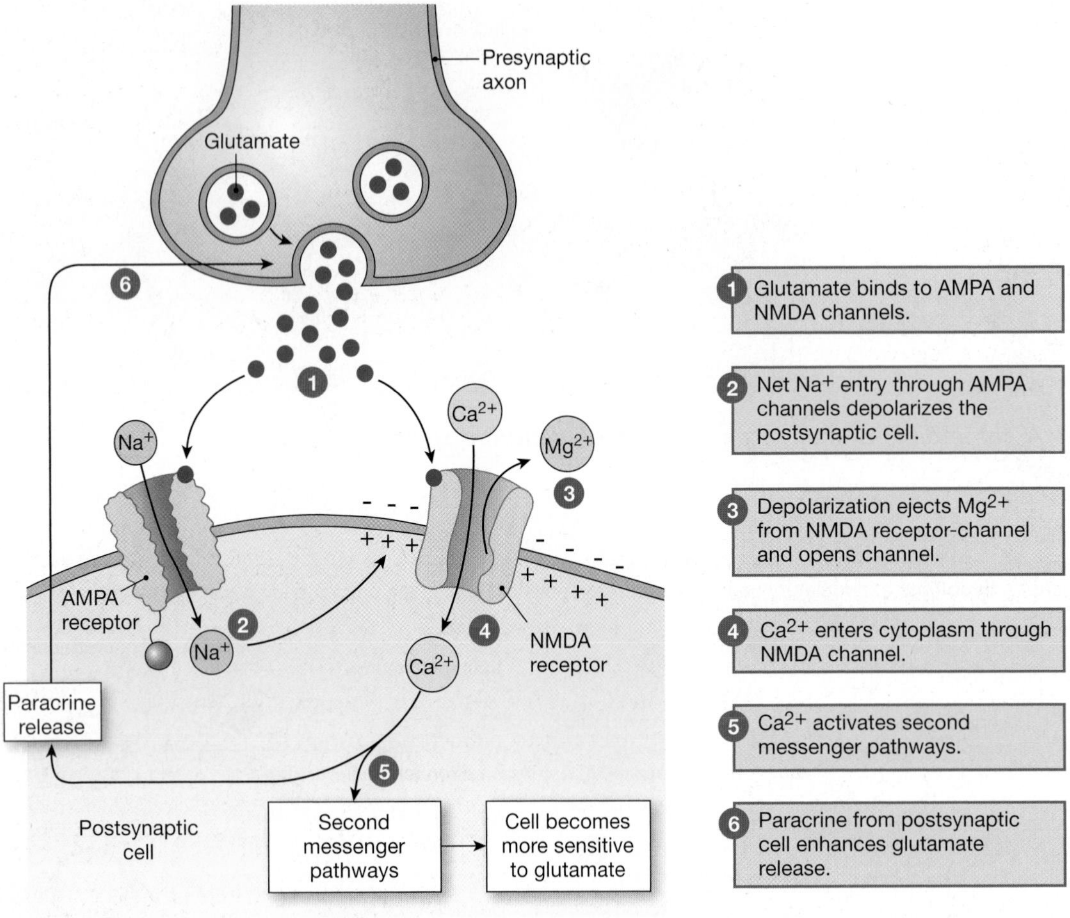
Presynaptic axon
Glutamate
6
1
Na+
Ca2+
Mg2+
3
AMPA receptor
2
Na+
4
Ca2+
NMDA receptor
Paracrine release
5
Postsynaptic cell
Second messenger pathways
Cell becomes more sensitive to glutamate
1 Glutamate binds to AMPA and NMDA channels.
2 Net Na+ entry through AMPA channels depolarizes the postsynaptic cell.
3 Depolarization ejects Mg2+ from NMDA receptor-channel and opens channel.
4 Ca2+ enters cytoplasm through NMDA channel.
5 Ca2+ activates second messenger pathways.
6 Paracrine from postsynaptic cell enhances glutamate release.

● **FIGURE 8-32** ***A mechanism for long-term potentiation***

Presynaptic modulation provides a more precise means of control than postsynaptic modulation. In postsynaptic modulation, if a modulatory neuron synapses on the dendrites and cell body of a neuron, the responsiveness of the entire postsynaptic neuron is altered. In that case, all target cells of the postsynaptic neuron are affected equally (Fig. 8-31b).

Synaptic activity can also be altered by changing the responsiveness of the target cell to neurotransmitter. This may be accomplished by changing the identity, affinity, or number of neurotransmitter receptors. Modulators can alter all of these parameters by influencing the synthesis of enzymes, membrane transporters, and receptors. Most neuromodulators act through second messenger systems that alter existing proteins, and their effects last much longer than do those of neurotransmitters. One signal molecule can act as either a neurotransmitter or a neuromodulator, depending upon its receptor (Fig. 8-23).

CONCEPT CHECK

24. Why are axon terminals sometimes called "biological transducers"?

Answers: p. 295

Long-Term Potentiation Alters Synapses

Two of the "hot topics" in neurobiology today are **long-term potentiation** (LTP) (*potentia,* power) and *long-term depression* (LTD), processes in which activity at a synapse brings about sustained changes in the quality or quantity of synaptic connections. Many times changes in synaptic transmission, such as the facilitation and inhibition we just discussed, are short-term processes of limited duration. However, if synaptic activity persists for longer periods, the neurons may adapt through LTP and LTD. Our understanding of LTP and LTD is changing rapidly, and the mechanisms may not be the same in different brain areas. The descriptions below reflect some of what we currently know about long-term adaptations of synaptic transmission.

A key element in long-term changes in the CNS is the amino acid glutamate, the main excitatory neurotransmitter in the CNS. As you learned previously, glutamate has two types of receptor-channels: AMPA receptors and NMDA receptors. The NMDA receptor has two unusual properties: its channel is blocked by both a gate and a Mg^{2+} ion, and it allows Ca^{2+} as well as Na^+ and K^+ to flow through it. The NMDA channel opens only when the receptor is bound to glutamate and the cell is depolarized.

In long-term potentiation, when presynaptic neurons release glutamate, the neurotransmitter binds to both AMPA and NMDA receptors on the postsynaptic cell (Fig. 8-32 (1) ●). Binding to the AMPA receptor opens a cation channel, and net Na^+ entry depolarizes the cell (2). Glutamate binding to the NMDA receptor opens the channel gate, and depolarization of the cell creates electrical repulsion that knocks the Mg^{2+} out of the NMDA channel (3). Once the NMDA channel is open, Ca^{2+} enters the cytosol (4).

The Ca^{2+} signal initiates second messenger pathways (5). As a result of these pathways, the postsynaptic cell becomes more sensitive to glutamate, possibly by inserting more glutamate receptors in the postsynaptic membrane (up-regulation, p. 194). In addition the postsynaptic cell releases a paracrine that acts on the presynaptic cell to enhance glutamate release (6).

Long-term depression seems to have two components: a change in the number of postsynaptic receptors and a change in the isoforms of the receptor proteins. In the face of continued neurotransmitter release from presynaptic neurons, the postsynaptic neurons withdraw AMPA receptors from the cell membrane by endocytosis [p. 152], a process similar to down-regulation of receptors discussed in the endocrine system [p. 236]. In addition, different subunits are inserted into the AMPA receptors, changing current flow through the ion channels.

Researchers believe that long-term potentiation and depression are related to the neural processes for learning and memory, and to changes in the brain that occur with clinical depression and other mental illnesses. The clinical link makes LTP and LTD hot topics in neuroscience research.

CONCEPT CHECK

25. Why would depolarization of the membrane repulse Mg^{2+} into the extracellular fluid? Answers: p. 295

Disorders of Synaptic Transmission Are Responsible for Many Diseases

Synaptic transmission is the most vulnerable step in the process of signaling through the nervous system. It is the point at which many things go wrong, leading to disruption of normal function. Yet, at the same time, the receptors at synapses are exposed to the extracellular fluid, making them more accessible to drugs than intracellular receptors are.

In recent years scientists have linked a variety of nervous system disorders to problems with synaptic transmission. These disorders include Parkinson's disease, schizophrenia, and depression. The best understood diseases of the synapse are those that involve the neuromuscular junction. Diseases resulting from synaptic transmission problems within the CNS have proved more difficult to study because they are more difficult to isolate anatomically.

RUNNING PROBLEM

Dr. McKhann suspected that the disease afflicting the Chinese children—which he named acute motor axonal polyneuropathy (AMAN)—might be triggered by a bacterial infection. He also thought that the disease initiates its damage of axons at the neuromuscular junctions.

Question 6:

Based on information provided in this chapter, what other diseases involve altered synaptic transmission?

247
249
252
273
275
279
287
290

Drugs that act on synaptic activity, particularly synapses in the CNS, are the oldest known and most widely used of all pharmacological agents. Caffeine, nicotine, and alcohol are common drugs in many cultures. Some of the drugs we use to treat conditions such as schizophrenia, depression, anxiety, and epilepsy act by influencing events at the synapse. In many disorders arising in the CNS, we do not yet fully understand either the cause of the disorder or the drug's mechanism of action. This subject is one major area of pharmacological research, and new classes of drugs are being formulated and approved every year.

Development of the Nervous System Depends on Chemical Signals

During the development of a system as complex as the nervous system, how can more than 100 billion neurons in the brain find their correct targets and make synapses among more than 10 times that many glial cells? How can a somatic motor neuron in the spinal cord find the correct pathway to form a synapse with its target muscle in the big toe? The answer is found in the chemical signals used by the developing embryo, ranging from factors that control differentiation of stem cells to those that direct an elongating axon to its target.

The axons of embryonic nerve cells send out special tips called **growth cones** that extend through the extracellular compartment until they find their target cell (Fig. 8-33 ●). In experiments in which target cells are moved to an unusual location in the embryo, the axons in many instances are still able to find their targets by "sniffing out" their chemical scent. Growth cones depend on many different types of signals to find their way: growth factors, molecules in the extracellular matrix, and membrane proteins on the growth cones and on cells along the path. For example, integrins [p. 74] on the growth cone membrane bind to laminins, protein fibers in the extracellular matrix. Nerve-cell adhesion molecules (NCAMs) [p. 72] interact with membrane proteins of other cells.

Once an axon reaches its target cell, a synapse forms. However, synapse formation must be followed by electrical and

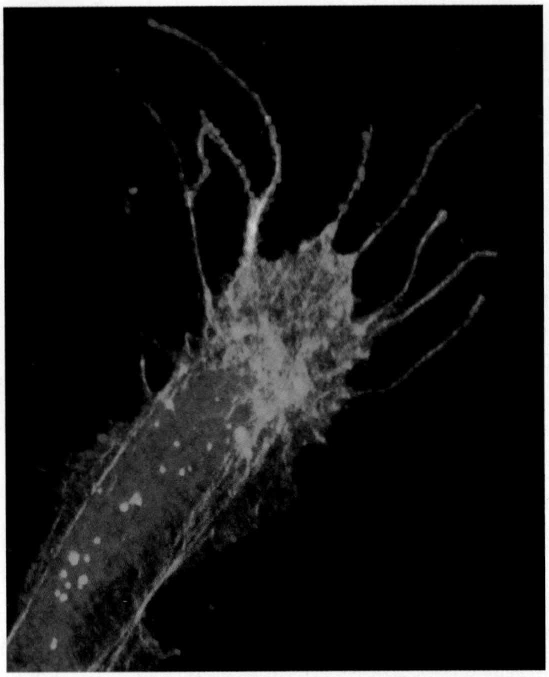

● **FIGURE 8-33** ***Growth cones of a developing axon***

chemical activity, or the synapse will disappear. The survival of neurons seems to depend on **neurotrophic factors** [*trophikos*, nourishment] secreted by neurons and glial cells. There is still much we have to learn about this complicated process, and it is an active area of physiological research.

This "use it or lose it" scenario is most dramatically reflected by the fact that the infant brain is only about one-fourth the size of the adult brain. Further brain growth is due not to an increase in cell number but to an increase in size and number of axons, dendrites, and synapses. Development depends on electrical activity in the brain—in other words, on action potentials moving through sensory pathways and interneurons.

Babies who are neglected or deprived of sensory input may experience delayed development because of the lack of nervous system stimulation. On the other hand, there is no evidence that extra stimulation in infancy enhances intellectual development, despite a popular movement to expose babies to art, music, and foreign languages before they can even walk. Once synapses form, they are not fixed for life. Variations in electrical activity can cause rearrangement of the connections. This process of synaptic plasticity continues throughout life. It is one reason that older adults are urged to keep learning new skills and information.

When Neurons Are Injured, Segments Separated from the Cell Body Die

We can grow neurons when we are young, but what happens when neurons are injured? The responses of mature neurons to injury are similar in many ways to the growth of neurons during development. Both processes rely on a combination of chemical and electrical signals. This is another area of active research because spinal cord injuries and brain damage from illnesses and accidents disable many people each year. The loss of one neuron from a reflex pathway can have drastic consequences for the entire pathway.

If the cell body dies when a neuron is injured, the entire neuron dies. If the cell body is intact and only the axon is severed, most of the neuron survives (Fig. 8-34 ●). At the site of in-

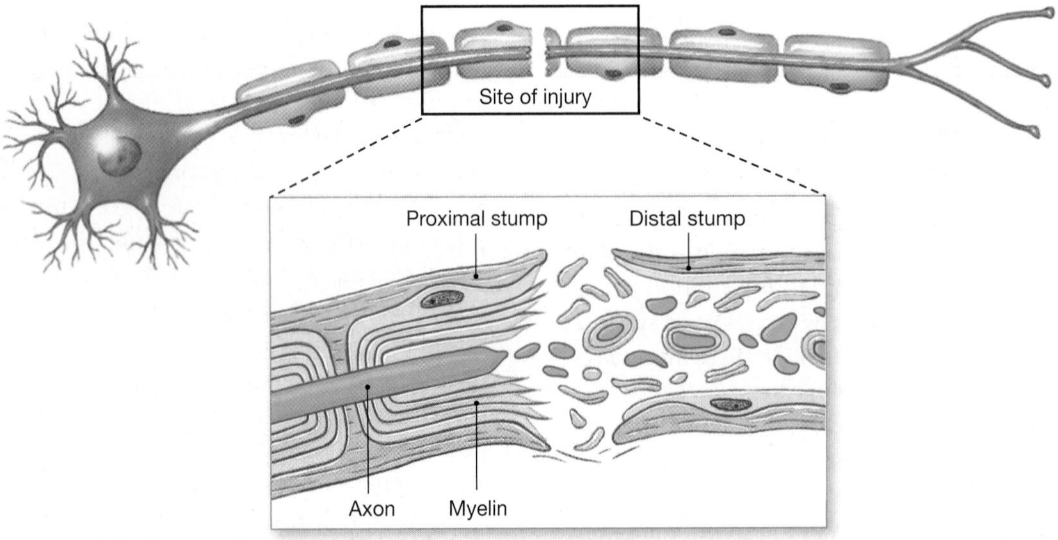
Site of injury
Proximal stump
Distal stump
Axon
Myelin

● **FIGURE 8-34** ***Injury to neurons.*** When an axon is cut, the section attached to the cell body (the proximal stump) continues to live, but the section of the axon distal to the cut (the distal stump) begins to disintegrate and die. Under some circumstances, the proximal stump may regrow through the existing sheath of Schwann cells and reform a synapse with the proper target.

jury, the cytoplasm leaks out until membrane is recruited to seal the opening. The proximal stump (the segment closer to the cell body) swells as organelles and filaments carried into the axon by axonal transport accumulate. Chemical factors produced by Schwann cells near the injury site move by retrograde transport to the cell body, telling it that an injury has occurred.

The distal segment of axon (the distal stump), deprived of its source of protein, begins to degenerate slowly. The death of this part of the neuron may take a month or longer, although synaptic transmission ceases almost immediately. The myelin sheath around the distal axon begins to unravel, and the axon itself collapses. The fragments are cleared away by scavenger microglia or phagocytes that ingest and digest the debris.

Under some conditions, axons in the peripheral nervous system can regenerate and reestablish their synaptic connections. The Schwann cells of the damaged neuron secrete certain neurotrophic factors that keep the cell body alive and stimulate regrowth of the axon. The growing tip of a regenerating axon behaves much like the growth cone of a developing axon, following chemical signals in the extracellular matrix along its former path until the axon rejoins its target cell. Sometimes the loss of the distal axon is permanent, however, and the pathway is destroyed.

Regeneration of axons in the central nervous system is less likely to occur naturally. CNS glial cells tend to seal off and scar the damaged region, and damaged CNS cells secrete factors that inhibit axon regrowth. Many scientists are studying these mechanisms of axon growth and inhibition in the hopes of finding treatments that will restore function to victims of spinal cord injury and degenerative neurological disorders.

RUNNING PROBLEM CONCLUSION

Mysterious Paralysis

In this running problem you learned about acute motor axonal polyneuropathy (AMAN), a baffling paralytic illness that physicians thought might be a new disease. Although its symptoms resemble those of classic Guillain-Barré syndrome, AMAN is not a demyelinating disease and it affects only motor neurons. However, in both classic GBS and AMAN, the body's immune system makes antibodies against nervous system components, leading experts eventually to conclude that AMAN is a subtype of GBS. The classic form of GBS has been renamed acute inflammatory demyelinating polyneuropathy, or AIDP. AIDP is more common in Europe and North America, while AMAN is the predominant form of GBS in China, Japan, and South America. A significant number of patients with AMAN develop their disease following a gastrointestinal illness caused by the bacterium *Campylobacter jejuni*, and experts suspect that antibodies to the bacterium also attack glycolipids called gangliosides in the axonal membrane. To learn more about the link between *Campylobacter* and GBS, see "*Campylobacter* Species and Guillain-Barré Syndrome," *Clinical Microbiology Reviews* 11: 555–567, July 1998 (*http://cmr.asm.org*). Check your understanding of this running problem by comparing your answers to the information in the summary table below.

	QUESTION	FACTS	INTEGRATION AND ANALYSIS
1	Which division(s) of the nervous system may be involved in Guillain-Barré syndrome (GBS)?	The nervous system is divided into peripheral nervous system, which has afferent (sensory) and efferent subdivisions, and central nervous system (CNS). Efferent neurons are either somatic motor neurons, which control skeletal muscles, or autonomic neurons, which control glands and smooth and cardiac muscle.	Patients with GBS can neither feel sensations nor move their muscles. This suggests a problem in both afferent and somatic motor neurons. However, it is also possible that there is a problem in the CNS integrating center. You do not have enough information to determine which division is affected.
2	Do you think the paralysis found in the Chinese children affected both sensory (afferent) and somatic motor neurons? Why or why not?	The Chinese children can feel a pin prick but cannot move their muscles.	Sensory (afferent) function is normal if they can feel the pin prick. Paralysis of the muscles suggests a problem with somatic motor neurons, with the CNS centers controlling movement, or with the muscles themselves.
3	In GBS, what would you expect the results of a nerve conduction test to be?	Nerve conduction tests measure conduction speed and strength of conduction action potentials. In GBS, myelin around neurons is destroyed.	Myelin insulates axons and increases speed. Without myelin, ions leak out of the axon. Thus, in GBS you would expect decreased conduction speed and decreased strength of action potentials.

RUNNING PROBLEM CONCLUSION *(continued)*

	QUESTION	FACTS	INTEGRATION AND ANALYSIS
4	Is the paralytic illness that affected the Chinese children a demyelinating condition? Why or why not?	Nerve conduction tests showed normal conduction speed but decreased strength of the summed action potentials.	Myelin loss should decrease conduction speed as well as action potential strength. Therefore, this illness is probably not a demyelinating disease.
5	Do the results of Dr. McKhann's investigation suggest that the Chinese children had classic Guillain-Barré syndrome? Why or why not?	Autopsy reports on children who died from the disease showed that the axons were damaged but the myelin was normal.	Classic GBS is a demyelinating disease that affects both sensory and motor neurons. The Chinese children had normal sensory function, and nerve conduction tests and histological studies indicated normal myelin. Therefore, it was reasonable to conclude that the disease was not GBS.
6	Based on information provided in this chapter, what other diseases involve altered synaptic transmission?	Synaptic transmission can be altered by blocking neurotransmitter release from the presynaptic cell, by interfering with the action of neurotransmitter on the target cell, or by removing neurotransmitter from the synapse.	Parkinson's disease, depression, schizophrenia, and myasthenia gravis are related to problems with synaptic transmission (p. 278).

247 249 252 273 275 279 287 290

CHAPTER SUMMARY

This chapter introduces the nervous system, one of the major control systems responsible for maintaining *homeostasis*. The divisions of the nervous system correlate with the steps in a reflex pathway. Sensory receptors monitor regulated variables and send input signals to the central nervous system through sensory (afferent) neurons. Output signals, both electrical and chemical, travel through the efferent divisions (somatic motor and autonomic) to their targets throughout the body. Information transfer and *communication* depend on electrical signals that pass along neurons, on *molecular interactions* between signal molecules and their receptors, and on signal transduction in the target cells. In Chapters 9 through 11 and 13 you will learn more details about the basic processes introduced here.

1. The **nervous system** is a complex network of neurons that form the rapid control system of the body. (p. 245)
2. **Emergent properties** of the nervous system include consciousness, intelligence, and emotion. (p. 245)

Organization of the Nervous System

3. The nervous system is divided into the **central nervous system (CNS)**, composed of the **brain** and **spinal cord**, and the **peripheral nervous system**. (p. 247; Fig. 8-1)
4. The peripheral nervous system has **afferent (sensory) neurons** that bring information into the CNS, and **efferent neurons** that carry information away from the CNS back to various parts of the body. (p. 247)
5. The efferent neurons include **somatic motor neurons**, which control skeletal muscles, and **autonomic neurons**, which control smooth and cardiac muscles, glands, and some adipose tissue. (p. 249)
6. Autonomic neurons are subdivided into **sympathetic** and **parasympathetic** branches. (p. 249)

Cells of the Nervous System

iP Nervous System I: Anatomy Review

7. Neurons have a **cell body** with a nucleus and organelles to direct cellular activity, **dendrites** to receive incoming signals, and an **axon** to transmit electrical signals from the cell body to the **axon terminal**. (p. 249; Fig. 8-2)
8. **Interneurons** are neurons that lie entirely within the CNS. (p. 250; Fig. 8-3)
9. The region where an axon terminal meets its target cell is called a **synapse**. The target cell is called the **postsynaptic cell**, and the neuron that releases the chemical signal is known as the **presynaptic cell**. The region between these two cells is the **synaptic cleft**. (p. 252)

10. Material is transported between the cell body and axon terminal by **axonal transport**. (p. 252; Fig. 8-4)
11. **Glial cells** provide physical support and communicate with neurons. **Schwann cells** and **satellite cells** are glial cells associated with the peripheral nervous system. **Microglia, oligodendrocytes, astrocytes**, and **ependymal cells** are glial cells found in the CNS. Microglia are modified immune cells that act as scavengers. (p. 253; Fig. 8-5)
12. Schwann cells and oligodendrocytes form insulating **myelin sheaths** around neurons. The **nodes of Ranvier** are sections of uninsulated membrane occurring at intervals along the length of an axon. (p. 253; Fig. 8-6)
13. **Neural stem cells** that can develop into new neurons and glia are found in the ependymal layer as well as in other parts of the nervous system. (p. 253)

Electrical Signals in Neurons

iP Nervous System I: The Membrane Potential; Ion Channels; The Action Potential

14. Membrane potential is influenced by the concentration gradients of ions across the membrane and by the permeability of the membrane to those ions. (p. 256)
15 The **Goldman-Hodgkin-Katz (GHK) equation** predicts membrane potential based on ion concentration gradients and membrane permeability. (p. 256)
16. The permeability of a cell to ions changes when ion channels in the membrane open and close. Movement of only a few ions significantly changes the membrane potential. (p. 257)
17. Gated ion channels in neurons open or close in response to chemical or mechanical signals or in response to depolarization of the cell membrane. Channels also close through inactivation. (p. 257)
18. **Graded potentials** are depolarizations or hyperpolarizations whose strength is directly proportional to the strength of the triggering event. Graded potentials lose strength as they move through the cell. (p. 258; Tbl. 8-3; Fig. 8-7)
19. The wave of depolarization that moves through the cell with a graded potential is known as **local current flow**. (p. 259)
20. **Action potentials** are rapid electrical signals that travel undiminished in amplitude (strength) from the cell body to the axon terminals. (p. 261)
21. Action potentials begin in the **trigger zone** if either a single graded potential or the sum of multiple graded potentials exceeds a minimum depolarization known as the **threshold**. (p. 260; Fig. 8-8)
22. Depolarizing graded potentials make a neuron more likely to fire an action potential. Hyperpolarizing graded potentials make a neuron less likely to fire an action potential. (p. 260)
23. Action potentials are uniform, **all-or-none** depolarizations. (p. 261)
24. The rising phase of the action potential is due to increased Na^+ permeability. The falling phase of the action potential is due to increased K^+ permeability. (p. 262; Fig. 8-9)
25. The voltage-gated Na^+ channels of the axon have a fast **activation gate** and a slower **inactivation gate**. (p. 263; Fig. 8-10)
26. Once an action potential has begun, there is a brief period of time known as the **absolute refractory period** during which a second action potential cannot be triggered, no matter how large the stimulus. Because of this, action potentials cannot be summed. (p. 264; Fig. 8-12)
27. During the **relative refractory period**, a higher-than-normal graded potential is required to trigger an action potential. (p. 264)
28. Information about the strength and duration of a stimulus is conveyed by the frequency of action potential propagation. (p. 265; Fig. 8-13)
29. Very few ions cross the membrane during an action potential. The Na^+-K^+-ATPase eventually restores Na^+ and K^+ to their original compartments. (p. 265)
30. The myelin sheath around an axon speeds up conduction by increasing membrane resistance and decreasing current leakage. Larger-diameter axons conduct action potentials faster than smaller-diameter axons do. (p. 270)
31. The apparent jumping of action potentials from node to node is called **saltatory conduction**. (p. 271; Fig. 8-18)
32. Changes in blood K^+ concentration affect resting membrane potential and the conduction of action potentials. (p. 272; Fig. 8-19)

Cell-to-Cell Communication in the Nervous System

iP Nervous System II: Anatomy Review; Synaptic Transmission; Ion Channels

33. In **electrical synapses**, an electrical signal passes directly from the cytoplasm of one cell to another through gap junctions. **Chemical synapses** use neurotransmitters to carry information from one cell to the next, with the neurotransmitters diffusing across the synaptic cleft. (p. 273)
34. Neurotransmitters are synthesized in the cell body or in the axon terminal. They are stored in **synaptic vesicles** and are released by exocytosis when an action potential reaches the axon terminal. Neurotransmitters combine with receptors on target cells. (p. 274; Fig. 8-21)
35. Neurotransmitters come in a variety of forms. **Cholinergic** neurons secrete **acetylcholine**. **Adrenergic** neurons secrete **norepinephrine**. **Glutamate, GABA, serotonin, adenosine**, and **nitric oxide** are other major neurotransmitters. (p. 277; Tbl. 8-4)
36. Neurotransmitter receptors are either ligand-gated ion channels or G protein–coupled receptors. Ion channels create **fast synaptic potentials**. G protein–coupled receptors either create **slow synaptic potentials** or modify cell metabolism. (p. 280; Fig. 8-23)
37. Neurotransmitter action is rapidly terminated by reuptake into cells, diffusion away from the synapse, or enzymatic breakdown. (p. 281; Fig. 8-24)

Integration of Neural Information Transfer

iP Nervous System II: Synaptic Potentials & Cellular Integration

38. When a presynaptic neuron synapses on a larger number of postsynaptic neurons, the pattern is known as **divergence**. When several presynaptic neurons provide input to a smaller number of postsynaptic neurons, the pattern is known as **convergence**. (p. 282; Fig. 8-25)

39. Synaptic transmission can be modulated in response to activity at the synapse, a process known as **synaptic plasticity**. (p. 282)
40. The summation of simultaneous graded potentials from different neurons is known as **spatial summation**. The summation of graded potentials that closely follow each other sequentially is called **temporal summation**. (p. 283; Figs. 8-28, 8-29)
41. **Presynaptic modulation** of an axon terminal allows selective modulation of collaterals and their targets. **Postsynaptic modulation** occurs when a modulatory neuron, usually inhibitory, synapses on a postsynaptic cell body or dendrites. (p. 283; Fig. 8-31)
42. **Long-term potentiation** and **long-term depression** are mechanisms by which neurons change the quality or quantity of their synaptic connections. (p. 285)
43. Developing neurons find their way to their targets by using chemical signals. (p. 287)

QUESTIONS

(Answers to the Review Questions begin on page A1.)

THE PHYSIOLOGY PLACE

Access more review material online at The Physiology Place web site. There you'll find review questions, problem-solving activities, case studies, flashcards, and direct links to both *Interactive Physiology®* and *PhysioEx™*. To access the site, go to *www.physiologyplace.com* and select *Human Physiology*, Fifth Edition.

LEVEL ONE REVIEWING FACTS AND TERMS

1. List the three functional classes of neurons, and explain how they differ structurally and functionally.
2. Somatic motor neurons control __________. __________ neurons control smooth and cardiac muscles, exocrine and some endocrine glands, and some types of adipose tissue.
3. Autonomic neurons are classified as either __________ or __________ neurons.
4. Match each term with its description:

(a) axon	1. process of a neuron that receives incoming signals
(b) dendrite	2. sensory neuron, transmits information to CNS
(c) afferent	3. long process that transmits signals to the target cell
(d) efferent	4. region of neuron where action potential begins
(e) trigger zone	5. neuron that transmits information from CNS to the rest of the body

5. Name the two primary cell types found in the nervous system.
6. Draw a typical neuron and label the cell body, axon, dendrites, nucleus, trigger zone, axon hillock, collaterals, and axon terminals. Draw mitochondria, rough endoplasmic reticulum, Golgi complex, and vesicles in the appropriate sections of the neuron.
7. Axonal transport refers to the
   (a) release of neurotransmitters into the synaptic cleft.
   (b) use of microtubules to send secretions from the cell body to axon terminal.
   (c) movement of organelles and cytoplasm up and down the axon.
   (d) movement of the axon terminal to synapse with a new postsynaptic cell.
   (e) none of these
8. Match the numbers of the appropriate characteristics with the two types of potentials. Characteristics may apply to one or both types.

(a) action potential	1. all-or-none
(b) graded potential	2. can be summed
	3. amplitude decreases with distance
	4. exhibits a refractory period
	5. amplitude depends on strength of stimulus
	6. has no threshold

9. Match the glial cell(s) on the right to the functions on the left. There may be more than one correct answer for each function.

(a) modified immune cells	1. astrocytes
(b) help form the blood-brain barrier	2. ependymal cells
(c) form myelin	3. microglia
(d) separates CNS fluid compartments	4. oligodendrocytes
(e) found in peripheral nervous system	5. satellite cells
(f) found in ganglia	6. Schwann cells

10. List the four major types of ion channels found in neurons. Are they chemically gated, mechanically gated, or voltage-gated?
11. Arrange the following events in the proper sequence:
    (a) Efferent neuron reaches threshold and fires an action potential.
    (b) Afferent neuron reaches threshold and fires an action potential.
    (c) Effector organ responds by performing output.
    (d) Integrating center reaches decision about response.
    (e) Sensory organ detects change in the environment.
12. An action potential is (circle all correct answers)
    (a) a reversal of the Na^+ and K^+ concentrations inside and outside the neuron.
    (b) the same size and shape at the beginning and end of the axon.
    (c) initiated by inhibitory postsynaptic graded potentials.
    (d) transmitted to the distal end of a neuron and causes release of neurotransmitter.

In questions 13–17, choose from the following ions to fill in the blanks correctly: Na^+, K^+, Ca^{2+}, Cl^-.

13. The resting cell membrane is more permeable to __________ than to __________. Although __________ contribute little to the resting

membrane potential, they play a key role in generating electrical signals in excitable tissues.

14. The concentration of __________ is 12 times greater outside the cell than inside.
15. The concentration of __________ is 30 times greater inside the cell than outside.
16. An action potential occurs when __________ enter the cell.
17. The resting membrane potential is due to the high __________ permeability of the cell.
18. What is the myelin sheath?
19. List two factors that enhance conduction speed.
20. List three ways neurotransmitters are removed from the synapse.
21. Draw and label a graph of an action potential. Below the graph, draw the positioning of the K^+ and Na^+ channel gates during each phase.

LEVEL TWO REVIEWING CONCEPTS

22. Create a map showing the organization of the nervous system using the following terms, plus any terms you choose to add:

afferent signals	neuron
astrocyte	neurotransmitter
autonomic division	oligodendrocyte
brain	parasympathetic division
CNS	peripheral division
efferent neuron	satellite cell
efferent signals	Schwann cell
ependymal cell	sensory division
glands	somatic motor division
glial cells	spinal cord
integration	stimulus
interneuron	sympathetic division
microglia	
muscles	

23. What causes the depolarization phase of an action potential? (Circle all that apply.)
    (a) K^+ leaving the cell through voltage-gated channels
    (b) K^+ being pumped into the cell by the Na^+-K^+-ATPase
    (c) Na^+ being pumped into the cell by the Na^+-K^+-ATPase
    (d) Na^+ entering the cell through voltage-gated channels
    (e) opening of the Na^+ channel inactivation gate
24. Name any four neurotransmitters, their receptor(s), and tell whether the receptor is an ion channel or a GPCR.
25. Arrange the following terms to describe the sequence of events after a neurotransmitter binds to a receptor on a postsynaptic neuron. Terms may be used more than once or not at all.
    (a) action potential fires at axon hillock
    (b) trigger zone reaches threshold
    (c) cell depolarizes
    (d) exocytosis
    (e) graded potential occurs
    (f) ligand-gated ion channel opens
    (g) local current flow occurs
    (h) saltatory conduction occurs
    (i) voltage-gated Ca^{2+} channels open
    (j) voltage-gated K^+ channels open
    (k) voltage-gated Na^+ channels open
26. Match the best term (hyperpolarize, depolarize, repolarize) to the following events. The cell in question has a resting membrane potential of −70 mV.
    (a) membrane potential changes from −70 mV to −50 mV
    (b) membrane potential changes from −70 mV to −90 mV
    (c) membrane potential changes from +20 mV to −60 mV
    (d) membrane potential changes from −80 mV to −70 mV
27. A neuron has a resting membrane potential of −70 mV. Will the neuron hyperpolarize or depolarize when each of the following events occurs? (More than one answer may apply; list all those that are correct.)
    (a) Na^+ enters the cell
    (b) K^+ leaves the cell
    (c) Cl^- enters the cell
    (d) Ca^{2+} enters the cell
28. Define, compare, and contrast the following concepts:
    (a) threshold, subthreshold, suprathreshold, all-or-none, overshoot, undershoot
    (b) graded potential, EPSP, IPSP
    (c) absolute refractory period, relative refractory period
    (d) afferent neuron, efferent neuron, interneuron
    (e) sensory neuron, somatic motor neuron, sympathetic neuron, autonomic neuron, parasympathetic neuron
    (f) fast synaptic potential, slow synaptic potential
    (g) temporal summation, spatial summation
    (h) convergence, divergence
29. If all action potentials within a given neuron are identical, how does the neuron transmit information about the strength and duration of the stimulus?
30. The presence of myelin allows an axon to
    (a) produce more frequent action potentials.
    (b) conduct impulses more rapidly.
    (c) produce action potentials of larger amplitude.
    (d) produce action potentials of longer duration.

LEVEL THREE PROBLEM SOLVING

31. If human babies' muscles and neurons are fully developed and functional at birth, why can't they focus their eyes, sit up, or learn to crawl within hours of being born? (*Hint:* Muscle strength is not the problem.)
32. The voltage-gated Na^+ channels of a neuron open when the neuron depolarizes. If depolarization opens the channels, why do they close when the neuron is maximally depolarized?
33. One of the pills that Jim takes for high blood pressure caused his blood K^+ level to decrease from 4.5 mM to 2.5 mM. What happens to the resting membrane potential of his liver cells? (Circle all that are correct.)
    (a) decreases
    (b) increases
    (c) does not change
    (d) becomes more negative
    (e) becomes less negative
    (f) fires an action potential
    (g) depolarizes
    (h) hyperpolarizes
    (i) repolarizes

34. Characterize each of the following stimuli as being mechanical, chemical, or thermal:
    (a) bath water at 106° F
    (b) acetylcholine
    (c) a hint of perfume
    (d) epinephrine
    (e) lemon juice
    (f) a punch on the arm
35. An unmyelinated axon has a much greater requirement for ATP than a myelinated axon of the same diameter and length. Can you explain why?

LEVEL FOUR QUANTITATIVE PROBLEMS

36. The GHK equation is sometimes abbreviated to exclude chloride, which plays a minimal role in membrane potential for most cells. In addition, because it is difficult to determine absolute membrane permeability values for Na^+ and K^+, the equation is revised to use the ratio of the two ion permeabilities as $\alpha = P_{Na}/P_K$:

$$V_m = 61 \log \frac{[K^+]_{out} + \alpha[Na^+]_{out}}{[K^+]_{in} + \alpha[Na^+]_{in}}$$

Thus, if you know the relative membrane permeabilities of the two ions and their intracellular (ICF) and extracellular (ECF) concentrations, you can predict the membrane potential for a cell.

    (a) A resting cell has an alpha value of 0.025 and the following ion concentrations:

    Na^+: ICF = 5 mM, ECF = 135 mM
    K^+: ICF = 150 mM, ECF = 4 mM

    What is the cell's membrane potential?
    (b) The Na^+ permeability of the cell in (a) suddenly increases so that $\alpha = 20$. Now what is the cell's membrane potential?
    (c) Mrs. Nguyen has high blood pressure and her physician puts her on a diuretc that decreases her plasma (ECF) K^+ from 4 mM to 2.5 mM. Using the other values in (a), now what is the membrane potential?
    (d) The physician prescribes a potassium supplement for Mrs. Nguyen, who decides that if two pills are good, four must be better. Her plasma (ECF) K^+ now goes to 6 mM. What happens to the membrane potential?
37. In each of the following scenarios, will an action potential be produced? The postsynaptic neuron has a resting membrane potential of −70 mV.
    (a) Fifteen neurons synapse on one postsynaptic neuron. At the trigger zone, 12 of the neurons produce EPSPs of 2 mV each, and the other three produce IPSPs of 3 mV each. The threshold for the postsynaptic cell is −50 mV.
    (b) Fourteen neurons synapse on one postsynaptic neuron. At the trigger zone, 11 of the neurons produce EPSPs of 2 mV each, and the other three produce IPSPs of 3 mV each. The threshold for the postsynaptic cell is −60 mV.
    (c) Fifteen neurons synapse on one postsynaptic neuron. At the trigger zone, 14 of the neurons produce EPSPs of 2 mV each, and the other one produces an IPSP of 9 mV. The threshold for the postsynaptic cell is −50 mV.

ANSWERS

Answers to Concept Check Questions

Page 249

1. Compare your answer to the map in Figure 8-1, p. 248.

Page 252

2. Neurons that secrete neurohormones terminate close to blood vessels so that the neurohormones can enter the circulation.
3. See Figure 8-2.

Page 255

4. Myelin insulates axon membranes. Microglia are scavenger cells in the CNS. Ependymal cells form epithelial barriers between fluid compartments of the CNS.
5. Schwann cells are in the PNS, and each Schwann cell forms myelin around a small portion of one axon. Oligodendrocytes are in the CNS, and one oligodendrocyte forms myelin around axons of several neurons.

Page 256

6. For Ca^{2+}, the electrical charge z is +2; the ratio of ion concentrations is 1/0.0001 = 10,000 or 10^4. Log of 10^4 is 4 (see Appendix B). Thus E_{ion} (in mV) = $(61 \times 4)/(+2)$ = 122 mV.

Page 257

7. (a) depolarizes (b) depolarizes
8. depolarize

Page 259

9. (a) 1, (b) 2, (c) 2, (d) 1

Page 259

10. The trigger zone for the sensory neurons is close to where the dendrites converge. You cannot tell where the trigger zone is for the anaxonic neuron. For multipolar neurons, the trigger zone is at the junction of the cell body and the axon.

Page 264

11. The membrane potential will depolarize and stay depolarized.
12. During resetting, the activation gate is closing, and the inactivation gate is opening.

Page 265

13. (b)

Page 270

14. The action potential will go in both directions because the Na^+ channels around the stimulation site have not been inactivated by a previous depolarization. See refractory periods, p. 264.

Page 271

15. a, c, b

Page 274

16. Proteins are synthesized on the ribosomes of the rough endoplasmic reticulum; then the proteins are directed into the Golgi complex to be packaged into vesicles.

17. Mitochondria are the primary sites of ATP synthesis.
18. Mitochondria reach the axon terminal by fast axonal transport along microtubules.

Page 275

19. The researchers concluded that some event between arrival of the action potential at the axon terminal and depolarization of the postsynaptic cell is dependent on extracellular Ca^{2+}. We now know that this event is neurotransmitter release.

Page 279

20. Because different receptor subtypes work through different signal transduction pathways, targeting drugs to specific receptor subtypes decreases the likelihood of unwanted side effects.

Page 281

21. SSRIs decrease reuptake of serotonin into the axon terminal, thereby increasing the time serotonin is active in the synapse.

Page 283

22. The postsynaptic neuron will fire an action potential, because the net effect would be a 17 mV depolarization to $-70 - (-17) = -53$ mV, which is just above the threshold of -55 mV.
23. The membrane potential does not change at the same time as the stimulus because the depolarization must travel from the point of the stimulus to the recording point.

Page 284

24. Axon terminals convert (transduce) the electrical action potential signal into a chemical neurotransmitter signal.

Page 286

25. Membrane depolarization makes the inside of the membrane more positive with respect to the outside. Like charges repel one another, so the more positive membrane potential tends to repel Mg^{2+}.

Answers to Figure Questions

Page 260

Fig. 8-7: The graded potential is stronger at B. On the graph, A is between 3 and 4, and B is about at 1.

Page 268

Fig. 8-15: a) 4; b) 2, 3; c) 1; d) 3; e) 4

Page 270

Fig. 8-17: Diameter would be 8 mm.

Page 282

Fig. 8-25: Amplification.

9

The Central Nervous System

BACKGROUND BASICS

Directions of the body: **Appendix D** Up-regulation: **194** Diffusion through membranes: **139** Cell-to-cell junctions: **72** Synapses: **274** Glial cells: **253** Transporting epithelium: **154** Ionic basis of action potentials: **258** Neurotransmitters and neuromodulators: **180** Posterior pituitary: **228** Fast and slow synaptic potentials: **280** Long-term potentiation: **285**

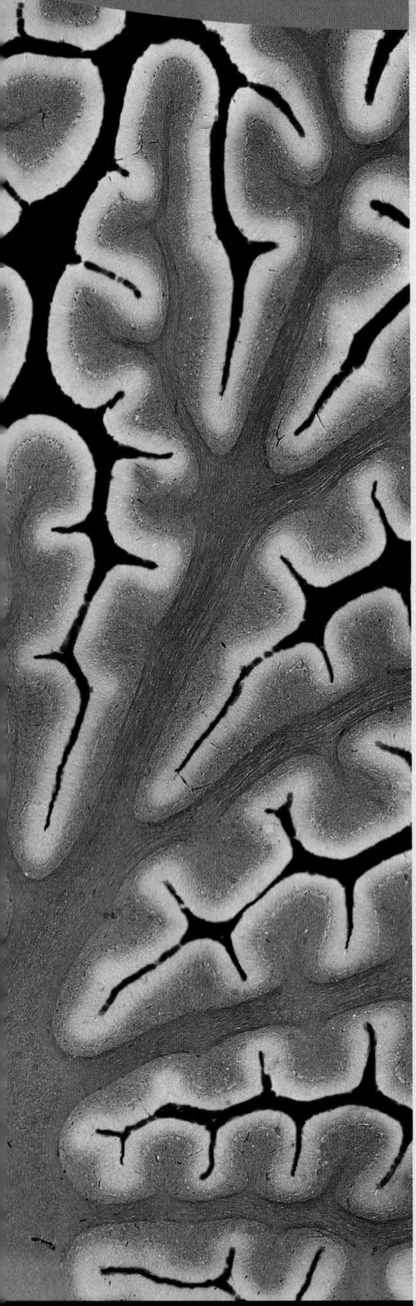

Cross-section of the cerebellum showing its complex folding.

Neuronal assemblies have important properties that cannot be explained by the additive qualities of individual neurons.

—O. Hechter, *in* Biology and Medicine into the 21st Century, 1991

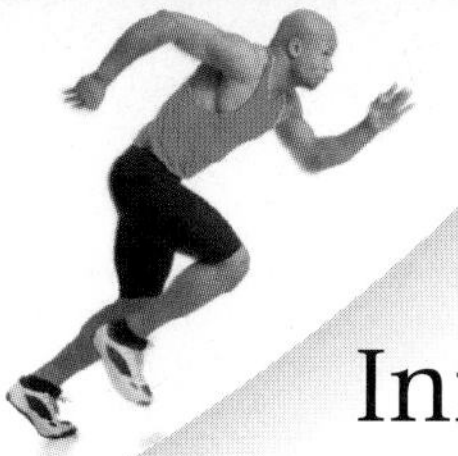

RUNNING PROBLEM

Infantile Spasms

At four months of age, Ben could roll over, hold up his head, and reach for things. At seven months, he was nearly paralyzed and lay listlessly in his crib. He had lost his abilities so gradually that it was hard to remember when each one had slipped away, but his mother could remember exactly when it began. She was preparing to feed him lunch one day when she heard a cry from the highchair where Ben was sitting. As she watched, Ben's head dropped to his chest, came back up, then went hurtling toward his lap, smacking into his highchair table. Ben's mother snatched him up into her arms, and she could feel him still convulsing against her shoulder. This was the first of many such spells that came with increasing frequency and duration.

297 305 320 322 326 327

Matt Nagle, paralyzed from the neck down and breathing with the aid of a ventilator, sat immobile in his wheelchair, a small box perched on top of his skull. But this was no ordinary box: it was part of a brain-computer interface (BCI) with 96 recording electrodes implanted in Matt's brain. On the computer screen in front of Matt was a cursor that moved across the screen as Matt thought about where he wanted it to go. By the end of the revolutionary one-year experiment in 2005, Matt could open email, play a game, and open and close a robotic hand using only his thoughts. This story may sound like science fiction, but the BrainGate® BCI and the experiment are real. The scientists who developed BrainGate were using what we know about the human brain to harness its electrical signals and create wireless bridges to external machines. In this chapter we take a look at the structure and organization of our main integrating center, the central nervous system.

EMERGENT PROPERTIES OF NEURAL NETWORKS

Neurons in the nervous system link together to form circuits that have specific functions. The most complex circuits are those of the brain, in which billions of neurons are linked into intricate networks that converge and diverge, creating an infinite number of possible pathways. Signaling within these pathways creates thinking, language, feeling, learning, and memory—the complex behaviors that make us human. Some neuroscientists have proposed that the functional unit of the nervous system be changed from the individual neuron to neural networks because even the most basic functions require circuits of neurons.

How is it that combinations of neurons linked together into chains or networks collectively possess emergent properties not found in any single neuron? We do not yet have an answer to this question. Some scientists seek to answer it by looking for parallels between the nervous system and the integrated circuits of computers.

Computer programs have been written that attempt to mimic the thought processes of humans. This field of study, called *artificial intelligence*, has created some interesting programs, such as the "psychiatrist" programmed to respond to typed complaints with appropriate comments and suggestions. We are nowhere near creating a brain as complex as that of a human, however, or even one as complex as that of Hal, the computer in the classic movie *2001: A Space Odyssey*.

Probably one reason computers cannot yet accurately model brain function is that computers lack *plasticity*, the ability to change circuit connections and function in response to sensory input and past experience [p. 282]. Although some computer programs can change their output under specialized conditions, they cannot begin to approximate the plasticity of human brain networks, which easily restructure themselves as the result of sensory input, learning, emotion, and creativity. In addition, we now know that the brain can add new connections when neural stem cells differentiate. Computers cannot add new circuits to themselves.

How can simply linking neurons together create **affective behaviors**, which are related to feeling and emotion, and **cognitive behaviors** [*cognoscere,* to get to know] related to thinking? In their search for the organizational principles that lead to these behaviors, scientists seek clues in the simplest animal nervous systems.

EVOLUTION OF NERVOUS SYSTEMS

All animals have the ability to sense and respond to changes in their environment. Even single-cell organisms such as *Paramecium* are able to carry out the basic tasks of life: finding food, avoiding becoming food, finding a mate. Yet these unicellular organisms have no obvious brain or integrating center, merely the resting membrane potential that exists in living cells.

The first multicellular animals to develop neurons were members of the phylum *Cnidaria*, the jellyfish and sea anemones. Their nervous system is a *nerve net* composed of sensory neurons, connective interneurons, and motor neurons that innervate muscles and glands (Fig. 9-1a ●). These animals respond to stimuli with complex behaviors, yet without input from an identifiable control center. If you watch a jellyfish swim or a sea anemone maneuver a piece of shrimp into its mouth, it is hard to imagine how a diffuse network of neurons can create such complex coordinated movements. However,

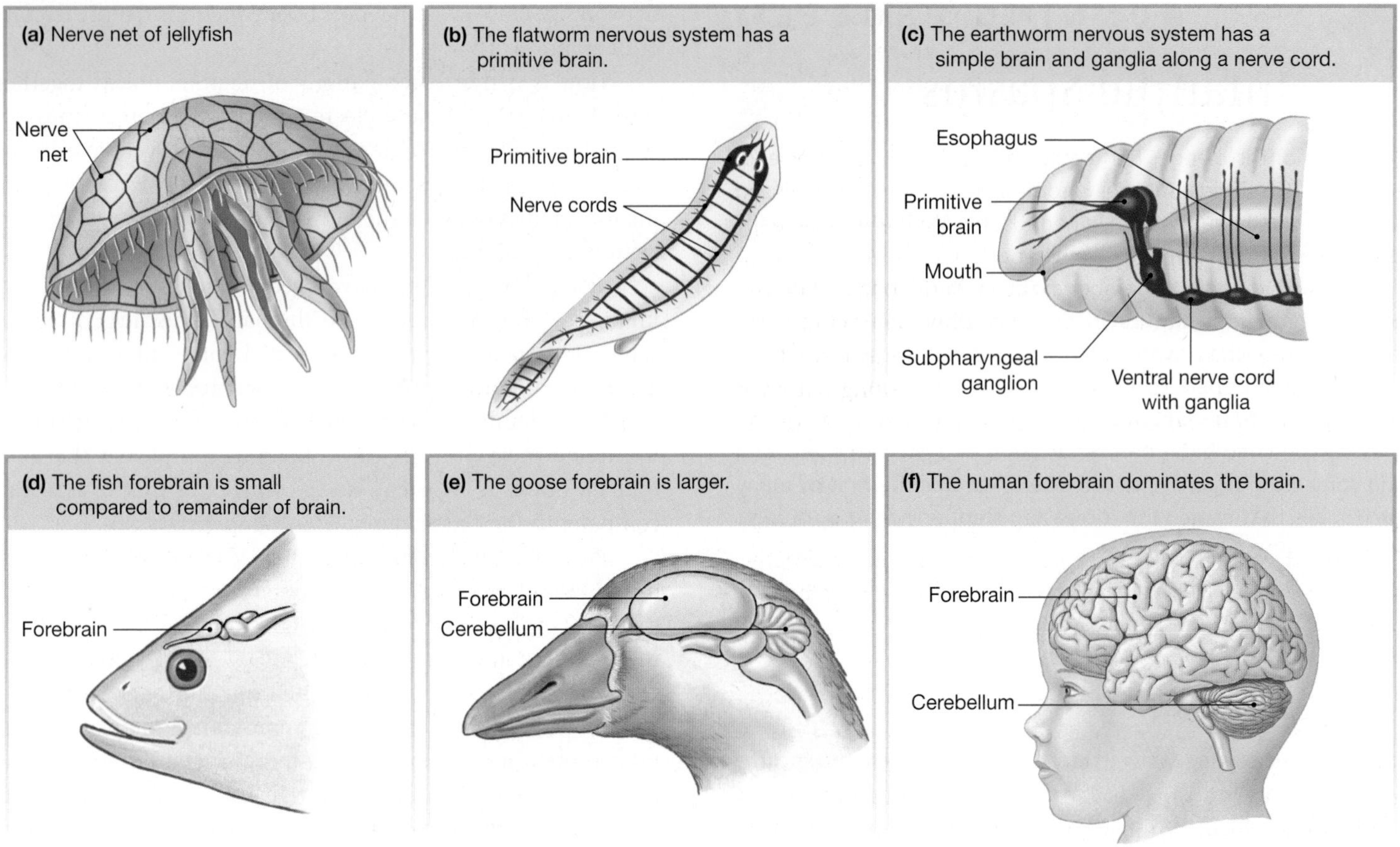
(a) Nerve net of jellyfish
Nerve net
(b) The flatworm nervous system has a primitive brain.
Primitive brain
Nerve cords
(c) The earthworm nervous system has a simple brain and ganglia along a nerve cord.
Esophagus
Primitive brain
Mouth
Subpharyngeal ganglion
Ventral nerve cord with ganglia
(d) The fish forebrain is small compared to remainder of brain.
Forebrain
(e) The goose forebrain is larger.
Forebrain
Cerebellum
(f) The human forebrain dominates the brain.
Forebrain
Cerebellum

FIGURE 9-1 ***Evolution of the nervous system***

the same basic principles that you learned in Chapter 8 apply to jellyfish and humans. Electrical signals in the form of action potentials, and chemical signals passing across synapses, are the same in all animals. It is only in the number and organization of the neurons that one species differs from another.

CONCEPT CHECK

1. Match each of the following terms with the appropriate neuron type(s).

(a) Afferent neuron	1. Interneuron
(b) Efferent signal	2. Motor neuron
(c) Integrating center	3. Sensory neuron
(d) Input signal	
(e) Output signal	

Answers: p. 331

In the primitive flatworms, we see the beginnings of a nervous system as we know it in higher animals, although in flatworms the distinction between central nervous system and peripheral nervous system is not clear. Flatworms have a rudimentary brain consisting of a cluster of nerve cell bodies concentrated in the head (*cephalic*) region. Two large nerves called *nerve cords* come off the primitive brain and lead to a nerve network that innervates distal regions of the flatworm body (Fig. 9-1b).

The segmented worms, or annelids, such as the earthworm, have a more advanced central nervous system (Fig. 9-1c). Clusters of cell bodies are no longer restricted to the head region, as they are in flatworms, but also occur in fused pairs, called *ganglia* (singular *ganglion*) [p. 253], along a nerve cord. Because each segment of the worm contains a ganglion, simple reflexes can be integrated within a segment without input from the brain. Reflexes that do not require integration in the brain also occur in higher animals and are called **spinal reflexes** in humans and other vertebrates.

Annelids and higher invertebrates have complex reflexes controlled through neural networks. Researchers use leeches (a type of annelid) and *Aplysia*, a type of shell-less mollusk, to study neural networks and synapse formation because the neurons in these species are 10 times larger than human brain neurons, and because the networks have identical numbers of neurons from animal to animal. The neural function of these invertebrates provides a simple model that we can apply to more complex vertebrate networks.

Nerve cell bodies clustered into brains persist throughout the more advanced phyla and become increasingly more complex. One advantage to cephalic brains is that in most animals, the head is the part of the body that first contacts the environment as the animal moves. For this reason, as brains evolved, they became associated with specialized cephalic receptors, such as eyes for vision and chemoreceptors for smell and taste.

In the higher arthropods, such as insects, specific regions of the brain are associated with particular functions. More complex brains are associated with complex behaviors, such as the ability of social insects like ants and bees to organize themselves into colonies, divide labor, and communicate with one another. The octopus (a cephalopod mollusk) has the most sophisticated brain development among the invertebrates, as well as the most sophisticated behavior.

In vertebrate brain evolution, the most dramatic change is seen in the *forebrain* region [*fore,* in front], which includes the **cerebrum** [*cerebrum,* brain; adjective *cerebral*]. In fish, the forebrain is a small bulge dedicated mainly to processing olfactory information about odors in the environment (Fig. 9-1d). In birds and rodents, part of the forebrain has enlarged into a cerebrum with a smooth surface (Fig. 9-1e). In humans, the cerebrum is the largest and most distinctive part of the brain, with deep grooves and folds (Fig. 9-1f). More than anything else, the cerebrum is what makes us human. All evidence indicates that it is the part of the brain that allows reasoning and cognition.

The other brain structure whose evolution is obvious in the vertebrates is the **cerebellum**, a region of the *hindbrain* devoted to coordinating movement and balance. Birds (Fig. 9-1e) and humans (Fig. 9-1f) both have well-developed cerebellar structures. The cerebellum, like the cerebrum, is readily identifiable in these phyla by its grooves and folds.

In this chapter we begin with an overview of CNS anatomy and functions. We then look at how neural networks create the higher brain functions of thought and emotion.

BIOTECHNOLOGY

TRACING NEURONS IN A NETWORK

One of the challenges facing neurophysiologists and neuroanatomists is tracing the networks of neurons that control specific functions, a task that can be likened to following one tiny thread through a tangled mass the size of a beach ball. In 1971, K. Kristensson and colleagues introduced the use of *horseradish peroxidase* (HRP), an enzyme that acts in the presence of its substrate to produce a visible product (colored or fluorescent). When injected into the extracellular fluid near axon terminals, HRP is brought into the neuron by endocytosis. The vesicles containing HRP are then transported by fast retrograde axonal transport to the cell body and dendrites [p. 252]. Once the enzyme-substrate reaction is completed, the neuron becomes visible, allowing the researcher to trace the entire neuron from its target back to its origin. Now, with the help of fluorescent antibodies, scientists can even tell which ion channels, neurotransmitters, and receptors the neuron uses.

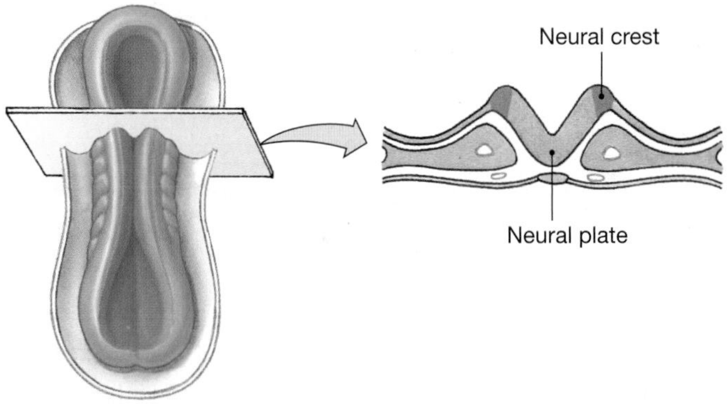

(a) In the 20-day embryo (dorsal view), neural plate cells (purple) migrate toward the midline. Neural crest cells migrate with the neural plate cells.

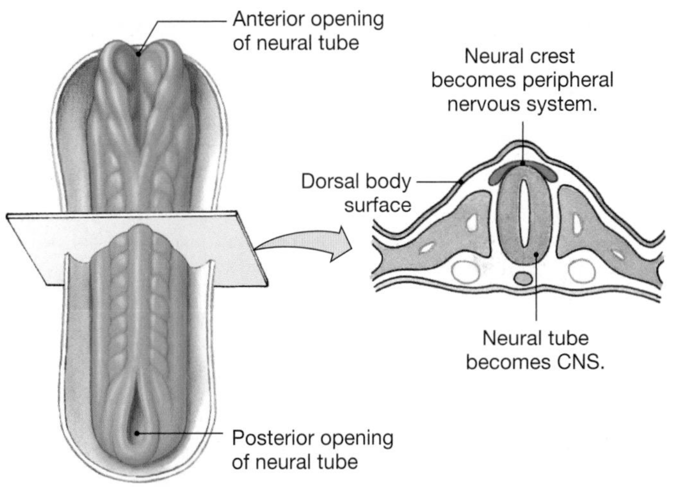

(b) By day 23 of embryonic development, neural tube formation is almost complete.

● **FIGURE 9-2** ***Development of the human nervous system***

ANATOMY OF THE CENTRAL NERVOUS SYSTEM

The vertebrate central nervous system (CNS) consists of the brain and the spinal cord. As you learned in the previous section, brains increase in complexity and degree of specialization as we move up the phylogenetic tree from fish to humans. However, if we look at the vertebrate nervous system during development, a basic anatomical pattern emerges. In all vertebrates, the CNS consists of layers of neural tissue surrounding a fluid-filled central cavity lined with epithelium.

The CNS Develops from a Hollow Tube

In the very early embryo, cells that will become the nervous system lie in a flattened region called the **neural plate**. As development proceeds (at about day 20 of human development), neural plate cells along the edge migrate toward the midline (Fig. 9-2a ●). By about day 23 of human development, the neural plate cells have fused with each other, creating a **neural**

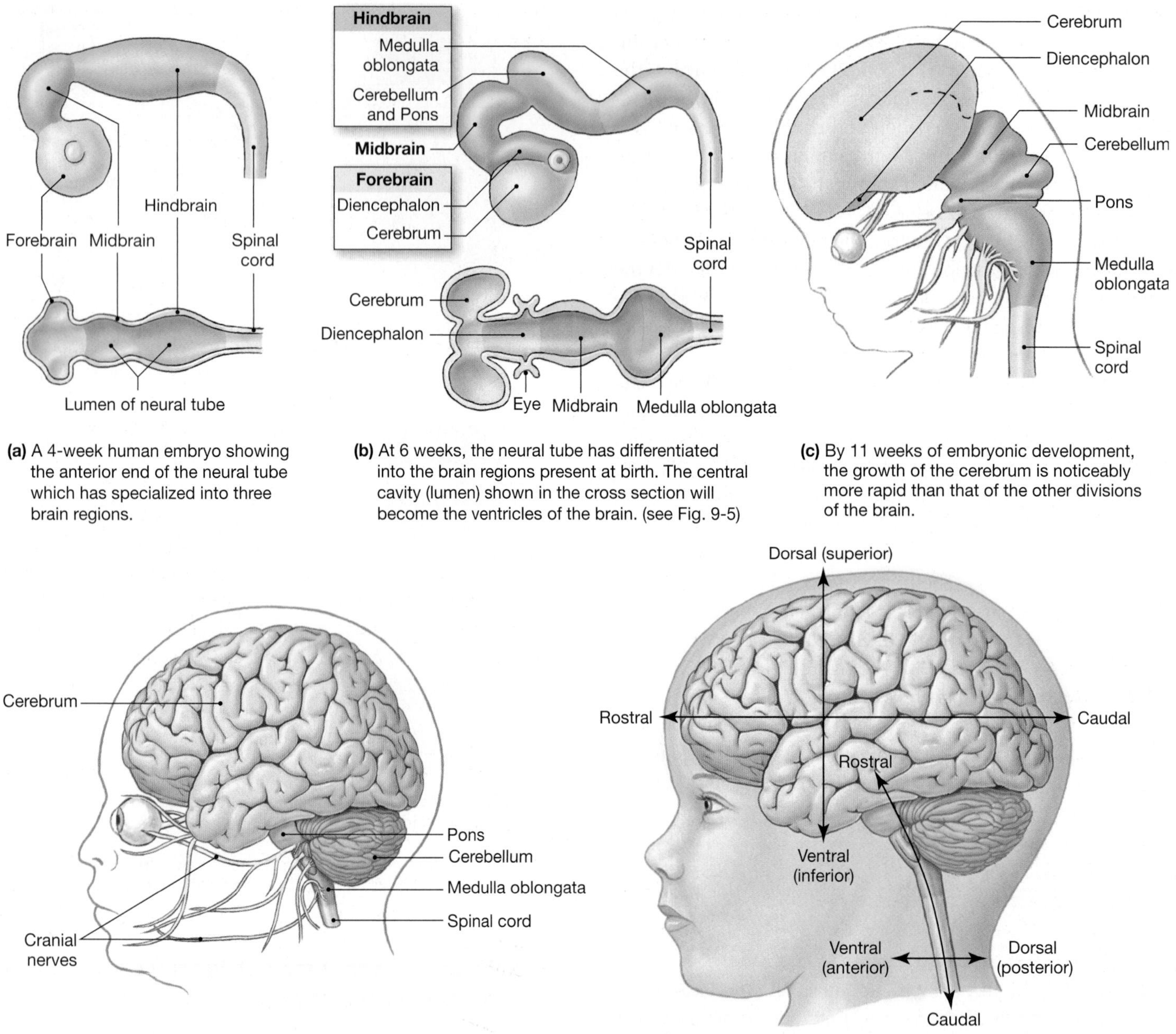

(a) A 4-week human embryo showing the anterior end of the neural tube which has specialized into three brain regions.

(b) At 6 weeks, the neural tube has differentiated into the brain regions present at birth. The central cavity (lumen) shown in the cross section will become the ventricles of the brain. (see Fig. 9-5)

(c) By 11 weeks of embryonic development, the growth of the cerebrum is noticeably more rapid than that of the other divisions of the brain.

(d) At birth, the cerebrum has covered most of the other brain regions. Its rapid growth within the rigid confines of the cranium forces it to develop a convoluted, furrowed surface.

(e) The directions "dorsal" and "ventral" are different in the brain because of flexion in the neural tube during development.

● **FIGURE 9-3** ***The neural tube specializes into the seven major regions of the nervous system.***

tube (Fig. 9-2b). *Neural crest cells* from the lateral edges of the neural plate now lie dorsal to the neural tube. The lumen of the neural tube will remain hollow and become the central cavity of the CNS. The cells lining the neural tube will either differentiate into the epithelial *ependyma* [p. 253] or remain as undifferentiated *neural stem cells*. The outer cell layers of the neural tube will become the neurons and glia of the CNS. Neural crest cells will become the sensory and motor neurons of the peripheral nervous system.

By week 4 of human development, the anterior portion of the neural tube has begun to specialize into the regions of the brain (Fig. 9-3a ●). Three divisions are obvious: a **forebrain**, a **midbrain**, and a **hindbrain**. The tube posterior to the hindbrain will become the spinal cord. At this stage, the portion of the forebrain that will become the cerebrum is not much larger than the other regions of the brain.

As development proceeds, the growth of the cerebrum begins to outpace that of the other regions (Fig. 9-3b). By week 6, the CNS has formed the seven major divisions that are present at birth. Six of these regions are in the brain—(1) the cerebrum, (2) the **diencephalon**, (3) the midbrain, (4) and (5) the cerebellum and **pons**, (6) the **medulla oblongata**—and the seventh is the spinal cord. The cerebrum and diencephalon develop from the forebrain. The cerebellum, pons, and medulla oblongata are divisions of the hindbrain.

By week 6 the central cavity (lumen) of the neural tube has begun to enlarge into the hollow **ventricles** [*ventriculus*, belly] of the brain. There are two *lateral ventricles* (the first and second) and two *descending ventricles* (the third and fourth). The central cavity of the neural tube also becomes the *central canal* of the spinal cord.

By week 11 the cerebrum is noticeably enlarged (Fig. 9-3c), and at birth the cerebrum is the largest and most obvious structure we see when looking at a human brain (Fig. 9-3d). The fully developed cerebrum surrounds the diencephalon, midbrain, and pons, leaving only the cerebellum and medulla oblongata visible below it. Because of the flexion (bending) of the neural tube early in development (see Fig. 9-3b), some directional terms have different meanings when applied to the brain (Fig. 9-3e).

The CNS Is Divided into Gray Matter and White Matter

The central nervous system, like the peripheral nervous system, is composed of neurons and supportive glial cells. As noted in Chapter 8, interneurons are neurons completely contained within the CNS. Sensory (afferent) and efferent neurons link interneurons to peripheral receptors and effectors.

When viewed on a macroscopic level, the tissues of the CNS are divided into gray matter and white matter (Fig. 9-4c ●). **Gray matter** consists of unmyelinated nerve cell bodies, dendrites, and axon terminals. The cell bodies are assembled in an organized fashion in both the brain and the spinal cord. They form layers in some parts of the brain and in other parts cluster into groups of neurons that have similar functions. Clusters of cell bodies in the brain and spinal cord are known as *nuclei,* and they are usually identified by specific names, such as the *lateral geniculate nucleus,* where visual information is processed.

White matter is made up mostly of myelinated axons and contains very few cell bodies. Its pale color comes from the myelin sheaths that surround the axons. Bundles of axons that connect different regions of the CNS are known as **tracts**. Tracts in the central nervous system are equivalent to nerves in the peripheral nervous system.

The consistency of the brain and spinal cord is soft and jellylike. Although individual neurons and glial cells have highly organized internal cytoskeletons that maintain cell shape and orientation, neural tissue has minimal extracellular matrix and must rely on external support for protection from trauma. This support comes in the form of an outer casing of bone, three layers of connective tissue membrane, and fluid between the membranes.

CONCEPT CHECK

2. Name the four kinds of glial cells found in the CNS, and describe the function(s) of each [p. 253]. Answers: p. 331

Bone and Connective Tissue Support the CNS

In vertebrates, the brain is encased in a bony **skull**, or **cranium** (Fig. 9-4a), and the spinal cord runs through a canal in the **vertebral column**. The body segmentation that is characteristic of many invertebrates can still be seen in the bony **vertebrae** (singular *vertebra*), which are stacked on top of one another and separated by disks of connective tissue. Nerves of the peripheral nervous system enter and leave the spinal cord by passing through notches between the stacked vertebrae (Fig. 9-4c).

Three layers of membrane, collectively called the **meninges** [singular *meninx,* membrane], lie between the bones and tissues of the central nervous system. These membranes help stabilize the neural tissue and protect it from bruising against the bones of the skeleton. Starting from the bones and moving toward the neural tissue, the membranes are (1) the dura mater, (2) the arachnoid membrane, and (3) the pia mater (Fig. 9-4b, c).

The **dura mater** [*durare,* to last + *mater,* mother] is the thickest of the three membranes (think *durable*). It is associated with veins that drain blood from the brain through vessels or cavities called *sinuses*. The middle layer, the **arachnoid** [*arachnoides,* cobweblike] **membrane,** is loosely tied to the inner membrane, leaving a *subarachnoid space* between the two layers. The inner membrane, the **pia mater** [*pius,* pious + *mater,* mother], is a thin membrane that adheres to the surface of the brain and spinal cord. Arteries that supply blood to the brain are associated with this layer.

The final protective component of the CNS is extracellular fluid, which helps cushion the delicate neural tissue. The cranium has an internal volume of 1.4 L, of which about 1 L is occupied by the cells. The remaining volume is divided into two distinct extracellular compartments: the blood (100–150 mL), and the cerebrospinal fluid and interstitial fluid (250–300 mL). The cerebrospinal fluid and interstitial fluid together form the extracellular environment for neurons. Interstitial fluid lies inside the pia mater. Cerebrospinal fluid is found in the ventricles and in the space between the pia mater and the arachnoid membrane. The cerebrospinal and interstitial fluid compartments communicate with each other across the leaky junctions of the pial membrane and the ependymal cell layer lining the ventricles.

ANATOMY SUMMARY

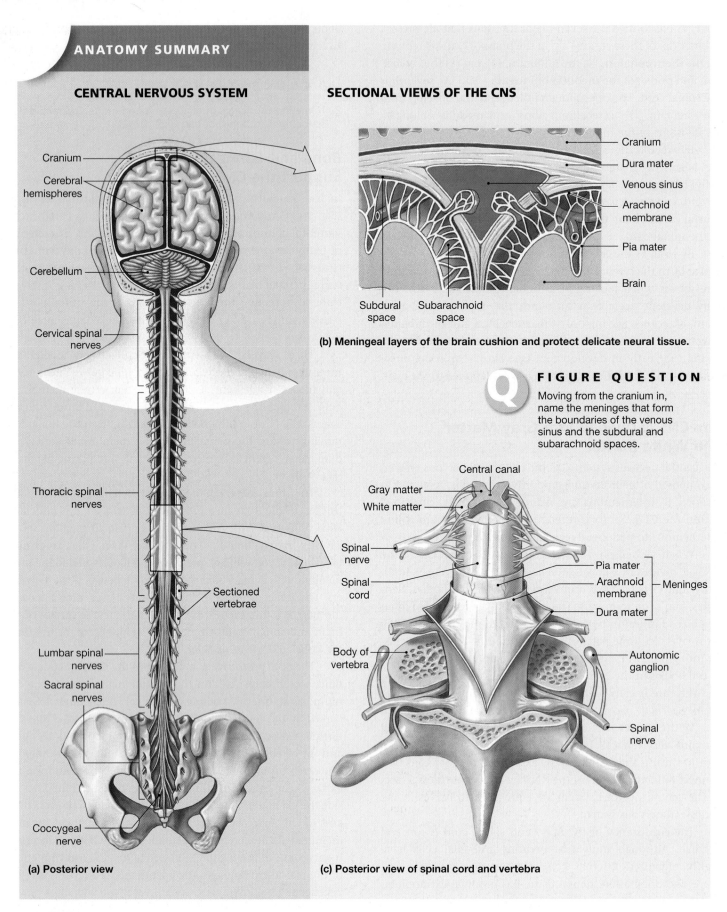

CENTRAL NERVOUS SYSTEM

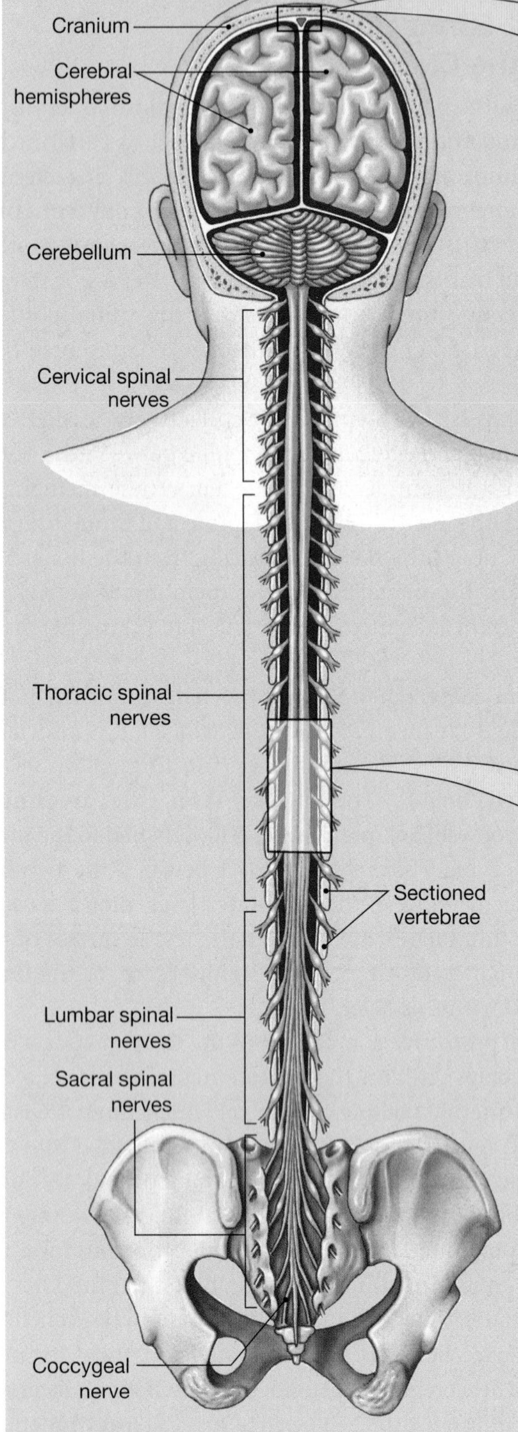

Cranium
Cerebral hemispheres
Cerebellum
Cervical spinal nerves
Thoracic spinal nerves
Sectioned vertebrae
Lumbar spinal nerves
Sacral spinal nerves
Coccygeal nerve

(a) Posterior view

SECTIONAL VIEWS OF THE CNS

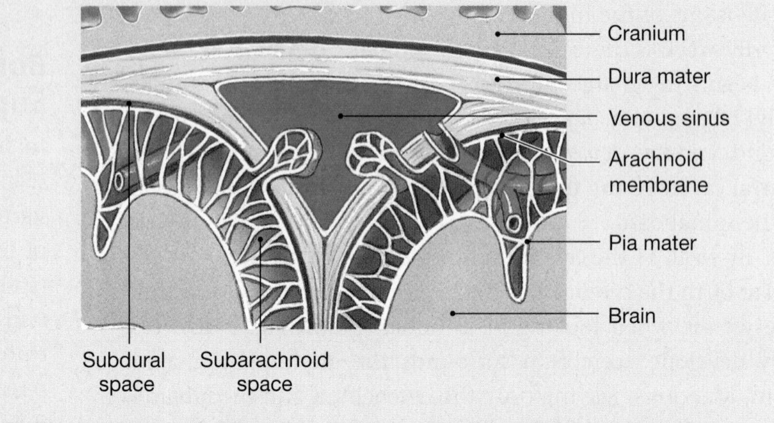

Cranium
Dura mater
Venous sinus
Arachnoid membrane
Pia mater
Brain
Subdural space
Subarachnoid space

(b) Meningeal layers of the brain cushion and protect delicate neural tissue.

FIGURE QUESTION

Moving from the cranium in, name the meninges that form the boundaries of the venous sinus and the subdural and subarachnoid spaces.

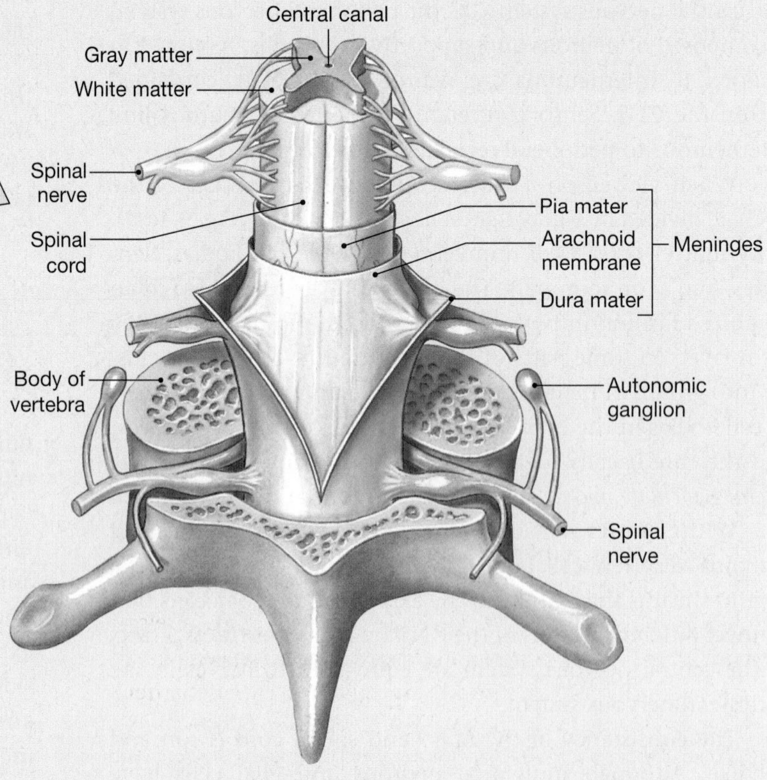

Central canal
Gray matter
White matter
Spinal nerve
Spinal cord
Pia mater
Arachnoid membrane
Dura mater
Meninges
Body of vertebra
Autonomic ganglion
Spinal nerve

(c) Posterior view of spinal cord and vertebra

● **FIGURE 9-4**

CONCEPT CHECK

3. What is a ganglion? What is the equivalent structure in the CNS?
4. Peripheral nerves are equivalent to what organizational structure in the CNS?

Answers: p. 331

The Brain Floats in Cerebrospinal Fluid

Cerebrospinal fluid, or **CSF**, is a salty solution that is continuously secreted by the **choroid plexus**, a specialized region on the walls of the ventricles (Fig. 9-5b ●). The choroid plexus is remarkably similar to kidney tissue and consists of capillaries and a transporting epithelium [p. 154] derived from the ependyma. The choroid plexus cells selectively pump sodium and other solutes from plasma into the ventricles, creating an osmotic gradient that draws water along with the solutes (Fig. 9-5c).

From the ventricles, cerebrospinal fluid flows into the **subarachnoid space** between the pia mater and the arachnoid membrane, surrounding the entire brain and spinal cord in fluid (Fig. 9-5b). The cerebrospinal fluid flows around the neural tissue and is finally absorbed back into the blood by special **villi** [singular *villus,* shaggy hair] on the arachnoid membrane in the cranium (Fig. 9-5d). The rate of fluid flow through the central nervous system is sufficient to replenish the entire volume of cerebrospinal fluid about three times a day.

Cerebrospinal fluid serves two purposes: physical protection and chemical protection. The brain and spinal cord float in the thin layer of fluid between the membranes. The buoyancy of cerebrospinal fluid reduces the weight of the brain nearly 30-fold. Lighter weight translates into less pressure on blood vessels and nerves attached to the CNS.

The cerebrospinal fluid also provides protective padding. When there is a blow to the head, the CSF must be compressed before the brain can hit the inside of the cranium. However, water is minimally compressible, which helps CSF cushion the brain. For a dramatic example of the protective power of cerebrospinal fluid, shake a block of tofu (representing the brain) in an empty jar. Then shake a second block of tofu in a jar completely filled with water to see how cerebrospinal fluid safeguards the brain.

In addition to physically protecting the delicate tissues of the CNS, cerebrospinal fluid creates a closely regulated extracellular environment for the neurons. The choroid plexus is selective about which substances it transports into the ventricles, and as a result, the composition of cerebrospinal fluid is different from that of the plasma. The concentrations of K^+, Ca^{2+}, HCO_3^-, and glucose are lower in the cerebrospinal fluid, and the concentration of H^+ is higher. Only the concentration of Na^+ in cerebrospinal fluid is similar to that in the blood. In addition, cerebrospinal fluid normally contains very little protein and no blood cells.

Cerebrospinal fluid exchanges solutes with the interstitial fluid of the CNS and provides a route by which wastes can be removed. Clinically, a sample of cerebrospinal fluid is presumed to be an indicator of the chemical environment in the brain. This sampling procedure, known as a *spinal tap* or *lumbar puncture,* is generally done by withdrawing fluid from the subarachnoid space between vertebrae at the lower end of the spinal cord. The presence of proteins or blood cells in cerebrospinal fluid suggests an infection.

CONCEPT CHECK

5. If the concentration of H^+ in cerebrospinal fluid is higher than that in the blood, what can you say about the pH of the CSF?
6. If a blood vessel running between the meninges ruptures as a result of a blow to the cranium, what do you predict might happen?
7. Is cerebrospinal fluid more like plasma or more like interstitial fluid? Defend your answer.

Answers: p. 331

The Blood-Brain Barrier Protects the Brain from Harmful Substances in the Blood

The final layer of protection for the brain is a functional barrier between the interstitial fluid and the blood. This barrier is necessary to isolate the body's main control center from potentially harmful substances in the blood and from blood-borne pathogens such as bacteria. To achieve this protection, most of the 400 miles of brain capillaries create a functional **blood-brain barrier** (Fig. 9-6 ●). Although not a literal barrier, the highly selective permeability of brain capillaries shelters the brain from toxins and from fluctuations in hormones, ions, and neuroactive substances such as neurotransmitters in the blood.

Why are brain capillaries so much less permeable than other capillaries? In most capillaries, leaky cell-cell junctions and pores allow free exchange of solutes between the plasma and interstitial fluid [p. 72]. In brain capillaries, however, the endothelial cells form tight junctions with one another, junctions that prevent solute movement between the cells. Tight junction formation apparently is induced by paracrine signals from adjacent astrocytes whose foot processes surround the capillary. As a result, it is the brain tissue itself that creates the blood-brain barrier.

The selective permeability of the blood-brain barrier can be attributed to its transport properties. The capillary endothelium uses selected membrane carriers and channels to move nutrients and other useful materials from the blood into the brain interstitial fluid. Other transporters move wastes from the interstitial fluid into the plasma. Any water-soluble molecule that is not transported on one of these carriers cannot cross the blood-brain barrier.

One interesting illustration of how the blood-brain barrier works is seen in *Parkinson's disease,* a neurological disorder in

ANATOMY SUMMARY

VENTRICLES OF THE BRAIN

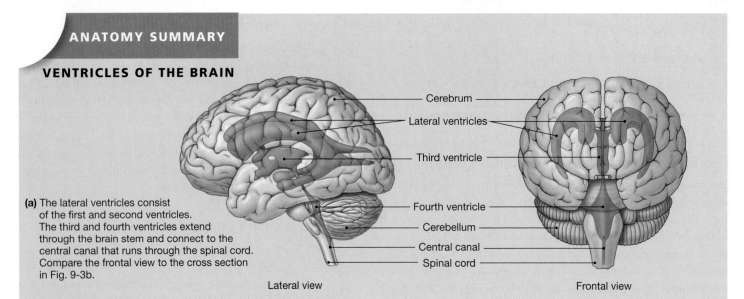

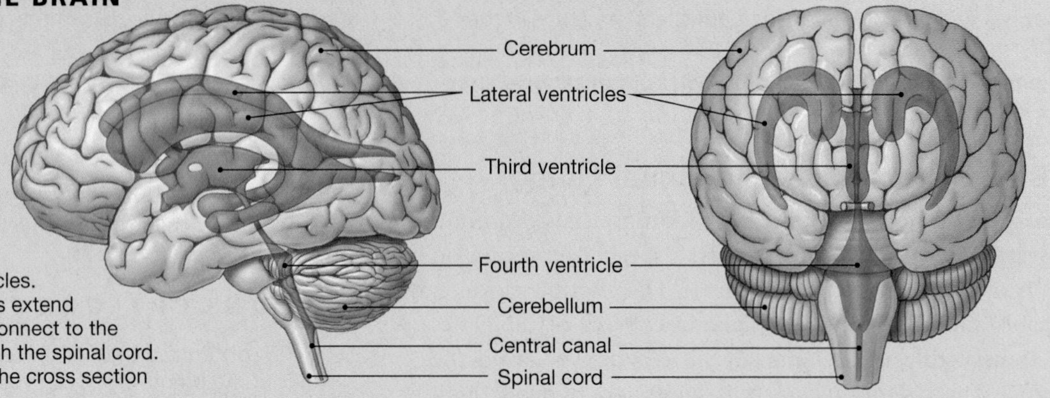
Cerebrum
Lateral ventricles
Third ventricle
Fourth ventricle
Cerebellum
Central canal
Spinal cord
Lateral view
Frontal view

(a) The lateral ventricles consist of the first and second ventricles. The third and fourth ventricles extend through the brain stem and connect to the central canal that runs through the spinal cord. Compare the frontal view to the cross section in Fig. 9-3b.

CEREBROSPINAL FLUID CIRCULATION

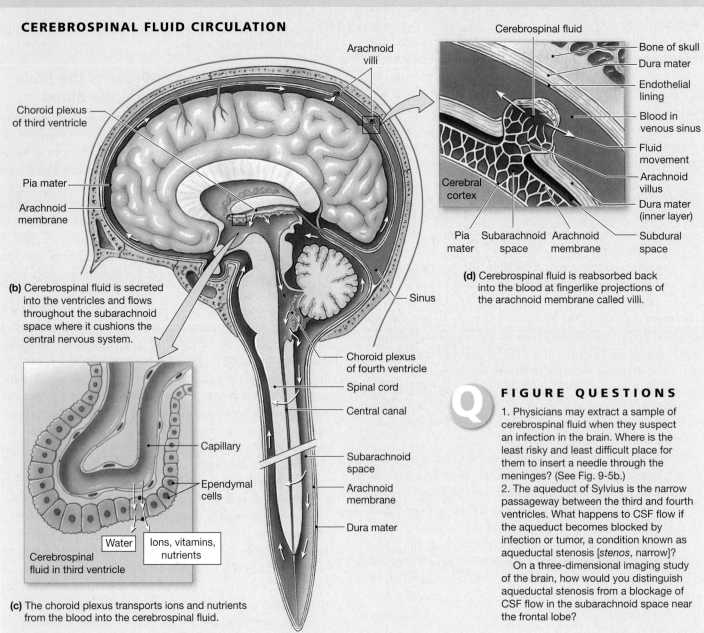

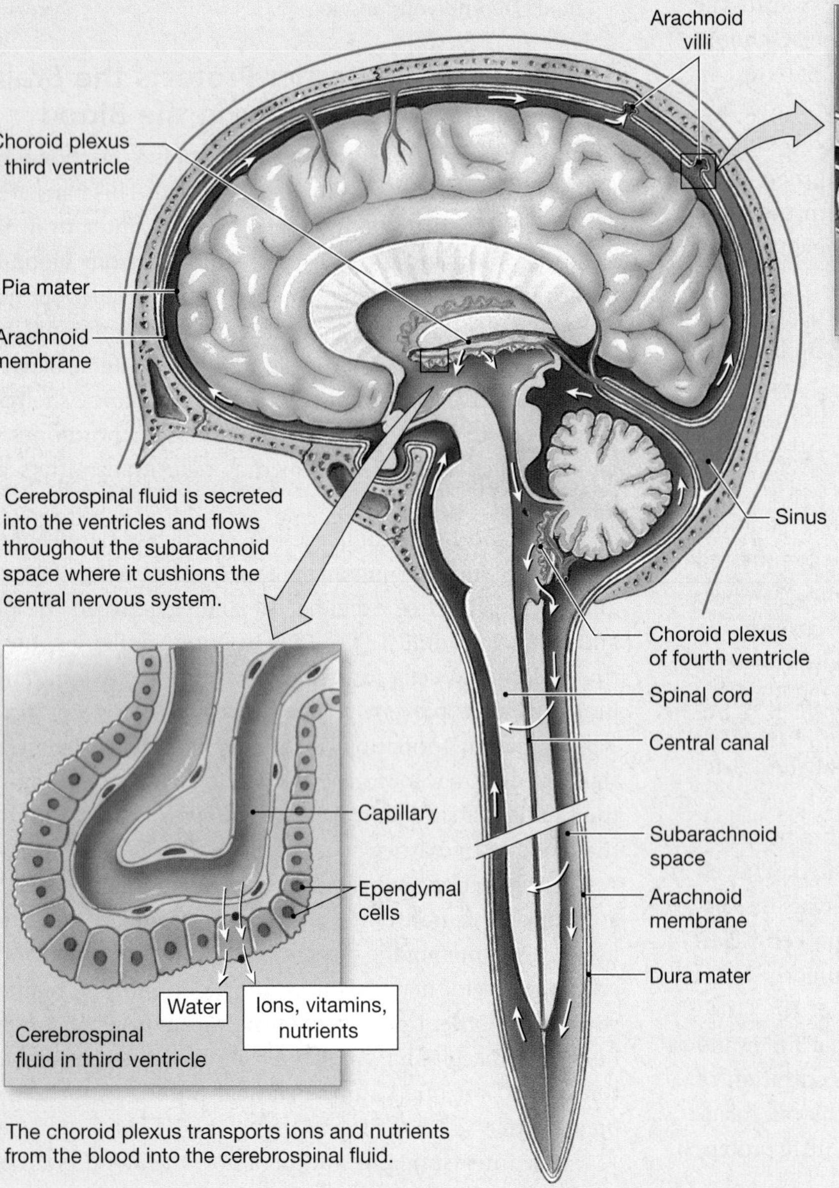
Arachnoid villi
Choroid plexus of third ventricle
Pia mater
Arachnoid membrane
Sinus
Choroid plexus of fourth ventricle
Spinal cord
Central canal
Subarachnoid space
Arachnoid membrane
Dura mater
Capillary
Ependymal cells
Water
Ions, vitamins, nutrients
Cerebrospinal fluid in third ventricle

(b) Cerebrospinal fluid is secreted into the ventricles and flows throughout the subarachnoid space where it cushions the central nervous system.

(c) The choroid plexus transports ions and nutrients from the blood into the cerebrospinal fluid.

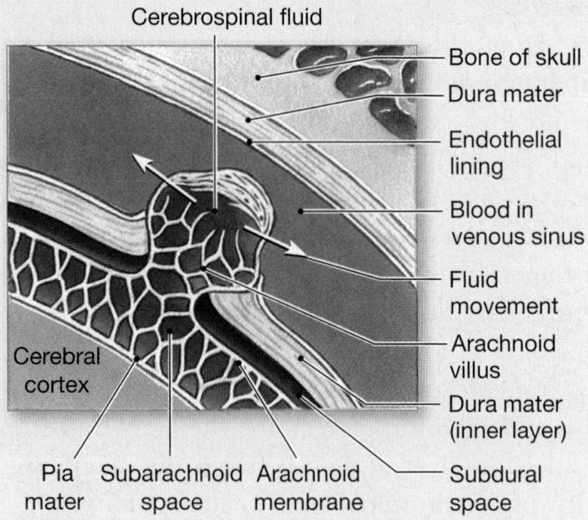
Cerebrospinal fluid
Bone of skull
Dura mater
Endothelial lining
Blood in venous sinus
Fluid movement
Arachnoid villus
Dura mater (inner layer)
Subdural space
Cerebral cortex
Pia mater
Subarachnoid space
Arachnoid membrane

(d) Cerebrospinal fluid is reabsorbed back into the blood at fingerlike projections of the arachnoid membrane called villi.

FIGURE QUESTIONS

1. Physicians may extract a sample of cerebrospinal fluid when they suspect an infection in the brain. Where is the least risky and least difficult place for them to insert a needle through the meninges? (See Fig. 9-5b.)
2. The aqueduct of Sylvius is the narrow passageway between the third and fourth ventricles. What happens to CSF flow if the aqueduct becomes blocked by infection or tumor, a condition known as aqueductal stenosis [*stenos*, narrow]?

On a three-dimensional imaging study of the brain, how would you distinguish aqueductal stenosis from a blockage of CSF flow in the subarachnoid space near the frontal lobe?

FIGURE 9-5

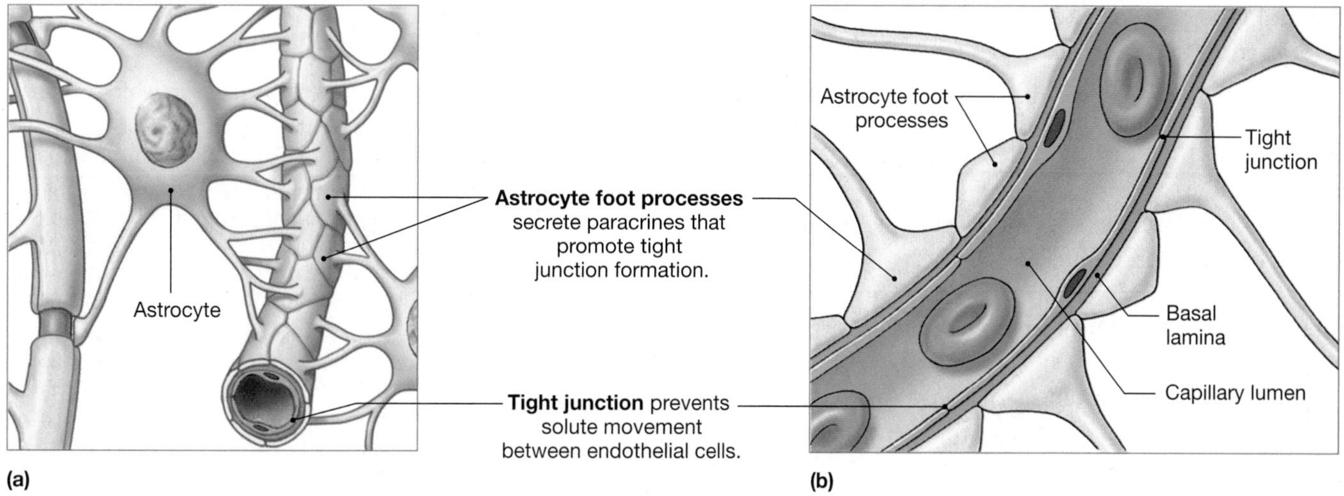

● **FIGURE 9-6** ***The blood-brain barrier.*** The movement of material across the blood-brain barrier is regulated to protect neurons from potentially harmful substances in the blood.

which brain levels of the neurotransmitter dopamine are too low because dopaminergic neurons are either damaged or dead. Dopamine administered in a pill or injection is ineffective because it is unable to cross the blood-brain barrier. The dopamine precursor L-*dopa,* however, is transported across the cells of the blood-brain barrier on an amino acid transporter [p. 147]. Once neurons have access to L-dopa in the interstitial fluid, they metabolize it to dopamine, thereby allowing the deficiency to be treated.

The blood-brain barrier effectively excludes many water-soluble substances, but smaller lipid-soluble molecules can diffuse through the cell membranes [p. 139]. This is one reason some antihistamines make you sleepy but others do not. Older antihistamines were lipid-soluble amines that readily crossed the blood-brain barrier and acted on brain centers controlling alertness. The newer drugs are much less lipid soluble and as a result do not have the same sedative effect.

A few areas of the brain lack a functional blood-brain barrier, and their capillaries have leaky endothelium like most of the rest of the body. In these areas of the brain, the function of adjacent neurons depends in some way on direct contact with the blood. For instance, the hypothalamus releases neurosecretory hormones that must pass into the capillaries of the *hypothalamic-hypophyseal portal system* for distribution to the anterior pituitary [p. 232]. Another region that lacks the blood-brain barrier is the vomiting center in the medulla oblongata. These neurons monitor the blood for possibly toxic foreign substances, such as drugs. If they sense something harmful, they initiate a vomiting reflex. Vomiting removes the contents of the digestive system and helps eliminate ingested toxins.

Neural Tissue Has Special Metabolic Requirements

A unique property of the central nervous system is its specialized metabolism. Neurons require a constant supply of

RUNNING PROBLEM

Ben was diagnosed with *infantile spasms,* a form of epilepsy characterized by the onset of head-drop seizures at four to seven months and by arrested or deteriorating mental development. Ben was started on a month-long regimen of adrenocorticotropin (ACTH) [p. 229] shots to control the seizures. Scientists are unsure why this hormone is so effective in controlling this type of seizure. They have found that among its effects, it increases myelin formation, increases blood-brain barrier integrity, and enhances binding of the neurotransmitter GABA at synapses. As expected, Ben's seizures disappeared completely before the month of treatment ended, and his development began to return to a normal level.

Question 1:
How might a leaky blood-brain barrier lead to a cascade of action potentials that trigger a seizure?

Question 2:
GABA opens Cl^- channels on the postsynaptic cell. What does this do to the cell's membrane potential? Does GABA make the cell more or less likely to fire action potentials

Question 3:
Why is it important to limit the duration of ACTH therapy, particularly in very young patients? [p. 235]

oxygen and glucose to make ATP for active transport of ions and neurotransmitters. Oxygen passes freely across the blood-brain barrier, and membrane transporters move glucose from the plasma to the brain's interstitial fluid. Unusually low levels of either substrate can have devastating results on brain function.

Because of its high demand for oxygen, the brain receives about 15% of the blood pumped by the heart. If blood flow to the brain is interrupted, brain damage occurs after only a few minutes without oxygen. Neurons are equally sensitive to lack of glucose.

Under normal circumstances the only energy source for neurons is glucose. (In starvation situations, the brain can metabolize ketones produced by fat breakdown [p. 115].) By some estimates, the brain is responsible for about half of the body's glucose consumption. Consequently, the body uses several homeostatic pathways to ensure that glucose concentrations in the blood always remain adequate to meet the brain's demand. If homeostasis fails, progressive **hypoglycemia** (low blood glucose levels) leads to confusion, unconsciousness, and eventually death.

Now that you have a broad overview of the central nervous system, we will examine the structure and function of the spinal cord and brain in more detail.

CLINICAL FOCUS

DIABETES

HYPOGLYCEMIA AND THE BRAIN

Neurons are picky about their food. Under most circumstances, the only biomolecule that neurons use for energy is glucose. Surprisingly, this can present a problem for diabetic patients, whose problem is too much glucose in the blood. In the face of sustained hyperglycemia (elevated blood glucose), the cells of the blood-brain barrier down-regulate [p. 194] their glucose transporters. Then, if the patient's blood glucose level falls below normal because of excess insulin or failing to eat, the neurons of the brain may not be able to take up glucose fast enough to sustain their electrical activity. Neighboring astrocytes have small amounts of glycogen that can be converted to glucose, but once glycogen stores are exhausted, neuronal function begins to fail. The individual may exhibit confusion, irritability, and slurred speech, and unless the neurons are provided with glucose promptly, they can sustain permanent damage. In extreme cases, hypoglycemia can cause coma or even death.

CONCEPT CHECK

8. Oxidative phosphorylation takes place in which organelle?
9. Name the two metabolic pathways for aerobic metabolism of glucose. What happens to NADH produced in these pathways?
10. In the late 1800s the scientist Paul Ehrlich injected blue dye into the bloodstream of animals. He noticed that all tissues except the brain stained blue. He was not aware of the blood-brain barrier and drew a different conclusion from his results. What other explanation might Ehrlich have proposed?
11. In a subsequent experiment, a student of Ehrlich's injected the dye into the cerebrospinal fluid of the same animals. What do you think he observed about staining in the brain and in other body tissues?

Answers: p. 331

THE SPINAL CORD

The spinal cord is the major pathway for information flowing back and forth between the brain and the skin, joints, and muscles of the body. In addition, the spinal cord contains neural networks responsible for locomotion. If the spinal cord is severed, there is loss of sensation from the skin and muscles as well as *paralysis,* loss of the ability to voluntarily control muscles.

The spinal cord is divided into four regions (*cervical, thoracic, lumbar,* and *sacral*), named to correspond to the adjacent vertebrae (see Fig. 9-4a). Each spinal region is subdivided into segments, and each segment gives rise to a bilateral pair of **spinal nerves**. Just before a spinal nerve joins the spinal cord, it divides into two branches called **roots** (Fig. 9-7a ●). The **dorsal root** of each spinal nerve is specialized to carry incoming sensory information. The **dorsal root ganglia**, swellings found on the dorsal roots just before they enter the cord (Fig. 9-7b), contain cell bodies of sensory neurons. The **ventral root** carries information from the CNS to muscles and glands.

In cross section, the spinal cord has a butterfly- or H-shaped core of gray matter and a surrounding rim of white matter. Sensory fibers from the dorsal roots synapse with interneurons in the **dorsal horns** of the gray matter. The dorsal horn cell bodies are organized into two distinct nuclei, one for somatic information and one for visceral information (Fig. 9-7b).

The **ventral horns** of the gray matter contain cell bodies of motor neurons that carry efferent signals to muscles and glands. The ventral horns are organized into somatic motor and autonomic nuclei. Efferent fibers leave the spinal cord via the ventral root.

The white matter of the spinal cord is the biological equivalent of fiber-optic cables that telephone companies use to carry our communications systems. White matter can be divided into a number of **columns** composed of tracts of axons that transfer information up and down the cord. **Ascending tracts** take sensory information to the brain. They occupy the dorsal and external lateral portions of the spinal

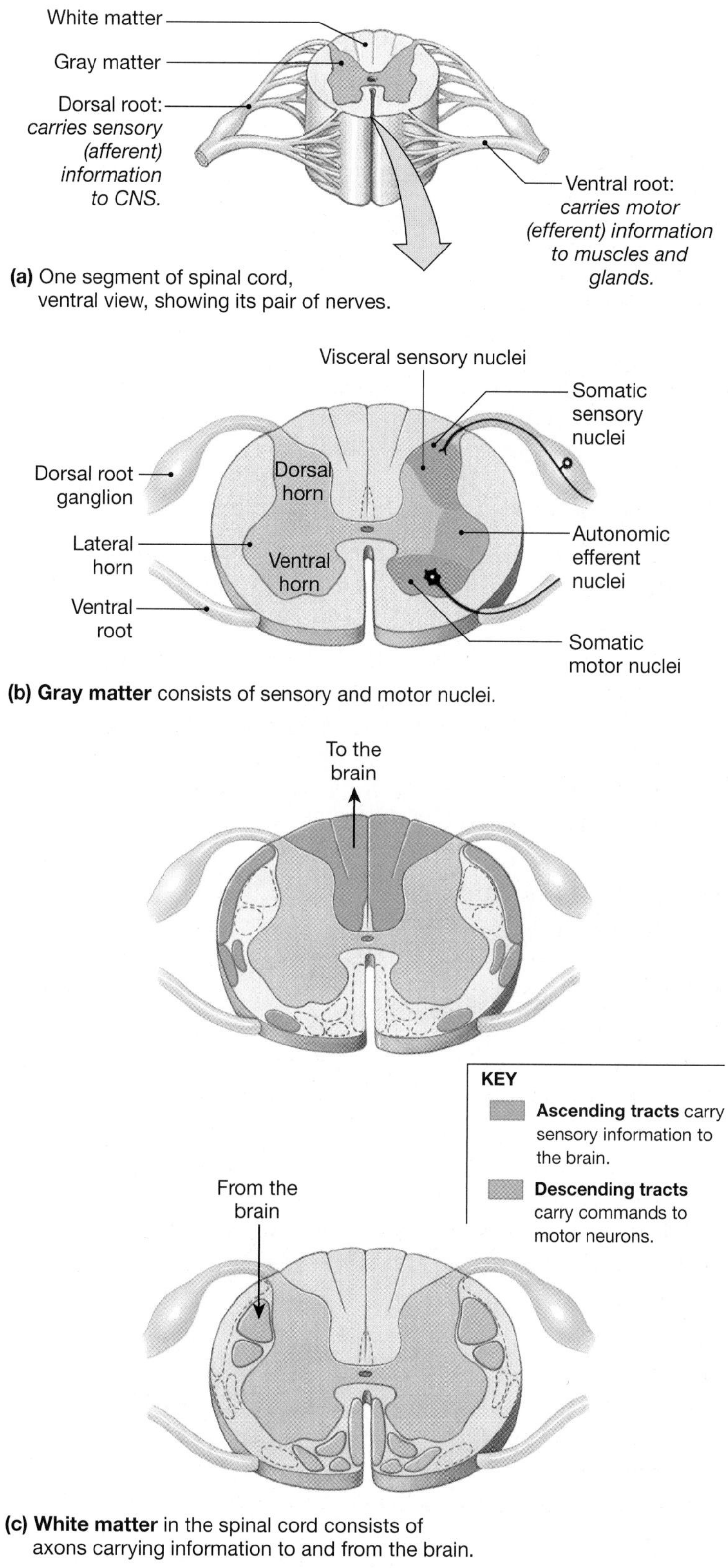
White matter
Gray matter
Dorsal root: *carries sensory (afferent) information to CNS.*
Ventral root: *carries motor (efferent) information to muscles and glands.*
(a) One segment of spinal cord, ventral view, showing its pair of nerves.
Visceral sensory nuclei
Somatic sensory nuclei
Dorsal root ganglion
Dorsal horn
Lateral horn
Ventral horn
Ventral root
Autonomic efferent nuclei
Somatic motor nuclei
(b) Gray matter consists of sensory and motor nuclei.
To the brain
KEY
Ascending tracts carry sensory information to the brain.
Descending tracts carry commands to motor neurons.
From the brain
(c) White matter in the spinal cord consists of axons carrying information to and from the brain.

● **FIGURE 9-7** ***The spinal cord contains cell bodies for efferent neurons and tracts of axons going to and from the brain.***

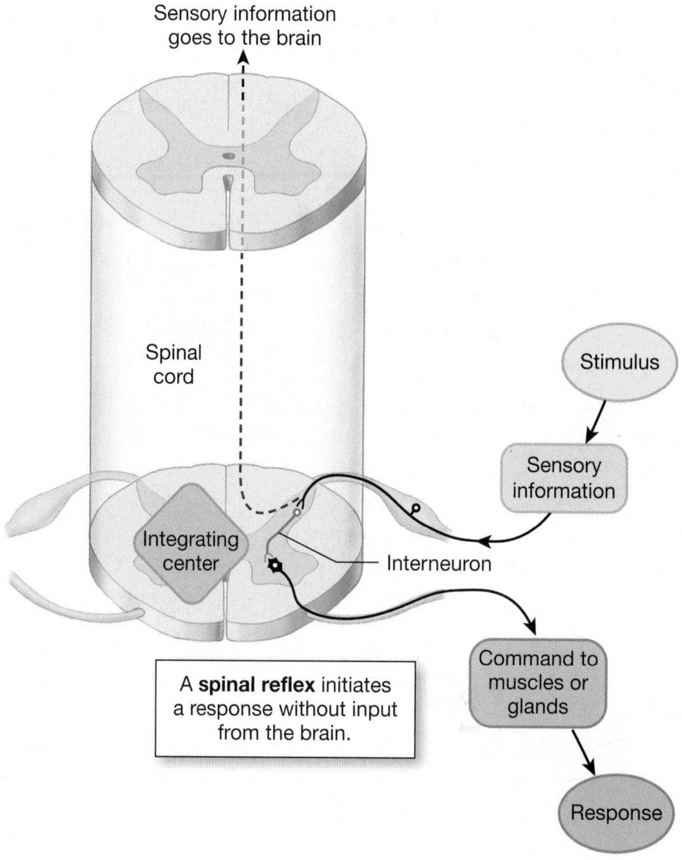
Sensory information goes to the brain
Spinal cord
Stimulus
Sensory information
Integrating center
Interneuron
Command to muscles or glands
Response
A **spinal reflex** initiates a response without input from the brain.

● **FIGURE 9-8** ***The spinal cord is an integrating center.*** In a spinal reflex, sensory information entering the spinal cord is acted on without input from the brain. However, sensory information about the stimulus may be sent to the brain.

cord (Fig. 9-7c). **Descending tracts** carry mostly efferent (motor) signals from the brain to the cord. They occupy the ventral and interior lateral portions of the white matter. **Propriospinal tracts** [*proprius,* one's own] are those that remain within the cord.

The spinal cord can function as a self-contained integrating center for simple *spinal reflexes,* with signals passing from a sensory neuron through the gray matter to an efferent neuron (Fig. 9-8 ●). In addition, spinal interneurons may route sensory information to the brain through ascending tracts or bring commands from the brain to motor neurons. In many cases, the interneurons also modify information as it passes through them. Reflexes play a critical role in the coordination of movement, and we discuss them in more detail in Chapter 13.

CONCEPT CHECK

12. What are the differences between horns, roots, tracts, and columns of the spinal cord?
13. If a dorsal root of the spinal cord is cut, what function will be disrupted?

Answers: p. 331

ANATOMY SUMMARY

LATERAL VIEW OF THE CNS

ANATOMY OF THE BRAIN

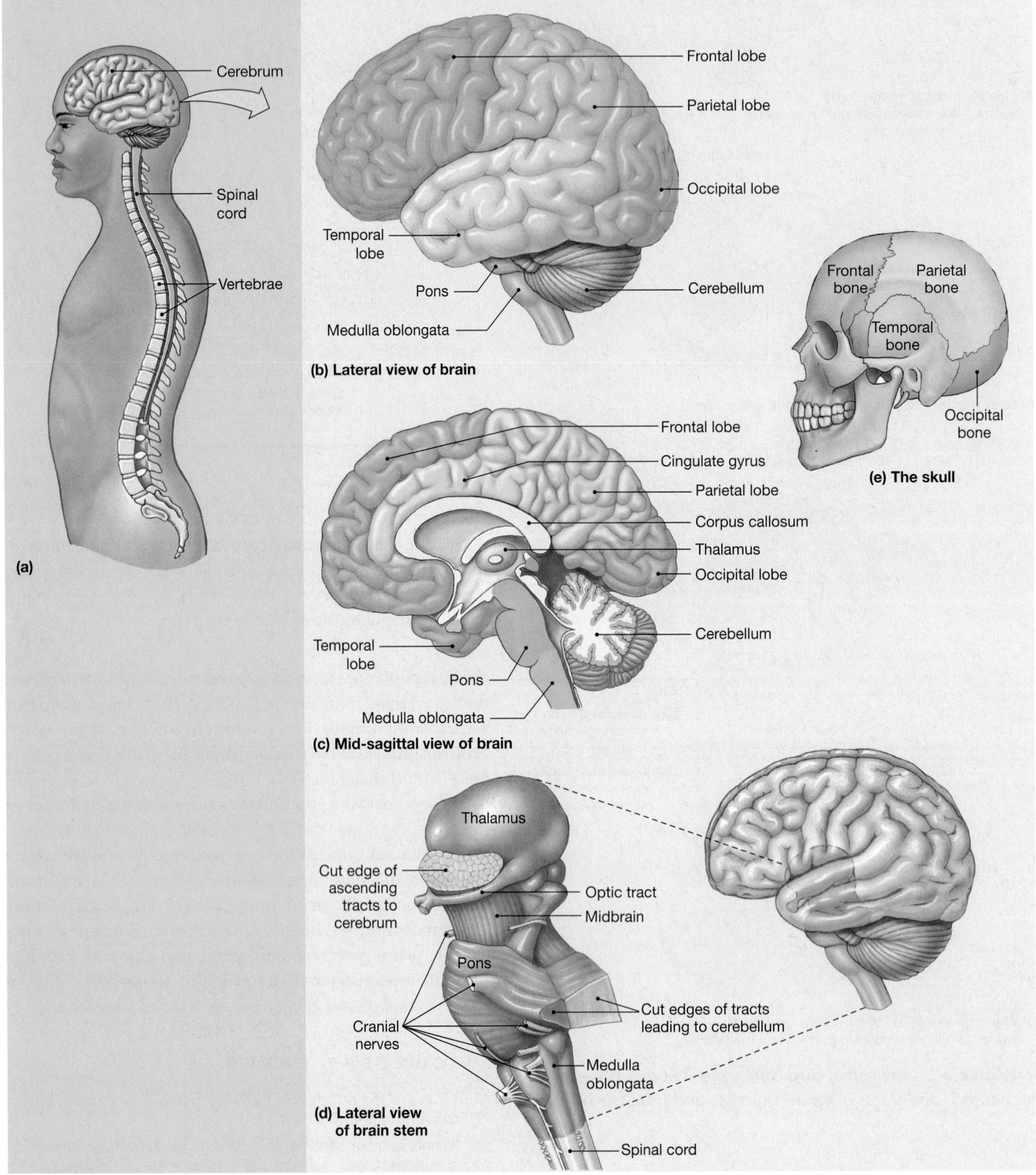

● FIGURE 9-9

Functions of the Brain

REGION	FUNCTION
Cerebrum (Frontal, Parietal, Occipital, and Temporal lobes)	
• Cerebral cortex (See Fig. 9.15)	
Sensory fields	Perception
Motor areas	Skeletal muscle movement
Association areas	Integration of information and direction of voluntary movement
• Basal ganglia (See Fig. 9-11)	Movement
• Limbic system (See Fig. 9-13)	
• Amygdala	Emotion and memory
• Hippocampus	Learning and memory
Diencephalon (See Fig. 9-10)	
• Thalamus	Integrating center and relay station for sensory and motor information
Hypothalamus	Homeostasis and behavioral drives (See Table 9-2)
• Pituitary	Hormone secretion
• Pineal gland	Melatonin secretion
Cerebellum	Movement coordination
Brain stem	
• Midbrain	Eye movement
• Pons	Relay station between cerebrum and cerebellum; coordination of breathing
• Medulla oblongata	Control of involuntary functions
Reticular formation (See Fig. 9-19)	Arousal, sleep, muscle tone, pain modulation

THE BRAIN

Thousands of years ago, Aristotle declared that the heart was the seat of the soul. However, most people now agree that the brain is the organ that gives the human species its unique attributes. The challenge facing today's scientists is to understand how circuits formed by millions of neurons result in complex behaviors such as speaking, writing a symphony, or creating imaginary worlds for an interactive computer game. Brain function may be the ultimate emergent property [p. 8]. The question remains whether we will ever be able to decipher how emotions such as happiness and love arise from the chemical and electrical signals passing along circuits of neurons.

It is possible to study the brain at many levels of organization. The most reductionist view looks at the individual neurons and at what happens to them in response to chemical or electrical signals. A more integrative study might look at groups of neurons and how they interact with one another in *circuits, pathways*, or networks. The most complicated approach starts with a behavior or physiological response and works backward to dissect the neural circuits that create the behavior or response.

For centuries, studies of brain function were restricted to anatomical descriptions. However, when we study the brain we see no tidy 1:1 relationship between structure and function. An adult human brain has a mass of about 1400 g and contains an estimated 10^{12} neurons. When you consider that each one of these millions of neurons may receive as many as 200,000 synapses, the number of possible neuronal connections is mind boggling. To complicate matters even more, those synapses are not fixed and are constantly changing.

A basic principle to remember when studying the brain is that one function, even an apparently simple one such as bending your finger, will involve multiple brain regions (as well as the spinal cord). Conversely, one brain region may be involved in several functions at the same time. In other words, understanding the brain is not simple and straightforward.

Figure 9-9 ● is an anatomy summary to follow as we discuss major brain regions, moving from the most primitive to the most complex. Of the six major divisions of the brain present at birth (see Fig. 9-3b), only the medulla, cerebellum, and cerebrum are visible when the intact brain is viewed in profile (see Fig. 9-3e). The remaining three divisions (diencephalon, midbrain, and pons) are covered by the cerebrum.

The Brain Stem Is the Transition Between Spinal Cord and Midbrain

The **brain stem** is the oldest and most primitive region of the brain and consists of structures that derive from the embryonic midbrain and hindbrain. The brain stem can be divided into white matter and gray matter, and in some ways its anatomy is similar to that of the spinal cord. Some ascending tracts from the spinal cord pass through the brain stem, while other

TABLE 9-1 The Cranial Nerves

NUMBER	NAME	TYPE	FUNCTION
I	Olfactory	Sensory	Olfactory (smell) information from nose
II	Optic	Sensory	Visual information from eyes
III	Oculomotor	Motor	Eye movement, pupil constriction, lens shape
IV	Trochlear	Motor	Eye movement
V	Trigeminal	Mixed	Sensory information from face, mouth; motor signals for chewing
VI	Abducens	Motor	Eye movement
VII	Facial	Mixed	Sensory for taste; efferent signals for tear and salivary glands, facial expression
VIII	Vestibulocochlear	Sensory	Hearing and equilibrium
IX	Glossopharyngeal	Mixed	Sensory from oral cavity, baro- and chemoreceptors in blood vessels; efferent for swallowing, parotid salivary gland secretion
X	Vagus	Mixed	Sensory and efferents to many internal organs, muscles, and glands
XI	Spinal accessory	Motor	Muscles of oral cavity, some muscles in neck and shoulder
XII	Hypoglossal	Motor	Tongue muscles

ascending tracts synapse there. Descending tracts from higher brain centers also travel through the brain stem on their way to the spinal cord.

Pairs of peripheral nerves branch off the brain stem, similar to spinal nerves along the spinal cord (Fig. 9-9d). Eleven of the 12 **cranial nerves** (numbers II–XII) originate along the brain stem. (The first cranial nerve, the olfactory nerve (I), enters the forebrain.) Cranial nerves carry sensory and motor information for the head and neck (Table 9-1 ●). The nerves are described according to whether they include sensory fibers, efferent fibers, or both (mixed nerves). For example, cranial nerve X, the **vagus nerve** [*vagus,* wandering], is a mixed nerve that carries both sensory and motor fibers for many internal organs. An important component of a clinical neurological examination is testing the functions controlled by these nerves.

Located throughout the brain stem are discrete groups of nerve cell bodies (*nuclei*). Many of these nuclei are associated with the **reticular formation**, a diffuse collection of neurons that extends throughout the brain stem. The name *reticular* means "network" and comes from the crisscrossed axons that branch profusely up into superior sections of the brain and down into the spinal cord. Nuclei in the brain stem are involved in many basic processes, including arousal and sleep, muscle tone and stretch reflexes, coordination of breathing, blood pressure regulation, and modulation of pain.

CONCEPT CHECK

14. Are the following white matter or gray matter: (a) ascending tracts, (b) reticular formation, (c) descending tracts?
15. Using the information from Table 9-1, describe the types of activities you might ask a patient to perform if you wished to test the function of each cranial nerve.
16. In anatomical directional terminology, the cerebrum, which is located next to the top of the skull, is said to be ________ to the brain stem.

Answers: p. 331

The Brain Stem Consists of Medulla, Pons, and Midbrain

Starting at the spinal cord and moving toward the top of the skull, the brain stem includes the medulla oblongata, the pons, and the midbrain (Fig. 9-9d). Some authorities include the cerebellum as part of the brain stem. The diamond-shaped fourth ventricle runs through the interior of the brain stem and connects to the central canal of the spinal cord (see Fig. 9-5a). The medulla oblongata, frequently just called the *medulla* [*medulla,* marrow; adjective *medullary*], is the transition from the spinal cord into the brain proper (Fig. 9-9d). Its white matter includes ascending **somatosensory tracts** [*soma,* body] that bring sensory information to the brain, and descending **corticospinal tracts** that convey information from the cerebrum to the spinal cord.

About 90% of corticospinal tracts cross the midline to the opposite side of the body in a region of the medulla known as the pyramids. As a result of this crossover, each side of the brain controls the opposite side of the body. Gray matter in the medulla includes nuclei that control many involuntary functions, such as blood pressure, breathing, swallowing, and vomiting.

The pons [*pons,* bridge; adjective *pontine*] is a bulbous protrusion on the ventral side of the brain stem above the medulla and below the midbrain. Because its primary function is to act as a relay station for information transfer between the cerebellum and cerebrum, the pons is often grouped with the cerebellum. The pons also coordinates the control of breathing along with centers in the medulla.

The third region of the brain stem, the midbrain, or *mesencephalon* [*mesos,* middle], is a relatively small area that lies between the lower brain stem and the diencephalon. The primary function of the midbrain is control of eye movement, but it also relays signals for auditory and visual reflexes.

The Cerebellum Coordinates Movement

The cerebellum is the second largest structure in the brain (Fig. 9-9a–c). It is located inside the base of the skull, just above the nape of the neck. The name *cerebellum* [adjective *cerebellar*] means "little brain," and, indeed, most of the nerve cells in the brain are in the cerebellum. The specialized function of the cerebellum is to process sensory information and coordinate the execution of movement. Sensory input into the cerebellum comes from somatic receptors in the periphery of the body and from receptors for equilibrium and balance located in the inner ear. The cerebellum also receives motor input from neurons in the cerebrum. You will learn more about cerebellar function in Chapter 13.

The Diencephalon Contains the Centers for Homeostasis

The diencephalon, or "between-brain," lies between the brain stem and the cerebrum. It is composed of two main sections, the thalamus and the hypothalamus, and two endocrine structures, the pituitary and pineal glands (Fig. 9-10 ●).

Most of the diencephalon is occupied by many small nuclei that make up the **thalamus** [*thalamus,* bedroom; adjective *thalamic*]. The thalamus receives sensory fibers from the optic tract, ears, and spinal cord as well as motor information from the cerebellum. It projects fibers to the cerebrum, where the information is processed. The thalamus is often described as a relay station because almost all sensory information from lower parts of the CNS passes through it. Like the spinal cord, the thalamus can modify information passing through it, making it an integrating center as well as a relay station.

The **hypothalamus** lies beneath the thalamus. Although the hypothalamus occupies less than 1% of total brain volume, it is the center for homeostasis and contains centers for various behavioral drives, such as hunger and thirst. Output from the hypothalamus also influences many functions of the autonomic division of the nervous system, as well as a variety of endocrine functions (Tbl. 9-2 ●). The hypothalamus receives input from multiple sources, including the cerebrum, the reticular formation, and various sensory receptors. Output from the hypothalamus goes first to the thalamus and eventually to multiple effector pathways.

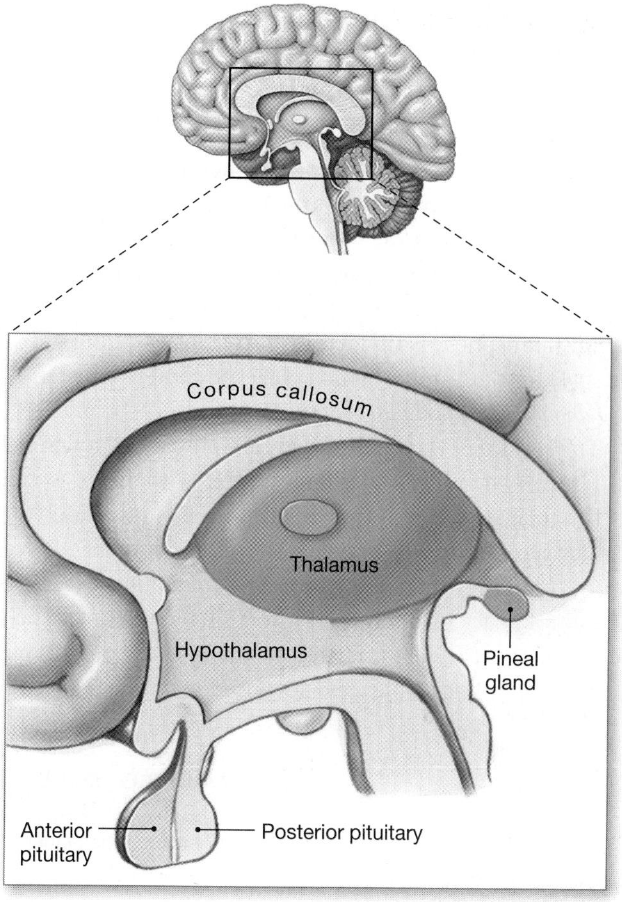

● **FIGURE 9-10** ***The diencephalon.*** The diencephalon lies between the brain stem and the cerebrum. It consists of thalamus, hypothalamus, pineal gland, and pituitary gland.

Two important endocrine structures are located in the diencephalon: the pituitary gland and the pineal gland. You learned about the endocrine function of the pituitary gland in Chapter 7 [p. 228]. The posterior pituitary (neurohypophysis) is a downgrowth of the hypothalamus and secretes neurohormones that are synthesized in hypothalamic nuclei. The anterior pituitary (adenohypophysis) is a true endocrine gland. Its hormones are regulated by hypothalamic neurohormones secreted into the hypothalamic-hypophyseal portal system. The pineal gland, which secretes the hormone melatonin, was also introduced in Chapter 7 [p. 239] and is discussed later in this chapter.

CONCEPT CHECK

17. Starting at the spinal cord and moving up, name the subdivisions of the brain stem.
18. What are the four primary structures of the diencephalon?

Answers: p. 332

The Cerebrum Is the Site of Higher Brain Functions

As noted earlier in the chapter, the cerebrum is the largest and most distinctive part of the human brain and fills most of the cranial cavity. It is composed of two hemispheres connected primarily at the **corpus callosum** (Figs. 9-9c and 9-10), a distinct structure formed by axons passing from one side of the brain to the other. This connection ensures that the two hemispheres communicate and cooperate with each other. Each cerebral hemisphere is divided into four lobes, named for the bones of the skull under which they are located: *frontal, parietal, temporal,* and *occipital* (Fig. 9-9b, c, e).

The surface of the cerebrum in humans and other primates has a furrowed, walnut-like appearance, with grooves called *sulci* [singular *sulcus,* a furrow] dividing convolutions called *gyri* [singular *gyrus,* a ring or circle]. During development, the cerebrum grows faster than the surrounding cranium, causing the tissue to fold back on itself to fit into a smaller volume. The degree of folding is directly related to the level of processing of which the brain is capable. Less-advanced mammals, such as rodents, have brains with a relatively smooth surface. The human brain, on the other hand, is so convoluted that if it were inflated enough to smooth the surfaces, it would be three times as large and would need a head the size of a beach ball.

TABLE 9-2 Functions of the Hypothalamus

1. Activates sympathetic nervous system
   - Controls catecholamine release from adrenal medulla (as in fight-or-flight reaction)
   - Helps maintain blood glucose concentrations through effects on endocrine pancreas
2. Maintains body temperature
   - Stimulates shivering and sweating
3. Controls body osmolarity
   - Motivates thirst and drinking behavior
   - Stimulates secretion of vasopressin [p. 229]
4. Controls reproductive functions
   - Directs secretion of oxytocin (for uterine contractions and milk release)
   - Directs trophic hormone control of anterior pituitary hormones FSH and LH [p. 233]
5. Controls food intake
   - Stimulates satiety center
   - Stimulates feeding center
6. Interacts with limbic system to influence behavior and emotions
7. Influences cardiovascular control center in medulla oblongata
8. Secretes trophic hormones that control release of hormones from anterior pituitary gland

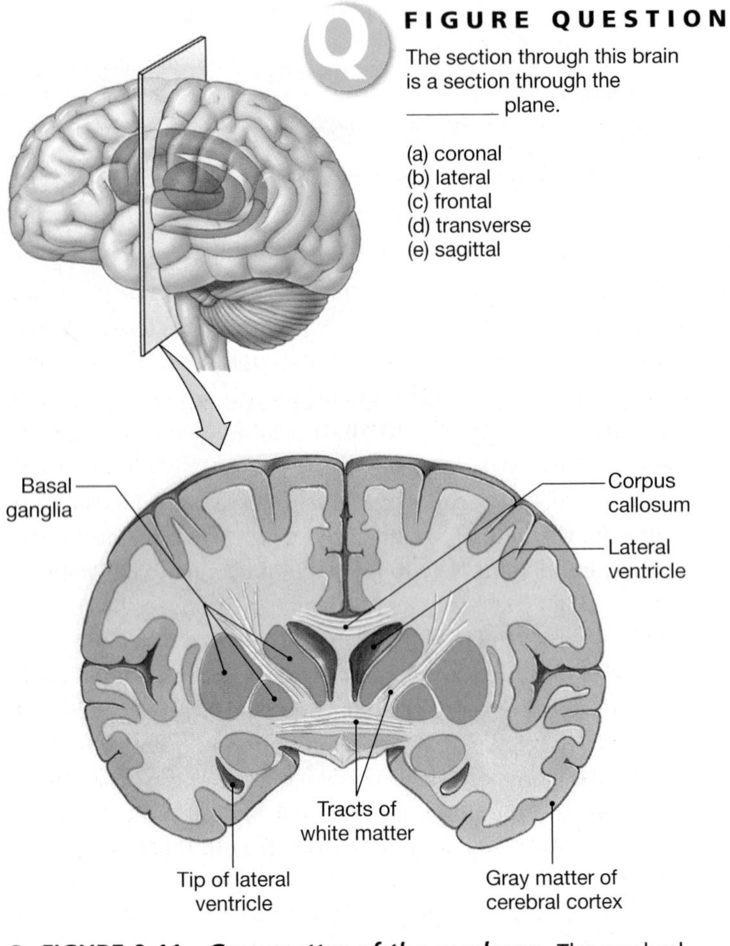
FIGURE QUESTION
The section through this brain is a section through the ________ plane.
(a) coronal
(b) lateral
(c) frontal
(d) transverse
(e) sagittal
Basal ganglia
Corpus callosum
Lateral ventricle
Tracts of white matter
Tip of lateral ventricle
Gray matter of cerebral cortex

● **FIGURE 9-11** ***Gray matter of the cerebrum.*** The cerebral cortex and basal ganglia are two of the three regions of gray matter in the cerebrum. The third region, the limbic system, is detailed in Figure 9-13. The frontal view shown here is similar to the sectional view obtained using modern diagnostic imaging techniques.

The Cerebrum Has Distinct Regions of Gray Matter and White Matter

Cerebral gray matter can be divided into three major regions: the cerebral cortex, the basal ganglia, and the limbic system. The **cerebral cortex** [*cortex,* bark or rind; adjective *cortical,* plural *cortices*] is the outer layer of the cerebrum, only a few millimeters thick (Fig. 9-11 ●). Neurons of the cerebral cortex are arranged in anatomically distinct vertical columns and horizontal layers (Fig. 9-12 ●). It is within these layers that our higher brain functions arise.

The second region of cerebral gray matter consists of the **basal ganglia** (Fig. 9-11), which are involved in the control of movement. The basal ganglia are also called the *basal nuclei.* Neuroanatomists prefer to reserve the term ganglia for clusters of nerve cell bodies outside the CNS, but the term basal ganglia is commonly used in clinical settings.

The third region of the cerebrum is the **limbic system** [*limbus,* a border], which surrounds the brain stem (Fig. 9-13 ●). The limbic system represents probably the most primitive region of the cerebrum. It acts as the link between higher cognitive

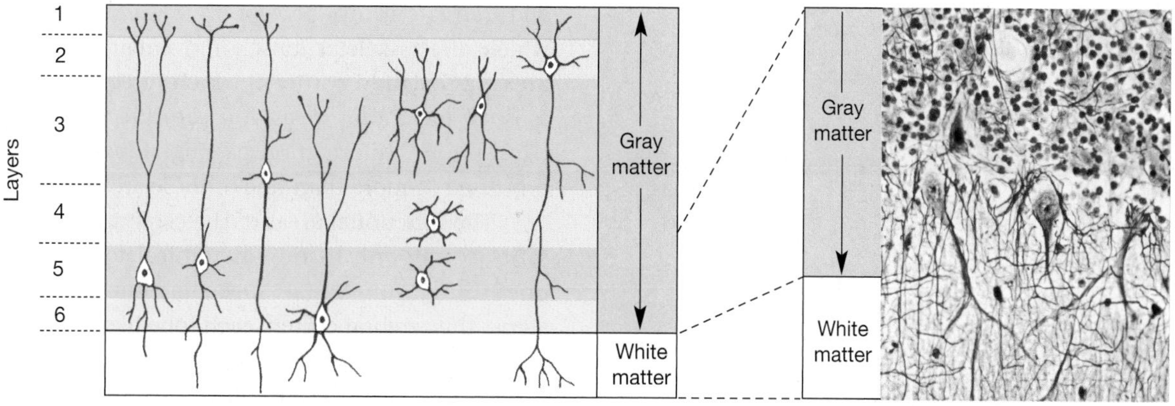
1
2
3
4
5
6
Layers
Gray matter
White matter
Gray matter
White matter

(a) Cell layers within the gray matter

(b) Photomicrograph of cerebral cortex

● **FIGURE 9-12** ***Cell bodies in the cerebral cortex form distinct layers.***

functions, such as reasoning, and more primitive emotional responses, such as fear. The major areas of the limbic system are the **amygdala** and **cingulate gyrus**, which are linked to emotion and memory, and the **hippocampus**, which is associated with learning and memory.

White matter in the cerebrum is found mostly in the interior (Fig. 9-11). Bundles of fibers allow different regions of the cortex to communicate with one another and transfer information from one hemisphere to the other, primarily through the corpus callosum. According to some estimates, the corpus callosum may have as many as 200 million axons passing through it! Information entering and leaving the cerebrum goes along tracts that pass through the thalamus (with the exception of olfactory information, which goes directly from olfactory receptors to the cerebrum).

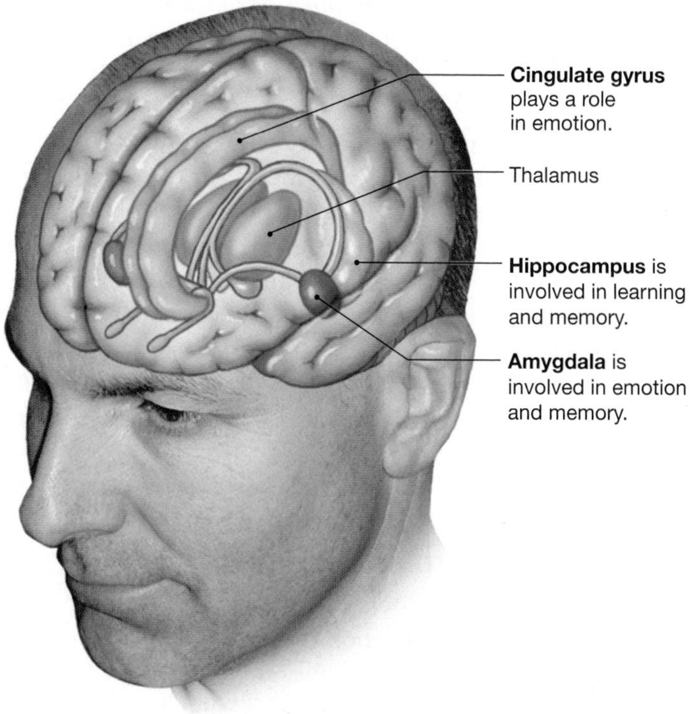
Cingulate gyrus plays a role in emotion.
Thalamus
Hippocampus is involved in learning and memory.
Amygdala is involved in emotion and memory.

● **FIGURE 9-13** ***The limbic system includes the amygdala, hippocampus, and cingulate gyrus.*** Anatomically, the limbic system is part of the gray matter of the cerebrum. The thalamus is shown for orientation purposes and is not part of the limbic system.

CONCEPT CHECK

19. Name the anatomical location in the brain where neurons from one side of the body cross to the opposite side.
20. Name the divisions of the brain in anatomical order, starting from the spinal cord.

Answers: p. 332

BRAIN FUNCTION

From a simplistic view, the brain is an information processor much like a computer. It receives sensory input from the internal and external environments, integrates and processes the information, and, if appropriate, creates a response (Fig. 9-14a ●). This is the basic reflex pathway introduced in Chapter 6 [p. 198]. What makes the brain more complicated than this simple reflex pathway, however, is its ability to generate information and output signals *in the absence of external input*. Modeling this intrinsic input requires a diagram more complex than the simple pathway illustrated in Figure 9-14a.

Larry Swanson of the University of Southern California presents one approach to modeling brain function in his book *Brain Architecture: Understanding the Basic Plan* (Oxford University Press, 2003). He describes three systems that influence output by the motor systems of the body: (1) the **sensory system**, which monitors the internal and external environments and initiates reflex responses; (2) a **cognitive system** that resides in the cerebral cortex and is able to initiate voluntary responses; and (3) a **behavioral state system**, which also resides in the brain and governs sleep-wake cycles and other intrinsic behaviors. Information about the physiological or behavioral responses created by motor output feeds back to the sensory system, which in turn communicates with the cognitive and behavioral state systems (Fig. 9-14b).

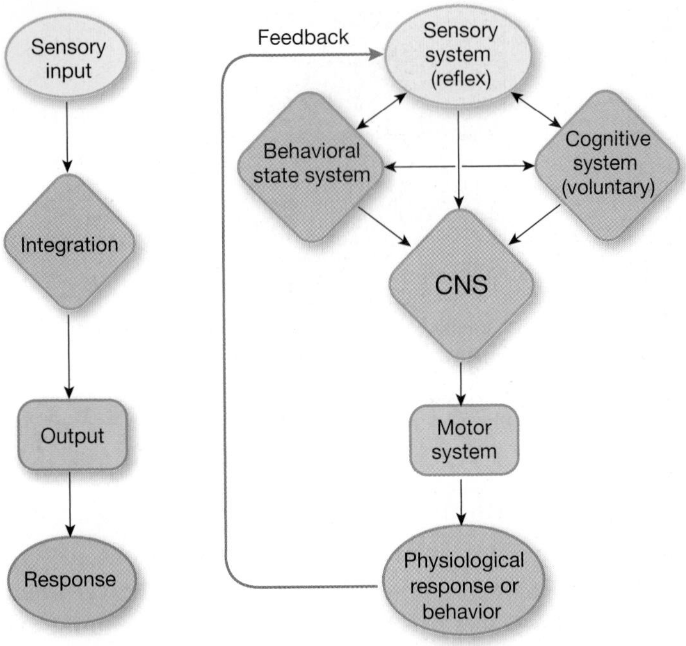

(a) A simple neural reflex

(b) Behavioral state and cognition influence brain output.

● **FIGURE 9-14** ***Reflex pathways in the brain may be simple or complex.***

In most of the physiological organ systems of the body that you will study in this book, simple reflex pathways initiated through the sensory system and executed by motor output are adequate to explain homeostatic control mechanisms. However, the cognitive and behavioral state systems remain potential sources of influence. At its simplest, this influence may take the form of voluntary behaviors, such as breath-holding, that override automatic functions. More subtle and complicated interactions include the effect of emotions on normal physiology, such as stress-induced heart palpitations, and the role of circadian rhythms in jet lag and shift work.

In the sections that follow we take a brief look at sensory and motor systems in the brain. The receptors and pathways of the sensory system are the subject of Chapter 10, and we discuss neural control of motor systems in Chapters 11 and 13. We conclude this chapter with a discussion of some aspects of the behavioral state system and the cognitive system, such as circadian rhythms, sleep-wake cycles, emotion, learning, and memory.

The Cerebral Cortex Is Organized into Functional Areas

The cerebral cortex serves as an integrating center for sensory information and a decision-making region for many types of motor output. If we examine the cortex from a functional viewpoint, it can be divided into three specializations: (1) **sensory areas** (also called sensory fields), which receive sensory input and translate it into perception (awareness); (2) **motor areas,** which direct skeletal muscle movement; and (3) **association areas** (association cortices), which integrate information from sensory and motor areas and can direct voluntary behaviors (Fig. 9-15 ●). Information passing along a pathway is usually processed in more than one of these areas.

The functional areas of the cerebral cortex do not necessarily correspond to the anatomical lobes of the brain. For one thing, functional specialization is not symmetrical across the cerebral cortex: each lobe has special functions not shared by the matching lobe on the opposite side. This **cerebral lateralization** of function is sometimes referred to as *cerebral dominance,* more popularly known as left brain–right brain dominance (Fig. 9-16 ●). Language and verbal skills tend to be concentrated on the left side of the brain, with spatial skills concentrated on the right side. The left brain is the dominant hemisphere for right-handed people, and it appears that the right brain is the dominant hemisphere for many left-handed people.

Even these generalizations are subject to change, however. Neural connections in the cerebrum, like those in other parts of the nervous system, exhibit a certain degree of plasticity. For example, if a person loses a finger, the regions of motor and sensory cortex previously devoted to control of the finger do not go dormant. Instead, adjacent regions of the cortex extend their functional fields and take over the parts of the cortex that are no longer used by the absent finger. Similarly, skills normally associated with one side of the cerebral cortex can be developed in the other hemisphere, as when a right-handed person with a broken hand learns to write with the left hand.

Much of what we know about functional areas of the cerebral cortex comes from study of patients who have either inherited neurological defects or suffered wounds in accidents or war. In some instances, surgical lesions made to treat some medical condition, such as uncontrollable epilepsy, have revealed functional relationships in particular brain regions. Imaging techniques such as *positron emission tomography* (PET) scans and *functional magnetic resonance imaging* (fMRI) provide noninvasive ways for us to watch the human brain at work (Fig. 9-17 ●).

Sensory Information Is Integrated in the Spinal Cord and Brain

The sensory system monitors the internal and external environments and sends information to neural integrating centers, which in turn initiate appropriate responses. In its simplest form, this pathway is the classic reflex, illustrated in Figure 9-14a. The simplest reflexes can be integrated in the spinal cord, without input from higher brain centers (see Fig. 9-8). However, even simple spinal reflexes usually send sensory information to the brain, creating perception of the stimulus. Brain functions

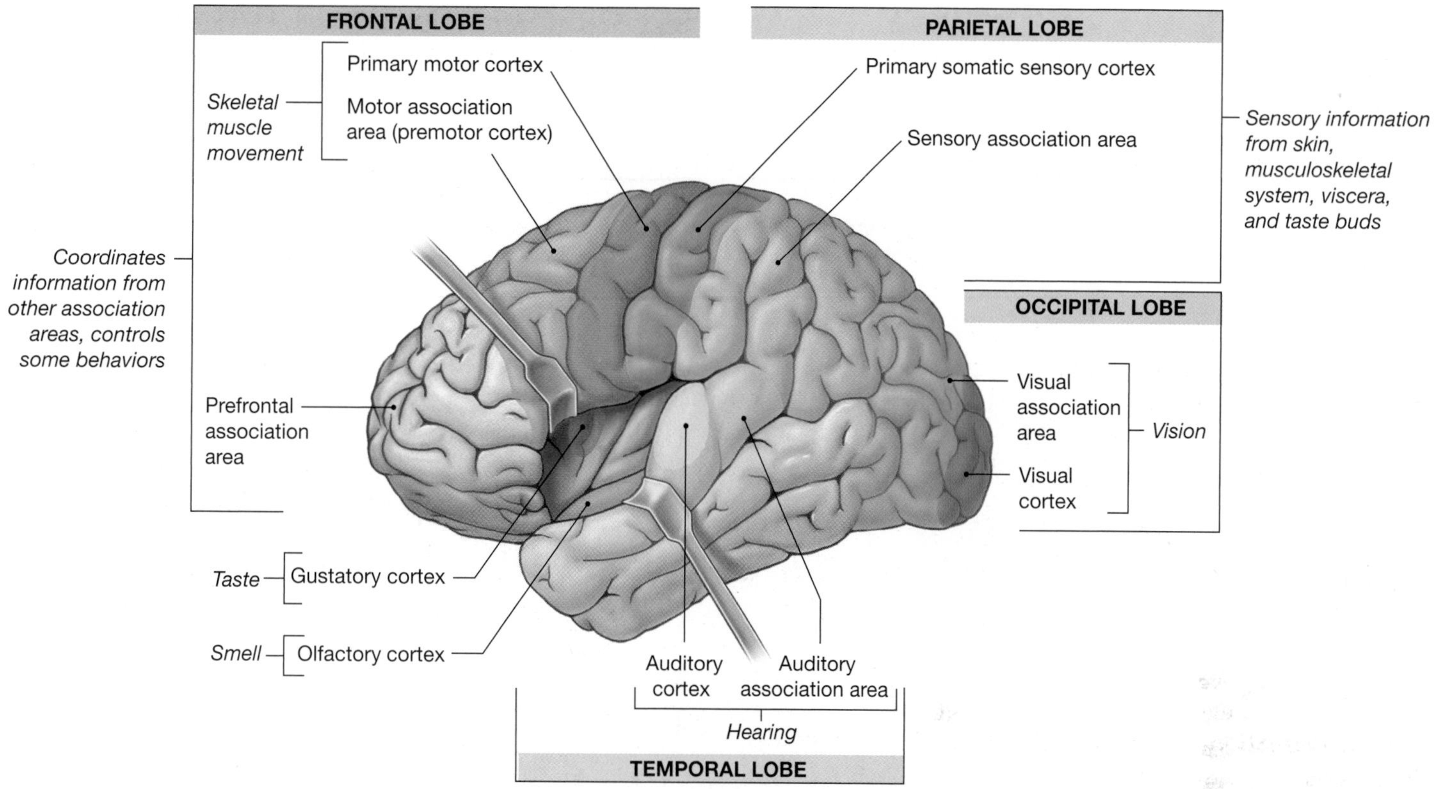
FRONTAL LOBE
Primary motor cortex
Skeletal muscle movement
Motor association area (premotor cortex)
Coordinates information from other association areas, controls some behaviors
Prefrontal association area
Taste
Gustatory cortex
Smell
Olfactory cortex
PARIETAL LOBE
Primary somatic sensory cortex
Sensory association area
Sensory information from skin, musculoskeletal system, viscera, and taste buds
OCCIPITAL LOBE
Visual association area
Visual cortex
Vision
Auditory cortex
Auditory association area
Hearing
TEMPORAL LOBE

● **FIGURE 9-15** ***The cerebral cortex is specialized into functional areas.*** The cerebral cortex contains sensory areas for perception, motor areas that direct movement, and association areas that integrate information.

dealing with perception are the most difficult to study because they require communication between the subject and the investigator—the subject must be able to tell the investigator what he or she is seeing, hearing, or feeling.

Sensory information from the body travels in ascending pathways to the brain. Information about muscle and joint position and movement goes to the cerebellum as well as to the cerebral cortex, allowing the cerebellum to assist with automatic subconscious coordination of movement. Most sensory information continues on to the cerebral cortex, where five sensory areas process information.

The **primary somatic sensory cortex** (also called the *somatosensory cortex*) in the parietal lobe is the termination point of pathways from the skin, musculoskeletal system, and viscera (see Fig. 9-15). The somatosensory pathways carry information about touch, temperature, pain, itch, and body position. Damage to this part of the brain leads to reduced sensitivity of the skin on the opposite side of the body because sensory fibers cross to the opposite side of the midline as they ascend through the spine or medulla.

The special senses of vision, hearing, taste, and olfaction (smell) each have different brain regions devoted to processing their sensory input (see Fig. 9-15). The **visual cortex**, located in the occipital lobe, receives information from the eyes. The **auditory cortex**, located in the temporal lobe, receives information from the ears. The **olfactory cortex**, a small region in the temporal lobe, receives input from chemoreceptors in the nose. The **gustatory cortex**, deeper in the brain near the edge of the frontal lobe, receives sensory information from the taste buds. The next chapter describes the somatic and special senses in detail.

Sensory Information Is Processed into Perception

Once sensory information reaches the appropriate cortical area, information processing has just begun. Neural pathways extend from sensory areas to appropriate association areas, which integrate somatic, visual, auditory, and other stimuli into *perception*, the brain's interpretation of sensory stimuli.

Often the perceived stimulus is very different from the actual stimulus. For instance, photoreceptors in the eye receive light waves of different frequencies, but we perceive the different wave energies as different colors. Similarly, the brain translates pressure waves hitting the ear into sound and interprets chemicals binding to chemoreceptors as taste or smell.

One interesting aspect of perception is the way our brain fills in missing information to create a complete picture, or translates a two-dimensional drawing into a three-dimensional

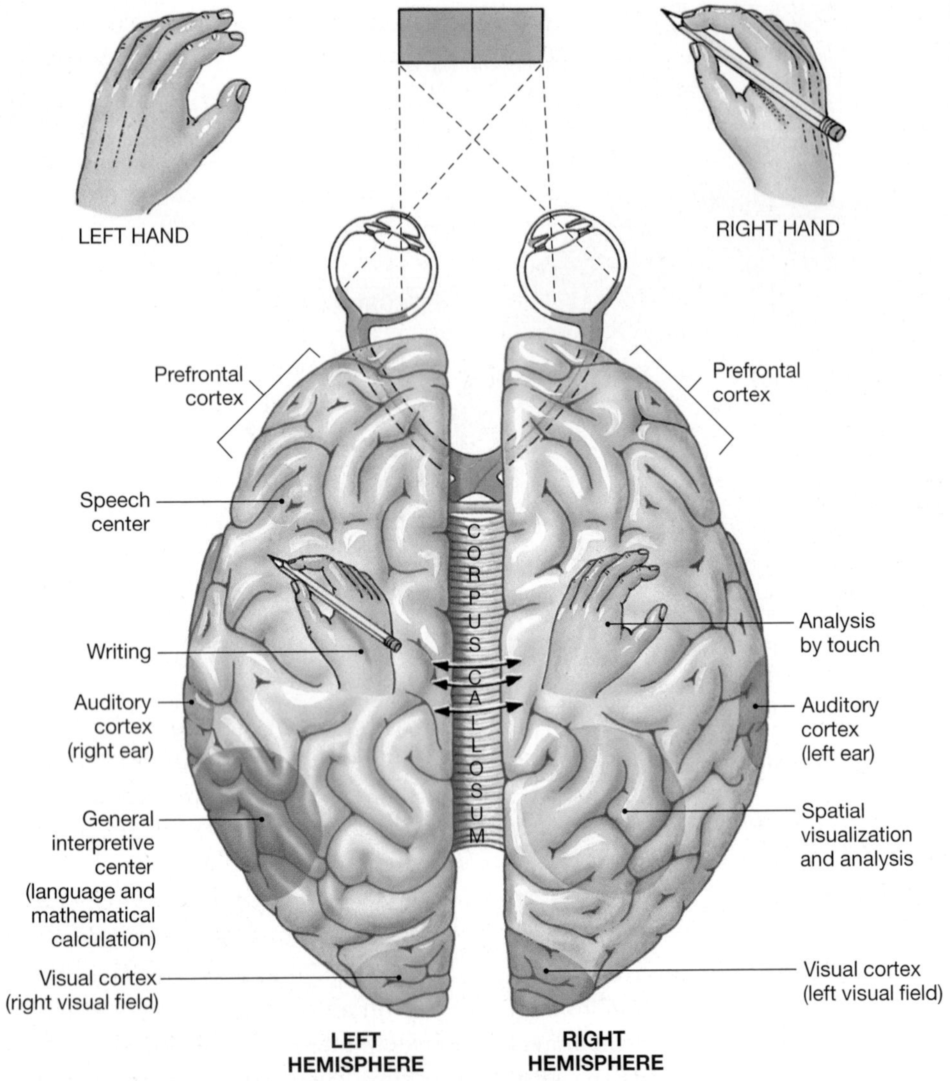
LEFT HAND
RIGHT HAND
Prefrontal cortex
Prefrontal cortex
Speech center
Writing
Auditory cortex (right ear)
General interpretive center (language and mathematical calculation)
Visual cortex (right visual field)
CORPUS CALLOSUM
Analysis by touch
Auditory cortex (left ear)
Spatial visualization and analysis
Visual cortex (left visual field)
LEFT HEMISPHERE
RIGHT HEMISPHERE

● **FIGURE 9-16** ***Cerebral lateralization.*** The distribution of functional areas in the two cerebral hemispheres is not symmetrical.

FIGURE QUESTIONS

- What would a person see if a stroke destroyed all function in the right visual cortex?
- What is the function of the corpus callosum?

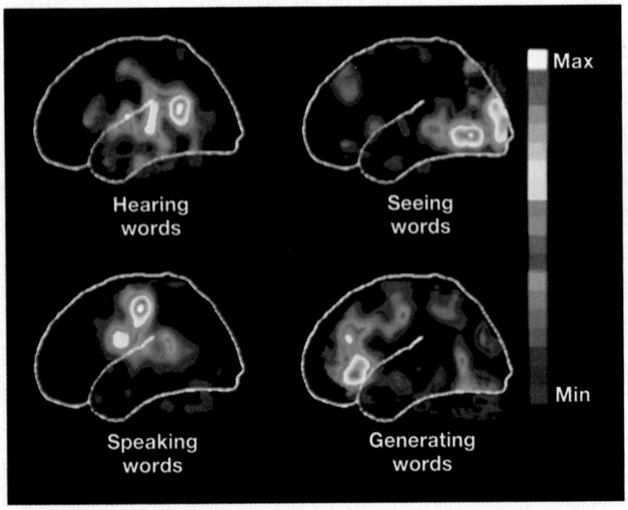
Max
Min
Hearing words
Seeing words
Speaking words
Generating words

FIGURE QUESTION

In the image above, the brain area active in seeing words is in the ________ lobe, and the brain area active during word generation is in the ________ lobe.

● **FIGURE 9-17** ***PET scan of the brain at work***

shape (Fig. 9-18 ●). Thus, we sometimes perceive what our brains expect to perceive. Our perceptual translation of sensory stimuli allows the information to be acted upon and used in voluntary motor control or in complex cognitive functions such as language.

The Motor System Governs Output from the CNS

The motor output component of the nervous system is associated with the efferent division, shown in Figure 8-1 [p. 248]. Motor output can be divided into three major types: (1) skeletal muscle movement, controlled by the somatic motor division; (2) neuroendocrine signals, neurohormones secreted into the blood by neurons located primarily in the hypothalamus and adrenal medulla; and (3) *visceral* responses, the actions of smooth and cardiac muscle or endocrine and exocrine glands. Visceral responses are governed by the autonomic division of the nervous system.

Information about skeletal muscle movement is processed in several regions of the CNS. Simple stimulus-response path-

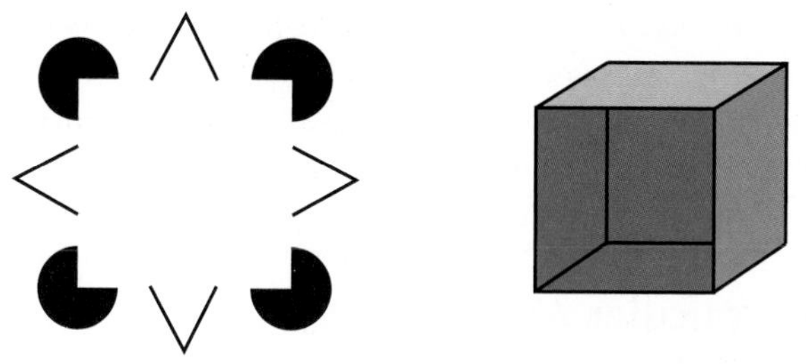

(a) (b)

FIGURE 9-18 *Perception.* The brain has the ability to interpret sensory information to create the perception of (a) shapes or (b) three-dimensional objects.

ways, such as the knee jerk reflex, are processed either in the spinal cord or in the brain stem. Although these reflexes do not require integration in the cerebral cortex, they can be modified or overridden by input from the cognitive system.

Voluntary movements are initiated by the cognitive system and originate in the **primary motor cortex** and **motor association area** in the frontal lobes of the cerebrum (see Fig. 9-15). These regions receive input from sensory areas as well as from the cerebellum and basal ganglia. Long output neurons called *pyramidal cells* project axons from the motor areas through the brain stem to the spinal cord. Other pathways go from the cortex to the basal ganglia and lower brain regions. Descending motor pathways cross to the opposite side of the body, which means that damage to a motor area manifests as paralysis or loss of function on the opposite side of the body. A detailed discussion of the coordination of body movement can be found in Chapter 13.

Neuroendocrine and visceral responses are coordinated primarily in the hypothalamus and medulla. The brain stem contains the control centers for many of the automatic life functions we take for granted, such as breathing and blood pressure. It receives sensory information from the body and relays motor commands to peripheral muscles and glands.

The hypothalamus contains centers for temperature regulation, eating, and control of body osmolarity, among others. The responses to stimulation of these centers may be neural or hormonal reflexes or a behavioral response. Stress, reproduction, and growth are also mediated by the hypothalamus by way of multiple hormones. You will learn more about these reflexes in later chapters as we discuss the various systems of the body.

Sensory input is not the only factor determining motor output by the brain. The behavioral state system can modulate reflex pathways, and the cognitive system exerts both voluntary and involuntary control over motor functions.

The Behavioral State System Modulates Motor Output

The behavioral state system is an important modulator of sensory and cognitive processing. Many neurons in the behavioral state system are found in regions of the brain outside the cerebral cortex, including parts of the reticular formation in the brain stem, the hypothalamus, and the limbic system.

The neurons collectively known as the **diffuse modulatory systems** originate in the reticular formation in the brain stem and project their axons to large areas of the brain (Tbl. 9-3 ●, Fig. 9-19 ●). There are four modulatory systems that are generally classified according to the neurotransmitter they

9

TABLE 9-3 The Diffuse Modulatory Systems

SYSTEM (NEUROMODULATOR)	SITE WHERE NEURONS ORIGINATE	STRUCTURES THAT NEURONS INNERVATE	FUNCTIONS MODULATED BY THE SYSTEM
Noradrenergic (norepinephrine)	Locus coeruleus of the pons	Cerebral cortex, thalamus, hypothalamus, olfactory bulb, cerebellum, midbrain, spinal cord	Attention, arousal, sleep-wake cycles, learning, memory, anxiety, pain, and mood
Serotonergic (serotonin)	Raphe nuclei along brain stem midline	Lower nuclei project to spinal cord	Pain, locomotion
		Upper nuclei project to most of brain	Sleep-wake cycle; mood and emotional behaviors, such as aggression and depression
Dopaminergic (dopamine)	Substantia nigra in midbrain	Cortex	Motor control
	Ventral tegmentum in midbrain	Cortex and parts of limbic system	"Reward" centers linked to addictive behaviors
Cholinergic (acetylcholine)	Base of cerebrum; pons and midbrain	Cerebrum, hippocampus, thalamus	Sleep-wake cycles, arousal, learning, memory, sensory information passing through thalamus

secrete: *noradrenergic* (norepinephrine), *serotonergic* (serotonin), *dopaminergic* (dopamine), and *cholinergic* (acetylcholine). The diffuse modulatory systems regulate brain function by influencing attention, motivation, wakefulness, memory, motor control, mood, and metabolic homeostasis.

The Reticular Activating System Influences States of Arousal

One function of the behavioral state system is control of levels of consciousness and sleep-wake cycles. **Consciousness** is the body's state of arousal or awareness of self and environment. Experimental evidence shows that the **reticular activating system**, a diffuse collection of neurons in the reticular formation, plays an essential role in keeping the "conscious brain" awake. If connections between the reticular formation and the cerebral cortex are disrupted surgically, an animal becomes comatose for long periods of time. Other evidence for the importance of the reticular formation in states of arousal comes from studies showing that general anesthetics depress synaptic transmission in that region of the brain. Presumably, blocking ascending pathways between the reticular formation and the cerebral cortex creates a state of unconsciousness.

Physiologically, what distinguishes being awake from various stages of sleep? One way to define arousal states is by the pattern of electrical activity created by the cortical neurons. The measurement of brain activity is recorded by a procedure known as **electroencephalography**. Surface electrodes placed on or in the scalp detect depolarizations of the cortical neurons in the region just under the electrode.

In awake states, many neurons are firing but not in a coordinated fashion. Presumably the desynchronization of electrical activity in waking states is produced by ascending signals from the reticular formation. An *electroencephalogram,* or **EEG**, of the waking-alert (eyes open) state shows a rapid, irregular pattern with no dominant waves. In awake-resting (eyes closed) states, sleep, or coma, electrical activity of the neurons begins to synchronize into waves with characteristic patterns (Fig. 9-20 ●). As the person's state of arousal lessens, the frequency of the waves decreases. The more synchronous the firing of cortical neurons, the larger the amplitude of the waves. Accordingly, the awake-resting state is characterized by low-amplitude, high-frequency waves, and deep sleep is marked by high-amplitude, low-frequency waves. The complete cessation of brain waves is one of the clinical criteria for determining death.

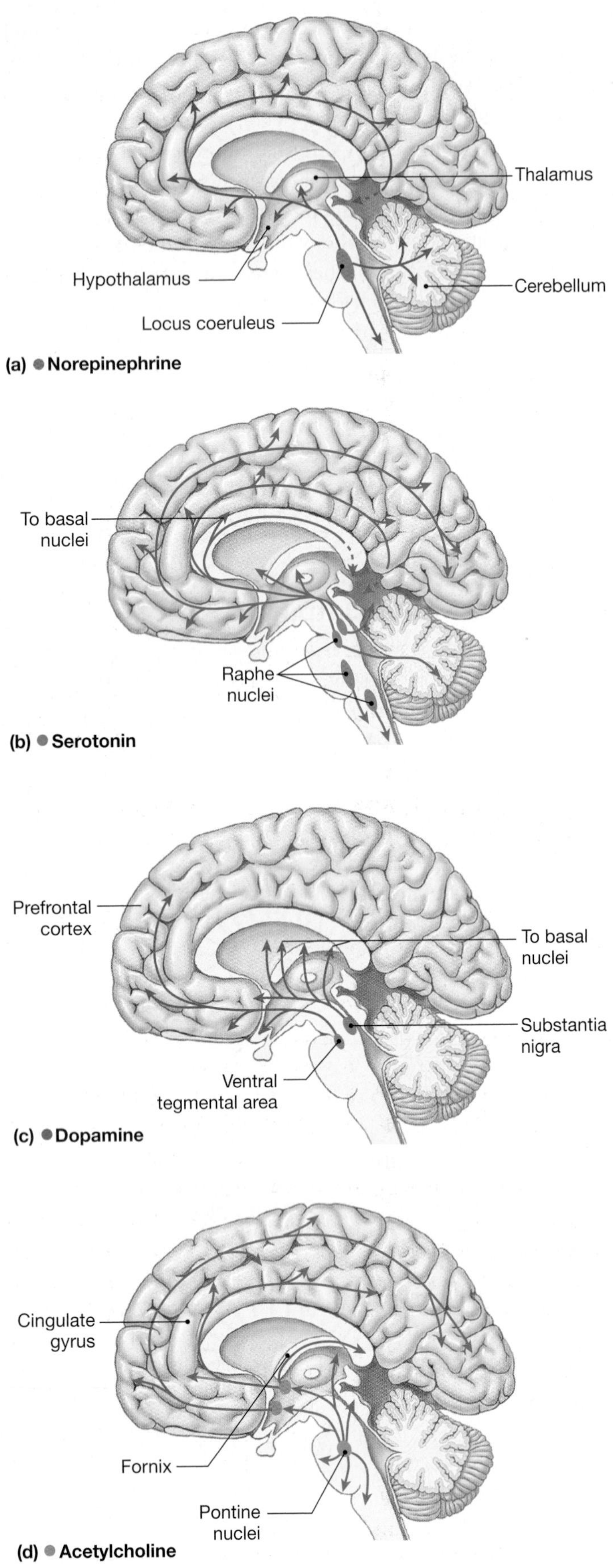

● **FIGURE 9-19** ***The diffuse modulatory systems modulate brain function.*** The neurons collectively known as the diffuse modulatory systems originate in the reticular formation of the brain stem and project their axons to large areas of the brain. The four systems are named for their neurotransmitters.

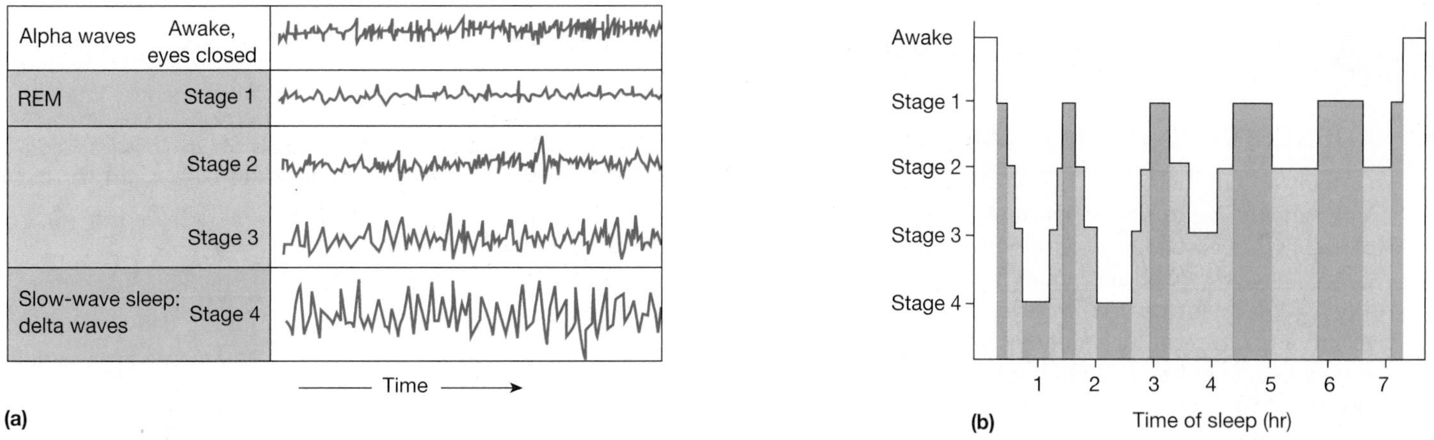

FIGURE QUESTIONS

Which EEG pattern has the fastest frequency? The greatest amplitude?

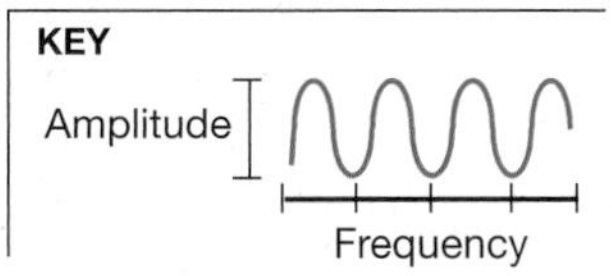

● **FIGURE 9-20** ***Electroencephalograms (EEGs) and the sleep cycle.*** Recordings of electrical activity in the brain during awake-resting and sleep periods show characteristic patterns.

Why Do We Sleep?

In humans, our major rest period is marked by a behavior known as **sleep**, defined as an easily reversible state of inactivity characterized by lack of interaction with the external environment. Why we need to sleep is one of the unsolved mysteries in neurophysiology. Some explanations that have been proposed include to conserve energy, to avoid predators, to allow the body to repair itself, and to process memories. Most mammals and birds show the same stages of sleep as humans, telling us that sleep is a very ancient property of vertebrate brains.

Until the 1960s, sleep was thought to be a passive state that resulted from withdrawal of stimuli to the brain. Then experiments showed that neuronal activity in ascending tracts from the brain stem to the cerebral cortex was required for sleep. From other studies, we know that the sleeping brain consumes as much oxygen as the awake brain, and sometimes even more. As a result, we now consider sleep to be an active state.

Sleep is divided into four stages, each marked by identifiable, predictable events associated with characteristic somatic changes and EEG patterns (Fig. 9-20a). The two major sleep phases are **slow-wave sleep** (also called **deep sleep** or **non-REM sleep**, stage 4) and **REM (rapid eye movement) sleep** (stage 1). Slow-wave sleep is apparent on the EEG by the presence of *delta waves,* high-amplitude, low-frequency waves of long duration that sweep across the cerebral cortex. During this phase of the sleep cycle, sleepers adjust body position without conscious commands from the brain to do so.

In contrast, REM sleep is marked by an EEG pattern closer to that of an awake person, with low-amplitude, high-frequency waves. During REM sleep, brain activity inhibits motor neurons to skeletal muscles, paralyzing them. Exceptions to this pattern are the muscles that move the eyes and those that control breathing. The control of homeostatic functions is depressed during REM sleep, and body temperature falls toward ambient temperature.

REM sleep is the period during which most dreaming takes place. The eyes move behind closed lids, as if following the action of the dream. Sleepers are most likely to wake up spontaneously from periods of REM sleep.

A typical eight-hour sleep consists of repeating cycles, as shown in Figure 9-20b. In the first hour, the person moves from wakefulness into a deep sleep (stage 4; first blue area in Figure 9-20b). The sleeper then cycles between deep sleep and REM sleep (stage 1), with stages 2–3 occurring in between. Near the end of an eight-hour sleep period a sleeper spends the most time in stage 2 and REM sleep, until finally awakening for the day.

If sleep is a neurologically active process, what is it that makes us sleepy? The possibility of a sleep-inducing factor was first proposed in 1913, when scientists found that cerebrospinal fluid from sleep-deprived dogs could induce sleep in normal animals. Since then, a variety of sleep-inducing factors have been identified. Curiously, many of them are also substances that enhance the immune response, such as interleukin-1, interferon, serotonin, and tumor necrosis factor. As a result of this finding, some investigators have suggested that one answer to the puzzle of the biological reason for sleep is that we need to sleep to enhance our immune response. Whether or not that is a reason for why we sleep, the link between the immune system and sleep induction may help explain why we tend to sleep more when we are sick.

EMERGING CONCEPTS

ADENOSINE AND THAT "JAVA JOLT"

Caffeine and its methylxanthine cousins *theobromine* and *theophylline* (found in chocolate and tea) are probably the most widely consumed psychoactive drugs, known since ancient times for their stimulant effect. Molecular research has revealed that the methylxanthines are receptor antagonists for *adenosine*, a molecule composed of the nitrogenous base adenine plus the sugar ribose [p. 34]. Adenosine acts as an important neuromodulator in the central nervous system. Four subtypes of adenosine receptor have been identified, and they are all G protein–coupled, cAMP-dependent membrane proteins. The discovery that the stimulant effect of caffeine comes from its blockade of adenosine receptors has led scientists to investigate adenosine's role in sleep-wake cycles. Evidence suggests that adenosine accumulates in the extracellular fluid during waking hours, increasingly suppressing activity of the neurons that promote wakefulness. Other roles for adenosine in the brain include its possible involvement in the addiction/reward system and in the development of depression.

Sleep disorders are relatively common, as you can tell by looking at the variety of sleep-promoting agents available over the counter in drugstores. Among the more common sleep disorders are *insomnia* (the inability to go to sleep or remain asleep long enough to awake refreshed), sleep apnea, and sleepwalking. *Sleep apnea* [*apnoos*, breathless] is a condition in which the sleeper awakes when the airway muscles relax to the point of obstructing normal breathing.

Sleepwalking, or *somnambulism* [*somnus*, sleep + *ambulare*, to walk], is a sleep behavior disorder that for many years was thought to represent the acting out of dreams. However, most dreaming occurs during REM sleep (stage 1), while sleepwalking takes place during deep sleep (stage 4). During sleepwalking episodes, which may last from 30 seconds to 30 minutes, the subject's eyes are open and registering the surroundings. The subject is able to avoid bumping into objects, can negotiate stairs, and in some cases is reported to perform such tasks as preparing food or folding clothes. The subject usually has little if any conscious recall of the sleepwalking episode upon awakening. Sleepwalking is most common in children, and the frequency of episodes declines with age. There is also a genetic component, as the tendency to sleepwalk runs in families. To learn more about the different sleep disorders, see the U.S. National Institutes of Health web site for the National Center for Sleep Disorder Research (*www.nhlbi.nih.gov/about/ncsdr*).

CONCEPT CHECK

21. During sleep, relay neurons in the thalamus reduce information reaching the cerebrum by altering their membrane potential. Are these neurons more likely to have depolarized or hyperpolarized? Explain your reasoning. Answers: p. 332

Physiological Functions Exhibit Circadian Rhythms

All organisms (even plants) have alternating daily patterns of rest and activity. Sleep-wake rhythms, like many other biological cycles, generally follow a 24-hour light-dark cycle and are known as *circadian rhythms* [p. 204]. When an organism is placed in conditions of constant light or darkness, these activity rhythms persist, apparently cued by an internal clock.

In mammals, the "clock" resides in networks of neurons located in the **suprachiasmatic nucleus** of the hypothalamus. A very simple interpretation of recent experiments on the molecular basis of the clock is that clock cycling is the result of a complex feedback loop in which specific genes turn on and direct protein synthesis. The proteins accumulate, turn off the genes, and then are themselves degraded. In the absence of the proteins, the genes turn back on and the cycle begins again. The clock has intrinsic activity that is synchronized with the external environment by sensory information about light cycles received through the eyes.

Circadian rhythms in humans can be found in most physiological functions and usually correspond to the phases of our sleep-wake cycles. For example, body temperature and cortisol secretion both cycle on a daily basis [Fig. 6-29, p. 205]. Melatonin secretion by the pineal gland also is strongly linked

RUNNING PROBLEM

About six months after the start of ACTH treatment, Ben's head-drop seizures returned, and his development began to decline once again. An EEG following Ben's relapse did not demonstrate the erratic wave patterns specific to infantile spasms but did show abnormal activity in the right cortex. A neurologist ordered a positron emission tomography (PET) scan to determine the focus of Ben's seizure activity.

Ben received an injection of radioactively labeled glucose. He was then placed in the center of a PET machine lined with radiation detectors that created a map of his brain showing areas of high and low radioactivity. Those parts of his brain that were more active absorbed more glucose and thus emitted more radiation when the radioactive compound began to decay.

Question 4:
What is the rationale for using radioactively labeled glucose (and not some other nutrient) for the PET scan?

297 305 320 322 326 327

to light-dark cycling and appears to feed back to the suprachiasmatic nucleus to modulate clock cycling.

Emotion and Motivation Involve Complex Neural Pathways

Emotion and motivation are two aspects of brain function that probably represent an overlap of the behavioral state system and cognitive system. The pathways involved are complex and form closed circuits that cycle information among various parts of the brain, including the hypothalamus, limbic system, and cerebral cortex. We still do not understand the underlying neural mechanisms, and this is a large and active area of neuroscience research.

Emotions are difficult to define. We know what they are and can name them, but in many ways they defy description. One characteristic of emotions is that they are difficult to voluntarily turn on or off. The most commonly described emotions, which arise in different parts of the brain, are anger, aggression, sexual feelings, fear, pleasure, contentment, and happiness.

The limbic system, particularly the region known as the *amygdala,* is the center of emotion in the human brain. Scientists have learned about the role of this brain region through experiments in humans and animals. When the amygdala is artificially stimulated in humans, as it might be during surgery for epilepsy, patients report experiencing feelings of fear and anxiety. Experimental lesions that destroy the amygdala in animals cause the animals to become tamer and to display hypersexuality. As a result, neurobiologists believe that the amygdala is the center for basic instincts such as fear and aggression.

The pathways for emotions are complex (Fig. 9-21 ●). Sensory stimuli feeding into the cerebral cortex are constructed in the brain to create a representation (perception) of the world. After information is integrated by the association areas, it is passed on to the limbic system. Feedback from the limbic system to the cerebral cortex creates awareness of the emotion, while descending pathways to the hypothalamus and brain stem initiate voluntary behaviors and unconscious responses mediated by autonomic, endocrine, immune, and somatic motor systems.

The physical result of emotions can be as dramatic as the pounding heart of a fight-or-flight reaction or as insidious as the development of an irregular heartbeat. The links between mind and body are difficult to study and will take many years of research to understand.

Motivation is defined as internal signals that shape voluntary behaviors. Some of these behaviors, such as eating, drinking, and having sex, are related to survival. Others, such as curiosity and having sex (again), are linked to emotions. Some motivational states are known as **drives** and generally have three properties in common: (1) they create an increased state of CNS arousal or alertness, (2) they create goal-oriented behavior, and (3) they are capable of coordinating disparate behaviors to achieve that goal.

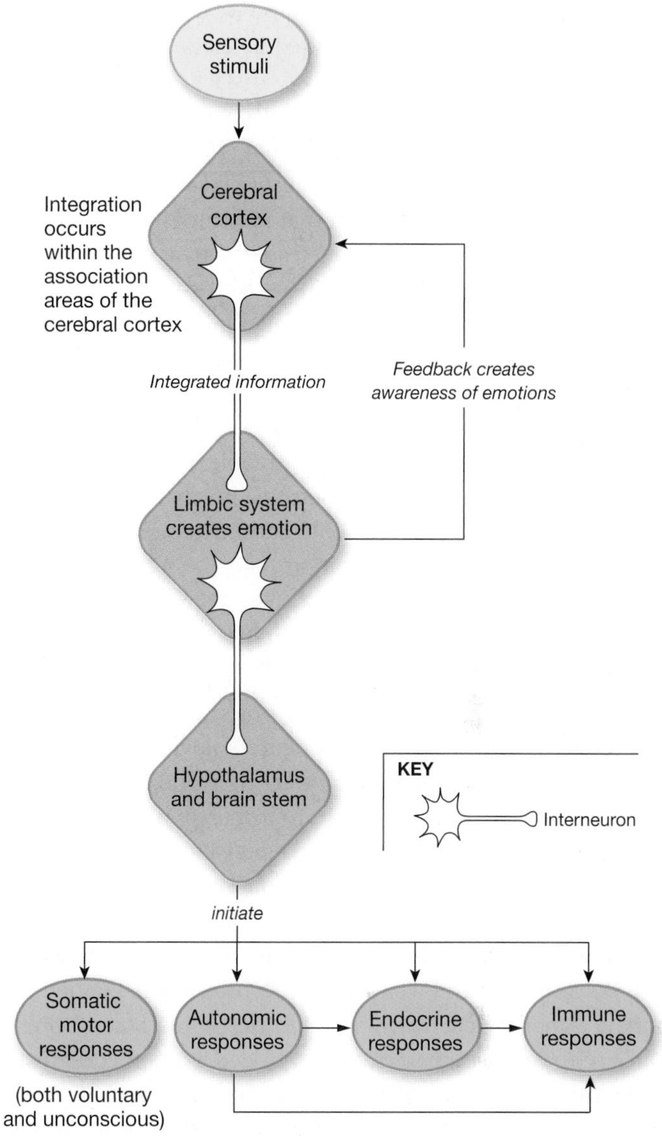

● **FIGURE 9-21** ***The link between emotions and physiological functions.*** The association between stress and increased susceptibility to viruses is an example of an emotionally linked immune response.

Motivated behaviors often work in parallel with autonomic and endocrine responses in the body, as you might expect with behaviors originating in the hypothalamus. For example, if you eat salty popcorn, your body osmolarity increases. This stimulus acts on the thirst center of the hypothalamus, motivating you to seek something to drink. Increased osmolarity also acts on an endocrine center in the hypothalamus, releasing a hormone that increases water retention by the kidneys. In this way one stimulus triggers both a motivated behavior and a homeostatic endocrine response.

Some motivated behaviors can be activated by internal stimuli that may not even be obvious to the person in whom they are occurring. Eating, curiosity, and sex drive are three examples of behaviors with complex stimuli underlying their onset. We may eat, for example, because we are hungry or because the food looks good or because we do not want to hurt someone's feelings. Many motivated behaviors stop when the person has reached a certain level of satisfaction, or **satiety**, but they may also continue *despite* feeling satiated.

Pleasure is a motivational state that is being intensely studied because of its relationship to *addictive behaviors,* such as drug use. Animal studies have shown that pleasure is a physiological state that is accompanied by increased activity of the neurotransmitter dopamine in certain parts of the brain. Drugs that are addictive, such as cocaine and nicotine, act by enhancing the effectiveness of dopamine, thereby increasing the pleasurable sensations perceived by the brain. As a result, use of these drugs rapidly becomes a learned behavior. Interestingly, not all behaviors that are addictive are pleasurable. For example, there are a variety of compulsive behaviors that involve self-mutilation, such as pulling out hair by the roots. Fortunately, many behaviors can be modulated, given motivation.

Moods Are Long-Lasting Emotional States

Moods are similar to emotions but are longer-lasting, relatively stable subjective feelings related to one's sense of well-being. Moods are difficult to define at a neurobiological level, but evidence obtained in studying and treating mood disorders indicates that what was once thought to be purely psychological in origin is actually a CNS function. Depression and other mood disorders result from abnormal neurotransmitter release or reception in different brain regions.

Mood disorders are estimated to be the fourth leading cause of illness in the world today. **Depression** is a mood disturbance that affects nearly 10% of the United States population each year. It is characterized by sleep and appetite disturbances and alterations of mood and libido that may seriously affect the person's ability to function at school or work or in personal relationships. Many people do not realize that depression is not a sign of mental or moral weakness, or that it can be treated successfully with drugs and psychotherapy. (For detailed information about depression, go to *www.nlm.nih.gov/medlineplus/depression.html*).

The drug therapy for depression has changed in recent years, but all the major categories of antidepressant drugs alter some aspect of synaptic transmission. The older *tricyclic antidepressants,* such as amitriptyline, block reuptake of norepinephrine into the presynaptic neuron, thus extending the active life of the neurotransmitter. The antidepressants known as *selective serotonin reuptake inhibitors,* or SSRIs, slow down the removal of serotonin (and possibly also norepinephrine) from the synapse. As a result of uptake inhibition, serotonin lingers in the synaptic cleft longer than usual, increasing serotonin-dependent activity in the postsynaptic neuron. Other antidepressant drugs alter brain levels of dopamine. The effectiveness of these different classes of antidepressant drugs suggests that norepinephrine, serotonin, and dopamine are all involved in brain pathways for mood and emotion.

Interestingly, patients need to take antidepressant drugs for several weeks before they experience their full effect. This delay suggests that the changes taking place in the brain are long-term modulation of pathways rather than simply enhanced fast synaptic responses. The causes of major depression are complex and probably involve a combination of genetic factors, the serotonergic and noradrenergic diffuse modulatory systems, trophic factors such as *brain-derived neurotrophic factor* (BDNF), and stress. The search to uncover the biological basis of disturbed brain function is a major focus of neuroscience research today.

Some research into brain function has become quite controversial, particularly that dealing with sexuality and the degree to which behavior in general is genetically determined in humans. We will not delve deeply into any of these subjects because they are complex and would require lengthy explanations to do them justice. Instead, we will look briefly at some of the recent models proposed to explain the mechanisms that are the basis for higher cognitive functions.

Learning and Memory Change Synaptic Connections in the Brain

For many years, motivation, learning, and memory (all of which are aspects of the cognitive state) were considered to be in the realm of psychology rather than biology. Neurobiologists in decades past were more concerned with the network and cellular aspects of neuronal function. In recent years, however, the two fields have overlapped more and more. Scientists have discovered that the underlying basis for cognitive function seems to be explainable in terms of cellular events that influence plasticity—events such as long-term potentiation [p. 285]. The ability of neuronal connections to change with experience is fundamental to the two cognitive processes of learning and memory.

RUNNING PROBLEM

Ben's halted development is a feature unique to infantile spasms. The abnormal portions of the brain send out continuous action potentials during frequent seizures and ultimately change the interconnections of brain neurons. The damaged portions of the brain harm normal portions to such an extent that medication or surgery should be started as soon as possible. If intervention is not begun early, the brain can be permanently damaged and development will never recover.

Question 5:

The brain's ability to change its synaptic connections as a result of neuronal activity is called ___________.

297 305 320 322 326 327

Learning Is the Acquisition of Knowledge

How do you know when you have learned something? Learning can be demonstrated by behavioral changes, but behavioral changes are not required in order for learning to occur. Learning can be internalized and is not always reflected by overt behavior while the learning is taking place. Would someone watching you read your textbook be able to tell whether you had learned anything?

Learning can be classified into two broad types: associative and nonassociative. **Associative learning** occurs when two stimuli are associated with each other, such as Pavlov's classic experiment in which he simultaneously presented dogs with food and rang a bell. After a period of time, the dogs came to associate the sound of the bell with food and began to salivate in anticipation of food whenever the bell was rung. Another form of associative learning occurs when an animal associates a stimulus with a given behavior. An example would be a mouse that gets a shock each time it touches a certain part of its cage. It soon associates that part of the cage with an unpleasant experience and avoids the area.

Nonassociative learning is a change in behavior that takes place after repeated exposure to a single stimulus. This type of learning includes habituation and sensitization, two adaptive behaviors that allow us to filter out and ignore background stimuli while responding more sensitively to potentially disruptive stimuli. In **habituation**, an animal shows a decreased response to an irrelevant stimulus that is repeated over and over. For example, a sudden loud noise may startle you, but if the noise is repeated over and over again, your brain begins to ignore it. Habituated responses allow us to filter out stimuli that we have evaluated and found to be insignificant.

Sensitization is the opposite of habituation, and the two behaviors combined help increase an organism's chances for survival. In sensitization learning, exposure to a noxious or intense stimulus causes an enhanced response upon subsequent exposure. For example, people who become ill while eating a certain food may find that they lose their desire to eat that food again. Sensitization is adaptive because it helps us avoid potentially harmful stimuli.

Memory Is the Ability to Retain and Recall Information

Memory is the ability to retain and recall information. We have several types of memory: short-term and long-term, reflexive and declarative. Processing for different types of memory appears to take place through different pathways. With noninvasive imaging techniques such as MRI and PET scans, researchers have been able to track brain activity as individuals learned to perform tasks.

Memories are stored throughout the cerebral cortex in pathways known as **memory traces**. Some components of memories are stored in the sensory cortices where they are

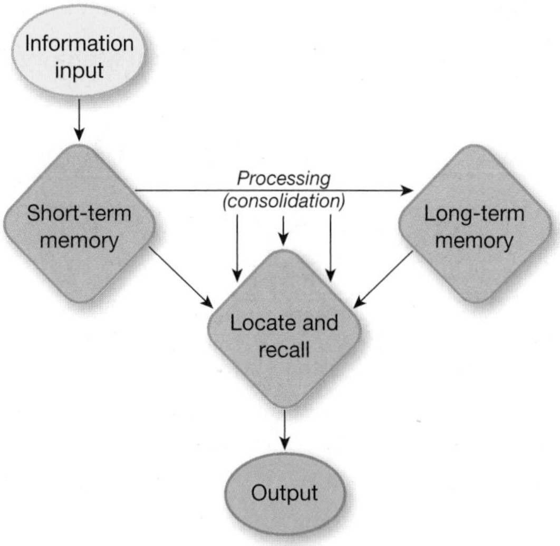

● **FIGURE 9-22** ***Memory processing.*** New information goes into short-term memory but is lost unless processed and stored in long-term memory.

processed. For example, pictures are stored in the visual cortex, and sounds in the auditory cortex.

Learning a task or recalling a task already learned may involve multiple brain circuits that work in parallel. This *parallel processing* helps provide backup in case one of the circuits is damaged. It is also believed to be the means by which specific memories are generalized, allowing new information to be matched to stored information. For example, a person who has never seen a volleyball will recognize it as a ball because the volleyball has the same general characteristics as all other balls the person has seen.

In humans, the hippocampus seems to be an important structure in both learning and memory. For example, patients who had part of the hippocampus destroyed to relieve a certain type of epilepsy also had trouble remembering new information. When given a list of words to repeat, they could remember the words as long as their attention stayed focused on the task. If they were distracted, however, the memory of the words disappeared, and they had to learn the list again. Information stored in long-term memory before the operation was not affected. This inability to remember newly acquired information is a defect known as **anterograde amnesia** [*amnesia,* oblivion].

Memory has multiple levels of storage, and our memory bank is constantly changing (Fig. 9-22 ●). When a stimulus comes into the CNS, it first goes into **short-term memory**, a limited storage area that can hold only about 7 to 12 pieces of information at a time. Items in short-term memory disappear unless an effort, such as repetition, is made to put them into a more permanent form.

Working memory is a special form of short-term memory processed in the prefrontal lobes. This region of the cerebral cortex is devoted to keeping track of bits of information long

TABLE 9-4 Types of Long-Term Memory

REFLEXIVE (IMPLICIT) MEMORY	DECLARATIVE (EXPLICIT) MEMORY
Recall is automatic and does not require conscious attention	Recall requires conscious attention
Acquired slowly through repetition	Depends on higher-level thinking skills such as inference, comparison, and evaluation
Includes motor skills and rules and procedures	Memories can be reported verbally
Procedural memories can be demonstrated	

enough to put them to use in a task that takes place after the information has been acquired. Working memory in these regions is linked to long-term memory stores, so that newly acquired information can be integrated with stored information and acted on. For example, suppose you are trying to cross a busy road. You look to the left and see that there are no cars coming for several blocks. You then look to the right and see that there are no cars coming from that direction either. Working memory has stored the information that the road to the left is clear, and so using stored knowledge about safety, you are able to conclude that there is no traffic from either direction and it is safe to cross the road.

In people with damage to the prefrontal lobes of the brain, this task becomes more difficult because they are unable to recall whether the road is clear from the left once they have looked away to assess traffic coming from the right. Working memory allows us to collect a series of facts from short- and long-term memory and connect them in a logical order to solve problems or plan actions.

Long-term memory is a storage area capable of holding vast amounts of information. The processing of information that converts short-term memory into long-term memory is known as **consolidation** (Fig. 9-22). Consolidation can take varying periods of time, from seconds to minutes. Information passes through many intermediate levels of memory during consolidation, and in each of these stages, the information can be located and recalled.

As scientists studied the consolidation of short-term memory into long-term memory, they discovered that the process involves changes in synaptic connections of the circuits involved in learning. In some cases, new synapses form; in others, the effectiveness of synaptic transmission is altered either through long-term potentiation or through long-term depression. These changes are evidence of plasticity and show us that the brain is not "hard-wired."

Long-term memory has been divided into two types that are consolidated and stored using different neuronal pathways (Table 9-4 ●). **Reflexive (implicit) memory**, which is automatic and does not require conscious processes for either creation or recall, involves the amygdala and the cerebellum. Information stored in reflexive memory is acquired slowly through repetition. Motor skills fall into this category, as do procedures and rules.

For example, you do not need to think about putting a period at the end of each sentence or about how to pick up a fork. Reflexive memory has also been called *procedural memory* because it generally concerns how to do things. Reflexive memories can be acquired through either associative or nonassociative learning processes, and these memories are stored.

Declarative (explicit) memory, on the other hand, requires conscious attention for its recall. Its creation generally depends on the use of higher-level cognitive skills such as inference, comparison, and evaluation. The neuronal pathways involved in this type of memory are in the temporal lobes. Declarative memories deal with knowledge about ourselves and the world around us that can be reported or described verbally.

Sometimes information can be transferred from declarative memory to reflexive memory. The quarterback on a football team is a good example. When he learned to throw the football as a small boy, he had to pay close attention to gripping the ball and coordinating his muscles to throw the ball accurately. At that point of learning to throw the ball, the process was in declarative memory and required conscious effort as the boy analyzed his movements.

With repetition, however, the mechanics of throwing the ball were transferred to reflexive memory: they became a reflex that could be executed without conscious thought. That transfer allowed the quarterback to use his conscious mind to analyze the path and timing of the pass while the mechanics of the pass became automatic. Athletes often refer to this automaticity of learned body movements as *muscle memory*.

Memory is an individual thing. We process information on the basis of our experiences and perception of the world. Because people have widely different experiences throughout their lives, it follows that no two people will process a given piece of information in the same way. If you ask a group of people about what happened during a particular event such as a lecture or an automobile accident, no two descriptions will be identical. Each person will have processed the event according to her or his own perceptions and experiences. Experiential processing is important to remember when studying in a group situation, because it is unlikely that all group members learn or recall information the same way.

Memory loss and the inability to process and store new memories are devastating medical conditions. In younger people, memory problems are usually associated with trauma to the brain from accidents. In older people, strokes and progressive *dementia* [*demens,* out of one's mind] are the main causes of memory loss. **Alzheimer's disease** is a progressive neurodegenerative disease of cognitive impairment that accounts for about half the cases of dementia in the elderly. By one estimate, it affects about 5.1 million Americans, with the number expected to rise as Baby Boomers age. Alzheimer's is characterized by memory loss that progresses to a point where the patient does not recognize family members. Over time, even the personality changes, and in the final stages, other cognitive functions fail so that patients cannot communicate with caregivers.

Diagnosis of Alzheimer's is usually made through the patient's declining performance on mental status examinations. The only definitive diagnosis comes after death, when brain tissue can be examined for neuronal degeneration, extracellular plaques made of *β-amyloid protein,* and intracellular tangles of *tau,* a protein that is normally associated with microtubules. Although the presence of plaques and tangles is diagnostic, the underlying cause of Alzheimer's is unclear. There is a known genetic component, and other theories include oxidative stress and chronic inflammation. Currently there is no proven prevention or treatment, although drugs that are acetylcholine agonists or acetylcholinesterase inhibitors slow the progression of the disease. The forecast of 14 million people with Alzheimer's by the year 2050 has put this disease in the forefront of neurobiological research.

Language Is the Most Elaborate Cognitive Behavior

One of the hallmarks of an advanced nervous system is the ability of one member of a species to exchange complex information with other members of the same species. Although found predominantly in birds and mammals, this ability also occurs in certain insects that convey amazingly detailed information by means of sound (crickets), touch and sight (bees), and odor (ants). In humans, the exchange of complex information takes place primarily through spoken and written language. Because language is considered the most elaborate cognitive behavior, it has received considerable attention from neurobiologists.

Language skills require the input of sensory information (primarily from hearing and vision), processing in various centers in the cerebral cortex, and the coordination of motor output for vocalization and writing. In most people the centers for language ability are found in the left hemisphere of the cerebrum. Even 70% of people who are either left-handed (right-brain dominant) or ambidextrous use their left brain for speech. The ability to communicate through speech has been divided into two processes: the combination of different sounds to form words (vocalization) and the combination of words into grammatically correct and meaningful sentences.

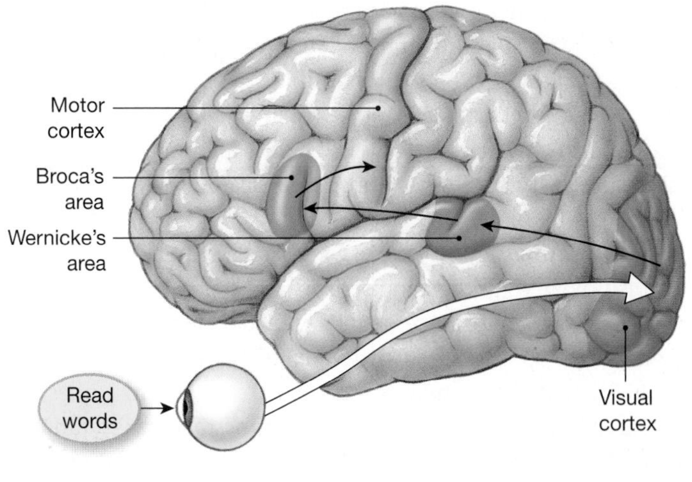

(a) Speaking a written word

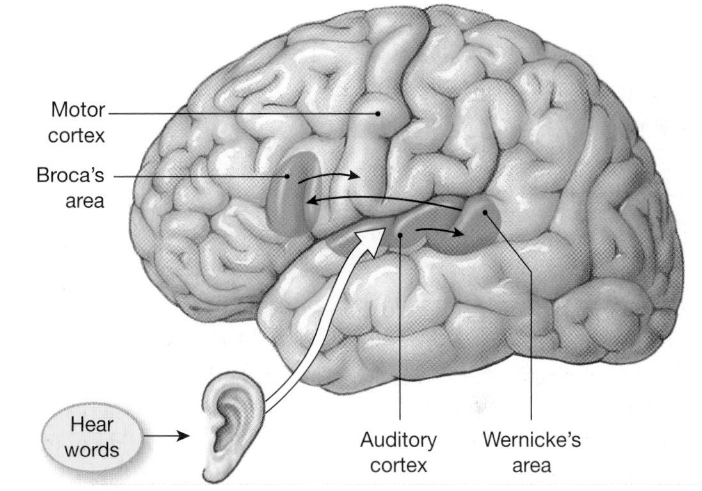

(b) Speaking a heard word

● **FIGURE 9-23** ***Cerebral processing of spoken and visual language.*** People with damage to Wernicke's area do not understand spoken or written communication. Those with damage to Broca's area understand but are unable to respond appropriately.

The integration of spoken language in the human brain involves two regions in the cerebral cortex: **Wernicke's area** in the temporal lobe and **Broca's area** in the frontal lobe close to the motor cortex (Fig. 9-23 ●). Most of what we know about these areas comes from studies of people with brain lesions (because nonhuman animals are not capable of speech). Even primates that communicate on the level of a small child through sign language and other visual means do not have the physical ability to vocalize the sounds of human language.

Input into the language areas comes from either the visual cortex (reading) or the auditory cortex (listening). Sensory input from either cortex goes first to Wernicke's area, then to Broca's area. After integration and processing, output from Broca's area to the motor cortex initiates a spoken or written action. If damage occurs to Wernicke's area, a person is unable to understand any spoken or visual information. The person's own speech, as a result, is nonsense, because the person is unaware of his or her own errors. This condition is known as **receptive aphasia** [*a*−, not + *phatos,* spoken] because the person is unable to understand sensory input.

On the other hand, people with damage to Broca's area understand spoken and written language but are unable to speak or write in normal syntax. Their response to a question often consists of appropriate words strung together in random order. These patients may have a difficult time dealing with their disability because they are aware of their mistakes but are powerless to correct them. Damage to Broca's area causes an **expressive aphasia**.

Mechanical forms of aphasia occur as a result of damage to the motor cortex. Patients with this type of damage find themselves unable to physically shape the sounds that make up words, or unable to coordinate the muscles of their arm and hand to write.

RUNNING PROBLEM

The PET scan revealed two abnormal spots, or *loci* (plural of *locus*), on Ben's right hemisphere, one on the parietal lobe and one overlapping a portion of the primary motor cortex. Because the loci triggering Ben's seizures were located on the same hemisphere and were in the cortex, Ben was a candidate for a *hemispherectomy,* removal of the cortex of the affected hemisphere. Surgeons removed 80 percent of his right cerebral cortex, sparing areas crucial to vision, hearing, and sensory processing. Normally the motor cortex would be spared as well, but in Ben's case a seizure locus overlapped much of the region.

Question 6:
In which lobes are the centers for vision, hearing, and sensory processing located?

Question 7:
Which of Ben's abilities might have suffered if his left hemisphere had been removed instead?

Question 8:
By taking only the cortex of the right hemisphere, what parts of the cerebrum did surgeons leave behind?

Question 9:
Why were the surgeons careful to spare Ben's right lateral ventricle?

297 305 320 322 326 327

Personality Is a Combination of Experience and Inheritance

One of the most difficult aspects of brain function to translate from the abstract realm of psychology into the physical circuits of neurobiology is the combination of attributes we call **personality**. What is it that makes us individuals? The parents of more than one child will tell you that their offspring were different from birth, and even before that in the womb. If we all have the same brain structure, what makes us different?

This question fascinates many people. The answer that is evolving from neurobiology research is that we are a combination of our experiences and the genetic constraints we inherit. One complicating factor is the developmental aspect of "experience," as scientists are showing that exposure of developing embryos to hormones while still in the womb can alter brain pathways.

What we learn or experience and what we store in memory create a unique pattern of neuronal connections in our brains. Sometimes these circuits malfunction, creating depression, schizophrenia, or any number of other personality disturbances. Psychiatrists for many years attempted to treat these disorders as if they were due solely to events in the person's life, but now we know that there is a genetic component to many of these disorders.

Schizophrenia [*schizein,* to split + *phren,* the mind] is an example of a brain disorder that has both a genetic and an environmental basis. In the American population as a whole, the risk of developing schizophrenia is about 1%. However, if one parent has schizophrenia, the risk increases to 10%, indicating that people can inherit a susceptibility to developing the disease. The cause of schizophrenia is not currently known. However, as with many other conditions involving altered mental states, schizophrenia can be treated with drugs that influence neurotransmitter release and activity in the brain. To learn more about diagnosis and treatment of schizophrenia, see the National Institutes of Health web site *www.nlm.nih.gov/medlineplus/schizophrenia.html*.

We still have much to learn about repairing damage to the CNS. One of the biggest tragedies in life is the personality change that sometimes accompanies head trauma. Physical damage to the delicate circuits of the brain not only can alter intelligence and memory storage but also can create a new personality. The person who exists after the injury may not seem to be the same person who inhabited that body before the injury. Although the change may not be noticeable to the injured person, it can be devastating to the victim's family and friends. Perhaps as we learn more about how neurons link to one another, we will be able to find a means of restoring damaged networks and preventing the lasting effects of head trauma and brain disorders.

RUNNING PROBLEM CONCLUSION

Infantile Spasms

Ben has remained seizure-free since the surgery and shows normal development in all areas except motor skills. He remains somewhat weaker and less coordinated on his left side, the side opposite (*contralateral*) to the surgery, but over time the weakness should subside with the aid of physical therapy. Ben's recovery stands as a testament to the incredible plasticity of the brain. Apart from the physical damage caused to the brain, a number of epileptics have developmental delays that stem from the social aspects of their disorder. Young children with frequent seizures often have difficulty socializing with their peers because of overprotective parents, missed school days, and the fear of people who do not understand epilepsy. Their problems can extend into adulthood, when epileptics may have difficulty finding employment or driving if their seizures are not controlled. There are numerous examples of adults who undergo successful epilepsy surgery but are still unable to fully enter society because they lack social and employment skills. Not surprisingly, the rate of depression is much higher among epileptics. To learn more about epilepsy, start with the Epilepsy Foundation (*www.epilepsyfoundation.org*).

This Running Problem was written by Susan E. Johnson while she was an undergraduate student at the University of Texas at Austin studying for a career in the biomedical sciences.

	QUESTION	FACTS	INTEGRATION AND ANALYSIS
1	How might a leaky blood-brain barrier lead to action potentials that trigger a seizure?	Neurotransmitters and other chemicals circulating freely in the blood are normally separated from brain tissue by the blood-brain barrier.	Negatively charged molecules and neurotransmitters entering the brain might depolarize neurons and trigger action potentials.
2	What does GABA do to the cell's membrane potential? Does GABA make the cell more or less likely to fire action potentials?	GABA opens Cl^- channels.	Cl^- entering a neuron hyperpolarizes the cell and makes it less likely to fire action potentials.
3	Why is it important to limit the duration of ACTH therapy?	Exogenous ACTH acts in a short negative feedback loop, decreasing the output of CRH from the hypothalamus and ACTH production by the anterior pituitary. See Figure 7-15, p. 231.	Long-term suppression of endogenous hormone secretion by ACTH can cause CRH- and ACTH-secreting neurons to atrophy, resulting in a lifelong cortisol deficiency.
4	What is the rationale for using radioactively labeled glucose (and not some other nutrient) for the PET scan?	Glucose is the primary energy source for the brain.	Glucose usage is more closely correlated to brain activity than any other nutrient in the body. Areas of abnormally high glucose usage are suggestive of overactive cells.
5	The brain's ability to change its synaptic connections as a result of neuronal activity is called ________.	Changes in synaptic connections as a result of neuronal activity are an example of plasticity.	N/A*
6	In which lobes are the centers for vision, hearing, and sensory processing located?	Vision is processed in the occipital lobe, hearing in the temporal lobe, and sensory information in the parietal lobe.	N/A
7	Which of Ben's abilities might have suffered if his left hemisphere had been removed instead?	In most people, the left hemisphere contains Wernicke's area and Broca's area, two centers vital to speech. The left brain controls right-sided sensory and motor functions.	Patients who have undergone left hemispherectomies have difficulty with speech (abstract words, grammar, and phonetics). They show loss of right-side sensory and motor functions.

*N/A—not applicable

RUNNING PROBLEM CONCLUSION *(continued)*

	QUESTION	FACTS	INTEGRATION AND ANALYSIS
8	By taking only the cortex of the right hemisphere, what parts of the cerebrum did surgeons leave behind?	The cerebrum consists of gray matter in the cortex and interior nuclei, white matter, and the ventricles.	The surgeons left behind the white matter, interior nuclei, and ventricles.
9	Why were the surgeons careful to spare Ben's right lateral ventricle?	The walls of the ventricles contain the choroid plexus, which secretes cerebrospinal fluid (CSF). CSF plays a vital protective role by cushioning the brain.	CSF protection is particularly important following removal of portions of brain tissue because the potential damage from jarring of the head is much greater.

297 305 320 322 326 327

CHAPTER SUMMARY

The brain is the primary control center of the body, and (as you will learn in later chapters), homeostatic responses in many organ systems are designed to maintain brain function. The ability of the brain to create complex thoughts and emotions in the absence of external stimuli is one of its *emergent properties*.

Emergent Properties of Neural Networks

1. Neural networks create **affective** and **cognitive behaviors**. (p. 297)
2. The brain exhibits **plasticity**, the ability to change connections as a result of experience. (p. 297)

Evolution of Nervous Systems

3. Nervous systems evolved from a simple network of neurons to complex brains. (p. 297; Fig. 9-1)
4. The **cerebrum** is responsible for thought and emotion. (p. 299)

Anatomy of the Central Nervous System

5. The central nervous system consists of layers of cells around a fluid-filled central cavity and develops from the **neural tube** of the embryo. (p. 299; Fig. 9-2)
6. The **gray matter** of the CNS consists of unmyelinated nerve cell bodies, dendrites, and axon terminals. The cell bodies either form layers in parts of the brain or else cluster into groups known as **nuclei**. (p. 301)
7. Myelinated axons form the **white matter** of the CNS and run in bundles called **tracts**. (p. 301)
8. The brain and spinal cord are encased in the **meninges** and the bones of the **cranium** and vertebrae. The meninges are the **pia mater**, the **arachnoid membrane**, and the **dura mater**. (p. 301; Fig. 9-4)
9. The **choroid plexus** secretes **cerebrospinal fluid** (CSF) into the **ventricles** of the brain. Cerebrospinal fluid cushions the tissue and creates a controlled chemical environment. (p. 303; Fig. 9-5)
10. Tight junctions in brain capillaries create a **blood-brain barrier** that prevents possibly harmful substances in the blood from entering the interstitial fluid. (p. 303; Fig. 9-6)
11. The normal fuel source for neurons is glucose, which is why the body closely regulates blood glucose concentrations. (p. 306)

The Spinal Cord

12. Each segment of the spinal cord is associated with a pair of **spinal nerves**. (p. 307)
13. The **dorsal root** of each spinal nerve carries incoming sensory information. The **dorsal root ganglia** contain the nerve cell bodies of sensory neurons. (p. 307; Fig. 9-7)
14. The **ventral roots** carry information from the central nervous system to muscles and glands. (p. 307)
15. **Ascending tracts** of white matter carry sensory information to the brain, and **descending tracts** carry efferent signals from the brain. **Propriospinal tracts** remain within the spinal cord. (p. 307)
16. **Spinal reflexes** are integrated in the spinal cord. (p. 307; Fig. 9-8)

The Brain

17. The brain has six major divisions: cerebrum, diencephalon, midbrain, cerebellum, pons, and medulla oblongata. (p. 309; Fig. 9-9)

18. The **brain stem** is divided into medulla oblongata, pons, and midbrain (mesencephalon). **Cranial nerves** II to XII originate here. (p. 309; Tbl. 9-1)
19. The **reticular formation** is a diffuse collection of neurons that play a role in many basic processes. (p. 310)
20. The **medulla oblongata** contains **somatosensory** and **corticospinal tracts** that convey information between the cerebrum and spinal cord. Most tracts cross the midline in the **pyramid** region. The medulla contains control centers for many involuntary functions. (p. 310)
21. The **pons** acts as a relay station for information between the cerebellum and cerebrum. (p. 311)
22. The **midbrain** controls eye movement and relays signals for auditory and visual reflexes. (p. 311)
23. The **cerebellum** processes sensory information and coordinates the execution of movement. (p. 311)
24. The **diencephalon** is composed of the thalamus and hypothalamus. The **thalamus** relays and modifies sensory and motor information going to and from the cerebral cortex. (p. 311; Fig. 9-10)
25. The **hypothalamus** contains centers for behavioral drives and plays a key role in homeostasis by its control over endocrine and autonomic function. (p. 311; Tbl. 9-2)
26. The **pituitary gland** and **pineal gland** are endocrine glands located in the diencephalon. (p. 311)
27. The cerebrum is composed of two hemispheres connected at the **corpus callosum**. Each cerebral hemisphere is divided into **frontal**, **parietal**, **temporal**, and **occipital lobes**. (p. 312)
28. Cerebral gray matter includes the **cerebral cortex**, basal ganglia, and limbic system. (p. 312; Fig. 9-11)
29. The **basal ganglia** help control movement. (p. 312)
30. The **limbic system** acts as the link between cognitive functions and emotional responses. It includes the **amygdala** and **cingulate gyrus,** linked to emotion and memory, and the **hippocampus,** associated with learning and memory. (p. 312; Fig. 9-13)

Brain Function

31. Three brain systems influence motor output: a **sensory system**, a **cognitive system**, and a **behavioral state system**. (p. 313; Fig. 9-14)
32. Higher brain functions, such as reasoning, arise in the cerebral cortex. The cerebral cortex contains three functional specializations: **sensory areas**, **motor areas**, and **association areas**. (p. 314; Fig. 9-15)
33. Each hemisphere of the cerebrum has developed functions not shared by the other hemisphere, a specialization known as **cerebral lateralization**. (p. 314; Fig. 9-16)
34. Sensory areas receive information from sensory receptors. The **primary somatic sensory cortex** processes information about touch, temperature, and other somatic senses. The **visual cortex**, **auditory cortex**, **gustatory cortex**, and **olfactory cortex** receive information about vision, sound, taste, and odors, respectively. (p. 315)
35. **Association areas** integrate sensory information into perception. **Perception** is the brain's interpretation of sensory stimuli. (p. 315)
36. Motor output includes skeletal muscle movement, neuroendocrine secretion, and visceral responses. (p. 316)
37. Motor areas direct skeletal muscle movement. Each cerebral hemisphere contains a **primary motor cortex** and **motor association area**. (p. 317)
38. The **behavioral state system** controls states of arousal and modulates the sensory and cognitive systems. (p. 317)
39. The **diffuse modulatory systems** of the reticular formation influence attention, motivation, wakefulness, memory, motor control, mood, and metabolic homeostasis. (p. 317; Fig. 9-19, Tbl. 9-3)
40. The **reticular activating system** keeps the brain **conscious**, or aware of self and environment. Electrical activity in the brain varies with levels of arousal and can be recorded by **electroencephalography**. (p. 318; Fig. 9-20)
41. **Circadian rhythms** are controlled by an internal clock in the **suprachiasmatic nucleus** of the hypothalamus. (p. 320)
42. **Sleep** is an easily reversible state of inactivity with characteristic stages. The two major phases of sleep are **REM (rapid eye movement) sleep** and **slow-wave sleep** (non-REM sleep). The physiological reason for sleep is uncertain. (p. 319)
43. The limbic system is the center of **emotion** in the human brain. Emotional events influence physiological functions. (p. 321; Fig. 9-21)
44. **Motivation** arises from internal signals that shape voluntary behaviors related to survival or emotions. Motivational **drives** create goal-oriented behaviors. (p. 321)
45. **Moods** are long-lasting emotional states. Many mood disorders can be treated by altering neurotransmission in the brain. (p. 322)
46. **Learning** is the acquisition of knowledge about the world around us. **Associative learning** occurs when two stimuli are associated with each other. **Nonassociative learning** includes imitative behaviors, such as learning a language. (p. 323)
47. In **habituation**, an animal shows a decreased response to a stimulus that is repeated over and over. In **sensitization**, exposure to a noxious or intense stimulus creates an enhanced response on subsequent exposure. (p. 323)
48. **Memory** has multiple levels of storage and is constantly changing. Information is first stored in **short-term memory** but disappears unless consolidated into long-term memory. (p. 323; Fig. 9-22)
49. **Long-term memory** includes **reflexive memory**, which does not require conscious processes for its creation or recall, and **declarative memory**, which uses higher-level cognitive skills for formation and requires conscious attention for its recall. (p. 324; Tbl. 9-4)
50. The **consolidation** of short-term memory into long-term memory appears to involve changes in the synaptic connections of the circuits involved in learning. (p. 324)
51. Language is considered the most elaborate cognitive behavior. The integration of spoken language in the human brain involves information processing in **Wernicke's area** and **Broca's area**. (p. 325; Fig. 9-23)

QUESTIONS

(Answers to the Review Questions begin on page A1.)

THE PHYSIOLOGY PLACE

Access more review material online at **The Physiology Place** web site. There you'll find review questions, problem-solving activities, case studies, flashcards, and direct links to both *Interactive Physiology®* and *PhysioEx™*. To access the site, go to *www.physiologyplace.com* and select *Human Physiology*, Fifth Edition.

LEVEL ONE REVIEWING FACTS AND TERMS

1. The ability of human brains to change circuit connections and function in response to sensory input and past experience is known as __________.
2. __________ behaviors are related to feeling and emotion. __________ behaviors are related to thinking.
3. The part of the brain called the __________ is what makes us human, allowing human reasoning and cognition.
4. In vertebrates, the central nervous system is protected by the bones of the __________ and __________.
5. Name the meninges, beginning with the layer next to the bones.
6. List and explain the purposes of cerebrospinal fluid (CSF). Where is CSF made?
7. Compare the CSF concentration of each of the following substances with its concentration in the blood plasma.
   (a) HCO_3^-
   (b) Ca^{2+}
   (c) glucose
   (d) H^+
   (e) Na^+
   (f) K^+
8. The only fuel source for neurons under normal circumstances is __________. Low concentration of this fuel in the blood is termed __________. To synthesize enough ATP to continually transport ions, the neurons consume large quantities of __________. To supply these needs, about __________% of the blood pumped by the heart goes to the brain.
9. Match each of the following areas with its function.

   (a) medulla oblongata
   (b) pons
   (c) midbrain
   (d) reticular formation
   (e) cerebellum
   (f) diencephalon
   (g) thalamus
   (h) hypothalamus
   (i) cerebrum

   1. coordinates execution of movement
   2. is composed of the thalamus and hypothalamus
   3. controls arousal and sleep
   4. fills most of the cranium
   5. contains control centers for blood pressure and breathing
   6. relays and modifies information going to and from the cerebrum
   7. transfers information to the cerebellum
   8. contains integrating centers for homeostasis
   9. relays signals and visual reflexes, plus eye movement

10. What is the blood-brain barrier, and what is its function?
11. How are gray matter and white matter different from each other, both anatomically and functionally?
12. Name the cerebral cortex areas that (a) direct perception, (b) direct movement, and (c) integrate information and direct voluntary behaviors.
13. What does *cerebral lateralization* refer to? What functions tend to be centered in each hemisphere?
14. Name the 12 cranial nerves in numerical order and their major functions.
15. Name and define the two major phases of sleep. How are they different from each other?
16. List several homeostatic reflexes and behaviors influenced by output from the hypothalamus. What is the source of emotional input into this area?
17. The __________ region of the limbic system is believed to be the center for basic instincts (such as fear) and learned emotional states.
18. What are the broad categories of learning? Define habituation and sensitization. What anatomical structure of the cerebrum is important in both learning and memory?
19. What two centers of the cortex are involved in integrating spoken language?

LEVEL TWO REVIEWING CONCEPTS

20. Map the following terms describing CNS anatomy. You may draw pictures or add additional terms if you wish.

arachnoid membrane	ependyma
ascending tracts	gray matter
blood-brain barrier	lumbar nerves
brain	meninges
capillaries	nuclei
cell bodies	pia mater
cerebrospinal fluid	propriospinal tracts
cervical nerves	sacral nerves
choroid plexus	spinal cord
cranial nerves	thoracic nerves
descending tracts	ventral root
dorsal root	ventricles
dorsal root ganglion	vertebral column
dura mater	white matter

21. Trace the pathway that the cerebrospinal fluid follows through the nervous system.
22. What are the three brain systems that regulate motor output by the CNS?
23. Explain the role of Wernicke's and Broca's areas in language.
24. Compare and contrast the following concepts:
    (a) diffuse modulatory systems, reticular formation, limbic system, and reticular activating system
    (b) different forms of memory
    (c) nuclei and ganglia
    (d) tracts, nerves, horns, nerve fibers, and roots

25. Replace each question mark in the following table with the appropriate word(s):

Cerebral Area	Lobe	Functions
Primary somatic sensory cortex	?	Receives sensory information from peripheral receptors
?	Occipital	Processes information from the eyes
Auditory cortex	Temporal	?
?	Temporal	Receives input from chemoreceptors in the nose
Motor cortices	?	?
Association areas	NA	?

26. Given the wave shown below, draw (a) a wave having a lower frequency, (b) a wave having a larger amplitude, (c) a wave having a higher frequency. (*Hint:* See Figure 9-20, p. 319.)

27. What properties do motivational states have in common?
28. What changes occur at synapses as memories are formed?

LEVEL THREE PROBLEM SOLVING

29. Mr. Andersen, a stroke patient, experiences expressive aphasia. His savvy therapist, Cheryl, teaches him to sing to communicate his needs. What signs did he exhibit before therapy? How do you know he did not have receptive aphasia? Using what you have learned about cerebral lateralization, hypothesize why singing worked for him.
30. A study was done in which 40 adults were taught about the importance of using seat belts in their cars. At the end of the presentation, all participants scored at least 90% on a comprehensive test covering the material taught. The people were also secretly videotaped entering and leaving the parking lot of the class site. Twenty subjects entered wearing their seat belts; 22 left wearing them. Did learning occur? What is the relationship between learning and actually buckling the seat belts?
31. In 1913, Henri Pieron kept a group of dogs awake for several days. Before allowing them to sleep, he withdrew cerebrospinal fluid from the sleep-deprived animals. He then injected this CSF into normal, rested dogs. The recipient dogs promptly went to sleep for periods ranging from two hours to six hours. What conclusion can you draw about the possible source of a sleep-inducing factor? What controls should Pieron have included?
32. A 2002 study* presented the results of a prospective study [p. 14] done in Utah. The study began in 1995 with cognitive assessment of 1889 women whose mean age was 74.5 years. Investigators asked about the women's history of taking calcium, multivitamin supplements, and postmenopausal hormone replacement therapy (estrogen or estrogen/progesterone). Follow-up interviews in 1998 looked for the development of Alzheimer's disease in the study population. Data showed that 58 of 800 women who had not used hormone replacement therapy developed Alzheimer's, compared with 26 of 1066 women who had used hormones.
    (a) Can the researchers conclude from the data given that hormone replacement therapy decreases the risk of developing Alzheimer's? Is there other information that should be factored into the data analysis?
    (b) How applicable are these findings to American women as a whole? What other information might you want to know about the study subjects before you draw any conclusions?

*"Hormone replacement therapy and incidence of Alzheimer disease in older women: The Cache County study." *JAMA* 288: 2123–2129, 2002 Nov. 6.

ANSWERS

Answers to Concept Check Questions

Page 298

1. (a) 3; (b) 2; (c) 1; (d) 3; (e) 2

Page 301

2. Glial cells in the CNS are astrocytes, oligodendrocytes, microglia, and ependyma. See Figure 8-5, p. 254, for functions.

Page 303

3. A ganglion is a cluster of nerve cell bodies outside the CNS. The CNS equivalent is a nucleus.
4. Tracts are the CNS equivalent of peripheral nerves.

Page 303

5. When H^+ concentration increases, pH decreases, which means CSF pH must be lower than blood pH.
6. Blood will collect in the space between the membranes, pushing on the soft brain tissue under the skull. (This is called a *subdural hematoma*.)
7. Cerebrospinal fluid is more like interstitial fluid because both these fluids contain little protein and no blood cells.

Page 307

8. Oxidative phosphorylation takes place in mitochondria.
9. The two pathways are glycolysis and the citric acid cycle. Glucose is metabolized to pyruvate through glycolysis and then enters the citric acid cycle (also called the tricarboxylic acid cycle). $NADH_2$ passes high-energy electrons to the electron transport system for ATP synthesis.
10. Another explanation would be that some property of brain tissue made it resistant to staining by the dye. This is in fact what Ehrlich concluded.
11. The brain stained blue this time, but none of the other body tissues were stained because the dye was unable to cross the blood-brain barrier and enter the bloodstream.

Page 307

12. Horns are areas of gray matter in the spinal cord. Roots are sections of spinal nerves just before they enter the spinal cord. Tracts are long projections of white matter (axons) that extend up and down the spinal cord. Columns are groups of tracts carrying similar information.
13. Cutting a dorsal root disrupts sensory function.

Page 310

14. (a) and (c) are white matter, (b) is gray matter.
15. Activities would include moving the eyes, jaw, or tongue and testing taste, smell, and hearing.
16. The cerebrum is dorsal or superior to the brain stem.

Page 311

17. The three subdivisions of the brain stem are medulla oblongata, pons, and midbrain.
18. The diencephalon is composed of thalamus, hypothalamus, pituitary gland, and pineal gland.

Page 313

19. Neurons cross from one side of the body to the other at the pyramids in the medulla (see Fig. 10-9 on p. 343).
20. The divisions of the brain, starting at the spinal cord, are medulla, pons, cerebellum, midbrain, diencephalon, and cerebrum.

Page 320

21. Neurons that are sending fewer signals have probably hyperpolarized because they would then require a larger stimulus to initiate an action potential.

Answers to Figure and Graph Questions

Page 302

Fig. 9-4: Dura mater completely surrounds the venous sinus and forms one boundary of the subdural space. The arachnoid membrane separates the subdural and subarachnoid spaces. Pia mater forms the other boundary of the subarachnoid space.

Page 304

Fig. 9-5: 1. The easiest access is into the subarachnoid space below the bottom of the spinal cord, where there is less risk of damaging the cord. This is called a spinal tap or lumbar puncture. 2. Blockage of the aqueduct will cause CSF to accumulate in the first, second, and third ventricles. Blockage near the frontal lobe will cause fluid build-up in all the ventricles. You would look for enlargement of the fourth ventricle to help localize the site of the blockage.

Page 312

Fig. 9-11: (a) and (c) are both correct. See Fig. D-1 in Appendix D.

Page 316

Fig. 9-16: (a) Losing function in the right visual cortex would mean that the person could see nothing in the left visual field, indicated by the red box at the top of the figure. (b) The tracts of the corpus callosum exchange information between the two sides of the cerebrum.

Page 316

Fig. 9-17: occipital, frontal

Page 319

Fig. 9-20: Alpha waves have the highest frequency, and delta waves have the greatest amplitude.

11

Efferent Division: Autonomic and Somatic Motor Control

The Autonomic Division

The Somatic Motor Division

BACKGROUND BASICS

Membrane receptors: **182** Neurotransmitters: **180** Second messenger systems: **184**
Catecholamines: **224** Up- and down-regulation: **44** Tonic and antagonistic control: **196**
Organization of the nervous system: **247** Neuron structure: **249** Synapses: **252** Nerves: **250**
Action potentials: **258** Slow synaptic potentials: **281**

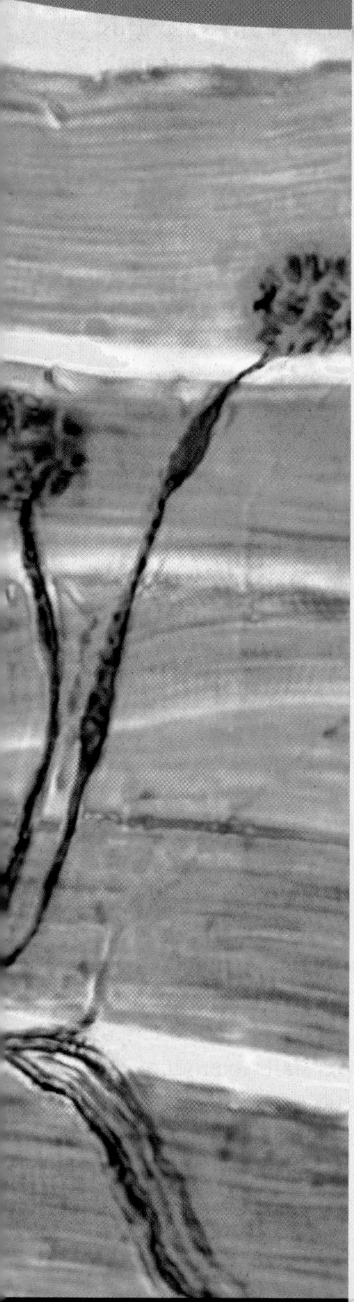

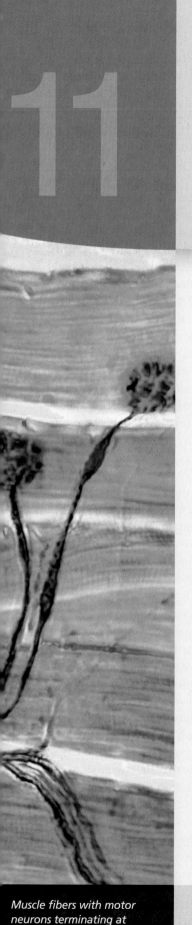

Muscle fibers with motor neurons terminating at neuromuscular junctions.

Because a number of cells in the autonomic nervous system act in conjunction, they have relinquished their independence to function as a coherent whole.

—Otto Appenzeller and Emilio Oribe, in *The Autonomic Nervous System*, 1997

RUNNING PROBLEM

A Powerful Addiction

Every day, more than 1.3 billion people around the world intentionally absorb a chemical that kills about 5 million people a year. Why would people knowingly poison themselves? If you've guessed that the chemical is nicotine, you already know part of the answer. One of more than 4000 chemicals found in tobacco, nicotine is highly addictive. So powerful is this addiction that fewer than 20% of tobacco users are able to quit smoking the first time they try. Shanika, a smoker for six years, is attempting for the second time to stop smoking. The odds are in her favor this time, however, because she has made an appointment with her physician to discuss all the options available to help her break her addiction to nicotine and smoking.

386 387 389 396 399 401

The picnic lunch was wonderful. You are now dozing on the grass in the warm spring sunlight as you let the meal digest. Suddenly you feel something moving across your lower leg. You open your eyes, and as they adjust to the bright light, you see a four-foot-long snake slithering over your foot. More by instinct than reason, you fling the snake into the grass while scrambling to a safe perch on top of the nearby picnic table. You are breathing heavily, and your heart is pounding.

In less than a second, your body has gone from a state of quiet rest and digestion to a state of panic and frantic activity. This reflex reaction is integrated and coordinated through the central nervous system (CNS), then carried out by the efferent division of the peripheral nervous system (PNS). The fibers of efferent neurons are bundled together into nerves that carry commands from the CNS to the muscles and glands of the body. Some nerves, called *mixed nerves,* also carry sensory information through afferent fibers [p. 250].

The efferent division of the peripheral nervous system can be subdivided into **somatic motor neurons**, which control skeletal muscles, and **autonomic neurons**, which control smooth muscle, cardiac muscle, many glands, and some adipose tissue. The somatic and autonomic divisions are sometimes called the voluntary and involuntary divisions of the nervous system, respectively. However, although it is true that movement controlled by somatic pathways usually requires conscious thought and that autonomic reflexes are mainly involuntary, this distinction does not always hold true. For example, some skeletal muscle reflexes, such as swallowing and the knee jerk reflex, are involuntary. And a person can use biofeedback training to learn to modulate some involuntary autonomic functions, such as heart rate and blood pressure.

We begin our study of the efferent division of the PNS by looking at the autonomic division. Then we consider the somatic motor division, as preparation for learning about muscles in Chapter 12.

THE AUTONOMIC DIVISION

The autonomic division of the efferent nervous system (or *autonomic nervous system* for short) is also known in older writings as the *vegetative nervous system,* reflecting the observation that its functions are not under voluntary control. The word *autonomic* comes from the same roots as *autonomous,* meaning *self-governing.* Another name for the autonomic division is *visceral nervous system* because of its control over internal organs.

The autonomic division is subdivided into **sympathetic** and **parasympathetic branches** (often called the *sympathetic* and *parasympathetic nervous systems*). Some parts of the sympathetic branch were first described by the Greek physician Claudius Galen (ca. A.D. 130–200), who is famous for his compilation of anatomy, physiology, and medicine as they were known during his time. As a result of his dissections, Galen proposed that "animal spirits" flowed from the brain to the tissues through hollow nerves, creating "sympathy" between the different parts of the body. Galen's "sympathy" later gave rise to the name for the sympathetic branch. The prefix *para-,* for the parasympathetic branch, means *beside* or *alongside.*

Although the sympathetic and parasympathetic branches can be distinguished anatomically, there is no simple way to separate the actions of the two branches on their targets. They are distinguished best by the type of situation in which they are most active. The picnic scene that began the chapter illustrates the two extremes at which the sympathetic and parasympathetic branches function. If you are resting quietly after a meal, the parasympathetic branch is dominant, taking command of the routine, quiet activities of day-to-day living, such as digestion. Consequently, parasympathetic neurons are sometimes said to control "rest and digest" functions.

In contrast, the sympathetic branch is dominant in stressful situations, such as the potential threat from the snake. One of the most dramatic examples of sympathetic action is the **fight-or-flight** response, in which the brain triggers massive simultaneous sympathetic discharge throughout the body. As the body prepares to fight or flee, the heart speeds up; blood vessels to muscles of the arms, legs, and heart dilate; and the liver starts to produce glucose to provide energy for muscle contraction. Digestion becomes a low priority when life and limb are threatened, and so blood is diverted from the gastrointestinal tract to skeletal muscles.

The massive sympathetic discharge that occurs in fight-or-flight situations is mediated through the hypothalamus and is a total-body response to a crisis. If you have ever been scared by the squealing of brakes or a sudden sound in the dark, you know how rapidly the nervous system can influence multiple body systems. Most sympathetic responses are not the all-out response of a fight-or-flight reflex, however, and more importantly, activating one sympathetic pathway does not automatically activate them all.

The role of the sympathetic nervous system in mundane daily activities is as important as a fight-or-flight response. For example, one key function of the sympathetic branch is control of blood flow to the tissues, as you will learn in Chapter 15. Most of the time, autonomic control of body function "see-saws" back and forth between the sympathetic and parasympathetic branches as they cooperate to fine-tune various processes (Fig. 11-1 ●). Only occasionally, as in the fight-or-flight example, does the seesaw move to one extreme or the other.

CONCEPT CHECK

1. The afferent division of the nervous system has what two components?
2. The central nervous system consists of the ________ and the ________.

Answers: p. 404

Autonomic Reflexes Are Important for Homeostasis

The autonomic nervous system works closely with the endocrine system and the behavioral state system [p. 317] to maintain homeostasis in the body. Sensory information from somatosensory and visceral receptors goes to homeostatic control centers in the hypothalamus, pons, and medulla (Fig. 11-2 ●). These centers monitor and regulate important functions such as blood pressure, temperature regulation, and water balance (Fig. 11-3 ●).

RUNNING PROBLEM

Neuroscientists have learned that addictive behaviors develop because certain chemicals act as *positive reinforcers* in the brain, creating physical and psychological dependence. Nicotine is an addictive drug that enhances dopamine release in the brain's reward centers and creates pleasurable sensations. Over time, the brain also begins to associate the social aspects of cigarette smoking with pleasure, a conditioned response that makes quitting difficult. If smokers do stop smoking, they may suffer from unpleasant physical withdrawal symptoms, including lethargy, hunger, and irritability.

Question 1:
To avoid withdrawal symptoms, people continue to smoke, resulting in chronically elevated nicotine levels in their blood. Nicotine binds to nicotinic acetylcholine receptors (nAChR). What is the usual response of cells that are chronically exposed to elevated concentrations of a signal molecule? [Hint: p. 194]

386 387 389 396 399 401

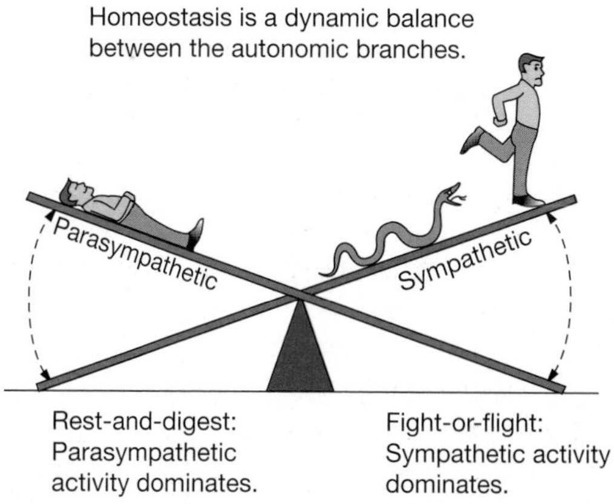

● **FIGURE 11-1** ***Most normal activities reflect a balance between the divisions of the autonomic division.***

The hypothalamus also contains neurons that act as sensors, such as osmoreceptors, which monitor osmolarity, and thermoreceptors, which monitor body temperature. Motor output from the hypothalamus and brain stem creates autonomic responses, endocrine responses, and behavioral responses such as drinking, food-seeking, and temperature regulation (getting out of the heat, putting on a sweater). These behavioral responses are integrated in brain centers responsible for motivated behaviors and control of movement.

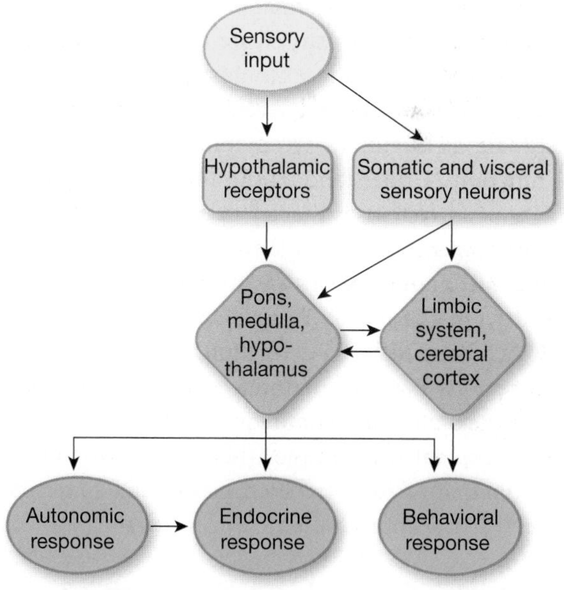

● **FIGURE 11-2** ***The hypothalamus, pons, and medulla initiate autonomic, endocrine, and behavioral responses.*** Hypothalamic trophic hormones control secretion of anterior pituitary hormones [p. 228]. The hypothalamus secretes neurohormones from the posterior pituitary [p. 228]. Autonomic neurons also control hormone release from peripheral endocrine cells, such as pancreatic beta cells [p. 227]. Emotional responses mediated through the limbic system can influence autonomic responses [p. 312].

11

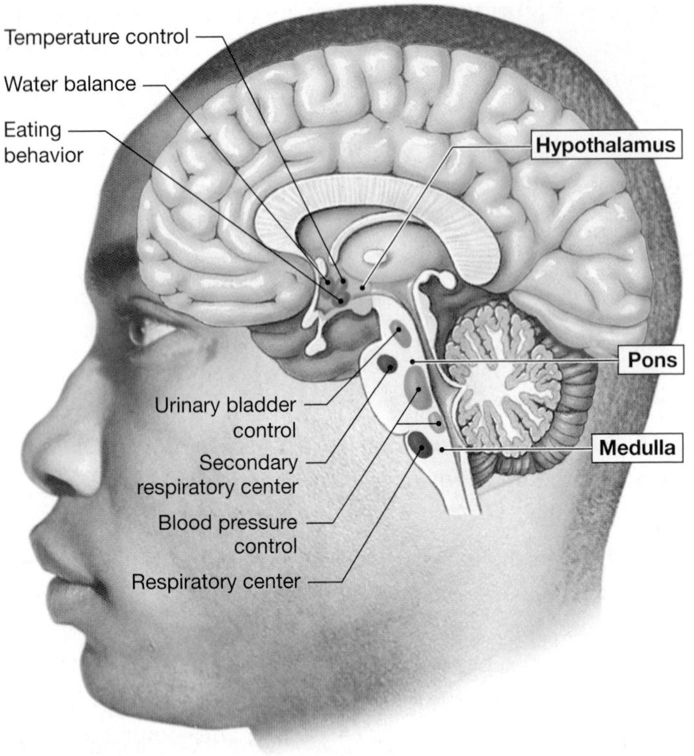

● **FIGURE 11-3** ***Autonomic control centers in the brain help maintain homeostasis.***

In addition, sensory information integrated in the cerebral cortex and limbic system can create emotions that influence autonomic output, as Figure 11-2 illustrates. Blushing, fainting at the sight of a hypodermic needle, and "butterflies in the stomach" are all examples of emotional influences on autonomic functions. Understanding the autonomic and hormonal control of organ systems is the key to understanding the maintenance of homeostasis in virtually every system of the body.

Some autonomic reflexes are capable of taking place without input from the brain. These *spinal reflexes* [Fig. 9-8, p. 307] include urination, defecation, and penile erection—bodily functions that can be influenced by descending pathways from the brain but do not require this input. For example, people with spinal cord injuries that disrupt communication between the brain and spinal cord may retain some spinal reflexes but lose the ability to sense or control them.

Antagonistic Control Is a Hallmark of the Autonomic Division

The sympathetic and parasympathetic branches of the autonomic nervous system display all four of Walter Cannon's properties of homeostasis: (1) preservation of the fitness of the internal environment, (2) up-down regulation by tonic control, (3) antagonistic control, and (4) chemical signals with different effects in different tissues [p. 196].

Most internal organs are under *antagonistic control,* in which one autonomic branch is excitatory and the other branch is inhibitory (see the table in Fig. 11-5). For example, sympathetic innervation increases heart rate, while parasympathetic stimulation decreases it. Consequently, heart rate can be regulated by altering the relative proportions of sympathetic and parasympathetic control.

Exceptions to dual antagonistic innervation include the sweat glands and the smooth muscle in most blood vessels. These tissues are innervated only by the sympathetic branch and rely strictly on tonic (up-down) control.

Although the two autonomic branches are usually antagonistic in their control of a given target tissue, they sometimes work cooperatively on different tissues to achieve a common goal. For example, blood flow for penile erection is under control of the parasympathetic branch, and muscle contraction for sperm ejaculation is directed by the sympathetic branch.

In some autonomic pathways, the neurotransmitter receptor determines the response of the target tissue. For instance, most blood vessels contain one type of *adrenergic receptor* [p. 279] that causes smooth muscle contraction (vasoconstriction). However, some blood vessels also contain a second type of adrenergic receptor that causes smooth muscle to relax (vasodilation). Both receptors are activated by catecholamines [p. 224]. In this example the receptor, not the chemical signal, determines the response.

CONCEPT CHECK

3. Define homeostasis. Answers: p. 404

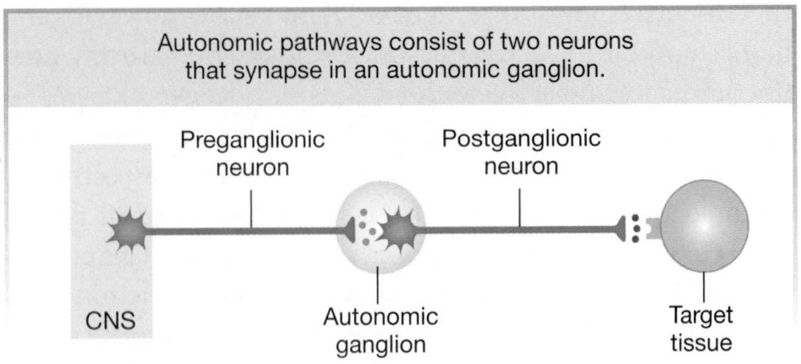

● **FIGURE 11-4** ***Autonomic pathways consist of two neurons.***

Autonomic Pathways Have Two Efferent Neurons in Series

All autonomic pathways (sympathetic and parasympathetic) consist of two neurons in series (Fig. 11-4 ●). The first neuron, called the **preganglionic neuron**, originates in the central nervous system and projects to an **autonomic ganglion** outside the CNS. There the preganglionic neuron synapses with the second neuron in the pathway, the **postganglionic neuron.** This neuron has its cell body in the ganglion and projects its axon to the target tissue. (A *ganglion* is a cluster of nerve cell bodies that lie outside the CNS. The equivalent in the CNS is a *nucleus* [p. 253].)

Divergence [p. 282] is an important feature of autonomic pathways. On average, one preganglionic neuron entering a ganglion synapses with eight or nine postganglionic neurons. Some synapse on as many as 32 neurons! Each postganglionic neuron may then innervate a different target, meaning that a single signal from the CNS can affect a large number of target cells simultaneously.

In the traditional view of the autonomic division, autonomic ganglia were simply a way station for the transfer of signals from preganglionic neurons to postganglionic neurons. We now know, however, that ganglia are more than a simple collection of axon terminals and nerve cell bodies: they also contain neurons that lie completely within them. These neurons enable the autonomic ganglia to act as mini-integrating centers, receiving sensory input from the periphery of the body and modulating outgoing autonomic signals to target tissues. Presumably this arrangement means that a reflex could be integrated totally within a ganglion, with no involvement of the CNS. That pattern of control is known to exist in the enteric nervous system [p. 249], which we discuss in Chapter 21.

Sympathetic and Parasympathetic Branches Exit the Spinal Cord in Different Regions

How, then, do the two autonomic branches differ anatomically? The main anatomical differences are (1) the pathways' point of origin in the CNS and (2) the location of the autonomic ganglia. As Figure 11-5 ● shows, most sympathetic pathways (red) originate in the thoracic and lumbar regions of the spinal cord. *Sympathetic ganglia* are found primarily in two chains that run along either side of the bony vertebral column, with additional ganglia along the descending aorta. Long nerves (axons of postganglionic neurons) project from the ganglia to the target tissues. Because most sympathetic ganglia lie close to the spinal cord, sympathetic pathways generally have short preganglionic neurons and long postganglionic neurons.

Many parasympathetic pathways (shown in blue in Figure 11-5) originate in the brain stem, and their axons leave the brain in several cranial nerves [p. 310]. Other parasympathetic pathways originate in the sacral region (near the lower end of the spinal cord) and control pelvic organs. In general, parasympathetic ganglia are located either on or near their target organs. Consequently, parasympathetic preganglionic neurons have long axons, and parasympathetic postganglionic neurons have short axons.

Parasympathetic innervation goes primarily to the head, neck, and internal organs. The major parasympathetic tract is the **vagus nerve** (cranial nerve X), which contains about 75% of all parasympathetic fibers. This nerve carries both sensory information from internal organs to the brain and parasympathetic output from the brain to organs (Fig. 11-6 ●).

Vagotomy, a procedure in which the vagus nerve is surgically cut, was an experimental technique used in the nineteenth and early twentieth centuries to study the effects of the autonomic nervous system on various organs. For a time, vagotomy was the preferred treatment for stomach ulcers because removal of parasympathetic innervation to the stomach decreased the secretion of stomach acid. However, this procedure had many unwanted side effects and has been abandoned in favor of drug therapies that treat the problem more specifically.

CONCEPT CHECK

4. A nerve that carries both sensory and motor information is called a ________ nerve.
5. Name the four regions of the spinal cord in order, starting from the brain stem.

Answers: p. 404

The Autonomic Nervous System Uses a Variety of Chemical Signals

Chemically, the sympathetic and parasympathetic branches can be distinguished by their neurotransmitters and receptors, using the following rules and Figure 11-7 ●:

1. Both sympathetic and parasympathetic preganglionic neurons release acetylcholine (ACh) onto *nicotinic cholinergic receptors* on the postganglionic cell [p. 279].
2. Most postganglionic sympathetic neurons secrete norepinephrine (NE) onto *adrenergic receptors* on the target cell.
3. Most postganglionic parasympathetic neurons secrete acetylcholine onto *muscarinic cholinergic receptors* on the target cell.

RUNNING PROBLEM

Shanika's doctor congratulates her for trying once more to stop smoking. He explains that quitting is most likely to be successful if the smoker uses a combination of behavioral modification strategies and drug therapy. Currently there are three types of pharmacological treatments used for nicotine addiction: nicotine replacement, buproprion (Zyban®), and varenicline (Chantix®), a drug that binds to nicotinic cholinergic receptors (nAChR). Nicotinic receptors are found throughout the nervous system, and evidence suggests that activation of nAChR by nicotine in certain regions of the brain plays a key role in nicotine addiction.

Question 2:

Cholinergic receptors are classified as either nicotinic or muscarinic, on the basis of the agonist molecules that bind to them. What happens to a postsynaptic cell when nicotine rather than ACh binds to a nicotinic cholinergic receptor?

386
387
389
396
399
401

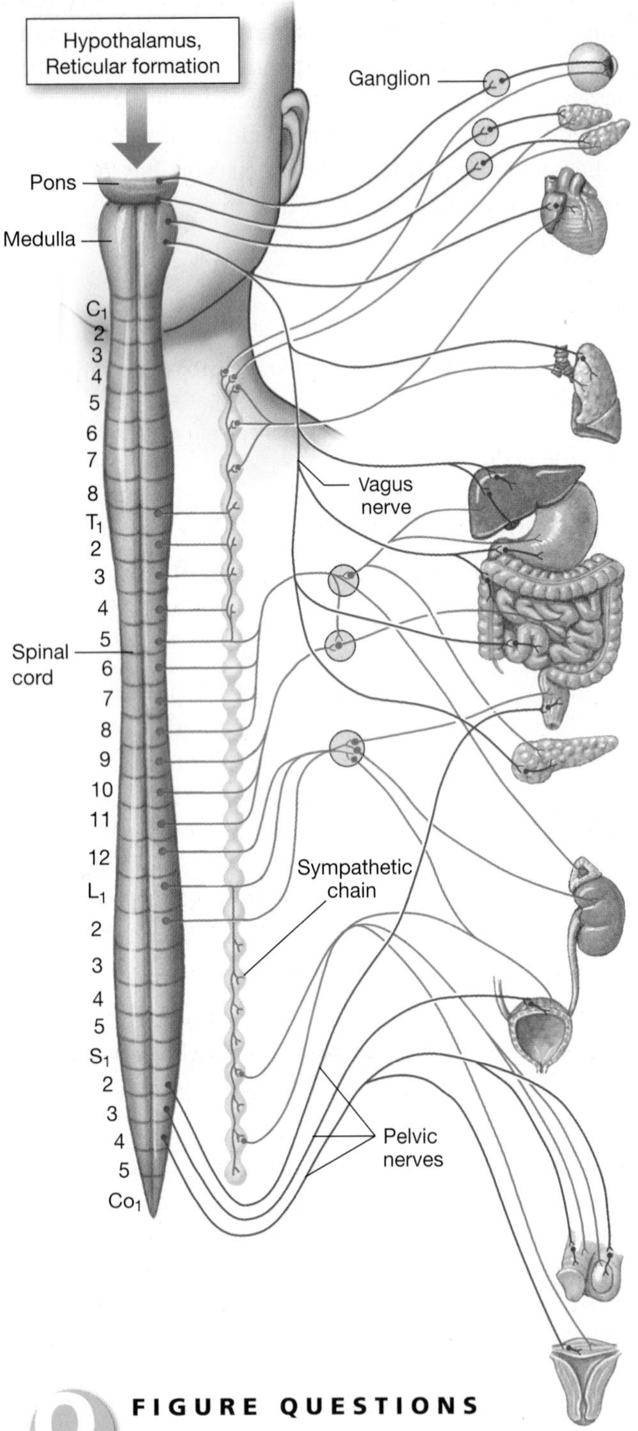

Effector Organ	Parasympathetic Response **	Sympathetic Response	Adrenergic Receptor
Pupil of eye	Constricts	Dilates	α
Salivary glands	Watery secretion	Mucus, enzymes	α and β_2
Heart	Slows rate	Increases rate and force of contraction	β_1
Arterioles and veins	—	Constricts Dilates	α β_2
Lungs	Bronchioles constrict	Bronchioles dilate	β_2*
Digestive tract	Increases motility and secretion	Decreases motility and secretion	α, β_2
Exocrine pancreas	Increases enzyme secretion	Decreases enzyme secretion	α
Endocrine pancreas	Stimulates insulin secretion	Inhibits insulin secretion	α
Adrenal medulla	—	Secretes catecholamines	—
Kidney	—	Increases renin secretion	β_1
Urinary bladder	Release of urine	Urinary retention	α, β_2
Adipose tissue	—	Fat breakdown	β
Sweat glands	Sweating	Localized sweating	α
Male and female sex organs	Erection	Ejaculation (male)	α
Uterus	Depends on stage of cycle	Depends on stage of cycle	α, β_2
Lymphoid tissue (not illustrated)	—	Generally inhibitory	α, β_2

**All parasympathetic responses are mediated by muscarinic receptors.

*Hormonal epinephrine only

KEY
- Parasympathetic
- Sympathetic

FIGURE QUESTIONS

1. Name the regions of the CNS where the two branches originate.
2. Describe where the ganglia for the two branches are located (relative to the spinal cord).
3. What is an advantage of having ganglia in the sympathetic chain linked to each other?

● **FIGURE 11-5** ***Autonomic sympathetic and parasympathetic pathways.*** There are actually two sympathetic ganglion chains, one on either side of the spinal cord.

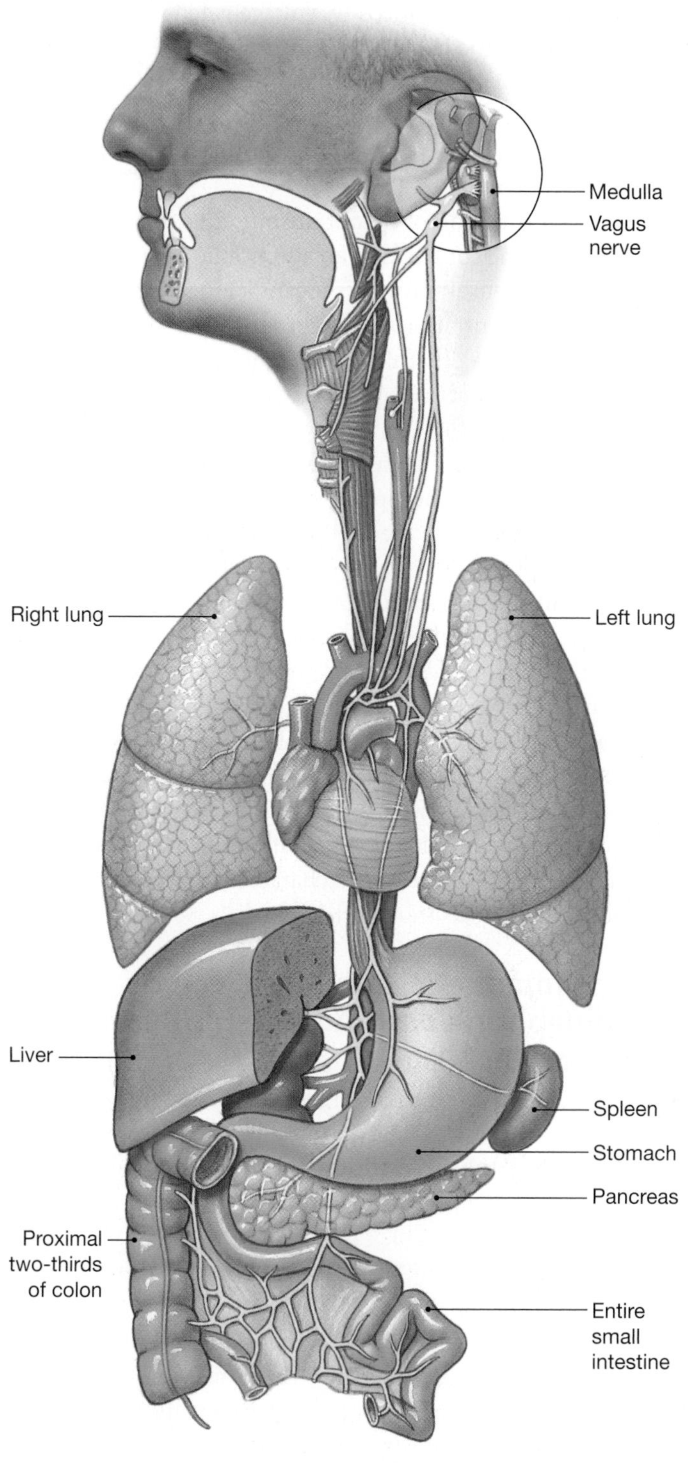

● **FIGURE 11-6** ***The vagus nerve carries parasympathetic fibers to many internal organs and sensory information from organs to the brain.***

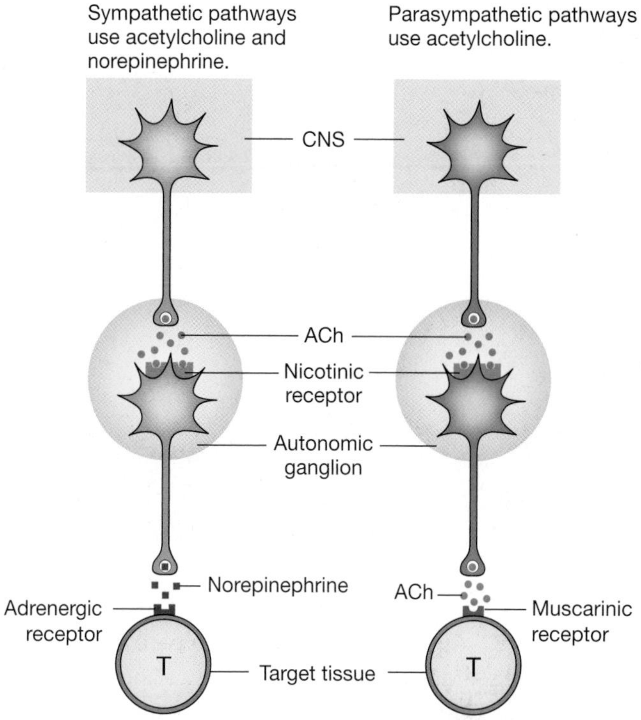

FIGURE QUESTION

- Identify all:
  - cholinergic neurons
  - adrenergic neurons
  - preganglionic neurons
  - postganglionic neurons
- Which pathway will have longer preganglionic neurons? (Hint: See Fig. 11-5)

● **FIGURE 11-7** ***Sympathetic and parasympathetic pathways differ in their neurotransmitters and receptors.***

However, there are some exceptions to these rules. A few sympathetic postganglionic neurons, such as those that terminate on sweat glands, secrete ACh rather than norepinephrine. These neurons are therefore called *sympathetic cholinergic neurons.*

A small number of autonomic neurons secrete neither norepinephrine nor acetylcholine and are known as *nonadrenergic, noncholinergic neurons*. Some of the chemicals they use as neurotransmitters include substance P, somatostatin, vasoactive intestinal peptide (VIP), adenosine, nitric oxide, and ATP. We mention these unusual neurotransmitters in later chapters when they play a significant role. The nonadrenergic, noncholinergic neurons are assigned to either the sympathetic or parasympathetic branch according to where their preganglionic fibers leave the nerve cord.

Autonomic Pathways Control Smooth and Cardiac Muscle and Glands

The targets of autonomic neurons are smooth muscle, cardiac muscle, many exocrine glands, a few endocrine glands, lymphoid tissues, and some adipose tissue. The synapse between a postganglionic autonomic neuron and its target cell is called the **neuroeffector junction.**

The structure of an autonomic synapse differs from the model synapse shown in Figure 8-20 [p. 274]. Autonomic postganglionic axons end with a series of swollen areas at their distal ends, like beads spaced out along a string (Fig. 11-8 ●). Each of

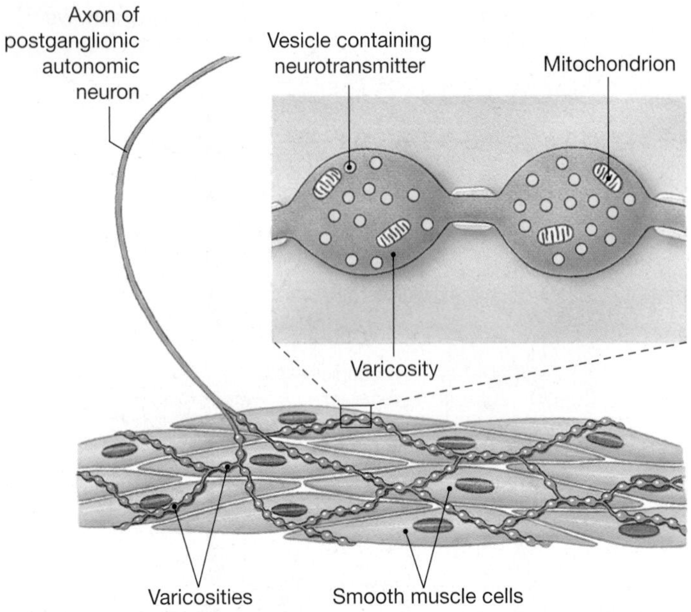
Axon of postganglionic autonomic neuron
Vesicle containing neurotransmitter
Mitochondrion
Varicosity
Varicosities
Smooth muscle cells

● **FIGURE 11-8** ***Autonomic varicosities release neurotransmitter over the surface of target cells.*** The swellings called varicosities are found along the distal ends of postganglionic axons.

these swellings, known as a **varicosity** [*varicosus,* abnormally enlarged or swollen], contains vesicles filled with neurotransmitter.

The branched ends of the axon lie across the surface of the target tissue, but the underlying target cell membrane does not possess clusters of neurotransmitter receptors in specific sites. Instead, the neurotransmitter is simply released into the interstitial fluid to diffuse to wherever the receptors are located. The result is a less-directed form of communication than that which occurs between a somatic motor neuron and a skeletal muscle. The diffuse release of autonomic neurotransmitter means that a single postganglionic neuron can affect a large area of target tissue.

The release of autonomic neurotransmitters is subject to modulation from a variety of sources. For example, sympathetic varicosities contain receptors for hormones and for paracrines such as histamine. These modulators may either facilitate or inhibit neurotransmitter release. Some preganglionic neurons co-secrete neuropeptides along with acetylcholine. The peptides act as neuromodulators, producing slow synaptic potentials that modify the activity of postganglionic neurons [p. 281].

Autonomic Neurotransmitters Are Synthesized in the Axon

In the autonomic division, neurotransmitter synthesis takes place in the axon varicosities. The primary autonomic neurotransmitters are acetylcholine (ACh) and norepinephrine, both small molecules easily synthesized by cytoplasmic enzymes. Neurotransmitter made in the varicosities is packaged into synaptic vesicles for storage.

The process of neurotransmitter release follows the same pattern you learned in Chapter 8 [p. 274]. When an action potential arrives at the varicosity, voltage-gated Ca^{2+} channels open, Ca^{2+} enters the neuron, and the synaptic vesicle contents are released by exocytosis. Once neurotransmitters are released into the synapse, they either diffuse through the interstitial fluid until they encounter a receptor on the target cell or drift away from the synapse.

The concentration of neurotransmitter in the synapse is a major factor in the control that an autonomic neuron exerts on its target: more neurotransmitter means a longer or stronger response. The concentration of neurotransmitter in a synapse is influenced by its rate of breakdown or removal. Neurotransmitter activation of its receptor terminates when the neurotransmitter either (1) diffuses away, (2) is metabolized by enzymes in the extracellular fluid, or (3) is actively transported into cells around the synapse. The uptake of neurotransmitter by varicosities allows neurons to reuse the chemicals.

These steps were illustrated for acetylcholine in Figure 8-22 [p. 278] and are shown for norepinephrine in Figure 11-9 ●. Norepinephrine is synthesized in the varicosity from the amino acid tyrosine. Once released into the synapse, norepinephrine may combine with an adrenergic receptor on the target cell, diffuse away, or be transported back into the varicosity. Inside the neuron, recycled norepinephrine is either repackaged into vesicles or broken down by **monoamine oxidase** (MAO), the main enzyme responsible for degradation of catecholamines.

Table 11-1 ● compares the characteristics of the two primary autonomic neurotransmitters.

Most Sympathetic Pathways Secrete Norepinephrine onto Adrenergic Receptors

Sympathetic pathways secrete catecholamines that bind to adrenergic receptors on their target cells. Adrenergic receptors come in two varieties: α (alpha) and β (beta), with several subtypes of each. **Alpha receptors**—the most common sympathetic receptor—respond strongly to norepinephrine and only weakly to epinephrine (Tbl. 11-2 ●).

The three main subtypes of beta receptors differ in their affinity for catecholamines. **β_1-receptors** respond equally strongly to norepinephrine and epinephrine. **β_2-receptors** are more sensitive to epinephrine than to norepinephrine. Interestingly, the β_2-receptors are not innervated (no sympathetic neurons terminate near them), which limits their exposure to the neurotransmitter norepinephrine. **β_3-receptors**, which are found primarily on adipose tissue, are innervated and more sensitive to norepinephrine than to epinephrine.

All adrenergic receptors are G protein–coupled receptors rather than ion channels [p. 186]. This means that the target cell response is slower to start and usually lasts longer. The different adrenergic receptor subtypes use different second messenger pathways (Table 11-2). Catecholamine binding to β-receptors increases cyclic AMP and triggers the phosphorylation of intracellular proteins. The target cell response then depends on

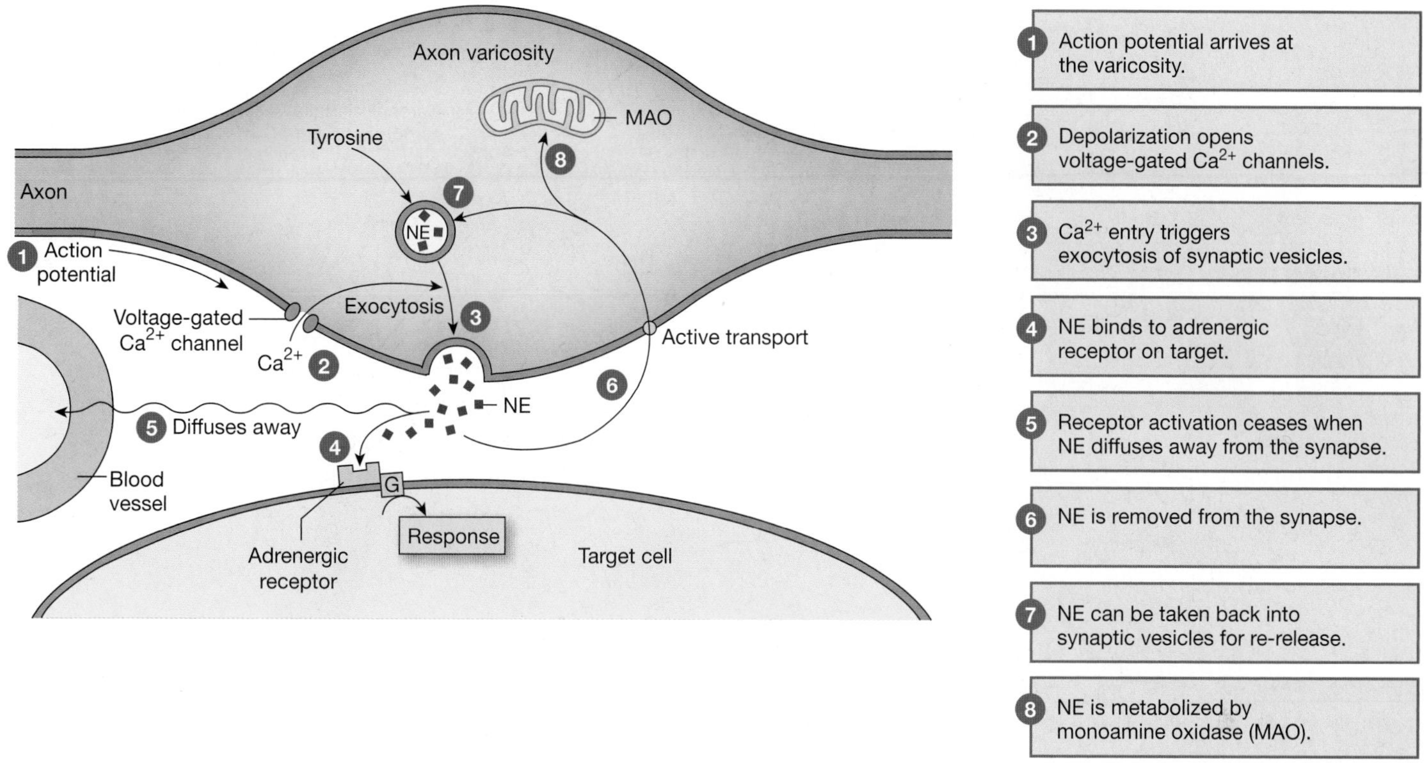

● **FIGURE 11-9** ***Norepinephrine (NE) release and removal at a sympathetic varicosity***

the specific downstream pathway. For example, activation of β_1-receptors enhances cardiac muscle contraction, but activation of β_2-receptors relaxes smooth muscle in many tissues.

α_1-receptors activate phospholipase C, creating inositol trisphosphate (IP_3) and diacylglycerol (DAG) [Fig. 6-12, p. 188]. DAG initiates a cascade that phosphorylates proteins. IP_3 opens Ca^{2+} channels, creating intracellular Ca^{2+} signals. In general, activation of α_1-receptors causes muscle contraction or secretion by exocytosis. **α_2-receptors** decrease intracellular cyclic AMP and cause smooth muscle relaxation (gastrointestinal tract) or decreased secretion (pancreas).

For all adrenergic receptors, second messenger activity in the target tissue can persist for a longer time than is usually associated with the rapid action of the nervous system. The long-lasting metabolic effects of some autonomic pathways result from modification of existing proteins or from the synthesis of new proteins. We discuss the specific effects of catecholamines on various tissues in subsequent chapters.

CONCEPT CHECK

6. In what organelle is most intracellular Ca^{2+} stored?
7. What enzyme (a) converts ATP to cAMP? (b) does cAMP activate? [Fig. 6-11, p. 187]

Answers: p. 404

TABLE 11-1 Postganglionic Autonomic Neurotransmitters

	SYMPATHETIC DIVISION	PARASYMPATHETIC DIVISION
Neurotransmitter	Norepinephrine (NE)	Acetylcholine (ACh)
Receptor types	α- and β-adrenergic	Nicotinic and muscarinic cholinergic
Synthesized from	Tyrosine	Acetyl CoA + choline
Inactivation enzyme	Monoamine oxidase (MAO) in mitochondria of varicosity	Acetylcholinesterase (AChE) in synaptic cleft
Varicosity membrane transporters for	Norepinephrine	Choline

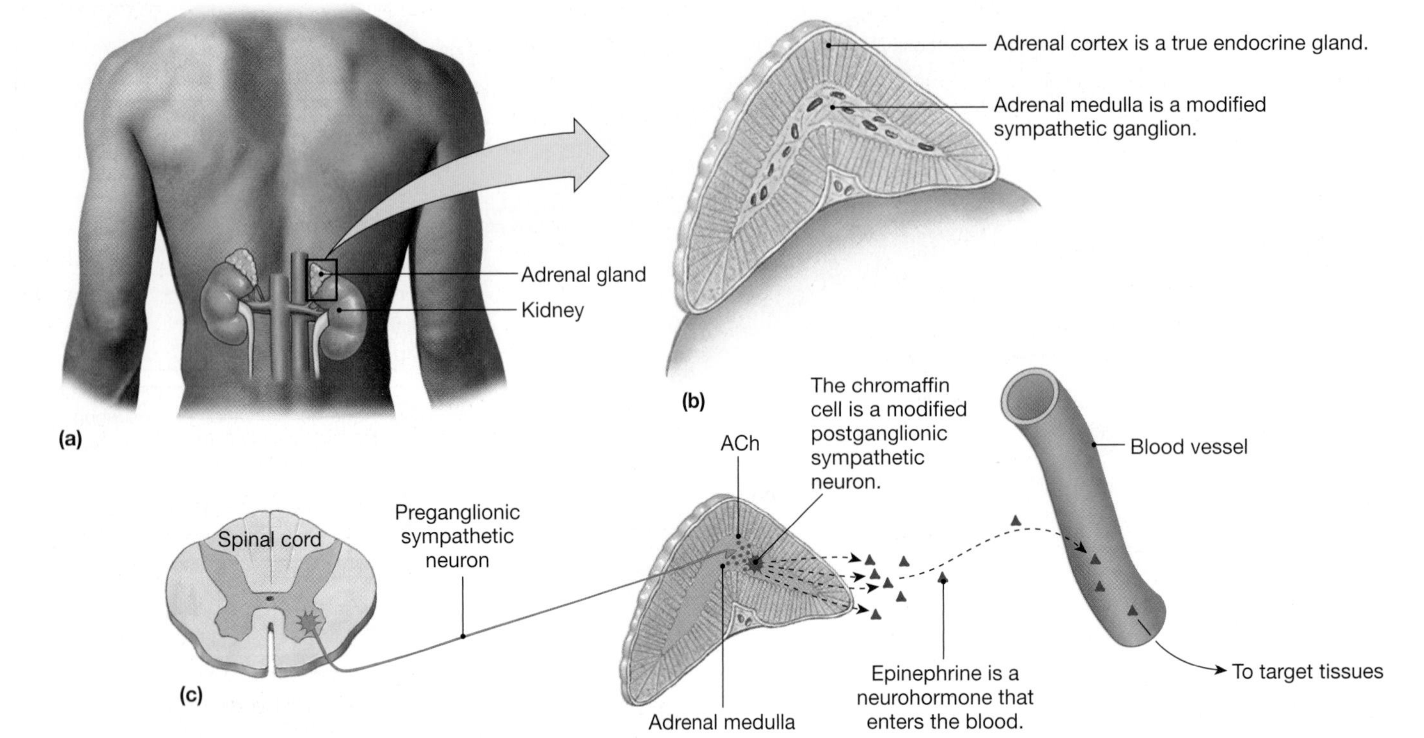

● **FIGURE 11-10** ***The adrenal medulla secretes epinephrine into the blood.***

The Adrenal Medulla Secretes Catecholamines

The **adrenal medulla** [*ad-,* upon + *renal,* kidney; *medulla,* marrow] is a specialized neuroendocrine tissue associated with the sympathetic nervous system. During development, the neural tissue destined to secrete the catecholamines norepinephrine and epinephrine splits into two functional entities: the sympathetic branch of the nervous system, which secretes norepinephrine, and the adrenal medulla, which secretes epinephrine primarily.

The adrenal medulla forms the core of the *adrenal glands,* which sit atop the kidneys (Fig. 11-10a ●). Like the pituitary gland, each adrenal gland is actually two glands of different embryological origin that fused during development (Fig. 11-10b). The outer portion, the *adrenal cortex,* is a true endocrine gland of epidermal origin that secretes steroid hormones [p. 79]. The adrenal medulla, which forms the small core of the gland, develops from the same embryonic tissue as sympathetic neurons and is a neurosecretory structure.

The adrenal medulla is often described as a *modified sympathetic ganglion.* Preganglionic sympathetic neurons project from the spinal cord to the adrenal medulla, where they synapse (Fig. 11-10c). However, the postganglionic neurons lack the axons that would normally project to target cells. Instead, the axonless cell bodies, called *chromaffin cells,* secrete the neurohormone epinephrine directly into the blood. In response to alarm signals from the CNS, the adrenal medulla releases large amounts of epinephrine for general distribution throughout the body as part of a fight-or-flight response.

TABLE 11-2 Properties of Adrenergic Receptors

RECEPTOR	FOUND IN	SENSITIVITY	EFFECT ON SECOND MESSENGER
α_1	Most sympathetic target tissues	NE > E*	Activates phospholipase C
α_2	Gastrointestinal tract and pancreas	NE > E	Decreases cAMP
β_1	Heart muscle, kidney	NE = E	Increases cAMP
β_2	Certain blood vessels and smooth muscle of some organs	E > NE	Increases cAMP
β_3	Adipose tissue	NE > E	Increases cAMP

*NE = norepinephrine, E = epinephrine.

✓ CONCEPT CHECK

8. Is the adrenal medulla most like the anterior pituitary or the posterior pituitary? Explain.
9. Which type of ACh receptors do you suppose chromaffin cells have, nicotinic or muscarinic? Answers: p. 404

Parasympathetic Pathways Secrete Acetylcholine onto Muscarinic Receptors

As a rule, parasympathetic neurons release ACh at their targets. As noted earlier, muscarinic cholinergic receptors [p. 279] are found at the neuroeffector junctions of the parasympathetic branch. Muscarinic receptors are all G protein–coupled receptors. Receptor activation initiates second messenger pathways, some of which open K^+ or Ca^{2+} channels. The tissue response to activation of a muscarinic receptor varies with the receptor subtype, of which there are at least five.

Autonomic Agonists and Antagonists Are Important Tools in Research and Medicine

The study of the two autonomic branches has been greatly simplified by advances in molecular biology. The genes for many autonomic receptors and their subtypes have been cloned, allowing researchers to create mutant receptors and study their properties. In addition, researchers have either discovered or synthesized a variety of agonist and antagonist molecules (Tbl. 11-3 ●). Direct agonists and antagonists combine with the target receptor to mimic or block neurotransmitter action. Indirect agonists and antagonists act by altering secretion, reuptake, or degradation of neurotransmitters.

For example, cocaine is an indirect agonist that blocks the reuptake of norepinephrine into adrenergic nerve terminals, thereby extending norepinephrine's excitatory effect on the target. *Anticholinesterases* (cholinesterase inhibitors) are indirect agonists that block ACh degradation and extend the active life of each ACh molecule. The toxic *organophosphate insecticides,* such as parathion and malathion, are anticholinesterases.

Many drugs used to treat depression are indirect agonists that act either on membrane transporters for neurotransmitters (tricyclic antidepressants and selective serotonin reuptake inhibitors) or on their metabolism (monoamine oxidase inhibitors). The older antidepressant drugs that act on norepinephrine transport and metabolism (tricyclics and MAO inhibitors) may have side effects related to their actions in the autonomic nervous system, including cardiovascular problems, constipation, urinary difficulty, and sexual dysfunction [*dys-,* abnormal or ill]. The newer serotonin reuptake inhibitors have fewer autonomic side effects.

Many new drugs have been developed from studies of agonists and antagonists. The discovery of α- and β-adrenergic receptors led to the development of drugs that block only one of the two receptor types. The drugs known as beta-blockers have given physicians a powerful tool for treating high blood pressure, one of the most common disorders in the United States today. Early α-adrenergic receptor antagonists had many unwanted side effects, but now pharmacologists can design drugs to target specific receptor subtypes. For example, tamsulosin (Flomax®) blocks alpha-1A adrenergic receptors (ADRA1A) found largely on smooth muscle of the prostate gland and bladder. Relaxing these muscles helps relieve the urinary symptoms of prostatic enlargement.

TABLE 11-3 Agonists and Antagonists of Neurotransmitter Receptors

RECEPTOR TYPE	NEUROTRANSMITTER	AGONIST	ANTAGONISTS	INDIRECT AGONISTS/ ANTAGONISTS
Cholinergic	Acetylcholine			AChE* *inhibitors:* neostigmine
Muscarinic		Muscarine	Atropine, scopolamine	
Nicotinic		Nicotine	α-bungarotoxin (muscle only), TEA (tetraethylammonium; ganglia only), curare	
Adrenergic	Norepinephrine (NE), epinephrine			*Stimulate NE release:* ephedrine, amphetamines *Prevents NE uptake:* cocaine
Alpha		Phenylephrine	"Alpha-blockers"	
Beta		Isoproterenol	"Beta-blockers": propranolol (β_1 and β_2), metoprolol (β_1 only)	

*AChE = acetylcholinesterase.

RUNNING PROBLEM

The action of nicotine on nAChR is complicated. Normally, chronic exposure of cells to a receptor agonist such as ACh or nicotine causes the cells to down-regulate their receptors. However, one research study that examined brains at autopsy found that smokers have a greater number of nAChR on their cell membranes than do nonsmokers. This increase in receptor numbers, or up-regulation [p. 194], is usually seen when cells are chronically exposed to receptor *antagonists*.

Question 3:
Although ACh and nicotine have been shown in short-term studies to be nAChR agonists, continued exposure of the receptors to ACh has been shown to close, or inactivate, the channel. Speculate why this could explain the up-regulation of nAChR observed in smokers.

Question 4:
Name another ion channel you have studied that opens in response to a stimulus but inactivates and closes shortly thereafter [p. 263].

386
387
389
396
399
401

CLINICAL FOCUS

AUTONOMIC NEUROPATHY

Primary disorders of the autonomic division are rare, but the secondary condition known as **diabetic autonomic neuropathy** is quite common. This complication of diabetes often begins as a sensory neuropathy, with tingling and loss of sensation in the hands and feet. In some patients, pain is the primary symptom [p. 348]. About 30% of diabetic patients go on to develop autonomic neuropathies, manifested by dysfunction of the cardiovascular, gastrointestinal, urinary, and reproductive systems (abnormal heart rate, constipation, incontinence, impotence). The cause of diabetic neuropathies is controversial. Patients who have chronically elevated blood glucose levels are more likely to develop neuropathies, but the underlying metabolic pathway has not been identified. Other contributing factors for neuropathy include oxidative stress [p. 24] and autoimmune reactions. Currently there is no prevention for diabetic neuropathies other than controlling blood glucose levels, and no cure. The only recourse for patients is taking drugs that treat the symptoms.

Primary Disorders of the Autonomic Nervous System Are Relatively Uncommon

Diseases and malfunction of the autonomic nervous system are relatively rare. Direct damage (trauma) to hypothalamic control centers may disrupt the body's ability to regulate water balance or temperature. Generalized sympathetic dysfunction may result from systemic diseases such as cancer and diabetes mellitus. There are also some conditions, such as *multiple system atrophy,* in which the CNS control centers for autonomic functions degenerate.

In many cases of sympathetic dysfunction, the symptoms are manifested most strongly in the cardiovascular system, when diminished sympathetic input to blood vessels results in abnormally low blood pressure. Other prominent symptoms of sympathetic pathology include urinary *incontinence* [*in-*, unable + *continere,* to contain], which is the loss of bladder control, and *impotence,* which is the inability to achieve or sustain a penile erection.

Occasionally, patients suffer from primary autonomic failure when sympathetic neurons degenerate. In the face of continuing diminished sympathetic input, target tissues up-regulate [p. 194], putting more receptors into the cell membrane to maximize the cell's response to available norepinephrine. This increase in receptor abundance leads to *denervation hypersensitivity,* a state in which the administration of exogenous adrenergic agonists causes a greater-than-expected response.

Summary of Sympathetic and Parasympathetic Branches

As you have seen in this discussion, the branches of the autonomic nervous system share some features but are distinguished by others. Many of these features are summarized in Figure 11-11 ● and compared in Table 11-4 ●.

1. Both sympathetic and parasympathetic pathways consist of two neurons (preganglionic and postganglionic) in series. One exception to this rule is the adrenal medulla, in which postganglionic sympathetic neurons have been modified into a neuroendocrine organ.
2. All preganglionic autonomic neurons secrete acetylcholine onto nicotinic receptors. Most sympathetic neurons secrete norepinephrine onto adrenergic receptors. Most parasympathetic neurons secrete acetylcholine onto muscarinic receptors.
3. Sympathetic pathways originate in the thoracic and lumbar regions of the spinal cord. Most sympathetic ganglia are located close to the spinal cord (are *paravertebral*). Parasympathetic pathways leave the CNS at the brain stem and in the sacral region of the spinal cord. Parasympathetic ganglia are located close to or in the target tissue.
4. The sympathetic branch controls functions that are useful in stress or emergencies (fight-or-flight). The parasympathetic branch is dominant during rest-and-digest activities.

THE SOMATIC MOTOR DIVISION

Somatic motor pathways, which control skeletal muscles, differ from autonomic pathways both anatomically and functionally (Tbl. 11-5 ●). Somatic motor pathways have a single neuron

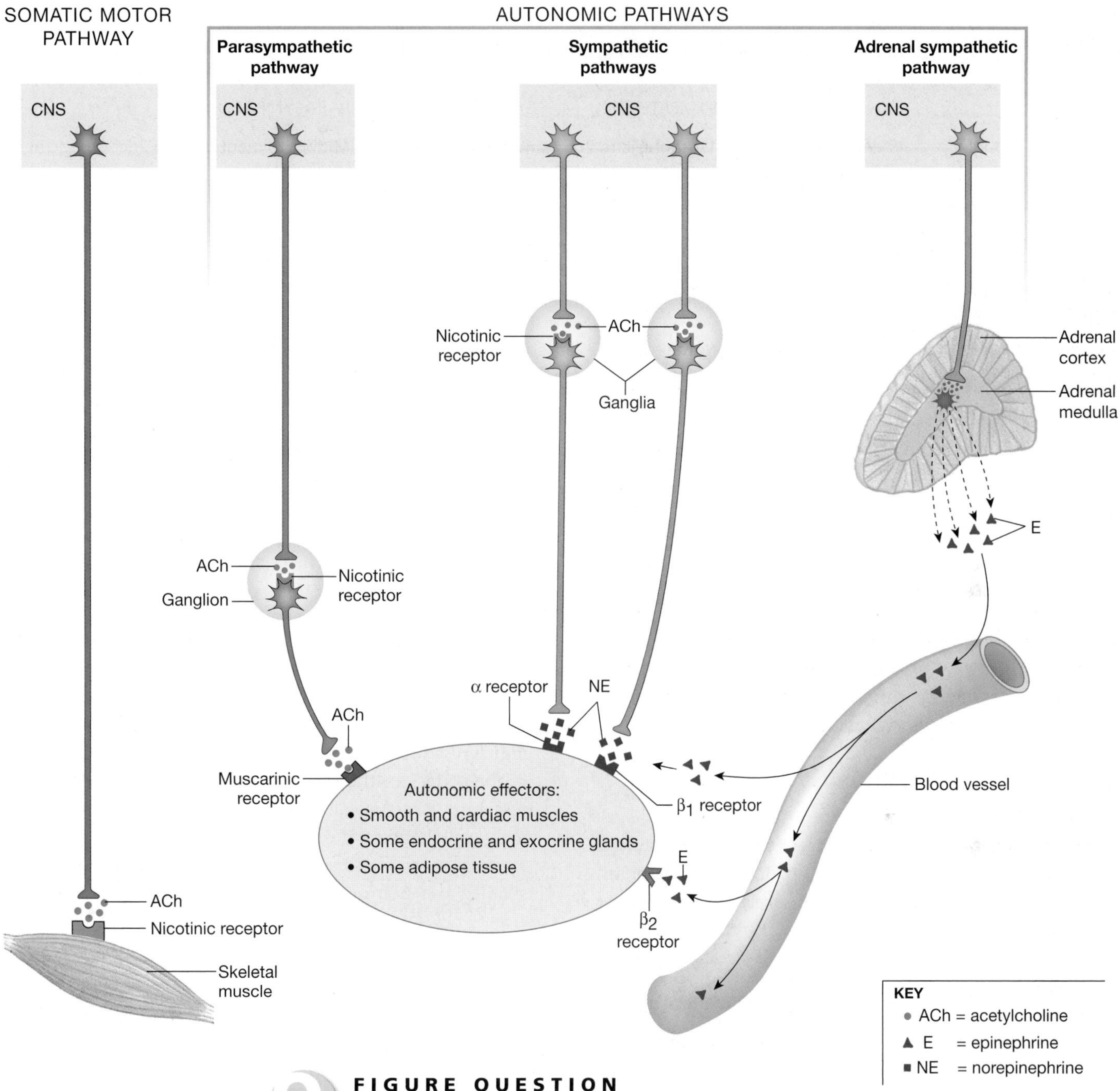
SOMATIC MOTOR PATHWAY
AUTONOMIC PATHWAYS
Parasympathetic pathway
Sympathetic pathways
Adrenal sympathetic pathway
CNS
CNS
CNS
CNS
Nicotinic receptor
ACh
Ganglia
Adrenal cortex
Adrenal medulla
E
ACh
Ganglion
Nicotinic receptor
α receptor
NE
ACh
Muscarinic receptor
Autonomic effectors:
• Smooth and cardiac muscles
• Some endocrine and exocrine glands
• Some adipose tissue
β1 receptor
Blood vessel
E
β2 receptor
ACh
Nicotinic receptor
Skeletal muscle
KEY
● ACh = acetylcholine
▲ E = epinephrine
■ NE = norepinephrine

FIGURE QUESTION

Using the figure, compare:
- (a) number of neurons in somatic motor and autonomic pathways
- (b) receptors on target cells of somatic motor, sympathetic, and parasympathetic pathways
- (c) neurotransmitters used on target cells of somatic motor, sympathetic, and parasympathetic pathways
- (d) receptor subtypes for epinephrine to subtypes for norepinephrine
- (e) ganglion location for sympathetic and parasympathetic pathways.

● **FIGURE 11-11** *Summary of efferent pathways*

TABLE 11-4 Comparison of Sympathetic and Parasympathetic Branches

	SYMPATHETIC	PARASYMPATHETIC
Point of CNS origin	1st thoracic to 2nd lumbar segments	Midbrain, medulla, and 2nd–4th sacral segments
Location of peripheral ganglia	Primarily in paravertebral sympathetic chain; 3 outlying ganglia located alongside descending aorta	On or near target organs
Structure of region from which neurotransmitter is released	Varicosities	Varicosities
Neurotransmitter at target synapse	Norepinephrine (adrenergic neurons)	ACh (cholinergic neurons)
Inactivation of neurotransmitter at synapse	Uptake into varicosity, diffusion	Enzymatic breakdown, diffusion
Neurotransmitter receptors on target cells	Adrenergic	Muscarinic
Ganglionic synapse	ACh on nicotinic receptor	ACh on nicotinic receptor
Neuron-target synapse	NE on α- or β-adrenergic receptor	ACh on muscarinic receptor

that originates in the CNS and projects its axon to the target tissue, which is always a skeletal muscle. Unlike autonomic pathways, which may be either excitatory or inhibitory, somatic pathways are always excitatory.

A Somatic Motor Pathway Consists of One Neuron

The cell bodies of somatic motor neurons are located either in the ventral horn of the spinal cord [p. 307] or in the brain, with a long single axon projecting to the skeletal muscle target (Fig. 11-11). These myelinated axons may be a meter or more in length, like the somatic motor neurons that innervate the muscles of the foot and hand.

Somatic motor neurons branch close to their targets. Each branch divides into a cluster of enlarged axon terminals that lie on the surface of the skeletal muscle fiber (Fig. 11-12 ●). This branching structure allows a single motor neuron to control many muscle fibers at one time.

The synapse of a somatic motor neuron on a muscle fiber is called the **neuromuscular junction**, or NMJ (Fig. 11-12).

TABLE 11-5 Comparison of Somatic and Autonomic Divisions

	SOMATIC	AUTONOMIC
Number of neurons in efferent path	1	2
Neurotransmitter/receptor at neuron-target synapse	ACh/nicotinic	ACh/muscarinic or NE/α- or β-adrenergic
Target tissue	Skeletal muscle	Smooth and cardiac muscle; some endocrine and exocrine glands; some adipose tissue
Neurotransmitter released from	Axon terminals	Varicosities and axon terminals
Effects on target tissue	Excitatory only: muscle contracts	Excitatory or inhibitory
Peripheral components found outside the CNS	Axons only	Preganglionic axons, ganglia, postganglionic neurons
Summary of function	Posture and movement	Visceral function, including movement in internal organs and secretion; control of metabolism

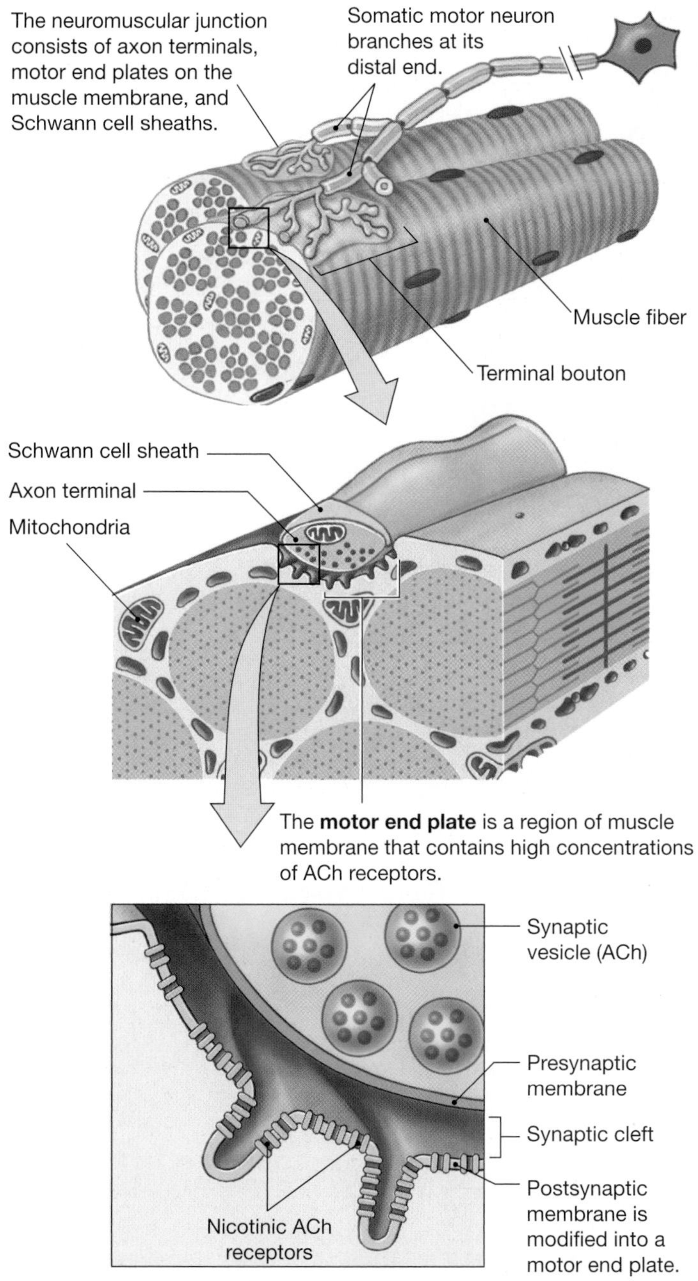
The neuromuscular junction consists of axon terminals, motor end plates on the muscle membrane, and Schwann cell sheaths.
Somatic motor neuron branches at its distal end.
Muscle fiber
Terminal bouton
Schwann cell sheath
Axon terminal
Mitochondria
The **motor end plate** is a region of muscle membrane that contains high concentrations of ACh receptors.
Synaptic vesicle (ACh)
Presynaptic membrane
Synaptic cleft
Postsynaptic membrane is modified into a motor end plate.
Nicotinic ACh receptors

● **FIGURE 11-12** ***Anatomy of the neuromuscular junction***

Like all other synapses, the NMJ has three components: (1) the motor neuron's presynaptic axon terminal filled with synaptic vesicles and mitochondria, (2) the synaptic cleft, and (3) the postsynaptic membrane of the skeletal muscle fiber.

In addition, the neuromuscular junction includes extensions of Schwann cells that form a thin layer covering the top of the axon terminals. For years it was thought that this cell layer simply provided insulation to speed up the conduction of the action potential, but we now know that Schwann cells secrete a variety of chemical signal molecules. These signal molecules play a critical role in the formation and maintenance of neuromuscular junctions.

On the postsynaptic side of the neuromuscular junction, the muscle cell membrane that lies opposite the axon terminal is modified into a **motor end plate**, a series of folds that look like shallow gutters. Along the upper edge of each gutter, nicotinic ACh receptor (nAChR) channels cluster together in an active zone. Between the axon and the muscle, the synaptic cleft is filled with a fibrous matrix whose collagen fibers hold the axon terminal and the motor end plate in the proper alignment. The matrix also contains **acetylcholinesterase** (AChE), the enzyme that rapidly deactivates ACh by degrading it into acetyl and choline [p. 281].

CONCEPT CHECK

10. Is the ventral horn of the spinal cord, which contains the cell bodies of somatic motor neurons, gray matter or white matter?

Answers: p. 404

The Neuromuscular Junction Contains Nicotinic Receptors

As in all neurons, action potentials arriving at the axon terminal open voltage-gated Ca^{2+} channels in the membrane. Calcium diffuses into the cell down its electrochemical gradient, triggering the release of ACh-containing synaptic vesicles. Acetylcholine diffuses across the synaptic cleft and combines with nicotinic receptor channels (nAChR) on the skeletal muscle membrane (Fig. 11-13 ●).

The nAChR channels of skeletal muscle are similar but not identical to the nicotinic ACh receptors found on neurons. This difference is illustrated by the fact that the snake toxin α-bungarotoxin binds to nicotinic skeletal muscle receptors but not to those in autonomic ganglia. Both muscle and neuronal nAChR proteins have five subunits encircling the central pore, but skeletal muscle has α, β, δ, and ε subunit isoforms while neuronal nAchR has only the α and β isoforms. Both forms of

RUNNING PROBLEM

After discussing her options with her doctor, Shanika decides to try the nicotine patch, one form of nicotine replacement therapy. These adhesive patches allow the former smoker to gradually decrease nicotine levels in the body, preventing withdrawal symptoms during the time the cells are down-regulating their receptors back to the normal number. When Shanika reads the package insert prior to applying her first nicotine patch, she notices a warning to keep the patches away from children. An overdose of nicotine (highly unlikely when the patch is used as directed) could result in complete paralysis of the respiratory muscles (the diaphragm and the skeletal muscles of the chest wall).

Question 5:

Why might excessive levels of nicotine cause respiratory paralysis?

386 387 389 396 399 401

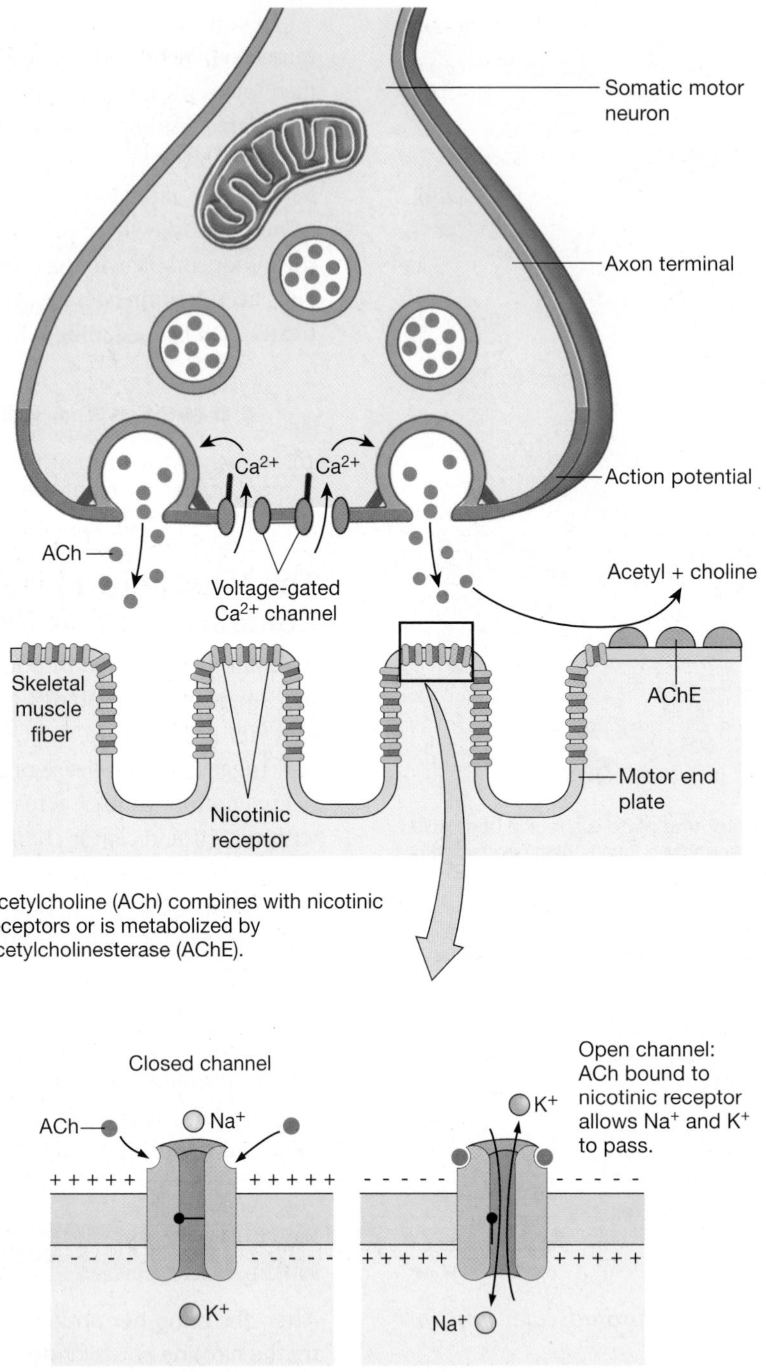

(a) Acetylcholine (ACh) combines with nicotinic receptors or is metabolized by acetylcholinesterase (AChE).

(b) The nicotinic cholinergic receptor binds two ACh molecules, opening a nonspecific monovalent cation channel.

● **FIGURE 11-13** ***Events at the neuromuscular junction***

nAChR will inactivate [p. 258] with extended exposure to ACh or other agonists.

Nicotinic cholinergic receptors are chemically gated ion channels with two binding sites for ACh (Fig. 11-13b). When ACh binds to the receptor, the channel gate opens and allows monovalent cations to flow through. In skeletal muscle, net Na^+ entry into the muscle fiber depolarizes it, triggering an action potential that causes contraction of the skeletal muscle cell.

Acetylcholine acting on a skeletal muscle's motor end plate is always excitatory and creates muscle contraction. There is no antagonistic innervation to relax skeletal muscles. Instead, relaxation occurs when the somatic motor neurons are inhibited in the CNS, preventing ACh release. In Chapter 13 you will learn more about how inhibition of somatic motor pathways controls body movement.

Somatic motor neurons do more than simply create contractions: they are necessary for muscle health. "Use it or lose it" is a cliché that is very appropriate to the dynamics of muscle mass because disrupting synaptic transmission at the neuromuscular junction has devastating effects on the entire body. Without communication between the motor neuron and the muscle, the skeletal muscles for movement and posture weaken, as do the skeletal muscles for breathing. In the severest cases, loss of respiratory function can be fatal unless the patient is placed on artificial ventilation. Myasthenia gravis, a disease characterized by loss of ACh receptors, is the most common disorder of the neuromuscular junction.

CONCEPT CHECK

11. Compare gating and ion selectivity of acetylcholine receptor-channels in the motor end plate with that of ion channels along the axon of a somatic motor neuron.
12. A nonsmoker who chews nicotine-containing gum might notice an increase in heart rate, a function controlled by sympathetic neurons. Postganglionic sympathetic neurons secrete norepinephrine, not ACh, so how could nicotine affect heart rate?
13. Patients with myasthenia gravis have a deficiency of ACh receptors on their skeletal muscles and have weak muscle function as a result. Why would administration of an anticholinesterase drug (one that inhibits acetylcholinesterase) improve muscle function in these patients?

Answers: p. 404

RUNNING PROBLEMS CONCLUSION

A Powerful Addiction

Shanika is determined to stop smoking this time because her grandfather, a smoker for many years, was just diagnosed with lung cancer. Finding that the patch alone does not stop her craving for a cigarette, she attends behavioral modification classes that help her avoid situations that make her likely to smoke and substitute other activities, such as chewing gum, for smoking. After six months, Shanika proudly informs her family that she thinks she has kicked the habit.

Nicotine replacement may not be the ideal treatment for smoking cessation because although the former smoker is no longer exposed to cigarette smoke, the nicotine addiction may remain. Chantix® acts as a partial nAChR agonist and may help break the addiction. However, unwanted side effects, such as nightmares, have been reported with its use. Some smokers have quit with the help of Zyban®, a drug that is also used as an antidepressant. Other treatments are still being investigated, including a drug that acts on cannabinoid receptors [p. 279] and a nicotine vaccine. To learn more about nicotine addiction and smoking cessation programs, try a Google search for *nicotine addiction*. Check your understanding of this running problem by comparing your answers to the information in the following summary table.

	QUESTION	FACTS	INTEGRATION AND ANALYSIS
1	What is the usual response of cells that are chronically exposed to elevated concentrations of a signal molecule?	A cell exposed to elevated concentrations of a signal molecule will decrease (down-regulate) its receptors for that molecule.	Down-regulation of receptors allows a cell to respond normally even if the concentration of ligand is elevated.
2	What happens to a postsynaptic cell when nicotine rather than ACh binds to a nicotinic cholinergic receptor?	Nicotine is an agonist of ACh. Agonists mimic the activity of a ligand.	Nicotine binding to a nAChR will open ion channels in the postsynaptic cell, and the cell will depolarize. This is the same effect that ACh binding creates.
3	Although ACh and nicotine have been shown in short-term studies to be nAChR agonists, continued exposure of the receptors to ACh has been shown to close, or inactivate, the channel. Speculate why this could explain the up-regulation of nAChR observed in smokers.	Chronic exposure to an agonist usually causes down-regulation. Chronic exposure to an antagonist usually causes up-regulation. nAChR channels open with initial exposure to agonists but close with continued exposure.	Although nicotine is a short-term agonist, it appears to be having the same effect as an antagonist during long-term exposure. With both antagonism and the inactivation described here, the cell's activity decreases. The cell subsequently up-regulates the number of receptors in an attempt to restore activity.
4	Name another ion channel you have studied that opens in response to a stimulus but inactivates and closes shortly thereafter.	The voltage-gated Na^+ channel of the axon first opens, then closes when the inactivation gate shuts.	N/A

RUNNING PROBLEMS CONCLUSION *(continued)*

	QUESTION	FACTS	INTEGRATION AND ANALYSIS
5	Why might excessive levels of nicotine cause respiratory paralysis?	Nicotinic receptors are found at the neuromuscular junction that controls skeletal muscle contraction. The diaphragm and chest wall muscles that regulate breathing are skeletal muscles.	The nicotinic receptors of the neuromuscular junction are not as sensitive to nicotine as are those of the CNS and autonomic ganglia. However, excessively high amounts of nicotine will activate the nAChR of the motor end plate, causing the muscle fiber to depolarize and contract. The continued presence of nicotine keeps these ion channels open, and the muscle remains depolarized. In this state, the muscle is unable to contract again, resulting in paralysis.

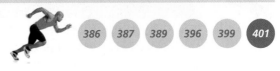

386 387 389 396 399 401

CHAPTER SUMMARY

This chapter completes our survey of the divisions of the nervous system. The central nervous system acts as the integrating center for neural reflexes. The sensory (afferent) system is the input division of the peripheral nervous system, and the autonomic and somatic motor divisions are the output pathways of the PNS. *Communication* among the divisions depends primarily on chemical signaling and *molecular interactions* between neurotransmitters and their receptors. *Homeostasis* requires constant surveillance of body parameters by the nervous system, working in conjunction with the endocrine and immune systems. As you learn about the function of other body systems, you will continue to revisit the principles of communication and coordination introduced in Chapters 6 through 11.

The Autonomic Division

1. The efferent division of the peripheral nervous system is divided into **somatic motor neurons**, which control skeletal muscles, and **autonomic neurons**, which control smooth muscle, cardiac muscle, many glands, lymphoid tissue, and some adipose tissue. (p. 386)
2. The autonomic division is subdivided into a **sympathetic branch** and a **parasympathetic branch**. (p. 386; Tbl. 11-4)
3. The maintenance of homeostasis within the body is a balance of autonomic control, endocrine control, and behavioral responses. (p. 387)
4. The autonomic division is controlled by centers in the hypothalamus, pons, and medulla. Some autonomic reflexes are spinal reflexes. Many of these can be modulated by input from the brain. (p. 387; Figs. 11-2, 11-3)
5. The two autonomic branches demonstrate Cannon's properties of homeostasis: maintenance of the internal environment, tonic control, antagonistic control, and variable tissue responses. (p. 388)
6. An autonomic pathway is composed of a **preganglionic neuron** from the CNS that synapses with a **postganglionic neuron** in an **autonomic ganglion**. Autonomic ganglia can modulate and integrate information passing through them. (p. 388; Fig. 11-4)
7. Most sympathetic pathways originate in the thoracic and lumbar regions of the spinal cord. Most sympathetic ganglia lie either close to the spinal cord or along the descending aorta. (p. 389; Fig. 11-5)
8. Parasympathetic pathways originate in the brain stem or the sacral region of the spinal cord. Parasympathetic ganglia are located on or near their target organs. (p. 389; Fig. 11-5)
9. The primary autonomic neurotransmitters are **acetylcholine** and **norepinephrine**. All preganglionic neurons secrete ACh onto **nicotinic cholinergic receptors**. As a rule, postganglionic sympathetic neurons secrete norepinephrine onto **adrenergic receptors**, and postganglionic parasympathetic neurons secrete ACh onto **muscarinic cholinergic receptors**. (p. 389; Fig. 11-7, Tbl. 11-1)
10. The synapse between an autonomic neuron and its target cells is called the **neuroeffector junction**. (p. 391)
11. Autonomic axons end with **varicosities** from which neurotransmitter is released. (p. 392; Figs. 11-8, 11-9)
12. The **adrenal medulla** secretes epinephrine and is controlled by sympathetic preganglionic neurons. (p. 394; Fig. 11-10)
13. Adrenergic receptors are G protein–coupled receptors. Alpha receptors respond most strongly to norepinephrine. **β_1-receptors** respond equally to norepinephrine and epinephrine. **β_2-receptors** are not associated with sympathetic neurons and respond most strongly to epinephrine. **β_3-receptors** respond most strongly to norepinephrine. (p. 392; Fig. 11-11, Tbl. 11-2)
14. Cholinergic muscarinic receptors are also G protein–coupled receptors. (p. 395)

The Somatic Motor Division

15. Somatic motor pathways, which control skeletal muscles, have a single neuron that originates in the CNS and terminates on a skeletal muscle. Somatic motor neurons are always excitatory and cause muscle contraction. (p. 396; Fig. 11-11)

16. A single **somatic motor neuron** controls many muscle fibers at one time. (p. 398)
17. The synapse of a somatic motor neuron on a muscle fiber is called the **neuromuscular junction.** The muscle cell membrane is modified into a **motor end plate** that contains a high concentration of nicotinic ACh receptors. (p. 398–399; Fig. 11-12)
18. ACh binding to nicotinic receptor opens cation channels. Net Na^+ entry into the muscle fiber depolarizes the fiber. Acetylcholine in the synapse is broken down by the enzyme **acetylcholinesterase.** (p. 400; Fig. 11-13)

QUESTIONS

(Answers to the Review Questions begin on page A1.)

THE PHYSIOLOGY PLACE

Access more review material online at The Physiology Place web site. There you'll find review questions, problem-solving activities, case studies, flashcards, and direct links to both *Interactive Physiology®* and *PhysioEx™*. To access the site, go to *www.physiologyplace.com* and *select Human Physiology,* Fifth Edition.

LEVEL ONE REVIEWING FACTS AND TERMS

1. Name the two efferent divisions of the peripheral nervous system. What type of effectors does each control?
2. The autonomic nervous system is sometimes called the __________ nervous system. Why is this an appropriate name? List some functions controlled by the autonomic nervous system.
3. What are the two branches of the autonomic nervous system? How are these branches distinguished from each other anatomically and physiologically?
4. Which neurosecretory endocrine gland is closely allied to the sympathetic branch?
5. Neurons that secrete acetylcholine are described as __________ neurons, whereas those that secrete norepinephrine are called either __________ or __________ neurons.
6. List four things that can happen to autonomic neurotransmitters after they are released into a synapse.
7. The main enzyme responsible for catecholamine degradation is __________, abbreviated __________.
8. Somatic motor pathways
   (a) are excitatory or inhibitory?
   (b) are composed of a single neuron or a preganglionic and a postganglionic neuron?
   (c) synapse with glands or with smooth, cardiac, or skeletal muscle?
9. What is acetylcholinesterase? Describe its action.
10. What kind of receptor is found on the postsynaptic cell in a neuromuscular junction?

LEVEL TWO REVIEWING CONCEPTS

11. What is the advantage of divergence of neural pathways in the autonomic nervous system?
12. Compare and contrast
    (a) neuroeffector junctions and neuromuscular junctions.
    (b) alpha, beta, muscarinic, and nicotinic receptors. Describe where each is found and the ligands that bind to them.
13. **Concept map:** Use the following terms to make a map comparing the somatic motor division and the sympathetic and parasympathetic branches of the autonomic division. You may add additional terms.

acetylcholine	muscarinic receptor
adipose tissue	nicotinic receptor
alpha receptor	norepinephrine
autonomic division	one-neuron pathway
beta receptor	parasympathetic branch
cardiac muscle	skeletal muscle
cholinergic receptor	smooth muscle
efferent division	somatic motor division
endocrine gland	sympathetic branch
exocrine gland	two-neuron pathway
ganglion	

14. Compare and contrast
    (a) autonomic ganglia and CNS nuclei.
    (b) the adrenal medulla and the posterior pituitary gland.
    (c) boutons and varicosities.
15. If a target cell's receptor is __________ (use items in left column), the neuron(s) releasing neurotransmitter onto the receptor must be __________ (use all appropriate items from the right column).

(a) nicotinic cholinergic	1. somatic motor neuron
(b) adrenergic α	2. autonomic preganglionic neuron
(c) muscarinic cholinergic	3. sympathetic postganglionic neuron
(d) adrenergic β	4. parasympathetic postganglionic neuron

16. Ganglia contain the cell bodies of (choose all that apply)
    (a) somatic motor neurons.
    (b) preganglionic autonomic neurons.
    (c) interneurons.
    (d) postganglionic autonomic neurons.
    (e) sensory neurons.

LEVEL THREE PROBLEM SOLVING

17. If nicotinic receptor channels allow both Na^+ and K^+ to flow through, why does Na^+ influx exceed K^+ efflux? [*Hint:* p. 256]
18. You have discovered a neuron that innervates an endocrine cell in the intestine. To learn more about this neuron, you place a marker substance at the endocrine cell synapse. The marker is taken into the neuron and transported in a vesicle by retrograde axonal transport to the nerve cell body.
    (a) By what process is the marker probably taken into the axon terminal?
    (b) The nerve cell body is found in a ganglion very close to the endocrine cell. To which branch of the peripheral nervous system does the neuron probably belong? (Be as specific as you can.)

(c) Which neurotransmitter do you predict will be secreted by the neuron onto the endocrine cell?

19. The Huaorani Indians of South America use blowguns to shoot darts poisoned with curare at monkeys. Curare is a plant toxin that binds to and inactivates nicotinic ACh receptors. What happens to a monkey struck by one of these darts?

LEVEL FOUR QUANTITATIVE PROBLEMS

20. The U.S. Centers for Disease Control and Prevention (CDC) conduct biennial Youth Risk Behavior Surveys (YRBS) in which they ask high school students to self-report risky behaviors such as alcohol consumption and smoking. The graphs that follow were created from data in the latest report on cigarette smoking among American high school students. *Current smoking* is defined as smoking cigarettes on at least one day in the 30 days preceding the survey. *(www.cdc.gov/mmwr/preview/mmwrhtml/mm5526a2.htm)*

(a) What can you say about cigarette smoking among high school students in the period from 1991 to 2005?

(b) Which high school students are most likely to be smokers? Least likely to be smokers?

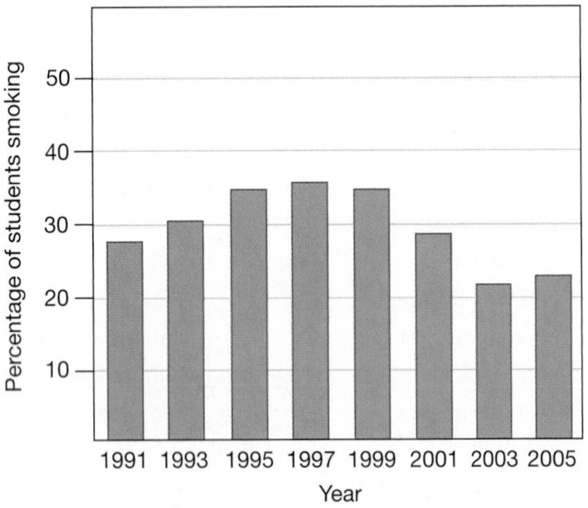

Percentage of students who reported current smoking (1991-2005)

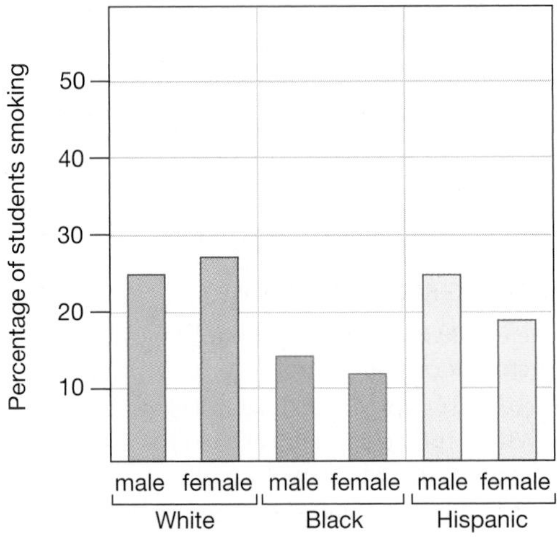

Percentage of students in 2005 who reported current smoking, separated by sex and race/ethnicity*

*Other race/ethnic groups are not shown because the numbers of students reporting were too small for meaningful statistical analysis.

ANSWERS

Answers to Concept Check Questions

Page 387

1. The afferent division consists of sensory receptors and sensory neurons.
2. The CNS consists of the brain and spinal cord.

Page 388

3. Homeostasis is the maintenance of a relatively stable internal environment.

Page 389

4. Mixed nerves carry sensory and motor signals.
5. The regions of the spinal cord are cervical, thoracic, lumbar, and sacral.

Page 393

6. Ca^{2+} is stored in the endoplasmic reticulum.
7. (a) Adenylyl cyclase converts ATP to cAMP; (b) cAMP activates protein kinase A.

Page 395

8. The adrenal medulla is neurosecretory and therefore like the posterior pituitary.
9. Chromaffin cells are modified postganglionic neurons, so they have nicotinic receptors.

Page 399

10. The ventral horn is gray matter.

Page 401

11. The nAChR of the motor end plate is a ligand-gated monovalent cation (Na^+ and K^+) channel. The axon contains voltage-gated channels, with separate channels for Na^+ and K^+ [p. 257].
12. Postganglionic sympathetic neurons are activated by ACh acting on nicotinic receptors. This means that nicotine also excites sympathetic neurons, such as those that increase heart rate.
13. Anticholinesterase drugs decrease the rate at which ACh is broken down at the motor end plate. Slower breakdown rate allows ACh to remain active at the motor end plate for a longer time and helps offset the decrease in active receptors.

Answers to Figure Questions

Page 390

Figure 11-5: 1. Sympathetic pathways originate in the thoracic and lumbar regions of the spinal cord; parasympathetic pathways originate in the brain stem or sacral region. 2. Sympathetic ganglia are located close to the spinal column or along the descending aorta (not shown); parasympathetic ganglia are located on or near their target organs. 3. Connections between the sympathetic ganglia allow rapid communication within the sympathetic branch.

Page 391

Figure 11-7: (a) The three neurons that secrete ACh are cholinergic. The one neuron that secretes norepinephrine is adrenergic. The cell bodies of preganglionic neurons are in the CNS; the cell bodies of postganglionic neurons are in a ganglion. (b) Parasympathetic pathways have the longer preganglionic neurons.

Page 397

Figure 11-11: (a) Somatic has one neuron, autonomic has two. (b) Somatic motor targets have nicotinic ACh receptors, parasympathetic targets have muscarinic ACh receptors, and sympathetic targets have adrenergic receptors. (c) Somatic motor and parasympathetic pathways use ACh; sympathetic uses norepinephrine. (d) Epinephrine is most active on β_1- and β_2-receptors; norepinephrine is most active on β_1- and α-receptors. (e) Sympathetic ganglia are close to the CNS; parasympathetic ganglia are closer to their target tissues.

12

Muscles

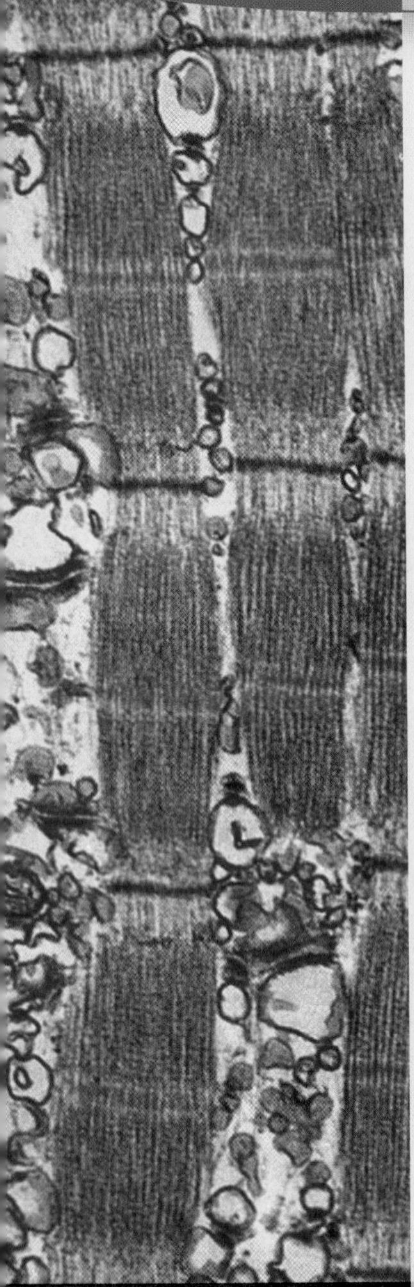

Striated muscle sarcomeres and sarcoplasmic reticulum between the fibers

BACKGROUND BASICS

Tendons: **81** Kinases and phosphatases: **104** Isozymes: **100** Anaerobic and aerobic metabolism: **107** Glycolysis: **107** Fatty acid metabolism: **115** Tonic control: **196** Nitric oxide: **191** Threshold: **200** Summation: **283** Autonomic neurons: **388** Somatic motor neurons: **398** Neuromuscular junction: **398**

A muscle is . . . an engine, capable of converting chemical energy into mechanical energy. It is quite unique in nature, for there has been no artificial engine devised with the great versatility of living muscle.

—Ralph W. Stacy and John A. Santolucito, in *Modern College Physiology*, 1966

RUNNING PROBLEM

Periodic Paralysis

This morning, Paul Leong, age 6, gave his mother the fright of her life. One minute he was happily playing in the backyard with his new beagle puppy. The next minute, after sitting down to rest, he could not move his legs. In answer to his screams, his mother came running and found her little boy unable to walk. Panic-stricken, she scooped him up, brought him into the house, and dialed 9-1-1. But as she hung up the phone and prepared to wait for the paramedics, Paul got to his feet and walked over to her. "I'm OK now, Mom," he announced. "I'm going outside."

407 420 422 431 433 440

It was his first time to be the starting pitcher. As he ran from the bullpen onto the field, his heart was pounding and his stomach felt as if it were tied in knots. He stepped onto the mound and gathered his thoughts before throwing his first practice pitch. Gradually, as he went through the familiar routine of throwing and catching the baseball, his heart slowed and his stomach relaxed. It was going to be a good game.

The pitcher's pounding heart, queasy stomach, and movements as he runs and throws all result from muscle contraction. Our muscles have two common functions: to generate motion and to generate force. Our skeletal muscles also generate heat and contribute significantly to the homeostasis of body temperature. When cold conditions threaten homeostasis, the brain may direct our muscles to shiver, creating additional heat.

The human body has three types of muscle tissue: skeletal muscle, cardiac muscle, and smooth muscle. Most **skeletal muscles** are attached to the bones of the skeleton, enabling these muscles to control body movement. **Cardiac muscle** [*kardia,* heart] is found only in the heart and moves blood through the circulatory system. Skeletal and cardiac muscles are classified as **striated muscles** [*stria,* groove] because of their alternating light and dark bands seen under the light microscope (Fig. 12-1a, b ●).

Smooth muscle is the primary muscle of internal organs and tubes, such as the stomach, urinary bladder, and blood vessels. Its primary function is to influence the movement of material into, out of, and within the body. An example is the passage of food through the gastrointestinal tract. Viewed under the microscope, smooth muscle lacks the obvious cross-bands of striated muscles (Fig. 12-1c). Its lack of banding results from the less organized arrangement of contractile fibers within the muscle cells.

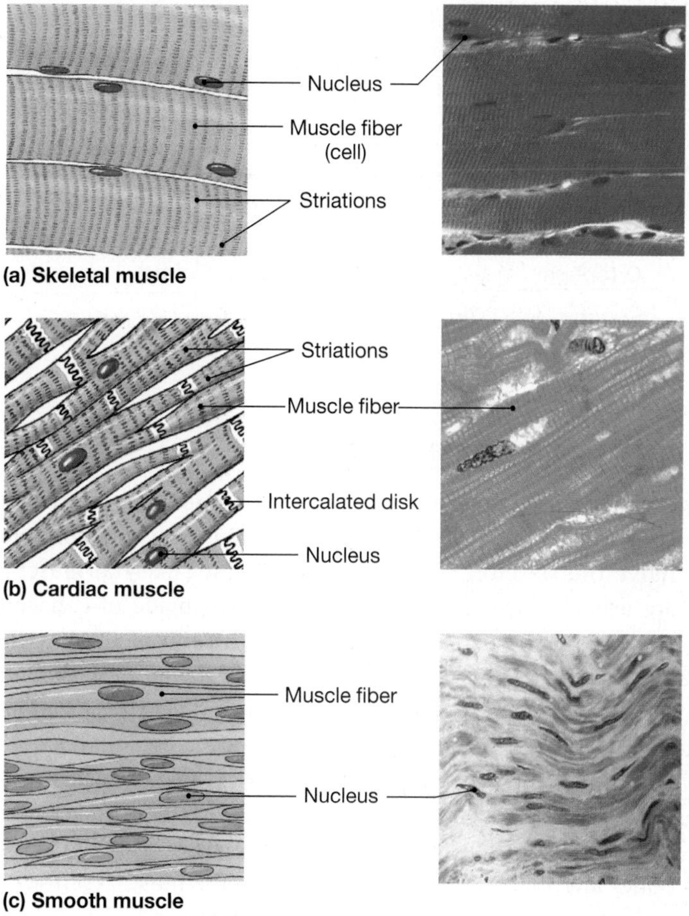
Nucleus
Muscle fiber (cell)
Striations
(a) Skeletal muscle
Striations
Muscle fiber
Intercalated disk
Nucleus
(b) Cardiac muscle
Muscle fiber
Nucleus
(c) Smooth muscle

● **FIGURE 12-1** ***The three types of muscles***

Skeletal muscles are often described as voluntary muscles, and smooth and cardiac muscle as involuntary. However, this is not a precise classification. Skeletal muscles can contract without conscious direction, and we can learn a certain degree of conscious control over some smooth and cardiac muscle [p. 386].

Skeletal muscles are unique in that they contract only in response to a signal from a somatic motor neuron. They cannot initiate their own contraction, and their contraction is not influenced directly by hormones.

In contrast, cardiac and smooth muscle have multiple levels of control. Their primary extrinsic control arises through autonomic innervation, but some types of smooth and cardiac muscle can contract spontaneously, without signals from the central nervous system. In addition, the activity of cardiac and some smooth muscle is subject to modulation by the endocrine system. Despite these differences, smooth and cardiac muscle share many properties with skeletal muscle.

In this chapter we discuss skeletal and smooth muscle anatomy and contraction, and conclude by comparing the properties of skeletal muscle, smooth muscle, and cardiac muscle. We will look at the details of cardiac muscle in Chapter 14 when we study the heart. The metabolism and endocrinology of skeletal muscle are covered in Chapters 22, 23, and 25.

TABLE 12-1 Muscle Terminology

GENERAL TERM	MUSCLE EQUIVALENT
Muscle cell	Muscle fiber
Cell membrane	Sarcolemma
Cytoplasm	Sarcoplasm
Modified endoplasmic reticulum	Sarcoplasmic reticulum

SKELETAL MUSCLE

Skeletal muscles make up the bulk of muscle in the body and constitute about 40% of total body weight. They position and move the skeleton, as their name suggests. Skeletal muscles are usually attached to bones by **tendons** made of collagen [p. 81]. The **origin** of a muscle is the end of the muscle that is attached closest to the trunk or to the more stationary bone. The **insertion** of the muscle is the more *distal* [*distantia,* distant] or more mobile attachment.

When the bones attached to a muscle are connected by a flexible joint, contraction of the muscle moves the skeleton. The muscle is called a **flexor** if the centers of the connected bones are brought closer together when the muscle contracts, and the movement is called *flexion*. The muscle is called an **extensor** if the bones move away from each other when the muscle contracts, and the movement is called *extension*.

Most joints in the body have both flexor and extensor muscles, because a contracting muscle can pull a bone in one direction but cannot push it back. Flexor-extensor pairs are called **antagonistic muscle groups** because they exert opposite effects. Figure 12-2 ● shows a pair of antagonistic muscles in the arm: the *biceps brachii* [*brachion,* arm], which acts as the flexor, and the *triceps brachii,* which acts as the extensor. When you do a "dumbbell curl" with a weight in your hand, the biceps muscle contracts and the hand and forearm move toward the shoulder. When you lower the weight, the triceps contracts, and the flexed forearm moves away from the shoulder. In each case, when one muscle contracts and shortens, the antagonistic muscle must relax and lengthen.

CONCEPT CHECK

1. Identify as many pairs of antagonistic muscle groups in the body as you can. If you cannot name them, point out the probable location of the flexor and extensor of each group.

Answers: p. 444

Skeletal Muscles Are Composed of Muscle Fibers

Muscles function together as a unit. A skeletal muscle is a collection of muscle cells, or **muscle fibers**, just as a nerve is a collection of neurons. Each skeletal muscle fiber is a long, cylindrical cell with up to several hundred nuclei on the surface of the fiber (see Anatomy Summary, Fig. 12-3a ●). Skeletal muscle fibers are the largest cells in the body, created by the fusion of many individual embryonic muscle cells.

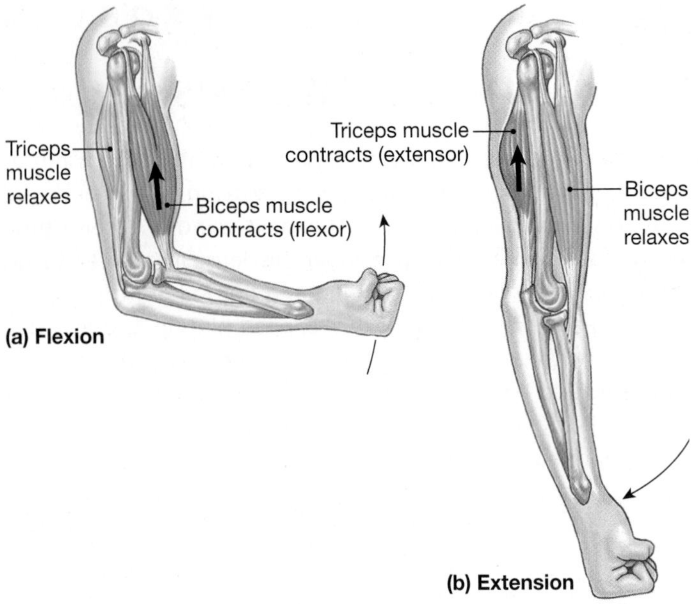

● **FIGURE 12-2** ***Antagonistic muscle groups move bones in opposite directions.*** Muscle contraction can pull on a bone but cannot push a bone away.

The fibers in a given muscle are arranged with their long axes in parallel (Fig. 12-3a). Each skeletal muscle fiber is sheathed in connective tissue, with groups of adjacent fibers bundled together into units called **fascicles**. Collagen, elastic fibers, nerves, and blood vessels are found between the fascicles. The entire muscle is enclosed in a connective tissue sheath that is continuous with the connective tissue around the muscle fibers and fascicles and with the tendons holding the muscle to underlying bones.

Muscle Fiber Anatomy Muscle physiologists, like neurobiologists, use specialized vocabulary (Tbl. 12-1 ●). The cell membrane of a muscle fiber is called the **sarcolemma** [*sarkos,* flesh + *lemma,* shell], and the cytoplasm is called the **sarcoplasm**. The main intracellular structures in striated muscles are **myofibrils** [*myo-,* muscle], highly organized bundles of contractile and elastic proteins that carry out the work of contraction.

Skeletal muscles also contain extensive **sarcoplasmic reticulum** (SR), a form of modified endoplasmic reticulum that wraps around each myofibril like a piece of lace (Figs. 12-3b, 12-4 ●). The sarcoplasmic reticulum consists of longitudinal tubules, which release Ca^{2+} ions, and the **terminal cisternae** [*cisterna,* a reservoir], enlarged regions at the ends of the tubules that concentrate and sequester Ca^{2+} [*sequestrare,* to put in the hands of a trustee]. Calcium plays a key role in contraction in all types of muscle.

The terminal cisternae are adjacent to and closely associated with a branching network of **transverse tubules**, also known as **t-tubules** (Fig. 12-4). One t-tubule and its two flanking terminal cisternae are called a *triad*. The membranes of t-tubules are a continuation of the muscle fiber membrane, which makes the lumen of t-tubules continuous with the extracellular fluid.

To understand how this network of t-tubules deep inside the muscle fiber communicates with the outside, take a lump of soft clay and poke your finger into the middle of it. Notice how the outside surface of the clay (analogous to the surface membrane of the muscle fiber) is now continuous with the sides of the hole that you poked in the clay (the membrane of the t-tubule).

T-tubules rapidly move action potentials from the cell surface into the interior of the fiber. Without t-tubules, the action potential could reach the center of the fiber only by the diffusion of positive charge through the cytosol, a slower process that would delay the response time of the muscle fiber.

The cytosol between the myofibrils contains many glycogen granules and mitochondria. Glycogen, the storage form of glucose found in animals, is a reserve source of energy. Mitochondria provide much of the ATP for muscle contraction through oxidative phosphorylation of glucose and other biomolecules.

Myofibrils Are the Contractile Structures of a Muscle Fiber

One muscle fiber contains a thousand or more myofibrils that occupy most of the intracellular volume, leaving little space for cytosol and organelles (Fig. 12-3b). Each myofibril is composed of several types of proteins: the contractile proteins *myosin* and *actin*, the regulatory proteins *tropomyosin* and *troponin*, and the giant accessory proteins *titin* and *nebulin*.

Myosin [*myo-*, muscle] is a motor protein with the ability to create movement [p. 67]. Various isoforms of myosin occur in different types of muscle and help determine the muscle's speed of contraction. Each myosin molecule is composed of protein chains that intertwine to form a long tail and a pair of tadpole-like heads (Fig. 12-3e). The rodlike tail is stiff, but the protruding myosin heads have an elastic hinge region where the heads join the rods. This hinge region allows the heads to swivel around their point of attachment.

In skeletal muscle, about 250 myosin molecules join to create a **thick filament**. Each thick filament is arranged so that the myosin heads are clustered at each end of the filament, and the central region of the filament is a bundle of myosin tails.

Actin [*actum,* to do] is a protein that makes up the **thin filaments** of the muscle fiber. One actin molecule is a globular protein (*G-actin*), represented in Figure 12-3f by a round ball. Usually, multiple G-actin molecules polymerize to form long chains or filaments, called *F-actin*. In skeletal muscle, two F-actin polymers twist together like a double strand of beads, creating the thin filaments of the myofibril.

Most of the time, the parallel thick and thin filaments of the myofibril are connected by myosin **crossbridges** that span the space between the filaments. Each G-actin molecule has a single *myosin-binding site*, and each myosin head has one actin-binding site and one binding site for ATP. Crossbridges form when the myosin heads of thick filaments bind to actin in the thin filaments (Fig. 12-3d). Crossbridges have two states: low-force (relaxed muscles) and high-force (contracting muscles).

Under a light microscope, the arrangement of thick and thin filaments in a myofibril creates a repeating pattern of alternating light and dark bands (Figs. 12-1a, 12-3c). One repeat of the pattern forms a **sarcomere** [*sarkos,* flesh + *-mere,* a unit or segment], which has the following elements (Fig. 12-5 ●):

1. **Z disks**. One sarcomere is composed of two Z disks and the filaments found between them. Z disks are zigzag protein structures that serve as the attachment site for thin filaments. The abbreviation *Z* comes from *zwischen,* the German word for "between."
2. **I band**. These are the lightest color bands of the sarcomere and represent a region occupied only by thin filaments. The abbreviation *I* comes from *isotropic,* a description from early microscopists meaning that this region reflects light uniformly under a polarizing microscope. A Z disk runs through the middle of every I band, so each half of an I band belongs to a different sarcomere.
3. **A band**. This is the darkest of the sarcomere's bands and encompasses the entire length of a thick filament. At the outer edges of the A band, the thick and thin filaments overlap. The center of the A band is occupied by thick filaments only. The abbreviation *A* comes from *anisotropic* [*an-*, not], meaning that the protein fibers in this region scatter light unevenly.
4. **H zone**. This central region of the A band is lighter than the outer edges of the A band because the H zone is occupied by thick filaments only. The *H* comes from *helles,* the German word for "clear."
5. **M line**. This band represents proteins that form the attachment site for thick filaments, equivalent to the Z disk for the thin filaments. Each M line divides an A band in half. *M* is the abbreviation for *mittel,* the German word for "middle."

In three-dimensional array, the actin and myosin molecules form a lattice of parallel, overlapping thin and thick filaments, held in place by their attachments to the Z-disk and M-line proteins, respectively (Fig. 12-5b). When viewed end-on, each thin filament is surrounded by three thick filaments, and six thin filaments encircle each thick filament (Fig. 12-5c, rightmost circle).

ANATOMY SUMMARY

SKELETAL MUSCLES

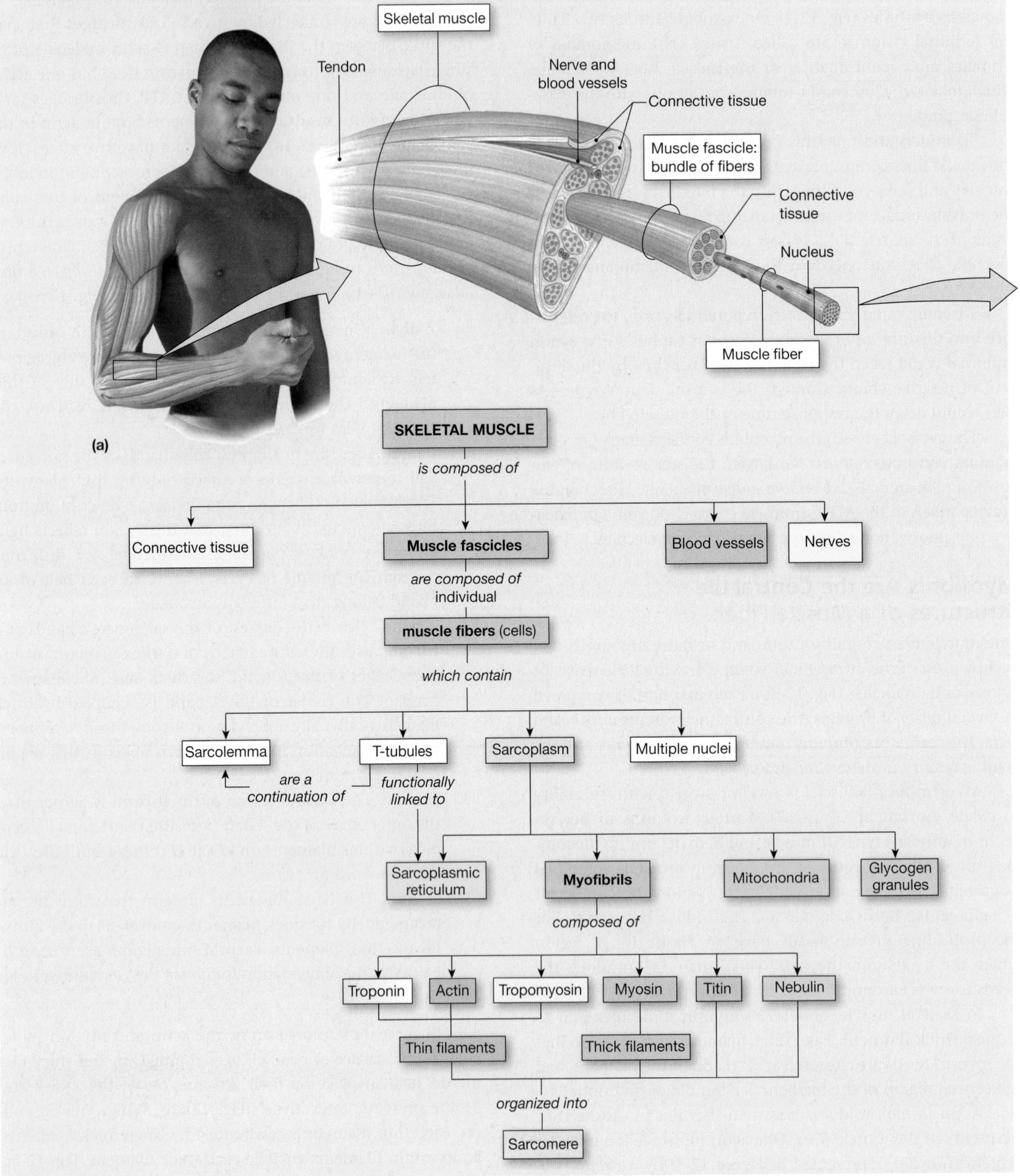

● **FIGURE 12-3**

ULTRASTRUCTURE OF MUSCLE

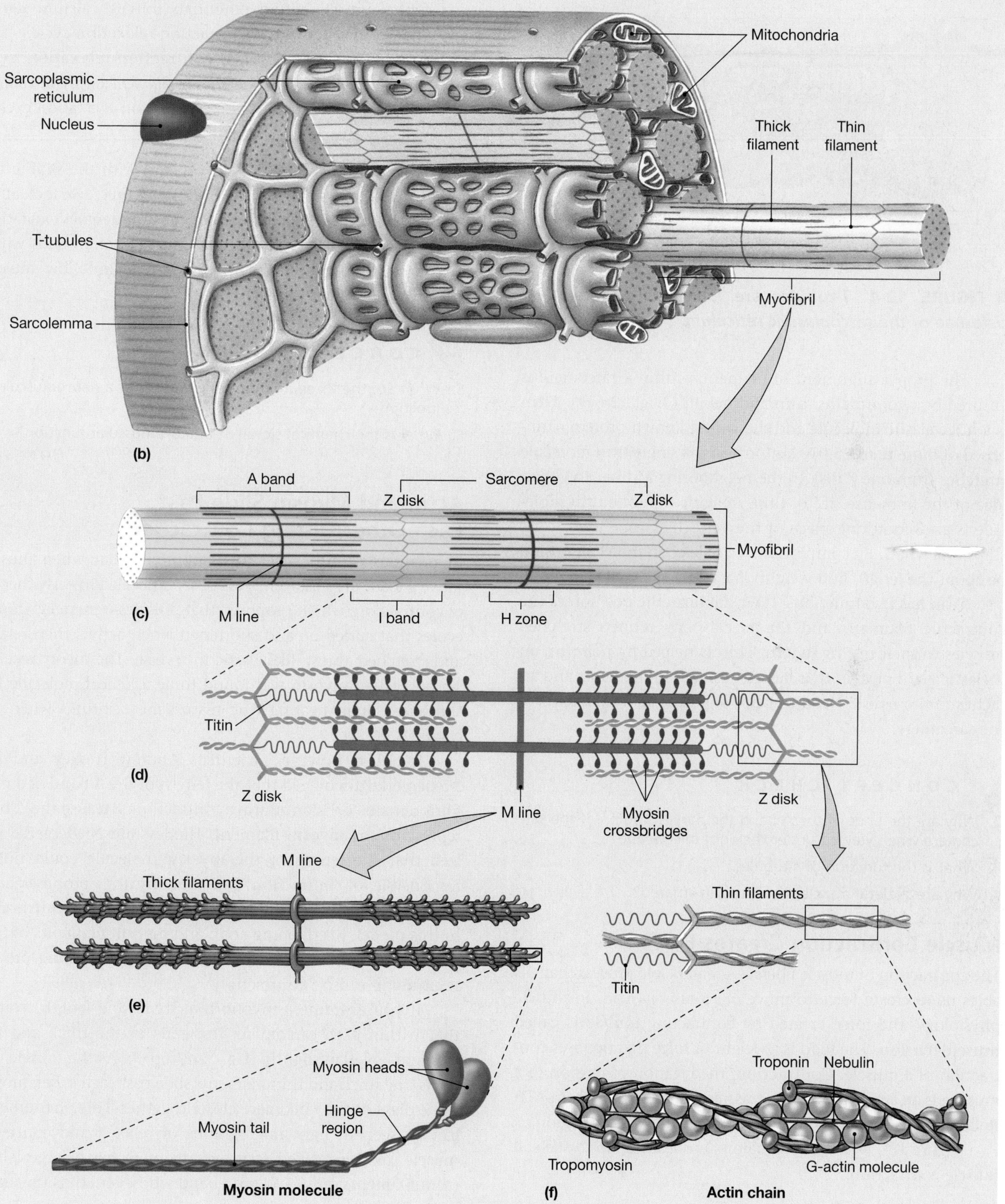

Mitochondria
Sarcoplasmic reticulum
Nucleus
Thick filament
Thin filament
T-tubules
Sarcolemma
Myofibril
(b)
A band
Sarcomere
Z disk
Z disk
Myofibril
(c)
M line
I band
H zone
Titin
(d)
Z disk
M line
Myosin crossbridges
Z disk
M line
Thick filaments
(e)
Thin filaments
Titin
Myosin heads
Hinge region
Myosin tail
Myosin molecule
Troponin
Nebulin
Tropomyosin
G-actin molecule
(f)
Actin chain

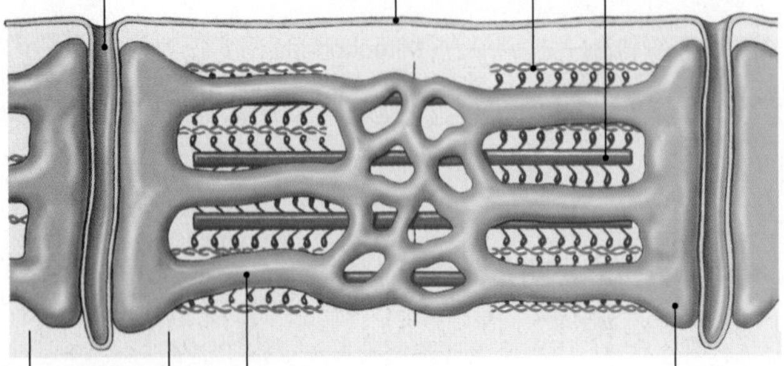

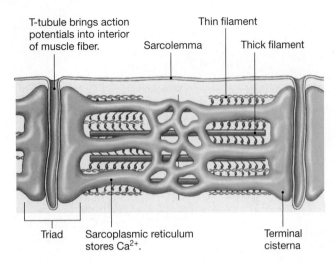

● **FIGURE 12-4** ***T-tubules are linked to the terminal cisternae of the sarcoplasmic reticulum.***

The proper alignment of filaments within a sarcomere is ensured by two proteins: titin and nebulin (Fig. 12-6 ●). **Titin** is a huge elastic molecule and the largest known protein, composed of more than 25,000 amino acids. A single titin molecule stretches from one Z disk to the neighboring M line. To get an idea of the immense size of titin, imagine that one titin molecule is an 8-foot-long piece of the very thick rope used to tie ships to a wharf. By comparison, a single actin molecule would be about the length and weight of a single eyelash.

Titin has two functions: (1) it stabilizes the position of the contractile filaments and (2) its elasticity returns stretched muscles to their resting length. Titin is helped by **nebulin**, an inelastic giant protein that lies alongside thin filaments and attaches to the Z disk. Nebulin helps align the actin filaments of the sarcomere.

CONCEPT CHECK

2. Why are the ends of the A band the darkest region of the sarcomere when viewed under the light microscope?
3. What is the function of t-tubules?
4. Why are skeletal muscles described as striated?

Answers: p. 444

Muscle Contraction Creates Force

The contraction of muscle fibers is a remarkable process that enables us to create force to move or to resist a load. In muscle physiology, the force created by contracting muscle is called **muscle tension**. The **load** is a weight or force that opposes contraction of a muscle. **Contraction**, the creation of tension in a muscle, is an active process that requires energy input from ATP. **Relaxation** is the release of tension created by a contraction.

Figure 12-7 ● maps the major steps leading up to skeletal muscle contraction.

1. **Events at the neuromuscular junction** convert an acetylcholine signal from a somatic motor neuron into an electrical signal in the muscle fiber. These events were described in Chapter 11 [p. 398].
2. **Excitation-contraction (E-C) coupling** is the process in which muscle action potentials initiate calcium signals that in turn activate a contraction-relaxation cycle.
3. At the molecular level, a **contraction-relaxation cycle** can be explained by the *sliding filament theory of contraction*. In intact muscles, one contraction-relaxation cycle is called a muscle *twitch*.

In the sections that follow, we start with the sliding filament theory for muscle contraction. From there, we look at the integrated function of a muscle fiber as it undergoes excitation-contraction coupling. The skeletal muscle section ends with a discussion of the innervation of muscles and how muscles move bones around joints.

CONCEPT CHECK

5. What are the three anatomical elements of a neuromuscular junction?
6. What is the chemical signal at a neuromuscular junction?

Answers: p. 445

Actin and Myosin Slide Past Each Other During Contraction

In previous centuries, scientists observed that when muscles move a load, they shorten. This observation led to early theories of contraction, which proposed that muscles were made of molecules that curled up and shortened when active, then relaxed and stretched at rest, like elastic in reverse. The theory received support when myosin was found to be a helical molecule that shortened upon heating (the reason meat shrinks when you cook it).

In 1954, however, scientists Andrew Huxley and Rolf Niedergerke discovered that the length of the A band of a myofibril remains constant during contraction. Because the A band represents the myosin filament, Huxley and Niedergerke realized that shortening of the myosin molecule could not be responsible for contraction. Subsequently, they proposed an alternative model, the **sliding filament theory of contraction**. In this model, overlapping actin and myosin filaments of fixed length slide past one another in an energy-requiring process, resulting in muscle contraction.

If you examine a myofibril at its resting length, you see that within each sarcomere, the ends of the thick and thin filaments overlap slightly (Fig. 12-8 top ●). As the muscle contracts, the thick and thin filaments slide past each other, moving the Z disks of the sarcomere closer together. This phenomenon can be seen in light micrographs of relaxed and contracted muscle. In the relaxed state, a sarcomere has a large I band (thin filaments only) and an A band whose length is the length of the thick filament.

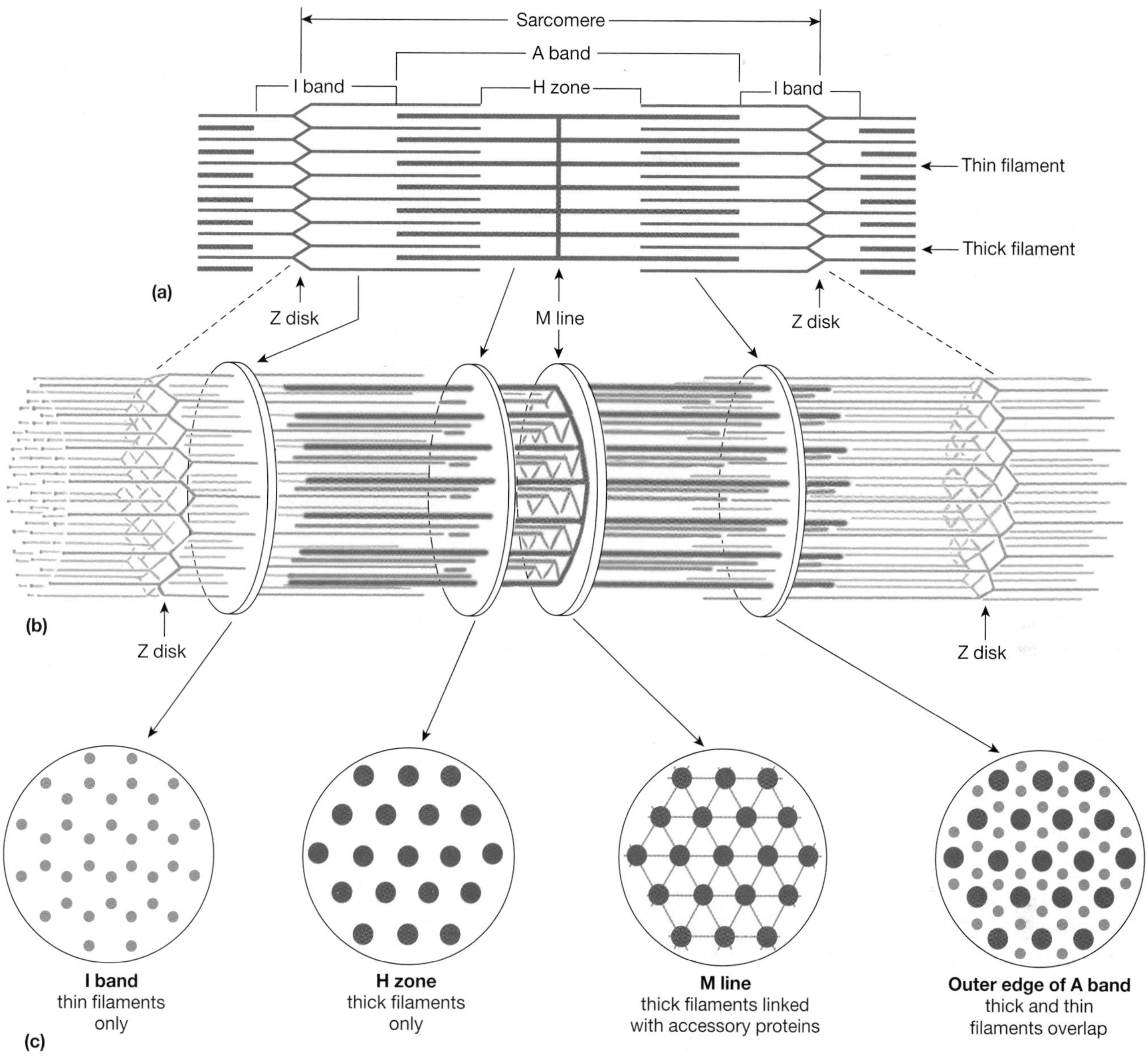

● **FIGURE 12-5** ***The two- and three-dimensional organization of a sarcomere.*** The Z disk (not shown in part c) has accessory proteins that link the thin filaments together, similar to the accessory proteins shown for the M line.

As contraction occurs, the sarcomere shortens (Fig. 12-8, bottom). The two Z disks at each end move closer together while the I band and H zone—regions where actin and myosin do not overlap in resting muscle—almost disappear. Despite shortening of the sarcomere, the length of the A band remains constant. These changes are consistent with the sliding of thin actin filaments along the thick myosin filaments as the actin filaments move toward the M line in the center of the sarcomere. It is from this process that the sliding filament theory of contraction derives its name.

The sliding filament theory explains how a muscle can contract and create force without creating movement. For example, if you push on a wall, you are creating tension in many muscles of your body without moving the wall. According to the sliding filament theory, tension generated in a muscle fiber is directly proportional to the number of high-force crossbridges between the thick and thin filaments.

Myosin Crossbridges Move Actin Filaments

The rotation of myosin crossbridges provides the force that pushes the actin filament during contraction. The process can be compared to a competitive sailing team, with many people holding the rope that raises a heavy mainsail. When the order to raise the mainsail comes, each person on the team begins pulling on the rope, hand over hand, grabbing, pulling, and releasing repeatedly as the rope moves past.

In muscle, myosin heads bind to actin molecules, which are the "rope." A calcium signal initiates the **power stroke**,

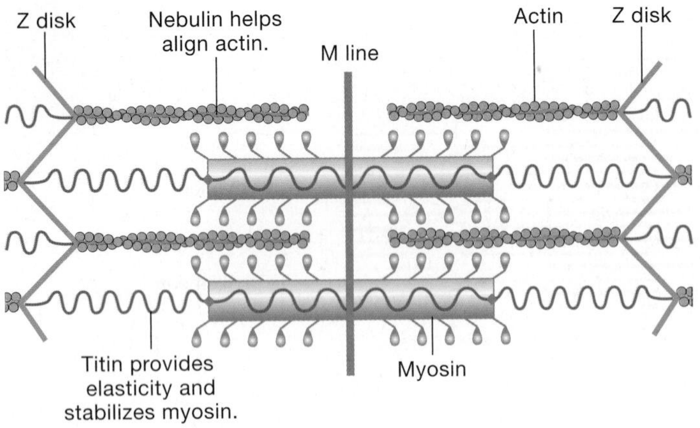

● **FIGURE 12-6** ***Titin and nebulin are giant accessory proteins.*** Titin spans the distance from one Z disk to the neighboring M line. Nebulin, lying along the thin filaments, attaches to a Z disk but does not extend to the M line.

when myosin crossbridges swivel and push the actin filaments toward the center of the sarcomere. At the end of its power stroke, each myosin head releases actin, then swivels back and binds to a new actin molecule, ready to start another contractile cycle. During contraction, the heads do not all release at the same time or the fibers would slide back to their starting position, just as the mainsail would fall if the sailors all released the rope at the same time.

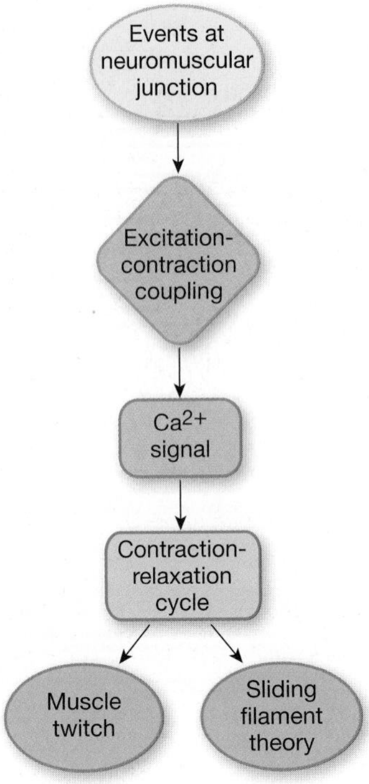

● **FIGURE 12-7** ***Summary map of muscle contraction***

N A V I G A T O R

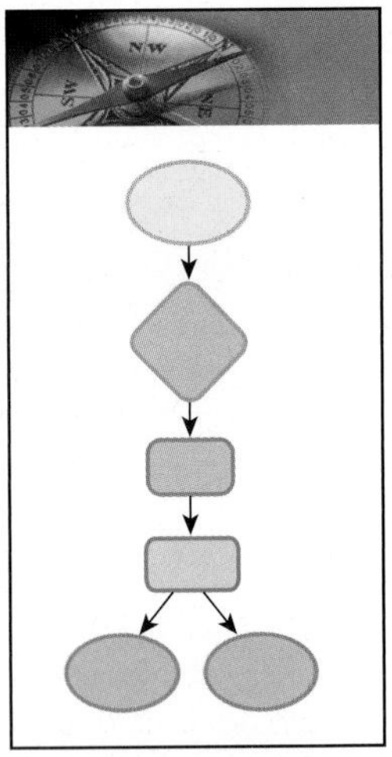

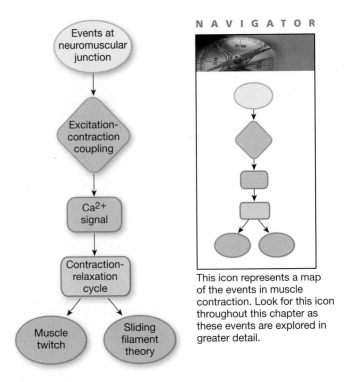

This icon represents a map of the events in muscle contraction. Look for this icon throughout this chapter as these events are explored in greater detail.

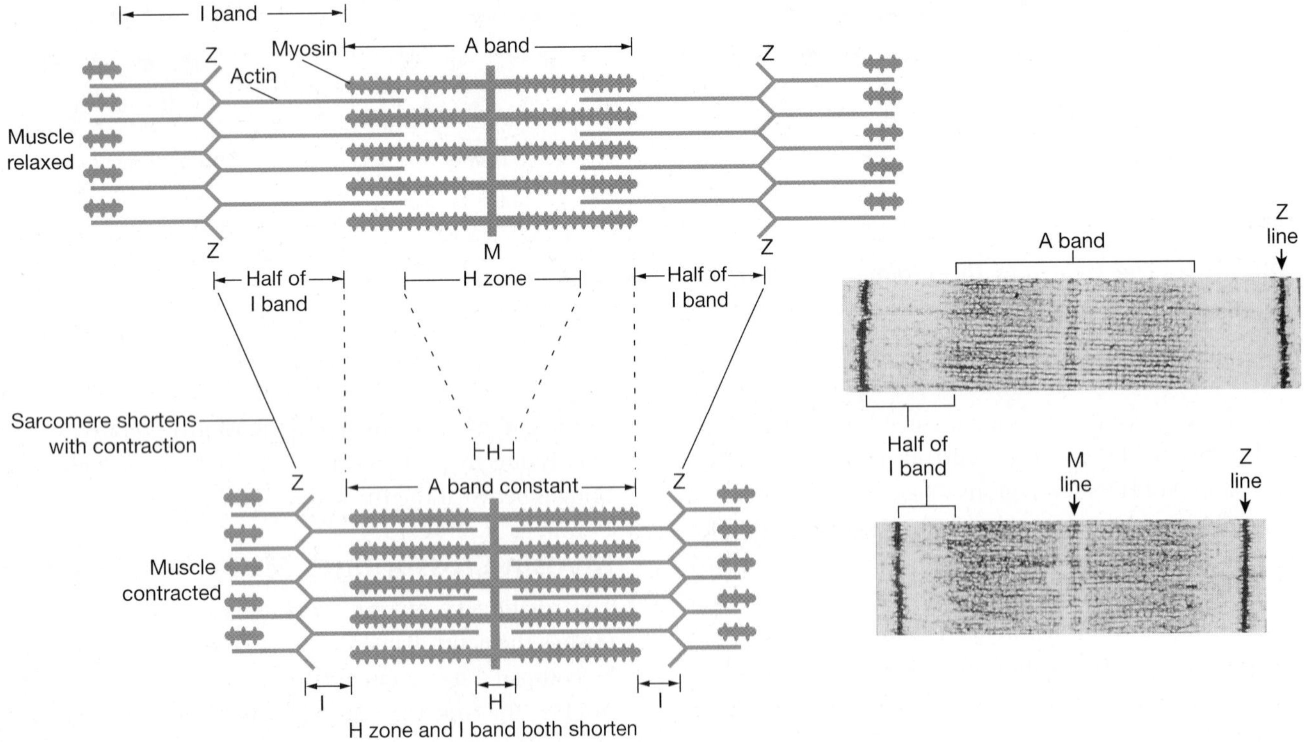

● **FIGURE 12-8** ***The sarcomere shortens during contraction.*** As contraction takes place, the thick and thin filaments do not change length but instead slide past one another.

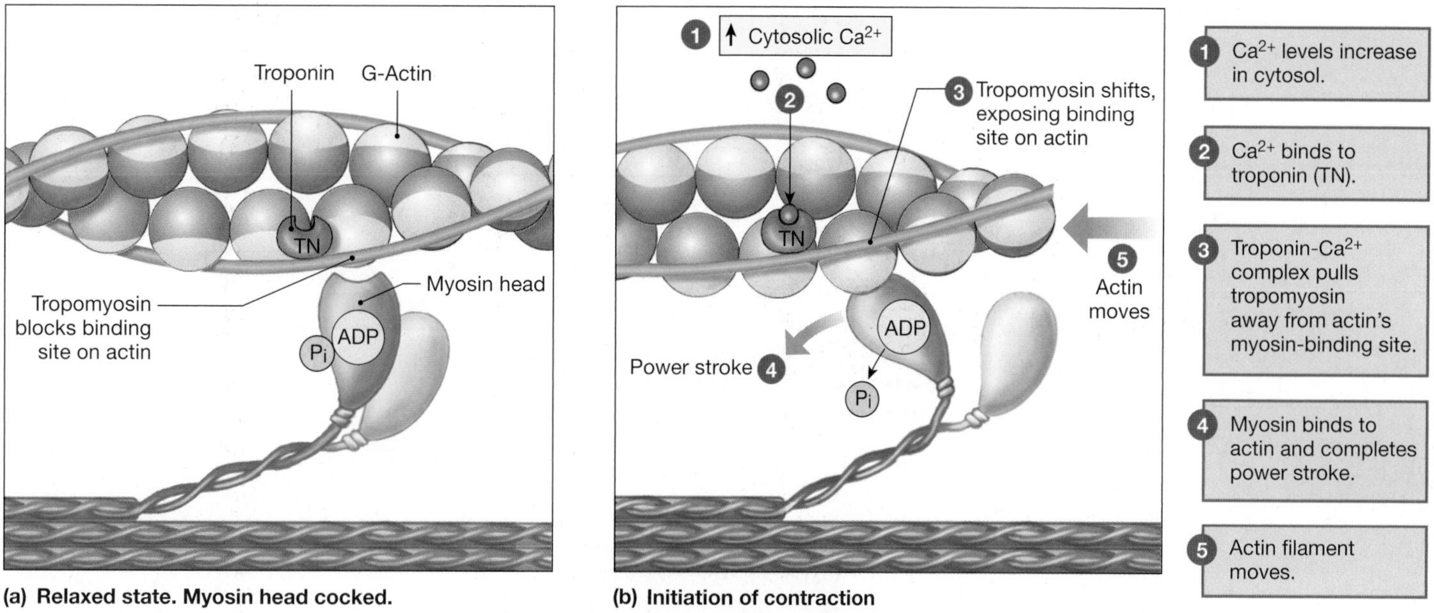
Troponin
G-Actin
TN
Myosin head
Tropomyosin blocks binding site on actin
ADP
Pi
(a) Relaxed state. Myosin head cocked.
1 ↑ Cytosolic Ca2+
2
3 Tropomyosin shifts, exposing binding site on actin
TN
5 Actin moves
ADP
Power stroke 4
Pi
(b) Initiation of contraction
1 Ca2+ levels increase in cytosol.
2 Ca2+ binds to troponin (TN).
3 Troponin-Ca2+ complex pulls tropomyosin away from actin's myosin-binding site.
4 Myosin binds to actin and completes power stroke.
5 Actin filament moves.

● **FIGURE 12-9** ***Calcium binds to troponin to initiate muscle contraction.***

The powerstroke repeats many times as a muscle fiber contracts. The myosin heads bind, push, and release actin molecules over and over as the thin filaments move toward the center of the sarcomere.

Myosin ATPase In the power stroke, what causes the myosin crossbridges to swivel? The answer is that myosin converts the chemical bond energy of ATP into the mechanical energy of crossbridge motion. Myosin is an ATPase (*myosin ATPase*), so it hydrolyzes ATP to ADP and inorganic phosphate (P_i). The energy released by ATP hydrolysis is trapped by myosin and stored as potential energy in the angle between the myosin head and the long axis of the myosin filament. Myosin heads in this position are said to be "cocked," or ready to rotate. The potential energy of the cocked heads becomes kinetic energy in the power stroke that moves actin.

Calcium Signals Initiate Contraction

How does a calcium signal turn muscle contraction on and off? The answer is found in **troponin** (TN), a calcium-binding complex of three proteins. Troponin controls the positioning of an elongated protein polymer, **tropomyosin** [*tropos,* to turn].

In resting skeletal muscle, tropomyosin wraps around actin filaments and partially covers actin's myosin-binding sites (Fig. 12-9a ●). This is tropomyosin's blocking or "off" position. Weak, low-force actin-myosin binding can still take place, but myosin is blocked from completing its power stroke, much as the safety latch on a gun keeps the cocked trigger from being pulled. Before contraction can occur, tropomyosin must be shifted to an "on" position that uncovers the remainder of actin's myosin-binding site.

The off-on positioning of tropomyosin is regulated by troponin. When contraction begins in response to a calcium signal (① in Fig. 12-9b), one protein of the complex—**troponin C**—binds reversibly to Ca^{2+} ②. The calcium-troponin C complex pulls tropomyosin completely away from actin's myosin-binding sites ③. This "on" position enables the myosin heads to form strong, high-force crossbridges and carry out their power strokes ④ , moving the actin filament ⑤. Contractile cycles repeat as long as the binding sites are uncovered.

For muscle relaxation to occur, Ca^{2+} concentrations in the cytosol must decrease. By the law of mass action, when cytosolic calcium decreases, Ca^{2+} unbinds from troponin. In the absence of Ca^{2+}, troponin allows tropomyosin to return to the "off" position, covering most of actin's myosin-binding sites. During the brief portion of the relaxation phase when actin and myosin are not bound to each other, the filaments of the sarcomere slide back to their original positions with the aid of titin and elastic connective tissues within the muscle.

In the next section we look in detail at the molecular events of the contractile cycle.

Myosin Heads Step Along Actin Filaments

Figure 12-10 ● shows the molecular events of a contractile cycle in skeletal muscle. We will start a cycle with the **rigor state** [*rigere,* to be stiff], where the myosin heads are tightly bound to G-actin molecules. No nucleotide (ATP or ADP) is bound to myosin. In living muscle, the rigor state occurs for only a very brief period. Then:

1. **ATP binds and myosin detaches.** An ATP molecule binds to the myosin head. ATP-binding decreases the actin-binding affinity of myosin, and myosin releases from actin.
2. **ATP hydrolysis provides energy for the myosin head to rotate and reattach to actin.** The ATP-binding site on

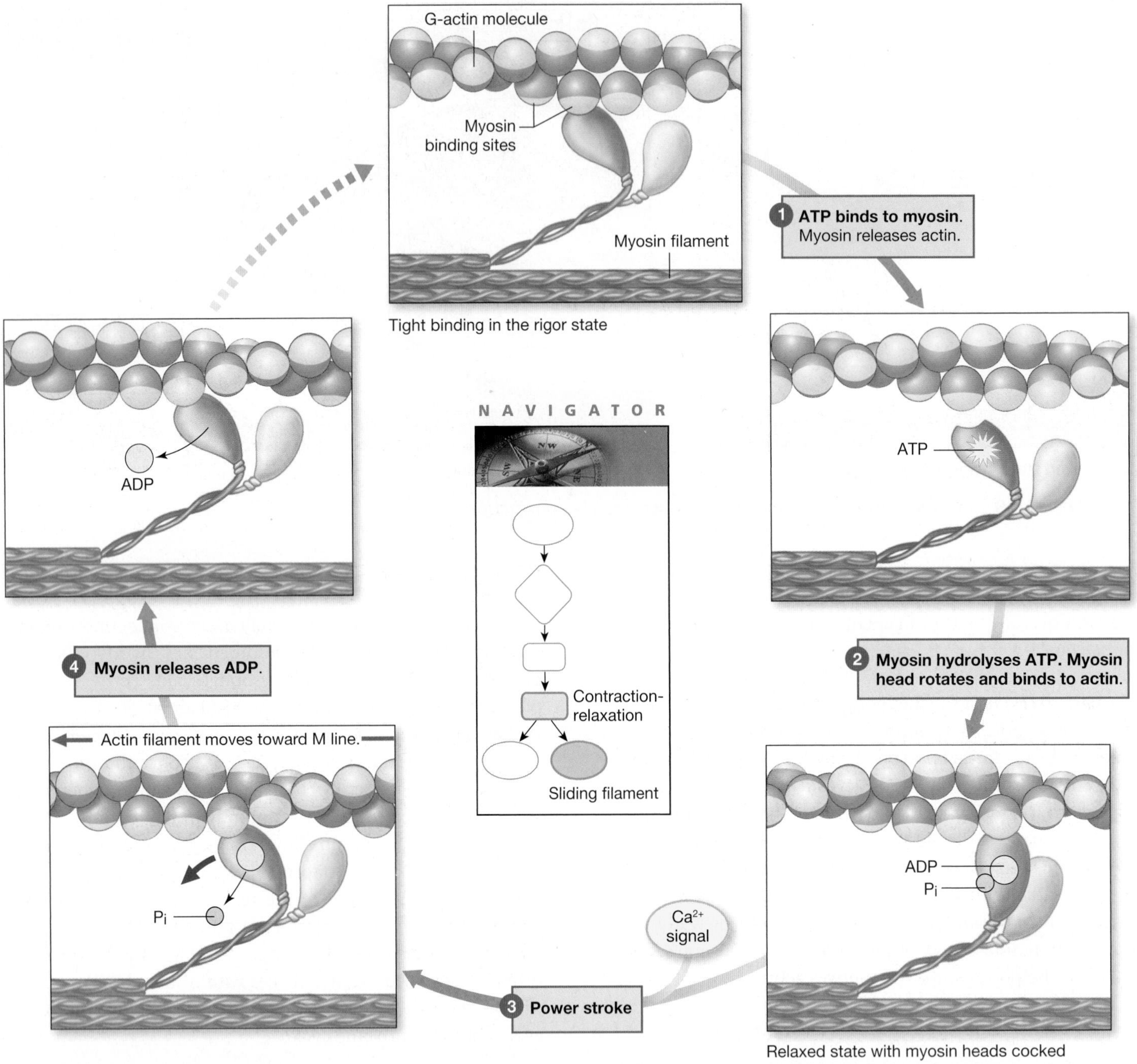

● **FIGURE 12-10** ***ATP provides energy for crossbridge tilting and the power stroke.*** To review actin and myosin structure, see Figure 12-3(d–f).

the myosin head closes around ATP and hydrolyzes it to ADP and inorganic phosphate (P_i). Both ADP and P_i remain bound to myosin as energy released by ATP hydrolysis rotates the myosin head until it forms a 90° angle with the long axis of the filaments. In this cocked position, myosin binds to a new actin that is 1–3 molecules away from where it started.

The newly formed actin-myosin crossbridge is weak and low-force because tropomyosin is partially blocking actin's binding site. However, in this rotated position myosin has stored potential energy, like a stretched spring. The head is cocked, just as someone preparing to fire a gun pulls back or cocks the spring-loaded hammer before firing. Most resting muscle fibers are in this state, cocked and prepared to contract, and just waiting for a calcium signal.

3. **The power stroke.** The power stroke (*crossbridge tilting*) begins after Ca^{2+} binds to troponin to uncover the rest of the myosin-binding site. The crossbridges transform into strong, high-force bonds as myosin releases P_i. Release of P_i allows the myosin head to swivel. The heads swing toward the M line, sliding the attached actin filament along with

them. The power stroke is also called crossbridge tilting because the myosin head and hinge region tilt from a 90° angle to a 45° angle.

4. **Myosin releases ADP.** At the end of the power stroke, myosin releases ADP, the second product of ATP hydrolysis. With ADP gone, the myosin head is again tightly bound to actin in the rigor state. The cycle is ready to begin once more as a new ATP binds to myosin.

The Rigor State Although the contractile cycle began with the rigor state in which no ATP or ADP was bound to myosin, relaxed muscle fibers remain mostly in step 2. The rigor state in living muscle is normally brief because the muscle fiber has a sufficient supply of ATP that quickly binds to myosin once ADP is released in step 4.

After death, however, when metabolism stops and ATP supplies are exhausted, muscles are unable to bind more ATP, so they remain in the tightly bound rigor state. In the condition known as *rigor mortis,* the muscles "freeze" owing to immovable crossbridges. The tight binding of actin and myosin persists for a day or so after death, until enzymes within the decaying fiber begin to break down the muscle proteins.

CONCEPT CHECK

7. Each myosin molecule has binding sites for what molecules?
8. What is the difference between F-actin and G-actin?
9. Myosin hydrolyzes ATP to ADP and P_i. Enzymes that hydrolyze ATP are collectively known as ________.

Answers: p. 445

Although the preceding discussion sounds as if we know everything there is to know about the molecular basis of muscle contraction, in reality this is simply our current model. The process is more complex than presented here, and it now appears that myosin can influence Ca^{2+}-troponin binding, depending on whether the myosin is bound to actin in a strong (rigor) state, bound to actin in a weak state, or not bound at all. The details of this influence are still being worked out.

Studying contraction and the movement of molecules in a myofibril has proved very difficult. Many research techniques rely on crystallized molecules, electron microscopy, and other tools that cannot be used with living tissues. Often we can see the thick and thin filaments only at the beginning and end of contraction. Progress is being made, however, and perhaps in the next decade you will see a "movie" of muscle contraction, constructed from photographs of sliding filaments.

CONCEPT CHECK

10. Name an elastic fiber in the sarcomere that aids relaxation.
11. In the sliding filament theory of contraction, what prevents the filaments from sliding back to their original position each time a myosin head releases to bind to the next actin binding site?

Answers: p. 445

BIOTECHNOLOGY

THE *IN VITRO* MOTILITY ASSAY

One big step forward in understanding the power stroke of myosin was the development of the *in vitro* motility assay in the 1980s. In this assay, isolated myosin molecules are randomly bonded to a specially coated glass coverslip. A fluorescently labeled actin molecule is placed on top of the myosin molecules. With ATP as a source of energy, the myosin heads bind to the actin and move it across the coverslip, marked by a fluorescent trail as it goes. In even more ingenious experiments, developed in 1995, a single myosin molecule is bound to a tiny bead that elevates it above the surface of the cover slip. An actin molecule is placed on top of the myosin molecule, like the balancing pole of a tightrope walker. As the myosin "motor" moves the actin molecule, lasers measure the nanometer movements and piconewton forces created with each cycle of the myosin head. Because of this technique, researchers can now measure the mechanical work being done by a single myosin molecule! For an animation and movie of the process, visit *http://physiology.med.uvm.edu/warshaw/TechspgInVitro.html.*

Acetylcholine Initiates Excitation-Contraction Coupling

Now let's start at the neuromuscular junction and follow the events leading up to contraction. As you learned earlier in the chapter, this combination of electrical and mechanical events in a muscle fiber is called *excitation-contraction coupling.* E-C coupling has four major events:

1. Acetylcholine (ACh) is released from the somatic motor neuron.
2. ACh initiates an action potential in the muscle fiber.
3. The muscle action potential triggers calcium release from the sarcoplasmic reticulum.
4. Calcium combines with troponin and initiates contraction.

Now let's look at these steps in detail. Acetylcholine released into the synapse at a neuromuscular junction binds to ACh receptor-channels on the motor end plate of the muscle fiber (Fig. 12-11 ① ●) [p. 399]. When these channels open, they allow both Na^+ and K^+ to cross the membrane. However, Na^+ influx exceeds K^+ efflux because the electrochemical driving force is greater for Na^+ [p. 168]. The addition of net positive charge to the muscle fiber depolarizes the membrane, creating an **end-plate potential (EPP)**. Normally, end-plate potentials always reach threshold and initiate a muscle action potential (Fig. 12-11a ②).

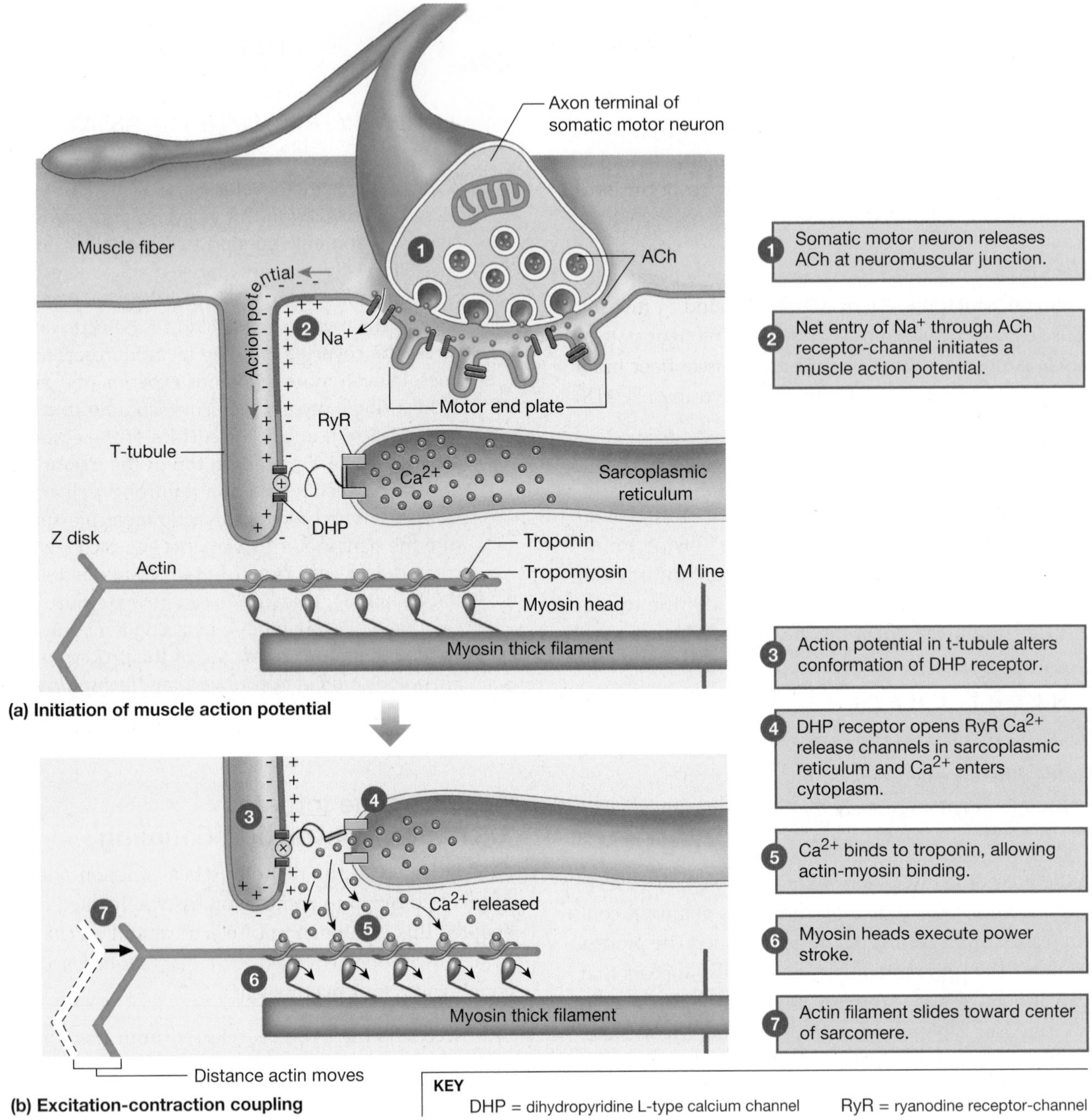

Axon terminal of somatic motor neuron
Muscle fiber
Action potential
ACh
Na+
Motor end plate
RyR
T-tubule
Ca2+
Sarcoplasmic reticulum
DHP
Z disk
Actin
Troponin
Tropomyosin
M line
Myosin head
Myosin thick filament
(a) Initiation of muscle action potential
Ca2+ released
Myosin thick filament
Distance actin moves
(b) Excitation-contraction coupling
1 Somatic motor neuron releases ACh at neuromuscular junction.
2 Net entry of Na+ through ACh receptor-channel initiates a muscle action potential.
3 Action potential in t-tubule alters conformation of DHP receptor.
4 DHP receptor opens RyR Ca2+ release channels in sarcoplasmic reticulum and Ca2+ enters cytoplasm.
5 Ca2+ binds to troponin, allowing actin-myosin binding.
6 Myosin heads execute power stroke.
7 Actin filament slides toward center of sarcomere.
KEY
DHP = dihydropyridine L-type calcium channel
RyR = ryanodine receptor-channel

FIGURE 12-11 ***Excitation-contraction coupling converts an electrical signal into a calcium signal.***

The action potential is conducted across the surface of the muscle fiber and into the t-tubules by the sequential opening of voltage-gated Na^+ channels. The process is similar to the conduction of action potentials in axons, although action potentials in skeletal muscle are conducted more slowly than action potentials in neurons [p. 258].

The action potential that moves down the t-tubules causes Ca^{2+} release from the sarcoplasmic reticulum (Fig. 12-11 ③ and ④). Free cytosolic Ca^{2+} levels in a resting muscle are normally quite low, but after an action potential, they increase about 100-fold. As you've learned, when cytosolic Ca^{2+} levels are high, Ca^{2+} binds to troponin, tropomyosin moves to the "on" position, and contraction occurs ⑤.

At the molecular level, transduction of the electrical signal into a calcium signal requires two key membrane proteins. The t-tubule membrane contains a type of voltage-sensing **L-type calcium channel** called a **dihydropyridine (DHP) receptor** (Fig. 12-11 ③). The specialized DHP receptors usually do not form open channels but instead are mechanically linked to **Ca^{2+} release channels** in the adjacent sarcoplasmic reticulum. The Ca^{2+} release channels are also known as **ryanodine receptors**, or **RyR**.

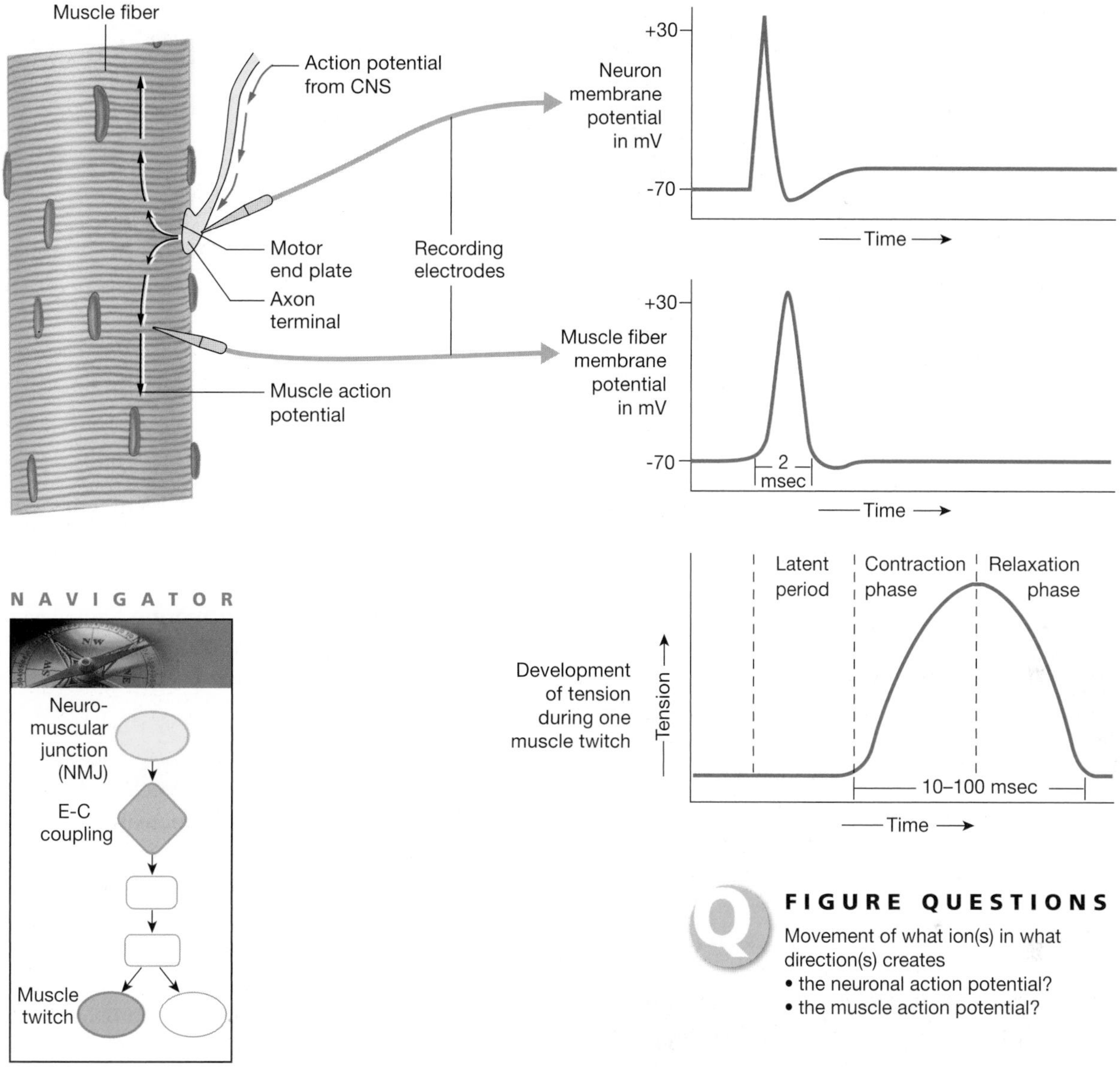

FIGURE QUESTIONS

Movement of what ion(s) in what direction(s) creates
- the neuronal action potential?
- the muscle action potential?

● **FIGURE 12-12** ***Electrical and mechanical events in muscle contraction.*** Action potentials in the axon terminal (top graph) and in the muscle fiber (middle graph) are followed by a muscle twitch (bottom graph).

When the depolarization of an action potential reaches a DHP receptor, the receptor changes conformation. The conformation change opens the RyR Ca^{2+} release channels in the sarcoplasmic reticulum (Fig. 12-11 ④). Stored Ca^{2+} then flows down its electrochemical gradient into the cytosol, where it initiates contraction, as depicted in Figure 12-9b.

To end the contraction, the sarcoplasmic reticulum pumps Ca^{2+} back into its lumen using a **Ca^{2+}-ATPase** [p. 147]. As the free cytosolic Ca^{2+} concentration decreases, the equilibrium between bound and unbound Ca^{2+} is disturbed. Calcium releases from troponin, which allows tropomyosin to slide back and block actin's myosin-binding site. As crossbridges release, the muscle fiber relaxes.

The discovery that Ca^{2+}, not the action potential, is the signal for contraction was the first piece of evidence suggesting that calcium acts as a messenger inside cells. Initially scientists thought that calcium signals occurred only in muscles, but we now know that calcium is an almost universal second messenger [p. 190].

The graphs in Figure 12-12 ● show the timing of electrical and mechanical events during E-C coupling. The somatic motor neuron action potential is followed by the skeletal muscle action potential, which in turn is followed by contraction. A single contraction-relaxation cycle in a skeletal muscle fiber is known as a **twitch**. Notice that there is a short delay—the **latent period**—between the muscle action potential and the beginning of muscle tension development. This delay represents the time required for E-C coupling to take place.

Once contraction begins, muscle tension increases steadily to a maximum value as crossbridge interaction increases.

Tension then decreases in the relaxation phase of the twitch. During relaxation, elastic elements of the muscle return the sarcomeres to their resting length.

A single action potential in a muscle fiber evokes a single twitch (Fig. 12-12, bottom graph). However, muscle twitches vary from fiber to fiber in the speed with which they develop tension (the rising slope of the twitch curve), the maximum tension they achieve (the height of the twitch curve), and the duration of the twitch (the width of the twitch curve). You will learn about factors that affect these parameters in upcoming sections. First we discuss how muscles produce ATP to provide energy for contraction and relaxation.

CONCEPT CHECK

12. Which part of contraction requires ATP? Does relaxation require ATP?
13. What events are taking place during the latent period before contraction begins? Answers: p. 445

Skeletal Muscle Contraction Requires a Steady Supply of ATP

The muscle fiber's use of ATP is a key feature of muscle physiology. Muscles require energy constantly: during contraction for crossbridge movement and release, during relaxation to pump Ca^{2+} back into the sarcoplasmic reticulum, and after E-C coupling to restore Na^+ and K^+ to the extracellular and intracellular compartments, respectively. Where do muscles get the ATP they need for this work?

RUNNING PROBLEM

Paul had experienced mild attacks of muscle weakness in his legs before, usually in the morning. Twice the weakness had come on after exposure to cold. Each attack had disappeared within minutes, and Paul seemed to suffer no lasting effects. On the advice of Paul's family doctor, Mrs. Leong takes her son to see a specialist in muscle disorders, who suspects a condition called periodic paralysis. The periodic paralyses are a family of disorders caused by Na^+ or Ca^{2+} ion channel mutations in the membranes of skeletal muscle fibers. The specialist believes that Paul has a condition in which defective voltage-gated Na^+ channels fail to inactivate after they open.

Question 1:
When Na^+ channels on the muscle membrane open, which way does Na^+ move?

Question 2:
What effect would continued movement of Na^+ have on the membrane potential of muscle fibers?

407
420
422
431
433
440

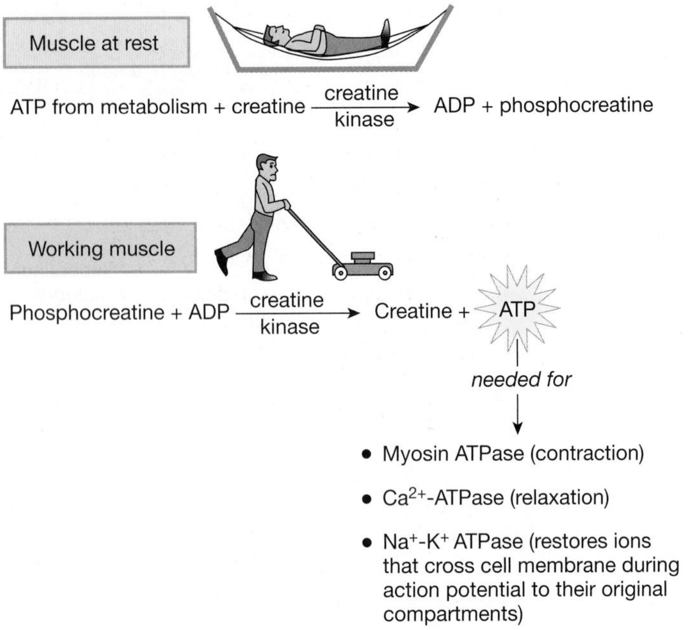
Muscle at rest
ATP from metabolism + creatine → (creatine kinase) ADP + phosphocreatine
Working muscle
Phosphocreatine + ADP → (creatine kinase) Creatine + ATP
needed for
• Myosin ATPase (contraction)
• Ca2+-ATPase (relaxation)
• Na+-K+ ATPase (restores ions that cross cell membrane during action potential to their original compartments)

FIGURE 12-13 ***Phosphocreatine.*** Resting muscle stores energy from ATP in the high-energy phosphate bonds of phosphocreatine. Working muscle then uses that stored energy.

The amount of ATP in a muscle fiber at any one time is sufficient for only about eight twitches. As a backup energy source, muscles contain **phosphocreatine**, a molecule whose high-energy phosphate bonds are created from creatine and ATP when muscles are at rest (Fig. 12-13 ●). When muscles become active, such as during exercise, the high-energy phosphate group of phosphocreatine is transferred to ADP, creating more ATP to power the muscles.

The enzyme that transfers the phosphate group from phosphocreatine to ADP is **creatine kinase** (CK), also known as *creatine phosphokinase* (CPK). Muscle cells contain large amounts of this enzyme. Consequently, elevated blood levels of creatine kinase usually indicate damage to skeletal or cardiac muscle. Because the two muscle types contain different isozymes [p. 100], clinicians can distinguish cardiac tissue damage during a heart attack from skeletal muscle damage.

Energy stored in high-energy phosphate bonds is very limited, so muscle fibers must use metabolism to transfer energy from the chemical bonds of nutrients to ATP. Carbohydrates, particularly glucose, are the most rapid and efficient source of energy for ATP production. Glucose is metabolized through glycolysis to pyruvate [p. 107]. In the presence of adequate oxygen, pyruvate goes into the citric acid cycle, producing about 30 ATP for each molecule of glucose.

When oxygen concentrations fall during strenuous exercise, muscle fiber metabolism relies more on *anaerobic glycolysis*. In this pathway, glucose is metabolized to lactate with a yield of only 2 ATP per glucose [p. 109]. Anaerobic metabolism of glucose is a quicker source of ATP but produces many fewer ATP per glucose. When muscle energy demands outpace the amount of ATP that can be produced through anaerobic metabolism of glucose, muscles can function for only a short time without fatiguing.

Muscle fibers also obtain energy from fatty acids, although this process always requires oxygen. During rest and light exercise, skeletal muscles burn fatty acids along with glucose, one reason that modest exercise programs of brisk walking are an effective way to reduce body fat. However, *beta-oxidation*—the process by which fatty acids are converted to acetyl CoA [p. 115]—is a slow process and cannot produce ATP rapidly enough to meet the energy needs of muscle fibers during heavy exercise. Under these conditions, muscle fibers rely more on glucose.

Proteins normally are not a source of energy for muscle contraction. Most amino acids found in muscle fibers are used to synthesize proteins rather than to produce ATP.

Do muscles ever run out of ATP? You might think so if you have ever exercised to the point of fatigue, the point at which you feel that you cannot continue or your limbs refuse to obey commands from your brain. Most studies show, however, that even intense exercise uses only 30% of the ATP in a muscle fiber. The condition we call fatigue must come from other changes in the exercising muscle.

CONCEPT CHECK

14. According to the convention for naming enzymes, what does the name *creatine kinase* tell you about this enzyme's function? [*Hint:* p. 103]
15. The reactions in Figure 12-13 show that creatine kinase catalyzes the creatine-phosphocreatine reaction in both directions. What then determines the direction that the reaction goes at any given moment? [*Hint:* p. 102]

Answers: p. 445

Fatigue Has Multiple Causes

The physiological term **fatigue** describes a reversible condition in which a muscle is no longer able to generate or sustain the expected power output. Fatigue is highly variable. It is influenced by the intensity and duration of the contractile activity, by whether the muscle fiber is using aerobic or anaerobic metabolism, by the composition of the muscle, and by the fitness level of the individual. The study of fatigue is quite complex, and research in this area is complicated by the fact that experiments are done under a wide range of conditions, from "skinned" (sarcolemma removed) single muscle fibers to exercising humans.

Factors that have been proposed to play a role in fatigue are classified into **central fatigue** mechanisms, which arise in the central nervous system, and **peripheral fatigue** mechanisms, which arise anywhere between the neuromuscular junction and the contractile elements of the muscle (Fig. 12-14 ●). Most experimental evidence suggests that muscle fatigue arises from excitation-contraction failure in the muscle fiber rather than from failure of control neurons or neuromuscular transmission.

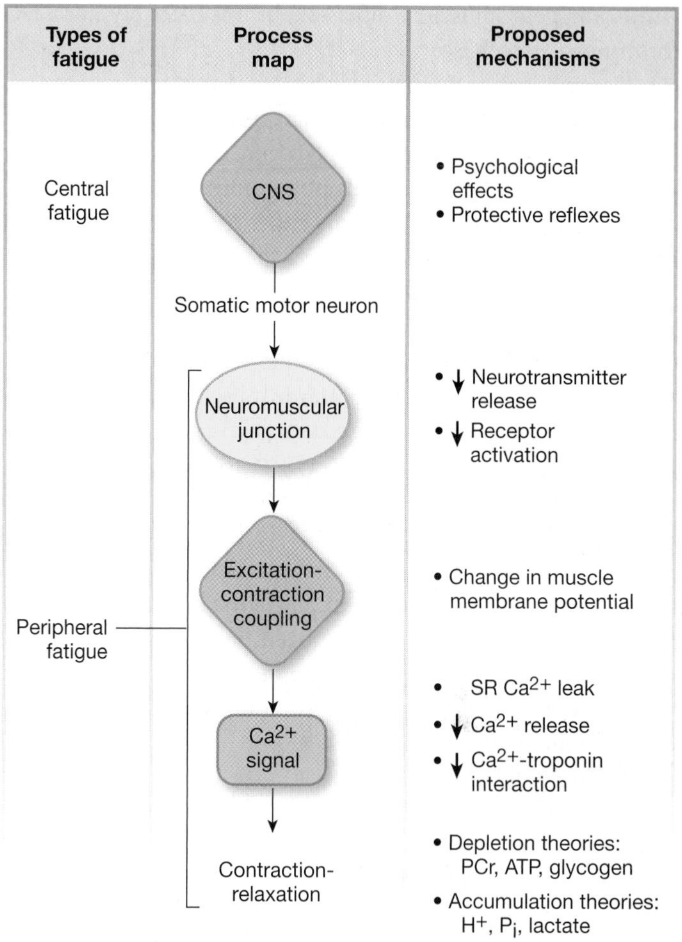

● **FIGURE 12-14** ***Locations and possible causes of muscle fatigue.*** In recent years, research indicated that lactate accumulation is no longer a likely cause of fatigue. A new theory that sarcoplasmic Ca^{2+} leaks cause fatigue has emerged.

Central fatigue includes subjective feelings of tiredness and a desire to cease activity. Several studies have shown that this psychological fatigue precedes physiological fatigue in the muscles and therefore may be a protective mechanism. Low pH from acid production during ATP hydrolysis is often mentioned as a possible cause of fatigue, and some evidence suggests that acidosis may influence the sensation of fatigue perceived by the brain. However, homeostatic mechanisms for pH balance maintain blood pH at normal levels until exertion is nearly maximal, so pH as a factor in central fatigue probably applies only in cases of maximal exertion.

Neural causes of fatigue could arise either from communication failure at the neuromuscular junction or from failure of the CNS command neurons. For example, if ACh is not synthesized in the axon terminal fast enough to keep up with neuron firing rate, neurotransmitter release at the synapse decreases. Consequently, the muscle end-plate potential fails to reach the threshold value needed to trigger a muscle fiber action potential, resulting in contraction failure. This type of fatigue is associated with some neuromuscular diseases, but it is probably not a factor in normal exercise.

Fatigue within the muscle fiber can occur in any of several sites. In extended submaximal exertion, fatigue is associated with the depletion of muscle glycogen stores. Because most studies show that lack of ATP is not a limiting factor, glycogen depletion may be affecting some other aspect of contraction, such as the release of Ca^{2+} from the sarcoplasmic reticulum.

The cause of fatigue in short-duration maximal exertion seems to be different. One theory is based on the increased levels of inorganic phosphate (P_i) produced when ATP and phosphocreatine are used for energy in the muscle fiber. Elevated cytoplasmic P_i may slow P_i release from myosin and thereby alter the power stroke (see Fig. 12-10 ③). Another theory suggests that elevated phosphate levels decrease Ca^{2+} release because the phosphate combines with Ca^{2+} to become calcium phosphate. Some investigators feel that alterations in Ca^{2+} release from the sarcoplasmic reticulum play a major role in fatigue.

Ion imbalances have also been implicated in fatigue. During maximal exercise, K^+ leaves the muscle fiber with each action potential, and as a result K^+ concentrations rise in the extracellular fluid of the t-tubules. The shift in K^+ alters the membrane potential of the muscle fiber. Changes in Na^+-K^+-ATPase activity may also be involved. In short, although many different factors have been *associated with* fatigue, the factors that *cause* fatigue are still uncertain.

CONCEPT CHECK

16. If K^+ concentration increases in the extracellular fluid surrounding a cell but does not change significantly in the cell's cytoplasm, the cell membrane _________ (*depolarizes/hyperpolarizes*) and becomes _________ (*more/less*) negative.

Answers: p. 445

Skeletal Muscle Is Classified by Speed and Resistance to Fatigue

Skeletal muscle fibers have traditionally been classified on the basis of their speed of contraction and their resistance to fatigue with repeated stimulation. But like so much in physiology, the more scientists learn, the more complicated the picture becomes. Muscles have plasticity and can shift their type depending on their activity. The currently accepted muscle fiber types include **slow-twitch fibers** (also called *ST* or *type I*), **fast-twitch oxidative-glycolytic fibers** (*FOG* or *type IIA*), and **fast-twitch glycolytic fibers** (*FG* or *type IIB*).

Fast-twitch muscle fibers (type II) develop tension two to three times faster than slow-twitch fibers (type I). The speed with which a muscle fiber contracts is determined by the isoform of myosin ATPase present in the fiber's thick filaments. Fast-twitch fibers split ATP more rapidly and can therefore complete multiple contractile cycles more rapidly than slow-twitch fibers. This speed translates into faster tension development in the fast-twitch fibers.

The duration of contraction also varies according to fiber type. Twitch duration is determined largely by how fast the sarcoplasmic reticulum removes Ca^{2+} from the cytosol. As cytosolic Ca^{2+} concentrations fall, Ca^{2+} unbinds from troponin, allowing tropomyosin to move into position to partially block the myosin-binding sites. With the power stroke inhibited in this way, the muscle fiber relaxes.

Fast-twitch fibers pump Ca^{2+} into their sarcoplasmic reticulum more rapidly than slow-twitch fibers do, so fast-twitch fibers have quicker twitches. The twitches in fast-twitch fibers last only about 7.5 msec, making these muscles useful for fine, quick movements, such as playing the piano. Contractions in slow-twitch muscle fibers may last more than 10 times as long. Fast-twitch fibers are used occasionally, but slow-twitch fibers are used almost constantly for maintaining posture, standing, or walking.

The second major difference between muscle fiber types is their ability to resist fatigue. Glycolytic fibers (fast-twitch type IIB) rely primarily on anaerobic glycolysis to produce ATP. However, the accumulation of H^+ from ATP hydrolysis contributes to acidosis, a condition implicated in the development of fatigue, as noted previously. As a result, glycolytic fibers fatigue more easily than do oxidative fibers, which do not depend on anaerobic metabolism.

Oxidative fibers rely primarily on oxidative phosphorylation [p. 112] for production of ATP—hence their descriptive name. These fibers, which include slow-twitch fibers and fast-twitch oxidative-glycolytic fibers, have more mitochondria (the site of enzymes for the citric acid cycle and oxidative phosphorylation) than glycolytic fibers do. They also have more blood vessels in their connective tissue to bring oxygen to the cells (Fig. 12-15 ●).

RUNNING PROBLEM

Two forms of periodic paralysis exist. One form, called *hypokalemic periodic paralysis,* is characterized by decreased blood levels of K^+ during paralytic episodes. The other form, *hyperkalemic periodic paralysis (hyperKPP)*, is characterized by either normal or increased blood levels of K^+ during episodes. Results of a blood test revealed that Paul has the hyperkalemic form.

Question 3:

In people with hyperKPP, attacks may occur after a period of exercise (that is, after a period of repeated muscle contractions). What ion is responsible for the repolarization phase of the muscle action potential, and in which direction does this ion move across the muscle fiber membrane? How might this be linked to hyperKPP?

407 420 422 431 433 440

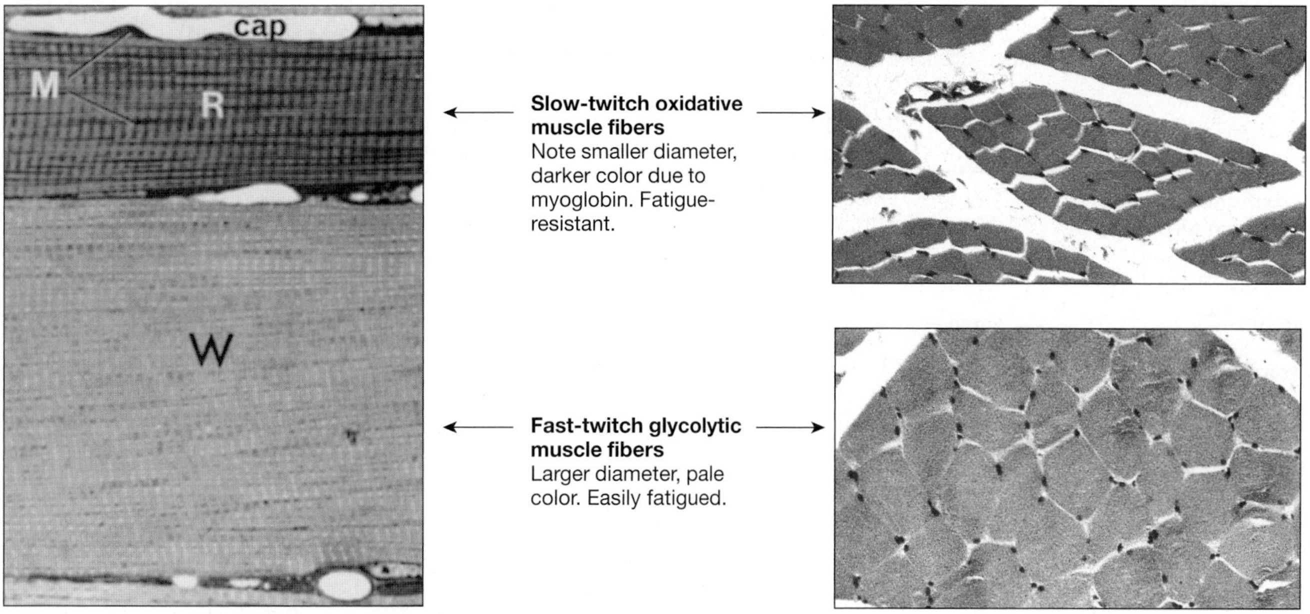

● **FIGURE 12-15** ***Fast-twitch glycolytic and slow-twitch oxidative muscle fibers.*** Slow-twitch oxidative muscle (labeled R here for red muscle) has large amounts of red myoglobin, numerous mitochondria (M), and extensive capillary blood supply (cap), in contrast to fast-twitch glycolytic muscle (labeled W for white muscle).

The efficiency with which muscle fibers obtain oxygen is a factor in their preferred method of glucose metabolism. Oxygen in the blood must diffuse into the interior of muscle fibers in order to reach the mitochondria. This process is facilitated by the presence of **myoglobin**, a red oxygen-binding pigment with a high affinity for oxygen. This affinity allows myoglobin to act as a transfer molecule, bringing oxygen more rapidly to the interior of the fibers. Because oxidative fibers contain more myoglobin, oxygen diffusion is faster than in glycolytic fibers. Oxidative fibers are described as *red muscle* because large amounts of myoglobin give them their characteristic color.

In addition to myoglobin, oxidative fibers have smaller diameters, so the distance through which oxygen must diffuse before reaching the mitochondria is shorter. Because oxidative fibers have more myoglobin and more capillaries to bring blood to the cells and are smaller in diameter, they maintain a better supply of oxygen and are able to use oxidative phosphorylation for ATP production.

Glycolytic fibers, in contrast, are described as *white muscle* because of their lower myoglobin content. These muscle fibers are also larger in diameter than slow-twitch fibers. The combination of larger size, less myoglobin, and fewer blood vessels means that glycolytic fibers are more likely to run out of oxygen after repeated contractions. Glycolytic fibers therefore rely primarily on anaerobic glycolysis for ATP synthesis and fatigue most rapidly.

Fast-twitch oxidative-glycolytic fibers exhibit properties of both oxidative and glycolytic fibers. They are smaller than fast-twitch glycolytic fibers and use a combination of oxidative and glycolytic metabolism to produce ATP. Because of their intermediate size and the use of oxidative phosphorylation for ATP synthesis, fast-twitch oxidative-glycolytic fibers are more fatigue resistant than their fast-twitch glycolytic cousins. Fast-twitch oxidative-glycolytic fibers, like slow-twitch fibers, are classified as red muscle because of their myoglobin content.

Human muscles are a mixture of fiber types, with the ratio of types varying from muscle to muscle and from one individual to another. For example, who would have more fast-twitch fibers in leg muscles, a marathon runner or a high-jumper? Characteristics of the three muscle fiber types are compared in Table 12-2 ●.

Tension Developed by Individual Muscle Fibers Is a Function of Fiber Length

In a muscle fiber, the tension developed during a twitch is a direct reflection of the length of individual sarcomeres before contraction begins (Fig. 12-16 ●). Each sarcomere contracts with optimum force if it is at optimum length (neither too long nor too short) before the contraction begins. Fortunately, the normal resting length of skeletal muscles usually ensures that sarcomeres are at optimum length when they begin a contraction.

At the molecular level, sarcomere length reflects the overlap between the thick and thin filaments (Fig. 12-16). The sliding filament theory predicts that *the tension a muscle fiber can generate is directly proportional to the number of crossbridges formed between the thick and thin filaments.* If the fibers start a contraction at a very long sarcomere length, the thick and thin filaments barely overlap and form few crossbridges (Fig. 12-16e).

TABLE 12-2 Characteristics of Muscle Fiber Types

	SLOW-TWITCH OXIDATIVE; RED MUSCLE	FAST-TWITCH OXIDATIVE-GLYCOLYTIC; RED MUSCLE	FAST-TWITCH GLYCOLYTIC; WHITE MUSCLE
Speed of development of maximum tension	Slowest	Intermediate	Fastest
Myosin ATPase activity	Slow	Fast	Fast
Diameter	Small	Medium	Large
Contraction duration	Longest	Short	Short
Ca^{2+}-ATPase activity in SR	Moderate	High	High
Endurance	Fatigue resistant	Fatigue resistant	Easily fatigued
Use	Most used: posture	Standing, walking	Least used: jumping; quick, fine movements
Metabolism	Oxidative; aerobic	Glycolytic but becomes more oxidative with endurance training	Glycolytic; more anaerobic than fast-twitch oxidative-glycolytic type
Capillary density	High	Medium	Low
Mitochondria	Numerous	Moderate	Few
Color	Dark red (myoglobin)	Red	Pale

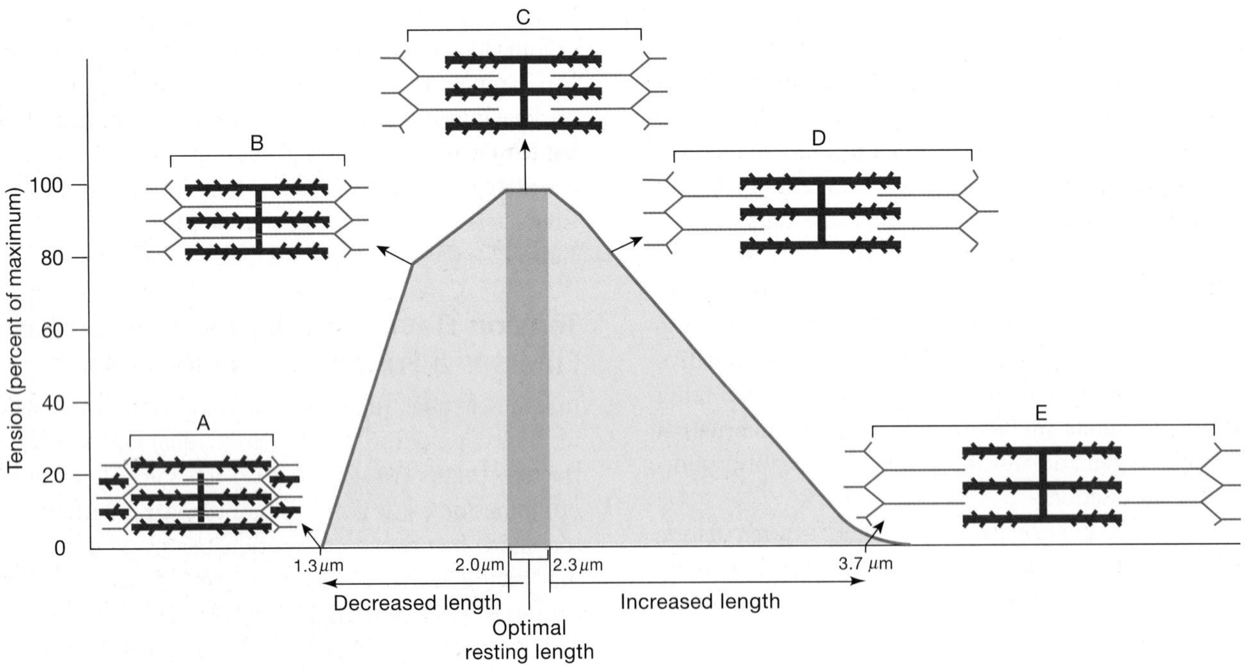

● **FIGURE 12-16** ***Too much or too little overlap of thick and thin filaments in resting muscle results in decreased tension.*** Adapted from A.M. Gordon *et al.*, *J Physiol* 184: 170–192, 1966.

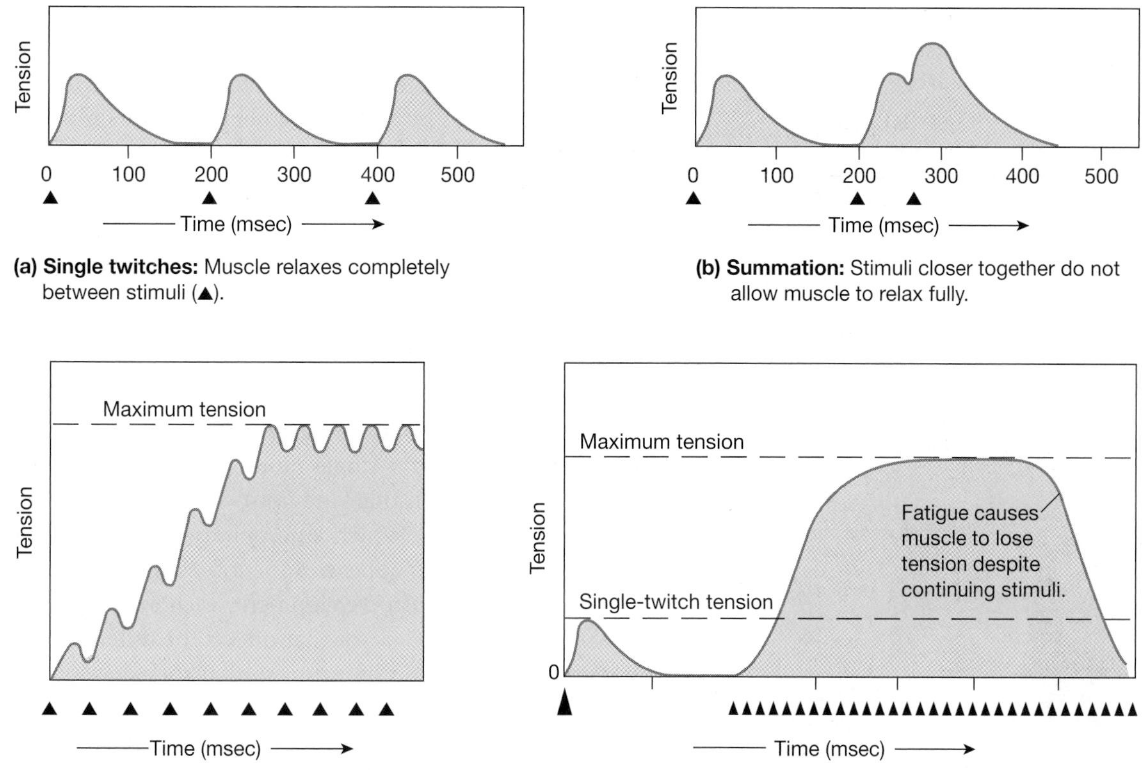
Tension
0
100
200
300
400
500
Time (msec)
Maximum tension
Single-twitch tension
Fatigue causes muscle to lose tension despite continuing stimuli.
0

(a) Single twitches: Muscle relaxes completely between stimuli (▲).

(b) Summation: Stimuli closer together do not allow muscle to relax fully.

(c) Summation leading to unfused tetanus: Stimuli are far enough apart to allow muscle to relax slightly between stimuli.

(d) Summation leading to complete tetanus: Muscle reaches steady tension.

● **FIGURE 12-17** ***Summation of contractions***

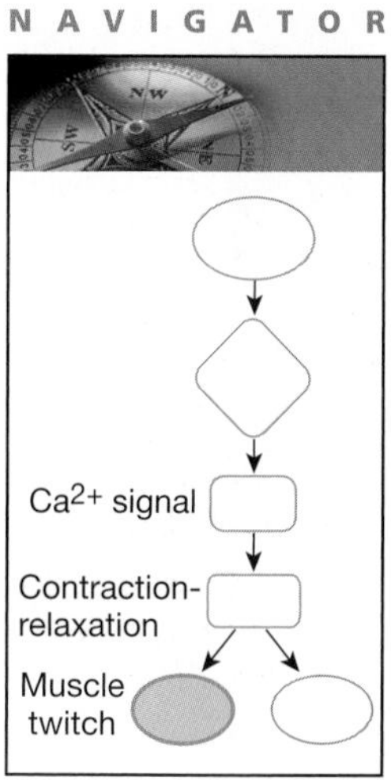
NAVIGATOR
Ca2+ signal
Contraction-relaxation
Muscle twitch

This means that in the initial part of the contraction, the sliding filaments interact only minimally and therefore cannot generate much force.

At the optimum sarcomere length (Fig. 12-16c), the filaments begin contracting with numerous crossbridges between the thick and thin filaments, allowing the fiber to generate optimum force in that twitch. If the sarcomere is shorter than optimum length at the beginning of the contraction (Fig. 12-16b), the thick and thin fibers have too much overlap before the contraction begins. Consequently, the thick filaments can move the thin filaments only a short distance before the thin actin filaments from opposite ends of the sarcomere start to overlap. This overlap prevents crossbridge formation. If the sarcomere is so short that the thick filaments run into the Z disks (Fig. 12-16a), myosin is unable to find new binding sites for crossbridge formation, and tension decreases rapidly. Thus the development of single-twitch tension in a muscle fiber is a passive property that depends on filament overlap and sarcomere length.

Force of Contraction Increases with Summation of Muscle Twitches

Although we have just seen that single-twitch tension is determined by the length of the sarcomere, it is important to note that a single twitch does not represent the maximum force that a muscle fiber can develop. The force generated by the contraction of a single muscle fiber can be increased by increasing the rate (frequency) at which muscle action potentials stimulate the muscle fiber.

A typical muscle action potential lasts between 1 and 3 msec, while the muscle contraction may last 100 msec (see Fig. 12-12). If repeated action potentials are separated by long intervals of time, the muscle fiber has time to relax completely between stimuli (Fig. 12-17a ●). If the interval of time between action potentials is shortened, the muscle fiber does not have time to relax completely between two stimuli, resulting in a more forceful contraction (Fig. 12-17b). This process is known as **summation** and is similar to the temporal summation of graded potentials that takes place in neurons [p. 283].

If action potentials continue to stimulate the muscle fiber repeatedly at short intervals (high frequency), relaxation between contractions diminishes until the muscle fiber achieves a state of maximal contraction known as **tetanus**. There are two types of tetanus. In *incomplete* (or *unfused*) *tetanus*, the stimulation rate of the muscle fiber is not at a maximum value, and consequently the fiber relaxes slightly between stimuli (Fig. 12-17c). In *complete* (or *fused*) *tetanus*, the stimulation rate is fast enough that the muscle fiber does not have time to relax. Instead, it reaches maximum tension and remains there (Fig. 12-17d).

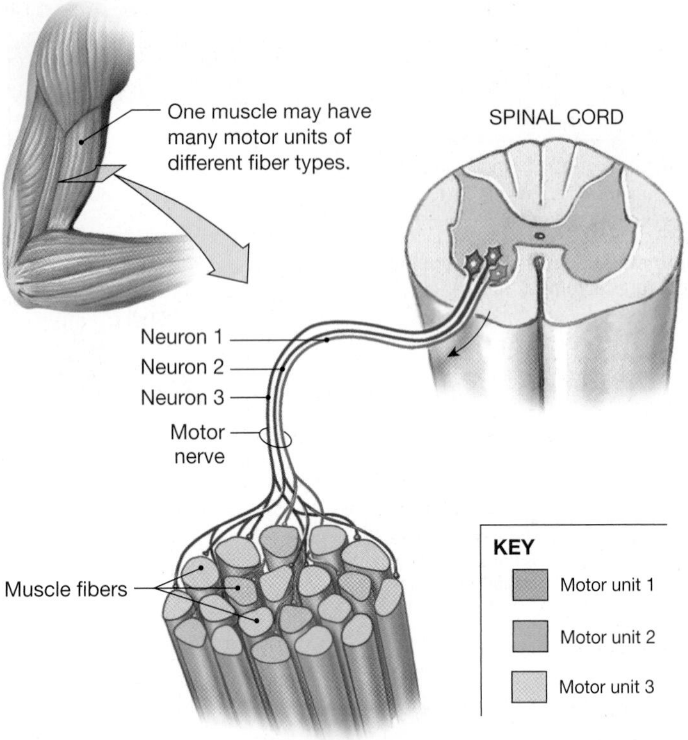

● **FIGURE 12-18** ***A motor unit consists of one motor neuron and all the muscle fibers it innervates.***

Thus it is possible to increase the tension developed in a single muscle fiber by changing the rate at which action potentials occur in the fiber. Muscle action potentials are initiated by the somatic motor neuron that controls the muscle fiber.

CONCEPT CHECK

17. Summation in muscle fibers means that the ________ of the fiber increases with repeated action potentials.
18. Temporal summation in neurons means that the ________ of the neuron increases when two depolarizing stimuli occur close together in time. Answers: p. 445

A Motor Unit Is One Somatic Motor Neuron and the Muscle Fibers It Innervates

The basic unit of contraction in an intact skeletal muscle is a **motor unit**, composed of a group of muscle fibers that function together and the somatic motor neuron that controls them (Fig. 12-18 ●). When the somatic motor neuron fires an action potential, all muscle fibers in the motor unit contract. Note that although one somatic motor neuron innervates multiple fibers, each muscle fiber is innervated by only a single neuron.

The number of muscle fibers in a motor unit varies. In muscles used for fine motor actions, such as the muscles that move the eyes or the muscles of the hand, a motor unit contains as few as three to five muscle fibers. If one such motor unit is activated, only a few fibers contract, and the muscle response is quite small. If additional motor units are activated, the response increases by small increments because only a few more muscle fibers contract with the addition of each motor unit. This arrangement allows fine gradations of movement.

In muscles used for gross motor actions such as standing or walking, each motor unit may contain hundreds or even thousands of muscle fibers. The gastrocnemius muscle in the calf of the leg, for example, has about 2000 muscle fibers in each motor unit. Each time an additional motor unit is activated in these muscles, many more muscle fibers contract, and the muscle response jumps by correspondingly greater increments.

All muscle fibers in a single motor unit are of the same fiber type. For this reason there are fast-twitch motor units and slow-twitch motor units. Which kind of muscle fiber associates with a particular neuron appears to be a function of the neuron. During embryological development, each somatic motor neuron secretes a growth factor that directs the differentiation of all muscle fibers in its motor unit so that they develop into the same fiber type.

Intuitively, it would seem that people who inherit a predominance of one fiber type over another would excel in certain sports. They do, to some extent. Endurance athletes, such as distance runners and cross-country skiers, have a predominance of slow-twitch fibers, whereas sprinters, ice hockey players, and weight lifters tend to have larger percentages of fast-twitch fibers.

Inheritance is not the only determining factor for fiber composition in the body, however, because the metabolic characteristics of muscle fibers have some plasticity. With endurance training, the aerobic capacity of some fast-twitch fibers can be enhanced until they are almost as fatigue-resistant as slow-twitch fibers. Because the conversion occurs only in those muscles that are being trained, a neuromodulator chemical is probably involved. In addition, endurance training increases the number of capillaries and mitochondria in the muscle tissue, allowing more oxygen-carrying blood to reach the contracting muscle and contributing to the increased aerobic capacity of the muscle fibers.

CONCEPT CHECK

19. Which type of runner would you expect to have more slow-twitch fibers, a sprinter or a marathoner? Answers: p. 445

Contraction Force Depends on the Types and Numbers of Motor Units

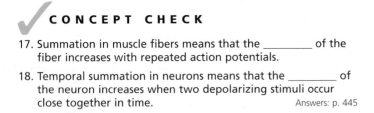

Within a skeletal muscle, each motor unit contracts in an all-or-none manner. How then can muscles create graded contractions of varying force and duration? The answer lies in the fact that muscles are composed of multiple motor units of different types (Fig. 12-18). This diversity allows the muscle to vary contraction by (1) changing the types of motor units that are active or (2) changing the number of motor units that are responding at any one time.

The force of contraction in a skeletal muscle can be increased by recruiting additional motor units. **Recruitment** is controlled by the nervous system and proceeds in a standardized sequence. A weak stimulus directed onto a pool of somatic motor neurons in the central nervous system activates only the neurons with the lowest thresholds [p. 257]. Studies have shown that these low-threshold neurons control fatigue-resistant slow-twitch fibers, which generate minimal force.

As the stimulus onto the motor neuron pool increases in strength, additional motor neurons with higher thresholds begin to fire. These neurons in turn stimulate motor units composed of fatigue-resistant fast-twitch oxidative-glycolytic fibers. Because more motor units (and thus more muscle fibers) are participating in the contraction, greater force is generated in the muscle.

As the stimulus increases to even higher levels, somatic motor neurons with the highest thresholds begin to fire. These neurons stimulate motor units composed of glycolytic fast-twitch fibers. At this point, the muscle contraction is approaching its maximum force. Because of differences in myosin and crossbridge formation, fast-twitch fibers generate more force than slow-twitch fibers do. However, because fast-twitch fibers fatigue more rapidly, it is impossible to hold a muscle contraction at maximum force for an extended period of time. You can demonstrate this by clenching your fist as hard as you can: how long can you hold it before some of the muscle fibers begin to fatigue?

Sustained contractions in a muscle require a continuous train of action potentials from the central nervous system to the muscle. As you learned earlier, however, increasing the stimulation rate of a muscle fiber results in summation of its contractions. If the muscle fiber is easily fatigued, summation leads to fatigue and diminished tension (Fig. 12-17d).

One way the nervous system avoids fatigue in sustained contractions is by **asynchronous recruitment** of motor units. The nervous system modulates the firing rates of the motor neurons so that different motor units take turns maintaining muscle tension. The alternation of active motor units allows some of the motor units to rest between contractions, preventing fatigue.

Asynchronous recruitment prevents fatigue only in submaximal contractions, however. In high-tension, sustained contractions, the individual motor units may reach a state of unfused tetanus, in which the muscle fibers cycle between contraction and partial relaxation. In general, we do not notice this cycling because the different motor units in the muscle are contracting and relaxing at slightly different times. As a result, the contractions and relaxations of the motor units average out and appear to be one smooth contraction. But as different motor units fatigue, we are unable to maintain the same amount of tension in the muscle, and the force of the contraction gradually decreases.

CONCEPT CHECK

20. What is the response of a muscle fiber to an increase in the firing rate of the somatic motor neuron?
21. How does the nervous system increase the force of contraction in a muscle composed of many motor units? Answers: p. 445

MECHANICS OF BODY MOVEMENT

Because one main role of skeletal muscles is to move the body, we now turn to the mechanics of body movement. The term *mechanics* refers to how muscles move loads and how the anatomical relationship between muscles and bones maximizes the work the muscles can do.

Isotonic Contractions Move Loads; Isometric Contractions Create Force Without Movement

When we described the function of muscles earlier in this chapter, we noted that they can create force to generate movement but can also create force without generating movement. You can demonstrate both properties with a pair of heavy weights. Pick up one weight in each hand and then bend your elbows so that the weights touch your shoulders. You have just performed an **isotonic contraction** [*iso,* equal + *teinein,* to stretch]. Any contraction that creates force and moves a load is an isotonic contraction.

When you bent your arms at the elbows and brought the weights to your shoulders, the biceps muscles shortened. Now slowly extend your arms, resisting the tendency of the weights to pull them down. The biceps muscles are again active, but now you are performing a *lengthening (eccentric) contraction.* Lengthening contractions are thought to contribute most to cellular damage after exercise and to lead to delayed muscle soreness.

If you pick up the weights and hold them stationary in front of you, the muscles of your arms are creating tension (force) to overcome the load of the weights but are not creating movement. Contractions that create force without moving a load are called **isometric** (static) **contractions** [*iso,* equal + *metric,* measurement]. Isotonic and isometric contractions are illustrated in Figure 12-19 ●. To demonstrate an isotonic contraction experimentally, we hang a weight (the load) from the muscle in Figure 12-19a and electrically stimulate the muscle to contract. The muscle contracts, lifting the weight. The graph on the right shows the development of force throughout the contraction.

To demonstrate an isometric contraction experimentally, we attach a heavier weight to the muscle, as shown in Figure

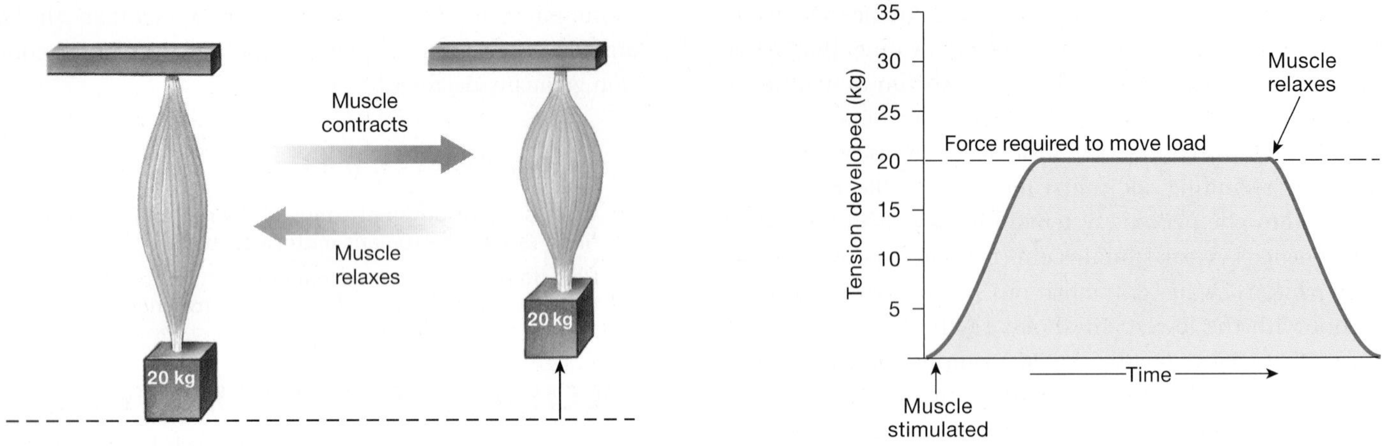

(a) Isotonic contraction: muscle contracts, shortens, and creates enough force to move the load.

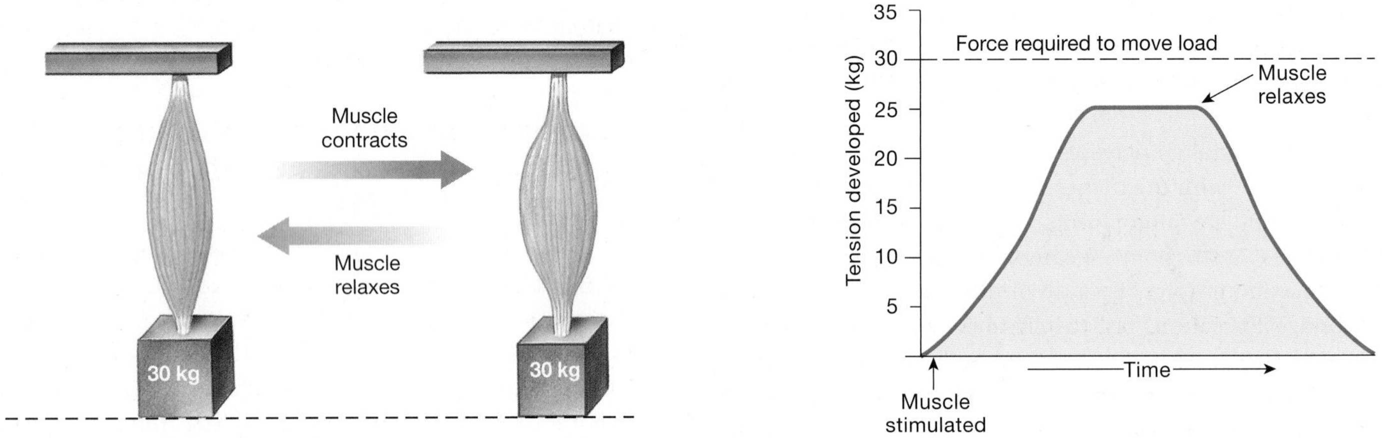

(b) Isometric contraction: muscle contracts but does not shorten. Force cannot move the load.

● **FIGURE 12-19** *Isotonic and isometric contractions*

12-19b. When the muscle is stimulated, it develops tension, but the force created is not enough to move the load. In isometric contractions, muscles create force without shortening significantly. For example, when your exercise instructor yells at you to "tighten those glutes," your response is isometric contraction of the gluteal muscles in your buttocks.

How can an isometric contraction create force if the length of the muscle does not change significantly? The elastic elements of the muscle provide the answer. All muscles contain elastic fibers in the tendons and other connective tissues that attach muscles to bone, and in the connective tissue between muscle fibers. In muscle fibers, elastic cytoskeletal proteins occur between the myofibrils and as part of the sarcomere. All of these elastic components behave collectively as if they were connected in series (one after the other) to the contractile elements of the muscle. Consequently, they are often called the **series elastic elements** of the muscle (Fig. 12-20 ●).

When the sarcomeres shorten in an isometric contraction, the elastic elements stretch. This stretching of the elastic elements allows the fibers to maintain a relatively constant length even though the sarcomeres are shortening and creating tension (Fig. 12-20 ②). Once the elastic elements have been stretched and the force generated by the sarcomeres equals the load, the muscle shortens in an isotonic contraction and lifts the load.

Bones and Muscles Around Joints Form Levers and Fulcrums

The anatomical arrangement of muscles and bones in the body is directly related to how muscles work. The body uses its bones and joints as levers and fulcrums on which muscles exert force to move or resist a load. A **lever** is a rigid bar that pivots around a point known as the **fulcrum** (Fig. 12-21a ●). In the body, bones form levers, flexible joints form the fulcrums, and muscles attached to bones create force by contracting. Most lever systems in the body are similar to the one shown in Figure 12-21a, where the fulcrum is located at one end of the lever, the load is near the other end of the lever, and the muscle attaches between the fulcrum and the load. This arrangement maximizes the distance and speed with which the lever can move the load but also requires that the muscles do more work. Let's see how flexion of the forearm illustrates lever system function.

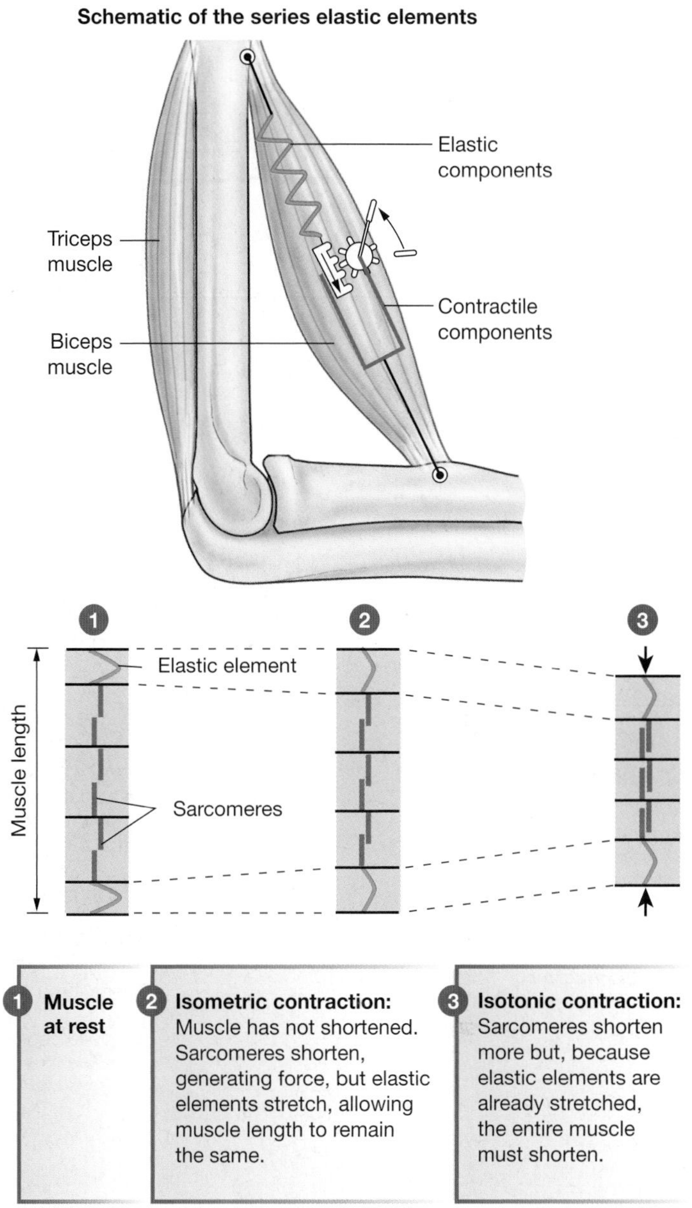

● **FIGURE 12-20** ***Series elastic elements in muscle.*** A muscle has both contractile components (sarcomeres, shown here as a gear and ratchet) and elastic components (shown here as a spring).

In the lever system of the forearm, the elbow joint acts as the fulcrum around which rotational movement of the forearm (the lever) takes place (Fig. 12-21a). The biceps muscle is attached at its origin at the shoulder and inserts onto the radius bone of the forearm a few centimeters away from the elbow joint. When the biceps contracts, it creates the upward force F_1 (Fig. 12-21b) as it pulls on the bone. The total rotational force* created by the biceps depends on the force of muscle contraction and on the distance between the fulcrum and the point at which the muscle inserts onto the radius.

If the biceps is to hold the forearm stationary and flexed at a 90° angle, the muscle must exert enough upward rotational force to exactly oppose the downward rotational force exerted by gravity on the forearm (Fig. 12-21b). The downward rotational force on the forearm is proportional to the weight of the forearm (F_2) times the distance from the fulcrum to the forearm's center of gravity (the point along the lever at which the forearm load exerts its force). For the arm illustrated in Figure 12-21b, the biceps must exert 6 kg of force to hold the arm at a 90° angle. Because the muscle is not shortening, this is an isometric contraction.

Now what happens if a 7-kg weight is placed in the hand? This weight places an additional load on the lever that is farther from the fulcrum than the forearm's center of gravity (Fig. 12-21c). Unless the biceps can create additional upward force to offset the downward force created by the weight, the hand falls. If you know the force exerted by the added weight and its distance from the elbow, you can calculate the additional muscle force needed to keep the arm from dropping the 7-kg weight.

What happens to the force required of the biceps to support a weight if the distance between the fulcrum and the muscle insertion point changes? Genetic variability in the insertion point can have a dramatic effect on the force required to move or resist a load. For example, if the biceps in Figure 12-21b inserted 6 cm from the fulcrum instead of 5 cm, it would only need to generate 5 kg of force to offset the weight of the arm. Some studies have shown a correlation between muscle insertion points and success in certain athletic events.

In the example so far, we have assumed that the load is stationary and that the muscle is contracting isometrically. What happens if we want to flex the arm and lift the load? To move the load from its position, the biceps must exert a force that exceeds the force created by the stationary load.

The disadvantage of a lever system in which the fulcrum is positioned near one end of the lever is that the muscle is required to create large amounts of force to move or resist a small load, as we just saw. However, the advantage of this type of lever-fulcrum system is that it maximizes speed and mobility. A small movement of the forearm at the point where the muscle inserts becomes a much larger movement at the hand (Fig. 12-22 ●). In addition, the two movements occur in the same amount of time, and so the speed of contraction at the insertion point is amplified at the hand. Thus, the lever-fulcrum system of the arm amplifies both the distance the load is moved and the speed at which this movement takes place.

In muscle physiology, the speed with which a muscle contracts depends on the type of muscle fiber (fast-twitch or slow-twitch) and on the load that is being moved. Intuitively, you can see that you can flex your arm much faster with nothing in your hand than you can while holding a 7-kg weight in your

*In physics, rotational force is expressed as *torque,* and the force of contraction is expressed in newtons (mass × acceleration due to gravity). For simplicity, we ignore the contribution of gravity in this discussion and use the mass unit "kilograms" for force of contraction.

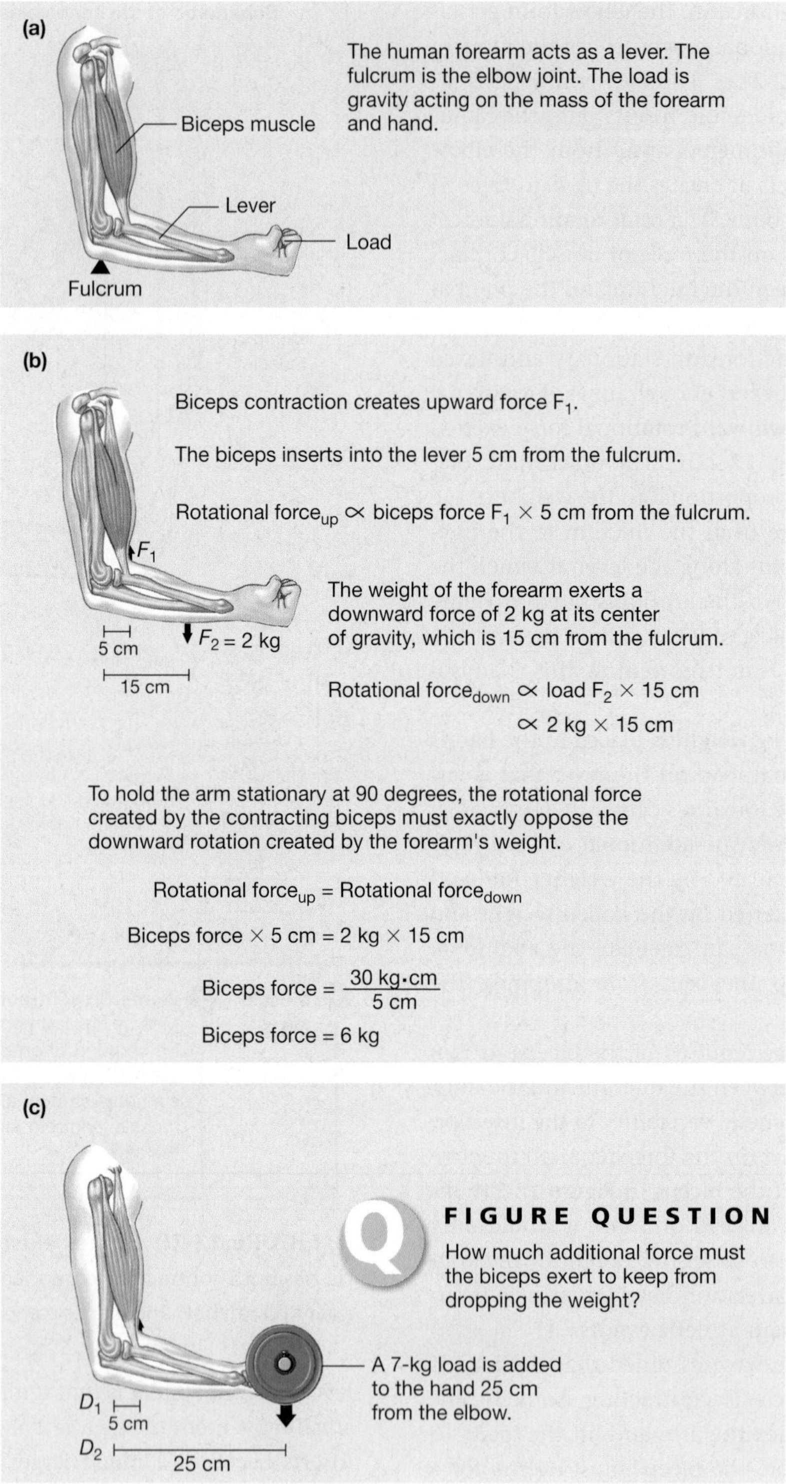
(a)
The human forearm acts as a lever. The fulcrum is the elbow joint. The load is gravity acting on the mass of the forearm and hand.
Biceps muscle
Lever
Load
Fulcrum
(b)
Biceps contraction creates upward force F_1.
The biceps inserts into the lever 5 cm from the fulcrum.
Rotational $force_{up} \propto$ biceps force $F_1 \times$ 5 cm from the fulcrum.
F_1
The weight of the forearm exerts a downward force of 2 kg at its center of gravity, which is 15 cm from the fulcrum.
5 cm
$F_2 = 2$ kg
15 cm
Rotational $force_{down} \propto$ load $F_2 \times$ 15 cm
$\propto$ 2 kg $\times$ 15 cm
To hold the arm stationary at 90 degrees, the rotational force created by the contracting biceps must exactly oppose the downward rotation created by the forearm's weight.
Rotational $force_{up}$ = Rotational $force_{down}$
Biceps force $\times$ 5 cm = 2 kg $\times$ 15 cm
Biceps force = $\frac{30 \text{ kg·cm}}{5 \text{ cm}}$
Biceps force = 6 kg
(c)
FIGURE QUESTION
How much additional force must the biceps exert to keep from dropping the weight?
A 7-kg load is added to the hand 25 cm from the elbow.
D_1
5 cm
D_2
25 cm

● **FIGURE 12-21** ***The arm is a lever and fulcrum system.***

hand. The relationship between load and velocity (speed) of contraction in a muscle fiber, determined experimentally, is graphed in Figure 12-23 ●. Contraction is fastest when the load on the muscle is zero. When the load on the muscle equals the ability of the muscle to create force, the muscle is unable to move the load and the velocity drops to zero. The muscle can still contract, but the contraction becomes isometric instead of isotonic. Because speed is a function of load and muscle fiber type, it cannot be regulated by the body except through recruitment of faster muscle fiber types. However, the arrangement of muscles, bones, and joints allows the body to amplify speed so that regulation at the cellular level becomes less important.

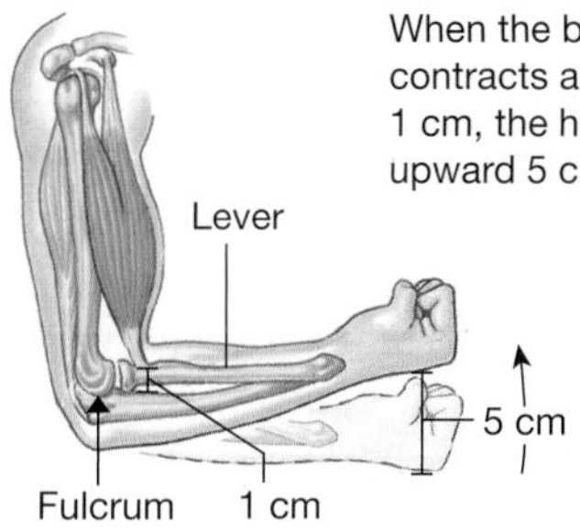
Because the insertion of the biceps is close to the fulcrum, a small movement of the biceps becomes a much larger movement of the hand.
When the biceps contracts and shortens 1 cm, the hand moves upward 5 cm.
Lever
5 cm
Fulcrum
1 cm

FIGURE QUESTION

If the biceps shortens 1 cm in 1 second, how fast does the hand move upward?

● **FIGURE 12-22** ***The arm amplifies speed of movement of the load.***

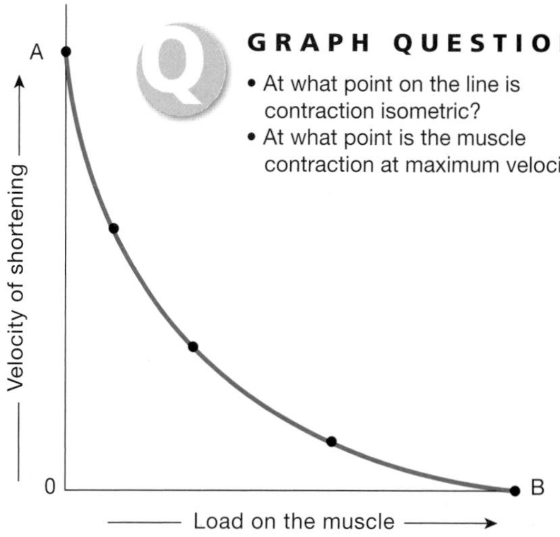
A
B
0
Velocity of shortening
Load on the muscle

GRAPH QUESTIONS

- At what point on the line is contraction isometric?
- At what point is the muscle contraction at maximum velocity?

● **FIGURE 12-23** ***Load-velocity relationship in skeletal muscle***

CONCEPT CHECK

22. One study found that many world-class athletes have muscle insertions that are farther from the joint than in the average person. Why would this trait translate into an advantage for a weight lifter? Answers: p. 445

Muscle Disorders Have Multiple Causes

Dysfunction in skeletal muscles can arise from a problem with the signal from the nervous system, from miscommunication at the neuromuscular junction, or from defects in the muscle. Unfortunately, in many muscle conditions, even the simple ones, we do not fully understand the mechanism of the primary defect. As a result, we can treat the symptoms but may not be able to cure the problem.

One common muscle disorder is a "charley horse," or *muscle cramp*—a sustained painful contraction of skeletal muscles. Many muscle cramps are caused by hyperexcitability of the somatic motor neurons controlling the muscle. As the neuron fires repeatedly, the muscle fibers of its motor unit go into a state of painful sustained contraction. Sometimes muscle cramps can be relieved by forcibly stretching the muscle. Apparently, stretching sends sensory information to the central nervous system that inhibits the somatic motor neuron, relieving the cramp.

The simplest muscle disorders arise from overuse. Most of us have exercised too long or too hard and suffered from fatigue or soreness as a result. With more severe trauma, muscle fibers, the connective tissue sheath, or the union of muscle and tendon may tear.

Disuse of muscles can be as traumatic as overuse. With prolonged inactivity, such as may occur when a limb is immobilized in a cast, the skeletal muscles atrophy. Blood supply to the muscle diminishes, and the muscle fibers get smaller. If activity is resumed in less than a year, the fibers usually regenerate. Atrophy of longer than one year is usually permanent. If the atrophy results from somatic motor neuron dysfunction, therapists now try to maintain muscle function by administering electrical impulses that directly stimulate the muscle fibers.

Acquired disorders that affect the skeletal muscle system include infectious diseases, such as influenza, that lead to weakness and achiness, and poisoning by toxins, such as those produced in botulism (*Clostridium botulinus*) and tetanus (*Clostridium tetani*). Botulinum toxin acts by decreasing the release of acetylcholine from the somatic motor neuron. Clinical investigators have successfully used injections of botulinum toxin as a treatment for writer's cramp, a disabling cramp of the hand that apparently arises as a result of hyperexcitability in the distal portion of the somatic motor neuron. Botox® injections are now widely used for cosmetic wrinkle reduction. Botulinum toxin injected under the skin temporarily paralyzes facial muscles that pull the skin into wrinkles.

RUNNING PROBLEM

Paul's doctor explains to Mrs. Leong that the paralytic attacks associated with hyperkalemic periodic paralysis last only a few minutes to a few hours and generally involve only the muscles of the extremities, which become weak and unable to contract (*flaccid paralysis*). "Is there any treatment?" asks Mrs. Leong. The doctor replies that although the inherited condition cannot be cured, attacks may be prevented with drugs. Diuretics, for example, increase the rate at which the body excretes water and ions (including Na^+ and K^+), and these medications have been shown to help prevent attacks of paralysis in people with hyperKPP.

Question 4:

Draw a map to explain why a Na^+ channel that does not inactivate results in a muscle that cannot contract (flaccid paralysis).

407 420 422 431 433 440

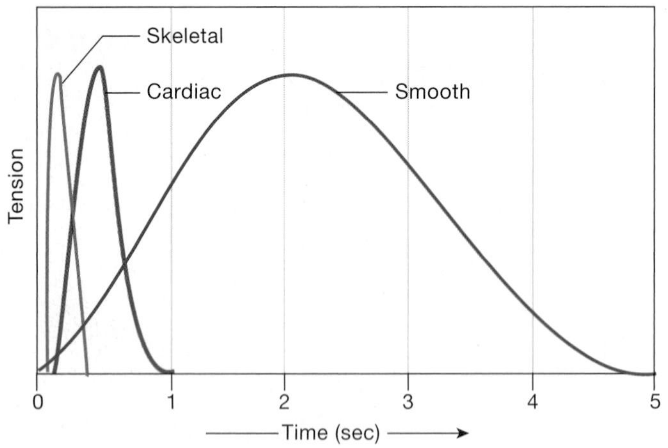

● **FIGURE 12-24** ***Duration of muscle contraction in the three types of muscle***

Inherited muscular disorders are the most difficult to treat. These conditions include various forms of muscular dystrophy as well as biochemical defects in glycogen and lipid storage. In **Duchenne muscular dystrophy**, the structural protein **dystrophin**, which links actin to proteins in the cell membrane, is absent. In muscle fibers that lack dystrophin, tiny tears in the membrane allow extracellular Ca^{2+} to enter the fiber. Consequently, intracellular enzymes are activated, resulting in breakdown of the fiber components. The major symptom of Duchenne dystrophy is progressive muscle weakness, and patients usually die before age 30 from failure of the respiratory muscles.

McArdle's disease, also known as *myophosphorylase deficiency,* is a condition in which the enzyme that converts glycogen to glucose 6-phosphate is absent in muscles. As a result, muscles lack a usable glycogen energy supply, and exercise tolerance is limited.

One way physiologists are trying to learn more about muscle diseases is by using animal models, such as genetically engineered mice that lack the genes for certain muscle proteins. Researchers are trying to correlate the absence of protein with particular disruptions in function.

SMOOTH MUSCLE

Although skeletal muscle has the most muscle mass in the body, cardiac and smooth muscle are more important in the maintenance of homeostasis. Smooth muscle is found predominantly in the walls of hollow organs and tubes, where its contraction changes the shape of the organ. Often smooth muscle generates force to move material through the lumen of the organ. For example, sequential waves of smooth muscle contraction in the intestinal tract move ingested material from the esophagus to the colon.

Smooth muscle is noticeably different from striated muscle in the way it develops tension. In a smooth muscle twitch, contraction and relaxation occur much more slowly than in either skeletal or cardiac muscle (Fig. 12-24 ●). At the same time, smooth muscle uses less energy to generate a given amount of force, and it can maintain its force for long periods. By one estimate, for example, a smooth muscle cell can generate maximum tension with only 25–30% of its crossbridges active. We still do not fully understand the mechanisms through which this is accomplished.

In addition, smooth muscle has low oxygen consumption rates yet can sustain contractions for extended periods without fatiguing. This property allows organs such as the bladder to maintain tension despite a continued load. It also allows some smooth muscles to be tonically contracted and maintain tension most of the time. The esophageal and urinary bladder **sphincters** [*sphingein,* to close] are examples of tonically contracted muscles that close off the opening to a hollow organ. These sphincters relax when it is necessary to allow material to enter or leave the organ.

Until recently, smooth muscle had not been studied as extensively as skeletal muscle for many reasons:

1. **Smooth muscle has more variety**. Many types of smooth muscle with widely differing properties are found throughout the animal kingdom, making a single model of smooth muscle function challenging. In humans, smooth muscle can be divided into six major groups: *vascular* (blood vessel walls), *gastrointestinal* (walls of digestive tract and associated organs, such as the gallbladder), *urinary* (walls of bladder and ureters), *respiratory* (airway passages), *reproductive* (uterus in females and other reproductive structures in both females and males), and *ocular* (eye). These muscles have different functions in the body, and their physiology reflects their specialized functions. In contrast, skeletal muscle is relatively uniform throughout the body.
2. **Smooth muscle anatomy makes functional studies difficult**. The contractile fibers of smooth muscle are arranged in oblique bundles rather than in parallel sarcomeres. Consequently, a contraction pulls the cell membrane in many directions at once. In addition, within an organ the layers of smooth muscle may run in several directions. For example, the intestine has one layer that encircles the lumen and a perpendicular layer that runs the length of the intestine. It is difficult to measure tension developing in both layers at once.
3. **Smooth muscle contraction is controlled by hormones and paracrines in addition to neurotransmitters**. Unlike skeletal muscle, which is controlled only by acetylcholine from somatic motor neurons, smooth muscle activity may be controlled by acetylcholine, norepinephrine, and a variety of other neurotransmitters, hormones, and paracrines.
4. **Smooth muscle has variable electrical properties**. Normal skeletal muscles always respond to an action potential with a twitch, but smooth muscles exhibit a

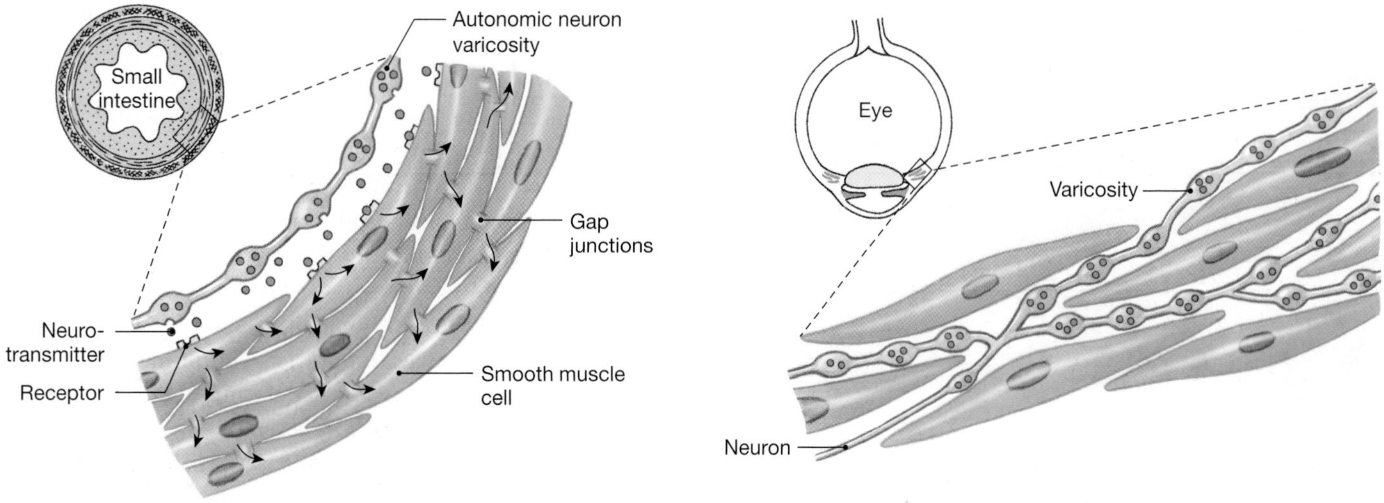

(a) Single-unit smooth muscle cells are connected by gap junctions, and the cells contract as a single unit.

(b) Multi-unit smooth muscle cells are not electrically linked, and each cell must be stimulated independently.

● **FIGURE 12-25** ***Two types of smooth muscle***

variety of electrical behaviors. They may hyperpolarize as well as depolarize, and they can depolarize without firing action potentials. Contraction may take place after an action potential, after a subthreshold graded potential, or without any change in membrane potential.

5. **Multiple pathways influence contraction and relaxation of smooth muscle.** Skeletal muscles contract in response to acetylcholine from a somatic motor neuron, and relax when the stimulus for contraction ceases. In marked contrast, multiple neurotransmitters, hormones, and paracrines acting on a smooth muscle fiber can inhibit contraction as well as stimulate it. And because several different signals might reach the muscle fiber simultaneously, smooth muscle fibers must act as integrating centers. For example, sometimes blood vessels receive contradictory messages from two sources: one message signals for contraction, the other for relaxation. The smooth muscle fibers must integrate the two signals and execute an appropriate response. The complexity of overlapping regulatory pathways influencing smooth muscle tone makes the tissue difficult to work with in the laboratory.

Because of the variability in smooth muscle types, we introduce only their general features in this chapter. Properties that are specific to a certain type are discussed when you learn about the different muscles in later chapters.

Smooth Muscles Are Much Smaller than Skeletal Muscle Fibers

Smooth muscles are composed of small, spindle-shaped cells with a single nucleus, in contrast to the large multinucleated fibers of skeletal muscles. In neurally controlled smooth muscle, neurotransmitter is released from autonomic neuron varicosities [p. 392] close to the surface of the muscle fibers. Smooth muscle lacks specialized receptor regions such as the motor end plates found in skeletal muscle synapses. Instead, the neurotransmitter simply diffuses across the cell surface until it finds a receptor.

Most smooth muscle is **single-unit smooth muscle** (*unitary smooth muscle*), so called because the individual muscle cells contract as a single unit. Single-unit smooth muscle is also called **visceral smooth muscle** because it forms the walls of internal organs (viscera), such as blood vessels and the intestinal tract. All the fibers of single-unit smooth muscle are electrically connected to one another, and an action potential in one cell spreads rapidly through gap junctions to make the entire sheet of tissue contract (Fig. 12-25a ●). Because all fibers contract every time, no reserve units are left to be recruited to increase contraction force. Instead, the amount of Ca^{2+} that enters the cell determines the force of contraction, as you will learn in the discussion that follows.

RUNNING PROBLEM

Three weeks later, Paul had another attack of paralysis, this time at kindergarten after a game of tag. He was rushed to the hospital and given glucose by mouth. Within minutes, he was able to move his legs and arms and asked for his mother.

Question 5:

Explain why oral glucose might help bring Paul out of his paralysis. (Hint: Glucose stimulates insulin release, and insulin increases Na^+-K^+-ATPase activity. What happens to the extracellular K^+ level when Na^+-K^+-ATPase is more active?)

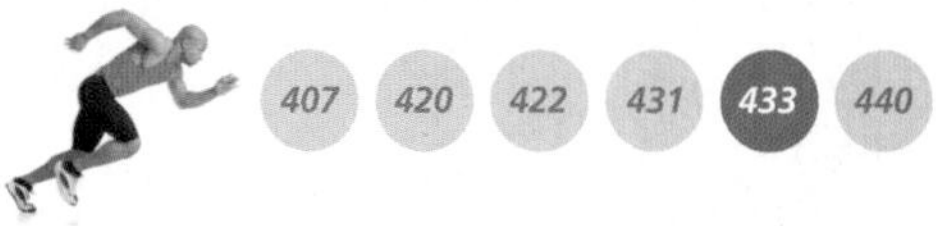

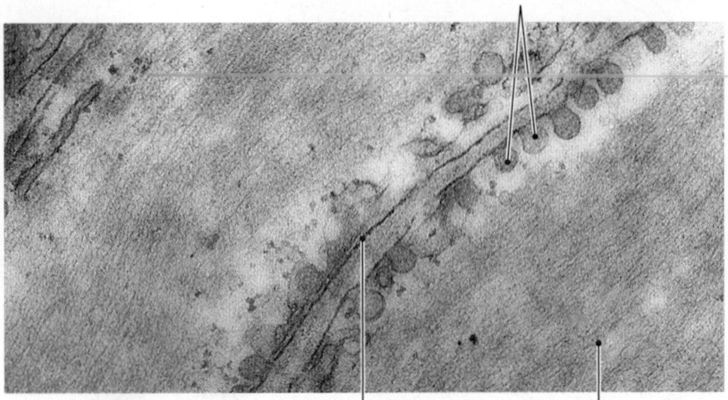
Caveolae are small invaginations of the sarcolemma that concentrate Ca^{2+}.
Sarcolemma
Smooth muscle cell

● **FIGURE 12-26** ***Caveolae in smooth muscle sequester calcium.***

Multi-unit smooth muscle consists of cells that are not linked electrically. Consequently, each individual muscle cell must be closely associated with an axon terminal or varicosity and stimulated independently (Fig. 12-25b). This arrangement allows fine control of contractions in these muscles through selective activation of individual muscle cells. As in skeletal muscle, increasing the force of contraction requires recruitment of additional fibers.

Multi-unit smooth muscle is found in the iris and ciliary body of the eye, in part of the male reproductive tract, and in the uterus except just prior to labor and delivery. Interestingly, the multi-unit smooth muscle of the uterus changes and becomes single-unit during the final stages of pregnancy. Genes for synthesis of gap junction connexin proteins turn on, apparently under the influence of pregnancy hormones. The addition of gap junctions to the uterine muscle cells synchronizes electrical signals, allowing the uterine muscle to contract more effectively while expelling the baby.

CONCEPT CHECK

23. What is the difference in how contraction force is varied in multi-unit and single-unit smooth muscle? Answers: p. 445

Smooth Muscle Has Longer Actin and Myosin Filaments

Smooth muscle uses many of the same contractile elements as skeletal muscle: actin-myosin crossbridges, sarcoplasmic reticulum with Ca^{2+} release channels, and a Ca^{2+} signal that initiates the process. However, details of the structural elements and the contraction process differ in the two muscle types.

Smooth muscles have longer actin and myosin filaments than skeletal muscles do, and the myosin isoform in smooth muscle is different from that in skeletal muscle. Smooth muscle myosin ATPase activity is much slower, decreasing the rate of crossbridge cycling and lengthening the contraction phase. In addition, one of the smaller protein chains in the myosin head plays a regulatory role in controlling contraction and relaxation. This small regulatory protein chain is called a **myosin light chain**.

Actin is more plentiful in smooth muscle than in striated muscle, with an actin-to-myosin ratio of 10–15 to 1, compared with 2–4 to 1 in striated muscle. Smooth muscle actin is associated with tropomyosin, as in skeletal muscle. However, unlike skeletal muscle, smooth muscle lacks troponin.

Smooth muscle has less sarcoplasmic reticulum than skeletal muscle does, although the amount varies from one type of smooth muscle to another. The primary Ca^{2+} release channel in smooth muscle sarcoplasmic reticulum is an **IP_3-receptor channel**. *Inositol trisphosphate* (IP_3) is a second messenger created in the phospholipase C pathway [p. 188]. The calcium-storage function of the sarcoplasmic reticulum may be supplemented by *caveolae* [p. 154], small vesicles that cluster close to the cell membrane (Fig. 12-26 ●).

Smooth Muscle Is Not Arranged in Sarcomeres

Smooth muscle gets its name from the homogeneous appearance of its cytoplasm under the microscope (Figs. 12-1c and 12-26). The contractile fibers are not arranged in sarcomeres, which is the reason smooth muscle does not have distinct banding patterns as striated muscle does. Instead, actin and myosin are arranged in long bundles that extend diagonally around the cell periphery, forming a lattice around a central nucleus (Fig. 12-27a ●). The oblique arrangement of contractile elements beneath the cell membrane causes smooth muscle fibers to become globular when they contract (Fig. 12-27b), rather than simply shortening as skeletal muscles do.

The long actin filaments of smooth muscle attach to **dense bodies** of protein in the cytoplasm and terminate at protein *attachment plaques* in the cell membrane (Fig. 12-27a, c). The less numerous myosin filaments lie bundled between the long actin filaments and are arranged so that their entire surface is covered by myosin heads (Fig. 12-27d). (Recall that in the sarcomere of skeletal muscles, the center of the myosin filament lacks myosin heads.)

The continuous line of myosin heads allows actin to slide along the myosin for longer distances. This unique organization enables smooth muscle to be stretched more while still maintaining enough overlap to create optimum tension. This is an important property for internal organs, such as the bladder, whose volume varies as it alternately fills and empties.

CONCEPT CHECK

24. The dense bodies that anchor smooth muscle actin are analogous to what structure in a sarcomere? (*Hint:* See Fig. 12-5.)
25. Name three ways smooth muscle myosin differs from skeletal muscle myosin.
26. Name one way actin and its associated proteins differ in skeletal and smooth muscle. Answers: p. 445

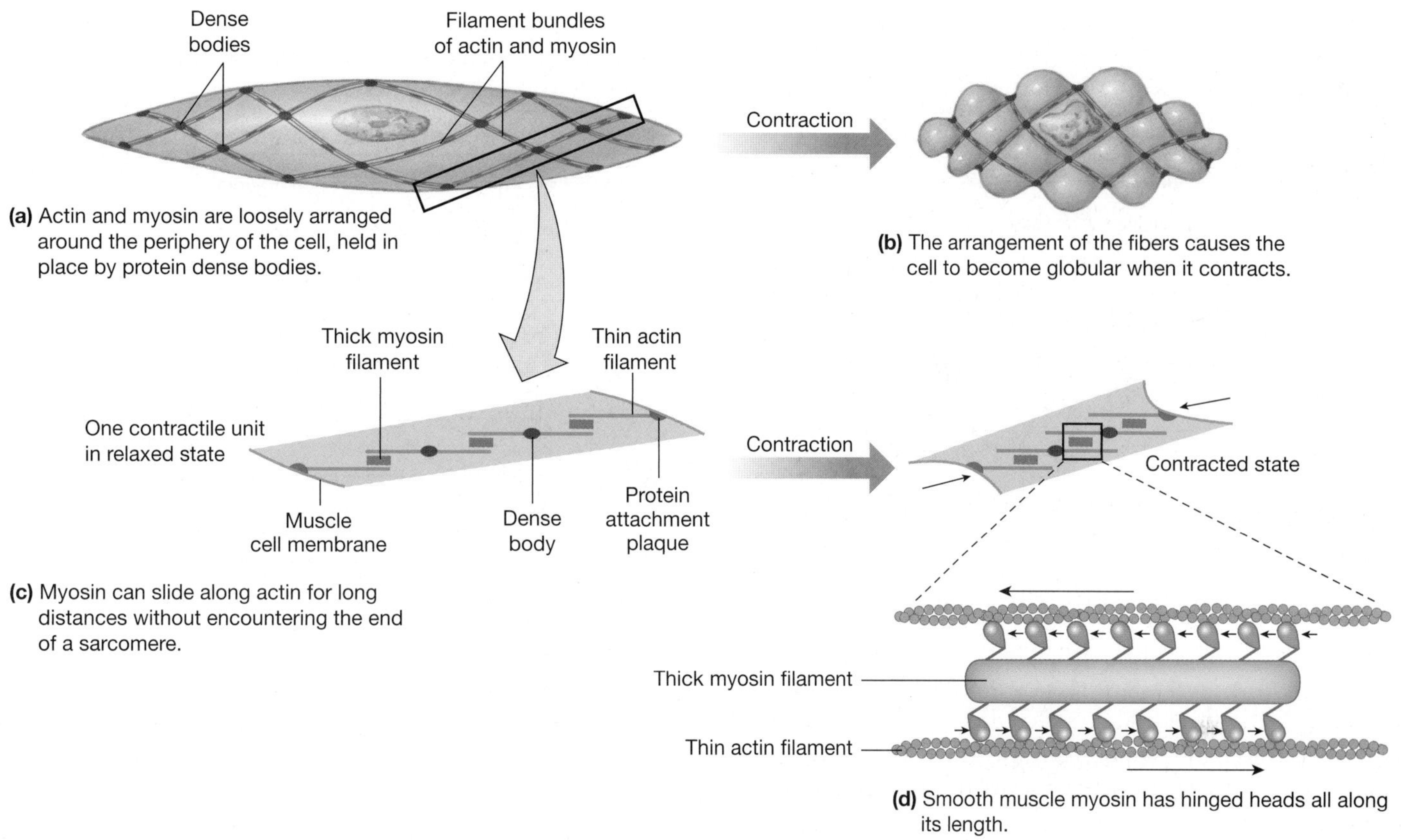
Dense bodies
Filament bundles of actin and myosin
Contraction
(a) Actin and myosin are loosely arranged around the periphery of the cell, held in place by protein dense bodies.
(b) The arrangement of the fibers causes the cell to become globular when it contracts.
Thick myosin filament
Thin actin filament
One contractile unit in relaxed state
Contraction
Contracted state
Muscle cell membrane
Dense body
Protein attachment plaque
(c) Myosin can slide along actin for long distances without encountering the end of a sarcomere.
Thick myosin filament
Thin actin filament
(d) Smooth muscle myosin has hinged heads all along its length.

● **FIGURE 12-27** *Anatomy of smooth muscle*

Protein Phosphorylation Plays a Key Role in Smooth Muscle Contraction

The molecular events of smooth muscle contraction are similar in many ways to those in skeletal muscle, but some important differences exist. In both types of muscle a Ca^{2+} signal initiates contraction. In skeletal muscle, the Ca^{2+} signal comes only from the sarcoplasmic reticulum, and it is always preceded by an action potential. In smooth muscle, Ca^{2+} comes from extracellular fluid as well as from the sarcoplasmic reticulum, and an action potential is not a requirement for Ca^{2+} release. In skeletal muscle the Ca^{2+} signal acts on troponin to initiate contraction. In smooth muscle there is no troponin. Instead the Ca^{2+} signal initiates a cascade that ends with phosphorylation of myosin.

Here is a summary of our current understanding of the key points of smooth muscle contraction. In smooth muscle:

1. An increase in cytosolic Ca^{2+} initiates contraction. Ca^{2+} is released from the sarcoplasmic reticulum and also enters from the extracellular fluid.
2. Ca^{2+} binds to **calmodulin**, a binding protein found in the cytosol.
3. Ca^{2+} binding to calmodulin is the first step in a cascade that ends in phosphorylation of myosin.
4. Phosphorylation of myosin enhances myosin ATPase activity and results in contraction.

We begin our discussion with steps 2-4 because those steps are common to all types of smooth muscle. We then go back and look at the different pathways that create Ca^{2+} signals.

Figure 12-28 ● illustrates the steps of smooth muscle contraction. Contraction begins when cytosolic Ca^{2+} concentrations increase following Ca^{2+} entry from the extracellular fluid and Ca^{2+} release from the sarcoplasmic reticulum ①. The Ca^{2+} ions bind to calmodulin (CaM) ②, obeying the law of mass action [p. 102]. The Ca^{2+}-calmodulin complex then activates an enzyme called **myosin light chain kinase (MLCK)** ③.

MLCK enhances myosin ATPase activity by phosphorylating light protein chains near the myosin head ④. When myosin ATPase activity is high, actin binding and crossbridge cycling increase tension in the muscle ⑤. As a result, smooth muscle contraction is primarily controlled through myosin-linked regulatory processes rather than through troponin and tropomyosin.

In some types of smooth muscle, myosin regulation of crossbridge cycling is supplemented by regulation of actin. Several actin-associated regulatory proteins, such as *caldesmon*, have been identified. In addition, second messengers may modulate contraction by acting on myosin light chain kinase, myosin phosphatase, or on the actin-associated regulatory proteins. The details of this modulation are still being worked out.

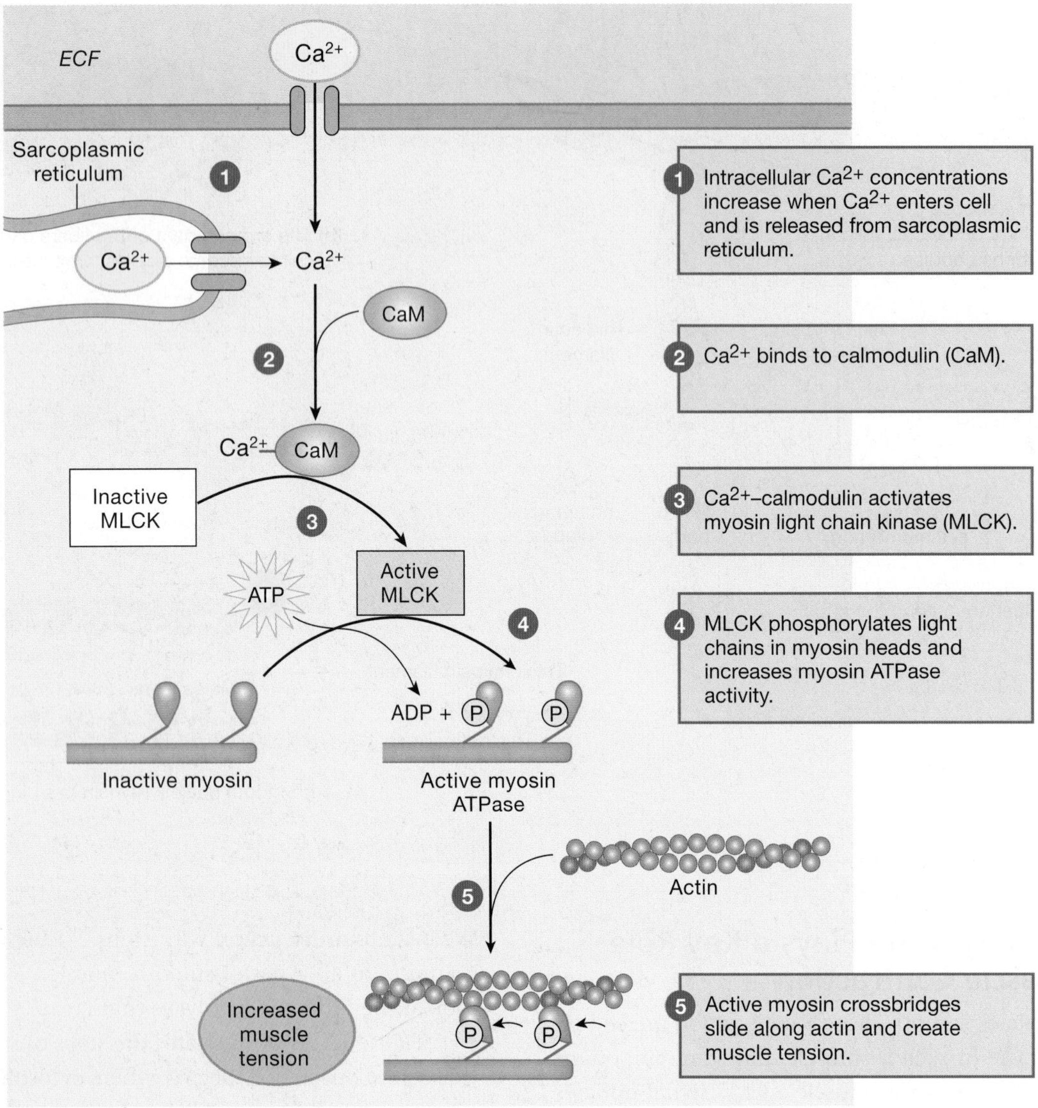

ECF
Ca2+
Sarcoplasmic reticulum
Ca2+
Ca2+
CaM
Ca2+ CaM
Inactive MLCK
Active MLCK
ATP
ADP + P
P
Inactive myosin
Active myosin ATPase
Actin
Increased muscle tension
P
P
1 Intracellular Ca2+ concentrations increase when Ca2+ enters cell and is released from sarcoplasmic reticulum.
2 Ca2+ binds to calmodulin (CaM).
3 Ca2+–calmodulin activates myosin light chain kinase (MLCK).
4 MLCK phosphorylates light chains in myosin heads and increases myosin ATPase activity.
5 Active myosin crossbridges slide along actin and create muscle tension.

● **FIGURE 12-28** ***Smooth muscle contraction***

Relaxation in Smooth Muscle Has Several Steps

Relaxation in a smooth muscle fiber is a multistep process (Fig. 12-29 ●). As in skeletal muscle, free Ca^{2+} is removed from the cytosol when Ca^{2+}-ATPase pumps it back into the sarcoplasmic reticulum. In addition, some Ca^{2+} is pumped out of the cell with the help of a Ca^{2+}-Na^{+} antiport exchanger [p. 144] and Ca^{2+}-ATPase ①. By the law of mass action, a decrease in free cytosolic Ca^{2+} causes Ca^{2+} to unbind from calmodulin ②. In the absence of Ca^{2+}-calmodulin, myosin light chain kinase inactivates.

An additional step in smooth muscle relaxation is dephosphorylation of the myosin light chain, accomplished with the aid of the enzyme **myosin phosphatase**. Removal of myosin's phosphate group decreases myosin ATPase activity ③.

Interestingly, dephosphorylation of myosin does not automatically result in relaxation. Under conditions that we do not fully understand, dephosphorylated myosin may remain attached to actin for a period of time in what is known as a **latch state**. This condition maintains tension in the muscle fiber without consuming ATP. It is a significant factor in the ability of smooth muscle to sustain contraction without fatiguing. The hinge muscles of certain bivalve mollusks such as oysters can enter a similar latch state that allows them to remain tightly closed under anaerobic conditions.

Calcium Entry Is the Signal for Smooth Muscle Contraction

We now step back to look in detail at the more complicated part of smooth muscle contraction: the Ca^{2+} signal that initiates the process. Smooth muscle Ca^{2+} comes from two sources:

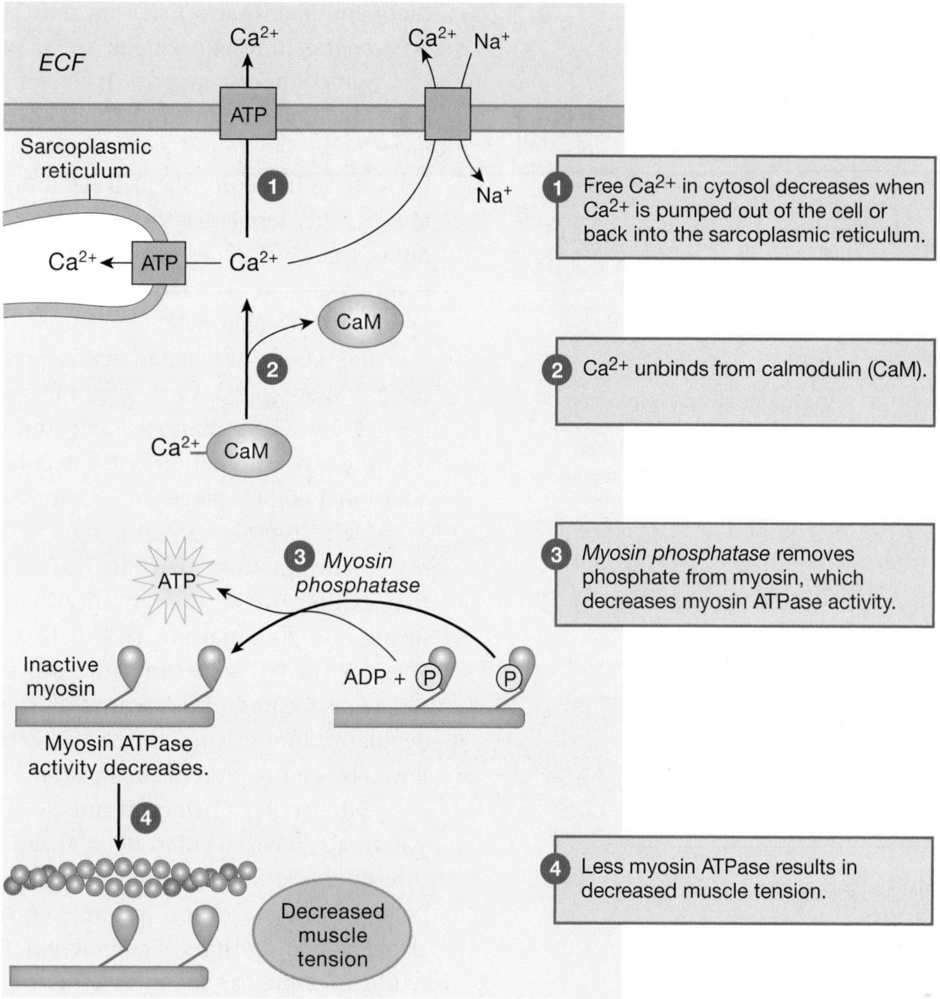

● **FIGURE 12-29** *Relaxation in smooth muscle*

the sarcoplasmic reticulum and the extracellular fluid. Variable amounts of Ca^{2+} enter the cytosol from these sources, creating *graded contractions* whose force varies according to the strength of the Ca^{2+} signal.

The smooth muscle fiber's intracellular Ca^{2+} store is the sarcoplasmic reticulum (SR). SR Ca^{2+} release is mediated primarily by an *IP_3-activated receptor-channel*, which opens in response to signal transduction pathways that produce IP_3. This is very different from skeletal muscle SR, where the calcium release channel is a ryanodine receptor that opens when an action potential reaches the DHP receptor. Because Ca^{2+} stores in smooth muscle are limited, sustained contractions also require influx of Ca^{2+} from the extracellular fluid.

Smooth muscle cells have an interesting mechanism for monitoring and replenishing their internal Ca^{2+} stores. The molecular details are still being worked out, but it appears that when SR Ca^{2+} stores become depleted, a protein sensor on the SR membrane communicates with a sarcolemma membrane protein. That protein then opens a set of **store-operated Ca^{2+} channels** to allow more Ca^{2+} into the cell.

CONCEPT CHECK

27. Compare the following aspects of skeletal and smooth muscle contraction:
    (a) signal for crossbridge activation
    (b) source(s) of calcium for the Ca^{2+} signal
    (c) signal that releases Ca^{2+} from the sarcoplasmic reticulum
28. What happens to contraction if a smooth muscle is placed in a saline bath from which all calcium has been removed?
29. Compare Ca^{2+} release channels in skeletal and smooth muscle sarcoplasmic reticulum.

Answers: p. 445

Ca^{2+} entry from the extracellular fluid takes place through membrane channels whose opening is regulated by membrane stretch, depolarization, or chemical signals. Figure 12-30 ● is a generalized summary of these pathways.

Some smooth muscle cells, such as those in blood vessels, contain stretch-activated Ca^{2+} channels that open when pressure or other force distorts the cell membrane. Because contraction in this instance originates from a property of the muscle fiber itself, it is known as a **myogenic contraction**. Myogenic

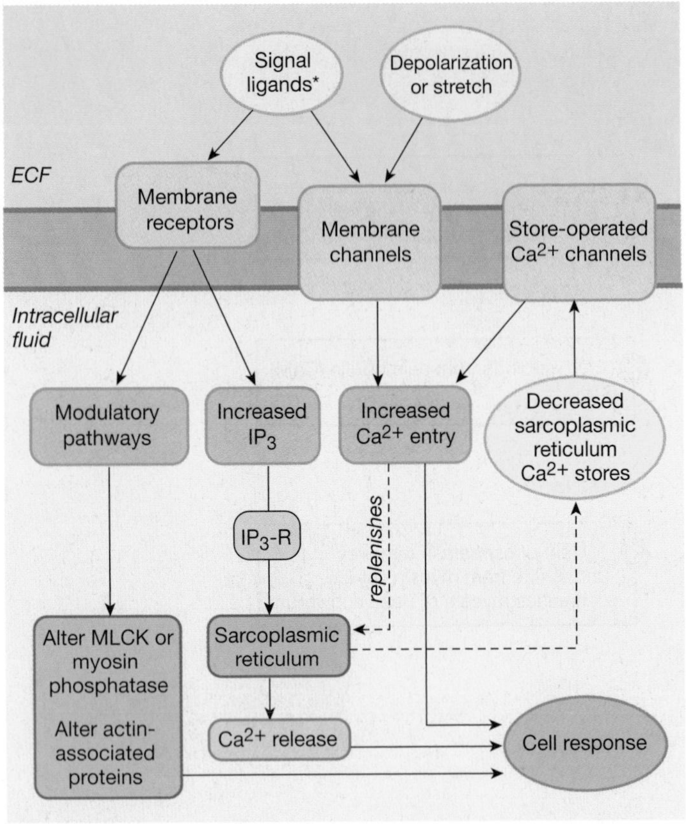

● **FIGURE 12-30** ***Control of smooth muscle contraction***

contractions are common in blood vessels that maintain a certain amount of tone at all times.

Although stretch may initiate a contraction, some types of smooth muscle adapt if the muscle cells are stretched for an extended period of time. As the stretch stimulus continues, the Ca^{2+} channels begin to close in a time-dependent fashion. Then, as Ca^{2+} is pumped out of the cell, the muscle relaxes. This adaptation response explains why the bladder develops tension as it fills, then relaxes as it adjusts to the increased volume. (There is a limit to the amount of stretch the muscle can endure, however, and once a critical volume is reached, the urination reflex empties the bladder.)

Some Smooth Muscles Have Unstable Membrane Potentials

A second major route of Ca^{2+} influx for smooth muscle is entry through voltage-gated Ca^{2+} channels in the cell membrane. In general, a depolarizing stimulus opens channels and makes the cell more likely to contract. Hyperpolarization of the cell decreases the likelihood of contraction. However, the role of membrane potentials in smooth muscle contraction is much more complex than in skeletal muscle, where contraction always begins in response to an action potential.

Some smooth muscles have action potentials that look very much like action potentials in neurons. At the cellular level, however, smooth muscle action potentials are different from those in neurons and skeletal muscle because in smooth muscle, the depolarization phase is due to the entry of Ca^{2+} rather than Na^+. The repolarization phase is similar to that of neurons and in skeletal muscle, however, and is due to the opening of K^+ channels.

In smooth muscle, an action potential is not required to open voltage-gated Ca^{2+} channels. Graded potentials may open a few Ca^{2+} channels, allowing small amounts of Ca^{2+} into the cell. This cation entry depolarizes the cell and opens additional voltage-gated Ca^{2+} channels.

Many types of smooth muscle display unstable resting membrane potentials that vary between −40 and −80 mV. Cells that exhibit cyclic depolarization and repolarization of their membrane potential are said to have **slow wave potentials** (Fig. 12-31a ●). Sometimes the cell simply cycles through a series of subthreshold slow waves. However, if the peak of the depolarization reaches threshold, action potentials fire, followed by contraction of the muscle.

Other types of smooth muscle with unstable membrane potentials have regular depolarizations that always reach threshold and fire an action potential (Fig. 12-31b). These depolarizations are called **pacemaker potentials** because they create regular rhythms of contraction. Pacemaker potentials are found in some cardiac muscles as well as in smooth muscle. Both slow wave and pacemaker potentials are due to ion channels in the cell membrane that spontaneously open and close.

Smooth muscle function does not always depend on firing action potentials. In **pharmacomechanical coupling**, smooth muscle contraction may occur without a significant change in membrane potential (Fig. 12-31c). Chemical signals may also relax muscle tension without a change in membrane potential.

CONCEPT CHECK

30. How do pacemaker potentials differ from slow wave potentials?
31. When tetrodotoxin (TTX), a poison that blocks sodium channels, is applied to certain types of smooth muscle, it does not alter the spontaneous generation of action potentials. From this observation, what conclusion can you draw about the action potentials of these types of smooth muscle? Answers: p. 445

Smooth Muscle Activity Is Regulated by Chemical Signals

In the following sections we look at how Ca^{2+} entry from the extracellular fluid is influenced by neurotransmitters, hormones, or paracrines. These chemical signals may be either excitatory or inhibitory, and they modulate contraction by second messenger action on myosin or actin as well as by influencing Ca^{2+} signals.

Autonomic Neurotransmitters Many smooth muscles have antagonistic control and are innervated by both sympathetic and parasympathetic neurons. However, other smooth muscles, such as those found in blood vessels, are controlled by only one of the two autonomic branches. In this type of *tonic control,* the response is graded by increasing or decreasing the amount of neurotransmitter released onto the muscle.

As we have seen, a neurotransmitter can have different effects in different tissues, depending on the receptors to which it binds. For this reason, both the neurotransmitter and its receptor determine the response of a smooth muscle to neural stimulation. Adrenergic and cholinergic muscarinic receptors act via IP_3 and cAMP second messenger systems. The exact response of the muscle depends on the adrenergic or cholinergic receptor subtype that is activated.

In addition to norepinephrine and acetylcholine, an amazing variety of other neurotransmitters are active in smooth muscle. In many instances we know how these chemicals affect smooth muscle contraction, but we do not understand the reflex pathways that trigger their release.

CONCEPT CHECK

32. How can a neuron alter the amount of neurotransmitter it releases? (*Hint:* See Fig. 8-13, p. 267.)
33. Explain how hyperpolarization decreases the likelihood of contraction in smooth muscle. Answers: p. 445

Hormones and Paracrines Hormones and paracrines also control smooth muscle contraction—unlike skeletal muscle, whose contraction is controlled only by the nervous system. Smooth muscles in the cardiovascular, gastrointestinal, urinary, respiratory, and reproductive systems respond either to blood-borne or to locally released chemicals. For example, asthma is a condition in which smooth muscle of the airways constricts in response to histamine release. This constriction can be reversed by the administration of epinephrine, a neurohormone that relaxes smooth muscle and dilates the airway. Note from this example that not all physiological responses are adaptive or favorable to the body: constriction of the airways triggered during an asthma attack, if left untreated, can be fatal.

Another important paracrine that affects smooth muscle contraction is *nitric oxide* [p. 191]. This gas is synthesized by the endothelial lining of blood vessels and relaxes adjacent smooth muscle that regulates the diameter of the blood vessels. For many years, the identity of this *endothelium-derived relaxing factor*, or EDRF, eluded scientists even though its presence could be demonstrated experimentally. We know now that EDRF is nitric oxide, an important paracrine in many systems of the body.

Although smooth muscles do not have nearly the mass of skeletal muscles, they play a critical role in the function of most organ systems. You will learn more about smooth muscle physiology in the chapters to come.

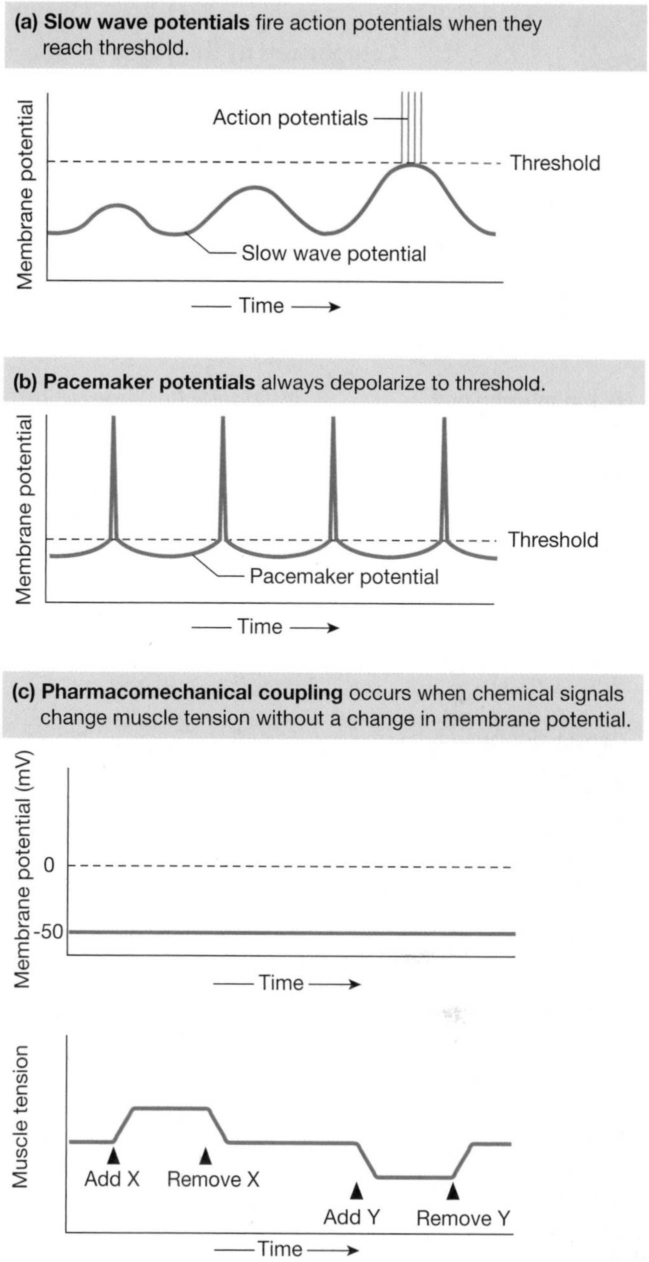
(a) Slow wave potentials fire action potentials when they reach threshold.
Membrane potential
Action potentials
Threshold
Slow wave potential
Time
(b) Pacemaker potentials always depolarize to threshold.
Membrane potential
Threshold
Pacemaker potential
Time
(c) Pharmacomechanical coupling occurs when chemical signals change muscle tension without a change in membrane potential.
Membrane potential (mV)
0
-50
Time
Muscle tension
Add X
Remove X
Add Y
Remove Y
Time

● **FIGURE 12-31** ***Membrane potentials vary in smooth muscle.***

CARDIAC MUSCLE

Cardiac muscle, the specialized muscle of the heart, shares features with both smooth and skeletal muscle (Tbl. 12-3 ●). Like skeletal muscle fibers, cardiac muscle fibers are striated and have a sarcomere structure. However, cardiac muscle fibers are shorter than skeletal muscle fibers, may be branched, and have a single nucleus (unlike multinucleate skeletal muscle fibers).

TABLE 12-3 Comparison of the Three Muscle Types

	SKELETAL	SMOOTH	CARDIAC
Appearance under light microscope	Striated	Smooth	Striated
Fiber arrangement	Sarcomeres	Oblique bundles	Sarcomeres
Location	Attached to bones; a few sphincters close off hollow organs	Forms the walls of hollow organs and tubes; some sphincters	Heart muscle
Tissue morphology	Multinucleate; large, cylindrical fibers	Uninucleate; small spindle-shaped fibers	Uninucleate; shorter branching fibers
Internal structure	T-tubule and sarcoplasmic reticulum	No t-tubules; sarcoplasmic reticulum reduced or absent	T-tubule and sarcoplasmic reticulum
Fiber proteins	Actin, myosin; troponin and tropomyosin	Actin, myosin, tropomyosin	Actin, myosin; troponin and tropomyosin
Control	• Ca^{2+} and troponin • Fibers independent of one another	• Ca^{2+} and calmodulin • Fibers electrically linked via gap junctions	• Ca^{2+} and troponin • Fibers electrically linked via gap junctions
Contraction speed	Fastest	Slowest	Intermediate
Contraction force of single fiber twitch	Not graded	Graded	Graded
Initiation of contraction	Requires ACh from motor neuron	Stretch, chemical signals. Can be autorhythmic	Autorhythmic
Neural control of contraction	Somatic motor neuron	Autonomic neurons	Autonomic neurons
Hormonal influence on contraction	None	Multiple hormones	Epinephrine

As in single-unit smooth muscle, cardiac muscle fibers are electrically linked to one another. The gap junctions are contained in specialized cell junctions known as *intercalated disks*. Some cardiac muscle, like some smooth muscle, exhibits pacemaker potentials. In addition, cardiac muscle is under sympathetic and parasympathetic control as well as hormonal control. In Chapter 14 you will learn more about cardiac muscle and how it functions within the heart.

RUNNING PROBLEM CONCLUSION

Periodic Paralysis

In this running problem, you were introduced to hyperkalemic periodic paralysis (hyperKPP), a condition caused by a genetic defect in voltage-gated Na^+ channels on muscle cell membranes. The periodic paralyses are a family of related disorders caused by muscle ion channel mutations. To learn more about periodic paralyses, visit the Periodic Paralysis Newsdesk at *www.hkpp.org*. Read the information there to compare the hyperkalemic and hypokalemic forms of the disease. For a more detailed discussion of these two conditions, read GeneReviews on the GeneTests web site (*www.genetests.org*).

Now check your understanding of this running problem by comparing your answers with the information in the following summary table.

(continued)

	QUESTION	FACTS	INTEGRATION AND ANALYSIS
1	When Na^+ channels on the muscle membrane open, which way does Na^+ move?	Na^+ is more concentrated in the ECF than in the ICF, and cells have a negative membrane potential.	The electrochemical gradient causes Na^+ to move into cells.
2	What effect would continued movement of Na^+ have on the membrane potential of muscle fibers?	The resting membrane potential of cells is negative relative to the extracellular fluid.	The influx of positive charge depolarizes the muscle, and it remains depolarized.
3	What ion is responsible for the repolarization phase of the muscle action potential, and in which direction does this ion move across the muscle fiber membrane? How might this be linked to hyperKPP?	In the repolarization phase of the action potential, K^+ leaves the cell.	During repeated contractions, K^+ leaves the muscle fiber, which could contribute to elevated extracellular $[K^+]$ (hyperkalemia).
4	Draw a map to explain why a Na^+ channel that does not inactivate results in a muscle that cannot contract (flaccid paralysis).	During an attack, the Na^+ channels remain open and continuously admit Na^+, and the muscle fiber remains depolarized.	If the muscle fiber is unable to repolarize, it cannot fire additional action potentials. The first action potential causes a twitch, but the muscle then goes into a state of flaccid (uncontracted) paralysis.
5	Explain why oral glucose might help bring Paul out of his paralysis. (Hint: What happens to the extracellular K^+ level when Na^+-K^+-ATPase is more active?)	The Na^+-K^+-ATPase moves K^+ into cells and Na^+ out of cells.	Providing glucose to cells triggers insulin release. Insulin increases Na^+-K^+-ATPase activity, which removes Na^+ from the cells and helps them repolarize.

407 420 422 431 433 433 440

CHAPTER SUMMARY

Muscles exhibit many of the physiological properties introduced in Chapter 1. They provide an excellent system for studying *structure-function* relationships at all levels, from actin, myosin, and sliding filaments in the cell to muscles pulling on bones and joints. *Mechanical properties* of muscles that influence contraction include elastic components, such as the protein titin and the series elastic elements of the intact muscle. *Compartmentation* is essential to muscle function, as demonstrated by the concentration of Ca^{2+} in the sarcoplasmic reticulum and the key role of Ca^{2+} signals in initiating contraction. The *law of mass action* is at work in the dynamics of Ca^{2+}-calmodulin and Ca^{2+}-troponin binding and unbinding. Muscles also show how *biological energy use* transforms stored energy in ATP's chemical bonds to the movement of motor proteins.

Muscles provide many examples of *communication* and *control* in the body. Communication occurs on a scale as small as electrical signals spreading among smooth muscle cells via gap junctions, or as large as a somatic motor neuron innervating multiple muscle fibers. Skeletal muscles are controlled only by somatic motor neurons, but smooth and cardiac muscle have complex regulation that ranges from neurotransmitters to hormones and paracrines.

1. Muscles generate motion, force, and heat. (p. 407)
2. The three types of muscle are **skeletal muscle**, **cardiac muscle**, and **smooth muscle**. Skeletal and cardiac muscles are **striated muscles**. (p. 407; Fig. 12-1)
3. Skeletal muscles are controlled by somatic motor neurons. Cardiac and smooth muscle are controlled by autonomic innervation, paracrines, and hormones. Some smooth and cardiac muscles are autorhythmic and contract spontaneously. (p. 407)

Skeletal Muscle

iP Muscular Physiology

4. Skeletal muscles are usually attached to bones by tendons. The **origin** is the end of the muscle attached closest to the trunk or to the more stationary bone. The **insertion** is the more distal or mobile attachment. (p. 408)
5. At a flexible joint, muscle contraction moves the skeleton. **Flexors** bring bones closer together; **extensors** move bones away from each other. Flexor-extensor pairs are examples of **antagonistic muscle groups**. (p. 408; Fig. 12-2)

6. A skeletal muscle is a collection of **muscle fibers**, large cells with many nuclei. (p. 408; Fig. 12-3, Tbl. 12-1)
7. **T-tubules** allow action potentials to move rapidly into the interior of the fiber and release calcium from the **sarcoplasmic reticulum**. (p. 408; Fig. 12-4)
8. **Myofibrils** are intracellular bundles of contractile and elastic proteins. **Thick filaments** are made of **myosin**. **Thin filaments** are made mostly of **actin**. **Titin** and **nebulin** hold thick and thin filaments in position. (pp. 408, 411; Figs. 12-3, 12-6)
9. Myosin binds to actin, creating **crossbridges** between the thick and thin filaments. (p. 411; Fig. 12-3d)
10. One **sarcomere** is composed of two **Z disks** and the filaments between them. A sarcomere is divided into **I bands** (thin filaments only), an **A band** that runs the length of a thick filament, and a central **H zone** occupied by thick filaments only. The **M line** and Z disks represent attachment sites for myosin and actin, respectively. (pp. 411–412; Fig. 12-5)
11. The force created by a contracting muscle is called **muscle tension**. The **load** is a weight or force that opposes contraction of a muscle. (p. 413)
12. The **sliding filament theory of contraction** states that during contraction, overlapping thick and thin filaments slide past each other in an energy-dependent manner as a result of actin-myosin crossbridge movement. (p. 414; Fig. 12-8)
13. In relaxed muscle, **tropomyosin** partially blocks the myosin-binding site on actin. To initiate contraction, Ca^{2+} binds to **troponin**. This unblocks the myosin-binding sites and allows myosin to complete its power stroke. (p. 415; Fig. 12-9)
14. During relaxation, the sarcoplasmic reticulum uses a **Ca^{2+}-ATPase** to pump Ca^{2+} back into its lumen. (p. 419)
15. Myosin converts energy from ATP into motion. **Myosin ATPase** hydrolyzes ATP to ADP and P_i. (p. 415; Fig. 12-10)
16. When myosin releases P_i, the myosin head moves in the **power stroke**. At the end of the power stroke, myosin releases ADP. The cycle ends in the **rigor state**, with myosin tightly bound to actin. (pp. 416–417; Fig. 12-10)
17. In **excitation-contraction coupling**, a somatic motor neuron releases ACh, which initiates a skeletal muscle action potential that leads to contraction. (p. 417; Fig. 12-11a)
18. Voltage-sensing **DHP receptors** in the t-tubules open **Ca^{2+} release channels** in the sarcoplasmic reticulum. (p. 418; Fig. 12-11b)
19. A single contraction-relaxation cycle is known as a **twitch**. The **latent period** between the end of the muscle action potential and the beginning of muscle tension development represents the time required for Ca^{2+} release and binding to troponin. (p. 419; Fig. 12-12)
20. Muscle fibers store energy for contraction in **phosphocreatine**. Anaerobic metabolism of glucose is a rapid source of ATP but is not efficient. Aerobic metabolism is very efficient but requires an adequate supply of oxygen to the muscles. (p. 420; Fig. 12-13)
21. **Muscle fatigue** is a reversible condition in which a muscle is no longer able to generate or sustain the expected power output. Fatigue has multiple causes. (p. 421; Fig. 12-14)
22. Skeletal muscle fibers can be classified on the basis of their speed of contraction and resistance to fatigue into **fast-twitch glycolytic fibers**, **fast-twitch oxidative-glycolytic fibers**, and **slow-twitch (oxidative) fibers**. Oxidative fibers are the most fatigue resistant. (p. 422; Fig. 12-15; Tbl. 12-2)
23. **Myoglobin** is an oxygen-binding pigment that transfers oxygen to the interior of the muscle fiber. (p. 423)
24. The tension of a skeletal muscle contraction is determined by the length of the sarcomeres before contraction begins. (p. 423; Fig. 12-16)
25. Increasing the stimulus frequency causes summation of twitches with an increase of tension. A state of maximal contraction is known as **tetanus**. (p. 425; Fig. 12-17)
26. A **motor unit** is composed of a group of muscle fibers and the somatic motor neuron that controls them. The number of muscle fibers in a motor unit varies, but all fibers in a single motor unit are of the same fiber type. (p. 426; Fig. 12-18)
27. The force of contraction within a skeletal muscle can be increased by **recruitment** of additional motor units. (p. 427)

Mechanics of Body Movement

28. An **isotonic contraction** creates force as the muscle shortens and moves a load. An **isometric contraction** creates force without moving a load. *Lengthening contractions* create force while the muscle lengthens. (p. 427; Fig. 12-19)
29. Isometric contractions occur because **series elastic elements** allow the fibers to maintain constant length even though the sarcomeres are shortening and creating tension. (p. 428; Fig. 12-20)
30. The body uses its bones and joints as **levers** and **fulcrums**. Most lever-fulcrum systems in the body maximize the distance and speed that a load can be moved but also require that muscles do more work than they would without the lever. (p. 428; Figs. 12-21, 12-22)
31. Contraction speed is a function of muscle fiber type and load. Contraction is fastest when the load on the muscle is zero. (p. 429; Fig. 12-23)

Smooth Muscle

32. Smooth muscle is slower than skeletal muscle but can sustain contractions for longer without fatiguing. (p. 432; Fig. 12-24)
33. **Single-unit smooth muscle** contracts as a single unit when depolarizations pass from cell to cell through gap junctions. In **multi-unit smooth muscle**, individual muscle fibers are stimulated independently. (pp. 433–434; Fig. 12-25)
34. Actin and myosin are arranged along the periphery of a smooth muscle cell. Smooth muscle actin lacks troponin. (p. 434; Fig. 12-27)
35. Smooth muscle has less sarcoplasmic reticulum, and its primary Ca^{2+} release channel is an **IP_3-receptor channel**. Calcium also enters the cell from the extracellular fluid (p. 434)
36. In smooth muscle contraction, Ca^{2+} binds to **calmodulin** and activates **myosin light chain kinase** (MLCK). (p. 435; Fig. 12-28)
37. MLCK phosphorylates **myosin light protein chains**, which activates myosin ATPase. This allows crossbridge power strokes. (p. 435; Fig. 12-28)
38. During relaxation, Ca^{2+} is pumped out of the cytosol, and myosin light chains are dephosphorylated by **myosin phosphatase**. (p. 436; Fig. 12-29)
39. Smooth muscle contraction is controlled by sympathetic and parasympathetic neurons and a variety of chemical signals. (p. 437; Fig. 12-30)
40. In **myogenic contraction**, stretch opens membrane Ca^{2+} channels. (p. 437)
41. The rising phase of smooth muscle action potentials is due to Ca^{2+} entry rather than Na^+ entry. (p. 438)
42. Unstable membrane potentials in smooth muscle take the form of either **slow wave potentials** or **pacemaker potentials**. (p. 438; Fig. 12-31a, b)

43. In **pharmacomechanical coupling**, Ca^{2+} entry causes smooth muscle contraction without a significant change in membrane potential. (p. 438; Fig. 12-31c)

Cardiac Muscle

44. Cardiac muscle fibers are striated, have a single nucleus, and are electrically linked through gap junctions. Cardiac muscle shares features with both skeletal and smooth muscle. (pp. 439–440; Tbl. 12-3)

QUESTIONS

(Answers to the Review Questions begin on page A1.)

THE PHYSIOLOGY PLACE

Access more review material online at **The Physiology Place** web site. There you'll find review questions, problem-solving activities, case studies, flashcards, and direct links to both *Interactive Physiology®* and *PhysioEx™*. To access the site, go to *www.physiologyplace.com* and select *Human Physiology*, Fifth Edition.

LEVEL ONE REVIEWING FACTS AND TERMS

1. The three types of muscle tissue found in the human body are ________, ________, and ________. Which type is attached to the bones, enabling it to control body movement?
2. Which two muscle types are striated?
3. Which type of muscle tissue is controlled only by somatic motor neurons?
4. Which of the following statement(s) is(are) true about skeletal muscles?
   (a) They constitute about 60% of a person's total body weight.
   (b) They position and move the skeleton.
   (c) The insertion of the muscle is more distal or mobile than the origin.
   (d) They are often paired into antagonistic muscle groups called flexors and extensors.
5. Arrange the following skeletal muscle components in order, from outermost to innermost: sarcolemma, connective tissue sheath, thick and thin filaments, myofibrils.
6. The modified endoplasmic reticulum of skeletal muscle is called the ________. Its role is to sequester ________ ions.
7. T-tubules allow ________ to move to the interior of the muscle fiber.
8. List six proteins that make up the myofibrils. Which protein creates the power stroke for contraction?
9. List the letters used to label the elements of a sarcomere. Which band has a Z disk in the middle? Which is the darkest band? Why? Which element forms the boundaries of a sarcomere? Name the line that divides the A band in half. What is the function of this line?
10. Briefly explain the functions of titin and nebulin.
11. During contraction, the ________ band remains a constant length. This band is composed primarily of ________ molecules. Which components approach each other during contraction?
12. Explain the sliding filament theory.
13. Explain the roles of troponin, tropomyosin, and Ca^{2+} in skeletal muscle contraction.
14. Which neurotransmitter is released by somatic motor neurons?
15. What is the motor end plate, and what kinds of receptors are found there? Explain how neurotransmitter binding to these receptors creates an action potential.
16. Match the following characteristics with the appropriate type(s) of muscle.

(a) has the largest diameter	1. fast-twitch glycolytic fibers
(b) uses anaerobic metabolism, thus fatigues quickly	2. fast-twitch oxidative-glycolytic fibers
(c) has the most blood vessels	3. slow-twitch oxidative fibers
(d) has some myoglobin	
(e) is used for quick, fine movements	
(f) is also called red muscle	
(g) uses a combination of oxidative and glycolytic metabolism	
(h) has the most mitochondria	

17. A single contraction-relaxation cycle in a skeletal muscle fiber is known as a(n) ________.
18. List the steps of skeletal muscle contraction that require ATP.
19. The basic unit of contraction in an intact skeletal muscle is the ________. The force of contraction within a skeletal muscle is increased by ________ additional motor units.
20. The two functional types of smooth muscle are ________ and ________.

LEVEL TWO REVIEWING CONCEPTS

21. Make a map of muscle fiber structure using the following terms. Add additional terms if you like.

actin	myosin
Ca^{2+}	nucleus
cell	regulatory protein
cell membrane	sarcolemma
contractile protein	sarcoplasm
crossbridges	sarcoplasmic reticulum
cytoplasm	titin
elastic protein	tropomyosin
glycogen	troponin
mitochondria	t-tubule
muscle fiber	

22. How does an action potential in a muscle fiber trigger a Ca^{2+} signal inside the fiber?
23. Muscle fibers depend on a continuous supply of ATP. How do the fibers in the different types of muscle generate ATP?
24. Define muscle fatigue. Summarize factors that could play a role in its development. How can muscle fibers adapt to resist fatigue?
25. Explain how you vary the strength and effort made by your muscles in picking up a pencil versus picking up a full gallon container of milk.
26. Compare and contrast the cellular anatomy and neural and chemical control of contraction in skeletal and smooth muscle.

27. Arrange the following terms to create a map of skeletal muscle excitation, contraction, and relaxation. Terms may be used more than once. Add any additional terms you like.

acetylcholine	motor end plate
ACh receptor	myosin
actin	Na^+
action potential	neuromuscular junction
ADP	P_i
ATP	power stroke
axon terminal	relaxation
Ca^{2+}	rigor state
Ca^{2+}-ATPase	sarcoplasmic reticulum
calcium-release channels	somatic motor neuron
contraction	tropomyosin
crossbridge	troponin
DHP receptor	t-tubules
end-plate potential	voltage-gated Ca^{2+} channels
exocytosis	

28. What is the role of the sarcoplasmic reticulum in muscular contraction? How can smooth muscle contract when it has so little sarcoplasmic reticulum?
29. Compare and contrast:
    (a) fast-twitch oxidative-glycolytic, fast-twitch glycolytic, and slow-twitch muscle fibers
    (b) a twitch and tetanus
    (c) action potentials in motor neurons and action potentials in skeletal muscles
    (d) temporal summation in motor neurons and summation in skeletal muscles
    (e) isotonic contraction and isometric contraction
    (f) slow-wave and pacemaker potentials
    (g) the source and role of Ca^{2+} in skeletal and smooth muscle contraction
30. Explain the different factors that influence Ca^{2+} entry and release in smooth muscle fibers.

LEVEL THREE PROBLEM SOLVING

31. One way that scientists study muscles is to put them into a state of rigor by removing ATP. In this condition, actin and myosin are strongly linked but unable to move. On the basis of what you know about muscle contraction, predict what would happen to these muscles in a state of rigor if you (a) added ATP but no free calcium ions; (b) added ATP with a substantial concentration of calcium ions.
32. When curare, a South American Indian arrow poison, is placed on a nerve-muscle preparation, the muscle does not contract when the nerve is stimulated, even though neurotransmitter is still being released from the nerve. Give all possible explanations for the action of curare that you can think of.
33. On the basis of what you have learned about muscle fiber types and metabolism, predict what variations in structure you would find among these athletes:
    (a) a 7 foot, 2 inch tall, 325-pound basketball player
    (b) a 5 foot, 10 inch tall, 180-pound steer wrestler
    (c) a 5 foot, 7 inch tall, 130-pound female figure skater
    (d) a 4 foot, 11 inch tall, 89-pound female gymnast

LEVEL FOUR QUANTITATIVE PROBLEMS

34. Look at the following graph, created from data published in "Effect of ambient temperature on human skeletal muscle metabolism during fatiguing submaximal exercise," *Journal of Applied Physiology* 86(3):902–908, 1999. What hypotheses might you develop about the cause(s) of muscle fatigue based on these data?

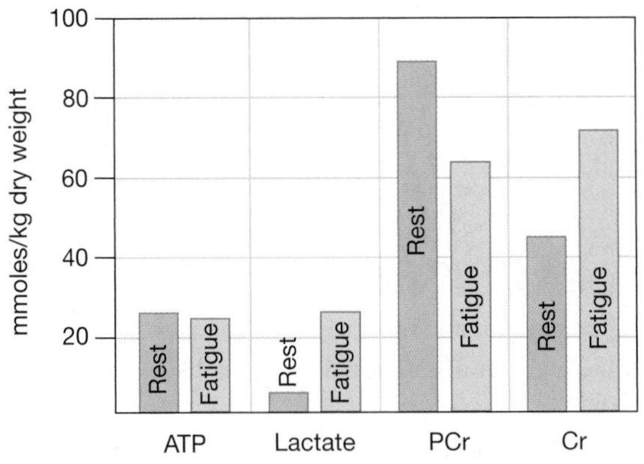

Muscle metabolites in resting muscle and after cycling exercise to fatigue

35. Use the arm in Figure 12-21b to answer the following questions.
    (a) How much force would a biceps muscle inserted 4 cm from the fulcrum need to exert to hold the arm stationary at a 90° angle? How does this force compare with the force needed when the insertion point is 5 cm from the fulcrum?
    (b) Suppose a 7-kg weight band is placed around the wrist 20 cm from the fulcrum. How much force does the biceps inserted 5 cm from the fulcrum need to exert to hold the arm stationary at a 90° angle? How does this force compare with the force needed to keep the arm horizontal in the situation shown in Figure 12.21c, with the same weight in the hand (25 cm from the fulcrum)?

ANSWERS

Answers to Concept Check Questions

Page 408

1. Some examples are biceps/triceps in the upper arm; hamstring (flexor)/quadriceps (extensor) in the upper leg; tibialis anterior (flexor)/gastrocnemius (extensor) for foot movement at the ankle.

Page 413

2. Ends of the A bands are darkest because they are where the thick and thin filaments overlap.
3. T-tubules allow action potentials to travel from the surface of the muscle fiber to its interior.
4. The banding pattern of organized filaments in the sarcomere forms striations in the muscle.

Page 413

5. A neuromuscular junction consists of axon terminals from one somatic motor neuron, the synaptic cleft, and the motor end plate on the muscle fiber.
6. The chemical signal at a neuromuscular junction is acetylcholine.

Page 417

7. Each myosin molecule has binding sites for ATP and actin.
8. F-actin is a polymer filament of actin made from globular G-actin molecules.
9. Enzymes that hydrolyze ATP are ATPases.

Page 417

10. Titin is an elastic fiber in the sarcomere.
11. The crossbridges do not all unlink at one time, so while some myosin heads are free and swiveling, others are still tightly bound.

Page 420

12. The release of myosin heads from actin requires ATP binding. Energy from ATP is required for the power stroke. Relaxation does not directly require ATP, but relaxation cannot occur unless Ca^{2+} is pumped back into the sarcoplasmic reticulum using a Ca^{2+}-ATPase.
13. The events of the latent period include creation of the muscle action potential, release of Ca^{2+} from the sarcoplasmic reticulum, and diffusion of Ca^{2+} to the contractile filaments.

Page 421

14. *Creatine* is the substrate, and *kinase* tells you that this enzyme phosphorylates the substrate.
15. Because creatine kinase catalyzes the reaction in both directions, the relative concentrations of the reactants and products determine the direction of the reaction. The reaction obeys the law of mass action and goes to equilibrium.

Page 422

16. Increasing extracellular K^+ causes the cell to depolarize and become less negative.

Page 426

17. Tension
18. Strength of the graded potential

Page 426

19. A marathoner probably has more slow-twitch muscle fibers, and a sprinter probably has more fast-twitch muscle fibers.

Page 427

20. Increased motor neuron firing rate causes summation in a muscle fiber, which increases the force of contraction.
21. The nervous system increases the force of contraction by recruiting additional motor units.

Page 431

22. If the muscle insertion point is farther from the joint, the leverage is better and a contraction creates more rotational force.

Page 434

23. Multi-unit smooth muscle increases force by recruiting additional muscle fibers; single-unit smooth muscle increases force by increasing Ca^{2+} entry.

Page 434

24. Dense bodies are analogous to Z disks.
25. Smooth muscle myosin is longer, has heads the entire length of the filament, and has slower ATPase activity.
26. Smooth muscle actin is longer than skeletal muscle actin, and it lacks troponin.

Page 437

27. (a) Skeletal muscle: Ca^{2+} binds to troponin. Smooth muscle: Myosin phosphorylated. (b) Skeletal muscles: all Ca^{2+} comes from the sarcoplasmic reticulum. Smooth muscle: Ca^{2+} from both SR and ECF. (c) Skeletal muscle: depolarization signal. Smooth muscle: IP_3 signal.
28. Without ECF Ca^{2+}, contraction either decreases or stops altogether because little or no Ca^{2+} is available to initiate the process.
29. Skeletal muscle Ca^{2+}-release (RyR) channels are mechanically linked to DHP receptors. Smooth muscle Ca^{2+}-release channels are activated by IP_3.

Page 438

30. Pacemaker potentials always reach threshold and create regular rhythms of contraction. Slow wave potentials are variable in magnitude and may not reach threshold each time.
31. The depolarization phase of the action potentials must not be due to Na^+ entry.

Page 439

32. More action potentials in the neuron increase neurotransmitter release.
33. Many Ca^{2+} channels open with depolarization; therefore, hyperpolarization decreases the likelihood that these channels open. The presence of Ca^{2+} is necessary for contraction.

Answers to Figure and Graph Questions

Page 419

Fig. 12-12: Both neuronal and muscle action potentials are due to Na^+ entering the fiber during depolarization, and K^+ leaving during repolarization. The neuronal channel for Na^+ entry is a voltage-gated Na^+ channel, but the muscle channel for Na^+ entry is the acetylcholine-gated monovalent cation channel.

Page 430

Fig. 12-21: Biceps force $\times$ 5 cm = 7 kg $\times$ 25 cm = 35 kg (additional force).

Page 431

Fig. 12-22: The hand moves upward at a speed of 5 cm/sec.

Page 431

Fig. 12-23: Contraction is isometric at B because at this point muscle does not shorten. Maximum velocity is at A, where the load on the muscle is zero.

13 Integrative Physiology I: Control of Body Movement

BACKGROUND BASICS

Reflex pathways: **198** Central nervous system: **298** Summation of action potentials: **283** Isometric contraction: **427** Sensory pathways and receptors: **334** Graded potentials: **258** Tonic control: **196** Tendons: **281**

Computer analysis of microarray data showing gene expression.

Extracting signals directly from the brain to directly control robotic devices has been a science fiction theme that seems destined to become fact.

—Dr. Eberhard E. Fetz, *Science News 156: 142, 8/28/99*

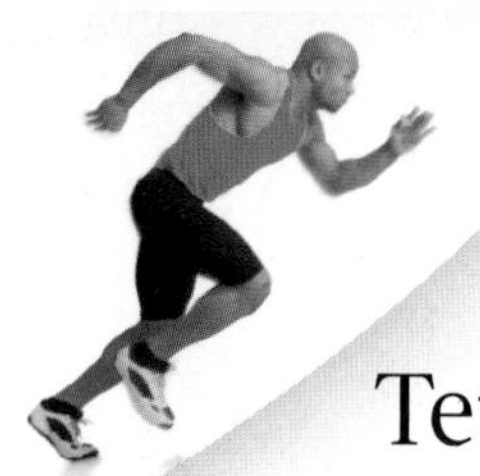

RUNNING PROBLEM

Tetanus

"She hasn't been able to talk to us. We're afraid she may have had a stroke." That is how her neighbors described 77-year-old Cecile Evans when they brought her to the emergency room. But when a neurological examination revealed no problems other than Mrs. Evans's inability to open her mouth and stiffness in her neck, emergency room physician Dr. Doris Ling began to consider other diagnoses. She noticed some scratches healing on Mrs. Evans's arms and legs and asked the neighbors if they knew what had caused them. "Oh, yes. She told us a few days ago that her dog jumped up and knocked her against the barbed wire fence." At that point, Dr. Ling realized she was probably dealing with her first case of tetanus.

447 448 456 457 462 463

Think back to the baseball pitcher in the last chapter. As he stands on the mound, looking in at the first batter, he receives sensory information from multiple sources: the sound of the crowd, the sight of the batter and the catcher, the smell of grass, the feel of the ball in his hand, and the alignment of his body as he begins his windup. Sensory receptors code this information and send it to the central nervous system (CNS), where it is integrated.

The pitcher acts consciously on some of the information: he decides to throw a fastball. But he processes other information at the subconscious level and acts on it without conscious thought. As he thinks about starting his motion, for instance, he shifts his weight to offset the impending movement of his arm. The integration of sensory information into an involuntary response is the hallmark of a *reflex* [p. 198].

NEURAL REFLEXES

All neural reflexes begin with a stimulus that activates a sensory receptor. The receptor sends information in the form of action potentials through sensory neurons to the CNS [p. 334]. The CNS is the integrating center that evaluates all incoming information and selects an appropriate response. It then initiates action potentials in efferent neurons to direct the response of muscles and glands—the *effectors*.

A key feature of many reflex pathways is *negative feedback,* a concept introduced in Chapter 6 [p. 203]. Feedback signals from muscle and joint receptors keep the CNS continuously informed of changing body position. Some reflexes have a *feedforward* component that allows the body to anticipate a stimulus and begin the response [p. 204]. Bracing yourself in anticipation of a collision is an example of a feedforward response.

TABLE 13-1 Classification of Neural Reflexes

Neural reflexes can be classified by:

1. **Efferent division that controls the effector**
   a. Somatic motor neurons control skeletal muscles.
   b. Autonomic neurons control smooth and cardiac muscle, glands, and adipose tissue.
2. **Integrating region within the central nervous system**
   a. Spinal reflexes do not require input from the brain.
   b. Cranial reflexes are integrated within the brain.
3. **Time at which the reflex develops**
   a. Innate (inborn) reflexes are genetically determined.
   b. Learned (conditioned) reflexes are acquired through experience.
4. **The number of neurons in the reflex pathway**
   a. Monosynaptic reflexes have only two neurons: one afferent (sensory) and one efferent. Only somatic motor reflexes can be monosynaptic.
   b. Polysynaptic reflexes include one or more interneurons between the afferent and efferent neurons. All autonomic reflexes are polysynaptic because they have three neurons: one afferent and two efferent.

Neural Reflex Pathways Can Be Classified in Different Ways

Reflex pathways in the nervous system consist of chains or networks of neurons that link sensory receptors to muscles or glands. Neural reflexes can be classified in several ways (Tbl. 13-1 ●):

1. *By the efferent division of the nervous system that controls the response.* Reflexes that involve somatic motor neurons and skeletal muscles are known as **somatic reflexes**. Reflexes whose responses are controlled by autonomic neurons are called **autonomic reflexes**.
2. *By the CNS location where the reflex is integrated.* **Spinal reflexes** are integrated in the spinal cord. These reflexes may be modulated by higher input from the brain, but they can occur without that input. Reflexes integrated in the brain are called **cranial reflexes**.
3. *By whether the reflex is innate or learned.* Many reflexes are **innate**; in other words, we are born with them, and they are genetically determined. One example is the knee jerk reflex, in which the lower leg kicks out when the patellar tendon at the lower edge of the kneecap is tapped. Other reflexes are acquired through experience [p. 323]. The example of Pavlov's dogs salivating upon hearing a bell is the classic example of a **learned reflex**, also referred to as a **conditioned reflex**.

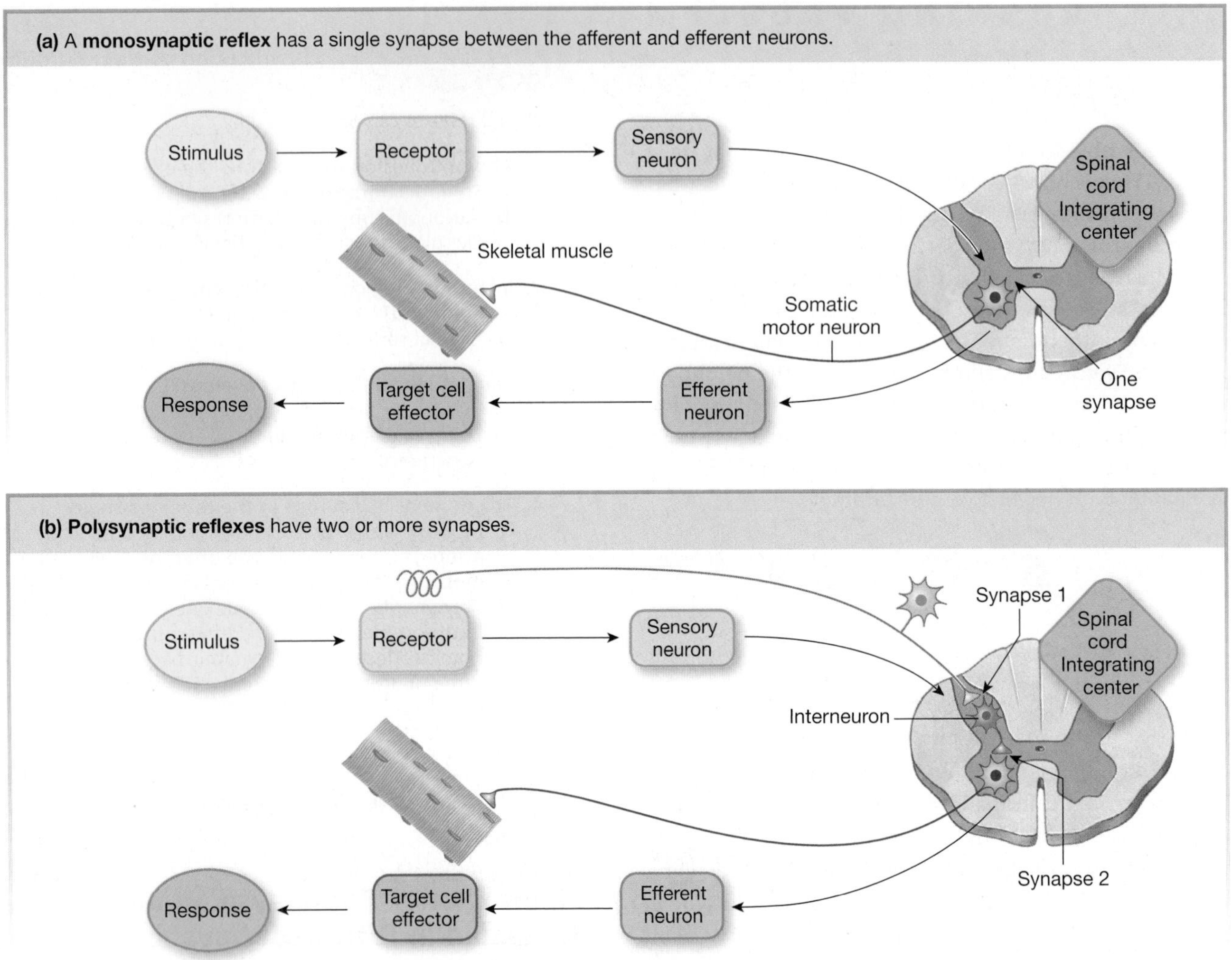

● **FIGURE 13-1** ***Monosynaptic and polysynaptic somatic motor reflexes***

4. *By the number of neurons in the reflex pathway.* The simplest reflex is a **monosynaptic reflex**, named for the single synapse between the two neurons in the pathway: an afferent sensory neuron and an efferent somatic motor neuron. These two neurons synapse in the spinal cord, allowing a signal initiated at the receptor to go directly from the sensory neuron to the motor neuron (Fig. 13-1a ●). (The synapse between the somatic motor neuron and its muscle target is ignored.)

Most reflexes have three or more neurons in the pathway (and at least two synapses), leading to their designation as **polysynaptic reflexes** (Fig. 13-1b). Polysynaptic reflexes may be quite complex, with extensive branching in the CNS to form networks involving multiple interneurons. *Divergence* of pathways allows a single stimulus to affect multiple targets [p. 282]. *Convergence* integrates the input from multiple sources to modulate the response. Recall from Chapter 8 that modulation in polysynaptic pathways may involve excitation or inhibition [p. 284].

RUNNING PROBLEM

Tetanus [*tetanus,* a muscle spasm], also known as lockjaw, is a devastating disease caused by the bacterium *Clostridium tetani.* These bacteria are commonly found in soil and enter the human body through a cut or wound. As the bacteria reproduce in the tissues, they release a protein neurotoxin. This toxin, called *tetanospasmin,* is taken up by somatic motor neurons at the axon terminals. Tetanospasmin then travels along the axons until it reaches the nerve cell body in the spinal cord.

Question 1:

a. ***Tetanospasmin is a protein. By what process is it taken up into neurons? [Hint: p. 158]***

b. ***By what process does it travel up the axon to the nerve cell body? [Hint: p. 252]***

447 448 456 457 462 463

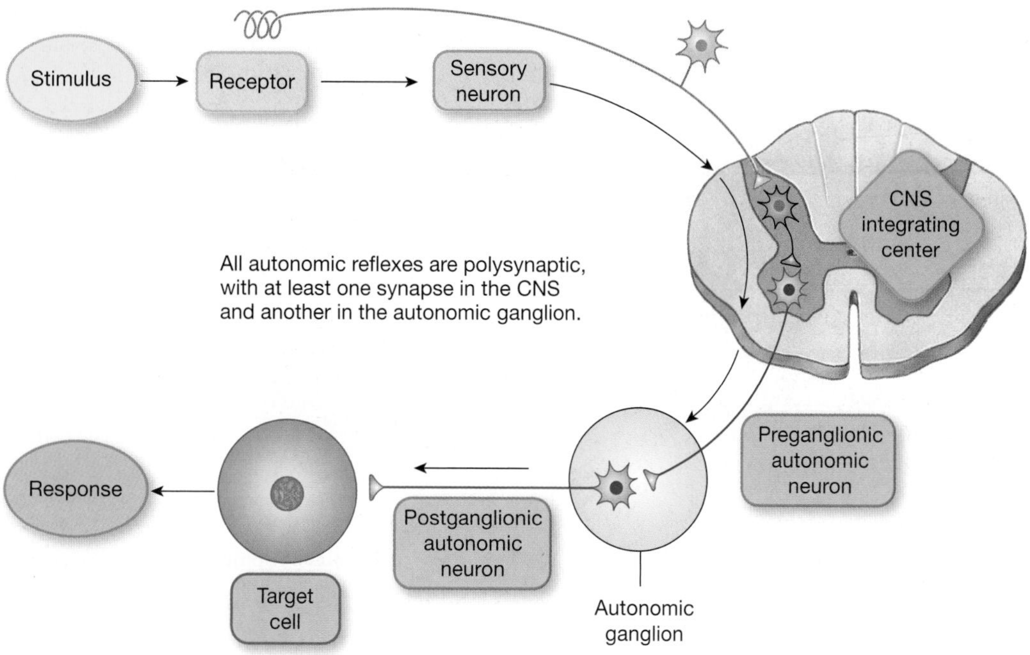

● **FIGURE 13-2** *Autonomic reflexes*

AUTONOMIC REFLEXES

Autonomic reflexes are also known as *visceral reflexes* because they often involve the internal organs of the body. Some visceral reflexes, such as urination and defecation, are spinal reflexes that can take place without input from the brain. However, spinal reflexes are often modulated by excitatory or inhibitory signals from the brain, carried by descending tracts from higher brain centers. For example, urination may be voluntarily initiated by conscious thought, or it may be inhibited by emotion or a stressful situation, such as the presence of other people (a syndrome known as "bashful bladder"). Often, the higher control of a spinal reflex is a learned response. The toilet training we master as toddlers is an example of a learned reflex that the CNS uses to modulate the simple spinal reflex of urination.

Other autonomic reflexes are integrated in the brain, primarily in the hypothalamus, thalamus, and brain stem. These regions contain centers that coordinate body functions needed to maintain homeostasis, such as heart rate, blood pressure, breathing, eating, water balance, and maintenance of body temperature [see Fig. 11-3, p. 388]. The brain stem also contains the integrating centers for autonomic reflexes such as salivating, vomiting, sneezing, coughing, swallowing, and gagging.

An interesting type of autonomic reflex is the conversion of emotional stimuli into visceral responses. The limbic system [p. 312]—the site of primitive drives such as sex, fear, rage, aggression, and hunger—has been called the "visceral brain" because of its role in these emotionally driven reflexes. We speak of "gut feelings" and "butterflies in the stomach"—all transformations of emotion into somatic sensation and visceral function. Other emotion-linked autonomic reflexes include urination, defecation, blushing, blanching, and *piloerection,* in which tiny muscles in the hair follicles pull the shaft of the hair erect ("I was so scared my hair stood on end!").

Autonomic reflexes are all polysynaptic, with at least one synapse in the CNS between the sensory neuron and the preganglionic autonomic neuron, and an additional synapse in the ganglion between the preganglionic and postganglionic neurons (Fig. 13-2 ●).

Many autonomic reflexes are characterized by tonic activity, a continuous stream of action potentials that creates ongoing activity in the effector. For example, the tonic control of blood vessels discussed in Chapter 6 is an example of a continuously active autonomic reflex [p. 196]. You will encounter many autonomic reflexes as you continue your study of the systems of the body.

CONCEPT CHECK

1. List the general steps of a reflex pathway, including the anatomical structures in the nervous system that correspond to each step.
2. If a cell hyperpolarizes, does its membrane potential become more positive or more negative? Does the potential move closer to threshold or farther from threshold?

Answers: p. 466

SKELETAL MUSCLE REFLEXES

Although we are not always aware of them, skeletal muscle reflexes are involved in almost everything we do. Receptors that sense changes in joint movements, muscle tension, and muscle length feed this information to the CNS, which responds in one of two ways. If muscle contraction is the appropriate

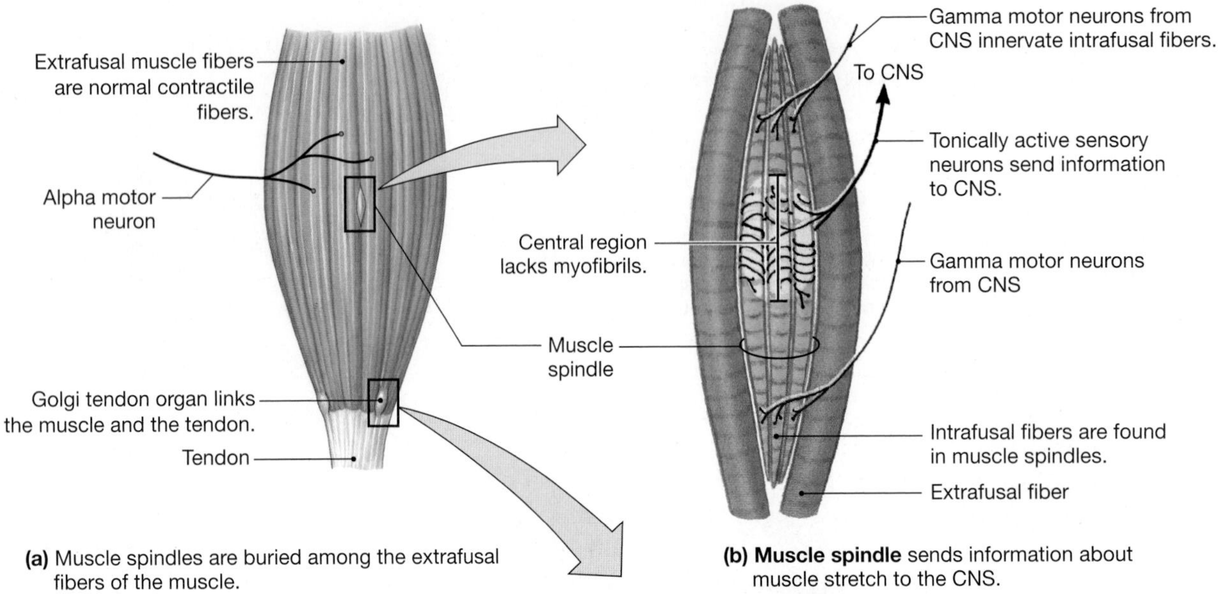

Extrafusal muscle fibers are normal contractile fibers.
Alpha motor neuron
Golgi tendon organ links the muscle and the tendon.
Tendon
Central region lacks myofibrils.
Muscle spindle
Gamma motor neurons from CNS innervate intrafusal fibers.
To CNS
Tonically active sensory neurons send information to CNS.
Gamma motor neurons from CNS
Intrafusal fibers are found in muscle spindles.
Extrafusal fiber

(a) Muscle spindles are buried among the extrafusal fibers of the muscle.

(b) Muscle spindle sends information about muscle stretch to the CNS.

FIGURE QUESTIONS

1. When the muscle shown in (a) is relaxed, which neurons are firing?
   a) muscle spindle gamma motor neuron
   b) muscle spindle sensory neuron
   c) Golgi tendon organ sensory neuron
   d) none of the above

2. Which neuron fires to cause contraction of the extrafusal muscle fibers?
   a) muscle alpha motor neuron
   b) muscle spindle gamma motor neuron
   c) muscle spindle sensory neuron
   d) Golgi tendon organ sensory neuron
   e) none of the above

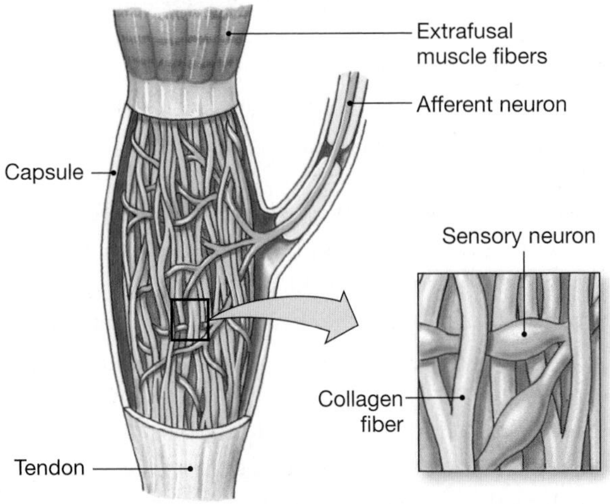

Extrafusal muscle fibers
Afferent neuron
Capsule
Sensory neuron
Collagen fiber
Tendon

(c) Golgi tendon organ consists of sensory nerve endings interwoven among collagen fibers.

● **FIGURE 13-3** ***Muscle spindles and Golgi tendon organs are sensory receptors in muscle.***

response, the CNS activates somatic motor neurons to the muscle fibers. If a muscle needs to be relaxed to achieve the response, sensory input activates inhibitory interneurons in the CNS, and these interneurons *inhibit* activity in somatic motor neurons controlling the muscle.

Recall that excitation of somatic motor neurons always causes contraction in skeletal muscle [p. 417]. There is no inhibitory neuron that synapses on skeletal muscles to cause them to relax. Instead, *relaxation results from the absence of excitatory input by the somatic motor neuron.* Inhibition and excitation of somatic motor neurons and their associated skeletal muscles must occur at synapses within the CNS.

Skeletal muscle reflexes have the following components:

1. *Sensory receptors,* known as **proprioceptors**, are located in skeletal muscles, joint capsules, and ligaments. They monitor the position of our limbs in space, our movements, and the effort we exert in lifting objects.
2. *Sensory neurons* carry the input signal from proprioceptors to the CNS.
3. *The central nervous system* integrates the input signal using networks and pathways of *excitatory and inhibitory interneurons*. In a reflex, sensory information is integrated and acted on subconsciously. However, some sensory information may be integrated in the cerebral cortex and become perception, and some reflexes can be modulated by conscious input.
4. *Somatic motor neurons* carry the output signal. The somatic motor neurons that innervate skeletal muscle contractile fibers are called **alpha motor neurons** (Fig. 13-3a ●).

5. The effectors are contractile skeletal muscle fibers, also known as **extrafusal muscle fibers**. Action potentials in alpha motor neurons cause extrafusal fibers to contract.

Three types of proprioceptors are found in the body: muscle spindles, Golgi tendon organs, and joint receptors. *Joint receptors* are found in the capsules and ligaments around joints in the body. They are stimulated by mechanical distortion that accompanies changes in the relative positioning of bones linked by flexible joints. Sensory information from joint receptors is integrated primarily in the cerebellum.

In the next two sections we examine the function of muscle spindles and Golgi tendon organs, two interesting and unique receptors. These receptors lie inside skeletal muscles and sense changes in muscle length and tension. Their sensory output activates muscle reflexes.

Muscle Spindles Respond to Muscle Stretch

Muscle spindles are stretch receptors that send information to the spinal cord and brain about muscle length and changes in muscle length. They are small, elongated structures scattered among and arranged parallel to the contractile extrafusal muscle fibers (Fig. 13-3a). With the exception of one muscle in the jaw, every skeletal muscle in the body has many muscle spindles. For example, a small muscle in the index finger of a newborn human has on average about 50 spindles.

Each muscle spindle consists of a connective tissue *capsule* that encloses a group of small muscle fibers known as **intrafusal fibers** [*intra-*, within + *fusus*, spindle]. Intrafusal muscle fibers are modified so that the ends are contractile but the central region lacks myofibrils (Fig. 13-3b). The contractile ends of the intrafusal fibers have their own innervation from **gamma motor neurons**. The noncontractile central region of each intrafusal fiber is wrapped by sensory nerve endings that are stimulated by stretch. These sensory neurons project to the spinal cord and synapse directly on alpha motor neurons innervating the muscle in which the spindles lie.

When a muscle is at its resting length, the central region of each muscle spindle is stretched enough to activate the sensory fibers (Fig. 13-4a ●). As a result, sensory neurons from the spindles are tonically active, sending a steady stream of action potentials to the CNS. Because of this tonic activity, even a muscle at rest maintains a certain level of tension, known as **muscle tone**.

Muscle spindles are anchored in parallel to the extrafusal muscle fibers. Any movement that increases muscle length also stretches the muscle spindles and causes their sensory fibers to fire more rapidly (Fig. 13-4b). This creates a reflex contraction of the muscle, which prevents damage from overstretching. The reflex pathway in which muscle stretch initiates a contraction response is known as a **stretch reflex**.

CONCEPT CHECK

3. Using the standard steps of a reflex pathway (stimulus, receptor, and so forth), draw a reflex map of the stretch reflex.

Answers: p. 466

If stretch activates muscle spindles, what happens to spindle activity when a resting muscle contracts and shortens? You might predict that the release of tension on the center of the intrafusal fibers would cause the afferent neurons to slow their firing rate or stop firing altogether, as shown in Figure 13-5b ● (when gamma motor neuron activity is silenced). However, the presence of gamma motor neurons in a normal muscle keeps the muscle spindles active, no matter what the muscle length is.

When alpha motor neurons fire, the muscle shortens and releases tension on the muscle spindle capsule (Fig. 13-5a). Simultaneously, gamma motor neurons innervating the contractile ends of the muscle spindle fire, which causes the ends of intrafusal fibers to contract and shorten. Contraction of the spindle ends lengthens the central region of the spindle and maintains stretch on the sensory nerve endings. As a result, the spindle remains active even when the muscle contracts. Excitation of gamma motor neurons and alpha motor neurons at the same time is a process known as **alpha-gamma coactivation**.

CLINICAL FOCUS

REFLEXES AND MUSCLE TONE

Clinicians use reflexes to investigate the condition of the nervous system and the muscles. For a reflex to be normal, there must be normal conduction through all neurons in the pathway, normal synaptic transmission at the neuromuscular junction, and normal muscle contraction. A reflex that is absent, abnormally slow, or greater than normal (hyperactive) suggests the presence of a pathology. Interestingly, not all abnormal reflexes are caused by neuromuscular disorders. For example, slowed relaxation of the ankle flexion reflex suggests hypothyroidism. (The cellular mechanism linking low thyroid to slow reflexes is not known.) Besides testing reflexes, clinicians assess muscle tone. Even when relaxed and at rest, muscles have a certain resistance to stretch that is the result of continuous (tonic) output by alpha motor neurons. The absence of muscle tone or a muscle's resistance to being passively stretched by the examiner (increased tone) indicates a problem with the pathways that control muscle contraction.

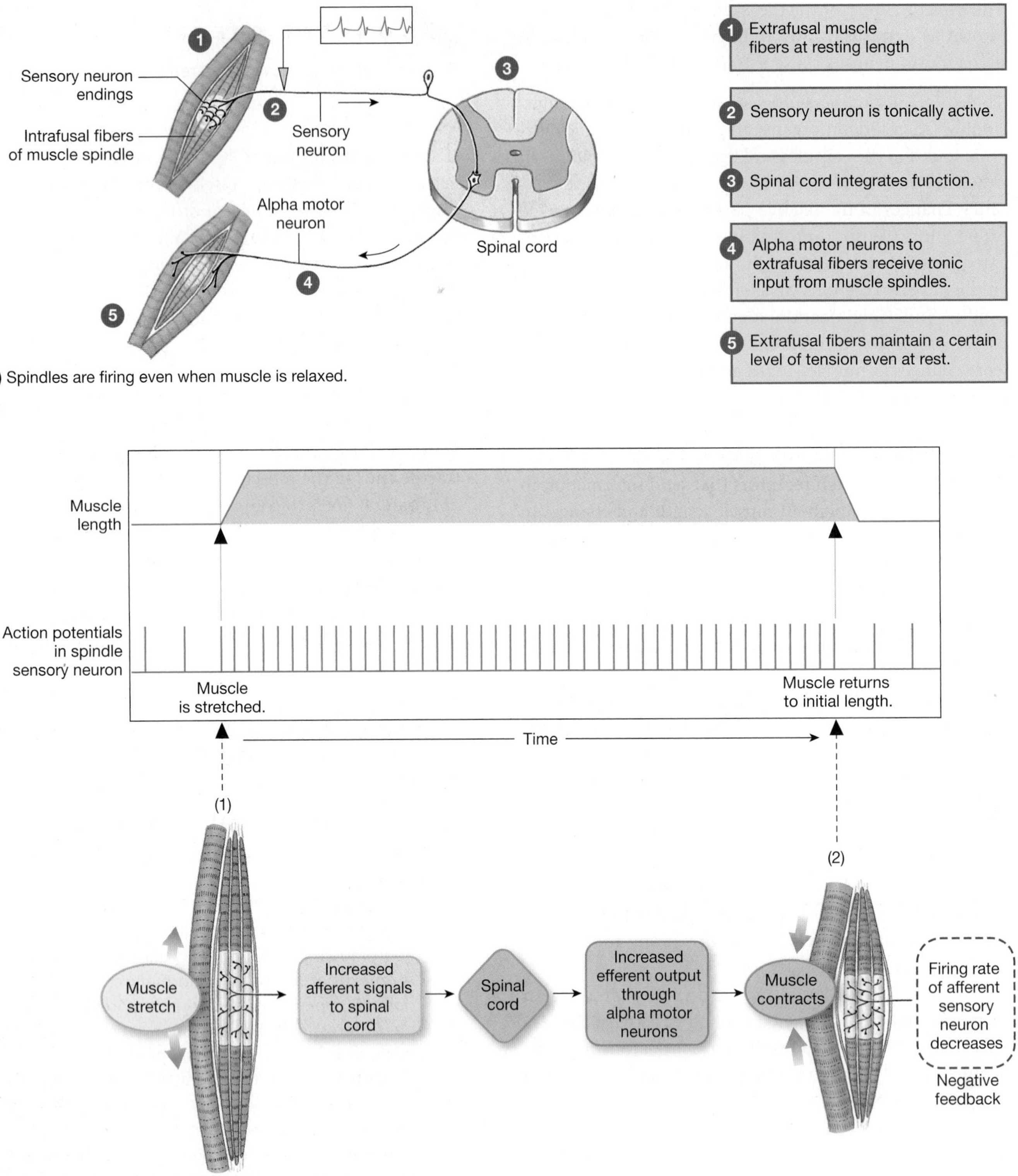

(a) Spindles are firing even when muscle is relaxed.

(b) Muscle stretch can trigger a stretch reflex, which contracts the muscle to avoid over-stretching.

● **FIGURE 13-4** ***Muscle spindles monitor muscle length and prevent over-stretching.***

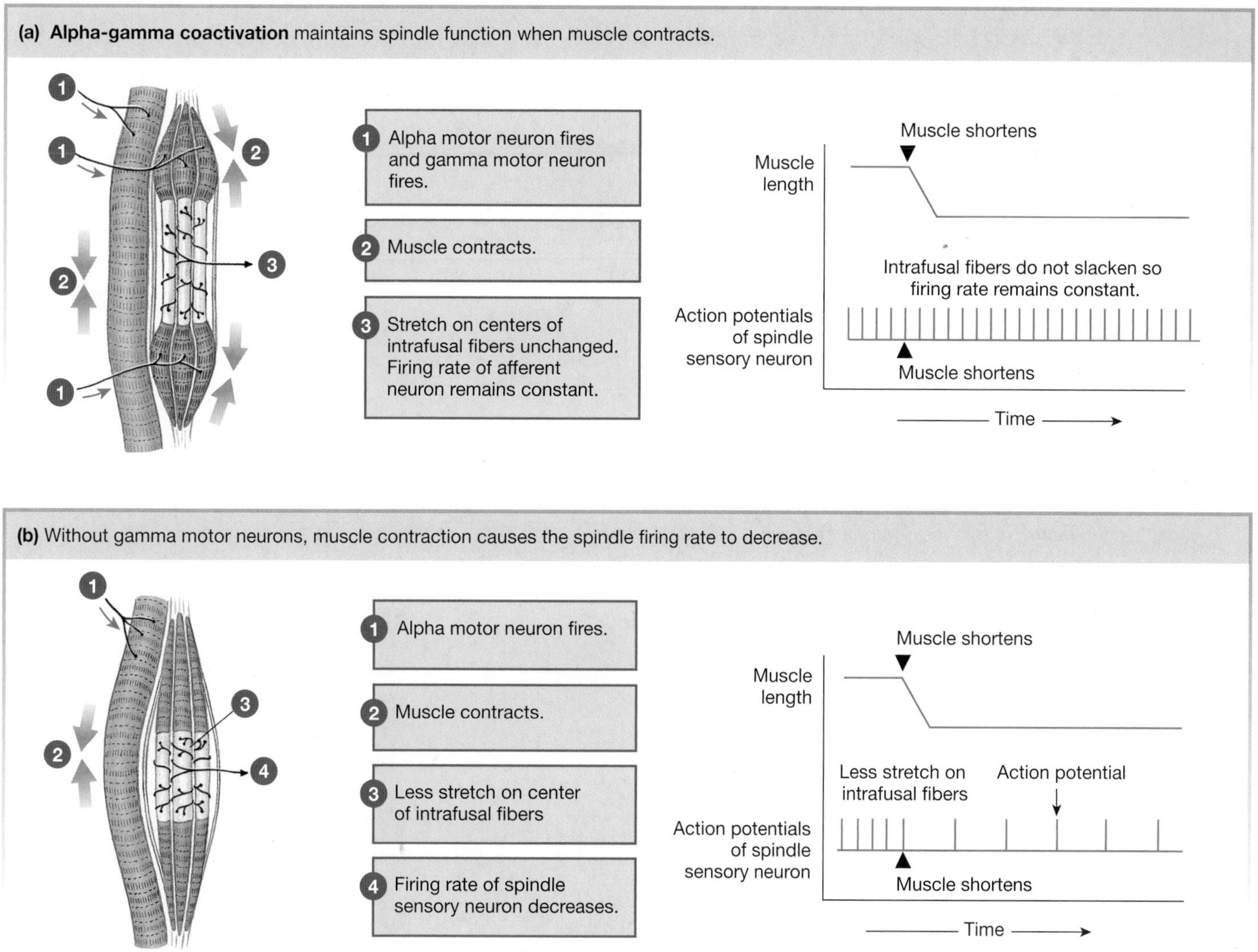
(a) Alpha-gamma coactivation maintains spindle function when muscle contracts.
1 Alpha motor neuron fires and gamma motor neuron fires.
2 Muscle contracts.
3 Stretch on centers of intrafusal fibers unchanged. Firing rate of afferent neuron remains constant.
Muscle length
Muscle shortens
Intrafusal fibers do not slacken so firing rate remains constant.
Action potentials of spindle sensory neuron
Muscle shortens
Time
(b) Without gamma motor neurons, muscle contraction causes the spindle firing rate to decrease.
1 Alpha motor neuron fires.
2 Muscle contracts.
3 Less stretch on center of intrafusal fibers
4 Firing rate of spindle sensory neuron decreases.
Muscle length
Muscle shortens
Less stretch on intrafusal fibers
Action potential
Action potentials of spindle sensory neuron
Muscle shortens
Time

● **FIGURE 13-5** ***Alpha-gamma coactivation.*** Gamma motor neurons innervate muscle fibers at the ends of muscle spindles. Alpha-gamma coactivation keeps the spindles stretched when the muscle contracts.

An example of how muscle spindles work during a stretch reflex is shown in Figure 13-6 a–c ●. You can demonstrate this yourself with an unsuspecting friend. Have your friend stand with eyes closed, one arm extended with the elbow at 90°, and the hand palm up. Place a small book or other flat weight in the outstretched hand and watch the arm muscles contract to compensate for the added weight. Then suddenly drop a heavier load, such as another book, onto the subject's hand. The added weight will send the hand downward, stretching the biceps muscle and activating its muscle spindles. Sensory input into the spinal cord then activates the alpha motor neurons of the biceps muscle. The biceps will contract, bringing the arm back to its original position.

Golgi Tendon Organs Respond to Muscle Tension

A second type of muscle proprioceptor is the **Golgi tendon organ**. These receptors are found at the junction of tendons and muscle fibers, placing them in series with the muscle fibers. Golgi tendon organs respond primarily to the tension a muscle develops during an isometric contraction, and they cause a relaxation reflex. This response is the opposite of the reflex contraction caused by muscle spindles. In contrast to the muscle spindle, the Golgi tendon organ is relatively insensitive to muscle stretch.

Golgi tendon organs are composed of free nerve endings that wind between collagen fibers inside a connective tissue capsule (Fig. 13-3c). When a muscle contracts, its tendons act as an elastic component during the isometric phase of the contraction [p. 428]. Contraction pulls collagen fibers within the Golgi tendon organ tight, pinching sensory endings of the afferent neurons and causing them to fire.

Afferent input from activation of the Golgi tendon organ excites *inhibitory* interneurons in the spinal cord. The interneurons inhibit alpha motor neurons innervating the

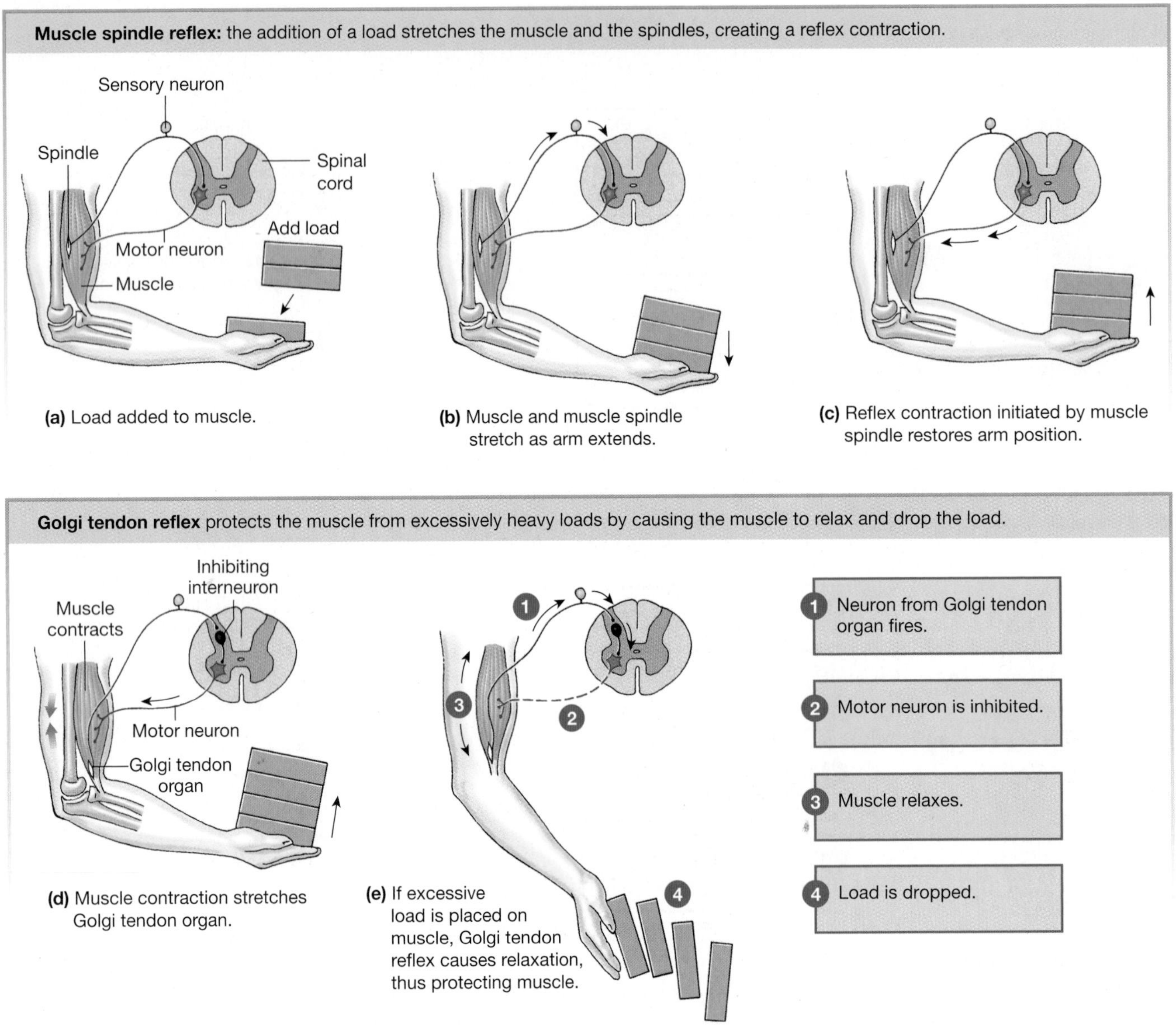

Muscle spindle reflex: the addition of a load stretches the muscle and the spindles, creating a reflex contraction.
Sensory neuron
Spindle
Spinal cord
Add load
Motor neuron
Muscle
(a) Load added to muscle.
(b) Muscle and muscle spindle stretch as arm extends.
(c) Reflex contraction initiated by muscle spindle restores arm position.
Golgi tendon reflex protects the muscle from excessively heavy loads by causing the muscle to relax and drop the load.
Inhibiting interneuron
Muscle contracts
Motor neuron
Golgi tendon organ
(d) Muscle contraction stretches Golgi tendon organ.
(e) If excessive load is placed on muscle, Golgi tendon reflex causes relaxation, thus protecting muscle.
1 Neuron from Golgi tendon organ fires.
2 Motor neuron is inhibited.
3 Muscle relaxes.
4 Load is dropped.

● **FIGURE 13-6** ***Muscle reflexes help prevent damage to the muscle.***

muscle, and muscle contraction decreases or ceases. Under most circumstances, this reflex slows muscle contraction as the force of contraction increases. In other instances, the Golgi tendon organs prevent excessive contraction that might injure the muscle.

Think back to the example of books placed on the outstretched hand. If supporting the added weight requires more tension than the muscle can develop, the Golgi tendon organ will respond as muscle tension nears its maximum. The Golgi tendon organ triggers reflex *inhibition* of the biceps motor neurons, causing the biceps to relax and the arm to fall. The person then drops the added weight before the muscle fibers can be damaged (Fig. 13-6d, e). Golgi tendon organ input is an important source of inhibition to alpha motor neurons.

CONCEPT CHECK

4. Using the standard steps of a reflex pathway, create a map showing alpha-gamma coactivation and the Golgi tendon reflex. Begin with the stimulus "Alpha motor neuron fires."

Answers: p. 466

Stretch Reflexes and Reciprocal Inhibition Control Movement Around a Joint

Movement around most flexible joints in the body is controlled by groups of synergistic and antagonistic muscles that act in a coordinated fashion. Sensory neurons from muscle receptors and efferent motor neurons that control the muscle are linked by diverging and converging pathways of interneurons within the spinal cord. The collection of pathways controlling a single joint is known as a **myotatic unit** [*myo-*, muscle + *tasis,* stretching].

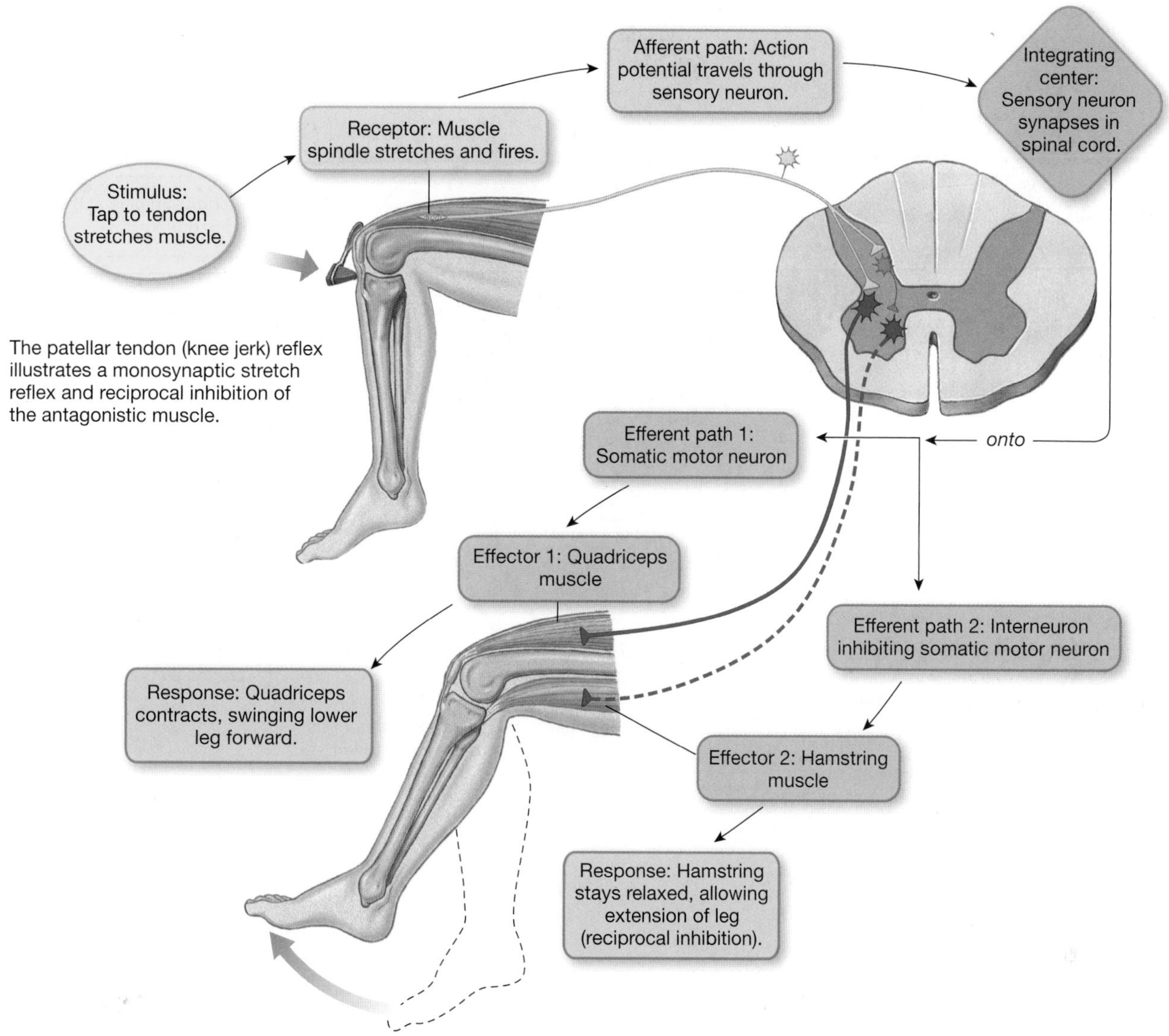

Stimulus: Tap to tendon stretches muscle.
Receptor: Muscle spindle stretches and fires.
Afferent path: Action potential travels through sensory neuron.
Integrating center: Sensory neuron synapses in spinal cord.
onto
The patellar tendon (knee jerk) reflex illustrates a monosynaptic stretch reflex and reciprocal inhibition of the antagonistic muscle.
Efferent path 1: Somatic motor neuron
Effector 1: Quadriceps muscle
Response: Quadriceps contracts, swinging lower leg forward.
Efferent path 2: Interneuron inhibiting somatic motor neuron
Effector 2: Hamstring muscle
Response: Hamstring stays relaxed, allowing extension of leg (reciprocal inhibition).

● **FIGURE 13-7** ***The patellar tendon (knee jerk) reflex***

The simplest reflex in a myotatic unit is the **monosynaptic stretch reflex**, which involves only two neurons: the sensory neuron from the muscle spindle and the somatic motor neuron to the muscle. The knee jerk reflex is an example of a monosynaptic stretch reflex (Fig. 13-7 ●).

To demonstrate the knee jerk reflex, a person sits on the edge of a table so that the lower leg hangs relaxed. When the patellar tendon below the kneecap is tapped with a small rubber hammer, the tap stretches the quadriceps muscle, which runs up the front of the thigh. This stretching activates muscle spindles and sends action potentials via the sensory fibers to the spinal cord. The sensory neurons synapse directly onto the motor neurons that control contraction of the quadriceps muscle (a monosynaptic reflex). Excitation of the motor neurons causes motor units in the quadriceps to contract, and the lower leg swings forward.

For muscle contraction to extend the leg, the antagonistic flexor muscles must relax (**reciprocal inhibition**). In the leg, this requires relaxation of the hamstring muscles running up the back of the thigh. The single stimulus of the tap to the tendon accomplishes both contraction of the quadriceps muscle and reciprocal inhibition of the hamstrings. The sensory fibers branch upon entering the spinal cord. Some of the branches activate motor neurons innervating the quadriceps, while the other branches synapse on inhibitory interneurons. The inhibitory interneurons suppress activity in the motor neurons controlling the hamstrings (a polysynaptic reflex). The result is a relaxation of the hamstrings that allows contraction of the quadriceps to proceed unopposed.

Flexion Reflexes Pull Limbs Away from Painful Stimuli

Flexion reflexes are polysynaptic reflex pathways that cause an arm or leg to be pulled away from a painful stimulus, such as a pinprick or a hot stove. These reflexes, like the reciprocal

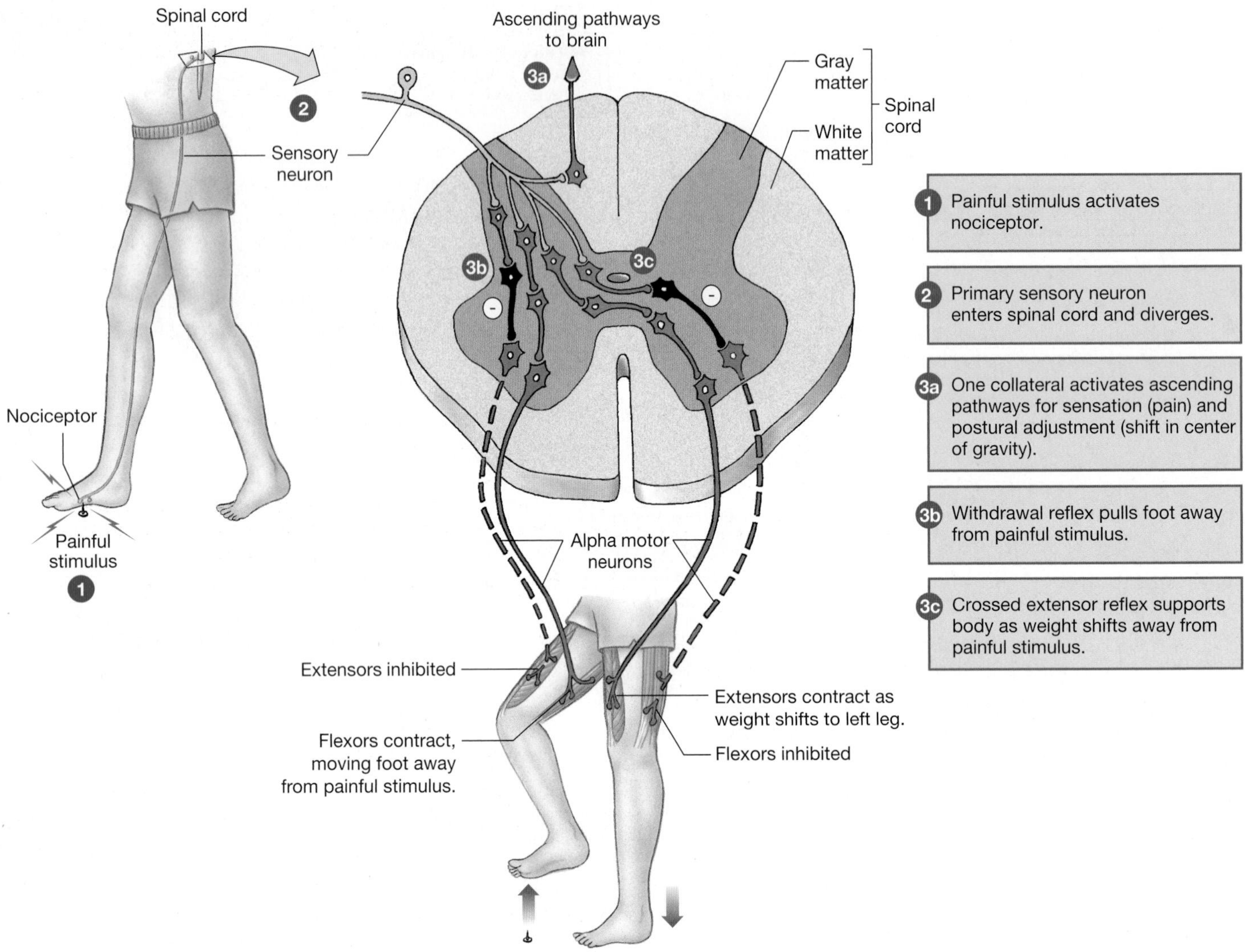

Spinal cord
Ascending pathways to brain
Gray matter
White matter
Spinal cord
Sensory neuron
2
3a
3b
3c
Nociceptor
Painful stimulus
1
Alpha motor neurons
Extensors inhibited
Flexors contract, moving foot away from painful stimulus.
Extensors contract as weight shifts to left leg.
Flexors inhibited
1 Painful stimulus activates nociceptor.
2 Primary sensory neuron enters spinal cord and diverges.
3a One collateral activates ascending pathways for sensation (pain) and postural adjustment (shift in center of gravity).
3b Withdrawal reflex pulls foot away from painful stimulus.
3c Crossed extensor reflex supports body as weight shifts away from painful stimulus.

● **FIGURE 13-8** ***A flexion reflex in one limb causes extension in the opposite limb through the crossed extensor reflex.*** The coordination of reflexes with postural adjustments is essential for maintaining balance.

inhibition reflex just described, rely on divergent pathways in the spinal cord. Figure 13-8 ● uses the example of stepping on a tack to illustrate a flexion reflex.

When the foot contacts the point of the tack, nociceptors (pain receptors) in the foot send sensory information to the spinal cord. Here the signal diverges, activating multiple excitatory interneurons. Some of these interneurons excite alpha motor neurons, leading to contraction of the flexor muscles of the stimulated limb. Other interneurons simultaneously activate inhibitory interneurons that cause relaxation of the antagonistic muscle groups. Because of this reciprocal inhibition, the limb is flexed, withdrawing it from the painful stimulus. This type of reflex requires more time than a stretch reflex (such as the knee jerk reflex) because it is a polysynaptic rather than a monosynaptic reflex.

RUNNING PROBLEM

Once in the spinal cord, tetanospasmin is released from the motor neuron. It then selectively blocks neurotransmitter release at inhibitory synapses. Patients with tetanus experience muscle spasms that begin in the jaw and may eventually affect the entire body. When the extremities become involved, the arms and legs may go into painful, rigid spasms.

Question 2:

Using the reflex pathways diagrammed in Figures 13-7 and 13-8, explain why inhibition of inhibitory interneurons might result in uncontrollable muscle spasms.

447 448 456 457 462 463

CONCEPT CHECK

5. Draw a reflex map of the flexion reflex initiated by a painful stimulus to the sole of a foot.

Answers: p. 466

Flexion reflexes, particularly in the legs, are usually accompanied by the **crossed extensor reflex**, a postural reflex that helps maintain balance when one foot is lifted from the ground. In this reflex, also shown in Figure 13-8, the quick withdrawal of the right foot from a painful stimulus (a tack) is matched by extension of the left leg so that it can support the sudden shift in weight. The extensors contract in the supporting left leg and relax in the withdrawing right leg, while the opposite occurs in the flexor muscles.

Note in Figure 13-8 how the one sensory neuron synapses on multiple interneurons. Divergence of the sensory signal permits a single stimulus to control two sets of antagonistic muscle groups as well as to send sensory information to the brain. This type of complex reflex with multiple neuron interactions is more typical of our reflexes than the simple monosynaptic knee jerk stretch reflex.

In the next section we look at how the CNS controls movements that range from involuntary reflexes to complex, voluntary movement patterns such as dancing, throwing a ball, or playing a musical instrument.

CONCEPT CHECK

6. Add the crossed extensor reflex in the supporting leg to the map you created in Concept Check 5.
7. As you pick up a heavy weight, which of the following are active in your biceps muscle: alpha motor neuron, gamma motor neuron, muscle spindle afferent neurons, Golgi tendon organ afferent neurons?
8. What distinguishes a stretch reflex from a crossed extensor reflex?

Answers: p. 466

RUNNING PROBLEM

Dr. Ling admits Mrs. Evans to the intensive care unit. There Mrs. Evans is given tetanus antitoxin to deactivate any toxin that has not yet entered motor neurons. She also receives penicillin, an antibiotic that kills the bacteria, and drugs to help relax her muscles. Despite these treatments, by the third day Mrs. Evans is having difficulty breathing because of spasms in her chest muscles. Dr. Ling calls in the chief of anesthesiology to administer metocurine, a drug similar to curare. Curare and metocurine induce temporary paralysis of muscles by binding to ACh receptors on the motor end plate. Patients receiving metocurine must be placed on respirators that breathe for them. For people with tetanus, however, metocurine can temporarily halt the muscle spasms and allow the body to recover.

Question 3:

a. ***Why does the binding of metocurine to ACh receptors on the motor end plate induce muscle paralysis? (Hint: what is the function of ACh in synaptic transmission?)***
b. ***Is metocurine an agonist or an antagonist of ACh?***

447 448 456 457 462 463

THE INTEGRATED CONTROL OF BODY MOVEMENT

Most of us never think about how our body translates thoughts into action. Even the simplest movement requires proper timing so that antagonistic and synergistic muscle groups contract in the appropriate sequence and to the appropriate degree. In addition, the body must continuously adjust its position to compensate for differences between the intended movement and the actual one. For example, the baseball pitcher steps off the mound to field a ground ball but in doing so slips on a wet patch of grass. His brain quickly compensates for the unexpected change in position through reflex muscle activity, and he stays on his feet to intercept the ball.

Skeletal muscles cannot communicate with one another directly, and so they send messages to the CNS, allowing the integrating centers to take charge and direct movement. Most body movements are highly integrated, coordinated responses that require input from multiple regions of the brain. In this section we examine a few of the CNS integrating centers that are responsible for control of body movement.

Movement Can Be Classified as Reflex, Voluntary, or Rhythmic

Movement can be loosely classified into three categories: reflex movement, voluntary movement, and rhythmic movement (Tbl. 13-2 ●). **Reflex movements** are the least complex and are integrated primarily in the spinal cord (for example, see the knee jerk reflex in Fig. 13-7). However, like other spinal reflexes, reflex movements can be modulated by input from higher brain centers. In addition, the sensory input that initiates reflex movements, such as the input from muscle spindles and Golgi tendon organs, goes to the brain and participates in the coordination of voluntary movements and postural reflexes.

Postural reflexes that help us maintain body position as we stand or move through space are integrated in the brain stem. They require continuous sensory input from visual and vestibular (inner ear) sensory systems and from the muscles themselves [p. 363]. Muscle, tendon, and joint receptors provide information about *proprioception,* the positions of various body parts relative to one another. You can tell if your arm is bent even when your eyes are closed because these receptors provide information about body position to the brain.

TABLE 13-2 Types of Movement

	REFLEX	VOLUNTARY	RHYTHMIC
Stimulus that initiates movement	Primarily external via sensory receptors; minimally voluntary	External stimuli or at will	Initiation and termination voluntary
Example	Knee jerk, cough, postural reflexes	Playing piano	Walking, running
Complexity	Least complex; integrated at level of spinal cord or brain stem with higher center modulation	Most complex; integrated in cerebral cortex	Intermediate complexity; integrated in spinal cord with higher center input required
Comments	Inherent, rapid	Learned movements that improve with practice; once learned, may become subconscious ("muscle memory")	Spinal circuits act as pattern generators; activation of these pathways requires input from brain stem

Information from the vestibular apparatus of the ear and visual cues help us maintain our position in space. For example, we use the horizon to tell us our spatial orientation relative to the ground. In the absence of visual cues, we rely on tactile input. People trying to move in a dark room instinctively reach for a wall or piece of furniture to help orient themselves. Without visual and tactile cues, our orientation skills may fail. The lack of cues is what makes flying airplanes in clouds or fog impossible without instruments. The effect of gravity on the vestibular system is such a weak input when compared with visual or tactile cues that pilots may find themselves flying upside down relative to the ground.

Voluntary movements are the most complex type of movement. They require integration at the cerebral cortex, and they can be initiated at will without external stimuli. Learned voluntary movements improve with practice, and some even become involuntary, like reflexes. Think about learning to ride a bicycle. It may have been difficult at first but once you learned to pedal smoothly and to keep your balance, the movements became automatic. "Muscle memory" is the name dancers and athletes give the ability of the unconscious brain to reproduce voluntary, learned movements and positions.

Rhythmic movements, such as walking or running, are a combination of reflex movements and voluntary movements. Rhythmic movements are initiated and terminated by input from the cerebral cortex, but once activated, networks of CNS interneurons called **central pattern generators** (CPGs) maintain the spontaneous repetitive activity. Changes in rhythmic activity, such as changing from walking to skipping, are also initiated by input from the cerebral cortex.

As an analogy, think of a battery-operated bunny. When the switch is thrown to "on," the bunny begins to hop. It continues its repetitive hopping until someone turns it off (or until the battery runs down). In humans, rhythmic movements controlled by central pattern generators include locomotion and the unconscious rhythm of quiet breathing.

An animal paralyzed by a spinal cord injury is unable to walk because damage to descending pathways blocks the "start walking" signal from the brain to the legs' motor neurons in the spinal cord. However, these paralyzed animals can walk if they are supported on a moving treadmill and given an electrical stimulus to activate the spinal CPG governing that motion. As the treadmill moves the animal's legs, the CPG, reinforced by sensory signals from muscle spindles, drives contraction of the leg muscles.

The ability of central pattern generators to sustain rhythmic movement without continued sensory input has proved important for research on spinal cord injuries. Researchers are trying to take advantage of CPGs and rhythmic reflexes in people with spinal cord injuries by artificially stimulating portions of the spinal cord to restore movement to formerly paralyzed limbs.

The distinctions among reflex, voluntary, and rhythmic movements are not always clear-cut. The precision of voluntary movements improves with practice, but so does that of some reflexes. Voluntary movements, once learned, can become reflexive. In addition, most voluntary movements require continuous input from postural reflexes. **Feedforward reflexes** allow the body to prepare for a voluntary movement, and feedback mechanisms are used to create a smooth, continuous motion. Coordination of movement requires cooperation from many parts of the brain.

The CNS Integrates Movement

Three levels of the nervous system control movement: (1) the spinal cord, which integrates spinal reflexes and contains central

TABLE 13-3 Neural Control of Movement

LOCATION	ROLE	RECEIVES INPUT FROM:	SENDS INTEGRATIVE OUTPUT TO:
Spinal cord	Spinal reflexes; locomotor pattern generators	Sensory receptors	Brain stem, cerebellum, thalamus/cerebral cortex
Brain stem	Posture, hand and eye movements	Cerebellum, visual and vestibular sensory receptors	Spinal cord
Motor areas of cerebral cortex	Planning and coordinating complex movement	Thalamus	Brain stem, spinal cord (corticospinal tract), cerebellum, basal ganglia
Cerebellum	Monitors output signals from motor areas and adjusts movements	Spinal cord (sensory), cerebral cortex (commands)	Brain stem, cerebral cortex (Note: All output is inhibitory.)
Thalamus	Contains relay nuclei that modulate and pass messages to cerebral cortex	Basal ganglia, cerebellum, spinal cord	Cerebral cortex
Basal nuclei	Motor planning	Cerebral cortex	Cerebral cortex, brain stem

pattern generators; (2) the brain stem and cerebellum, which control postural reflexes and hand and eye movements; and (3) the cerebral cortex and basal ganglia [p. 312], which are responsible for voluntary movements. The thalamus relays and modifies signals being sent from the spinal cord, basal ganglia, and cerebellum to the cerebral cortex (Tbl. 13-3 ●).

Reflex movements do not require input from the cerebral cortex. Proprioceptors such as muscle spindles, Golgi tendon organs, and joint capsule receptors provide information to the spinal cord, brain stem, and cerebellum (Fig. 13-9 ●). The brain stem is in charge of postural reflexes and hand and eye movements. It also gets commands from the cerebellum, the part of the brain responsible for "fine-tuning" movement. The result is reflex movement. However, some sensory information is sent through ascending pathways to sensory areas of the cortex, where it can be used to plan voluntary movements.

Voluntary movements require coordination between the cerebral cortex, cerebellum, and basal ganglia. The control of voluntary movement can be divided into three steps: (1) decision-making and planning, (2) initiating the movement, and (3) executing the movement (Fig. 13-10 ●). The cerebral cortex plays a key role in the first two steps. Behaviors such as movement require knowledge of the body's position in space (where am I?), a decision on what movement should be executed (what shall I do?), a plan for executing the movement (how shall I do it?), and the ability to hold the plan in memory long enough to carry it out (now, what was I just doing?). As with reflex movements, sensory feedback is used to continuously refine the process.

Let's return to our baseball pitcher and trace the process as he decides whether to throw a fastball or a slow curve. Standing out on the mound, the pitcher is acutely aware of his surroundings: the other players on the field, the batter in the box, and the dirt beneath his feet. With the help of visual and somatosensory input to the sensory areas of the cortex, he is aware of his body position as he steadies himself for the pitch (Fig. 13-11 ●). Deciding which type of pitch to throw and

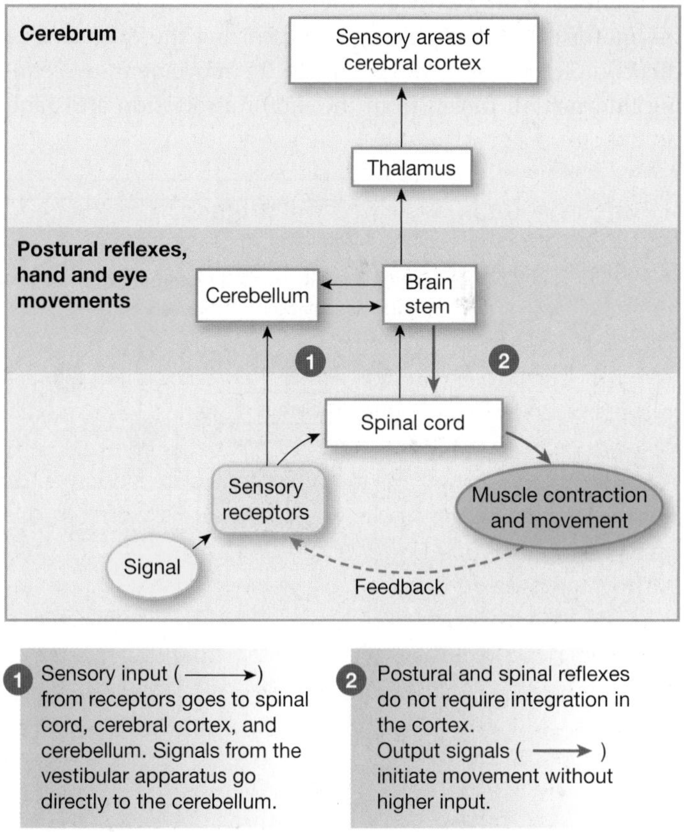
Cerebrum
Sensory areas of cerebral cortex
Thalamus
Postural reflexes, hand and eye movements
Cerebellum
Brain stem
1
2
Spinal cord
Sensory receptors
Muscle contraction and movement
Signal
Feedback
1 Sensory input (→) from receptors goes to spinal cord, cerebral cortex, and cerebellum. Signals from the vestibular apparatus go directly to the cerebellum.
2 Postural and spinal reflexes do not require integration in the cortex. Output signals (→) initiate movement without higher input.

● **FIGURE 13-9** *Integration of muscle reflexes*

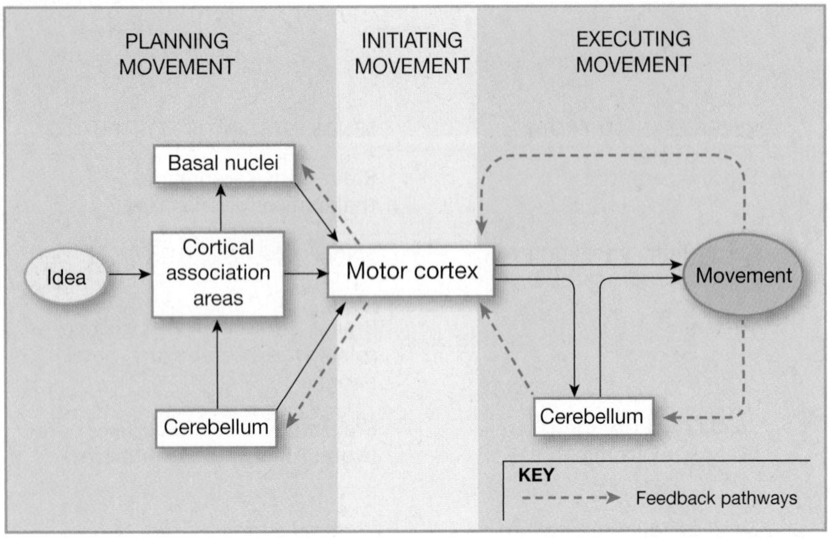

● **FIGURE 13-10** ***CNS control of voluntary movement.*** Voluntary movements can be divided into three phases: planning, initiation, and execution. Sensory feedback allows the brain to correct for any deviation between the planned movement and the actual movement.

anticipating the consequences occupy many pathways in his prefrontal cortex and association areas. These pathways loop down through the basal ganglia and thalamus for modulation before cycling back to the cortex.

Once the pitcher makes the decision to throw a fastball, the motor cortex takes charge of organizing the execution of this complex movement. To initiate the movement, descending information travels from the motor association areas and motor cortex to the brain stem, the spinal cord, and the cerebellum. The cerebellum assists in making postural adjustments by integrating feedback from peripheral sensory receptors. The basal ganglia, which assisted the cortical motor areas in planning the pitch, also provide information about posture, balance, and gait to the brain stem.

The pitcher's decision to throw a fastball now is translated into action potentials that travel down through the **corticospinal**

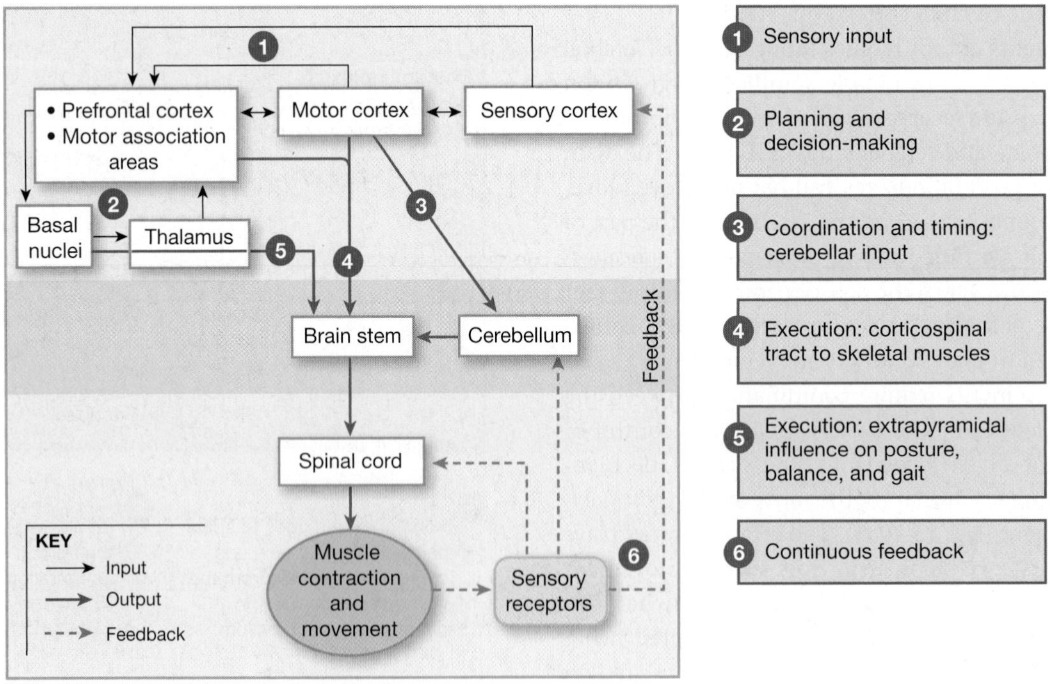

● **FIGURE 13-11** *Control of voluntary movements*

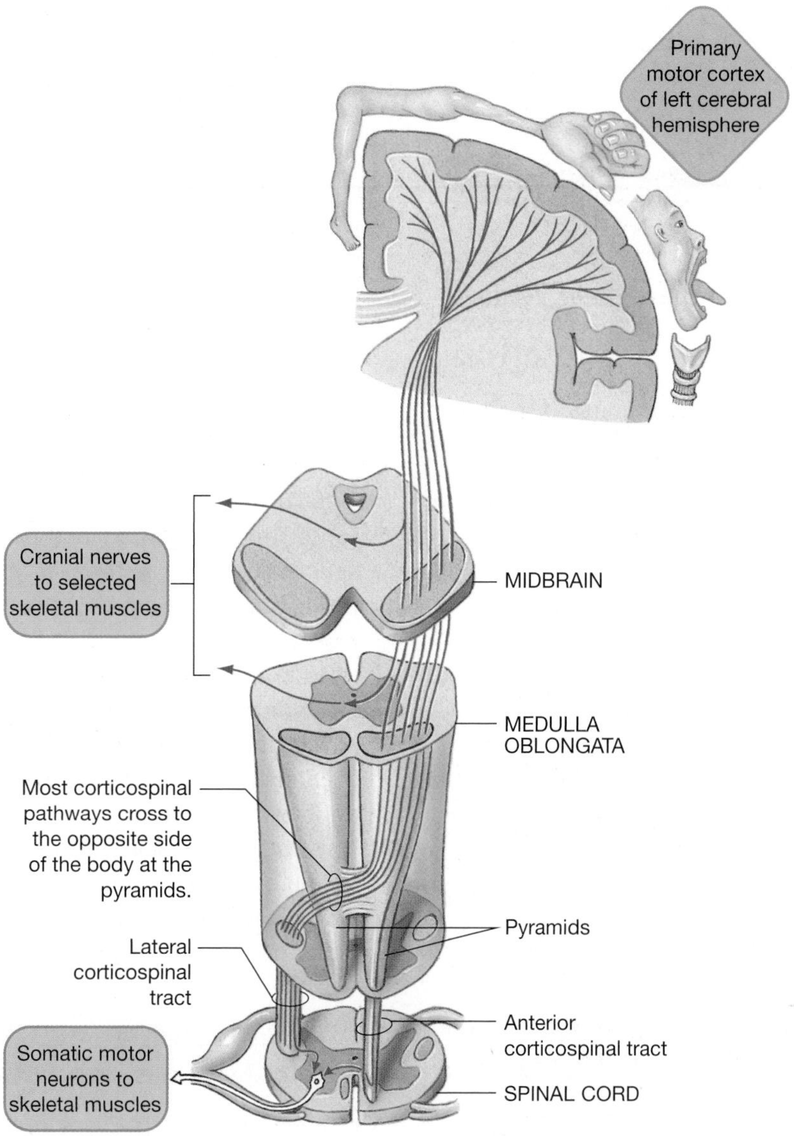

● **FIGURE 13-12** ***The corticospinal tract.*** These interneurons run directly from the motor cortex to their synapses with somatic motor neurons. Most corticospinal neurons cross the midline at the pyramids.

tract, a group of interneurons controlling voluntary movement that run from the motor cortex to the spinal cord, where they synapse directly onto somatic motor neurons (Fig. 13-12 ●). As noted in Chapter 9, most of these descending pathways cross to the opposite side of the body in a region of the medulla known as the *pyramids*. Consequently, this pathway is sometimes called the *pyramidal tract*.

Neurons from the basal ganglia [p. 312] also influence body movement. These neurons have multiple synapses in the CNS and make up what is sometimes called the *extrapyramidal tract* or the *extrapyramidal system*. It was once believed that the pyramidal and extrapyramidal pathways were separate systems, but we now know that they interact and are not as distinct in their function as was once believed.

As the pitcher begins the pitch, *feedforward postural reflexes* adjust the body position, shifting weight slightly in anticipation of the changes about to occur (Fig. 13-13 ●). Through the appropriate divergent pathways, action potentials race to the somatic motor neurons that control the muscles used for pitching: some are excited, others are inhibited. The neural circuitry allows precise control over antagonistic muscle groups as the pitcher flexes and retracts his right arm. His weight shifts onto his right foot as his right arm moves back.

Each of these movements activates sensory receptors that feed information back to the spinal cord, brain stem, and cerebellum, initiating postural reflexes. These reflexes adjust his body position so that the pitcher does not lose his balance and fall over backward. Finally, he releases the ball, catching his

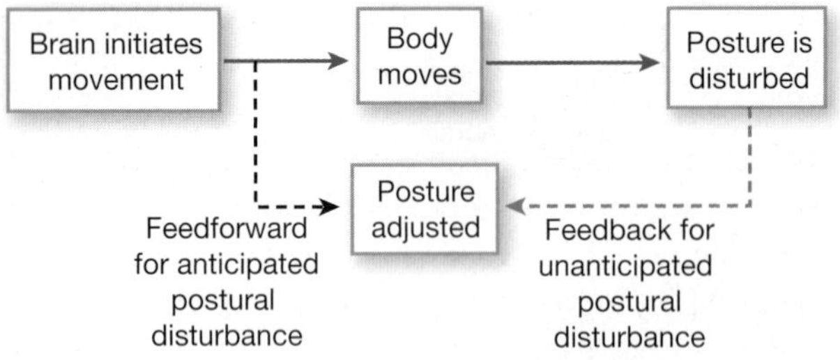

● **FIGURE 13-13** ***Feedforward reflexes and feedback of information during movement***

balance on the follow-through—another example of postural reflexes mediated through sensory feedback. His head stays erect, and his eyes track the ball as it reaches the batter. WHACK ... home run. As the pitcher's eyes follow the ball and he evaluates the result of his pitch, his brain is preparing for the next batter, hoping to use what it has learned from these pitches to improve those to come.

Symptoms of Parkinson's Disease Reflect the Functions of the Basal Ganglia

Our understanding of the role of the basal ganglia in the control of movement has been slow to develop because, for many years, animal experiments yielded little information. Randomly destroying portions of the basal ganglia did not appear to affect research animals. However, research focusing on **Parkinson's disease** (Parkinsonism) in humans has been more fruitful. From studying patients with Parkinson's, scientists have learned that the basal ganglia play a role in cognitive function and memory as well as in the coordination of movement.

Parkinson's disease is a progressive neurological disorder characterized by abnormal movements, speech difficulties, and cognitive changes. These signs and symptoms are associated with loss of neurons in the basal ganglia that release the neurotransmitter dopamine. One abnormal sign that most Parkinson patients have is tremors in the hands, arms, and legs, particularly at rest. In addition, they have difficulty initiating movement and walk slowly with stooped posture and shuffling gait. They lose facial expression, fail to blink (the reptilian stare), and may develop depression, sleep disturbances, and personality changes.

The cause of Parkinson's disease is usually not known and appears to be a combination of environmental factors and genetic susceptibility. However, a few years ago, a number of young drug users were diagnosed with Parkinsonism. Their disease was traced to the use of homemade heroin containing a toxic contaminant that destroyed *dopaminergic* (dopamine-secreting) neurons. This contaminant has been isolated and now enables researchers to induce Parkinson's disease in experimental animals so that we have an animal model on which to test new treatments.

The primary current treatment for Parkinson's is administration of drugs designed to enhance dopamine activity in the brain. Dopamine cannot cross the blood-brain barrier, so patients take *L-dopa*, a precursor of dopamine that crosses the

EMERGING CONCEPTS

VISUALIZATION TECHNIQUES IN SPORTS

Researchers now believe that *presynaptic facilitation,* in which modulatory input increases neurotransmitter release, is the physiological mechanism that underlies the success of visualization techniques in sports. Visualization, also known as *guided imagery,* enables athletes to maximize their performance by "psyching" themselves, picturing in their minds the perfect vault or the perfect fast ball. By pathways that we still do not understand, the mental image conjured up by the cerebral cortex is translated into signals that find their way to the muscles. Guided imagery is also being used in medicine as an *adjunct* (supplementary) therapy for cancer treatment and pain management. The ability of the conscious brain to alter physiological function is only one example of the many fascinating connections between the higher brain and the body. To learn more about this, go to *http://sportsmedicine.about.com* and search for *visualization.*

RUNNING PROBLEM

Four weeks later, Mrs. Evans is ready to go home, completely recovered and showing no signs of lingering effects. Once she could talk, Mrs. Evans, who was born on the farm where she still lived, was able to tell Dr. Ling that she had never had immunization shots for tetanus or any other diseases. "Well, that made you one of only a handful of people in the United States who will develop tetanus this year," Dr. Ling told her. "You've been given your first two tetanus shots here in the hospital. Be sure to come back in six months for the last one so that this won't happen again." Because of national immunization programs begun in the 1950s, tetanus is now a rare disease in the United States. However, in developing countries without immunization programs, tetanus is still a common and serious condition.

Question 4:

On the basis of what you know about who receives immunization shots in the United States, predict the age and background of people who are most likely to develop tetanus this year.

447 448 456 457 462 463

blood-brain barrier, then is metabolized to dopamine. Other drug treatments include dopamine agonists and inhibitors of enzymes that break down dopamine, such as MAO [p. 392]. In severe cases, selected parts of the brain may be destroyed to reduce tremors and rigidity. Experimental treatments include transplants of dopamine-secreting neurons. Proponents of stem cell research feel that Parkinson's may be one of the conditions that would benefit from the transplant of stem cells into affected brains. For more information on Parkinson's treatments, see *www.parkinson.org*, the National Parkinson Foundation.

CONTROL OF MOVEMENT IN VISCERAL MUSCLES

Movement created by contracting smooth and cardiac muscles is very different from that created by skeletal muscles, in large part because smooth and cardiac muscle are not attached to bone. In the internal organs, or viscera, muscle contraction usually changes the shape of an organ, narrowing the lumen of a hollow organ or shortening the length of a tube. In many hollow internal organs, muscle contraction pushes material through the lumen of the organ: the heart pumps blood, the digestive tract moves food, the uterus expels a baby.

Visceral muscle contraction is often reflexively controlled by the autonomic nervous system, but not always. Some types of smooth and cardiac muscle are capable of generating their own action potentials, independent of an external signal. Both the heart and digestive tract have spontaneously depolarizing muscle fibers (often called *pacemakers*) that give rise to regular, rhythmic contractions.

Reflex control of visceral smooth muscle varies from that of skeletal muscle. Skeletal muscles are controlled only by the nervous system, but in many types of visceral muscle, hormones are important in regulating contraction. In addition, some visceral muscle cells are connected to one another by gap junctions that allow electrical signals to pass directly from cell to cell.

Because smooth and cardiac muscle have such a variety of control mechanisms, we will discuss their control as we cover the appropriate organ system for each type of muscle. In the next chapter, we examine cardiac muscle and its function in the heart.

RUNNING PROBLEM CONCLUSION

Tetanus

In this running problem, you learned about the tetanus toxin tetanospasmin, a potent poison made by the bacterium *Clostridium tetani*. As little as 175 billionths of a gram (175 nanograms) can be fatal to a 70-kg human. Both tetanus toxin and botulinum toxin cause paralysis, but tetanus is a rigid (contracted muscle) paralysis, while botulism is a *flaccid* (relaxed muscle) paralysis. To learn more about tetanus, visit the web site of the U.S. Centers for Disease Control and Prevention (*www.cdc.gov*). Now check your understanding of this running problem by comparing your answers with the information in the summary table.

	QUESTION	FACTS	INTEGRATION AND ANALYSIS
1a	By what process is tetanospasmin taken up into neurons?	Tetanospasmin is a protein.	Proteins are too large to cross cell membranes by mediated transport. Therefore, tetanospasmin must be taken up by endocytosis [p. 152].
1b	By what process does tetanospasmin travel up the axon to the nerve cell body?	Movement of substances from the axon terminal to the cell body is called retrograde axonal transport [p. 252].	Tetanospasmin is taken up by endocytosis, so it will be contained in endocytotic vesicles. These vesicles "walk" along microtubules through retrograde axonal transport.
2	Using the reflex pathways diagrammed in Figures 13-7 and 13-8, explain why inhibition of inhibitory interneurons might result in uncontrollable muscle spasms.	Muscles often occur in antagonistic pairs. When one muscle is contracting, its antagonist must be inhibited.	If the inhibitory interneurons are not functioning, both sets of antagonistic muscles can contract at the same time. This would lead to muscle spasms and rigidity because the bones attached to the muscles would be unable to move in any direction.

RUNNING PROBLEM CONCLUSION *(continued)*

	QUESTION	FACTS	INTEGRATION AND ANALYSIS
3a	Why does the binding of metocurine to ACh receptors on the motor end plate induce muscle paralysis?	ACh is the somatic motor neuron neurotransmitter that initiates skeletal muscle contraction.	If metocurine binds to ACh receptors, it prevents ACh from binding. Without ACh binding, the muscle fiber will not depolarize and cannot contract, resulting in paralysis.
3b	Is metocurine an agonist or an antagonist of ACh?	Agonists mimic the effects of a substance; antagonists block the effects of a substance.	Metocurine blocks ACh action; therefore, it is an antagonist.
4	On the basis of what you know about who receives immunization shots in the United States, predict the age and background of people who are most likely to develop tetanus this year.	Immunizations are required for all children of school age. This practice has been in effect since about the 1950s. In addition, most people who suffer puncture wounds or dirty wounds are given tetanus booster shots when they are treated for those wounds.	Most cases of tetanus in the United States will occur in people over the age of 60 who have never been immunized, in immigrants (particularly migrant workers), and in newborn infants. Another source of the disease is contaminated heroin; injection of the drug under the skin may cause tetanus.

447 448 456 457 462 463

CHAPTER SUMMARY

How many times have you heard people say, "I did it without thinking"? In effect, they were saying that their action was a reflex response. There are many ways to control the functions of muscles and glands of the body, but a neural reflex is the simplest and the fastest.

This chapter integrates the material you learned in Chapters 8–12 and shows how the nervous *control system* controls body movement. Postural and spinal reflexes follow the basic pattern of a reflex, with sensory input being integrated in the CNS and acted on when an output signal goes to skeletal muscles. Voluntary movements do not require sensory input to be initiated, but they integrate sensory feedback to ensure smooth execution.

Neural Reflexes

1. A neural reflex consists of the following elements: stimulus, receptor, sensory neurons, integrating center, efferent neurons, effectors (muscles and glands), and response. (p. 447)
2. Neural reflexes can be classified in several ways. **Somatic reflexes** involve somatic motor neurons and skeletal muscles. **Autonomic** (or **visceral**) **reflexes** are controlled by autonomic neurons. (p. 447; Tbl. 13-1)
3. **Spinal reflexes** are integrated in the spinal cord. **Cranial reflexes** are integrated in the brain. (p. 447)
4. Many reflexes are innate. Others are acquired through experience. (p. 447)
5. The simplest reflex pathway is a **monosynaptic reflex** with only two neurons. **Polysynaptic reflexes** have three or more neurons in the pathway. (p. 448 ; Fig. 13-1)

Autonomic Reflexes

6. Some autonomic reflexes are spinal reflexes that are modulated by input from the brain. Other reflexes needed to maintain homeostasis are integrated in the brain, primarily in the hypothalamus, thalamus, and brain stem. (p. 449)
7. Autonomic reflexes are all polysynaptic, and many are characterized by tonic activity. (p. 449; Fig. 13-2)

Skeletal Muscle Reflexes

8. Skeletal muscle relaxation must be controlled by the CNS because somatic motor neurons always cause contraction in skeletal muscle. (p. 449)
9. The normal contractile fibers of a muscle are called **extrafusal muscle fibers**. Their contraction is controlled by **alpha motor neurons**. (p. 449; Fig. 13-3)
10. **Muscle spindles** send information about muscle length to the CNS. These receptors consist of **intrafusal fibers** with sensory neurons wrapped around the noncontractile center. **Gamma motor neurons** innervate the contractile ends of the intrafusal fibers. (p. 451; Fig. 13-3)
11. Muscle spindles are tonically active stretch receptors. Their output creates tonic contraction of extrafusal muscle fibers. Because of this tonic activity, a muscle at rest maintains a certain level of tension, known as **muscle tone**. (p. 451; Fig. 13-4a)
12. If a muscle stretches, the intrafusal fibers of its spindles stretch and initiate reflex contraction of the muscle. The contraction prevents

damage from overstretching. This reflex pathway is known as a **stretch reflex**. (p. 451; Fig. 13-4b)

13. When a muscle contracts, **alpha-gamma coactivation** ensures that its muscle spindle remains active. Activation of gamma motor neurons causes contraction of the ends of the intrafusal fibers. This contraction lengthens the central region of the intrafusal fibers and maintains stretch on the sensory nerve endings. (p. 451; Fig. 13-5)
14. **Golgi tendon organs** are found at the junction of the tendons and muscle fibers. They consist of free nerve endings that wind between collagen fibers. Golgi tendon organs respond to muscle contraction by causing a reflexive relaxation. (p. 453; Figs. 13-3, 13-6)
15. The synergistic and antagonistic muscles that control a single joint are known as a **myotatic unit**. When one set of muscles in a myotatic unit contracts, the antagonistic muscles must relax through a reflex known as **reciprocal inhibition**. (pp. 454–455; Fig. 13-7)
16. **Flexion reflexes** are polysynaptic reflexes that cause an arm or leg to be pulled away from a painful stimulus. Flexion reflexes that occur in the legs are usually accompanied by the **crossed extensor reflex**, a postural reflex that helps maintain balance when one foot is lifted from the ground. (pp. 455–457, Fig. 13-8)
17. **Central pattern generators** are networks of neurons in the CNS that can produce rhythmic motor movements without sensory feedback or higher brain commands. (p. 458)

The Integrated Control of Body Movement

18. Movement can be loosely classified into three categories: reflex movement, voluntary movement, and rhythmic movement. (p. 457; Tbl. 13-2)
19. **Reflex movements** are integrated primarily in the spinal cord. **Postural reflexes** are integrated in the brain stem. (p. 457; Fig. 13-9, Tbl. 13-3)
20. **Voluntary movements** are integrated in the cerebral cortex and can be initiated at will. Learned voluntary movements improve with practice and may even become involuntary, like reflexes. (p. 460; Fig. 13-11)
21. **Rhythmic movements**, such as walking, are a combination of reflexes and voluntary movements. Rhythmic movements can be sustained by central pattern generators. (p. 458)
22. Most signals for voluntary movement travel from cortex to spinal cord through the **corticospinal tract**. Signals from the **basal ganglia** also influence movement through extrapyramidal pathways. (pp. 460–461; Fig. 13-12)
23. **Feedforward reflexes** allow the body to prepare for a voluntary movement; feedback mechanisms are used to create a smooth, continuous motion. (p. 461; Fig. 13-13)

Control of Movement in Visceral Muscles

24. Contraction in smooth and cardiac muscles may occur spontaneously or may be controlled by hormones or by the autonomic division of the nervous system. (p. 463)

13

QUESTIONS

(Answers to the Review Questions begin on page A1.)

THE PHYSIOLOGY PLACE

Access more review material online at **The Physiology Place** web site. There you'll find review questions, problem-solving activities, case studies, flashcards, and direct links to both *Interactive Physiology®* and *PhysioEx™*. To access the site, go to *www.physiologyplace.com* and select *Human Physiology,* Fifth Edition.

LEVEL ONE REVIEWING FACTS AND TERMS

1. All neural reflexes begin with a(n) ________ that activates a receptor.
2. Somatic reflexes involve ________ muscles; ________ (or visceral) reflexes are controlled by autonomic neurons.
3. The pathway pattern that brings information from many neurons into a smaller number of neurons is known as ________.
4. When the axon terminal of a modulatory neuron (cell M) terminates close to the axon terminal of a presynaptic cell (cell P) and decreases the amount of neurotransmitter released by cell P, the resulting type of modulation is called ________. (*Hint:* See p. 284.)
5. Autonomic reflexes are also called ________ reflexes. Why?
6. Some autonomic reflexes are spinal reflexes; others are integrated in the brain. List some examples of each.
7. Which part of the brain transforms emotions into somatic sensation and visceral function? List three autonomic reflexes that are linked to emotions.
8. How many synapses occur in the simplest autonomic reflexes? Where do the synapses occur?
9. List the three types of sensory receptors that convey information for muscle reflexes.
10. Because of tonic activity in neurons, a resting muscle maintains a low level of tension known as ________.
11. Stretching a skeletal muscle causes sensory neurons to (increase/decrease) their rate of firing, causing the muscle to contract, thereby relieving the stretch. Why is this a useful reflex?
12. Match the structure to all correct statements about it.

(a) muscle spindle	1. is strictly a sensory receptor
(b) Golgi tendon organ	2. has sensory neurons that send information to the CNS
(c) joint capsule mechanoreceptor	3. is associated with two types of motor neurons
	4. conveys information about the relative positioning of bones
	5. is innervated by gamma motor neurons
	6. modulates activity in alpha motor neurons

13. The Golgi tendon organ responds to both ________ and ________, although ________ elicits the stronger response. Its activation (increases/decreases) muscle contraction via the ________ neuron.
14. The simplest reflex requires a minimum of how many neurons? How many synapses? Give an example.
15. List and differentiate the three categories of movement. Give an example of each.

LEVEL TWO REVIEWING CONCEPTS

16. What is the purpose of alpha-gamma coactivation? Explain how it occurs.
17. Modulatory neuron M synapses on the axon terminal of neuron P, just before P synapses with the effector organ. If M is an inhibitory neuron, what happens to neurotransmitter release by P? What effect does M's neurotransmitter have on the postsynaptic membrane potential of P? (*Hint:* Draw this pathway.)
18. At your last physical, your physician checked your patellar tendon reflex by tapping just below your knee while you sat quietly on the edge of the table. (a) What was she checking when she did this test? (b) What would happen if you were worried about falling off the table and were very tense? Where does this additional input to the efferent motor neurons originate? Are these modulatory neurons causing EPSPs or IPSPs [p. 281] at the spinal motor neuron? (c) Your physician notices that you are tense and asks you to count backward from 100 by 3's while she repeats the test. Why would carrying out this counting task enhance your reflex?

LEVEL THREE PROBLEM SOLVING

19. There are several theories about how presynaptic inhibition works at the cellular level. Use what you have learned about membrane potentials and synaptic transmission to explain how each of the following mechanisms would result in presynaptic inhibition:
    (a) Voltage-gated Ca^{2+} channels in axon terminal are inhibited.
    (b) Cl^- channels in axon terminal open.
    (c) K^+ channels in axon terminal open.
20. Andy is working on improving his golf swing. He must watch the ball, swing the club back and then forward, twist his hips, straighten his left arm, then complete the follow-through, where the club arcs in front of him. Which parts of the brain are involved in adjusting how hard he hits the ball, keeping all his body parts moving correctly, watching the ball, and then repeating these actions once he has verified that this swing is successful?
21. It's Halloween, and you are walking through the scariest haunted house around. As you turn a corner and enter the dungeon, a skeleton reaches out and grabs your arm. You let out a scream. Your heart rate quickens, and you feel the hairs on your arm stand on end. (a) What has just happened to you? (b) Where in the brain is fear processed? What are the functions of this part of the brain? Which branch (somatic or autonomic) of the motor output does it control? What are the target organs for this response? (c) How is it possible for your hair to stand on end when hair is made of proteins that do not contract? (*Hint:* See p. 86.) Given that the autonomic nervous system is mediating this reflex response, which type of tissue do you expect to find attached to hair follicles?
22. Using what you've learned about tetanus and botulinum toxins, make a table to compare the two. In what ways are tetanus and botulinum toxin similar? How are they different?

ANSWERS

Answers to Concept Check Questions

Page 449

1. Sensor (sensory receptor), afferent pathway (sensory neuron), integrating center (central nervous system), efferent pathway (autonomic or somatic motor neuron), effector (muscles, glands, some adipose tissue).
2. Upon hyperpolarization, the membrane potential becomes more negative and moves farther from threshold.

Page 451

3. Your map of a stretch reflex should match the components shown in Figure 13-4b.

Page 454

4. Your map of alpha-gamma coactivation should match the steps in Figure 13-5b. The stimulus of muscle contraction is the same for the Golgi tendon reflex, but your map should then branch to show the steps in Figure 13-6d and e.

Page 457

5. Your flexion reflex map should match the steps shown for the knee jerk in Figure 13-7, with the added contraction of hip flexor muscles in addition to the quadriceps.

Page 457

6. The initial steps of the crossed extensor reflex are the same as those of the flexion reflex until the CNS. There the crossed extensor reflex follows the diagram shown in Figure 13-8, step 3c.
7. When you pick up a weight, alpha and gamma neurons, spindle afferents, and Golgi tendon organ afferents are all active.
8. A stretch reflex is initiated by stretch and causes a reflex contraction. A crossed extensor reflex is a postural reflex initiated by withdrawal from a painful stimulus; the extensor muscles contract, but the corresponding flexors are inhibited.

Answers to Figure Questions

Page 450

Fig. 13-3: 1. b 2. (a) Firing of the alpha motor neuron causes extrafusal fibers to contract. However, the tonic activity of (c) spindle afferents will activate the alpha motor neuron.

14 Cardiovascular Physiology

BACKGROUND BASICS

Diffusion: **136** Striated muscle: **407** Desmosomes: **74** Excitation-contraction coupling: **417** Length-tension relationship in muscle: **423** Tetanus in skeletal muscle: **425** Muscle contraction: **415** Gap junctions: **179** Catecholamines: **224** Vagus nerve: **389** Isometric contraction: **427**

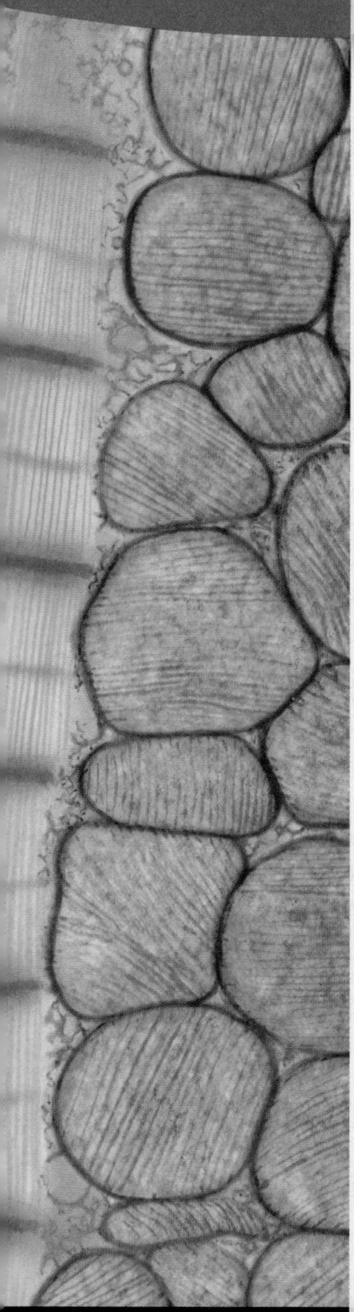

Cardiac muscle fibers showing sarcomeres and mitochondria.

Only in the 17th century did the brain displace the heart as the controller of our actions.

—Mary A. B. Brazier, *A History of Neurophysiology in the 19th Century,* 1988

RUNNING PROBLEM

Myocardial Infarction

At 9:06 A.M., the blood clot that had silently formed in Walter Parker's left anterior descending coronary artery made its sinister presence known. The 53-year-old advertising executive had arrived at the Dallas Convention Center feeling fine, but suddenly a dull ache started in the center of his chest, and he became nauseated. At first he brushed it off as the after-effects of the convention banquet the night before. When the chest pain persisted, however, he thought of his family history of heart disease and took an aspirin, remembering a radio ad that said to do this if you were having symptoms of a heart attack. Walter then made his way to the Center's Aid Station. "I'm not feeling very well," he told the emergency medical technician (EMT). The EMT, on hearing Walter's symptoms and seeing his pale, sweaty face, immediately thought of a heart attack. "Let's get you over to the hospital and get this checked out."

468 472 483 487 494 500 505

In the classic movie *Indiana Jones and the Temple of Doom,* the evil priest reaches into the chest of a sacrificial victim and pulls out his heart, still beating. This act was not dreamed up by some Hollywood scriptwriter—it was taken from rituals of the ancient Mayans, who documented this grisly practice in their carvings and paintings. The heart has been an object of fascination for centuries, but how can this workhorse muscle, which pumps 7200 liters of blood a day, keep beating outside the body? Before we can answer that question, we must first consider the role of hearts in cardiovascular systems.

As life evolved, simple one-celled organisms began to band together, first into cooperative colonies and then into multicelled organisms. In most multicellular animals, only the surface layer of cells is in direct contact with the environment. This body plan presents a problem because diffusion slows as distance increases [p. 138]. For example, oxygen consumption in the interior cells of larger animals exceeds the rate at which oxygen can diffuse from the body surface.

One solution to overcome slow diffusion was the evolutionary development of circulatory systems that move fluid between the body's surface and its deepest parts. In simple animals, muscular activity creates fluid flow when the animal moves. More complex animals have muscular pumps called hearts to circulate internal fluid.

In the most efficient circulatory systems, the heart pumps blood through a closed system of vessels. This one-way circuit steers the blood along a specific route and ensures systematic distribution of gases, nutrients, signal molecules, and wastes. A circulatory system comprising a heart, blood vessels, and blood is known as a **cardiovascular system** [*kardia,* heart + *vasculum,* little vessel].

Although the idea of a closed cardiovascular system that cycles blood in an endless loop seems intuitive to us today, it has not always been so. **Capillaries** [*capillus,* hair], the microscopic vessels where blood exchanges material with the interstitial fluid, were not discovered until Marcello Malpighi, an Italian anatomist, observed them through a microscope in the middle of the seventeenth century. At that time European medicine was still heavily influenced by the ancient belief that the cardiovascular system distributed both blood and air.

Blood was thought to be made in the liver and distributed throughout the body in the veins. Air went from the lungs to the heart, where it was digested and picked up "vital spirits." From the heart, air was distributed to the tissues through vessels called arteries. Anomalies—such as the fact that a cut artery squirted blood rather than air—were ingeniously explained by unseen links between arteries and veins that opened upon injury.

According to this model of the circulatory system, the tissues consumed all blood delivered to them, and the liver had to synthesize new blood continuously. It took the calculations of William Harvey (1578–1657), court physician to King Charles I of England, to show that the weight of blood pumped by the heart in a single hour exceeds the weight of the entire body! Once it became obvious that the liver could not make blood as rapidly as the heart pumped it, Harvey looked for an anatomical route that would allow the blood to recirculate rather than be consumed in the tissues. He showed that valves in the heart and veins created a one-way flow of blood, and that veins carried blood back to the heart, not out to the limbs. He also showed that blood entering the right side of the heart had to go to the lungs before it could go to the left side of the heart.

These studies created a furor among Harvey's contemporaries, leading Harvey to say in a huff that no one under the age of 40 could understand his conclusions. Ultimately, Harvey's work became the foundation of modern cardiovascular physiology. Today, we understand the structure of the cardiovascular system at microscopic and molecular levels that Harvey never dreamed existed. Yet some things have not changed. Even now, with our sophisticated technology, we are searching for "spirits" in the blood, although today we call them by such names as *hormone* and *cytokine.*

OVERVIEW OF THE CARDIOVASCULAR SYSTEM

In the simplest terms, a cardiovascular system is a series of tubes (the blood vessels) filled with fluid (blood) and connected to a pump (the heart). Pressure generated in the heart propels blood through the system continuously. The blood picks up oxygen at the lungs and nutrients in the intestine and then delivers these substances to the body's cells while simultaneously removing cellular wastes and heat for excretion. In addition, the cardiovascular system plays an important role in cell-to-cell communication and in defending the body against foreign invaders. This chapter focuses on an overview of the cardiovascular system and on the heart as a pump. You will learn about the properties of the blood vessels and the homeostatic controls that regulate blood flow and blood pressure in Chapter 15.

The Cardiovascular System Transports Materials Throughout the Body

The primary function of the cardiovascular system is the transport of materials to and from all parts of the body. Substances transported by the cardiovascular system can be divided into (1) nutrients, water, and gases that enter the body from the external environment, (2) materials that move from cell to cell within the body, and (3) wastes that the cells eliminate (Tbl. 14-1 ●).

Oxygen enters the body at the exchange surface of the lungs. Nutrients and water are absorbed across the intestinal epithelium. Once all these materials are in the blood, the cardiovascular system distributes them. A steady supply of oxygen for the cells is particularly important because many cells deprived of oxygen become irreparably damaged within a short period of time. For example, about 5–10 seconds after blood flow to the brain is stopped, a person loses consciousness. If oxygen delivery stops for 5–10 minutes, permanent brain damage results. Neurons of the brain have a very high rate of oxygen consumption and cannot meet their metabolic need for ATP by using anaerobic pathways, which have low yields of ATP/glucose [p. 109]. Because of the brain's sensitivity to *hypoxia* [*hypo-*, low + *oxia,* oxygen], homeostatic controls do everything possible to maintain cerebral blood flow, even if it means depriving other cells of oxygen.

Cell-to-cell communication is a key function of the cardiovascular system. For example, hormones secreted by endocrine glands travel in the blood to their targets. Blood also carries nutrients, such as glucose from the liver and fatty acids from adipose tissue, to metabolically active cells. Finally, the defense team of white blood cells and antibodies patrols the circulation to intercept foreign invaders.

The cardiovascular system also picks up carbon dioxide and metabolic wastes released by cells and transports them to the lungs and kidneys for excretion. Some waste products are transported to the liver for processing before they are excreted in the urine or feces. Heat also circulates through the blood, moving from the body core to the surface, where it dissipates.

Table 14-1 Transport in the Cardiovascular System

SUBSTANCE MOVED	FROM	TO
Materials entering the body		
Oxygen	Lungs	All cells
Nutrients and water	Intestinal tract	All cells
Materials moved from cell to cell		
Wastes	Some cells	Liver for processing
Immune cells, antibodies, clotting proteins	Present in blood continuously	Available for any cell that needs them
Hormones	Endocrine cells	Target cells
Stored nutrients	Liver and adipose tissue	All cells
Materials leaving the body		
Metabolic wastes	All cells	Kidneys
Heat	All cells	Skin
Carbon dioxide	All cells	Lungs

The Cardiovascular System Consists of the Heart, Blood Vessels, and Blood

The cardiovascular system is composed of the heart, the blood vessels (also known as the *vasculature*), and the cells and plasma of the blood. Blood vessels that carry blood away from the heart are called **arteries**. Blood vessels that return blood to the heart are called **veins**.

As blood moves through the cardiovascular system, a system of valves in the heart and veins ensures that the blood flows in one direction only. Like the turnstiles at an amusement park, the valves keep blood from reversing its direction of flow. Figure 14-1 ● is a schematic diagram that shows these components and the route that blood follows through the body. Notice in this illustration, as well as in most other diagrams of the heart, that the right side of the heart is on the left side of the page, which means that the heart is labeled as if you were viewing the heart of a person facing you.

The heart is divided by a central wall, or **septum**, into left and right halves. Each half functions as an independent pump that consists of an **atrium** [*atrium,* central room; plural *atria*] and a **ventricle** [*ventriculus,* belly]. The atrium receives blood returning to the heart from the blood vessels, and the ventricle pumps blood out into the blood vessels. The right side of the heart receives blood from the tissues and sends it to the lungs for oxygenation. The left side of the heart receives newly oxygenated blood from the lungs and pumps it to tissues throughout the body.

Starting in the right atrium in Figure 14-1, trace the path taken by blood as it flows through the cardiovascular system. Note that blood in the right side of the heart is colored blue.

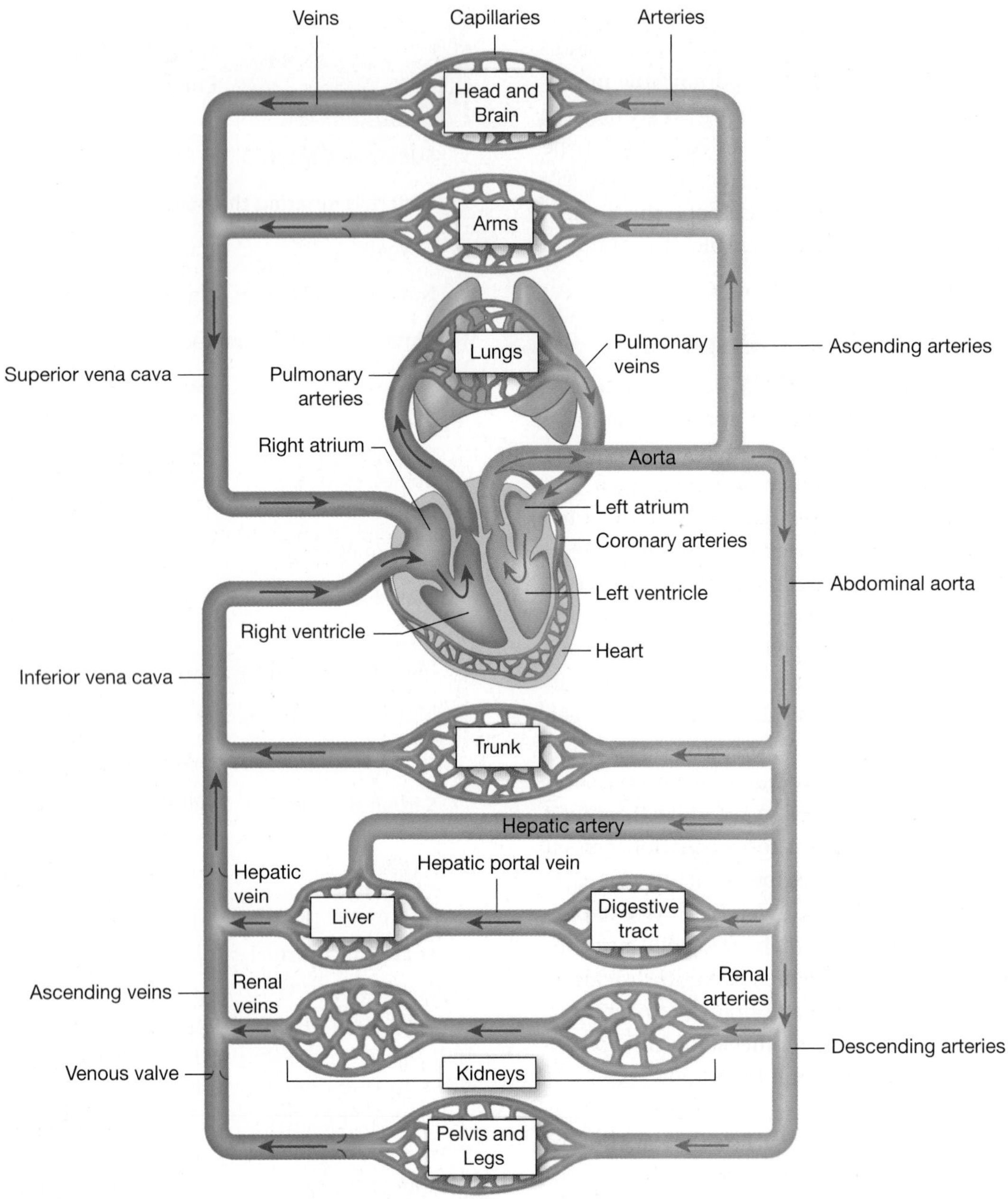

Veins
Capillaries
Arteries
Head and Brain
Arms
Lungs
Superior vena cava
Pulmonary arteries
Pulmonary veins
Ascending arteries
Right atrium
Aorta
Left atrium
Coronary arteries
Left ventricle
Abdominal aorta
Right ventricle
Heart
Inferior vena cava
Trunk
Hepatic artery
Hepatic vein
Hepatic portal vein
Liver
Digestive tract
Ascending veins
Renal veins
Renal arteries
Descending arteries
Venous valve
Kidneys
Pelvis and Legs

FIGURE QUESTION

A portal system is two capillary beds joined in series. Identify the two portal systems shown in this figure.

● **FIGURE 14-1** ***The heart is a pump that circulates blood through the blood vessels.***

This is a convention used to show blood from which the tissues have extracted oxygen. Although this blood is often described as *deoxygenated,* it is not completely devoid of oxygen. It simply has less oxygen than blood going from the lungs to the tissues.

In living people, well-oxygenated blood is bright red, and low-oxygen blood is a darker red. Under some conditions, low-oxygen blood can impart a bluish color to certain areas of the skin, such as around the mouth and under the fingernails. This condition, known as *cyanosis* [*kyanos,* dark blue], is the reason blue is used in drawings to indicate blood with lower oxygen content.

From the right atrium, blood flows into the right ventricle of the heart. From there it is pumped through the **pulmonary arteries** [*pulmo*, lung] to the lungs, where it is oxygenated. Note the color change from blue to red in Figure 14-1, indicating higher oxygen content after the blood leaves the lungs. From the lungs, blood travels to the left side of the heart through the **pulmonary veins**. The blood vessels that go from the right ventricle to the lungs and back to the left atrium are known collectively as the **pulmonary circulation**.

Blood from the lungs enters the heart at the left atrium and passes into the left ventricle. Blood pumped out of the left ventricle enters the large artery known as the **aorta**. The aorta branches into a series of smaller and smaller arteries that finally lead into networks of capillaries. Notice at the top of Figure 14-1 the color change from red to blue as the blood passes through the capillaries, indicating that oxygen has left the blood and diffused into the tissues.

After leaving the capillaries, blood flows into the venous side of the circulation, moving from small veins into larger and larger veins. The veins from the upper part of the body join to form the **superior vena cava**. Those from the lower part of the body form the **inferior vena cava**. The two *venae cavae* empty into the right atrium. The blood vessels that carry blood from the left side of the heart to the tissues and back to the right side of the heart are collectively known as the **systemic circulation**.

Return to Figure 14-1 and follow the divisions of the aorta after it leaves the left ventricle. The first branch represents the *coronary arteries,* which nourish the heart muscle itself. Blood from these arteries flows into capillaries, then into the *coronary veins,* which empty directly into the right atrium at the *coronary sinus*. Ascending branches of the aorta go to the arms, head, and brain. The abdominal aorta supplies blood to the trunk, the legs, and the internal organs such as liver (*hepatic artery*), digestive tract, and the kidneys (*renal arteries*).

Notice two special arrangements of the circulation. One is the blood supply to the digestive tract and liver. Both regions receive well-oxygenated blood through their own arteries, but, in addition, blood leaving the digestive tract goes directly to the liver by means of the *hepatic portal vein*. The liver is an important site for nutrient processing and plays a major role in the detoxifying foreign substances. Most nutrients absorbed in the intestine are routed directly to the liver, allowing that organ to process material before it is released into the general circulation. The two capillary beds of the digestive tract and liver, joined by the hepatic portal vein, are an example of a *portal system*.

A second portal system occurs in the kidneys, where two capillary beds are connected in series. You will learn more about this special vascular arrangement in Chapter 19. A third portal system, discussed earlier but not shown here, is the hypothalamic-hypophyseal portal system, which connects the hypothalamus and the anterior pituitary [p. 232].

CONCEPT CHECK

1. A cardiovascular system has what three major components?
2. What is the difference between (a) the pulmonary and systemic circulations, (b) an artery and a vein, (c) an atrium and a ventricle?

Answers: p. 509

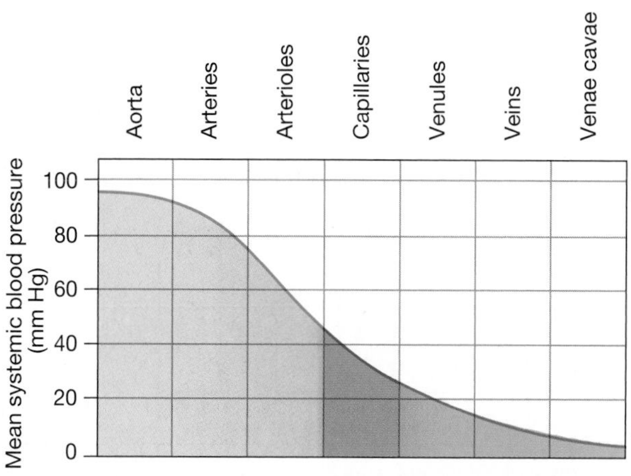

● **FIGURE 14-2** ***Pressure gradient in the systemic circulation.*** The mean blood pressure of the systemic circulation ranges from a high of 93 mm Hg (millimeters of mercury) in the aorta to a low of a few mm Hg in the venae cavae.

PRESSURE, VOLUME, FLOW, AND RESISTANCE

If you ask people why blood flows through the cardiovascular system, many of them respond, "So that oxygen and nutrients can get to all parts of the body." This is true, but it is a teleological answer, one that describes the purpose of blood flow. In physiology, we are also concerned with how blood flows—in other words, with the mechanisms or forces that create blood flow.

A simple mechanistic answer to "Why does blood flow?" is that liquids and gases flow down **pressure gradients (ΔP)** from regions of higher pressure to regions of lower pressure. For this reason, blood can flow in the cardiovascular system only if one region develops higher pressure than other regions.

In humans, the heart creates high pressure when it contracts. Blood flows out of the heart (the region of highest pressure) into the closed loop of blood vessels (a region of lower pressure). As blood moves through the system, pressure is lost because of friction between the fluid and the blood vessel walls. Consequently, pressure falls continuously as blood moves farther from the heart (Fig. 14-2 ●). The highest pressure in the vessels of the cardiovascular system is found in the aorta and systemic arteries as they receive blood from the left ventricle. The lowest pressure is in the venae cavae, just before they empty into the right atrium.

Now let's review the laws of physics that explain the interaction of pressure, volume, flow, and resistance in the cardiovascular system. Many of these principles apply broadly to the flow of all types of liquids and gases, including the flow of air in the respiratory system. However, in this chapter we focus on blood flow and its relevance to the function of the heart.

14

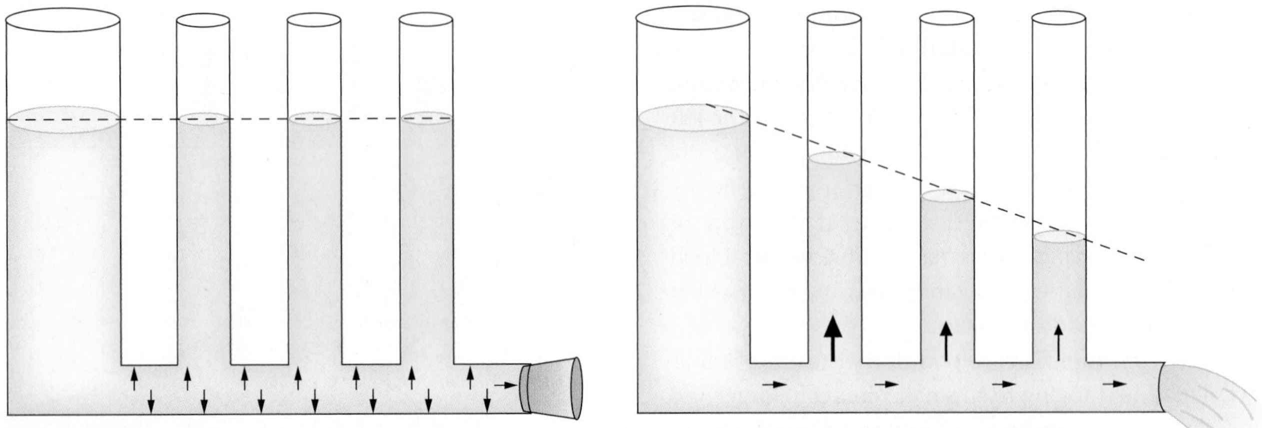

(a) Hydrostatic pressure is the pressure exerted on the walls of the container by the fluid within the container. Hydrostatic pressure is proportional to the height of the water column.

(b) Once fluid begins to flow through the system, pressure falls with distance as energy is lost because of friction. This is the situation in the cardiovascular system.

● **FIGURE 14-3** ***Pressure differences in static and flowing fluids***

The Pressure of Fluid in Motion Decreases over Distance

Pressure in a fluid is the force exerted by the fluid on its container. If the fluid is not moving, the pressure it exerts is called **hydrostatic pressure** (Fig. 14-3a ●), and force is exerted equally in all directions. For example, a column of fluid in a tube exerts hydrostatic pressure on the floor and sides of the tube. In the heart and blood vessels, pressure is commonly measured in *millimeters of mercury* (mm Hg), where one millimeter of mercury is equivalent to the hydrostatic pressure exerted by a 1-mm-high column of mercury on an area of 1 cm^2. Some physiological literature reports pressures in *torr* (1 torr = 1 mm Hg) or in *centimeters of water:* 1 cm H_2O = 0.74 mm Hg.

In a system in which fluid is flowing, pressure falls over distance as energy is lost because of friction (Fig. 14-3b). In addition, the pressure exerted by moving fluid has two components: a dynamic, flowing component that represents the kinetic energy of the system, and a lateral component that represents the hydrostatic pressure (potential energy) exerted on the walls of the system. Pressure within our cardiovascular system is usually called hydrostatic pressure even though it is a system in which fluid is in motion. Some textbooks are beginning to replace the term *hydrostatic pressure* with the term *hydraulic pressure*. Hydraulics is the study of fluid in motion.

RUNNING PROBLEM

When people speak of a "heart attack," they are actually referring to a clot that stops the blood supply to part of the heart, creating a condition known as *ischemia* [*ischien,* to suppress + *emia,* blood]. In medical terms, a heart attack is called a *myocardial infarction* (MI), referring to an area of heart muscle that is dying because of a lack of blood supply. The clot in Walter's coronary artery had restricted blood flow to part of his left ventricle, and its cells were beginning to die from lack of oxygen. When someone has a heart attack, immediate medical intervention is critical. In the ambulance on the way to the emergency room, the EMT gave Walter oxygen, hooked him up to a heart monitor, and started an intravenous (IV) injection of normal (isotonic) saline. With an IV line in place, other drugs could be given rapidly if Walter's condition should suddenly worsen.

Question 1:
Why did the EMT give Walter oxygen?

Question 2:
What effect would the injection of isotonic saline have on Walter's extracellular fluid volume? On his intracellular fluid volume? On his total body osmolarity? *[Hint:* *p. 161]*

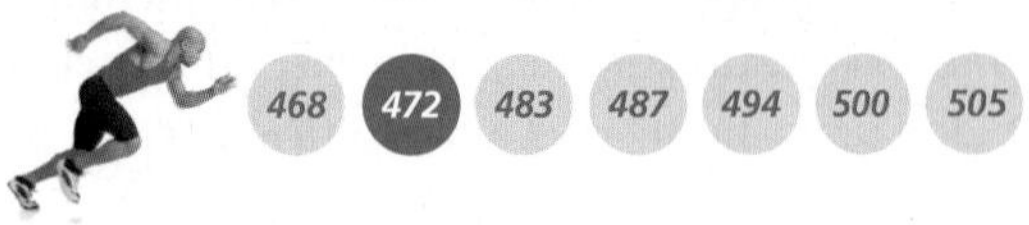

Pressure Changes in Liquids Without a Change in Volume

If the walls of a fluid-filled container contract, the pressure exerted on the fluid in the container increases. You can demonstrate this principle by filling a balloon with water and squeezing the water balloon in your hand. Water is minimally compressible, and so the pressure you apply to the balloon is transmitted throughout the fluid. As you squeeze, higher pressure in the fluid causes parts of the balloon to bulge. If the pressure becomes high enough, the stress on the balloon causes it to pop. The water volume inside the balloon did not change, but the pressure in the fluid increased.

In the human heart, contraction of the blood-filled ventricles is similar to squeezing a water balloon: pressure created by the contracting muscle is transferred to the blood. This high-pressure blood then flows out of the ventricle and into the blood vessels, displacing lower-pressure blood already in the vessels. The pressure created in the ventricles is called the **driving pressure** because it is the force that drives blood through the blood vessels.

When the walls of a fluid-filled container expand, the pressure exerted on the fluid decreases. For this reason, when the heart relaxes and expands, pressure in the fluid-filled chambers falls.

Pressure changes can also take place in the blood vessels. If blood vessels dilate, blood pressure inside them falls. If blood vessels constrict, blood pressure increases. Volume changes of the blood vessels and heart are major factors that influence blood pressure in the cardiovascular system.

Blood Flows from Higher Pressure to Lower Pressure

As stated earlier, blood flow through the cardiovascular system requires a pressure gradient. This pressure gradient is analogous to the difference in pressure between two ends of a tube through which fluid flows (Fig. 14-4a ●). Flow through the tube is directly proportional to ($\propto$) the pressure gradient (ΔP):

$$\text{Flow} \propto \Delta P \qquad (1)$$

where $\Delta P = P_1 - P_2$. This relationship says that the higher the pressure gradient, the greater the fluid flow.

A pressure gradient is not the same thing as the absolute pressure in the system. For example, the tube in Figure 14-4b has an absolute pressure of 100 mm Hg at each end. However, because there is no pressure gradient between the two ends of the tube, there is no flow through the tube.

On the other hand, two identical tubes can have very different absolute pressures but the same flow. The top tube in Figure 14-4c has a hydrostatic pressure of 100 mm Hg at one end and 75 mm Hg at the other end, which means that the pressure gradient between the ends of the tube is 25 mm Hg. The identical bottom tube has a hydrostatic pressure of 40 mm Hg at one end and 15 mm Hg at the other end. This tube has lower absolute pressure all along its length but the same pressure gradient as the top tube—25 mm Hg. Because the pressure difference in the two tubes is identical, fluid flow through the tubes is the same.

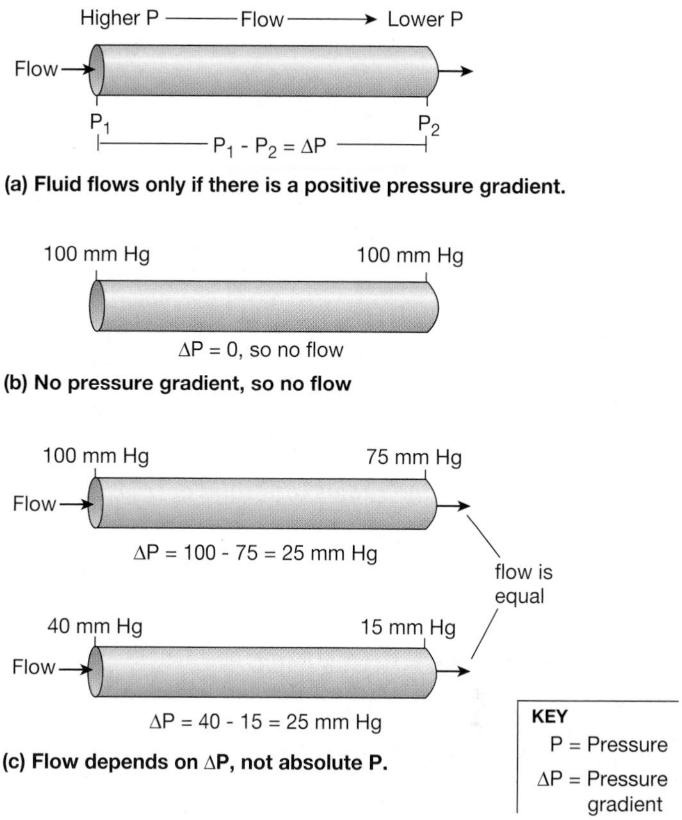

● **FIGURE 14-4** ***Fluid flow through a tube depends on the pressure gradient.***

Resistance Opposes Flow

In an ideal system, a substance in motion would remain in motion. However, no system is ideal because all movement creates friction. Just as a ball rolled across the ground loses energy to friction, blood flowing through blood vessels encounters friction from the walls of the vessels and from cells within the blood rubbing against one another as they flow.

The tendency of the cardiovascular system to oppose blood flow is called the system's **resistance** to flow. Resistance (R) is a term that most of us understand from everyday life. We speak of people being resistant to change or taking the path of least resistance. This concept translates well to the cardiovascular system because blood flow also takes the path of least resistance. An increase in the resistance of a blood vessel results in a decrease in the flow through that vessel. We can express that relationship as

$$\text{Flow} \propto 1/R \qquad (2)$$

This expression says that flow is inversely proportional to resistance: if resistance increases, flow decreases; and if resistance decreases, flow increases.

What parameters determine resistance? For fluid flowing through a tube, resistance is influenced by three components: the radius of the tube (r), the length of the tube (L), and the **viscosity** (thickness) of the fluid (η, the Greek letter eta). The following equation, derived by the French physician Jean Leonard Marie Poiseuille and known as **Poiseuille's law**, shows the relationship of these factors:

$$R = 8L\eta/\pi r^4 \qquad (3)$$

Because the value of $8/\pi$ is a constant, this factor can be removed from the equation, and the relationship can be rewritten as

$$R \propto L\eta/r^4 \qquad (4)$$

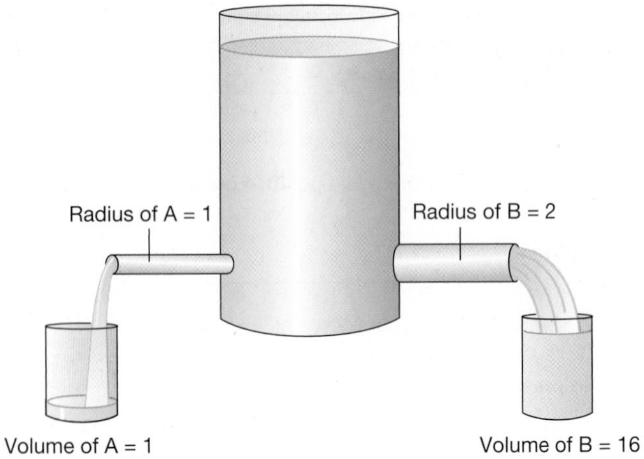

Resistance ∝ $\frac{1}{\text{radius}^4}$	
Tube A	Tube B
$R \propto \frac{1}{1^4}$	$R \propto \frac{1}{2^4}$
$R \propto 1$	$R \propto \frac{1}{16}$

Flow ∝ $\frac{1}{\text{resistance}}$	
Tube A	Tube B
$\text{Flow} \propto \frac{1}{1}$	$\text{Flow} \propto \frac{1}{\frac{1}{16}}$
$\text{Flow} \propto 1$	$\text{Flow} \propto 16$

FIGURE QUESTION

If the radius of A changes to 3, the flow through A will be about ______ times the flow through B.

● **FIGURE 14-5** ***As the radius of a tube decreases, the resistance to flow increases.***

This expression says that (1) the resistance to fluid flow offered by a tube increases as the length of the tube increases, (2) resistance increases as the viscosity of the fluid increases, but (3) resistance decreases as the tube's radius increases.

To remember these relationships, think of drinking through a straw. You do not need to suck as hard on a short straw as on a long one (the resistance offered by the straw increases with length). Drinking water through a straw is easier than drinking a thick milkshake (resistance increases with viscosity). And drinking the milkshake through a fat straw is much easier than through a skinny cocktail straw (resistance increases as radius decreases).

How significant are tube length, fluid viscosity, and tube radius to blood flow in a normal individual? The length of the systemic circulation is determined by the anatomy of the system and is essentially constant. Blood viscosity is determined by the ratio of red blood cells to plasma and by how much protein is in the plasma. Normally, viscosity is constant, and small changes in either length or viscosity have little effect on resistance. This leaves changes in the radius of the blood vessels as the main variable that affects resistance in the systemic circulation.

Let's return to the example of the straw and the milkshake to illustrate how changes in radius affect resistance. If we assume that the length of the straw and the viscosity of the milkshake do not change, this system is similar to the cardiovascular system—the radius of the tube has the greatest effect on resistance. If we consider only resistance (R) and radius (r) from equation 4, the relationship between resistance and radius can be expressed as

$$R \propto 1/r^4 \qquad (5)$$

If the skinny straw has a radius of 1, its resistance is proportional to $1/1^4$, or 1. If the fat straw has a radius of 2, the resistance it offers is $1/2^4$, or 1/16th, that of the skinny straw (Fig. 14-5 ●). Because flow is inversely proportional to resistance, flow increases 16-fold when the radius doubles.

As you can see from this example, a small change in the radius of a tube has a large effect on the flow of a fluid through that tube. Similarly, a small change in the radius of a blood vessel has a large effect on the resistance to blood flow offered by that vessel. A decrease in blood vessel diameter is known as **vasoconstriction** [*vas,* a vessel or duct]. An increase in blood vessel diameter is called **vasodilation**. Vasoconstriction decreases blood flow through a vessel, and vasodilation increases blood flow through a vessel.

In summary, by combining equations 1 and 2, we get the equation

$$\text{Flow} \propto \Delta P/R \qquad (6)$$

which, translated into words, says that the flow of blood in the cardiovascular system is directly proportional to the pressure gradient in the system, and inversely proportional to the resistance of the system to flow. If the pressure gradient remains constant, then flow varies inversely with resistance.

CONCEPT CHECK

3. Which is more important for determining flow through a tube: absolute pressure or the pressure gradient?
4. The two identical tubes below have the pressures shown at each end. Which tube has the greater flow? Defend your choice.

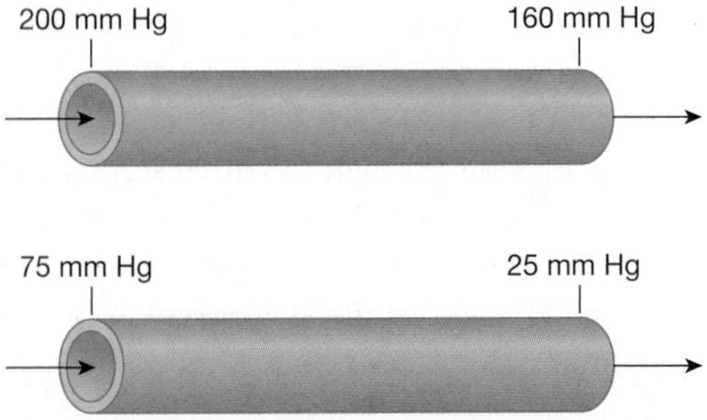

5. All four tubes below have the same driving pressure. Which tube has the greatest flow? Which has the least flow? Defend your choices.

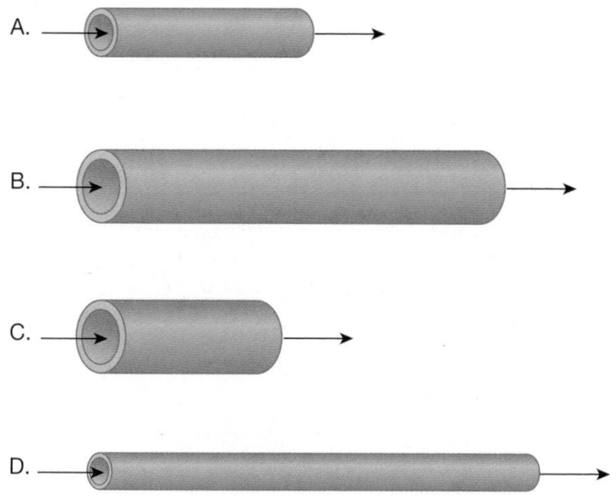

Answers: p. 509

Velocity Depends on the Flow Rate and the Cross-Sectional Area

The word *flow* is sometimes used imprecisely in cardiovascular physiology, leading to confusion. Flow usually means **flow rate**, the volume of blood that passes a given point in the system per unit time. In the circulation, flow is expressed in either liters per minute (L/min) or milliliters per minute (mL/min). For instance, blood flow through the aorta of a 70-kg man at rest is about 5 L/min.

Flow rate should not be confused with **velocity of flow** (or simply *velocity*), the distance a fixed volume of blood travels in a given period of time. Velocity is a measure of *how fast* blood flows past a point. In contrast, flow rate measures *how much* (volume) blood flows past a point in a given period of time. For example, look through the open door at the hallway outside your classroom. The number of people passing the door in one minute is the flow rate of people through the hallway. How quickly those people are walking past the door is their velocity.

The relationship between velocity of flow (v), flow rate (Q), and cross-sectional area of the tube (A) is expressed by the equation

$$v = Q/A \qquad (7)$$

which says that the velocity of flow through a tube equals the flow rate divided by the tube's cross-sectional area. In a tube of fixed diameter (and thus fixed cross-sectional area), velocity is directly related to flow rate. In a tube of variable diameter, if the flow rate is constant, velocity varies inversely with the diameter. In other words, velocity is faster in narrow sections, and slower in wider sections.

Figure 14-6 ● shows how the velocity of flow varies as the cross-sectional area of the tube changes. The vessel in the figure has variable width, from narrow, with a cross-sectional area of 1 cm^2, to wide, with a cross-sectional area of 12 cm^2. The flow rate is identical along the length of the vessel: 12 cm^3 per minute (1 cm^3 = 1 cubic centimeter (cc) = 1 mL). This flow rate means that in one minute, 12 cm^3 of fluid flows past point X in the narrow section, and 12 cm^3 of fluid flows past point Y in the wide section.

But *how fast* does the fluid need to flow to accomplish that rate? According to equation 7, the velocity of flow at point X is 12 cm/min, but at point Y it is only 1 cm/min. As you can see, fluid flows more rapidly through narrow sections of a tube than through wide sections.

To see this principle in action, watch a leaf as it floats down a stream. Where the stream is narrow, the leaf moves rapidly, carried by the fast velocity of the water. In sections where the stream widens into a pool, the velocity of the water decreases and the leaf meanders more slowly.

In this chapter and the next, we apply the physics of fluid flow to the cardiovascular system. The heart generates pressure when it contracts and pumps blood into the arterial side of the circulation. Arteries act as a pressure reservoir during the heart's relaxation phase, maintaining the *mean arterial pressure* (MAP) that is the primary driving force for blood flow. Mean arterial pressure is influenced by two parameters: *cardiac output* (the

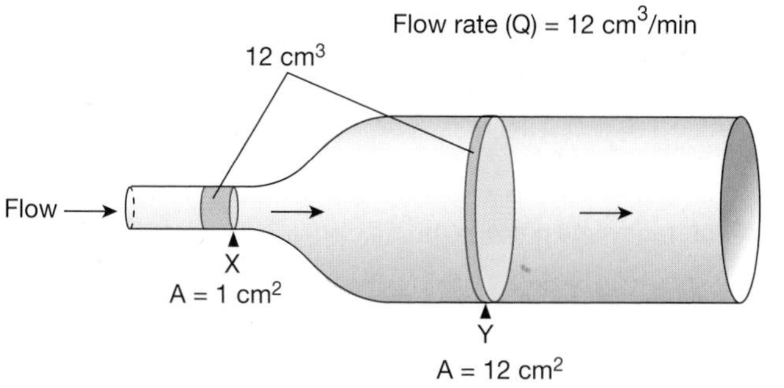

The narrower the vessel, the faster the velocity of flow.

Velocity (v) = $\frac{\text{Flow rate (Q)}}{\text{Cross-sectional area (A)}}$

At point X	At point Y
$v = \frac{12\ cm^3/min}{1\ cm^2}$	$v = \frac{12\ cm^3/min}{12\ cm^2}$
v = 12 cm/min	v = 1 cm/min

FIGURE QUESTION

If the cross-sectional area of this pipe is 3 cm^2, what is the velocity of the flow?

● **FIGURE 14-6** ***Flow rate is not the same as velocity of flow.***

ANATOMY SUMMARY

THE HEART

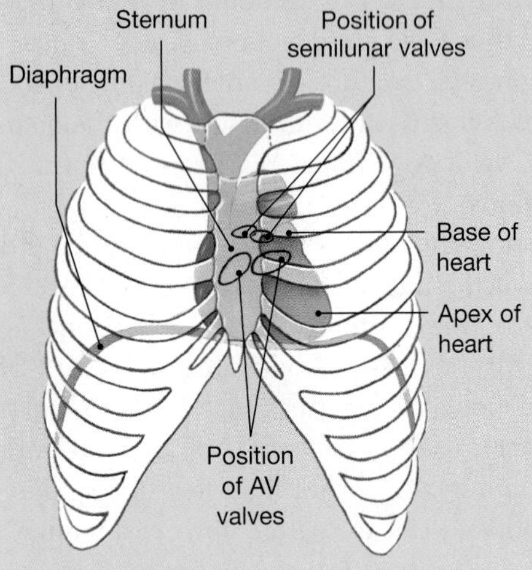
Sternum
Position of semilunar valves
Diaphragm
Base of heart
Apex of heart
Position of AV valves

(a) The heart lies in the center of the thorax.

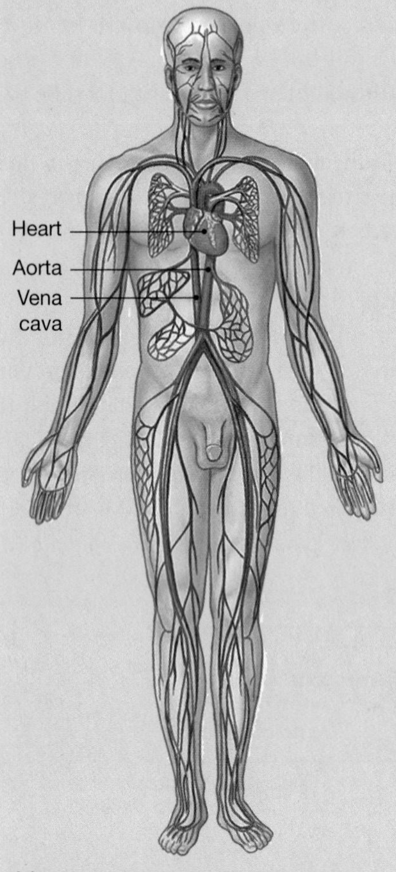
Heart
Aorta
Vena cava

(c) Vessels that carry well-oxygenated blood are red; those with less well-oxygenated blood are blue.

ANATOMY OF THE THORACIC CAVITY

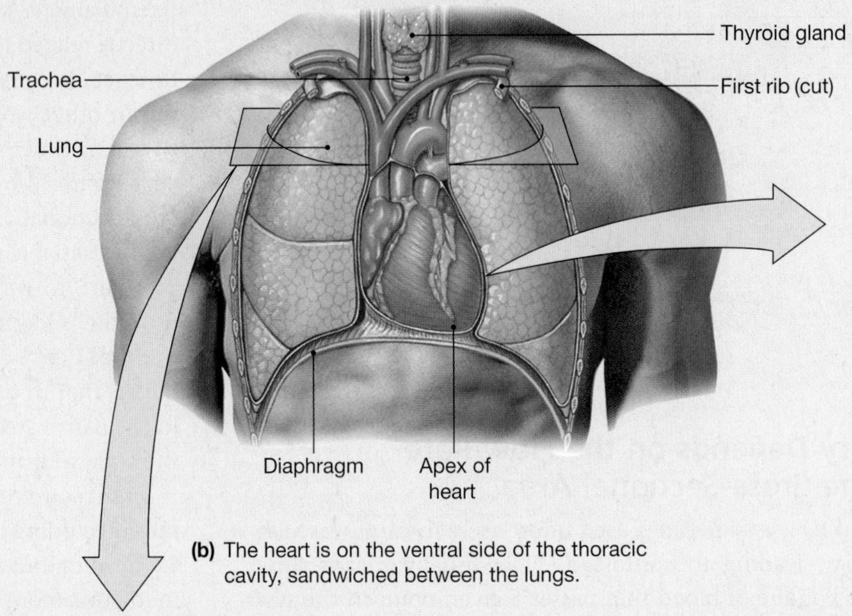
Thyroid gland
Trachea
First rib (cut)
Lung
Diaphragm
Apex of heart

(b) The heart is on the ventral side of the thoracic cavity, sandwiched between the lungs.

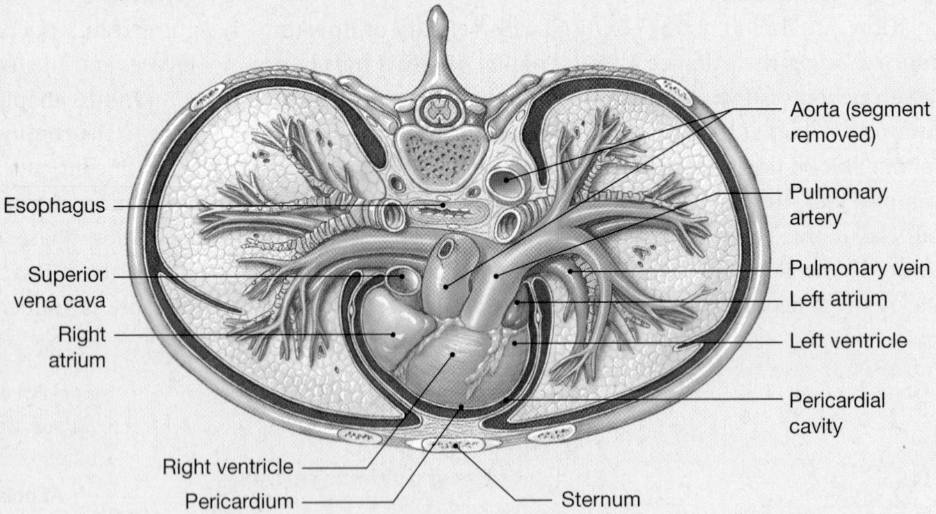
Aorta (segment removed)
Esophagus
Pulmonary artery
Superior vena cava
Pulmonary vein
Left atrium
Right atrium
Left ventricle
Pericardial cavity
Right ventricle
Pericardium
Sternum

(d) Superior view of transverse plane in (b)

● **FIGURE 14-7**

STRUCTURE OF THE HEART

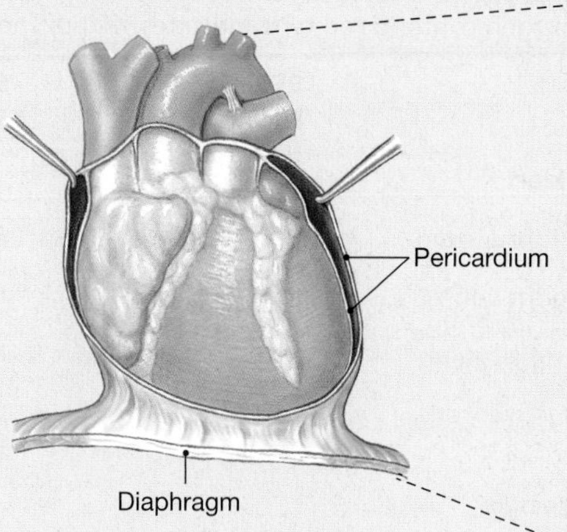
Pericardium
Diaphragm

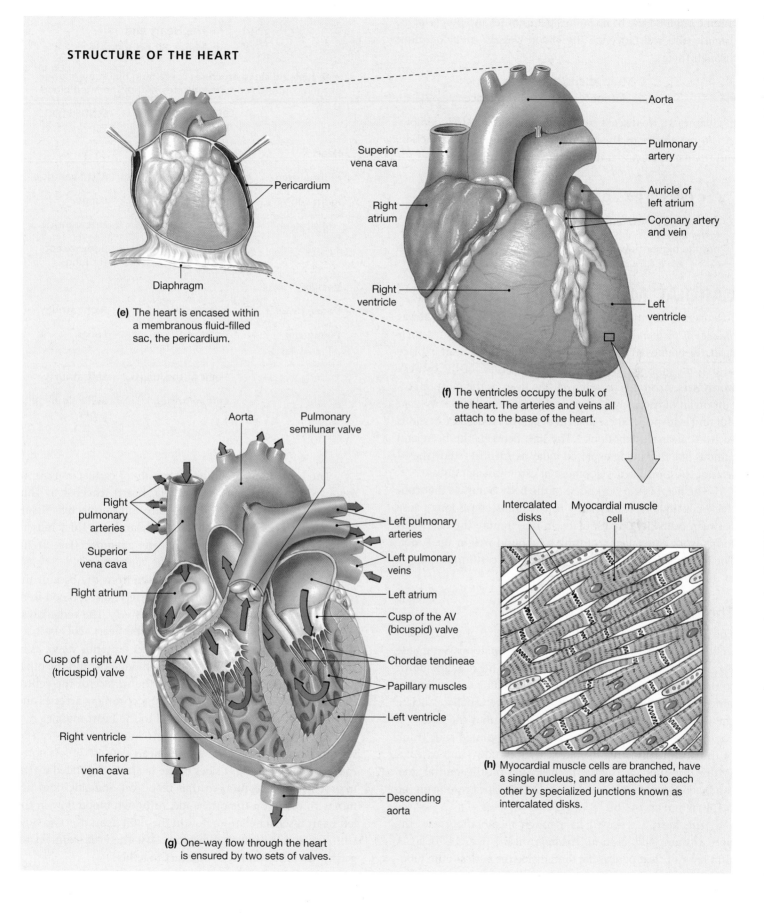

(e) The heart is encased within a membranous fluid-filled sac, the pericardium.

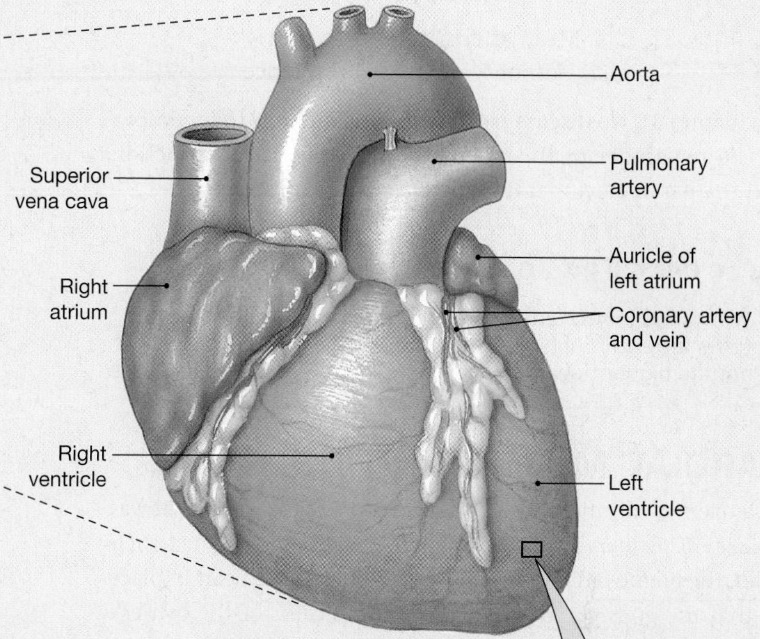
Aorta
Superior vena cava
Pulmonary artery
Auricle of left atrium
Right atrium
Coronary artery and vein
Right ventricle
Left ventricle

(f) The ventricles occupy the bulk of the heart. The arteries and veins all attach to the base of the heart.

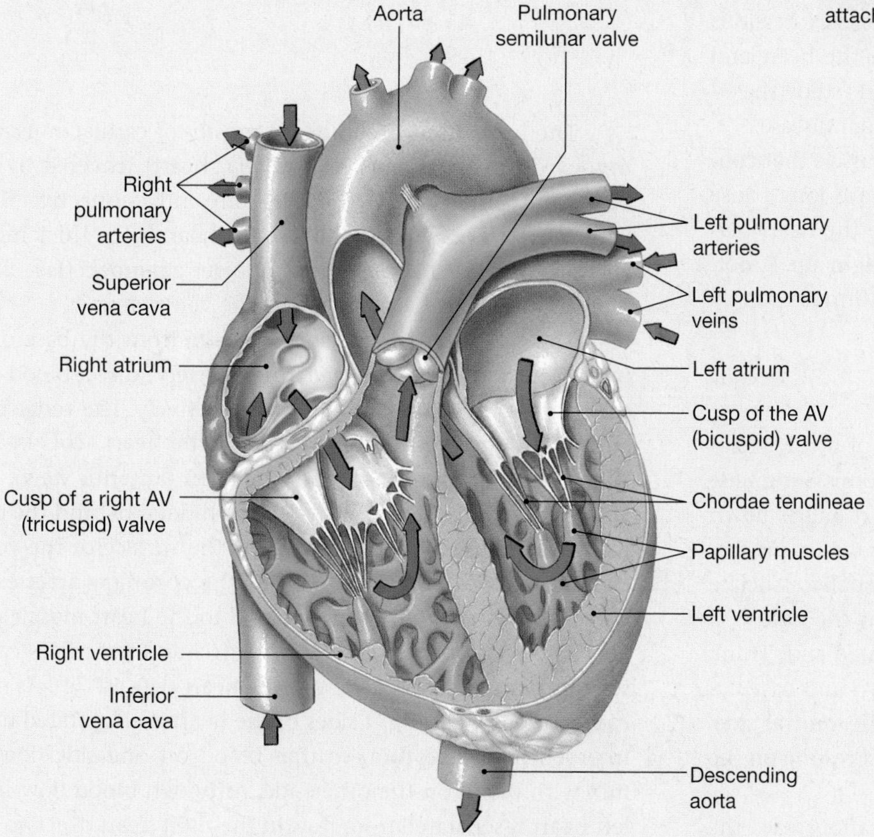
Aorta
Pulmonary semilunar valve
Right pulmonary arteries
Superior vena cava
Right atrium
Cusp of a right AV (tricuspid) valve
Right ventricle
Inferior vena cava
Left pulmonary arteries
Left pulmonary veins
Left atrium
Cusp of the AV (bicuspid) valve
Chordae tendineae
Papillary muscles
Left ventricle
Descending aorta

(g) One-way flow through the heart is ensured by two sets of valves.

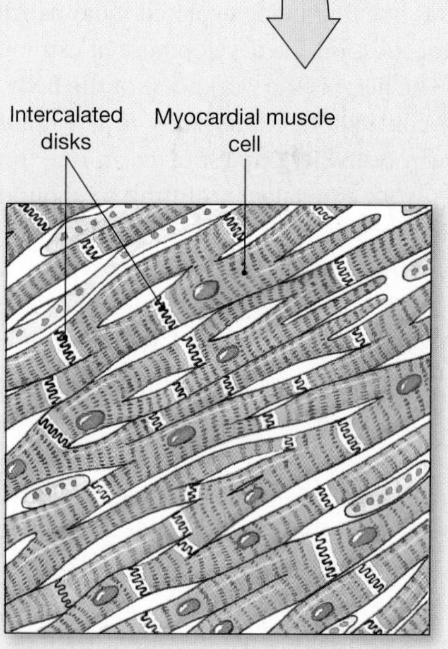
Intercalated disks
Myocardial muscle cell

(h) Myocardial muscle cells are branched, have a single nucleus, and are attached to each other by specialized junctions known as intercalated disks.

volume of blood the heart pumps per minute) and *peripheral resistance* (the resistance of the blood vessels to blood flow through them):

$$\text{Mean arterial pressure} \propto \text{cardiac output} \times \text{peripheral resistance}$$

In Chapter 15 we discuss peripheral resistance and blood flow. In the remainder of this chapter we examine heart function and the parameters that influence cardiac output.

CONCEPT CHECK

6. Two canals in Amsterdam are identical in size, but the water flows faster through one than through the other. Which canal has the higher flow rate? Answers: p. 509

CARDIAC MUSCLE AND THE HEART

To ancient civilizations, the heart was more than a pump—it was *the seat of the mind.* When ancient Egyptians mummified their dead, they removed most of the viscera but left the heart in place so that the gods could weigh it as an indicator of the owner's worthiness. Aristotle characterized the heart as the most important organ of the body, as well as *the seat of intelligence.* We can still find evidence of these ancient beliefs in modern expressions such as "heartfelt emotions." The link between the heart and mind is one that is still explored today as scientists study the effects of stress on the development of cardiovascular disease.

The heart is the workhorse of the body, a muscle that contracts continually, resting only in the milliseconds-long pause between beats. By one estimate, in one minute the heart performs work equivalent to lifting a 5-pound weight up 1 foot. The energy demands of this work require a continuous supply of nutrients and oxygen to the heart muscle.

The Heart Has Four Chambers

The heart is a muscular organ, about the size of a fist. It lies in the center of the *thoracic cavity* (see Anatomy Summary, Fig. 14-7a, b, d ●). The pointed *apex* of the heart angles down to the left side of the body, while the broader *base* lies just behind the breastbone, or *sternum.* Because we usually associate the word *base* with the bottom, remember that the base of a cone is the broad end, and the apex is the pointed end. Think of the heart as an inverted cone with apex down and base up. Within the thoracic cavity, the heart lies on the ventral side, sandwiched between the two lungs, with its apex resting on the diaphragm (Fig. 14-7b).

The heart is encased in a tough membranous sac, the **pericardium** [*peri,* around + *kardia,* heart] (Fig. 14-7d, e). A thin layer of clear pericardial fluid inside the pericardium lubricates the external surface of the heart as it beats within the sac. Inflammation of the pericardium (*pericarditis*) may reduce this lubrication to the point that the heart rubs against the pericardium, creating a sound known as a *friction rub.*

Table 14-2 The Heart and Major Blood Vessels

Blue type indicates structures containing blood with lower oxygen content; red type indicates well-oxygenated blood.

	RECEIVES BLOOD FROM	SENDS BLOOD TO
Heart		
Right atrium	Venae cavae	Right ventricle
Right ventricle	Right atrium	Lungs
Left atrium	Pulmonary veins	Left ventricle
Left ventricle	Left atrium	Body except for lungs
Vessels		
Venae cavae	Systemic veins	Right atrium
Pulmonary trunk (artery)	Right ventricle	Lungs
Pulmonary vein	Veins of the lungs	Left atrium
Aorta	Left ventricle	Systemic arteries

The heart itself is composed mostly of cardiac muscle, or **myocardium** [*myo,* muscle + *kardia,* heart], covered by thin outer and inner layers of epithelium and connective tissue. Seen from the outside, the bulk of the heart is the thick muscular walls of the ventricles, the two lower chambers (Fig. 14-7f). The thinner-walled atria lie above the ventricles.

The major blood vessels all emerge from the base of the heart. The aorta and *pulmonary trunk* (artery) direct blood from the heart to the tissues and lungs, respectively. The venae cavae and pulmonary veins return blood to the heart (Tbl. 14-2 ●). When the heart is viewed from the front (anterior view), as in Figure 14-7f, the pulmonary veins are hidden behind the other major blood vessels. Running across the surface of the ventricles are shallow grooves containing the **coronary arteries** and **coronary veins**, which supply blood to the heart muscle.

The relationship between the atria and ventricles can be seen in a cross-sectional view of the heart (Fig. 14-7g). As noted earlier, the left and right sides of the heart are separated by the interventricular septum, so that blood on one side does not mix with blood on the other side. Although blood flow in the left heart is separated from flow in the right heart, the two sides contract in a coordinated fashion. First the atria contract together, then the ventricles contract together.

Blood flows from veins into the atria and from there through one-way valves into the ventricles, the pumping chambers. Blood leaves the heart via the pulmonary trunk from the right ventricle and via the aorta from the left ventricle. A second set of valves guards the exits of the ventricles so that blood cannot flow back into the heart once it has been ejected.

Notice in Figure 14-7g that blood enters each ventricle at the top of the chamber but also leaves at the top. This is because during development, the tubular embryonic heart twists back on itself (Fig. 14-8b ●). This twisting puts the arteries (through which blood leaves) close to the top of the ventricles. Functionally, this means that the ventricles must contract from the bottom up so that blood is squeezed out of the top.

Four fibrous connective tissue rings surround the four heart valves (Fig. 14-9a ●). These rings form both the origin and insertion for the cardiac muscle, an arrangement that pulls the apex and base of the heart together when the ventricles contract. In addition, the fibrous connective tissue acts as an electrical insulator, blocking most transmission of electrical signals between the atria and the ventricles. This arrangement ensures that the electrical signals can be directed through a specialized conduction system to the apex of the heart for the bottom-to-top contraction.

Heart Valves Ensure One-Way Flow in the Heart

As the arrows in Figure 14-7g indicate, blood flows through the heart in one direction. Two sets of heart valves ensure this one-way flow: one set (the **atrioventricular valves**) between the atria and ventricles, and the second set (the **semilunar valves**, named for their crescent-moon shape) between the ventricles and the arteries. Although the two sets of valves are very different in structure, they serve the same function: preventing the backward flow of blood.

The opening between each atrium and its ventricle is guarded by an atrioventricular (AV) valve (Fig. 14-7g). The AV valve is formed from thin flaps of tissue joined at the base to a connective tissue ring. The flaps are slightly thickened at the edge and connect on the ventricular side to collagenous tendons, the **chordae tendineae** (Fig. 14-9b, d).

Most of the chordae fasten to the edges of the valve flaps. The opposite ends of the chordae are tethered to moundlike extensions of ventricular muscle known as the **papillary muscles** [*papilla,* nipple]. These muscles provide stability for the chordae, but they cannot actively open and close the AV valves. The valves move passively when flowing blood pushes on them.

When a ventricle contracts, blood pushes against the bottom side of its AV valve and forces it upward into a closed position (Fig. 14-9b). The chordae tendineae prevent the valve from being pushed back into the atrium, just as the struts on an umbrella keep the umbrella from turning inside out in a high wind. Occasionally, the chordae fail, and the valve is pushed back into the atrium during ventricular contraction, an abnormal condition known as *prolapse.*

The two AV valves are not identical. The valve that separates the right atrium and right ventricle has three flaps and is called the **tricuspid valve** [*cuspis,* point] (Fig. 14-9a). The valve

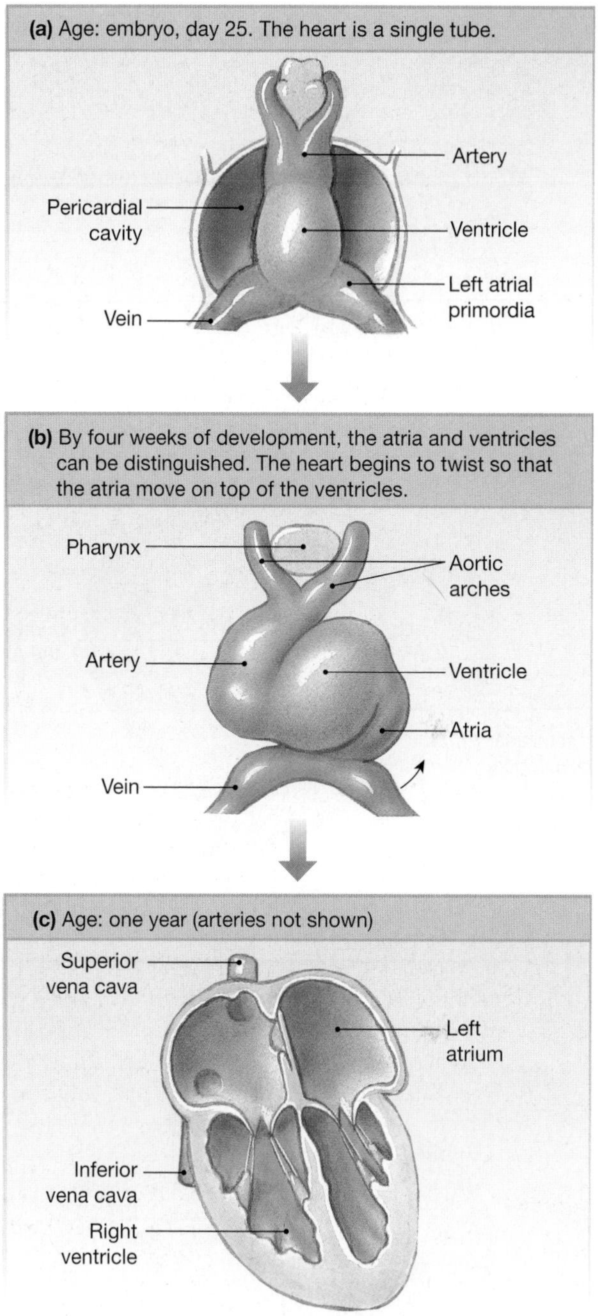
(a) Age: embryo, day 25. The heart is a single tube.
Artery
Pericardial cavity
Ventricle
Left atrial primordia
Vein
(b) By four weeks of development, the atria and ventricles can be distinguished. The heart begins to twist so that the atria move on top of the ventricles.
Pharynx
Aortic arches
Artery
Ventricle
Atria
Vein
(c) Age: one year (arteries not shown)
Superior vena cava
Left atrium
Inferior vena cava
Right ventricle

● **FIGURE 14-8** ***In the embryo, the heart develops from a single tube.***

between the left atrium and left ventricle has only two flaps and is called the **bicuspid valve**. The bicuspid is also called the **mitral valve** because of its resemblance to the tall headdress, known as a miter, worn by popes and bishops. You can match AV valves to the proper side of the heart by remembering that the Right Side has the Tricuspid (R-S-T).

The semilunar valves separate the ventricles from the major arteries. The **aortic valve** is between the left ventricle and the aorta, and the **pulmonary valve** lies between the right ventricle and the pulmonary trunk. Each semilunar valve has three cuplike leaflets that snap closed when blood attempting to flow

14

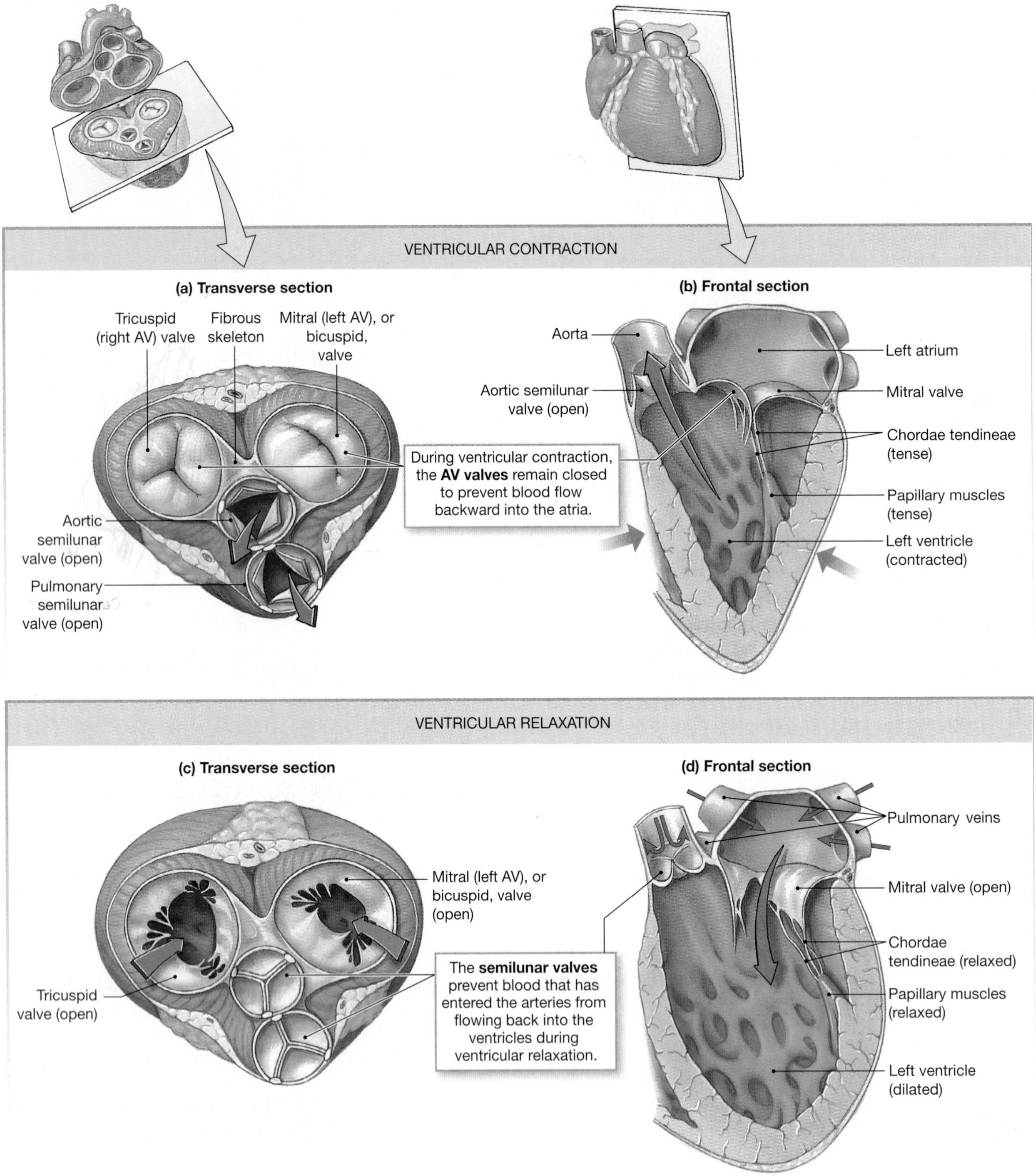
VENTRICULAR CONTRACTION
(a) Transverse section
Tricuspid (right AV) valve
Fibrous skeleton
Mitral (left AV), or bicuspid, valve
Aortic semilunar valve (open)
Pulmonary semilunar valve (open)
During ventricular contraction, the AV valves remain closed to prevent blood flow backward into the atria.
(b) Frontal section
Aorta
Aortic semilunar valve (open)
Left atrium
Mitral valve
Chordae tendineae (tense)
Papillary muscles (tense)
Left ventricle (contracted)
VENTRICULAR RELAXATION
(c) Transverse section
Mitral (left AV), or bicuspid, valve (open)
Tricuspid valve (open)
The semilunar valves prevent blood that has entered the arteries from flowing back into the ventricles during ventricular relaxation.
(d) Frontal section
Pulmonary veins
Mitral valve (open)
Chordae tendineae (relaxed)
Papillary muscles (relaxed)
Left ventricle (dilated)

● **FIGURE 14-9** ***Heart valves create one-way flow through the heart.*** Views **(a)** and **(c)** show the AV valves as viewed from the atria, and the semilunar valves as viewed from inside the arteries.

back into the ventricles fills them (Fig. 14-9c, d). Because of their shape, the semilunar valves do not need connective tendons as the AV valves do.

CONCEPT CHECK

7. What prevents electrical signals from passing through the connective tissue in the heart?
8. Trace a drop of blood from the superior vena cava to the aorta, naming all structures the drop encounters along its route.
9. What is the function of the AV valves? What happens to blood flow if one of these valves fails? Answers: p. 509

Cardiac Muscle Cells Contract Without Innervation

The bulk of the heart is composed of cardiac muscle cells, or myocardium. Most cardiac muscle is contractile, but about 1% of the myocardial cells are specialized to generate action potentials spontaneously. These cells account for a unique property of the heart: its ability to contract without any outside signal. As mentioned in the introduction to this chapter, records tell us of Spanish explorers in the New World witnessing human sacrifices in which hearts torn from the chests of living victims continued to beat for minutes. The heart can contract without a connection to other parts of the body because the signal for contraction is *myogenic,* originating within the heart muscle itself.

The signal for myocardial contraction comes not from the nervous system but from specialized myocardial cells known as **autorhythmic cells**. The autorhythmic cells are also called **pacemakers** because they set the rate of the heartbeat. Myocardial autorhythmic cells are anatomically distinct from contractile cells: autorhythmic cells are smaller and contain few contractile fibers. Because they do not have organized sarcomeres, autorhythmic cells do not contribute to the contractile force of the heart.

Contractile cells are typical striated muscle, however, with contractile fibers organized into sarcomeres [p. 411]. Cardiac muscle differs in significant ways from skeletal muscle and shares some properties with smooth muscle:

1. Cardiac muscle fibers are much smaller than skeletal muscle fibers and usually have a single nucleus per fiber.
2. Individual cardiac muscle cells branch and join neighboring cells end-to-end to create a complex network (Fig. 14-7h, 14-10b ●). The cell junctions, known as **intercalated disks** [*inter-,* between + *calare,* to proclaim], consist of interdigitated membranes. Intercalated disks have two components: *desmosomes* [p. 74] and gap junctions [p. 72]. Desmosomes are strong connections that tie adjacent cells together, allowing force created in one cell to be transferred to the adjacent cell.
3. *Gap junctions* in the intercalated disks electrically connect cardiac muscle cells to one another. They allow waves of depolarization to spread rapidly from cell to cell, so that all the heart muscle cells contract almost simultaneously. In this respect, cardiac muscle resembles single-unit smooth muscle.
4. The t-tubules of myocardial cells are larger than those of skeletal muscle, and they branch inside the myocardial cells.
5. Myocardial sarcoplasmic reticulum is smaller than that of skeletal muscle, reflecting the fact that cardiac muscle depends in part on extracellular Ca^{2+} to initiate contraction. In this respect, cardiac muscle resembles smooth muscle.
6. Mitochondria occupy about one-third the cell volume of a cardiac contractile fiber, a reflection of the high energy demand of these cells. By one estimate, cardiac muscle consumes 70–80% of the oxygen delivered to it by the blood, more than twice the amount extracted by other cells in the body.

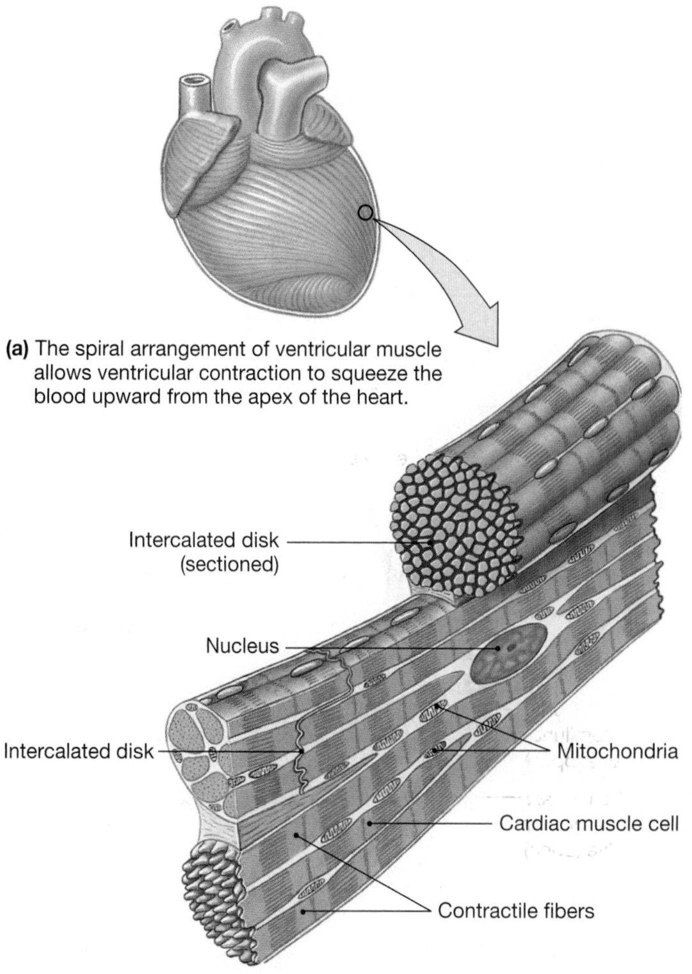
Intercalated disk (sectioned)
Nucleus
Intercalated disk
Mitochondria
Cardiac muscle cell
Contractile fibers

(a) The spiral arrangement of ventricular muscle allows ventricular contraction to squeeze the blood upward from the apex of the heart.

(b) Intercalated disks contain desmosomes that transfer force from cell to cell, and gap junctions that allow electrical signals to pass rapidly from cell to cell.

● **FIGURE 14-10** ***Cardiac muscle.*** For an electron micrograph of gap junctions, see Figure 3-21c on p. 73.

During periods of increased activity, the heart uses almost all the oxygen brought to it by the coronary arteries. As a result, the only way to get more oxygen to exercising heart

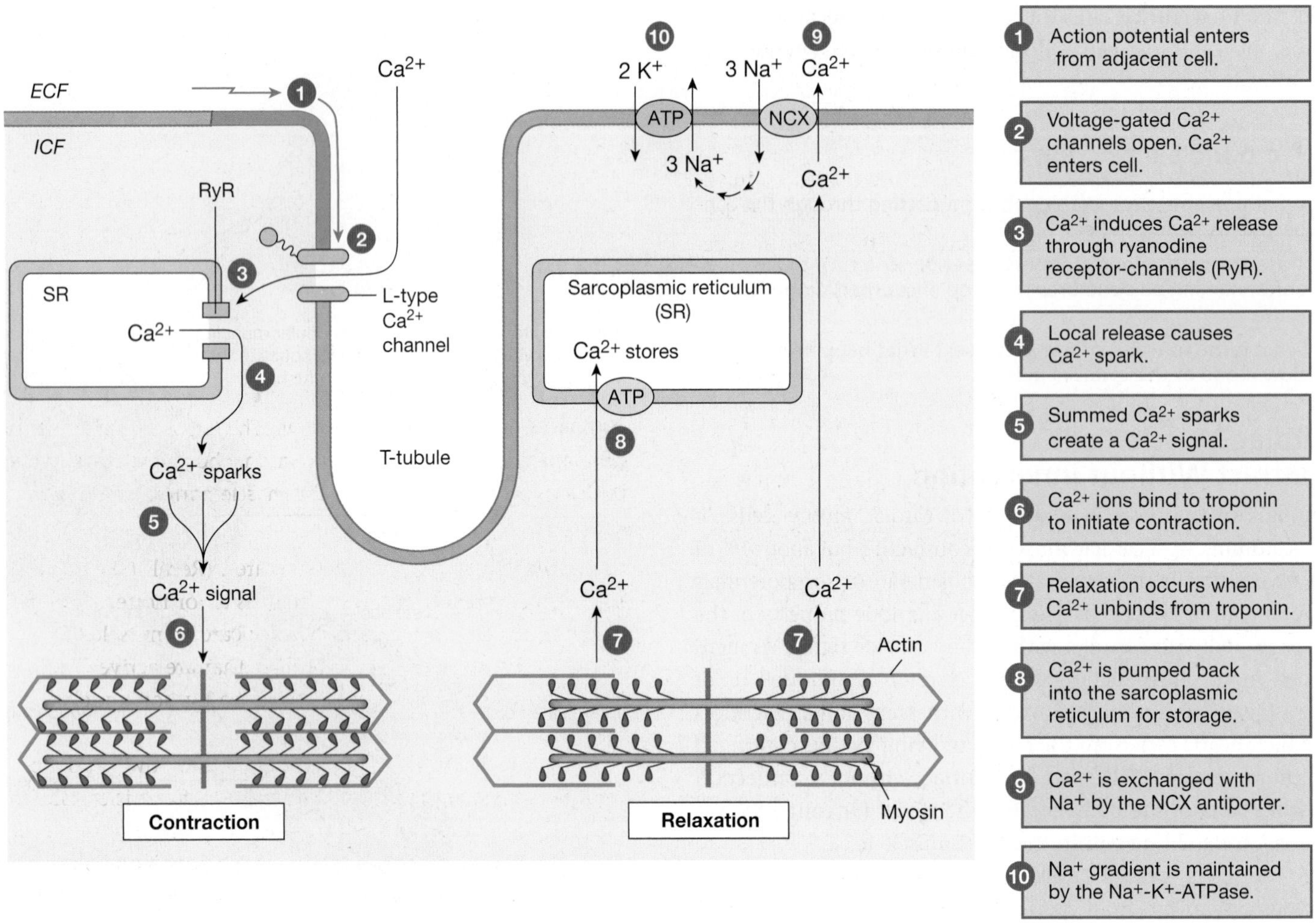

● **FIGURE 14-11** ***EC coupling and relaxation in cardiac muscle***

muscle is to increase the blood flow. Reduced myocardial blood flow from narrowing of a coronary vessel by a clot or fatty deposit can damage or even kill myocardial cells.

See Table 12-3, p. 440, for a summary comparison of the three muscle types.

Calcium Entry Is a Feature of Cardiac EC Coupling

In Chapters 11 and 12 you learned how acetylcholine from a somatic motor neuron causes a skeletal muscle action potential to begin excitation-contraction coupling (EC coupling) [p. 417]. In cardiac muscle, an action potential also initiates EC coupling, but the action potential originates spontaneously in the heart's pacemaker cells and spreads into the contractile cells through gap junctions. (Neurotransmitters modulate the pacemaker rate, as you will learn later in this chapter). Other aspects of cardiac EC coupling repeat processes you encountered in skeletal and smooth muscle contraction.

Figure 14-11 ● illustrates EC coupling and relaxation in cardiac muscle. An action potential that enters a contractile cell moves across the sarcolemma and into the t-tubules ①, where it opens voltage-gated L-type Ca^{2+} channels in the cell membrane ②. Ca^{2+} enters the cell and opens *ryanodine receptor Ca^{2+} release channels (RyR)* in the sarcoplasmic reticulum ③. When the RyR channels open, stored Ca^{2+} flows out of the sarcoplasmic reticulum and into the cytosol ④, creating a Ca^{2+} "spark" that can be seen using special biochemical methods [p. 191]. Multiple sparks from different RyR channels sum to create a Ca^{2+} signal ⑤. This process of EC coupling in cardiac muscle is also called **Ca^{2+}-induced Ca^{2+} release** because the myocardial RyR channels open in response to Ca^{2+} binding.

Calcium released from the sarcoplasmic reticulum provides about 90% of the Ca^{2+} needed for muscle contraction, with the remaining 10% entering the cell from the extracellular fluid. Calcium diffuses through the cytosol to the contractile elements, where the ions bind to troponin and initiate the cycle of crossbridge formation and movement ⑥. Contraction takes place by the same type of sliding filament movement that occurs in skeletal muscle [p. 415].

Relaxation in cardiac muscle is generally similar to that in skeletal muscle. As cytoplasmic Ca^{2+} concentrations decrease, Ca^{2+} unbinds from troponin, myosin releases actin, and the contractile filaments slide back to their relaxed position ⑦. As in skeletal muscle, Ca^{2+} is transported back into the sarcoplasmic reticulum with the help of a Ca^{2+}-ATPase ⑧. However, in cardiac muscle Ca^{2+} is also removed from the cell in exchange for Na^+ via the **Na^+-Ca^{2+} exchanger** (NCX) ⑨. Each Ca^{2+} moves out of the cell against its electrochemical gradient in exchange for 3 Na^+ entering the cell down their electrochemical gradient. Sodium that enters the cell during this transfer is removed by the Na^+-K^+-ATPase ⑩.

CONCEPT CHECK

10. Compare the receptors and channels involved in cardiac EC coupling to those found in skeletal muscle EC coupling. [Hint: p. 417]
11. If a myocardial contractile cell is placed in interstitial fluid and depolarized, the cell contracts. If Ca^{2+} is removed from the fluid surrounding the myocardial cell and the cell is depolarized, it does not contract. If the experiment is repeated with a skeletal muscle fiber, the skeletal muscle contracts when depolarized, whether or not Ca^{2+} is present in the surrounding fluid. What conclusion can you draw from the results of this experiment? Answers: p. 509

Cardiac Muscle Contraction Can Be Graded

A key property of cardiac muscle cells is the ability of a single muscle fiber to execute *graded contractions,* in which the fiber

RUNNING PROBLEM

When Walter arrived at the University of Texas Southwestern Medical Center emergency room, one of the first tasks was to determine whether he had actually had a heart attack. A nurse took Walter's vital signs (pulse and breathing rates, blood pressure, and temperature) and he was given nitroglycerin to dilate his coronary blood vessels [p. 192]. The doctor was pleased to hear that Walter had taken an aspirin to decrease blood clotting. A technician then drew blood for enzyme assays to determine the level of cardiac creatine kinase (CK-MB) in Walter's blood. When heart muscle cells die, they release various enzymes such as creatine kinase that serve as markers of a heart attack. A second tube of blood was sent for an assay of its troponin I level. Troponin I (TnI) is a good indicator of heart damage following a heart attack.

Question 3:
A related form of creatine kinase, CK-MM, is found in skeletal muscle. What are related forms of an enzyme called? [Hint: p. 100]

Question 4:
What is troponin, and why would elevated blood levels of troponin indicate heart damage? [Hint: p. 415]

468 472 483 487 494 500 505

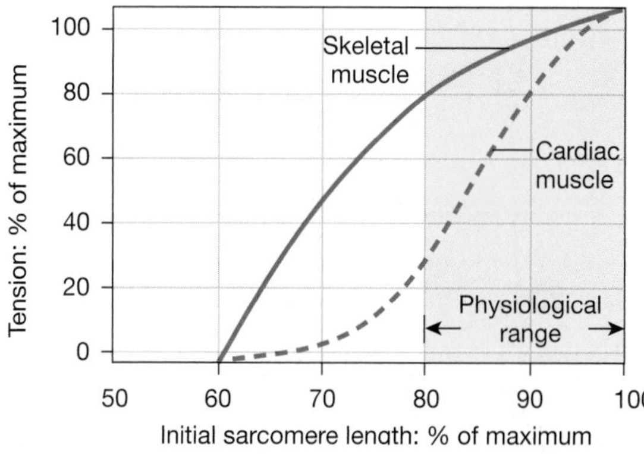

● **FIGURE 14-12** ***Increasing stretch on a cardiac muscle increases its force of contraction.*** These data represent tension developed during isometric contraction. The physiological range is the sarcomere length in which the muscle normally functions.

varies the amount of force it generates. (Recall that in skeletal muscle, contraction in a single fiber is all-or-none at any given fiber length). The force generated by cardiac muscle is proportional to the number of crossbridges that are active. The number of active crossbridges is determined by how much Ca^{2+} is bound to troponin.

If cytosolic Ca^{2+} concentrations are low, some crossbridges are not activated and contraction force is small. If additional Ca^{2+} enters the cell from the extracellular fluid, more Ca^{2+} is released from the sarcoplasmic reticulum. This additional Ca^{2+} binds to troponin, enhancing the ability of myosin to form crossbridges with actin and creating additional force.

Another factor that affects the force of contraction in cardiac muscle is the sarcomere length at the beginning of contraction. For both cardiac and skeletal muscle, the tension generated is directly proportional to the initial length of the muscle fiber [p. 423]. The longer the muscle fiber and sarcomere when a contraction begins, the greater the tension developed, up to a maximum (Fig. 14-12 ●).

In the intact heart, stretch on the individual fibers is a function of how much blood is in the chambers of the heart. The relationship between force and ventricular volume is an important property of cardiac function, and we discuss it in detail later in this chapter.

CONCEPT CHECK

12. A drug that blocks all Ca^{2+} channels in the myocardial cell membrane is placed in the solution around the cell. What happens to the force of contraction in that cell? Answers: p. 570

Myocardial Action Potentials Vary

Cardiac muscle, like skeletal muscle and neurons, is an excitable tissue with the ability to generate action potentials. Each of the two types of cardiac muscle cells has a distinctive action potential. In both types, Ca^{2+} plays an important role in

14

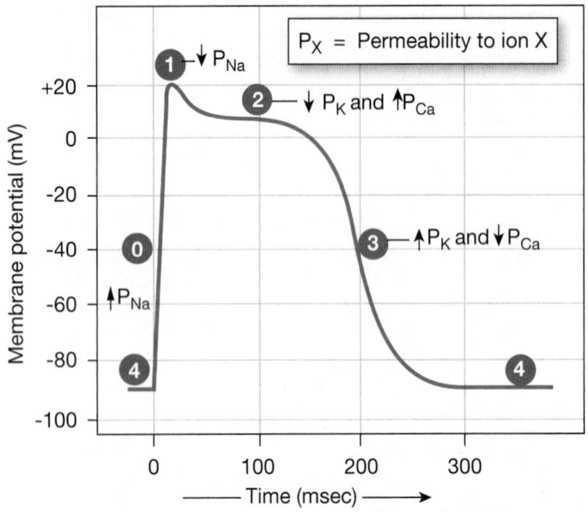

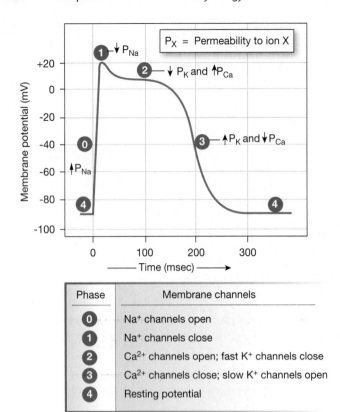

Phase	Membrane channels
0	Na^+ channels open
1	Na^+ channels close
2	Ca^{2+} channels open; fast K^+ channels close
3	Ca^{2+} channels close; slow K^+ channels open
4	Resting potential

● **FIGURE 14-13** ***Action potential of a cardiac contractile cell.*** The phase numbers are a convention.

the action potential, in contrast to the action potentials of skeletal muscle and neurons.

Myocardial Contractile Cells The action potentials of myocardial contractile cells are similar in several ways to those of neurons and skeletal muscle [p. 258]. The rapid depolarization phase of the action potential is the result of Na^+ entry, and the steep repolarization phase is due to K^+ leaving the cell. The main difference between the action potential of the myocardial contractile cell and that of a skeletal muscle fiber or a neuron is that in the myocardial cell, there is a longer action potential due to Ca^{2+} entry. Let's take a look at these longer action potentials (Fig. 14-13 ●).

Phase 4: resting membrane potential. Myocardial contractile cells have a stable resting potential of about −90 mV.

Phase 0: depolarization. When a wave of depolarization moves into a contractile cell through gap junctions, the membrane potential becomes more positive. Voltage-gated Na^+ channels open, allowing Na^+ to enter the cell and rapidly depolarize it. The membrane potential reaches about +20 mV before the Na^+ channels close. These are double-gated Na^+ channels, similar to the voltage-gated Na^+ channels of the axon [p. 263].

Phase 1: initial repolarization. When the Na^+ channels close, the cell begins to repolarize as K^+ leaves through open K^+ channels.

Phase 2: the plateau. The initial repolarization is very brief. The action potential then flattens into a plateau as the result of two events: a decrease in K^+ permeability and an increase in Ca^{2+} permeability. Voltage-gated Ca^{2+} channels activated by depolarization have been slowly opening during phases 0 and 1. When they finally open, Ca^{2+} enters the cell. At the same time, some "fast" K^+ channels close. The combination of Ca^{2+} influx and decreased K^+ efflux causes the action potential to flatten out into a plateau.

Phase 3: rapid repolarization. The plateau ends when Ca^{2+} channels close and K^+ permeability increases once more. The "slow" K^+ channels responsible for this phase are similar to those in the neuron: they are activated by depolarization but are slow to open. When the slow K^+ channels open, K^+ exits rapidly, returning the cell to its resting potential (phase 4).

The influx of Ca^{2+} during phase 2 lengthens the total duration of a myocardial action potential. A typical action potential in a neuron or skeletal muscle fiber lasts between 1 and 5 msec. In a contractile myocardial cell, the action potential typically lasts 200 msec or more. The longer myocardial action potential helps prevent the sustained contraction called tetanus. Prevention of tetanus in the heart is important because cardiac muscles must relax between contractions so the ventricles can fill with blood.

How does a longer action potential prevent tetanus? To understand this, compare the relationship between action potentials, refractory periods [p. 264], and contraction in skeletal and cardiac muscle cells (Fig. 14-14 ●). As you may recall from Chapter 8, the refractory period is the time following an action potential during which a normal stimulus cannot trigger a second action potential. In skeletal muscle, the action potential (red curve) and refractory period (yellow background) are ending as contraction (blue curve) begins. For this reason, a second action potential fired immediately after the refractory period causes summation of the contractions. If a series of action potentials occurs in rapid succession, the sustained contraction known as tetanus results (Fig. 14-14b).

In cardiac muscle, tetanus cannot occur because the extended action potential means the refractory period and the contraction end almost simultaneously (Fig. 14-14c). By the time a second action potential can take place, the myocardial cell has almost completely relaxed. Consequently, no summation occurs (Fig. 14-14d).

CONCEPT CHECK

13. Which ions moving in what directions cause the depolarization and repolarization phases of a neuronal action potential?
14. At the molecular level, what is happening during the refractory period in neurons and muscle fibers?
15. Lidocaine is a molecule that blocks the action of voltage-gated cardiac Na^+ channels. What happens to the action potential of a myocardial contractile cell if lidocaine is applied to the cell?

Answers: p. 510

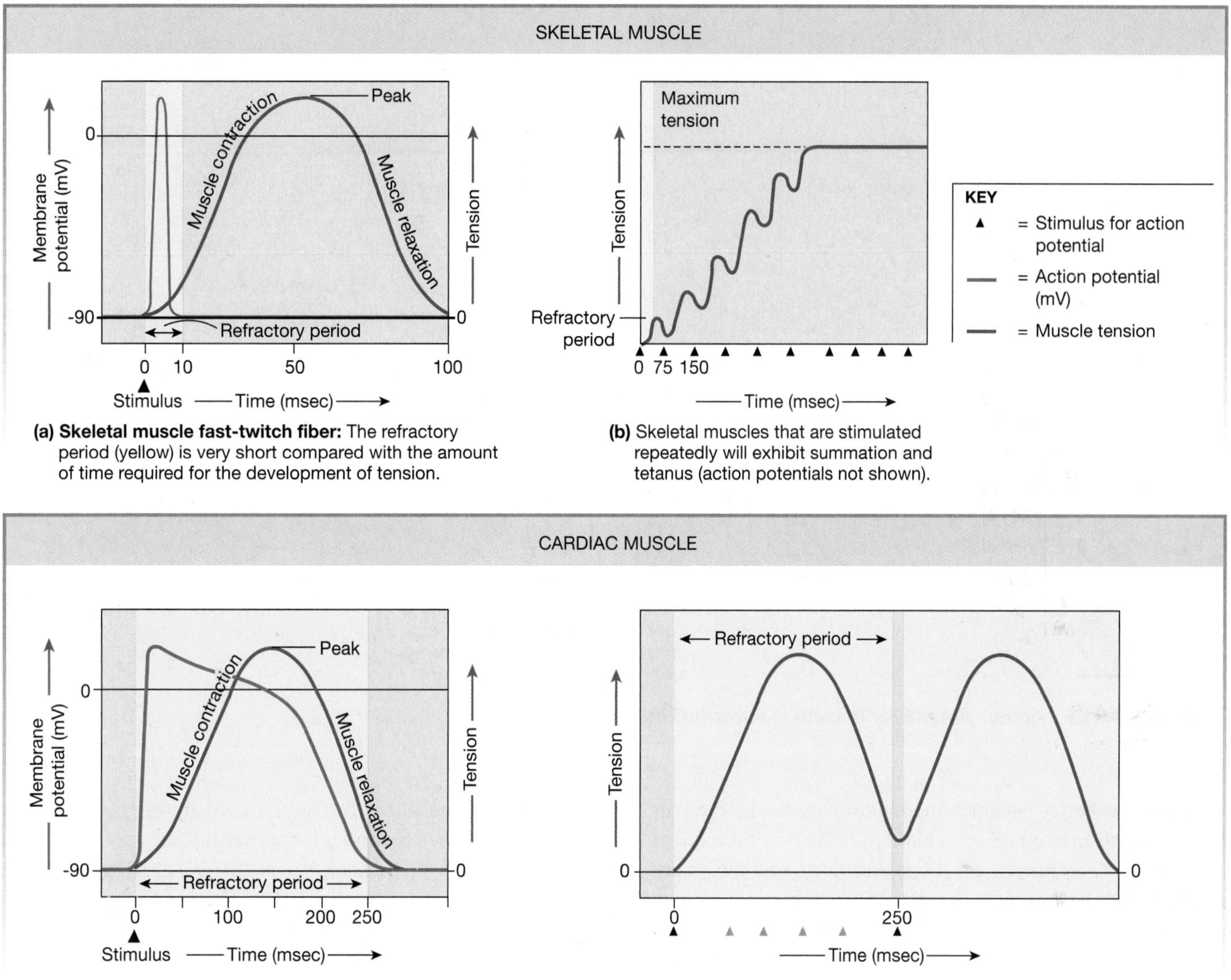

(a) Skeletal muscle fast-twitch fiber: The refractory period (yellow) is very short compared with the amount of time required for the development of tension.

(b) Skeletal muscles that are stimulated repeatedly will exhibit summation and tetanus (action potentials not shown).

(c) Cardiac muscle fiber: The refractory period lasts almost as long as the entire muscle twitch.

(d) Long refractory period in a cardiac muscle prevents tetanus.

● **FIGURE 14-14** ***Refractory periods and summation in skeletal and cardiac muscle***

Myocardial Autorhythmic Cells What gives myocardial autorhythmic cells their unique ability to generate action potentials spontaneously in the absence of input from the nervous system? This ability results from their unstable membrane potential, which starts at −60 mV and slowly drifts upward toward threshold (Fig. 14-15a ●). This unstable membrane potential is called a **pacemaker potential** rather than a resting membrane potential because it never "rests" at a constant value. Whenever a pacemaker potential depolarizes to threshold, the autorhythmic cell fires an action potential.

What causes the membrane potential of these cells to be unstable? Our current understanding is that the autorhythmic cells contain channels that are different from the channels of other excitable tissues. When the cell membrane potential is −60 mV, **I_f channels** that are permeable to both K^+ and Na^+ open (Fig. 14-15c). These channels are called I_f channels because they allow current (I) to flow and because of their unusual properties. The researchers who first described the ion current through these channels initially did not understand its behavior and named it *funny* current—hence the subscript *f*. The I_f channels belong to the family of *HCN channels*, or *hyperpolarization-activated cyclic nucleotide-gated channels*. Other members of the HCN family are found in neurons.

When I_f channels open at negative membrane potentials, Na^+ influx exceeds K^+ efflux (Fig. 14-15b). (This is similar to what happens at the neuromuscular junction when nonspecific cation channels open [p. 398]). The net influx of positive charge slowly depolarizes the autorhythmic cell. As the

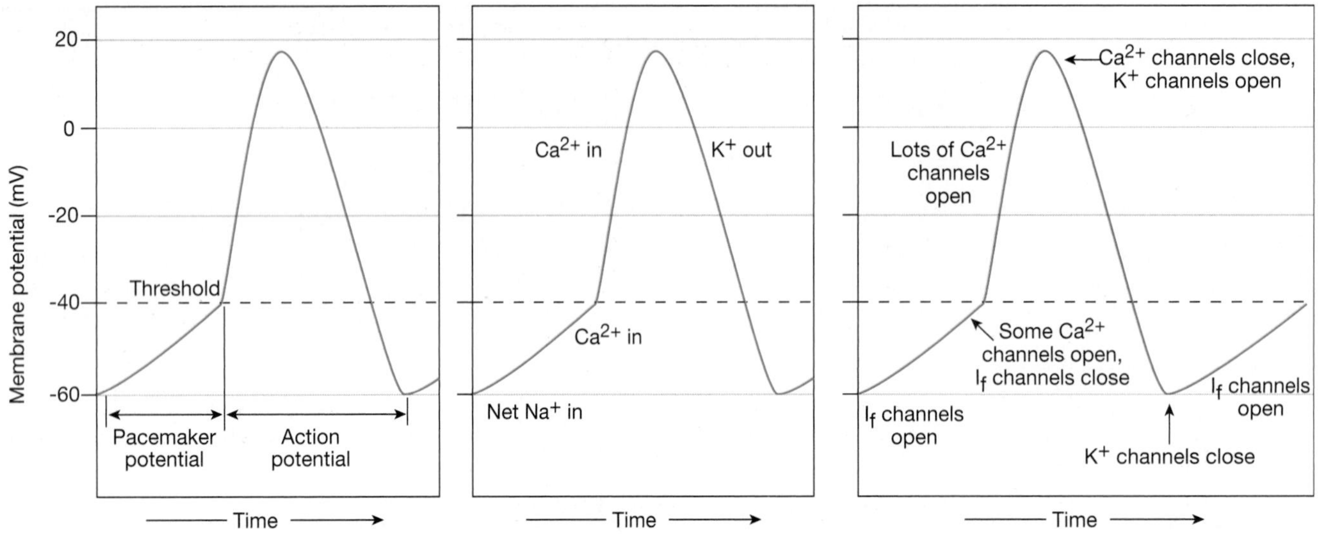

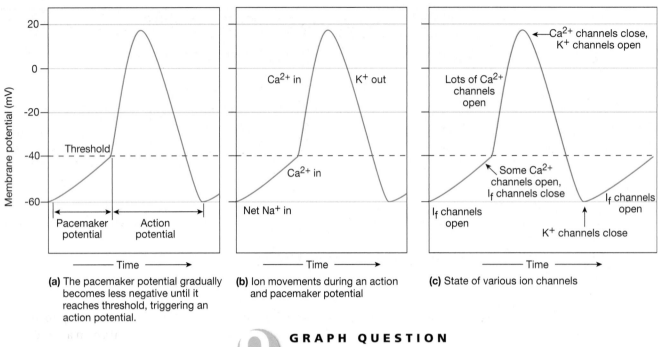

(a) The pacemaker potential gradually becomes less negative until it reaches threshold, triggering an action potential.

(b) Ion movements during an action and pacemaker potential

(c) State of various ion channels

GRAPH QUESTION

Match the appropriate phases of the myocardial contractile cell action potential (Fig.14-13) to the pacemaker action potential above.

● **FIGURE 14-15** ***Action potentials in cardiac autorhythmic cells***

membrane potential becomes more positive, the I_f channels gradually close and some Ca^{2+} channels open. The subsequent influx of Ca^{2+} continues the depolarization, and the membrane potential moves steadily toward threshold.

When the membrane potential reaches threshold, additional Ca^{2+} channels open. Calcium rushes into the cell, creating the steep depolarization phase of the action potential. Note that this process is different from that in other excitable cells, in which the depolarization phase is due to the opening of voltage-gated Na^+ channels.

When the Ca^{2+} channels close at the peak of the action potential, slow K^+ channels have opened. The repolarization phase of the autorhythmic action potential is due to the resultant efflux of K^+. This phase is similar to repolarization in other types of excitable cells.

CONCEPT CHECK

16. What does increasing K^+ permeability do to the membrane potential of the cell? Answers: p. 510

Autonomic Neurotransmitters Modulate Heart Rate

The speed with which pacemaker cells depolarize determines the rate at which the heart contracts (the heart rate). The interval between action potentials can be modified by altering the permeability of the autorhythmic cells to different ions. Increased permeability to Na^+ and Ca^{2+} during the pacemaker potential phase speeds up depolarization and heart rate. Decreased Ca^{2+} permeability or increased K^+ permeability slows depolarization and thus slows the heart rate.

Sympathetic stimulation of pacemaker cells speeds up heart rate. The catecholamines norepinephrine (from sympathetic neurons) and epinephrine (from the adrenal medulla) increase ion flow through both I_f and Ca^{2+} channels. More rapid cation entry speeds up the rate of the pacemaker depolarization, causing the cell to reach threshold faster and increasing the rate of action potential firing (Fig. 14-16a ●). When the pacemaker fires action potentials more rapidly, heart rate increases.

Catecholamines exert their effect by binding to and activating β_1-adrenergic receptors on the autorhythmic cells. The β_1-receptors use a cAMP second messenger system to alter the transport properties of the ion channels. In the case of the I_f channels, which are cyclic nucleotide-gated channels, cAMP itself is the messenger. When cAMP binds to open I_f channels, they remain open longer.

The parasympathetic neurotransmitter acetylcholine (ACh) slows heart rate. Acetylcholine activates muscarinic cholinergic receptors that influence K^+ and Ca^{2+} channels in the pacemaker cell. Potassium permeability increases, hyperpolarizing the cell so that the pacemaker potential begins at a more negative value (Fig. 14-16b). At the same time,

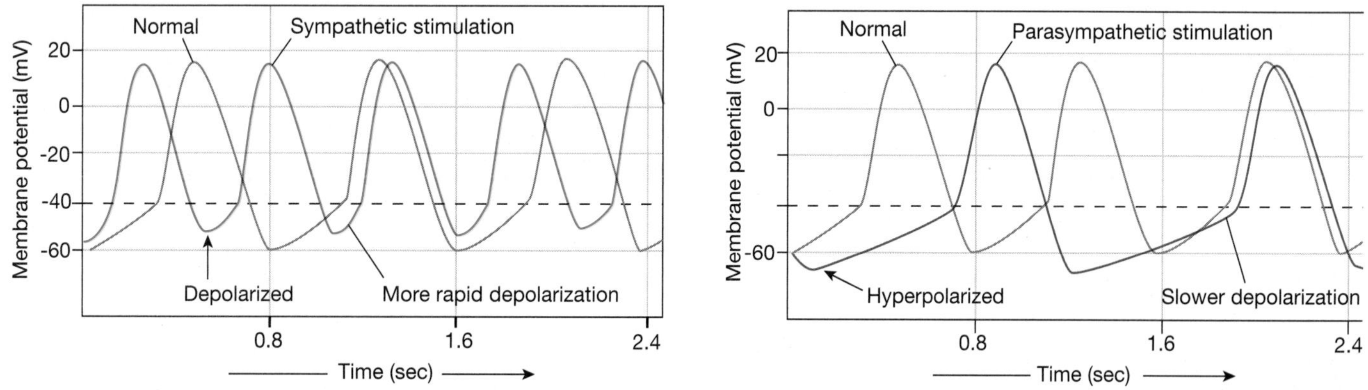

(a) Sympathetic stimulation and epinephrine depolarize the autorhythmic cell and speed up the depolarization rate, increasing the heart rate.

(b) Parasympathetic stimulation hyperpolarizes the membrane potential of the autorhythmic cell and slows depolarization, slowing down the heart rate.

● **FIGURE 14-16** ***Modulation of heart rate by the autonomic nervous system***

Ca^{2+} permeability of the pacemaker decreases. Decreased Ca^{2+} permeability slows the rate at which the pacemaker potential depolarizes. The combination of the two effects causes the cell to take longer to reach threshold, delaying the onset of the action potential in the pacemaker and slowing the heart rate.

Table 14-3 ● compares action potentials of the two types of myocardial muscle with those of skeletal muscle. Next we will see how action potentials of autorhythmic cells spread throughout the heart to coordinate contraction.

CONCEPT CHECK

17. Do you think that the Ca^{2+} channels in autorhythmic cells are the same as the Ca^{2+} channels in contractile cells? Defend your answer.
18. What happens to the action potential of a myocardial autorhythmic cell if tetrodotoxin, which blocks voltage-gated Na^+ channels, is applied to the cell?
19. In an experiment, the vagus nerve [p. 389] to the heart was cut. The investigators noticed that heart rate increased. What can you conclude about the vagal neurons that innervate the heart?

Answers: p. 510

THE HEART AS A PUMP

We now turn from single myocardial cells to the intact heart. How can one tiny noncontractile autorhythmic cell cause the entire heart to beat? And why do those doctors on TV shows shock patients with electric paddles when their hearts malfunction? You're about to learn the answers to these questions.

Electrical Conduction in the Heart Coordinates Contraction

The heart is like a group of people around a stalled car. One person can push on the car, but it's not likely to move very far unless everyone pushes together. In the same way, individual myocardial cells must depolarize and contract in a coordinated fashion if the heart is to create enough force to circulate the blood.

RUNNING PROBLEM

The results of creatine kinase and troponin I assays may not come back from the laboratory for an hour. If a coronary artery were blocked, damage to the heart muscle could be severe by that time. In Walter's case, an electrocardiogram (ECG) showed an abnormal pattern of electrical activity. "He's definitely had an MI," said the ER physician, referring to a myocardial infarction, or heart attack. "Let's start him on a beta-blocker and tPA." tPA (short for *tissue plasminogen activator*) activates plasminogen, a substance that is produced in the body and dissolves blood clots. Given within a couple of hours of a heart attack, tPA can help dissolve blood clots that are blocking blood flow to the heart muscle. This will help limit the extent of ischemic damage.

Question 5:
How do electrical signals move from cell to cell in the myocardium?

Question 6:
What happens to contraction in a myocardial contractile cell if a wave of depolarization passing through the heart bypasses it?

Question 7:
A beta-blocker is an antagonist to β_1-adrenergic receptors. What will this drug do to Walter's heart rate? Why is that response helpful following a heart attack?

468 472 483 487 494 500 505

Table 14-3 Comparison of Action Potentials in Cardiac and Skeletal Muscle

	SKELETAL MUSCLE	CONTRACTILE MYOCARDIUM	AUTORHYTHMIC MYOCARDIUM
Membrane potential	Stable at −70 mV	Stable at −90 mV	Unstable pacemaker potential; usually starts at −60 mV
Events leading to threshold potential	Net Na^+ entry through ACh-operated channels	Depolarization enters via gap junctions	Net Na^+ entry through I_f channels; reinforced by Ca^{2+} entry
Rising phase of action potential	Na^+ entry	Na^+ entry	Ca^{2+} entry
Repolarization phase	Rapid; caused by K^+ efflux	Extended plateau caused by Ca^{2+} entry; rapid phase caused by K^+ efflux	Rapid; caused by K^+ efflux
Hyperpolarization	Due to excessive K^+ efflux at high K^+ permeability when K^+ channels close; leak of K^+ and Na^+ restores potential to resting state	None; resting potential is −90 mV, the equilibrium potential for K^+	Normally none; when repolarization hits −60 mV, the I_f channels open again. ACh can hyperpolarize the cell.
Duration of action potential	Short: 1–2 msec	Extended: 200+ msec	Variable; generally 150+ msec
Refractory period	Generally brief	Long because resetting of Na^+ channel gates delayed until end of action potential	None

Electrical communication in the heart begins with an action potential in an autorhythmic cell. The depolarization spreads rapidly to adjacent cells through gap junctions in the intercalated disks (Fig. 14-17 ●). The depolarization wave is followed by a wave of contraction that passes across the atria, then moves into the ventricles.

The depolarization begins in the **sinoatrial node (SA node)**, autorhythmic cells in the right atrium that serve as the main pacemaker of the heart (Fig. 14-18 ●). The depolarization wave then spreads rapidly through a specialized conducting system of noncontractile autorhythmic fibers. A branched **internodal pathway** connects the SA node to the **atrioventricular node (AV node)**, a group of autorhythmic cells near the floor of the right atrium.

From the AV node, the depolarization moves into the ventricles. **Purkinje fibers**, specialized conducting cells, transmit electrical signals very rapidly down the **atrioventricular bundle (AV bundle**, also called the **bundle of His** ("hiss")) in the ventricular septum. A short way down the septum, the AV bundle fibers divide into left and right **bundle branches**. The bundle branch fibers continue downward to the apex of the heart, where they divide into smaller Purkinje fibers that spread outward among the contractile cells.

The electrical signal for contraction begins when the SA node fires an action potential and the depolarization spreads to

CLINICAL FOCUS

FIBRILLATION

Coordination of myocardial contraction is essential for normal cardiac function. In extreme cases in which the myocardial cells contract in a disorganized manner, a condition known as *fibrillation* results. Atrial fibrillation is a common condition, often without symptoms, that can lead to serious consequences (such as stroke) if not treated. Ventricular fibrillation, on the other hand, is an immediately life-threatening emergency because without coordinated contraction of the muscle fibers, the ventricles cannot pump enough blood to supply adequate oxygen to the brain. One way to correct this problem is to administer an electrical shock to the heart. The shock creates a depolarization that triggers action potentials in all cells simultaneously, coordinating them again. You have probably seen this procedure on television hospital shows, when a doctor places flat paddles on the patient's chest and tells everyone to stand back ("Clear!") while the paddles pass an electrical current through the body.

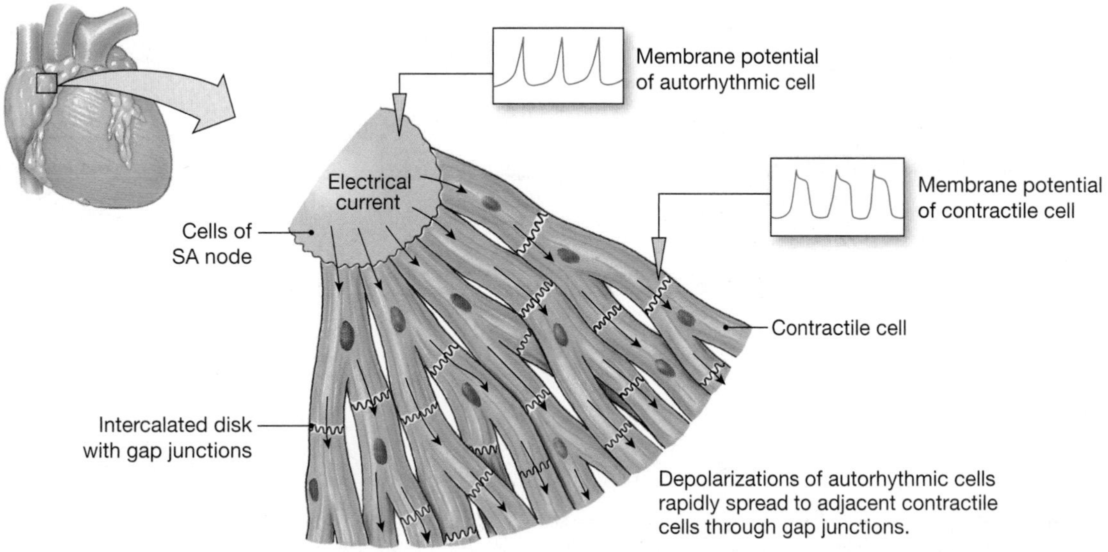

● **FIGURE 14-17** ***Electrical conduction in myocardial cells depends on gap junctions.***

adjacent cells through gap junctions (Fig. 14-18 ①). Electrical conduction is rapid through the internodal conducting pathways ② but slower through the contractile cells of the atria ③.

As action potentials spread across the atria, they encounter the fibrous skeleton of the heart at the junction of the atria and ventricles. This barricade prevents the transfer of electrical signals from the atria to the ventricles. Consequently, the AV node is the only pathway through which action potentials can reach the contractile fibers of the ventricles.

The electrical signal passes from the AV node through the AV bundle and bundle branches to the apex of the heart (Fig. 14-18 ④). The Purkinje fibers transmit impulses very rapidly, with speeds up to 4 m/sec, so that all contractile cells in the apex contract nearly simultaneously ⑤.

Why is it necessary to direct the electrical signals through the AV node? Why not allow them to spread downward from the atria? The answer lies in the fact that blood is pumped out of the ventricles through openings at the top of the chambers (see Fig. 14-9b). If electrical signals from the atria were conducted directly into the ventricles, the ventricles would start contracting at the top. Then blood would be squeezed downward and would become trapped in the bottom of the ventricles (think of squeezing a toothpaste tube at the top). The apex-to-base contraction squeezes blood toward the arterial openings at the base of the heart.

The ejection of blood from the ventricles is aided by the spiral arrangement of the muscles in the walls (see Fig. 14-10a). As these muscles contract, they pull the apex and base of the heart closer together, squeezing blood out the openings at the top of the ventricles.

A second function of the AV node is to delay the transmission of action potentials slightly, allowing the atria to complete their contraction before ventricular contraction begins. The **AV node delay** is accomplished by slowing conduction through the nodal cells. Action potentials here move at only 1/20 the rate of action potentials in the atrial internodal pathway.

Pacemakers Set the Heart Rate

The cells of the SA node set the pace of the heartbeat. Other cells in the conducting system, such as the AV node and the Purkinje fibers, have unstable resting potentials and can also act as pacemakers under some conditions. However, because their rhythm is slower than that of the SA node, they do not usually have a chance to set the heartbeat. The Purkinje fibers, for example, can spontaneously fire action potentials, but their firing rate is very slow, between 25 and 40 beats per minute.

Why does the fastest pacemaker determine the pace of the heartbeat? Consider the following analogy. A group of people are playing "follow the leader" as they walk. Initially, everyone is walking at a different pace—some fast, some slow. When the game starts, everyone must match his or her pace to the pace of the person who is walking the fastest. The fastest person in the group is the SA node, walking at 70 steps per minute. Everyone else in the group (autorhythmic and contractile cells) sees that the SA node is fastest, and so they pick up their pace and follow the leader. In the heart, the cue to follow the leader is the electrical signal sent from the SA node to the other cells.

Now suppose the SA node gets tired and drops out of the group. The role of leader defaults to the next fastest person, the AV node, who is walking at a rate of 50 steps per minute. The group slows to match the pace of the AV node, but everyone is still following the fastest walker.

What happens if the group divides? Suppose that when they reach a corner, the AV node leader goes left but a renegade Purkinje fiber decides to go right. Those people who follow the AV node continue to walk at 50 steps per minute, but the people who follow the Purkinje fiber slow down to match his pace

14

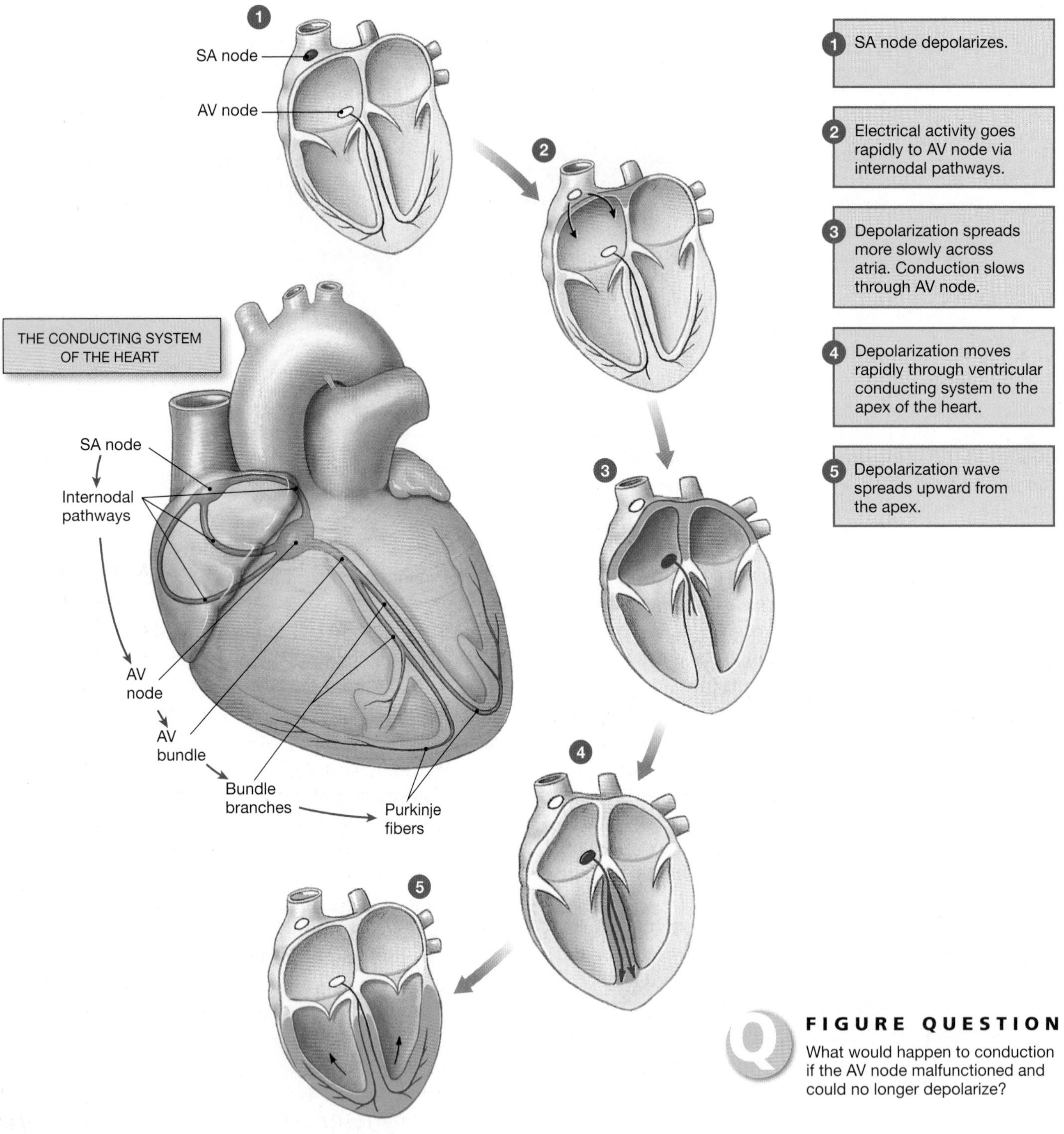

THE CONDUCTING SYSTEM OF THE HEART
SA node
AV node
SA node
Internodal pathways
AV node
AV bundle
Bundle branches
Purkinje fibers
1
2
3
4
5
1 SA node depolarizes.
2 Electrical activity goes rapidly to AV node via internodal pathways.
3 Depolarization spreads more slowly across atria. Conduction slows through AV node.
4 Depolarization moves rapidly through ventricular conducting system to the apex of the heart.
5 Depolarization wave spreads upward from the apex.
FIGURE QUESTION
What would happen to conduction if the AV node malfunctioned and could no longer depolarize?

● **FIGURE 14-18** ***Electrical conduction in the heart.*** Purple shading in steps 2–5 represents depolarization.

of 35 steps per minute. Now there are two leaders, each walking at a different pace.

In the heart, the SA node is the fastest pacemaker and normally sets the heart rate. If this node is damaged and cannot function, one of the slower pacemakers in the heart takes over. Heart rate then matches the rate of the new pacemaker. It is even possible for different parts of the heart to follow different pacemakers, just as the walking group split at the corner.

In a condition known as *complete heart block,* the conduction of electrical signals from the atria to the ventricles through the AV node is disrupted. The SA node fires at its rate of 70 beats per minute, but those signals never reach the ventricles. So the ventricles coordinate with their fastest pacemaker. Because ventricular autorhythmic cells discharge only about 35 times a minute, the rate at which the ventricles contract is much slower than the rate at which the atria contract. If ventricular contraction is too slow to maintain adequate blood flow, it may be necessary for the heart's rhythm to be set artificially by a surgically implanted mechanical pacemaker. These battery-powered devices artificially stimulate the heart at a predetermined rate.

✓ CONCEPT CHECK

20. Name two functions of the AV node. What is the purpose of AV node delay?
21. Where is the SA node located?
22. Occasionally an ectopic pacemaker [*ektopos*, out of place] develops in part of the heart's conducting system. What happens to heart rate if an ectopic atrial pacemaker depolarizes at a rate of 120 times per minute? Answers: p. 510

The Electrocardiogram Reflects Electrical Activity

At the end of the nineteenth century, physiologists discovered that they could place electrodes on the skin's surface and record the electrical activity of the heart. These recordings, called **electrocardiograms** (ECGs or sometimes EKGs—from the Greek word *kardia,* meaning *heart*) provide indirect information about heart function. It is possible to use surface electrodes to record internal electrical activity because salt solutions, such as our NaCl-based extracellular fluid, are good conductors of electricity.

The first human electrocardiogram was recorded in 1887, but the procedure was not refined for clinical use until the first years of the twentieth century. The father of the modern ECG was a Dutch physiologist named Walter Einthoven. He named the parts of the ECG as we know them today and created "Einthoven's triangle," a hypothetical triangle created around the heart when electrodes are placed on both arms and the left leg (Fig. 14-19 ●). The sides of the triangle are numbered to correspond with the three *leads* ("leeds"), or pairs of electrodes, used for a recording.

An ECG is recorded from one lead at a time. One electrode acts as the positive electrode of a lead, and a second electrode acts as the negative electrode of the lead. (The third electrode is inactive). For example, in lead I, the left arm electrode is designated as positive and the right arm electrode is designated as negative.

An ECG tracing shows the summed electrical potentials generated by all cells of the heart. Different components of the ECG reflect depolarization or repolarization of the atria and ventricles. Because depolarization initiates muscle contraction, these *electrical events* (waves) of an ECG can be associated with contraction or relaxation (collectively referred to as the *mechanical events* in the heart). Let's follow an ECG through a single contraction-relaxation cycle, otherwise known as a **cardiac cycle**.

There are two major components of an ECG: waves and segments. *Waves* appear as deflections above or below the baseline. *Segments* are sections of baseline between two waves. *Intervals* are combinations of waves and segments.

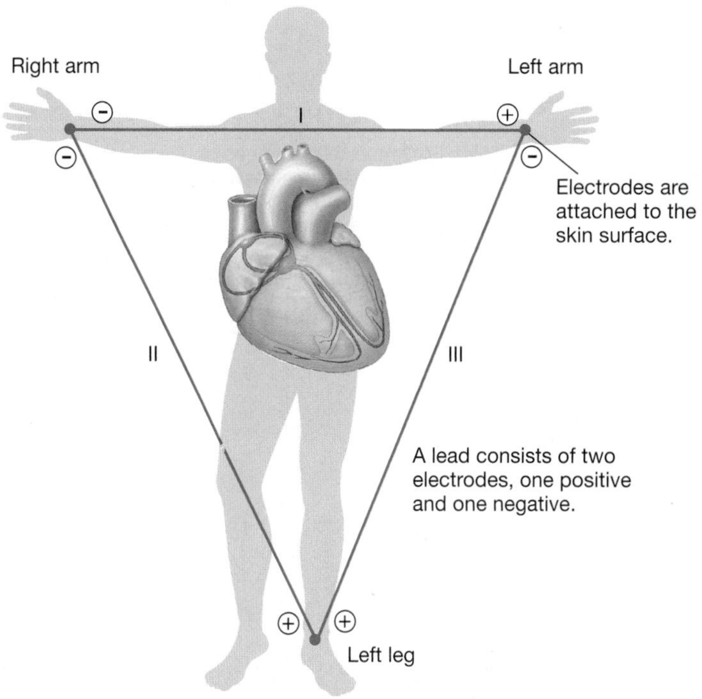
Right arm
Left arm
I
II
III
Electrodes are attached to the skin surface.
A lead consists of two electrodes, one positive and one negative.
Left leg

● **FIGURE 14-19** ***Einthoven's triangle.*** ECG electrodes attached to both arms and the left leg form a triangle. Each two-electrode pair constitutes one *lead* (pronounced "leed"), and only one lead is active at a time. Lead I, for instance, has the negative electrode attached to the right arm and the positive electrode attached to the left arm.

Three major waves can be seen on a normal ECG recorded from lead I (Fig. 14-20 ●). The first wave is the **P wave**, which corresponds to depolarization of the atria (Fig. 14-21 ●). The next trio of waves, the **QRS complex**, represents the progressive wave of ventricular depolarization. The final wave, the **T wave**, represents the repolarization of the ventricles. Atrial repolarization is not represented by a special wave but is incorporated into the QRS complex.

The mechanical events of the cardiac cycle lag slightly behind the electrical signals, just as the contraction of a single cardiac muscle cell follows its action potential (see Fig. 14-14c). Atrial contraction begins during the latter part of the P wave and continues during the PR segment. Ventricular contraction begins just after the Q wave and continues through the T wave.

One thing many people find confusing is that you cannot tell if an ECG recording represents depolarization or repolarization by looking at the shape of the waves relative to the baseline. For example, the P wave represents atrial depolarization and the T wave represents ventricular repolarization, but both the P wave and the T wave are deflections above the baseline. This is very different from the action potential recordings of neurons and muscle fibers, in which an upward deflection always represents depolarization [p. 169].

GRAPH QUESTION

If the ECG records at a speed of 25 mm/sec, what is the heart rate of the person?
(1 little square = 1 mm)

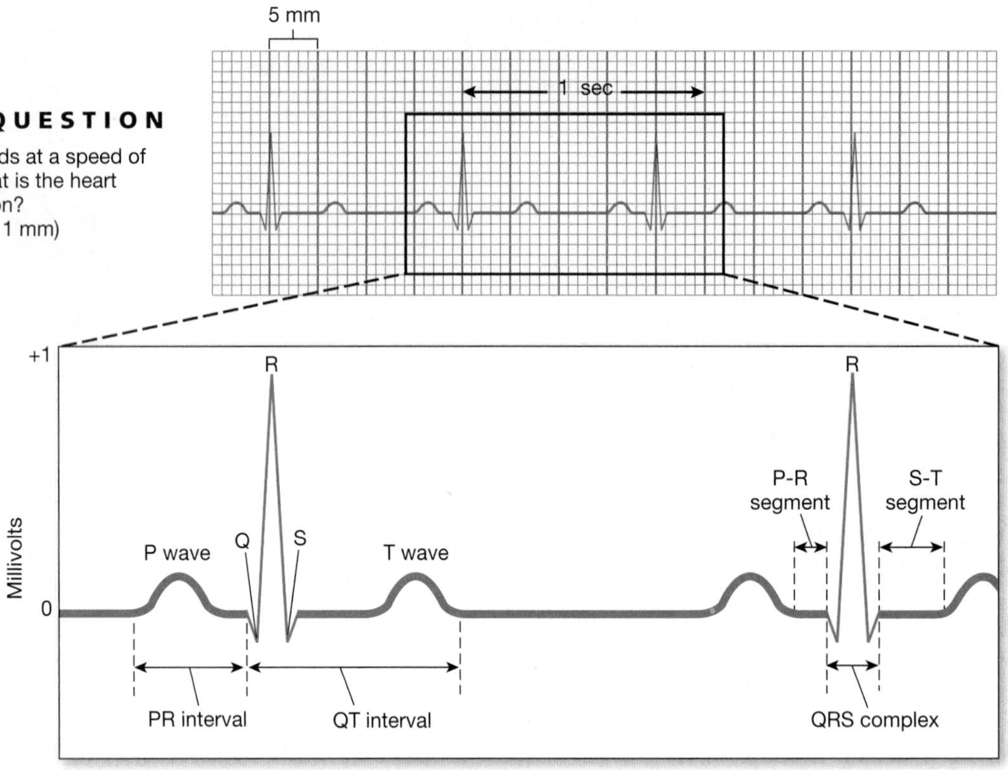

● **FIGURE 14-20** ***The electrocardiogram.*** An electrocardiogram is divided into waves (P, Q, R, S, and T), segments between the waves (the P-R and S-T segments, for example), and intervals consisting of a combination of waves and segments (such as the PR and QT intervals). This ECG tracing was recorded from lead I.

An ECG is not the same as a single action potential (Fig. 14-22 ●). An action potential is one electrical event in a single cell, recorded using an intracellular electrode. The ECG is an extracellular recording that represents the sum of multiple action potentials taking place in many heart muscle cells.

When an electrical wave moving through the heart is directed toward the positive electrode, the ECG wave goes up from the baseline. If net charge movement through the heart is toward the negative electrode, the wave points downward. In addition, the amplitudes of action potential and ECG recordings are very different. A ventricular action potential has a voltage change of 110 mV, for example, but the ECG signal has an amplitude of only 1 mV by the time it reaches the surface of the body.

An important point to remember is that an ECG is an electrical "view" of a three-dimensional object. This is one reason we use multiple leads to assess heart function. Think of looking at an automobile. From the air, it looks like a rectangle, but from the side and front it has different shapes. Not everything that you see from the front of the car can be seen from its side, and vice versa. In the same way, the leads of an ECG provide different electrical "views" and give information about different regions of the heart. A 12-lead ECG (the three limb electrodes plus nine more electrodes placed on the chest and trunk) is the standard for clinical use. The additional leads provide detailed information about electrical conduction in the heart. Electrocardiograms are important diagnostic tools in medicine because they are quick, painless, and noninvasive (that is, do not puncture the skin).

An ECG provides information on heart rate and rhythm, conduction velocity, and even the condition of tissues in the heart. Thus, although obtaining an ECG is simple, interpreting some of its subtleties can be quite complicated. The interpretation of an ECG begins with the following questions (Fig. 14-23 ●).

1. *What is the heart rate?* Heart rate is normally timed either from the beginning of one P wave to the beginning of the next P wave or from the peak of one R wave to the peak of the next R wave. A normal resting heart rate is 60–100 beats per minute, although trained athletes often have slower heart rates at rest. A faster-than-normal rate is known as *tachycardia,* and a slower-than-normal rate is called *bradycardia* [*tachys,* swift; *bradys,* slow].
2. *Is the rhythm of the heartbeat regular (that is, occurs at regular intervals) or irregular?* An irregular rhythm, or *arrhythmia* [*a-,* without + rhythm], can result from a benign extra beat or from more serious conditions such as atrial fibrillation, in which the SA node has lost control of the pacemaking.
3. *Are all normal waves present in recognizable form?* After determining heart rate and rhythm, the next step in analyzing

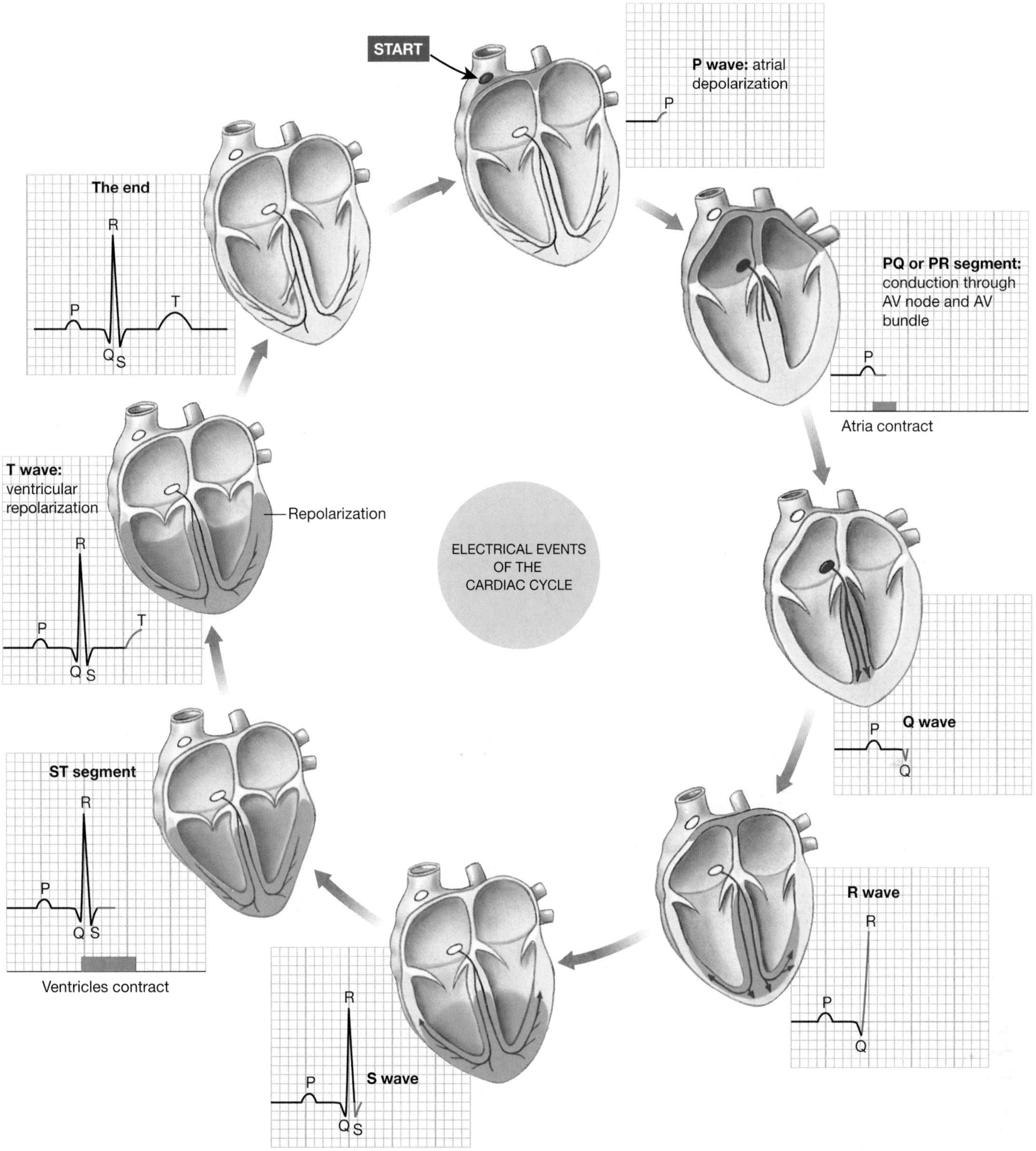

● **FIGURE 14-21** ***Correlation between an ECG and electrical events in the heart.*** The figure shows the correspondence between electrical events in the ECG and depolarizing (purple) and repolarizing (peach) regions of the heart.

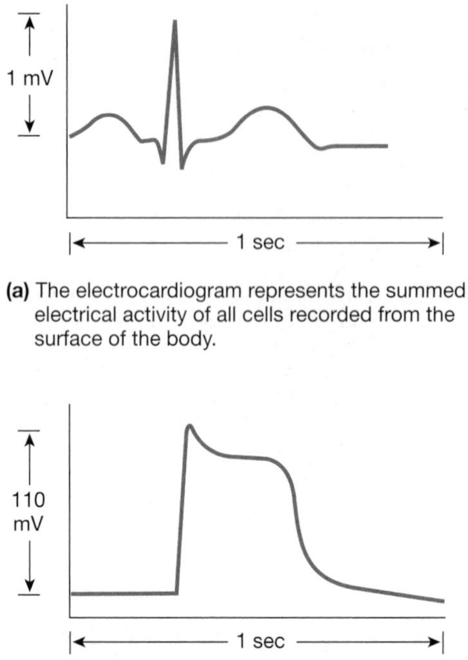

(a) The electrocardiogram represents the summed electrical activity of all cells recorded from the surface of the body.

(b) The ventricular action potential is recorded from a single cell using an intracellular electrode. Notice that the voltage change is much greater when recorded intracellularly.

● **FIGURE 14-22** ***Comparison of an ECG and a myocardial action potential***

an ECG is to look at the individual waves. To help your analysis, you might want to write the letters above the P, R, and T waves.

4. *Does a QRS complex follow each P wave, and is the P-R segment constant in length?* If not, a problem with conduction of signals through the AV node may exist. In heart block (the conduction problem mentioned earlier), action potentials from the SA node sometimes fail to be transmitted through the AV node to the ventricles. In these conditions, one or more P waves may occur without initiating a QRS complex. In the most severe form of heart block (third-degree), the atria depolarize regularly at one pace while the ventricles contract at a much slower pace (Fig. 14-23b).

The more difficult aspects of interpreting an ECG include looking for subtle changes, such as alterations in the shape or duration of various waves or segments. An experienced clinician can find signs pointing to changes in conduction velocity, enlargement of the heart, or tissue damage resulting from periods of ischemia. An amazing number of conclusions can be drawn about heart function simply by looking at alterations in the heart's electrical activity as recorded on an ECG.

Cardiac arrhythmias are a family of cardiac pathologies that range from benign to those with potentially fatal consequences. Arrhythmias are electrical problems that arise during the generation or conduction of action potentials through the heart, and they can usually be seen on an ECG. Some arrhythmias are "dropped beats" that result when the ventricles do not get their usual signal to contract. Other arrhythmias, such as *premature ventricular contractions* (*PVCs*), are extra beats that occur when an autorhythmic cell other than the SA node jumps in and fires an action potential out of sequence.

One interesting heart condition that can be observed on an ECG is *long QT syndrome* (*LQTS*), named for the change in the QT interval. LQTS has several forms. Some are inherited channelopathies, in which mutations occur in myocardial Na^+ or K^+ channels [p. 258]. In another form of LQTS, the ion channels are normal but the protein *ankyrin-B* that anchors the channels to the cell membrane is defective. *Iatrogenic* (physician-caused) forms of LQTS can occur as a side effect of taking certain medications. One well-publicized incident occurred in the 1990s when patients took a non-sedating antihistamine called terfenadine (Seldane®) that binds to K^+ repolarization channels. After at least eight deaths were attributed to the drug, the U.S. Food and Drug Administration removed Seldane from the market.

The Heart Contracts and Relaxes During a Cardiac Cycle

Each cardiac cycle has two phases: **diastole**, the time during which cardiac muscle relaxes, and **systole**, the time during which the muscle is contracting [*diastole,* dilation; *systole,* contraction]. Because the atria and ventricles do not contract and relax at the same time, we will discuss atrial and ventricular events separately.

In thinking about blood flow during the cardiac cycle, remember that blood flows from an area of higher pressure to one of lower pressure, and that contraction increases pressure while relaxation decreases pressure. In this discussion, we divide the cardiac cycle into the five phases shown in Figure 14-24 ●:

1. **The heart at rest: atrial and ventricular diastole**. We enter the cardiac cycle at the brief moment during which both the atria and the ventricles are relaxing. The atria are filling with blood from the veins, and the ventricles have just completed a contraction. As the ventricles relax, the AV valves between the atria and ventricles open. Blood

RUNNING PROBLEM

The electrocardiogram indicated that Walter suffered a myocardial infarction, resulting from blockage of blood vessels nourishing the left ventricle. The exact location of the damage depends on which artery and which branch or branches have become occluded.

Question 8:

If the ventricle of the heart is damaged, in which wave or waves of the electrocardiogram would you expect to see abnormal changes?

468 472 483 487 494 500 505

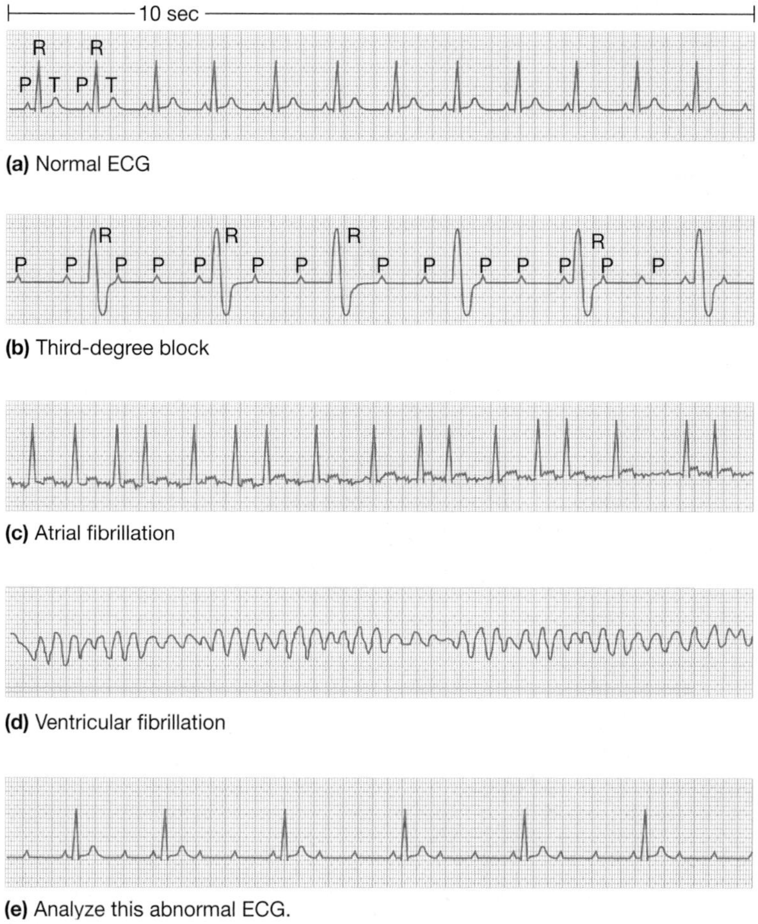
10 sec
R R
P T P T
(a) Normal ECG
R R R R
P P P P P P P P P P P P P P P
(b) Third-degree block
(c) Atrial fibrillation
(d) Ventricular fibrillation
(e) Analyze this abnormal ECG.

FIGURE 14-23 ***Normal and abnormal electrocardiograms.*** All tracings represent 10-sec recordings.

QUESTIONS TO ASK WHEN ANALYZING ECG TRACINGS:

1. What is the rate? Is it within the normal range of 60–100 beats per minute?
2. Is the rhythm regular?
3. Are all normal waves present in recognizable form?
4. Is there one QRS complex for each P wave? If yes, is the P-R segment constant in length?
5. If there is not one QRS complex for each P wave, count the heart rate using the P waves, then count it according to the R waves. Are the rates the same? Which wave would agree with the pulse felt at the wrist?

FIGURE QUESTIONS

a. Three abnormal ECGs are shown at left. Study them and see if you can relate the ECG changes to disruption of the normal electrical conduction pattern in the heart.

b. Identify the waves on the ECG in part (e). Look at the pattern of their occurrence and describe what has happened to electrical conduction in the heart.

flows by gravity from the atria into the ventricles. The relaxing ventricles expand to accommodate the entering blood.

CONCEPT CHECK

23. During atrial filling, is pressure in the atrium higher or lower than pressure in the venae cavae? Answers: p. 510

2. **Completion of ventricular filling: atrial systole.** Although most blood enters the ventricles while the atria are relaxed, the last 20% of filling is accomplished when the atria contract and push blood into the ventricles. (This applies to a normal person at rest. When heart rate increases, as during exercise, atrial contraction plays a greater role in ventricular filling). Atrial systole, or contraction, begins following the wave of depolarization that sweeps across the atria. The pressure increase that accompanies contraction pushes blood into the ventricles.

   A small amount of blood is forced backward into the veins because there are no one-way valves to block backward flow, although the openings of the veins do narrow during contraction. This retrograde movement of blood back into the veins may be observed as a pulse in the jugular vein of a normal person who is lying with the head and chest elevated about 30°. (Look in the hollow formed where the sternocleidomastoid muscle runs under the clavicle). An observable jugular pulse higher on the neck of a person sitting upright is a sign that pressure in the right atrium is higher than normal.

3. **Early ventricular contraction and the first heart sound.** As the atria are contracting, the depolarization wave is moving slowly through the conducting cells of the AV node, then rapidly down the Purkinje fibers to the apex of the heart. Ventricular systole begins there as spiral bands of muscle squeeze the blood upward toward the base. Blood pushing against the underside of the AV valves forces them closed so that blood cannot flow back into the atria. Vibrations following closure of the AV valves create the **first heart sound, S_1**, the "lub" of "lub-dup."

   With both sets of AV and semilunar valves closed, blood in the ventricles has nowhere to go. Nevertheless, the ventricles continue to contract, squeezing on the blood in the same way that you might squeeze a water balloon in your hand. This is similar to an isometric contraction, in which muscle fibers create force without movement [p. 427]. To return to the toothpaste tube

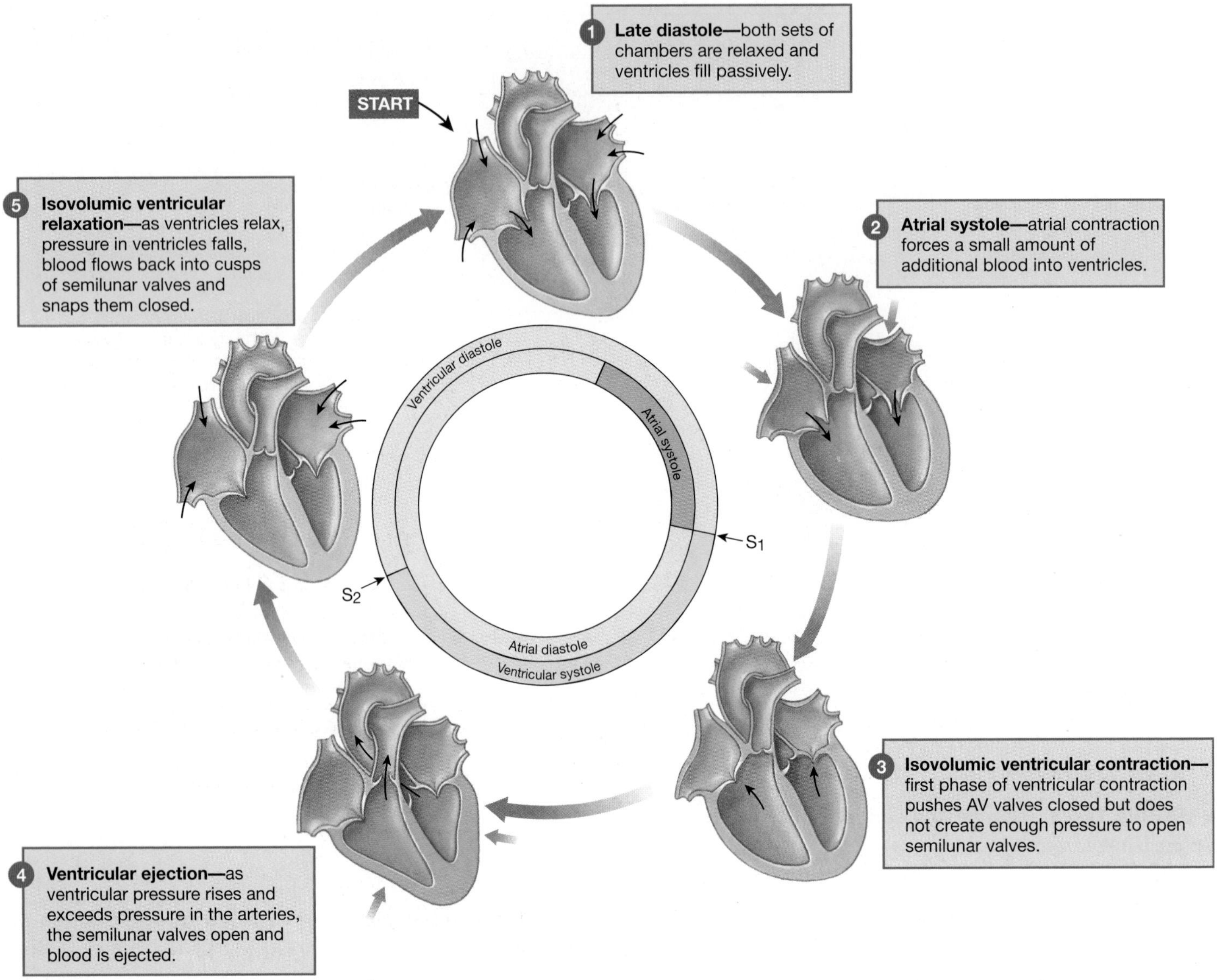

1 Late diastole—both sets of chambers are relaxed and ventricles fill passively.
START
2 Atrial systole—atrial contraction forces a small amount of additional blood into ventricles.
3 Isovolumic ventricular contraction—first phase of ventricular contraction pushes AV valves closed but does not create enough pressure to open semilunar valves.
4 Ventricular ejection—as ventricular pressure rises and exceeds pressure in the arteries, the semilunar valves open and blood is ejected.
5 Isovolumic ventricular relaxation—as ventricles relax, pressure in ventricles falls, blood flows back into cusps of semilunar valves and snaps them closed.
Ventricular diastole
Atrial systole
S1
S2
Atrial diastole
Ventricular systole

● **FIGURE 14-24** ***Systole and diastole are the mechanical events of the cardiac cycle.***

analogy, it is like squeezing the tube with the cap on: high pressure develops within the tube, but the toothpaste has nowhere to go. This phase is called **isovolumic ventricular contraction** [*iso-*, equal], to underscore the fact that the volume of blood in the ventricle is not changing.

While the ventricles begin to contract, the atrial muscle fibers are repolarizing and relaxing. When atrial pressure falls below that in the veins, blood flows from the veins into the atria again. Closure of the AV valves isolates the upper and lower cardiac chambers, meaning that atrial filling is independent of events taking place in the ventricles.

4. **The heart pumps: ventricular ejection**. As the ventricles contract, they generate enough pressure to open the semilunar valves and push blood into the arteries. The pressure created by ventricular contraction becomes the driving force for blood flow. High-pressure blood is forced into the arteries, displacing the low-pressure blood that fills them and pushing it farther into the vasculature. During this phase, the AV valves remain closed and the atria continue to fill.

5. **Ventricular relaxation and the second heart sound.** At the end of ventricular ejection, the ventricles begin to repolarize and relax. As they do so, ventricular pressure decreases. Once ventricular pressure falls below the pressure in the arteries, blood starts to flow backward into the heart. This backflow of blood fills the cuplike cusps of the semilunar valves, forcing them together into the closed position. The vibrations created by semilunar valve closure are the **second heart sound, S_2**, the "dup" of "lub-dup."

Once the semilunar valves close, the ventricles again become sealed chambers. The AV valves remain closed because ventricular pressure, although falling, is still higher

CLINICAL FOCUS

GALLOPS, CLICKS, AND MURMURS

The simplest direct assessment of heart function consists of listening to the heart through the chest wall, a process known as **auscultation** [*auscultare,* to listen to] that has been practiced since ancient times. In its simplest form, auscultation is done by placing an ear against the chest. Today, however, it is usually performed by listening through a stethoscope placed against the chest and the back. Normally, there are two audible heart sounds. The first ("lub") is associated with closure of the AV valves. The second ("dup") is associated with closure of the semilunar valves.

Two additional heart sounds can be recorded with very sensitive electronic stethoscopes. The third heart sound is caused by turbulent blood flow into the ventricles during ventricular filling, and the fourth sound is associated with turbulence during atrial contraction. In certain abnormal conditions, these latter two sounds may become audible through a regular stethoscope. They are called gallops because their timing puts them close to one of the normal heart sounds: "lub—dup-dup," or "lub-lub—dup." Other abnormal heart sounds include clicking, caused by abnormal movement of one of the valves, and murmurs, caused by the "whoosh" of blood leaking through an incompletely closed or excessively narrowed (*stenotic*) valve.

than atrial pressure. This period is called **isovolumic ventricular relaxation** because the volume of blood in the ventricles is not changing.

When ventricular relaxation causes ventricular pressure to become less than atrial pressure, the AV valves open. Blood that has been accumulating in the atria during ventricular contraction rushes into the ventricles. The cardiac cycle has begun again.

CONCEPT CHECK

24. Which chamber—atrium or ventricle—has higher pressure during the following phases of the cardiac cycle? (a) ventricular ejection, (b) isovolumic ventricular relaxation, (c) atrial and ventricular diastole, (d) isovolumic ventricular contraction
25. *Murmurs* are abnormal heart sounds caused either by blood forced through a narrowed valve opening or by backward flow (regurgitation) through a valve that has not closed completely. *Valvular stenosis* [*stenos,* narrow] may be an inherited condition or may result from inflammation or other disease processes. At which step(s) in the cardiac cycle (Fig. 14-24) would you expect to hear a murmur caused by the following pathologies? (a) aortic valvular stenosis, (b) mitral valve regurgitation, (c) aortic valve regurgitation

Answers: p. 510

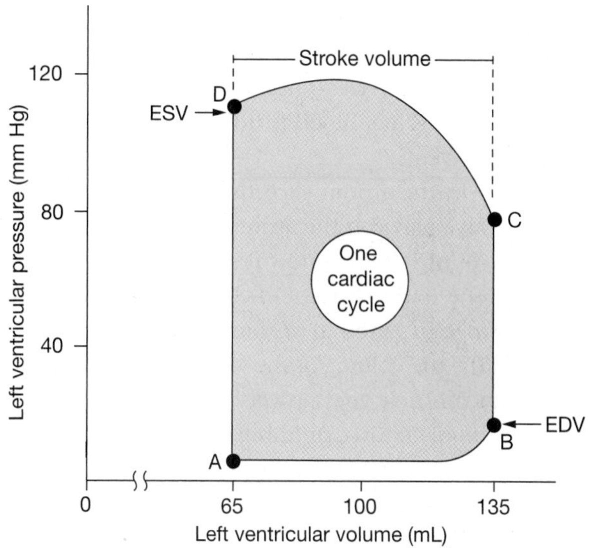

KEY
EDV = End-diastolic volume
ESV = End-systolic volume

GRAPH QUESTIONS

Match the following segments to the corresponding ventricular events:

A → B: (a) Ejection of blood into aorta
B → C: (b) Isovolumic contraction
C → D: (c) Isovolumic relaxation
D → A: (d) Passive filling and atrial contraction

Match the following events to points A–D:
(a) aortic valve opens
(b) mitral valve opens
(c) aortic valve closes
(d) mitral valve closes

● **FIGURE 14-25** ***Left ventricular pressure-volume changes during one cardiac cycle.***

Pressure-Volume Curves Represent One Cardiac Cycle

Another way to describe the cardiac cycle is with a pressure-volume graph, shown in Figure 14-25 ●. This figure represents the changes in volume (*x*-axis) and pressure (*y*-axis) that occur during one cardiac cycle.

The flow of blood through the heart is governed by the same principle that governs the flow of all liquids and gases: flow proceeds from areas of higher pressure to areas of lower pressure. When the heart contracts, the pressure increases and blood flows out of the heart into areas of lower pressure. Figure 14-25 represents pressure and volume changes in the left ventricle, which sends blood into the systemic circulation. The left side of the heart creates higher pressures than the right side, which sends blood through the shorter pulmonary circuit.

The cycle begins at point A. The ventricle has completed a contraction and contains the minimum amount of blood that it will hold during the cycle. It has relaxed, and its pressure is also at its minimum value. Blood is flowing into the atrium from the pulmonary veins.

Once pressure in the atrium exceeds pressure in the ventricle, the mitral valve between the atrium and ventricle opens (Fig. 14-25, point A). Atrial blood now flows into the ventricle, increasing its volume (point A to point B). As blood flows in, the relaxing ventricle expands to accommodate the entering blood. Consequently, the volume of the ventricle increases, but the pressure in the ventricle goes up very little.

The last portion of ventricular filling is completed by atrial contraction. The ventricle now contains the maximum volume of blood that it will hold during this cardiac cycle (point B). Because maximum filling occurs at the end of ventricular relaxation (diastole), this volume is called the **end-diastolic volume (EDV)**. In a 70-kg man at rest, end-diastolic volume is about 135 mL, but this value varies under different conditions. During periods of very high heart rate, for instance, when the ventricle does not have time to fill completely between beats, the end-diastolic value may be less than 135 mL.

When ventricular contraction begins, the mitral valve closes. With both the AV valve and the semilunar valve closed, blood in the ventricle has nowhere to go. Nevertheless, the ventricle continues to contract, causing the pressure in this chamber to increase rapidly during isovolumic contraction ($B \rightarrow C$ in Fig. 14-25). Once ventricular pressure exceeds the pressure in the aorta, the aortic valve opens (point C). Pressure continues to increase as the ventricle contracts further, but ventricular volume decreases as blood is pushed out into the aorta ($C \rightarrow D$).

The heart does not empty itself completely of blood each time the ventricle contracts. The amount of blood left in the ventricle at the end of contraction is known as the **end-systolic volume (ESV)**. The ESV (point D) is the minimum amount of blood the ventricle contains during one cycle. An average ESV value in a person at rest is 65 mL, meaning that nearly half of the 135 mL that was in the ventricle at the start of the contraction is still there at the end of the contraction.

At the end of each ventricular contraction, the ventricle begins to relax. As it does so, ventricular pressure decreases. Once pressure in the ventricle falls below aortic pressure, the semilunar valve closes, and the ventricle again becomes a sealed chamber. The remainder of relaxation occurs without a change in blood volume, and so this phase is called *isovolumic relaxation* (Fig. 14-25, $D \rightarrow A$). When ventricular pressure finally falls to the point at which atrial pressure exceeds ventricular pressure, the mitral valve opens and the cycle begins again.

The electrical and mechanical events of the cardiac cycle are summarized together in Figure 14-26 ●, known as a Wiggers diagram after the physiologist who first created it.

CONCEPT CHECK

26. In Figure 14-24, at what points in the cycle do EDV and ESV occur?
27. On the Wiggers diagram in Figure 14-26, match the following events to the lettered boxes: (a) end diastolic volume, (b) aortic valve opens, (c) mitral valve opens, (d) aortic valve closes, (e) mitral valve closes, (f) end systolic volume
28. Why does atrial pressure increase just to the right of point C in Figure 14-26? Why does it decrease during the initial part of ventricular systole, then increase? Why does it decrease to the right of point D?
29. Why does ventricular pressure shoot up suddenly at point C in Figure 14-26?

Answers: p. 510

Stroke Volume Is the Volume of Blood Pumped per Contraction

What is the purpose of blood remaining in the ventricles at the end of each contraction? For one thing, the resting end-systolic volume of 65 mL provides a safety margin. With a more forceful contraction, the heart can decrease its ESV, sending additional blood to the tissues. Like many organs of the body, the heart does not usually work "all out."

Stroke volume is the amount of blood pumped by one ventricle during a contraction. It is measured in milliliters per beat and can be calculated as follows:

$$\begin{array}{c}\text{Volume of blood before contraction} \\ -\ \text{volume of blood after contraction} = \text{stroke volume}\end{array}$$

$$\text{EDV} - \text{ESV} = \text{stroke volume}$$

For the average contraction in a person at rest:

$$135\ \text{mL} - 65\ \text{mL} = 70\ \text{mL, the normal stroke volume}$$

Stroke volume is not constant and can increase to as much as 100 mL during exercise. Stroke volume, like heart rate, is regulated by mechanisms we discuss later in this chapter.

Cardiac Output Is a Measure of Cardiac Performance

How can we assess the effectiveness of the heart as a pump? One way is to measure **cardiac output** (CO), the volume of blood pumped by one ventricle in a given period of time. Because all blood that leaves the heart flows through the tissues, cardiac output is an indicator of total blood flow through the body. However, cardiac output does not tell us how blood is distributed to various tissues. That aspect of blood flow is regulated at the tissue level.

Cardiac output (CO) can be calculated by multiplying heart rate (beats per minute) by stroke volume (mL per beat, or per contraction):

$$\text{Cardiac output} = \text{heart rate} \times \text{stroke volume}$$

For an average resting heart rate of 72 beats per minute and a stroke volume of 70 mL per beat, we have

$$\begin{aligned}\text{CO} &= 72\ \text{beats/min} \times 70\ \text{mL/beat} \\ &= 5040\ \text{mL/min (or approx. 5/L min)}\end{aligned}$$

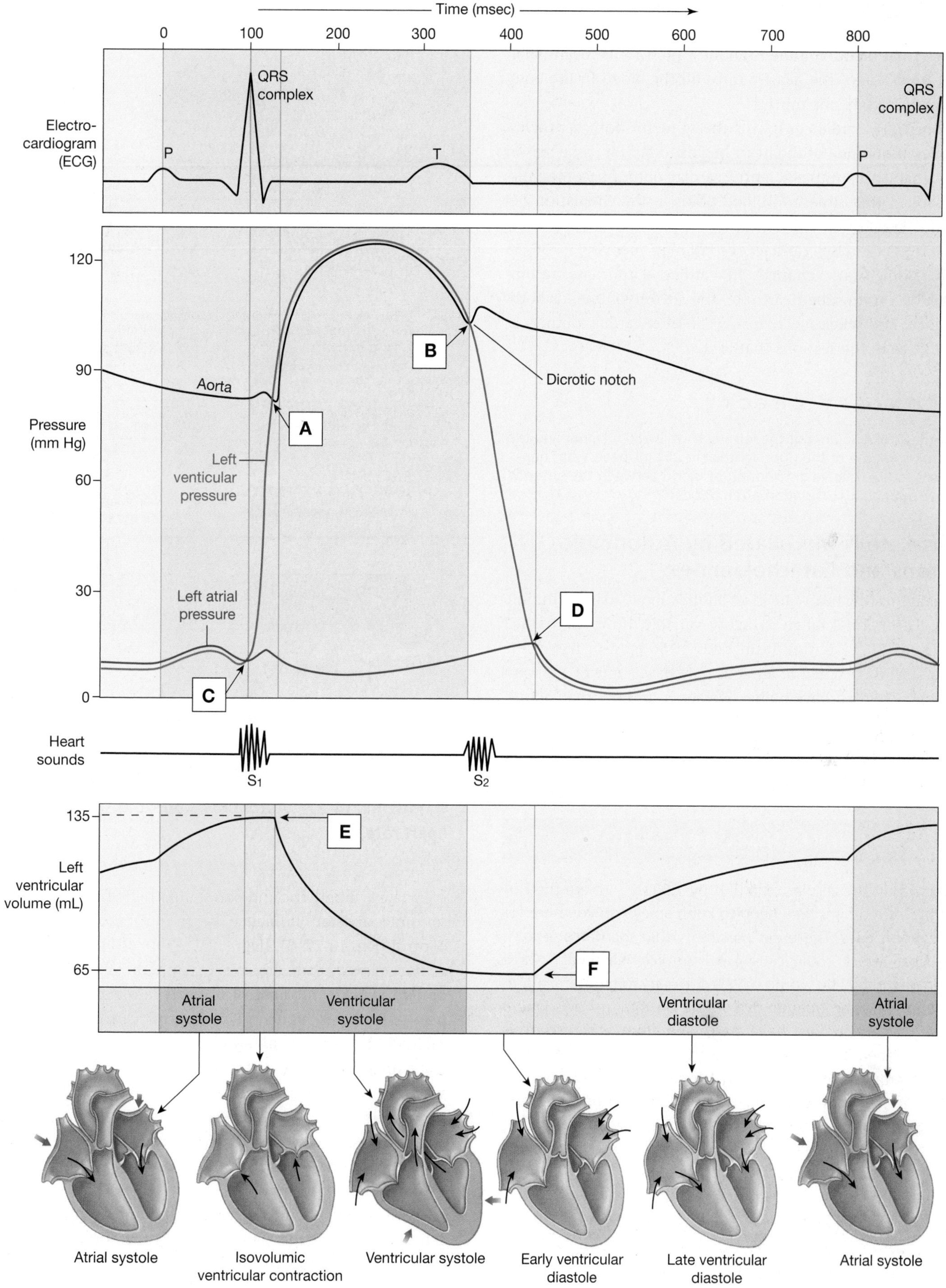

● **FIGURE 14-26** ***The Wiggers diagram of the cardiac cycle.*** The boxed letters refer to Concept Checks 27–29.

Average total blood volume is about 5 liters. This means that, at rest, one side of the heart pumps all the blood in the body through it in only one minute!

Normally, cardiac output is the same for both ventricles. However, if one side of the heart begins to fail for some reason and is unable to pump efficiently, cardiac output becomes mismatched. In that situation, blood pools in the circulation behind the weaker side of the heart.

During exercise, cardiac output may increase to 30–35 L/min. Homeostatic changes in cardiac output are accomplished by varying the heart rate, the stroke volume, or both. Both local and reflex mechanisms can alter cardiac output, as you will see in the sections that follow.

CONCEPT CHECK

30. If the stroke volume of the left ventricle is 250 mL/beat and the stroke volume of the right ventricle is 251 mL/beat, what happens to the relative distribution of blood between the systemic and pulmonary circulation after 10 beats? Answers: p. 510

Heart Rate Is Modulated by Autonomic Neurons and Catecholamines

An average resting heart rate in an adult is about 70 beats/minute (bpm). The normal range is highly variable, however. Trained athletes may have resting heart rates of 50 bpm or less, while someone who is excited or anxious may have a rate of 125 bpm or higher. Children have higher average heart rates than adults. Although heart rate is initiated by autorhythmic cells in the SA node, it is modulated by neural and hormonal input.

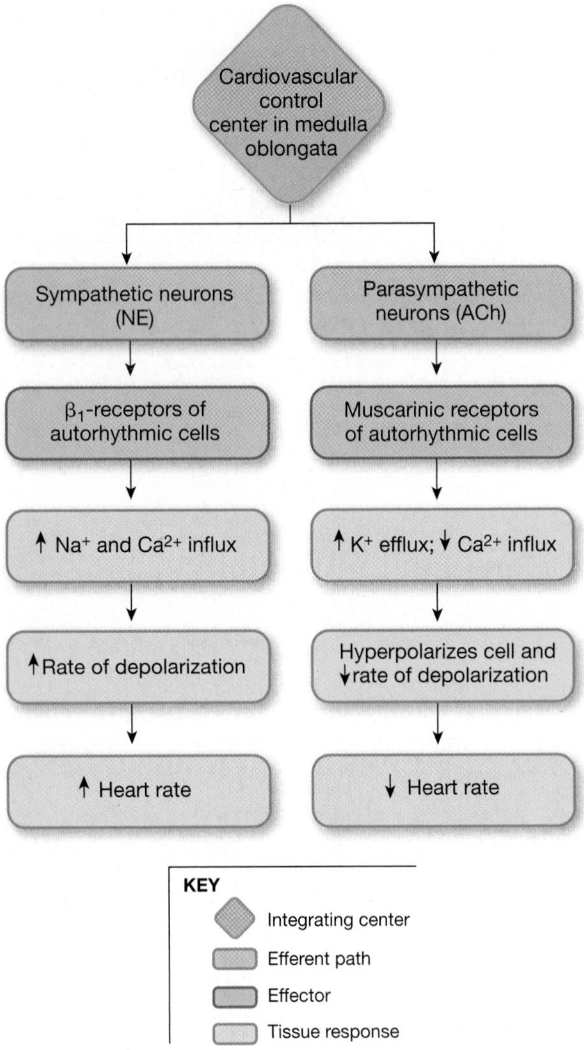

● **FIGURE 14-27** ***Autonomic neurotransmitters alter heart rate.***

RUNNING PROBLEM

Walter was in the cardiac care unit by 1:00 P.M., where the cardiologist visited him. "We need to keep an eye on you here for the next few days. There is a possibility that the damage from your heart attack could cause an irregular heartbeat." Once Walter was stable, he would have a coronary angiogram, a procedure in which an opaque dye visible on X-rays shows where coronary artery lumens have narrowed from atherosclerotic plaques. Depending on the results of that test, the physician might recommend either balloon angioplasty, in which a tube passed into the coronary artery is inflated to open up the blockage, or coronary bypass surgery, in which veins from other parts of the body are grafted onto the heart arteries to provide bypass channels around blocked regions.

Question 9:

If Walter's heart attack has damaged the muscle of his left ventricle, what do you predict will happen to his cardiac output?

The sympathetic and parasympathetic branches of the autonomic division influence heart rate through antagonistic control (Fig. 14-27 ●). [Fig. 6-21, p. 197]. Parasympathetic activity slows heart rate, while sympathetic activity speeds it up. Normally, tonic control of heart rate is dominated by the parasympathetic branch. This control can be shown experimentally by blocking all autonomic input to the heart. When all sympathetic and parasympathetic input is blocked, the spontaneous depolarization rate of the SA node is 90–100 times per minute. To achieve a resting heart rate of 70 beats per minute, tonic parasympathetic activity must slow the intrinsic rate down from 90 beats per minute.

An increase in heart rate can be achieved in two ways. The simplest method for increasing rate is to decrease parasympathetic activity. As parasympathetic influence is withdrawn from the autorhythmic cells, they resume their intrinsic rate of depolarization, and heart rate increases to 90–100 beats per minute. Alternatively, sympathetic input is required to increase heart rate above the intrinsic rate. As you learned earlier, norepinephrine (or epinephrine) on β_1-receptors speeds up the depolarization rate of the autorhythmic cells and increases heart rate.

Both autonomic branches also alter the rate of conduction through the AV node. Acetylcholine secreted by parasympathetic neurons slows the conduction of action potentials through the AV node, thereby increasing AV node delay. In contrast, the catecholamines epinephrine and norepinephrine enhance conduction of action potentials through the AV node and through the conducting system.

Multiple Factors Influence Stroke Volume

Stroke volume, the volume of blood pumped per ventricle per contraction, is directly related to the force generated by cardiac muscle during a contraction. Normally, as contraction force increases, stroke volume increases. In the isolated heart, the force of ventricular contraction is affected by two parameters: the length of muscle fibers at the beginning of contraction and the contractility of the heart. The volume of blood in the ventricle at the beginning of contraction (the end-diastolic volume) determines the length of the muscle. **Contractility** is the intrinsic ability of a cardiac muscle fiber to contract at any given fiber length and is a function of Ca^{2+} interaction with the contractile filaments.

Length-Tension Relationships and the Frank-Starling Law of the Heart As you learned earlier in this chapter, the force created by a myocardial muscle fiber is directly related to the length of the sarcomere. As sarcomere length increases (up to an optimum length), contraction force increases. In the intact heart, as stretch of the ventricular wall increases, so does the stroke volume. If additional blood flows into the ventricles, the muscle fibers stretch, then contract more forcefully, ejecting more blood. The degree of myocardial stretch before contraction begins is called the **preload** on the heart because this stretch represents the load placed on cardiac muscles before they contract.

This relationship between stretch and force in the intact heart was first described by a German physiologist, Otto Frank. A British physiologist, Ernest Starling, then expanded on Frank's work. Starling attached an isolated heart-lung preparation from a dog to a reservoir so that he could regulate the amount of blood returning to the heart. He found that in the absence of any nervous or hormonal control, the heart pumped all the blood that returned to it.

The relationship between stretch and force in the intact heart is plotted on a *Starling curve* (Fig. 14-28 ●). The *x*-axis represents the end-diastolic volume. This volume is a measure of stretch in the ventricles, which in turn determines sarcomere length. The *y*-axis of the Starling curve represents the stroke volume and is an indicator of the force of contraction.

The graph shows that stroke volume is proportional to EDV. As additional blood enters the heart, the heart contracts more forcefully and ejects more blood. This relationship is known as the **Frank-Starling law of the heart.** It means that within physiological limits, the heart pumps all the blood that returns to it.

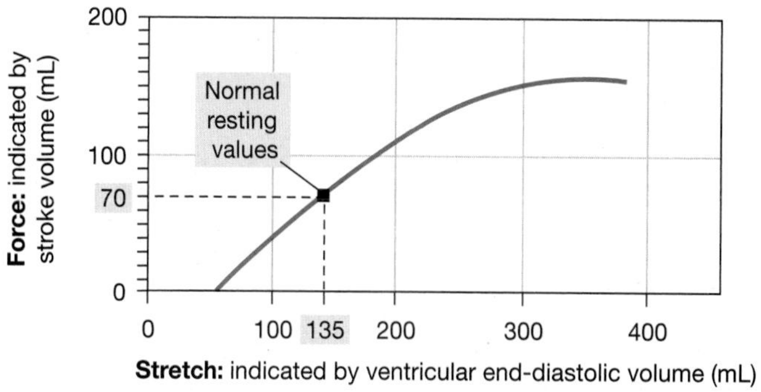

GRAPH QUESTION

What is the maximum stroke volume achieved in this experiment? At what end-diastolic volume is maximum stroke volume first achieved?

● **FIGURE 14-28** ***Length-force relationships in the intact heart: a Starling curve.*** In the intact heart, stroke volume is used as an indicator of contractile force.

Stroke Volume and Venous Return According to the Frank-Starling law, stroke volume increases as end-diastolic volume increases. End-diastolic volume is normally determined by **venous return**, the amount of blood that enters the heart from the venous circulation. Three factors affect venous return: (1) contraction or compression of veins returning blood to the heart (the skeletal muscle pump), (2) pressure changes in the abdomen and thorax during breathing (the respiratory pump), and (3) sympathetic innervation of veins.

Skeletal muscle pump is the name given to skeletal muscle contractions that squeeze veins (particularly in the legs), compressing them and pushing blood toward the heart. During exercise that involves the lower extremities, the skeletal muscle pump helps return blood to the heart. During periods of sitting or standing motionless, the skeletal muscle pump does not assist venous return.

The **respiratory pump** is created by movement of the thorax during inspiration (breathing in). As the chest expands and the diaphragm moves toward the abdomen, the thoracic cavity enlarges and develops a subatmospheric pressure. This low pressure decreases pressure in the inferior vena cava as it passes through the thorax, which helps draw more blood into the vena cava from veins in the abdomen. The respiratory pump is aided by the higher pressure placed on the outside of abdominal veins when the abdominal contents are compressed during inspiration. The combination of increased pressure in the abdominal veins and decreased pressure in thoracic veins enhances venous return during inspiration.

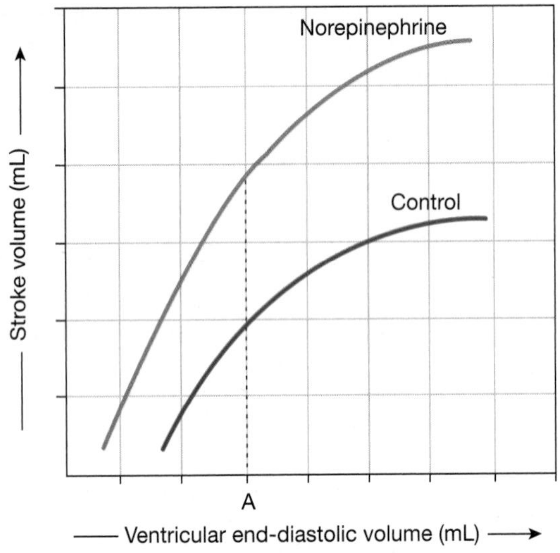

GRAPH QUESTION

At the end-diastolic volume indicated by point A, which heart will create more force: the control heart or the heart under the influence of norepinephrine?

● **FIGURE 14-29** ***The effect of norepinephrine on contractility of the heart.*** Norepinephrine is a positive inotropic agent.

Constriction of veins by sympathetic activity is the third factor that affects venous return. When the veins constrict, their volume decreases, squeezing more blood out of them and into the heart. With a larger ventricular volume at the beginning of the next contraction, the ventricle contracts more forcefully, sending the blood out into the arterial side of the circulation. In this manner, sympathetic innervation of veins allows the body to redistribute some venous blood to the arterial side of the circulation.

Contractility Is Controlled by the Nervous and Endocrine Systems

Any chemical that affects contractility is called an **inotropic agent** [*ino,* fiber], and its influence is called an **inotropic effect.** If a chemical increases the force of contraction, it is said to have a positive inotropic effect. For example, the catecholamines epinephrine and norepinephrine and drugs such as digitalis enhance contractility and are therefore considered to have a positive inotropic effect. Chemicals with negative inotropic effects decrease contractility.

Figure 14-29 ● shows a normal Starling curve (the control curve) along with a curve showing how the stroke volume changes with increased contractility due to norepinephrine. Note that contractility is distinct from the length-tension relationship. A muscle can remain at one length (for example, the end-diastolic volume marked A in Figure 14-29) but show increased contractility. Contractility increases as the amount of calcium available for contraction increases. Contractility was once considered to be distinct from changes in force resulting from variations in muscle (sarcomere) length. However, it now appears that increasing sarcomere length also makes cardiac muscle more sensitive to Ca^{2+}, thus linking contractility to muscle length.

The mechanism by which catecholamines increase Ca^{2+} entry and storage and exert their positive inotropic effect is mapped in Figure 14-30 ●. The signal molecules bind to and activate β_1-adrenergic receptors [⇄ p. 279] on the contractile myocardial cell membrane. Activated β_1-receptors use a cyclic AMP second messenger system to phosphorylate specific intracellular proteins [⇄ p. 186]. Phosphorylation of voltage-gated Ca^{2+} channels increases the probability that they will open and stay open longer. More open channels allow more Ca^{2+} to enter the cell.

The catecholamines increase Ca^{2+} storage through the use of a regulatory protein called **phospholamban** (Fig. 14-30). Phosphorylation of phospholamban enhances Ca^{2+}-ATPase activity in the sarcoplasmic reticulum. The ATPase concentrates Ca^{2+} in the sarcoplasmic reticulum, making more Ca^{2+} available for calcium-induced calcium release. Because more cytosolic Ca^{2+}

EMERGING CONCEPTS

STEM CELLS FOR HEART DISEASE

One of the interesting (and scary) aspects of translating basic scientific research into medicine is that sometimes therapies work but no one knows why. An example is the use of bone marrow stem cells to treat heart disease. After a heart attack, portions of the myocardium may be so damaged from lack of oxygen that they can no longer contract and contribute to cardiac function. A therapy that could replace dead and damaged cells and restore function would be a dream come true. In 2001 a group of researchers reported that bone marrow stem cells injected into mice with damaged hearts differentiated into new myocardial cells. This dramatic result prompted rapid translation of the basic research into human clinical trials. By 2008 there were more than 251 clinical trials looking at whether stem cell injections could help impaired cardiac function. Early results indicated that some patients were exhibiting small (about 5%) functional improvement. At the same time, however, scientists reported that they had been unable to duplicate the 2001 findings that bone marrow stem cells differentiate into myocardial cells. At this time, no one has an explanation for the mechanism(s) by which stem cell injections improve function. Theories with supporting evidence include stem cell secretion of growth factors that prevent tissue death or scarring or that cause new blood vessels to grow into damaged areas. One study is looking at whether skeletal muscle stem cells (*myoblasts*) can differentiate into functional cardiac muscle.

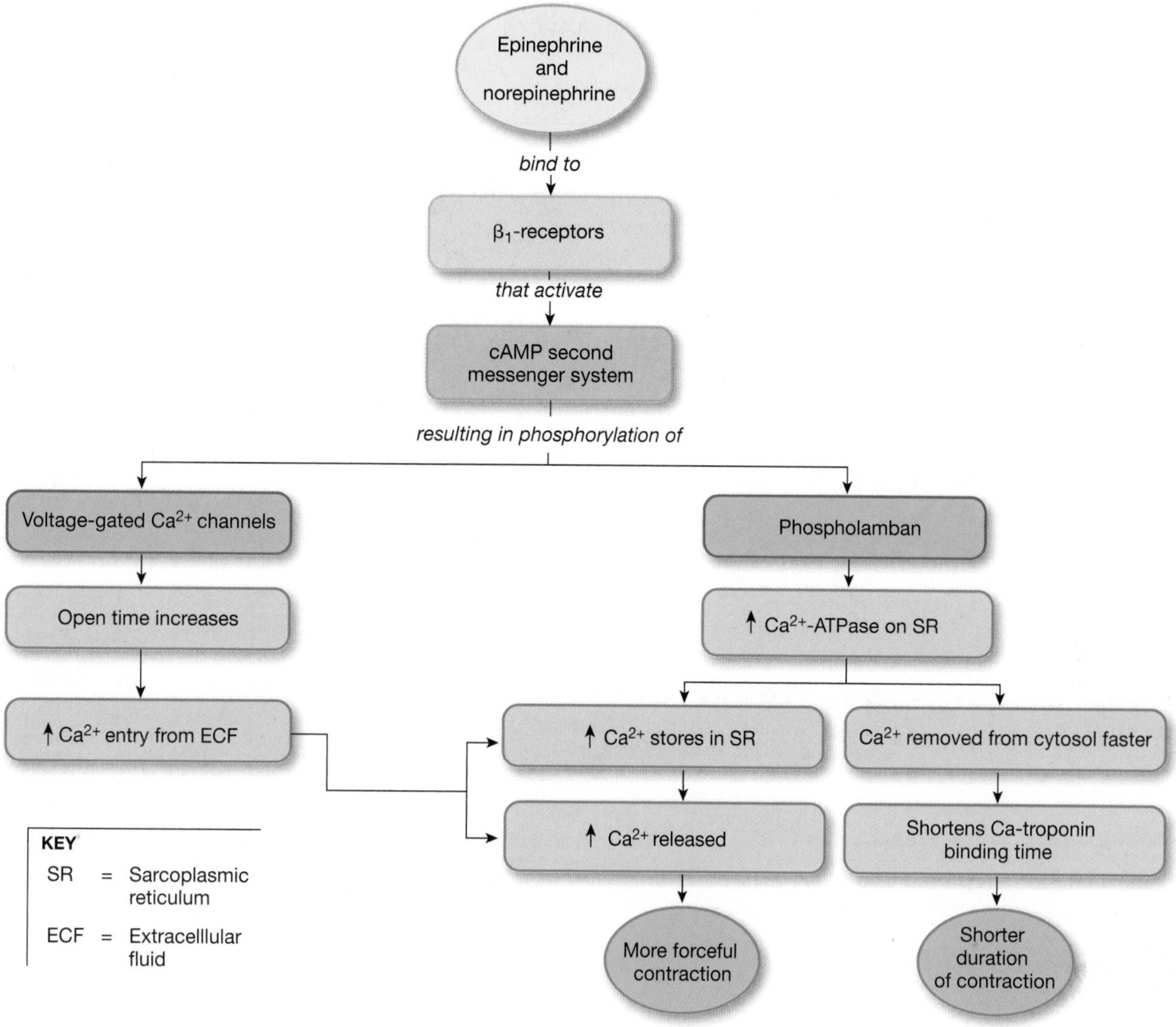

● **FIGURE 14-30** ***Catecholamines modulate cardiac contraction.***

means more active crossbridges, and because the force of contraction is proportional to the number of active crossbridges, the net result of catecholamine stimulation is a stronger contraction.

In addition to increasing the force of cardiac contraction, catecholamines also shorten the duration of contraction. The enhanced Ca^{2+}-ATPase speeds up removal of Ca^{2+} from the cytosol. This in turn shortens the time that Ca^{2+} is bound to troponin and decreases the active time of the myosin crossbridges. The muscle twitch is therefore briefer.

A different mechanism that enhances contractility can be triggered by the administration of cardiac glycosides, a class of molecules first discovered in the plant *Digitalis purpurea* (purple foxglove). Cardiac glycosides include digitoxin and the related compound *ouabain,* a molecule used to inhibit sodium transport in research studies. Glycosides increase contractility by slowing Ca^{2+} removal from the cytosol (in contrast to the catecholamines just discussed, which speed up Ca^{2+} removal). This mechanism is a pharmacological effect and does not occur in the absence of the drug.

Cardiac glycosides have been used since the eighteenth century as a remedy for *heart failure,* a pathological condition in which the heart is unable to contract forcefully. These highly toxic drugs depress Na^+-K^+-ATPase activity in all cells, not just those of the heart. With depressed Na^+-K^+-ATPase activity, Na^+ builds up in the cytosol, and the concentration gradient for Na^+ across the cell membrane diminishes. This in turn decreases the potential energy available for indirect active transport [p. 147]. In the myocardial cell, cardiac glycosides decrease the cell's ability to remove Ca^{2+} by means of the Na^+-Ca^{2+} exchanger. The resultant increase in cytosolic Ca^{2+} causes more forceful myocardial contractions.

CONCEPT CHECK

31. Using the myocardial cell in Figure 14-11 as a model, draw a contractile cell and show how catecholamines increase myocardial contractility.

Answers: p. 510

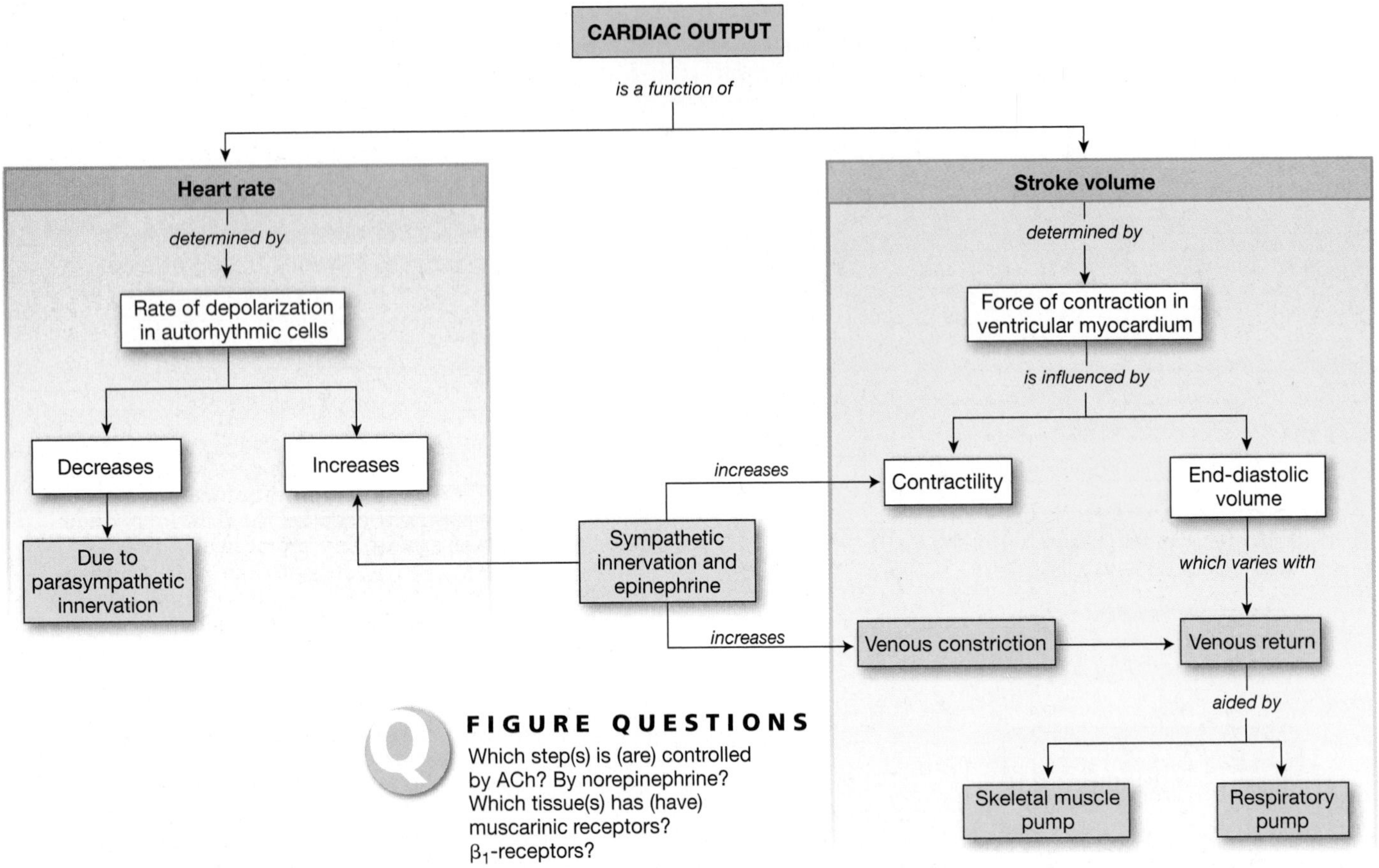

FIGURE QUESTIONS

Which step(s) is (are) controlled by ACh? By norepinephrine? Which tissue(s) has (have) muscarinic receptors? β_1-receptors?

● **FIGURE 14-31** ***Stroke volume and heart rate determine cardiac output.***

EDV and Arterial Blood Pressure Determine Afterload

Many of the experiments that uncovered the relationship between myocardial stretch and contractile force were conducted using isolated hearts. In the intact animal, ventricular force must be used to overcome the resistance created by blood filling the arterial system. The combined load of EDV and arterial resistance during ventricular contraction is known as **afterload.**

As an analogy, think of waiters carrying trays of food through a swinging door. A tray is a load equivalent to blood in the ventricles at the beginning of contraction. The door is an additional load that the waiter must push against to leave the kitchen. Normally this additional load is relatively minor. If someone decides to play a prank, however, and piles furniture against the dining room side of the door (increased afterload), the waiter must expend considerably more force to push through the door. Similarly, ventricular contraction must push a load of blood through a semilunar valve and out into the blood-filled arteries.

Increased afterload is found in several pathological situations, including elevated arterial blood pressure and loss of stretchability (*compliance*) in the aorta. To maintain constant stroke volume when afterload increases, the ventricle must increase its force of contraction, which then increases the muscle's need for oxygen and ATP production. If increased afterload becomes a chronic situation, the myocardial cells hypertrophy, resulting in increased thickness of the ventricular wall.

Clinically, arterial blood pressure is often used as an indirect indicator of afterload. Other aspects of ventricular function can be assessed noninvasively by echocardiography, an ultrasound procedure in which sound waves are reflected off heart tissue. A common functional index derived from this procedure is the **ejection fraction**, or percentage of EDV ejected with one contraction (stroke volume/EDV). Using our standard values for the 70-kg man, ejection fraction at rest is 70 mL/135 mL, or 52%. If stroke volume increases to 100 mL with exercise, the ejection fraction increases to 74%.

CONCEPT CHECK

32. A person's aortic valve opening has become constricted, creating a condition known as *aortic stenosis.* Which ventricle is affected by this change? What happens to the afterload on this ventricle? Answers: p. 510

The factors that determine cardiac output are summarized in Figure 14-31 ●. Cardiac output varies with both heart rate and stroke volume. Heart rate is modulated by the autonomic division of the nervous system and by epinephrine. The determination of stroke volume is more complex because stroke volume is a function of an intrinsic myocardial response to stretch (the length-tension relationship of the Frank-Starling law) interacting with adrenergically mediated changes in contractility. Venous return is a major determinant of end-diastolic volume and stretch.

The heart is a complex organ with many parts that can malfunction. In the next chapter we examine how cardiac output plays a key role in blood flow through the circulation. You will learn about high blood pressure and atherosclerosis, and how these conditions can cause the heart to fail in its role as a pump.

RUNNING PROBLEM CONCLUSION

Myocardial Infarction

Walter's angiogram showed two small blocked arteries, which were opened by balloon angioplasty. He returned home with instructions from his doctor for modifying his lifestyle to include a better diet, regular exercise, and no cigarette smoking. As part of his follow-up, Walter had a *myocardial perfusion imaging* test, in which he was administered radioactive thallium. The distribution of thallium throughout the heart is an indicator of blood flow to the heart muscle.

In this running problem, you learned about some current techniques for diagnosing and treating heart attacks. Walter's symptoms are the classic ones, but many women have symptoms that are different. For more information on heart attack symptoms and other cardiovascular diseases, visit *www.americanheart.org*, the American Heart Association web site. Check your understanding of this physiology by comparing your answers with the information in the summary table.

	QUESTION	FACTS	INTEGRATION AND ANALYSIS
1	Why did the EMT give Walter oxygen?	The EMT suspects that Walter has had a heart attack. Blood flow and oxygen supply to the heart muscle may be blocked.	If the heart is not pumping effectively, the brain may not receive adequate oxygen. Administration of oxygen increases the amount of oxygen that reaches both the heart and the brain.
2	What effect would the injection of isotonic saline have on Walter's extracellular fluid volume? On his intracellular fluid volume? On his total body osmolarity?	An isotonic solution is one that does not change cell volume [p. 161]. Isotonic saline (NaCl) is isosmotic to the body.	The extracellular volume will increase because all of the saline administered will remain in that compartment. Intracellular volume and total body osmolarity will not change.
3	A related form of creatine kinase is found in skeletal muscle. What are related forms of an enzyme called?	Related forms of an enzyme are called isozymes.	Although isozymes are variants of the same enzymes, their activity may vary under different conditions, and their structures are slightly different. Cardiac and skeletal muscle isozymes can be distinguished by their different structures.
4	What is troponin, and why would elevated blood levels of troponin indicate heart damage?	Troponin is the regulatory protein bound to tropomyosin [p. 415]. Ca^{2+} binding to troponin uncovers the myosin-binding site of actin to allow contraction.	Troponin is part of the contractile apparatus of the muscle cell. If troponin escapes from the cell and enters the blood, this is an indication that the cell either has been damaged or is dead.
5	How do electrical signals move from cell to cell in the myocardium?	Electrical signals pass through gap junctions in intercalated disks [p. 179].	The cells of the heart are electrically linked by gap junctions.
6	What happens to contraction in a myocardial contractile cell if a wave of depolarization passing through the heart bypasses it?	Depolarization in a muscle cell is the signal for contraction.	If a myocardial cell is not depolarized, it will not contract. Failure to contract creates a nonfunctioning region of heart muscle and impairs the pumping function of the heart.

RUNNING PROBLEM CONCLUSION *(continued)*

	QUESTION	FACTS	INTEGRATION AND ANALYSIS
7	What will a beta-blocker do to Walter's heart rate? Why is that response helpful following a heart attack?	A beta-blocker is an antagonist to β_1-adrenergic receptors. Activation of β_1-receptors increases heart rate.	A beta-blocker therefore decreases heart rate and lowers oxygen demand. Cells that need less oxygen are less likely to die if their blood supply is diminished.
8	If the ventricle of the heart is damaged, in which wave or waves of the electrocardiogram would you expect to see abnormal changes?	The P wave represents atrial depolarization. The QRS complex and T wave represent ventricular depolarization and repolarization, respectively.	The QRS complex and the T wave are most likely to show changes after a heart attack. Changes indicative of myocardial damage include enlargement of the Q wave, shifting of the S-T segment off the baseline (elevated or depressed), and inversion of the T wave.
9	If Walter's heart attack has damaged the muscle of his left ventricle, what do you predict will happen to his left cardiac output?	Cardiac output equals stroke volume times heart rate.	If the ventricular myocardium has been weakened, stroke volume may decrease. Decreased stroke volume in turn decreases cardiac output.

468 472 483 487 494 500 505

CHAPTER SUMMARY

The cardiovascular system exemplifies many of the basic themes in physiology. Blood flows through vessels as a result of high pressure created during ventricular contraction (*mass flow*). The circulation of blood provides an essential route for *cell-to-cell communication,* particularly for hormones and other chemical signals. Myocardial contraction, like contraction in skeletal and smooth muscle, demonstrates the importance of *molecular interactions, biological energy use,* and the *mechanical properties* of cells and tissues. This chapter also introduced the *control systems* for cardiovascular physiology, a theme that will be expanded in the next chapter.

Overview of the Cardiovascular System

iP Cardiovascular—Anatomy Review: The Heart

1. The human **cardiovascular system** consists of a **heart** that pumps **blood** through a closed system of **blood vessels**. (p. 469; Fig. 14-1)
2. The primary function of the cardiovascular system is the transport of nutrients, water, gases, wastes, and chemical signals to and from all parts of the body. (p. 469; Tbl. 14-1)
3. Blood vessels that carry blood away from the heart are called **arteries**. Blood vessels that return blood to the heart are called **veins. Valves** in the heart and veins ensure unidirectional blood flow. (p. 469; Fig. 14-1)
4. The heart is divided into two **atria** and two **ventricles**. (p. 469; Fig. 14-1)
5. The **pulmonary circulation** goes from the right side of the heart to the lungs and back to the heart. The **systemic circulation** goes from the left side of the heart to the tissues and back to the heart. (p. 471; Fig. 14-1)

Pressure, Volume, Flow, and Resistance

6. Blood flows down a **pressure gradient** (ΔP), from the highest pressure in the **aorta** and arteries to the lowest pressure in the **venae cavae** and **pulmonary veins**. (p. 471; Fig. 14-2)
7. In a system in which fluid is flowing, pressure decreases over distance. (p. 472; Fig. 14-3)
8. The pressure created when the ventricles contract is called the **driving pressure** for blood flow. (p. 473)
9. **Resistance** of a fluid flowing through a tube increases as the length of the tube and the **viscosity** (thickness) of the fluid increase, and as the radius of the tube decreases. Of these three factors, radius has the greatest effect on resistance. (pp. 473–474)
10. If resistance increases, flow rate decreases. If resistance decreases, flow rate increases. (p. 474; Fig. 14-5)
11. Fluid flow through a tube is proportional to the pressure gradient (ΔP). A pressure gradient is not the same thing as the absolute pressure in the system. (p. 474 Fig. 14-4)
12. **Flow rate** is the volume of blood that passes one point in the system per unit time. (p. 475)
13. **Velocity** is the distance a volume of blood travels in a given period of time. At a constant flow rate, the velocity of flow through a small tube is faster than the velocity through a larger tube. (p. 475; Fig. 14-6)

Cardiac Muscle and the Heart

iP Cardiovascular: Cardiac Action Potential

14. The heart is composed mostly of cardiac muscle, or **myocardium**. Most cardiac muscle is typical striated muscle. (p. 478; Fig. 14-7h)
15. The signal for contraction originates in **autorhythmic cells** in the heart. Autorhythmic cells are noncontractile myocardium. (p. 481)
16. Myocardial cells are linked to one another by **intercalated disks** that contain gap junctions. The junctions allow depolarization to spread rapidly from cell to cell. (p. 481; Fig. 14-10)
17. In contractile cell excitation-contraction coupling, an action potential opens Ca^{2+} channels. Ca^{2+} entry into the cell triggers the release of additional Ca^{2+} from the sarcoplasmic reticulum through **calcium-induced calcium release**. (p. 482; Fig. 14-11)
18. The force of cardiac muscle contraction can be graded according to how much Ca^{2+} enters the cell. (p. 483)
19. The longer a muscle fiber is when it begins to contract, the greater the force of contraction. (p. 483; Fig. 14-12)
20. The action potentials of myocardial contractile cells have a rapid depolarization phase created by Na^+ influx, and a steep repolarization phase due to K^+ efflux. The action potential also has a plateau phase created by Ca^{2+} influx. (pp. 483–484; Fig. 14-13)
21. Autorhythmic myocardial cells have an unstable membrane potential called a **pacemaker potential**. The pacemaker potential is due to I_f **channels** that allow net influx of positive charge. (p. 485; Fig. 14-15)
22. The steep depolarization phase of the autorhythmic cell action potential is caused by Ca^{2+} influx. The repolarization phase is due to K^+ efflux. (p. 486; Fig. 14-15)
23. Norepinephrine and epinephrine act on β_1-receptors to speed up the rate of the pacemaker depolarization and increase heart rate. Acetylcholine activates muscarinic receptors and slows down heart rate. (p. 486; Fig. 14-16)

The Heart as a Pump

iP Cardiovascular: Intrinsic Conduction System

24. Action potentials originate at the **sinoatrial node** (SA node) and spread rapidly from cell to cell in the heart. Action potentials are followed by a wave of contraction. (p. 488; Fig. 14-17)
25. The electrical signal moves from the SA node through the **internodal pathway** to the **atrioventricular node** (AV node), then into the **AV bundle**, **bundle branches**, terminal **Purkinje fibers**, and myocardial contractile cells. (p. 488; Fig. 14-18)
26. The SA node sets the pace of the heartbeat. If the SA node malfunctions, other autorhythmic cells in the AV node or ventricles take control of heart rate. (p. 489)
27. An **electrocardiogram** (ECG) is a surface recording of the electrical activity of the heart. The **P wave** represents atrial depolarization. The **QRS complex** represents ventricular depolarization. The **T wave** represents ventricular repolarization. Atrial repolarization is incorporated in the QRS complex. (p. 491; Figs. 14-20, 14-21)
28. An ECG provides information on heart rate and rhythm, conduction velocity, and the condition of cardiac tissues. (p. 492)

iP Cardiovascular: The Cardiac Cycle

29. One **cardiac cycle** includes one cycle of contraction and relaxation. **Systole** is the contraction phase; **diastole** is the relaxation phase. (p. 494; Fig. 14-24)
30. Most blood enters the ventricles while the atria are relaxed. Only 20% of ventricular filling at rest is due to atrial contraction. (p. 495)
31. The **AV valves** prevent backflow of blood into the atria. Vibrations following closure of the AV valves create the **first heart sound**. (p. 495; Figs. 14-9, 14-24)
32. During **isovolumic ventricular contraction**, the ventricular blood volume does not change, but pressure rises. When ventricular pressure exceeds arterial pressure, the **semilunar valves** open, and blood is ejected into the arteries. (pp. 495–497; Figs. 14-9, 14-24)
33. When the ventricles relax and ventricular pressure falls, the semilunar valves close, creating the **second heart sound**. (p. 496; Fig. 14-9, 14-24)
34. The amount of blood pumped by one ventricle during one contraction is known as the **stroke volume**. (p. 498; Fig. 14-25)

iP Cardiovascular: Cardiac Output

35. **Cardiac output** is the volume of blood pumped per ventricle per unit time. It is equal to heart rate times stroke volume. The average cardiac output at rest is 5 L/min. (p. 498)
36. Homeostatic changes in cardiac output are accomplished by varying heart rate, stroke volume, or both. (p. 500; Fig. 14-31)
37. Parasympathetic activity slows heart rate; sympathetic activity speeds it up. (p. 500; Fig. 14-27)
38. The **Frank-Starling law of the heart** says that an increase in **end-diastolic volume** results in a greater stroke volume. (p. 501; Fig. 14-28)
39. Epinephrine and norepinephrine increase the force of myocardial contraction when they bind to β_1-adrenergic receptors. They also shorten the duration of cardiac contraction. (pp. 500–501; Fig. 14-30)
40. End-diastolic volume and **preload** are determined by **venous return**. Venous return is affected by skeletal muscle contractions, the respiratory pump, and constriction of veins by sympathetic activity. (p. 501)
41. **Contractility** of the heart is enhanced by catecholamines and certain drugs. Chemicals that alter contractility are said to have an **inotropic effect**. (p. 502; Fig. 14-29)
42. **Afterload** is the load placed on the ventricle as it contracts. Afterload reflects the preload and the effort required to push the blood out into the arterial system. Mean arterial pressure is a clinical indicator of afterload. (p. 504)
43. **Ejection fraction**, the percent of EDV ejected with one contraction (stroke volume/EDV), is one measure for evaluating ventricular function. (p. 504)

QUESTIONS

(Answers to the Review Questions begin on page A1).

THE PHYSIOLOGY PLACE

Access more review material online at The Physiology Place web site. There you'll find review questions, problem-solving activities, case studies, flashcards, and direct links to both *Interactive Physiology®* and *PhysioEx™*. To access the site, go to *www.physiologyplace.com* and select *Human Physiology*, Fifth Edition.

LEVEL ONE REVIEWING FACTS AND TERMS

1. What contributions to understanding the cardiovascular system did each of the following people make?
   (a) William Harvey
   (b) Otto Frank and Ernest Starling
   (c) Marcello Malpighi
2. List three functions of the cardiovascular system.
3. Put the following structures in the order in which blood passes through them, starting and ending with the left ventricle:
   (a) left ventricle
   (b) systemic veins
   (c) pulmonary circulation
   (d) systemic arteries
   (e) aorta
   (f) right ventricle
4. The primary factor causing blood to flow through the body is a(n) __________ gradient. In humans, the value of this gradient is highest at the __________ and in the __________. It is lowest in the __________. In a system in which fluid is flowing, pressure decreases over distance because __________.
5. If vasodilation occurs in a blood vessel, pressure (increases/decreases).
6. The specialized cell junctions between myocardial cells are called __________. These areas contain __________ that allow rapid conduction of electrical signals.
7. Trace an action potential from the SA node through the conducting system of the heart.
8. Distinguish between the two members of each of the following pairs:
   (a) end-systolic volume and end-diastolic volume
   (b) sympathetic and parasympathetic control of heart rate
   (c) diastole and systole
   (d) systemic and pulmonary circulation
   (e) AV node and SA node
9. Match the descriptions with the correct anatomic term(s). Not all terms are used and terms may be used more than once. Give a definition for the unused terms.
   (a) tough membranous sac that encases the heart
   (b) valve between ventricle and a main artery
   (c) a vessel that carries blood away from the heart
   (d) lower chamber of the heart
   (e) valve between left atrium and left ventricle
   (f) primary artery of the systemic circulation
   (g) muscular layer of the heart
   (h) narrow end of the heart; points downward
   (i) valve with papillary muscles
   (j) the upper chambers of the heart

   1. aorta
   2. apex
   3. artery
   4. atria
   5. atrium
   6. AV valve
   7. base
   8. bicuspid valve
   9. endothelium
   10. myocardium
   11. pericardium
   12. semilunar valve
   13. tricuspid valve
   14. ventricle
10. What events cause the two principal heart sounds?
11. What is the proper term for each of the following?
   (a) number of heart contractions per minute
   (b) volume of blood in the ventricle before the heart contracts
   (c) volume of blood that enters the aorta with each contraction
   (d) volume of blood that leaves the heart in one minute
   (e) volume of blood in the entire body

LEVEL TWO REVIEWING CONCEPTS

12. Concept maps:
   (a) Create a map showing blood flow through the heart and body. Label as many structures as you can.
   (b) Create a map for control of cardiac output using the following terms. You may add additional terms.

ACh	heart rate
adrenal medulla	length-tension relationship
autorhythmic cells	muscarinic receptor
β_1-receptor	norepinephrine
Ca^{2+}	parasympathetic neurons
Ca^{2+}-induced Ca^{2+} release	respiratory pump
cardiac output	skeletal muscle pump
contractile myocardium	stroke volume
contractility	sympathetic neurons
force of contraction	venous return

13. List the events of the cardiac cycle in sequence, beginning with atrial and ventricular diastole. Note when valves open and close. Describe what happens to pressure and blood flow in each chamber at each step of the cycle.
14. Compare and contrast the structure of a cardiac muscle cell with that of a skeletal muscle cell. What unique properties of cardiac muscle are essential to its function?
15. Explain why contractions in cardiac muscle cannot sum or exhibit tetanus.
16. Correlate the waves of an ECG with mechanical events in the atria and ventricles. Why are there only three electrical events but four mechanical events?

17. Match the following ion movements with the appropriate phrase. More than one ion movement may apply to a single phrase. Some choices may not be used.

(a) slow rising phase of autorhythmic cells	1. K^+ from ECF to ICF
(b) plateau phase of contractile cells	2. K^+ from ICF to ECF
(c) rapid rising phase of contractile cells	3. Na^+ from ECF to ICF
(d) rapid rising phase of autorhythmic cells	4. Na^+ from ICF to ECF
(e) rapid falling phase of contractile cells	5. Ca^{2+} from ECF to ICF
(f) falling phase of autorhythmic cells	6. Ca^{2+} from ICF to ECF
(g) cardiac muscle contraction	
(h) cardiac muscle relaxation	

18. List and briefly explain four types of information that an ECG provides about the heart.

19. Define inotropic effect. Name two drugs that have a positive inotropic effect on the heart.

LEVEL THREE PROBLEM SOLVING

20. Two drugs used to reduce cardiac output are calcium channel blockers and beta (receptor) blockers. What effect do these drugs have on the heart that explains how they decrease cardiac output?

21. Police Captain Jeffers has suffered a myocardial infarction.
    (a) Explain to his (nonmedically oriented) family what has happened to his heart.
    (b) When you analyzed his ECG, you referred to several different leads, such as lead I and lead III. What are leads?
    (c) Why is it possible to record an ECG on the body surface without direct access to the heart?

22. What might cause a longer-than-normal PR interval in an ECG?

23. The following paragraph is a summary of a newspaper article:

    A new treatment for atrial fibrillation due to an excessively rapid rate at the SA node involves a high-voltage electrical pulse administered to the AV node to destroy its autorhythmic cells. A ventricular pacemaker is then implanted in the patient.

    Briefly explain the physiological rationale for this treatment. Why is a rapid atrial depolarization rate dangerous? Why is the AV node destroyed in this procedure? Why must a pacemaker be implanted?

LEVEL FOUR QUANTITATIVE PROBLEMS

24. Police Captain Jeffers in question 21 has an ejection fraction (SV divided by EDV) of only 25%. His stroke volume is 40 mL/beat, and his heart rate is 100 beats/min. What are his EDV, ESV, and CO? Show your calculations.

25. If 1 cm water = 0.74 mm Hg:
    (a) Convert a pressure of 120 mm Hg to cm H_2O.
    (b) Convert a pressure of 90 cm H_2O to mm Hg.

26. Calculate cardiac output if stroke volume is 65 mL/beat and heart rate is 80 beats/min.

27. Calculate end-systolic volume if end-diastolic volume is 150 mL and stroke volume is 65 mL/beat.

28. A person has a total blood volume of 5 L. Of this total, assume that 4 L is contained in the systemic circulation and 1 L is in the pulmonary circulation. If the person has a cardiac output of 5 L/min, how long will it take (a) for a drop of blood leaving the left ventricle to return to the left ventricle and (b) for a drop of blood to go from the right ventricle to the left ventricle?

ANSWERS

Answers to Concept Check Questions

Page 471

1. A cardiovascular system has tubes (vessels), fluid (blood), and a pump (heart).
2. (a) The pulmonary circulation takes blood to and from the lungs; the systemic circulation takes blood to and from the rest of the body. (b) An artery carries blood away from the heart; a vein carries blood to the heart. (c) An atrium is an upper heart chamber that receives blood entering the heart; a ventricle is a lower heart chamber that pumps blood out of the heart.

Page 474

3. The pressure gradient is more important.
4. The bottom tube has the greater flow because it has the larger pressure gradient (50 mm Hg versus 40 mm Hg for the top tube).
5. Tube C has the highest flow because it has the largest radius of the four tubes (less resistance) and the shorter length (less resistance). (Tube B has the same radius as tube C but a longer length and therefore offers greater resistance to flow). Tube D, with the greatest resistance due to longer length and narrow radius, has the lowest flow.

Page 478

6. If the canals are identical in size and therefore in cross-sectional area A, the canal with the higher velocity of flow v has the higher flow rate Q. (From equation 7, $Q = v \times A$).

Page 481

7. Connective tissue is not excitable and is therefore unable to conduct action potentials.
8. Superior vena cava → right atrium → tricuspid (right AV) valve right ventricle → pulmonary (right semilunar) valve → pulmonary trunk → pulmonary vein → left atrium → mitral (bicuspid, left AV) valve → left ventricle → aortic (left semilunar) valve → aorta
9. The AV valves prevent backward flow of blood. If one fails, blood leaks back into the atrium.

Page 483

10. Skeletal muscle L-type Ca^{2+} channels (also called DHP receptors) remain closed but are mechanically linked to the RyR Ca^{2+} release

channels of the sarcoplasmic reticulum. Myocardial L-type Ca^{2+} channels open to allow Ca^{2+} into the cell. In both muscles, sarcolemma Ca^{2+} channels are associated with RyR Ca^{2+} release channels on the SR.

11. From this experiment, it is possible to conclude that myocardial cells require extracellular calcium for contraction but skeletal muscle cells do not.

Page 483

12. If all calcium channels in the muscle cell membrane are blocked, there will be no contraction. If only some are blocked, the force of contraction will be smaller than the force created with all channels open.

Page 484

13. Na^+ influx causes neuronal depolarization, and K^+ efflux causes neuronal repolarization.
14. The refractory period represents the time required for the Na^+ channel gates to reset (activation gate closes, inactivation gate opens).
15. If cardiac Na^+ channels are blocked with lidocaine, the cell will not depolarize and therefore will not contract.

Page 486

16. Increasing K^+ permeability hyperpolarizes the membrane potential.

Page 487

17. The Ca^{2+} channels in autorhythmic cells are not the same as those in contractile cells. Autorhythmic Ca^{2+} channels open rapidly when the membrane potential reaches about −50 mV and close when it reaches about +20 mV. The Ca^{2+} channels in contractile cells are slower and do not open until the membrane has depolarized fully.
18. If tetrodotoxin is applied to a myocardial autorhythmic cell, nothing will happen because there are no voltage-gated Na^+ channels in the cell.
19. Cutting the vagus nerve caused heart rate to increase, so the nerve must contain parasympathetic fibers that slow heart rate.

Page 491

20. The AV node conducts action potentials from atria to ventricles. It also slows down the speed at which those action potentials are conducted, allowing atrial contraction to end before ventricular contraction begins.
21. The SA node is in the upper right atrium.
22. The fastest pacemaker sets the heart rate, so the heart rate increases to 120 beats/min.

Page 495

23. The atrium has lower pressure than the venae cavae.

Page 497

24. (a) ventricle, (b) ventricle, (c) atrium, (d) ventricle
25. (a) ventricular ejection, (b) isovolumic ventricular contraction and ventricular ejection (c) from isovolumic ventricular relaxation until ventricular contraction begins again

Page 498

26. EDV occurs in step 3, and ESV occurs in step 5.
27. (a) E, (b) A, (c) D, (d) B, (e) C, (f) F
28. Atrial pressure increases because pressure on the mitral valve pushes the valve back into the atrium, decreasing atrial volume. Atrial pressure decreases during the initial part of ventricular systole as the atrium relaxes. The pressure then increases as the atrium fills with blood. Atrial pressure begins to decrease at point D, when the mitral valve opens and blood flows down into the ventricles.
29. Ventricular pressure shoots up when the ventricles contract on a fixed volume of blood.

Page 500

30. After 10 beats, the pulmonary circulation will have gained 10 mL of blood and the systemic circulation will have lost 10 mL.

Page 503

31. Your drawing should show a β_1-receptor on the cell membrane activating intracellular cAMP, which should have an arrow drawn to Ca^{2+} channels on the sarcoplasmic reticulum. Open channels should be shown increasing cytoplasmic Ca^{2+}. A second arrow should go from cAMP to Ca^{2+}-ATPase on the SR and the cell membrane, showing increased uptake in the SR and increased removal of Ca^{2+} from the cell.

Page 504

32. The aortic valve is found between the left ventricle and the aorta. A stenotic aortic valve would increase afterload on the ventricle.

Answers to Figure and Graph Questions

Page 470

Fig. 14-1: The two portal systems are in the GI tract and in the kidneys, with two capillary beds connected in series for each portal system.

Page 474

Fig. 14-5: If radius = 3, R = 1/81 and flow = 81, which is about 5× flow through B.

Page 475

Fig. 14-6: If A = 3, $v = 4\ cm^2/min$.

Page 486

Fig. 14-15: Phase 2 (the plateau) of the contractile cell action potential has no equivalent in the autorhythmic cell action potential. Phase 4 is approximately equivalent to the pacemaker potential. Both action potentials have rising phases, peaks, and falling phases.

Page 490

Fig. 14-18: If the AV node could not depolarize, there would be no conduction of electrical activity into the ventricles.

Page 492

Fig. 14-20: The heart rate is either 75 beats/min or 80 beats/min, depending on how you calculate it. If you use the data from one R peak to the next, the time interval between the two peaks is 0.8 sec; therefore, 1 beat /0.8 sec × 60 sec / 1 min = 75 beats/min. However, it is more accurate to estimate rate by using several seconds of the ECG tracing rather than one RR interval because beat-to-beat intervals may vary. If you start counting at the first R wave on the top graph and go right for 3 sec, there are 4 beats in that time period, which means 4 beats/3 sec × 60 sec/1 min = 80 beats/min.

Page 495

Fig. 14-23: (a) In (b), notice that there is no regular association between the P waves and the QRS complexes (the P-R segment varies in length). Notice also that not every P wave has an associated QRS complex. Both

P waves and QRS complexes appear at regular intervals, but the atrial rate (P waves) is faster than the ventricular rate (QRS complexes). The QRS complexes are not their usual shape, and the T wave is absent because the ventricular depolarization is not following its normal path. In (c), there are identifiable R waves but no P waves. In (d), there are no recognizable waves at all, indicating that the depolarizations are not following the normal conduction path.

(b) Starting at left, the waves are P, P, QRS, T, P, P, QRS, T, P, P, P, and so on. Each P wave that is not followed by a QRS wave suggests an intermittent conduction block at the AV node. See also Figure 14-23b.

Page 497

Fig. 14-25: Match segments to events: (a) C → D, (b) B → C, (c) D → A, (d) A → B. Match events to points: (a) C, (b) A, (c) D, (d) B.

Page 501

Fig. 14-28: Maximum stroke volume is about 160 mL/beat, first achieved when end-diastolic volume is about 330 mL.

Page 502

Fig. 14-29: At point A, the heart under the influence of norepinephrine has a larger stroke volume and is therefore creating more force.

Page 504

Fig. 14-31: Heart rate is the only parameter controlled by ACh. Heart rate and contractility are both controlled by norepinephrine. The SA node has muscarinic receptors. The SA node and contractile myocardium have β_1-receptors.

15

Blood Flow and the Control of Blood Pressure

BACKGROUND BASICS

Basal lamina: **75** Nitric oxide: **191** Transcytosis: **157** Fight-or-flight response: **386** Exchange epithelium: **76** Catecholamines and receptors: **224** Caveolae: **154** Diffusion: **136** Tonic control: **196** Smooth muscle: **432**

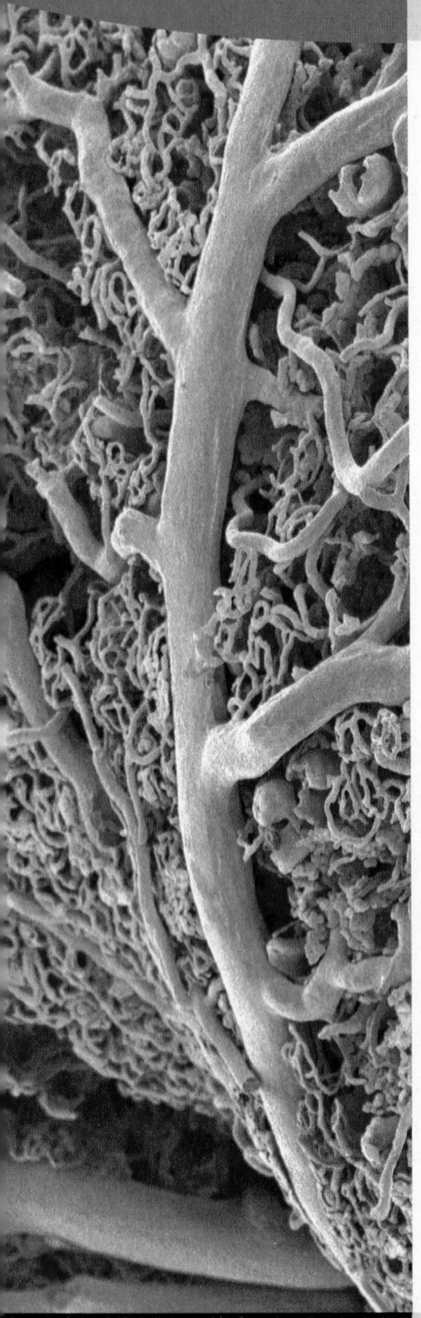

Blood vessels of the small intestine

Since 1900, CVD (cardiovascular disease) has been the No. 1 killer in the United States every year but 1918.

—American Heart Association, ***Heart Disease and Stroke Statistics***

RUNNING PROBLEM

Essential Hypertension

"Doc, I'm as healthy as a horse," says Kurt English, age 56, during his long-overdue annual physical examination. "I don't want to waste your time. Let's get this over with." But to Dr. Arthur Cortez, Kurt does not appear to be the picture of health: he is about 30 pounds overweight. When Dr. Cortez asks about his diet, Kurt replies, "Well, I like to eat." Exercise? "Who has the time?" replies Kurt. Dr. Cortez wraps a blood pressure cuff around Kurt's arm and takes a reading. "Your blood pressure is 164 over 100," says Dr. Cortez. "We'll take it again in 15 minutes. If it's still high, we'll need to discuss it further." Kurt stares at his doctor, flabbergasted. "But how can my blood pressure be too high? I feel fine!" he protests.

513 519 523 524 532 540

Anthony was sure he was going to be a physician, until the day in physiology laboratory they studied blood types. When the lancet pierced his fingertip and he saw the drop of bright red blood well up, the room started to spin, and then everything went black. He awoke, much embarrassed, to the sight of his classmates and the teacher bending over him.

Anthony suffered an attack of *vasovagal syncope* (syncope = fainting), a benign and common emotional reaction to blood, hypodermic needles, or other upsetting sights. Normally, homeostatic regulation of the cardiovascular system maintains blood flow, or *perfusion*, to the heart and brain. In vasovagal syncope, signals from the nervous system cause a sudden decrease in blood pressure, and the individual faints from lack of oxygen to the brain. In this chapter you will learn how the heart and blood vessels work together most of the time to prevent such problems.

A simplified model of the cardiovascular system (Fig. 15-1 ●) illustrates the key points we discuss in this chapter. This model shows the heart as two separate pumps, with the right heart pumping blood to the lungs and back to the left heart. The left heart then pumps blood through the rest of the body and back to the right heart.

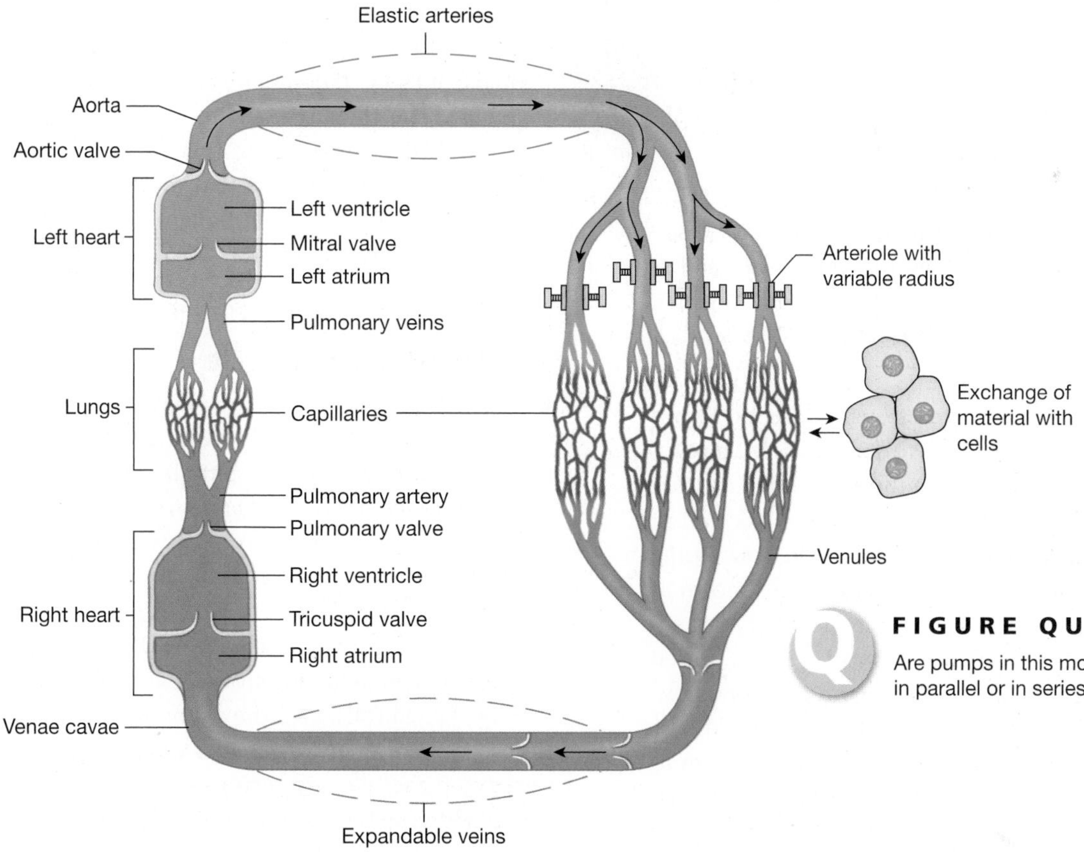

FIGURE QUESTION

Are pumps in this model operating in parallel or in series?

● **FIGURE 15-1** ***Functional model of the cardiovascular system.*** Each side of the heart functions as an independent pump. The systemic arteries are a pressure reservoir that maintains blood flow during ventricular relaxation. The arterioles, shown with adjustable screws that alter their diameter, are the site of variable resistance. Exchange between the blood and cells takes place only at the capillaries. Veins serve as an expandable volume reservoir.

15

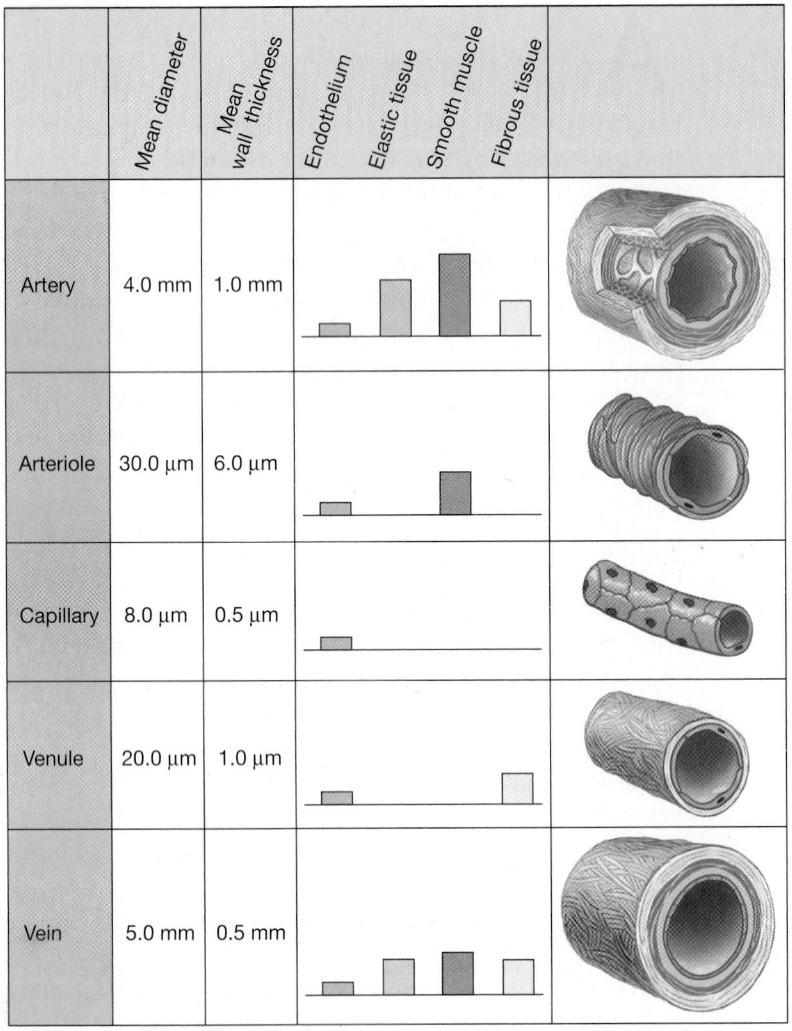
Mean diameter
Mean wall thickness
Endothelium
Elastic tissue
Smooth muscle
Fibrous tissue
Artery
4.0 mm
1.0 mm
Arteriole
30.0 μm
6.0 μm
Capillary
8.0 μm
0.5 μm
Venule
20.0 μm
1.0 μm
Vein
5.0 mm
0.5 mm

● **FIGURE 15-2** ***Blood vessel structure.*** The walls of blood vessels vary in diameter and composition. The endothelium and its underlying elastic tissue together form the tunica intima. (Adapted from A. C. Burton, *Physiol. Rev.* 34:619–642, 1954).

Blood leaving the left heart enters systemic arteries, shown here as an expandable, elastic region. Pressure produced by contraction of the left ventricle is stored in the elastic walls of arteries and slowly released through *elastic recoil*. This mechanism maintains a continuous driving pressure for blood flow during ventricular relaxation. For this reason, the arteries are known as the *pressure reservoir* [*reservare*, to retain] of the circulatory system.

Downstream from the arteries, small vessels called **arterioles** create a high-resistance outlet for arterial blood flow. Arterioles direct distribution of blood flow to individual tissues by selectively constricting and dilating, so they are known as the site of *variable resistance*. Arteriolar diameter is regulated both by local factors, such as tissue oxygen concentrations, and by the autonomic nervous system and hormones.

When blood flows into the capillaries, their leaky epithelium allows exchange of materials between the plasma, the interstitial fluid, and the cells of the body. At the distal end of the capillaries, blood flows into the venous side of the circulation. The veins act as a *volume reservoir* from which blood can be sent to the arterial side of the circulation if blood pressure falls too low. From the veins, blood flows back to the right heart.

Total blood flow through any level of the circulation is equal to cardiac output. For example, if cardiac output is 5 L/min, blood flow through all the systemic capillaries is 5 L/min. In the same manner, blood flow through the pulmonary side of the circulation is equal to blood flow through the systemic circulation.

THE BLOOD VESSELS

The walls of blood vessels are composed of layers of smooth muscle, elastic connective tissue, and fibrous connective tissue (Fig. 15-2 ●). The inner lining of all blood vessels is a thin layer of **endothelium,** a type of epithelium. For years, the endothelium was thought to be simply a passive barrier. However, we now know that endothelial cells secrete many paracrines and play important roles in the regulation of blood pressure, blood vessel growth, and absorption of materials. Some biologists have even proposed that endothelium be considered a separate physiological organ system.

In most vessels, layers of connective tissue and smooth muscle surround the endothelium. The endothelium and its adjacent elastic connective tissue together make up the *tunica intima,* usually called simply the *intima*. The thickness of the smooth muscle–connective tissue layers surrounding the intima varies in different vessels. The descriptions that follow apply to the vessels of the systemic circulation, although those of the pulmonary circulation are generally similar.

Blood Vessels Contain Vascular Smooth Muscle

The smooth muscle of blood vessels is known as **vascular smooth muscle**. Most blood vessels contain smooth muscle, arranged in either circular or spiral layers. *Vasoconstriction* narrows the diameter of the vessel lumen, and *vasodilation* widens it.

In most blood vessels, smooth muscle cells maintain a state of partial contraction at all times, creating the condition known as *muscle tone* [p. 451]. Contraction of smooth muscle, like that of cardiac muscle, depends on the entry of Ca^{2+} from the extracellular fluid through Ca^{2+} channels [p. 435]. A variety of chemicals, including neurotransmitters, hormones, and paracrines, influences vascular smooth muscle tone. Many vasoactive paracrines are secreted either by endothelial cells lining blood vessels or by tissues surrounding the vessels.

Arteries and Arterioles Carry Blood Away from the Heart

The aorta and major arteries are characterized by walls that are both stiff and springy. Arteries have a thick smooth muscle layer and large amounts of elastic and fibrous connective tissue (Fig. 15-2). Because of the stiffness of the fibrous tissue, substantial amounts of energy are required to stretch the walls of an artery outward, but that energy can be stored by the stretched elastic fibers and released through elastic recoil.

The arteries and arterioles are characterized by a divergent [*divergere,* bend apart] pattern of blood flow. As major arteries divide into smaller and smaller arteries, the character of the wall changes, becoming less elastic and more muscular. The walls of arterioles contain several layers of smooth muscle that contract and relax under the influence of various chemical signals.

Some arterioles branch into vessels known as **metarterioles** [*meta-,* beyond] (Fig. 15-3 ●). True arterioles have a continuous smooth muscle layer, but the wall of a metarteriole is only partially surrounded by smooth muscle. Blood flowing through metarterioles can take one of two paths. If muscle rings called **precapillary sphincters** [*sphingein,* to hold tight] are relaxed, blood flowing into a metarteriole is directed into adjoining capillary beds.

If the precapillary sphincters are constricted, metarteriole blood bypasses the capillaries and goes directly to the venous circulation. In addition, metarterioles allow white blood cells to go directly from the arterial to the venous circulation. Capillaries are barely large enough to let red blood cells through, much less white blood cells, which are twice as large.

Arterioles, along with capillaries and small postcapillary vessels called venules, form the *microcirculation*. Regulation of blood flow through the microcirculation is an active area of physiological research.

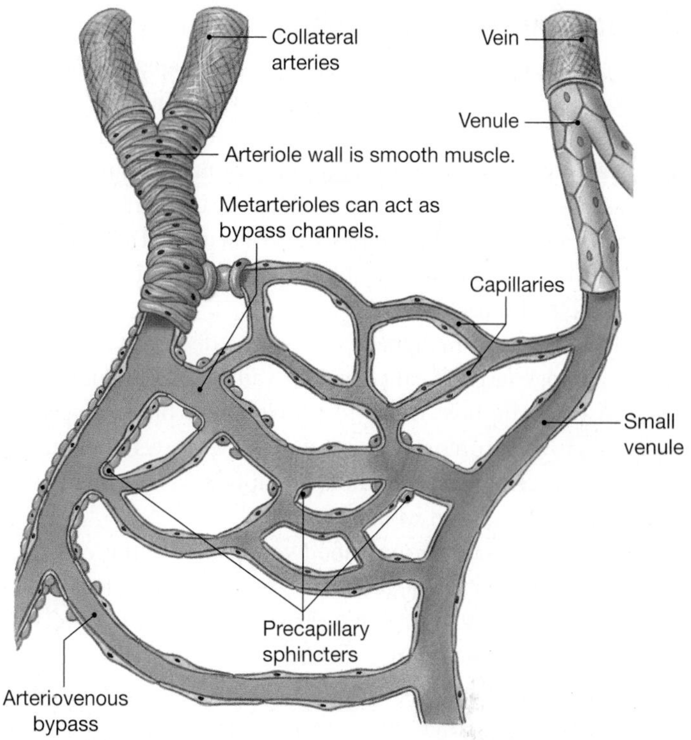

● **FIGURE 15-3** ***Metarterioles regulate flow into capillary beds.***

Exchange Takes Place in the Capillaries

Capillaries are the smallest vessels in the cardiovascular system. They and the postcapillary venules are the site of exchange between the blood and the interstitial fluid. To facilitate exchange of materials, capillaries lack smooth muscle and elastic or fibrous tissue reinforcement (Fig. 15-2). Instead, their walls consist of a flat layer of endothelium, one cell thick, supported on an acellular matrix called the *basal lamina* (basement membrane) [p. 75].

Many capillaries are closely associated with cells known as **pericytes** [*peri-,* around]. In most tissues, these highly branched contractile cells surround the capillaries, forming a meshlike outer layer between the capillary endothelium and the interstitial fluid. Pericytes contribute to the "tightness" of capillary permeability: the more pericytes, the less leaky the capillary endothelium. Cerebral capillaries, for example, are surrounded by pericytes and glial cells, and have tight junctions that create the *blood-brain barrier* [p. 303].

Pericytes secrete factors that influence capillary growth, and they can differentiate to become new endothelial or smooth muscle cells. Loss of pericytes around capillaries of the retina is a hallmark of the disease *diabetic retinopathy,* a leading cause of blindness. Scientists are now trying to determine whether pericyte loss is a cause or consequence of the retinopathy.

Blood Flow Converges in the Venules and Veins

Blood flows from the capillaries into small vessels called **venules**. The very smallest venules are similar to capillaries, with a thin exchange epithelium and little connective tissue (Fig. 15-2). They are distinguished from capillaries by their convergent pattern of flow.

Smooth muscle begins to appear in the walls of larger venules. From venules, blood flows into veins that become larger in diameter as they travel toward the heart. Finally, the largest veins, the venae cavae, empty into the right atrium.

Veins are more numerous than arteries and have a larger diameter. As a result of their large volume, the veins hold more than half of the blood in the circulatory system, making them the volume reservoir. Veins lie closer to the surface of the body than arteries, forming the bluish blood vessels that you see running just under the skin. Veins have thinner walls than arteries, with less elastic tissue. As a result, they expand easily when they fill with blood.

When you have blood drawn from your arm (*venipuncture*), the technician uses a tourniquet to exert pressure on the blood vessels. Blood flow into the arm through deep high-pressure arteries is not affected, but pressure exerted by the tourniquet stops outflow through the low-pressure veins. As a result, blood collects in the surface veins, making them stand out against the underlying muscle tissue.

Angiogenesis Creates New Blood Vessels

One topic of great interest to researchers is **angiogenesis** [*angeion,* vessel + *gignesthai,* to beget], the process by which new blood vessels develop, especially after birth. In children, blood vessel growth is necessary for normal development. In adults, angiogenesis takes place as wounds heal and as the uterine lining grows after menstruation. Angiogenesis also occurs with endurance exercise training, enhancing blood flow to the heart muscle and to skeletal muscles.

The growth of malignant tumors is a disease state that requires angiogenesis. As cancer cells invade tissues and multiply, they instruct the host tissue to develop new blood vessels to feed the growing tumor. Without these new vessels, the interior cells of a cancerous mass would be unable to get adequate oxygen and nutrients, and would die.

From studies of normal blood vessels and tumor cells, scientists learned that angiogenesis is controlled by a balance of angiogenic and antiangiogenic cytokines. A number of related growth factors, including *vascular endothelial growth factor* (VEGF) and *fibroblast growth factor* (FGF), promote angiogenesis. These growth factors are *mitogens,* meaning they promote mitosis, or cell division. They are normally produced by smooth muscle cells and pericytes.

Cytokines that inhibit angiogenesis include *angiostatin,* made from the blood protein plasminogen, and *endostatin* [*stasis,* a state of standing still]. Scientists are currently testing these cytokines for treating cancer, to see if they can block angiogenesis and literally starve tumors to death.

In contrast, **coronary heart disease,** also known as *coronary artery disease,* is a condition in which blood flow to the myocardium is decreased by fatty deposits that narrow the lumen of the coronary arteries. In some individuals, new blood vessels develop spontaneously and form *collateral circulation* that supplements flow through the partially blocked artery. Researchers are testing angiogenic cytokines to see if they can duplicate this natural process and induce angiogenesis to replace *occluded* vessels [*occludere,* to close up].

BLOOD PRESSURE

Recall from Chapter 14 that the pressure created by ventricular contraction is the driving force for blood flow through the cardiovascular system [p. 469]. As blood is ejected from the left ventricle, the aorta and arteries expand to accommodate it (Fig. 15-4a ●). When the ventricle relaxes and the semilunar valve closes, the elastic arterial walls recoil, propelling the blood forward into smaller arteries and arterioles (Fig. 15-4b). By sustaining the *driving pressure* for blood flow during ventricular relaxation, the arteries keep blood flowing continuously through the blood vessels.

Blood flow obeys the rules of fluid flow that were introduced in Chapter 14 [p. 474]. Flow is directly proportional to the pressure gradient between any two points, and inversely proportional to the resistance of the vessels to flow (Tbl. 15-1 ●). Unless otherwise noted, the discussion that follows is restricted to the events that take place in the systemic circuit. We discuss pulmonary blood flow in Chapter 17.

Blood Pressure Is Highest in Arteries and Lowest in Veins

Blood pressure is highest in the arteries and decreases continuously as blood flows through the circulatory system (Fig. 15-5 ●). The decrease in pressure occurs because energy is lost as a result of the resistance to flow offered by the vessels. Resistance to blood flow also results from friction between the blood cells.

In the systemic circulation, the highest pressure occurs in the aorta and results from pressure created by the left ventricle. Aortic pressure reaches an average high of 120 mm Hg during ventricular systole (**systolic pressure**), then falls steadily to a low of 80 mm Hg during ventricular diastole (**diastolic pressure**). Notice that pressure in the ventricle falls to 0 mm Hg as the ventricle relaxes, but diastolic pressure in the large arteries remains relatively high. The high diastolic pressure in arteries reflects the ability of those vessels to capture and store energy in their elastic walls.

The rapid pressure increase that occurs when the left ventricle pushes blood into the aorta can be felt as a **pulse,** or pressure wave, transmitted through the fluid-filled arteries. The pressure wave travels about 10 times faster than the blood itself. Even so, a pulse felt in the arm is occurring slightly after the ventricular contraction that created the wave.

The amplitude of the pressure wave decreases over distance because of friction, and the wave finally disappears at the capillaries (Fig. 15-5). **Pulse pressure,** a measure of the strength of the pressure wave, is defined as systolic pressure minus diastolic pressure:

$$\text{Systolic pressure} - \text{diastolic pressure} = \text{pulse pressure}$$

For example, in the aorta:

$$120 \text{ mm Hg} - 80 \text{ mm Hg} = 40 \text{ mm Hg pressure}$$

By the time blood reaches the veins, pressure has fallen because of friction, and a pressure wave no longer exists. Low-pressure blood in veins below the heart must flow "uphill," or against gravity, to return to the heart. Try holding your arm straight down without moving for several minutes and notice how the veins in the back of your hand begin to stand out as they fill with blood. (This effect may be more evident in older people, whose subcutaneous connective tissue has lost elasticity). Then raise your hand so that gravity assists the venous flow and watch the bulging veins disappear.

To assist venous flow, some veins have internal one-way valves (Fig. 15-6 ●). These valves, like those in the heart, ensure that blood passing the valve cannot flow backward. Once blood reaches the vena cava, there are no valves. Venous blood flow is steady rather than pulsatile, pushed along by the continuous movement of blood out of the capillaries.

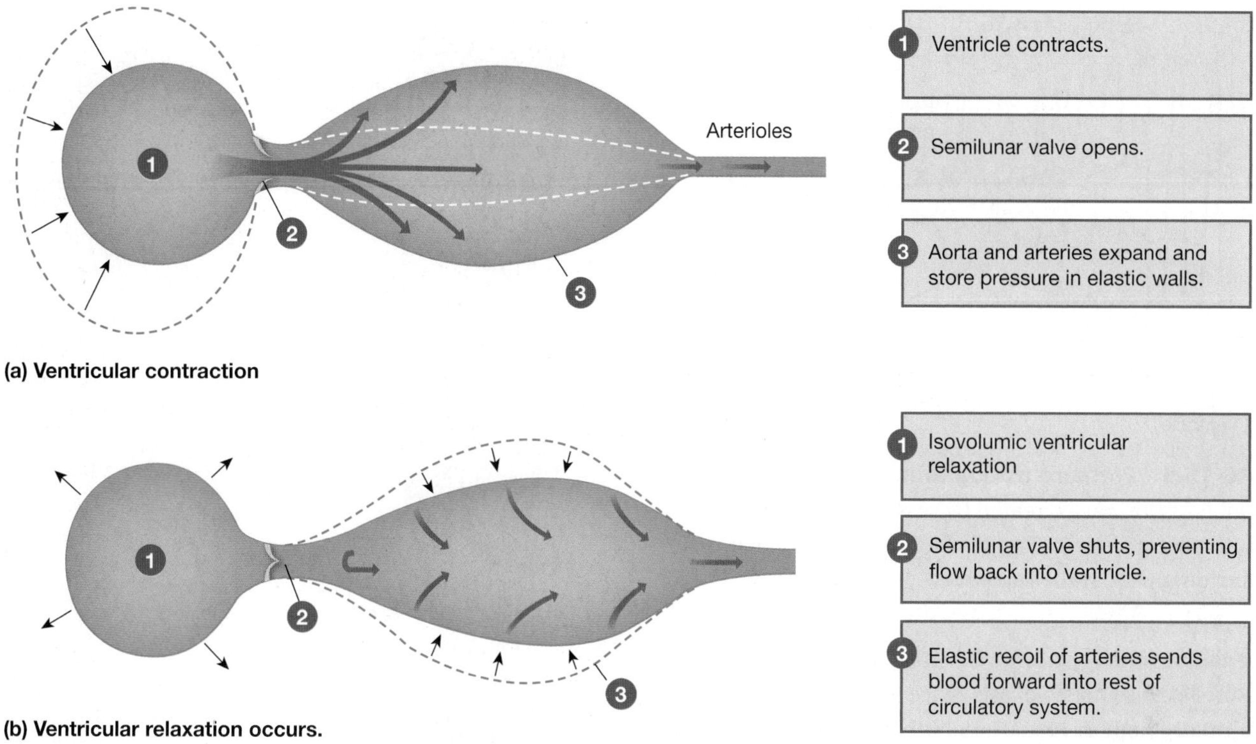

FIGURE 15-4 ***Elastic recoil in the arteries maintains driving pressure during ventricular diastole.***

Venous return to the heart is aided by the *skeletal muscle pump* and the *respiratory pump* [p. 501]. When muscles such as those in the calf of the leg contract, they compress the veins, forcing blood upward past the valves. While your hand is hanging down, try clenching and unclenching your fist to see the effect muscle contraction has on distention of the veins.

CONCEPT CHECK

1. Would you expect to find valves in the veins leading from the brain to the heart? Defend your answer.
2. If you checked the pulse in a person's carotid artery and left wrist at the same time, would the pressure waves occur simultaneously? Explain.
3. Who has the higher pulse pressure, someone with blood pressure of 90/60 or someone with blood pressure of 130/95?

Answers: p. 544

Arterial Blood Pressure Reflects the Driving Pressure for Blood Flow

Arterial blood pressure, or simply "blood pressure," reflects the driving pressure created by the pumping action of the heart. Because ventricular pressure is difficult to measure, it is customary to assume that arterial blood pressure reflects ventricular pressure. Because arterial pressure is pulsatile, we use a single value—the **mean arterial pressure** (MAP)—to represent driving pressure. Mean arterial pressure is estimated as diastolic pressure plus one-third of pulse pressure:

$$\text{MAP} = \text{diastolic P} + 1/3\ (\text{systolic P} - \text{diastolic P})$$

For a person whose systolic pressure is 120 and diastolic pressure is 80:

$$\text{MAP} = 80 \text{ mm Hg} + 1/3\ (120 - 80 \text{ mm Hg})$$
$$= 93 \text{ mm Hg}$$

TABLE 15-1 Pressure, Flow, and Resistance in the Cardiovascular System

FLOW $\propto \Delta P/R$

1. Blood flows if a pressure gradient (ΔP) is present.
2. Blood flows from areas of higher pressure to areas of lower pressure.
3. Blood flow is opposed by the resistance (R) of the system.
4. Three factors affecting resistance are radius of the blood vessels, viscosity of the blood, and length of the system [p. 473].
5. Flow is usually expressed in either liters or milliliters per minute (L/min or mL/min).
6. Velocity of flow is usually expressed in either centimeters per minute (cm/min) or millimeters per second (mm/sec).
7. The primary determinant of velocity (when flow rate is constant) is the total cross-sectional area of the vessel(s).

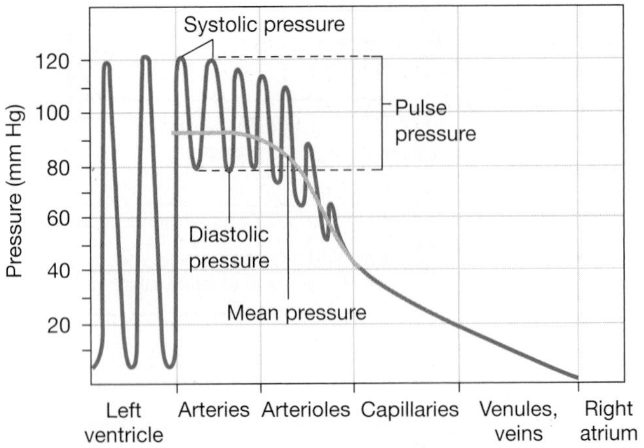

● **FIGURE 15-5** ***Pressure throughout the systemic circulation.*** Pressure waves created by ventricular contraction travel into the blood vessels. They diminish in amplitude with distance and disappear at the capillaries.

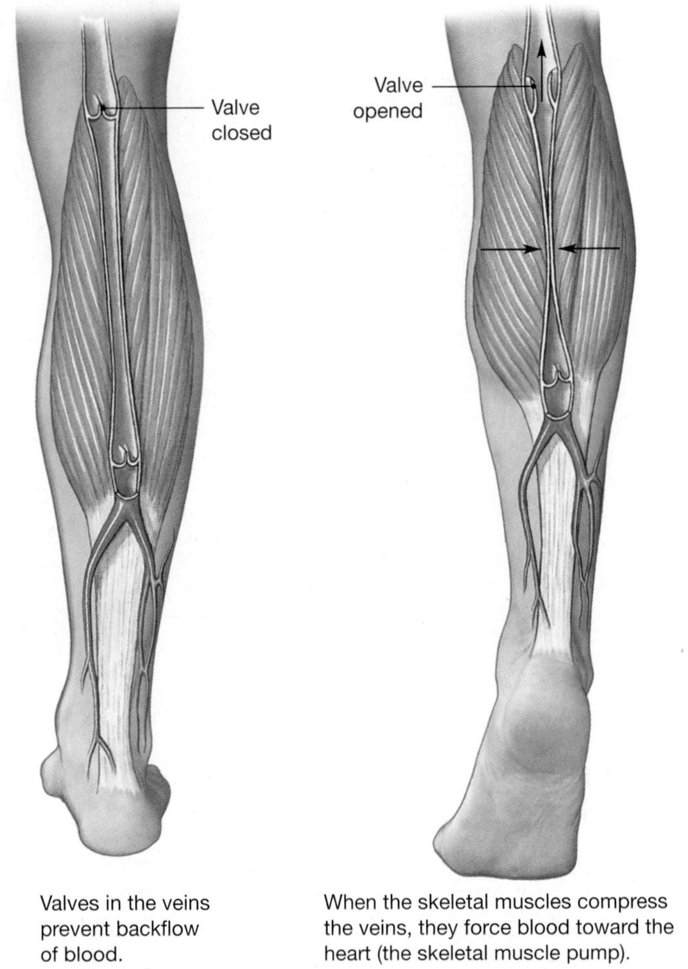

● **FIGURE 15-6** ***Valves ensure one-way flow in veins.***

Mean arterial pressure is closer to diastolic pressure than to systolic pressure because diastole lasts twice as long as systole.

Abnormally high or low arterial blood pressure can be indicative of a problem in the cardiovascular system. If blood pressure falls too low (*hypotension*), the driving force for blood flow is unable to overcome opposition by gravity. In this instance, blood flow and oxygen supply to the brain are impaired, and the person may become dizzy or faint.

On the other hand, if blood pressure is chronically elevated (a condition known as *hypertension,* or high blood pressure), high pressure on the walls of blood vessels may cause weakened areas to rupture and bleed into the tissues. If a rupture occurs in the brain, it is called a *cerebral hemorrhage* and may cause the loss of neurological function commonly called a *stroke*. If a weakened area ruptures in a major artery, such as the descending aorta, rapid blood loss into the abdominal cavity causes blood pressure to fall below the critical minimum. Without prompt treatment, rupture of a major artery is fatal.

CONCEPT CHECK

4. The formula given for calculating MAP applies to a typical resting heart rate of 60–80 beats/min. If heart rate increases, would the contribution of systolic pressure to mean arterial pressure decrease or increase, and would MAP decrease or increase?
5. Peter's systolic pressure is 112 mm Hg, and his diastolic pressure is 68 mm Hg (written 112/68). What is his pulse pressure? His mean arterial pressure?

Answers: p. 544

Blood Pressure Is Estimated by Sphygmomanometry

We estimate arterial blood pressure in the radial artery of the arm using a *sphygmomanometer,* an instrument consisting of an inflatable cuff and a pressure gauge [*sphygmus,* pulse + *manometer,* an instrument for measuring pressure of a fluid]. The cuff encircles the upper arm and is inflated until it exerts pressure higher than the systolic pressure driving arterial blood. When cuff pressure exceeds arterial pressure, blood flow into the lower arm stops (Fig. 15-7a ●).

Now pressure on the cuff is gradually released. When cuff pressure falls below systolic arterial blood pressure, blood begins to flow again. As blood squeezes through the still-compressed artery, a thumping noise called a **Korotkoff sound** can be heard with each pressure wave (Fig. 15-7b). Once the cuff pressure no longer compresses the artery, the sounds disappear (Fig. 15-7c).

The pressure at which a Korotkoff sound is first heard represents the highest pressure in the artery and is recorded as the systolic pressure. The point at which the Korotkoff sounds disappear is the lowest pressure in the artery and is recorded as the diastolic pressure. By convention, blood pressure is written as systolic pressure over diastolic pressure.

For years the "average" value for blood pressure has been stated as 120/80. Like many average physiological values, however, these numbers are subject to wide variability, both from one person to another and within a single individual from moment to moment. A systolic pressure that is consistently over 140 mm Hg at rest, or a diastolic pressure that is chronically over 90 mm Hg, is considered a sign of hypertension in an otherwise healthy person. Furthermore, the guidelines published in the

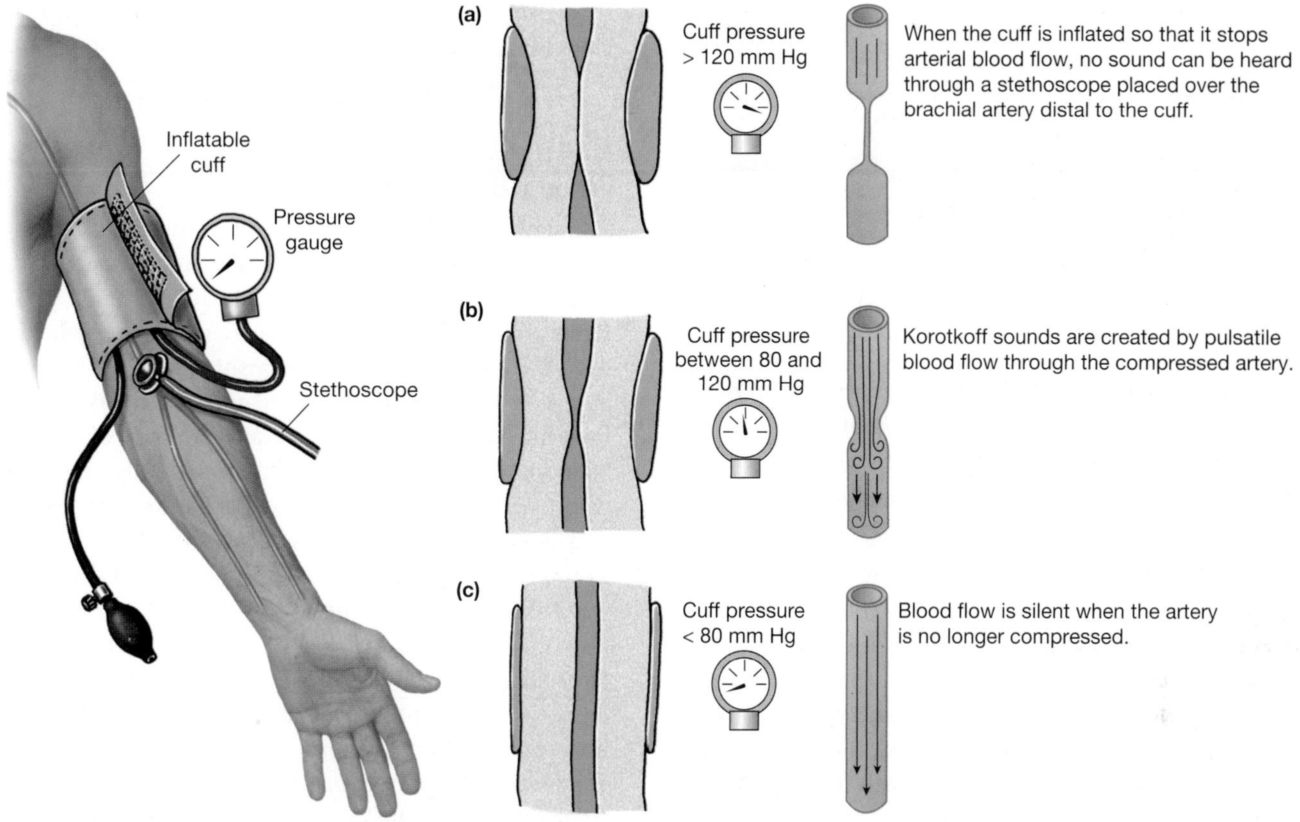
Inflatable cuff
Pressure gauge
Stethoscope
(a)
Cuff pressure > 120 mm Hg
When the cuff is inflated so that it stops arterial blood flow, no sound can be heard through a stethoscope placed over the brachial artery distal to the cuff.
(b)
Cuff pressure between 80 and 120 mm Hg
Korotkoff sounds are created by pulsatile blood flow through the compressed artery.
(c)
Cuff pressure < 80 mm Hg
Blood flow is silent when the artery is no longer compressed.

● **FIGURE 15-7** ***Measurement of arterial blood pressure.*** Arterial blood pressure is measured with a sphygmomanometer (an inflatable cuff plus a pressure gauge) and a stethoscope. The inflation pressure shown is for a person whose blood pressure is 120/80.

2003 JNC 7 Report* recommend that individuals maintain their blood pressure *below* 120/80. Persons whose systolic pressure is consistently in the range of 120–139 or whose diastolic pressure is in the range of 80–89 are now considered to be prehypertensive and should be counseled on lifestyle modification strategies to reduce their blood pressure.

Cardiac Output and Peripheral Resistance Determine Mean Arterial Pressure

Mean arterial pressure is the driving force for blood flow, but what determines mean arterial pressure? Arterial pressure is a balance between blood flow into the arteries and blood flow out of the arteries. If flow in exceeds flow out, blood collects in the arteries, and mean arterial pressure increases. If flow out exceeds flow in, mean arterial pressure falls.

Blood flow into the aorta is equal to the cardiac output of the left ventricle. Blood flow out of the arteries is influenced primarily by **peripheral resistance**, defined as the resistance to flow offered by the arterioles (Fig. 15-8 ●). Mean arterial pressure (MAP) then is proportional to cardiac output (CO) times resistance (R) of the arterioles:

$$\text{MAP} \propto \text{CO} \times R_{\text{arterioles}}$$

Let's consider how this works. If cardiac output increases, the heart pumps more blood into the arteries per unit time. If

*Seventh Report of the Joint National Committee on Prevention, Detection, Evaluation, and Treatment of High Blood Pressure, National Institutes of Health. *www.nhlbi.nih.gov/guidelines/hypertension*

RUNNING PROBLEM

Kurt's second blood pressure reading is 158/98. Dr. Cortez asks him to take his blood pressure at home daily for two weeks and then return to the doctor's office. When Kurt comes back with his diary, the story is the same: his blood pressure continues to average 160/100. After running some tests, Dr. Cortez concludes that Kurt is one of approximately 50 million adult Americans with high blood pressure, also called hypertension. If not controlled, hypertension can lead to heart failure, stroke, and kidney failure.

Question 1:
Why are people with high blood pressure at greater risk for having a hemorrhagic (or bleeding) stroke?

513 519 523 524 532 540

15

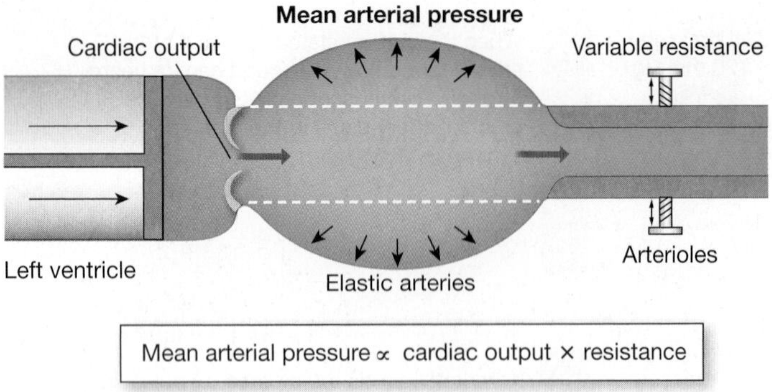

● **FIGURE 15-8** ***Mean arterial pressure is a function of cardiac output and resistance in the arterioles.*** In this model, the ventricle is represented by a syringe. The variable diameter of the arterioles is represented by adjustable screws.

resistance to blood flow out of the arteries does not change, flow into the arteries is greater than flow out, blood volume in the arteries increases, and arterial blood pressure increases.

In another example, suppose cardiac output remains unchanged but peripheral resistance increases. Flow into arteries is unchanged, but flow out is decreased. Blood again accumulates in the arteries, and the arterial pressure again increases. Most cases of hypertension are believed to be caused by increased peripheral resistance without changes in cardiac output.

Two additional factors can influence arterial blood pressure: total blood volume and the distribution of blood in the systemic circulation.

Changes in Blood Volume Affect Blood Pressure

Although the volume of the blood in the circulation is usually relatively constant, changes in blood volume can affect arterial blood pressure. If blood volume increases, blood pressure increases. When blood volume decreases, blood pressure decreases.

To understand the relationship between blood volume and pressure, think of the circulatory system as an elastic balloon filled with water. If only a small amount of water is in the balloon, little pressure is exerted on the walls, and the balloon is soft and flabby. As more water is added to the balloon, more pressure is exerted on the elastic walls. If you fill a balloon close to the bursting point, you risk popping the balloon. The best way to reduce this pressure is to remove some of the water.

Small increases in blood volume occur throughout the day due to ingestion of food and liquids, but these increases usually do not create long-lasting changes in blood pressure because of homeostatic compensations. Adjustments for increased blood volume are primarily the responsibility of the kidneys. If blood volume increases, the kidneys restore normal volume by excreting excess water in the urine (Fig. 15-9 ●).

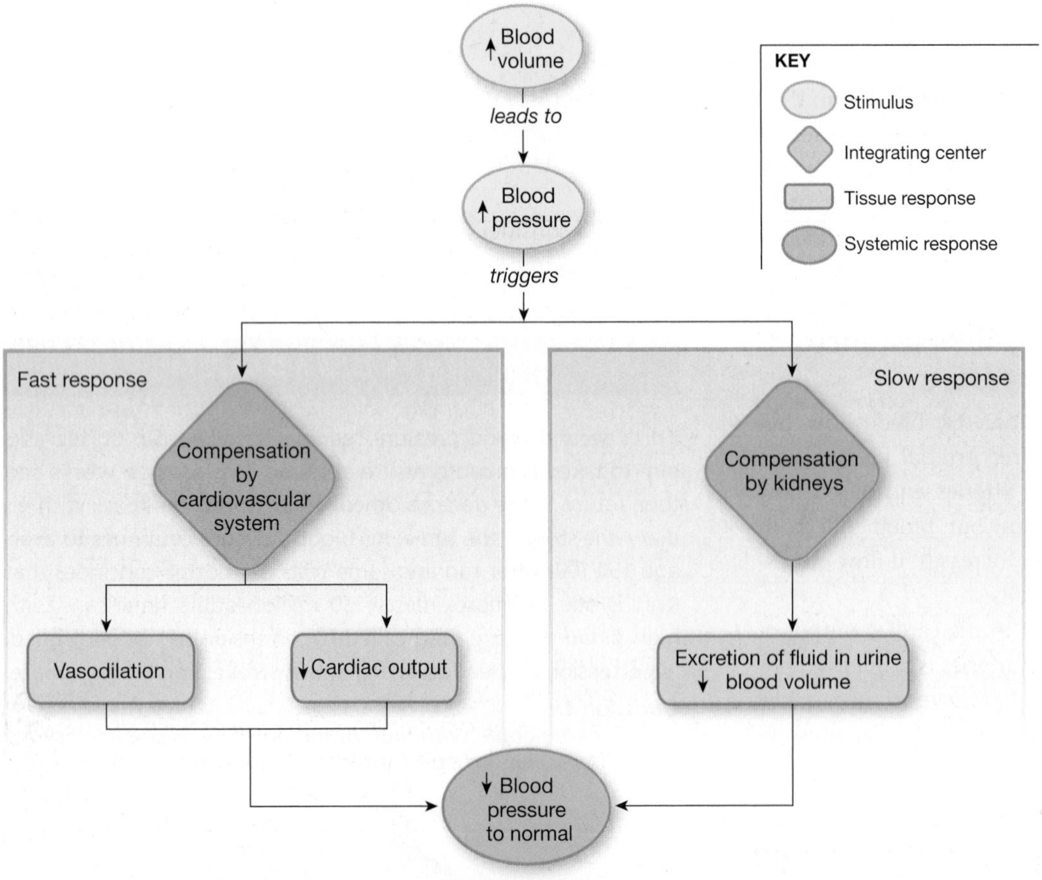

● **FIGURE 15-9** ***Blood pressure control includes rapid responses from the cardiovascular system and slower responses by the kidneys.***

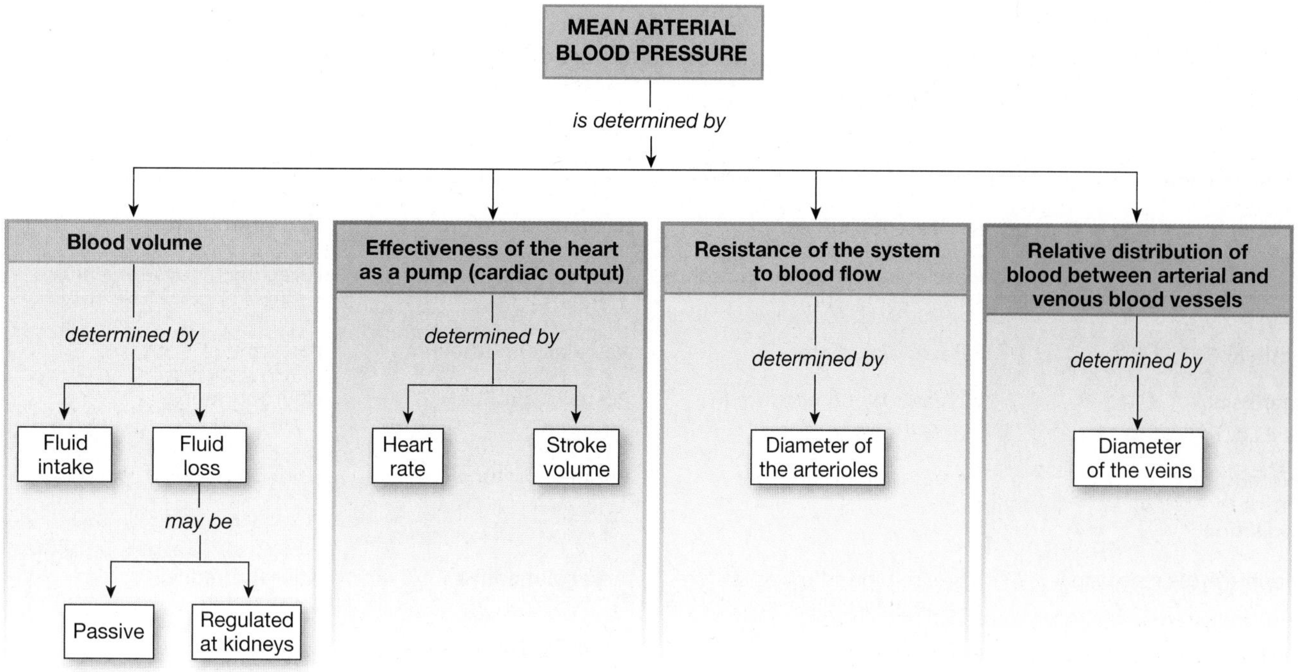

● **FIGURE 15-10** ***Factors that influence mean arterial pressure***

Compensation for decreased blood volume is more difficult and requires an integrated response from the kidneys and the cardiovascular system. If blood volume decreases, *the kidneys cannot restore the lost fluid*. The kidneys can only *conserve* blood volume and thereby prevent further decreases in blood pressure.

The only way to restore lost fluid volume is through drinking or intravenous infusions. This is an example of mass balance: volume lost to the external environment must be replaced from the external environment.

Cardiovascular compensation for decreased blood volume includes vasoconstriction and increased sympathetic stimulation of the heart [Fig. 14-31, p. 504]. However, there are limits to the effectiveness of cardiovascular compensation, and if fluid loss is too great, the body cannot maintain adequate blood pressure. Typical events that might cause significant changes in blood volume include dehydration, hemorrhage, and ingestion of a large quantity of fluid. We discuss the integrated compensation for these events in Chapter 20.

In addition to the absolute volume of blood in the cardiovascular system, the relative distribution of blood between the arterial and venous sides of the circulation can be an important factor in maintaining arterial blood pressure. Arteries are low-volume vessels that usually contain only about 11% of total blood volume at any one time. Veins, in contrast, are high-volume vessels that hold about 60% of the circulating blood volume at any one time. The veins act as a volume reservoir, holding blood that can be redistributed to the arteries if needed. When arterial blood pressure falls, increased sympathetic activity constricts veins, decreasing their holding capacity and redistributing blood to the arterial side of the circulation. Figure 15-10 ● summarizes the four key factors that influence mean arterial blood pressure.

RESISTANCE IN THE ARTERIOLES

As we saw in Chapter 14 [p. 473], resistance to blood flow (R) is directly proportional to the length of the tubing through which the fluid flows (L) and to the viscosity (η) of the fluid,

CLINICAL FOCUS

SHOCK

Shock is a broad term that refers to generalized, severe circulatory failure. Shock can arise from multiple causes: failure of the heart to maintain normal cardiac output (*cardiogenic shock*), decreased circulating blood volume (*hypovolemic shock*), bacterial toxins (*septic shock*), and miscellaneous causes, such as the massive immune reactions that cause *anaphylactic shock*. No matter what the cause, the results are similar: low cardiac output and falling peripheral blood pressure. When tissue perfusion can no longer keep up with tissue oxygen demand, the cells begin to sustain damage from inadequate oxygen and from the buildup of metabolic wastes. Once this damage occurs, a positive feedback cycle begins. The shock becomes progressively worse until it becomes irreversible, and the patient dies. The management of shock includes administration of oxygen, fluids, and norepinephrine, which stimulates vasoconstriction and increases cardiac output. If the shock arises from a cause that is treatable, such as a bacterial infection, measures must also be taken to remove the precipitating cause.

TABLE 15-2 Chemicals Mediating Vasoconstriction and Vasodilation

CHEMICAL	PHYSIOLOGICAL ROLE	SOURCE	TYPE
Vasoconstriction			
Norepinephrine (α-receptors)	Baroreceptor reflex	Sympathetic neurons	Neurotransmitter
Serotonin	Platelet aggregation, smooth muscle contraction	Neurons, digestive tract, platelets	Paracrine, neurotransmitter
Endothelin	Paracrine mediator	Vascular endothelium	Paracrine
Vasopressin	Increases blood pressure in hemorrhage	Posterior pituitary	Neurohormone
Angiotensin II	Increases blood pressure	Plasma hormone	Hormone
Vasodilation			
Epinephrine (β_2-receptors)	Increase blood flow to skeletal muscle, heart, liver	Adrenal medulla	Neurohormone
Acetylcholine	Erection reflex	Parasympathetic neurons	Neurotransmitter
Nitric oxide (NO)	Paracrine mediator	Endothelium	Paracrine
Bradykinin (via NO)	Increases blood flow	Multiple tissues	Paracrine
Adenosine	Increases blood flow to match metabolism	Hypoxic cells	Paracrine
$\downarrow O_2$, $\uparrow CO_2$, $\uparrow H^+$, $\uparrow K^+$	Increase blood flow to match metabolism	Cell metabolism	Paracrine
Histamine	Increases blood flow	Mast cells	Paracrine
Natriuretic peptides (example—ANP)	Reduce blood pressure	Atrial myocardium, brain	Hormone, neurotransmitter
Vasoactive intestinal peptide	Digestive secretion, relax smooth muscle	Neurons	Neurotransmitter, neurohormone

and inversely proportional to the fourth power of the tubing radius (r):

$$R \propto L\,\eta/r^4$$

Normally the length of the systemic circulation and the blood's viscosity are relatively constant. That leaves only the radius of the blood vessels as the primary resistance to blood flow:

$$R \propto 1/r^4$$

The arterioles are the main site of variable resistance in the systemic circulation and contribute more than 60% of the total resistance to flow in the system. Resistance in arterioles is variable because of the large amounts of smooth muscle in the arteriolar walls. When the smooth muscle contracts or relaxes, the radius of the arterioles changes.

Arteriolar resistance is influenced by both local and systemic control mechanisms:

1. *Local control of arteriolar resistance* matches tissue blood flow to the metabolic needs of the tissue. In the heart and skeletal muscle, these local controls often take precedence over reflex control by the central nervous system.
2. *Sympathetic reflexes* mediated by the CNS maintain mean arterial pressure and govern blood distribution for certain homeostatic needs, such as temperature regulation.
3. *Hormones*—particularly those that regulate salt and water excretion by the kidneys—influence blood pressure by acting directly on the arterioles and by altering autonomic reflex control.

Table 15-2 ● lists significant chemicals that mediate arteriolar resistance by producing vasoconstriction or vasodilation. In the following sections we look at the factors that influence blood flow at the tissue level.

Myogenic Autoregulation Automatically Adjusts Blood Flow

Vascular smooth muscle has the ability to regulate its own state of contraction, a process called **myogenic autoregulation**. In the absence of autoregulation, an increase in blood pressure increases blood flow through an arteriole. However, when smooth muscle fibers in the wall of the arteriole stretch because of increased blood pressure, the arteriole constricts. This vasoconstriction increases the resistance offered by the arteriole, automatically decreasing blood flow through the vessel. With this simple and direct response to pressure, arterioles regulate their own blood flow.

How does myogenic autoregulation work at the cellular level? When vascular smooth muscle cells in arterioles are stretched, mechanically gated Ca^{2+} channels in the muscle membrane open. Calcium entering the cell combines with calmodulin and activates myosin light chain kinase, which in turn increases myosin ATPase activity and crossbridge activity [p. 435], resulting in contraction.

Paracrines Alter Vascular Smooth Muscle Contraction

Local control of arteriolar resistance is an important method by which individual tissues regulate their own blood supply. Local regulation is accomplished by paracrines (including the gases O_2, CO_2, and NO) secreted by the vascular endothelium or by cells to which the arterioles are supplying blood (Tbl. 15-2).

The concentrations of many paracrines change as cells become more or less metabolically active. For example, if aerobic metabolism increases, tissue O_2 levels decrease while CO_2 production goes up. Both low O_2 and high CO_2 dilate arterioles. This vasodilation increases blood flow into the tissue, bringing additional O_2 to meet the increased metabolic demand and removing waste CO_2 (Fig. 15-11a ●). The process in which an increase in blood flow accompanies an increase in metabolic activity is known as **active hyperemia** [*hyper-*, above normal + *(h)aimia*, blood].

If blood flow to a tissue is occluded for a few seconds to a few minutes, O_2 levels fall and metabolically produced

RUNNING PROBLEM

Most hypertension is *essential hypertension,* which means high blood pressure that cannot be attributed to any particular cause. "Since your blood pressure is only mildly elevated," Dr. Cortez tells Kurt, "let's see if we can control it with lifestyle changes and a diuretic. You need to reduce salt and fat in your diet, get some exercise, and lose some weight. The diuretic will help your kidneys get rid of excess fluid." "Looks like you're asking me to turn over a whole new leaf," says Kurt. "I'll try it."

Question 2:
What is the rationale for reducing salt intake and taking a diuretic to control hypertension? (Hint: Salt causes water retention).

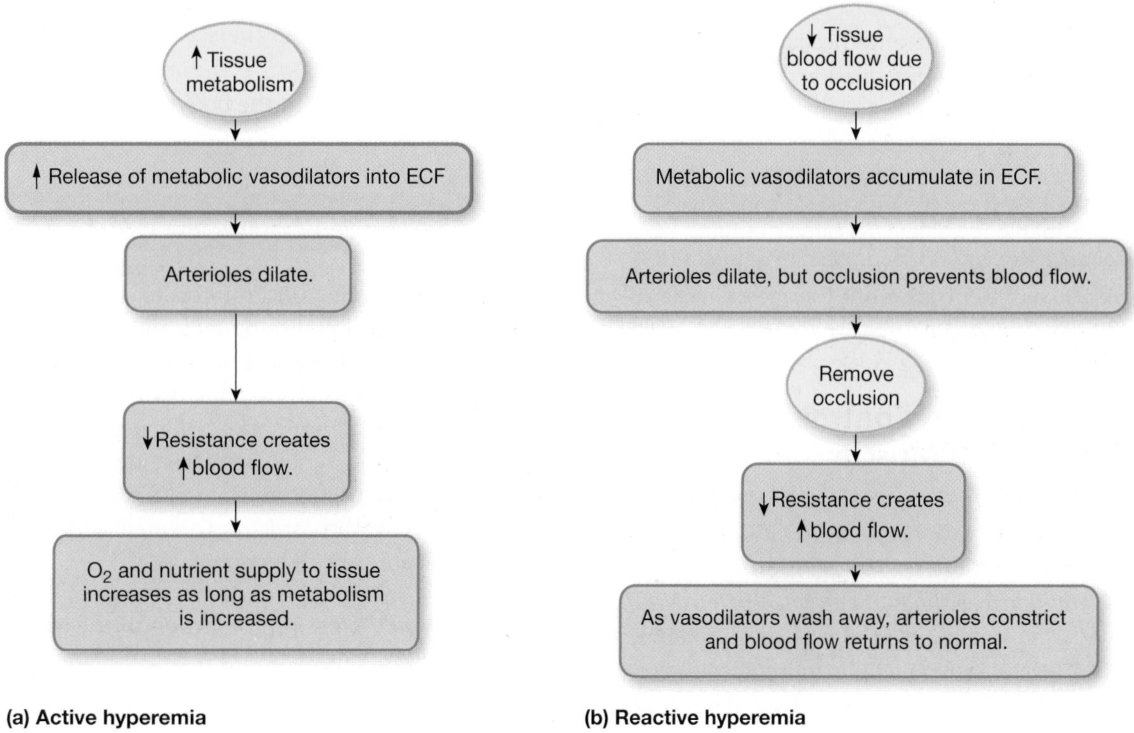

● **FIGURE 15-11** ***Hyperemia is a locally mediated increase in blood flow.***

15

paracrines such as CO_2 and H^+ accumulate in the interstitial fluid. Local *hypoxia* [*hypo-*, low + *oxia,* oxygen] causes endothelial cells to synthesize the vasodilator nitric oxide. When blood flow to the tissue resumes, the increased concentrations of NO, CO_2, and other paracrines immediately trigger significant vasodilation. As the vasodilators are metabolized or washed away by the restored tissue blood flow, the radius of the arteriole gradually returns to normal. An increase in tissue blood flow following a period of low perfusion is known as **reactive hyperemia** (Fig. 15-11b).

NO is probably best known for its role in the male erection reflex (see Ch. 26), and drugs used to treat erectile dysfunction prolong NO activity. Decreases in endogenous NO activity are suspected to play a role in several significant conditions, including hypertension and *pre-eclampsia,* the elevated blood pressure that sometimes occurs during pregnancy.

Another vasodilator paracrine is the nucleotide **adenosine**. If oxygen consumption in heart muscle exceeds the rate at which oxygen is supplied by the blood, myocardial hypoxia results. In response to low tissue oxygen, the myocardial cells release adenosine. Adenosine dilates coronary arterioles in an attempt to bring additional blood flow into the muscle.

Not all vasoactive paracrines reflect changes in metabolism. For example, *kinins* and *histamine* are potent vasodilators that play a role in inflammation. *Serotonin* (5-HT), previously mentioned as a CNS neurotransmitter [p. 277], is also a vasoconstricting paracrine released by activated platelets. When damaged blood vessels activate platelets, the subsequent serotonin-mediated vasoconstriction helps slow blood loss. Serotonin agonists called triptans (for example, *sumatriptan*) are drugs that bind to 5-HT_1 receptors and cause vasoconstriction. These drugs are used to treat migraine headaches, which are caused by inappropriate cerebral vasodilation.

CONCEPT CHECK

6. Resistance to blood flow is determined *primarily* by which? (a) blood viscosity, (b) blood volume, (c) cardiac output, (d) blood vessel diameter, or (e) blood pressure gradient (ΔP)
7. The extracellular fluid concentration of K^+ increases in exercising skeletal muscles. What effect does this increase in K^+ have on blood flow in the muscles?

Answers: p. 545

The Sympathetic Branch Controls Most Vascular Smooth Muscle

Smooth muscle contraction in arterioles is regulated by neural and hormonal signals in addition to locally produced paracrines. Among the hormones with significant vasoactive properties are *atrial natriuretic peptide* and *angiotensin II (ANG II).* These hormones also have significant effects on the kidney's excretion of ions and water, as you will learn in Chapter 20.

Most systemic arterioles are innervated by sympathetic neurons. A notable exception is arterioles involved in the erection reflex of the penis and clitoris. They are controlled indirectly by parasympathetic innervation that causes paracrine release of nitric oxide, resulting in vasodilation.

Tonic discharge of norepinephrine from sympathetic neurons helps maintain myogenic tone of arterioles (Fig. 15-12 ●). Norepinephrine binding to α-receptors on vascular smooth muscle causes vasoconstriction. If sympathetic release of norepinephrine decreases, the arterioles dilate. If sympathetic stimulation increases, the arterioles constrict.

Epinephrine from the adrenal medulla travels through the blood and binds with α-receptors, reinforcing vasoconstriction. However, α-receptors have a lower affinity for epinephrine and do not respond as strongly to it as they do to norepinephrine [p. 394].

Epinephrine also binds to β_2-receptors, found on vascular smooth muscle of heart, liver, and skeletal muscle arterioles. These receptors are not innervated and therefore respond primarily to circulating epinephrine [p. 397]. Activation of vascular β_2-receptors by epinephrine causes vasodilation.

One way to remember which arterioles have β_2-receptors is to think of a fight-or-flight response to a stressful event [p. 386]. This response includes a generalized increase in sympathetic activity, along with the release of epinephrine. Blood vessels that have β_2-receptors respond to epinephrine by vasodilating. Such β_2-mediated vasodilation enhances blood flow to the heart, skeletal muscles, and liver, tissues that are active during the fight-or-flight response. (The liver produces glucose for muscle contraction.)

During fight or flight, increased sympathetic activity at arteriolar α-receptors causes vasoconstriction. The increase in resistance diverts blood from nonessential organs, such as the gastrointestinal tract, to the skeletal muscles, liver, and heart. The map in Figure 15-13 ● summarizes the many factors that influence blood flow in the body.

RUNNING PROBLEM

After two months, Kurt returns to the doctor's office for a checkup. He has lost five pounds and is walking at least a mile daily, but his blood pressure has not changed. "I swear, I'm trying to do better," says Kurt, "but it's difficult." Because lifestyle changes and the diuretic have not lowered Kurt's blood pressure, Dr. Cortez adds an antihypertensive drug. "This drug, called an ACE inhibitor, blocks production of a chemical called angiotensin II, a powerful vasoconstrictor. This medication should bring your blood pressure back to a normal value."

Question 3:

Why would blocking the action of a vasoconstrictor lower blood pressure?

513 519 523 524 532 540

● **FIGURE 15-12** *Tonic control of arteriolar diameter*

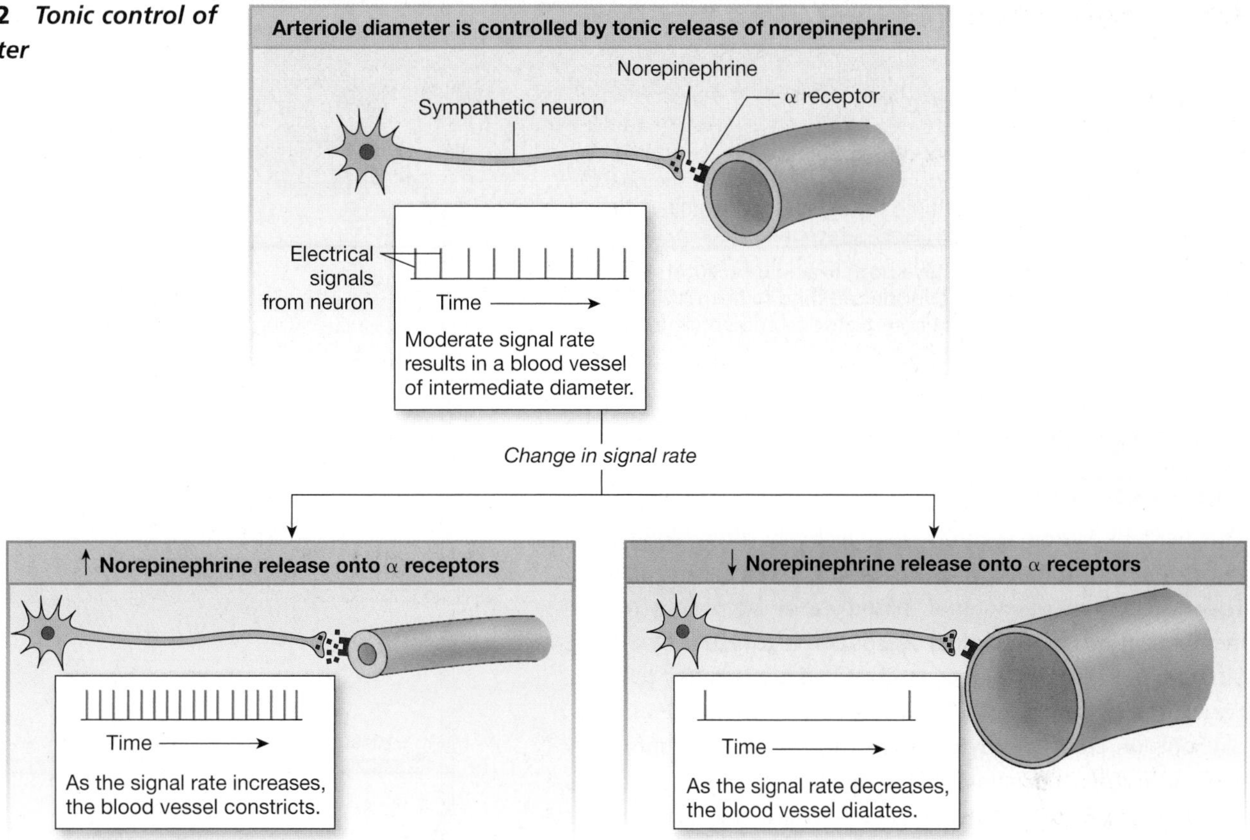

Arteriole diameter is controlled by tonic release of norepinephrine.
Norepinephrine
α receptor
Sympathetic neuron
Electrical signals from neuron
Time
Moderate signal rate results in a blood vessel of intermediate diameter.
Change in signal rate
↑ Norepinephrine release onto α receptors
Time
As the signal rate increases, the blood vessel constricts.
↓ Norepinephrine release onto α receptors
Time
As the signal rate decreases, the blood vessel dialates.

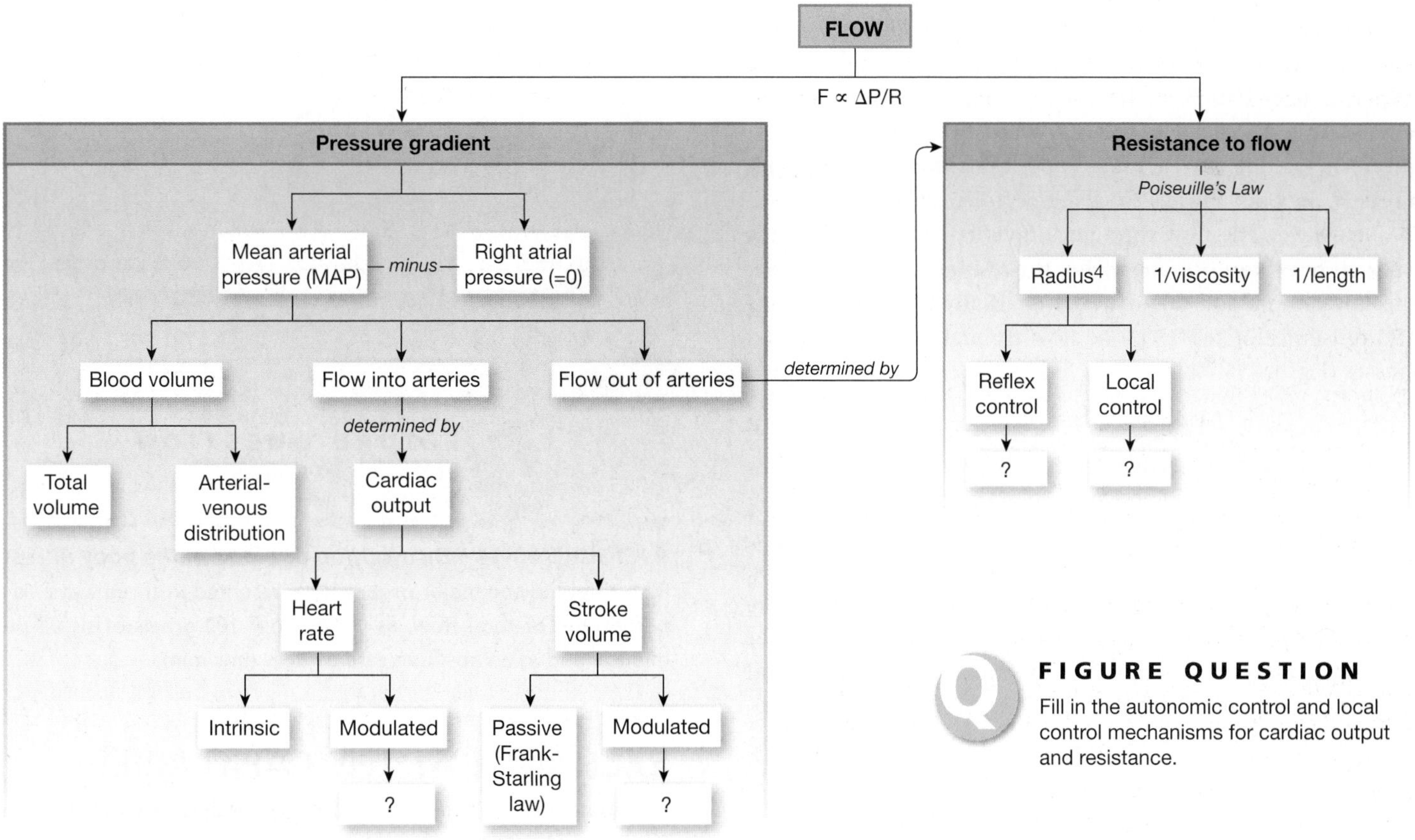

FLOW
F ∝ ΔP/R
Pressure gradient
Mean arterial pressure (MAP)
minus
Right atrial pressure (=0)
Blood volume
Flow into arteries
Flow out of arteries
determined by
Total volume
Arterial-venous distribution
determined by
Cardiac output
Heart rate
Stroke volume
Intrinsic
Modulated
?
Passive (Frank-Starling law)
Modulated
?
Resistance to flow
Poiseuille's Law
Radius4
1/viscosity
1/length
Reflex control
Local control
?
?

FIGURE QUESTION

Fill in the autonomic control and local control mechanisms for cardiac output and resistance.

● **FIGURE 15-13** *Summary map of factors influencing peripheral blood flow*

CONCEPT CHECK

8. What happens when epinephrine combines with β_1-receptors in the heart? With β_2-receptors in the heart? (*Hint:* "in the heart" is vague. The heart has multiple tissue types. Which heart tissues possess the different types of β-receptors? [p. 502])
9. Skeletal muscle arterioles have both α- and β-receptors on their smooth muscle. Epinephrine can bind to both. Will the arterioles constrict or dilate in response to epinephrine? Explain. Answers: p. 545

DISTRIBUTION OF BLOOD TO THE TISSUES

The nervous system's ability to selectively alter blood flow to organs is an important aspect of cardiovascular regulation. The distribution of systemic blood varies according to the metabolic needs of individual organs and is governed by a combination of local control mechanisms and homeostatic reflexes. For example, skeletal muscles at rest receive about 20% of cardiac output. During exercise, when the muscles use more oxygen and nutrients, they receive as much as 85%.

Blood flow to individual organs is set to some degree by the number and size of arteries feeding the organ. Figure 15-14 ● shows how blood is distributed to various organs when the body is at rest. Usually, more than two-thirds of the cardiac output is routed to the digestive tract, liver, muscles, and kidneys.

Variations in blood flow to individual tissues are possible because the arterioles in the body are arranged in parallel. In other words, all arterioles receive blood at the same time from the aorta (see Fig. 15-1). Total blood flow through *all* the arterioles of the body always equals the cardiac output.

However, the flow through individual arterioles depends on their resistance (R). The higher the resistance in an arteriole, the lower the blood flow through it. If an arteriole constricts and resistance increases, blood flow through that arteriole decreases (Fig. 15-15 ●):

$$\text{Flow}_{\text{arteriole}} \propto 1/\text{R}_{\text{arteriole}}$$

In other words, blood is diverted from high-resistance arterioles to lower-resistance arterioles. You might say that blood traveling through the arterioles takes the path of least resistance.

In a tissue, blood flow into individual capillaries can be regulated by the precapillary sphincters described earlier in the chapter. When these small bands of smooth muscle at metarteriole-capillary junctions constrict, they restrict blood flow into the capillaries (Fig. 15-16 ●). When the sphincters dilate, blood flow into the capillaries increases. This mechanism provides an additional site for local control of blood flow.

CONCEPT CHECK

10. Use Figure 15-14 to answer these questions. (a) Which tissue has the highest blood flow per unit weight? (b) Which tissue has the least blood flow, regardless of weight? Answers: p. 545

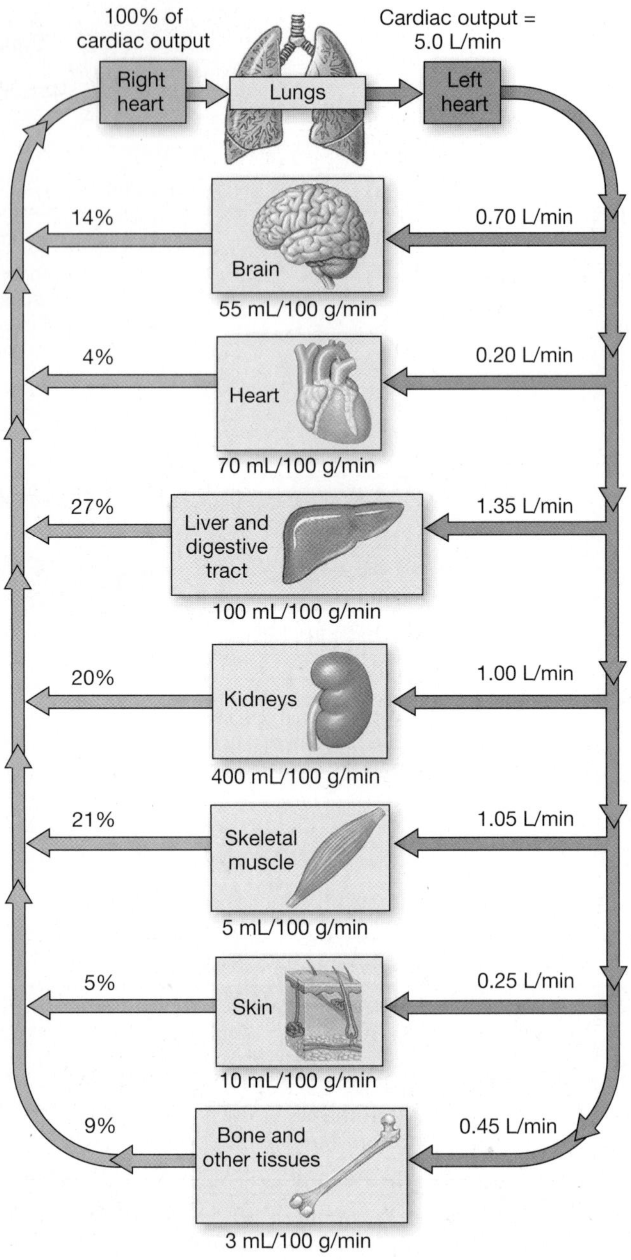

FIGURE QUESTION

What is the rate of blood flow through the lungs?

● **FIGURE 15-14** ***Distribution of blood in the body at rest.*** Blood flow to the major organs is represented in three ways: as a percentage of total flow, as volume per 100 grams of tissue per minute, and as an absolute rate of flow (in L/min).

EXCHANGE AT THE CAPILLARIES

The transport of materials around the body is only part of the function of the cardiovascular system. Once blood reaches the capillaries, the plasma and the cells exchange materials across the thin capillary walls. Most cells are located within 0.1 mm

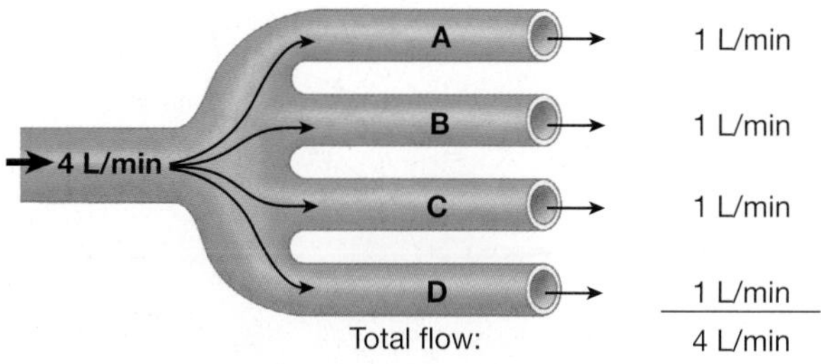

(a) Blood flow through four identical vessels (A–D) is equal. Total flow into vessels equals total flow out.

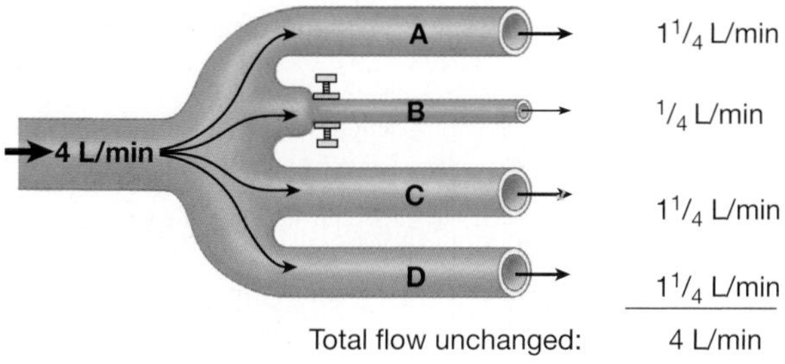

(b) When vessel B constricts, resistance of B increases and flow through B decreases. Flow diverted from B is divided among the lower-resistance vessels A, C, and D.

● **FIGURE 15-15** ***Blood flow through individual blood vessels is determined by the vessel's resistance to flow.***

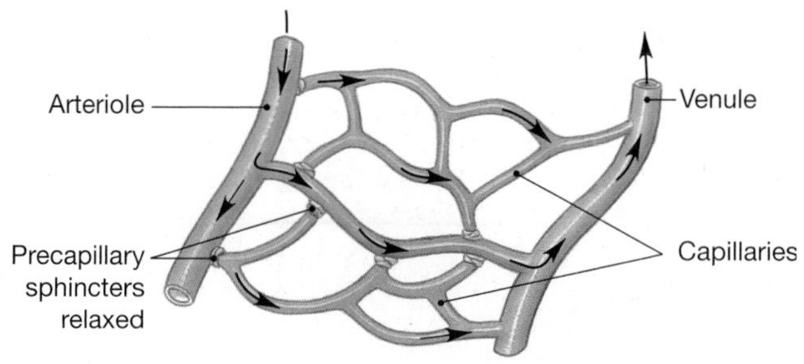

(a) When precapillary sphincters are relaxed, blood flows through all capillaries in the bed.

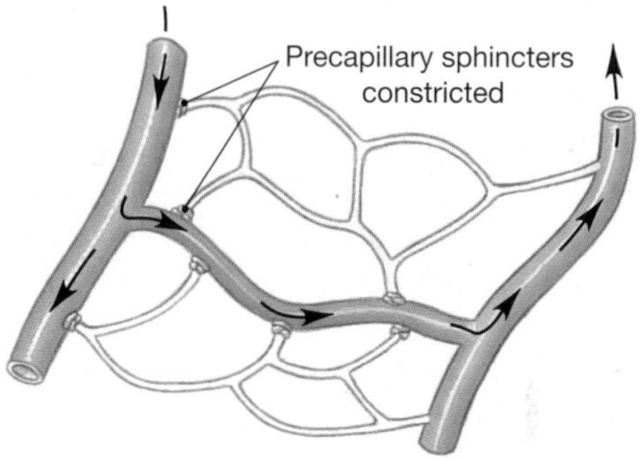

(b) If precapillary sphincters constrict, blood flow bypasses capillaries completely and flows through metarterioles.

● **FIGURE 15-16** ***Precapillary sphincters***

of the nearest capillary, and diffusion over this short distance proceeds rapidly.

The capillary density in any given tissue is directly related to the metabolic activity of the tissue's cells. Tissues with a higher metabolic rate require more oxygen and nutrients. Those tissues have more capillaries per unit area. Subcutaneous tissue and cartilage have the lowest capillary density. Muscles and glands have the highest. By one estimate, the adult human body has about 50,000 miles of capillaries, with a total exchange surface area of more than 6300 m^2, nearly the surface area of two football fields.

Capillaries have the thinnest walls of all the blood vessels, composed of a single layer of flattened endothelial cells supported on a basal lamina (Fig. 15-2). The diameter of a capillary is barely larger than that of a red blood cell, forcing the RBCs to pass through in single file. Cell junctions between the endothelial cells vary from tissue to tissue and help determine the "leakiness" of the capillary.

The most common capillaries are **continuous capillaries**, whose endothelial cells are joined to one another with leaky junctions (Fig. 15-17a ●). These capillaries are found in muscle, connective tissue, and neural tissue. The continuous capillaries of the brain have evolved to form the *blood-brain barrier*, with tight junctions that protect neural tissue from toxins that may be present in the bloodstream [p. 303].

Fenestrated capillaries [*fenestra,* window] have large pores (*fenestrae*) that allow high volumes of fluid to pass rapidly between the plasma and interstitial fluid (Fig. 15-17b). These capillaries are found primarily in the kidney and the intestine, where they are associated with absorptive transporting epithelia.

Three tissues—the bone marrow, the liver, and the spleen—do not have typical capillaries. Instead they have modified vessels called **sinusoids** that are as much as five times wider than a capillary. The sinusoid endothelium has fenestrations, and there may be gaps between the cells as well. Sinusoids are found in locations where blood cells and plasma proteins need to cross the endothelium to enter the blood. Figure 16-4c, Focus on Bone Marrow, shows blood cells leaving the bone marrow by squeezing between endothelial cells. In the liver, the sinusoidal endothelium lacks a basal lamina, which allows even more free exchange between plasma and interstitial fluid.

15

Velocity of Blood Flow Is Lowest in the Capillaries

In Chapter 14 you learned that at a constant flow rate, velocity of flow is higher in a smaller vessel than in a larger vessel [p. 475]. From this, you might conclude that blood moves very rapidly through the capillaries because they are the smallest blood vessels. However, the primary determinant for velocity is not the diameter of an individual capillary but the *total cross-sectional area* of *all* the capillaries.

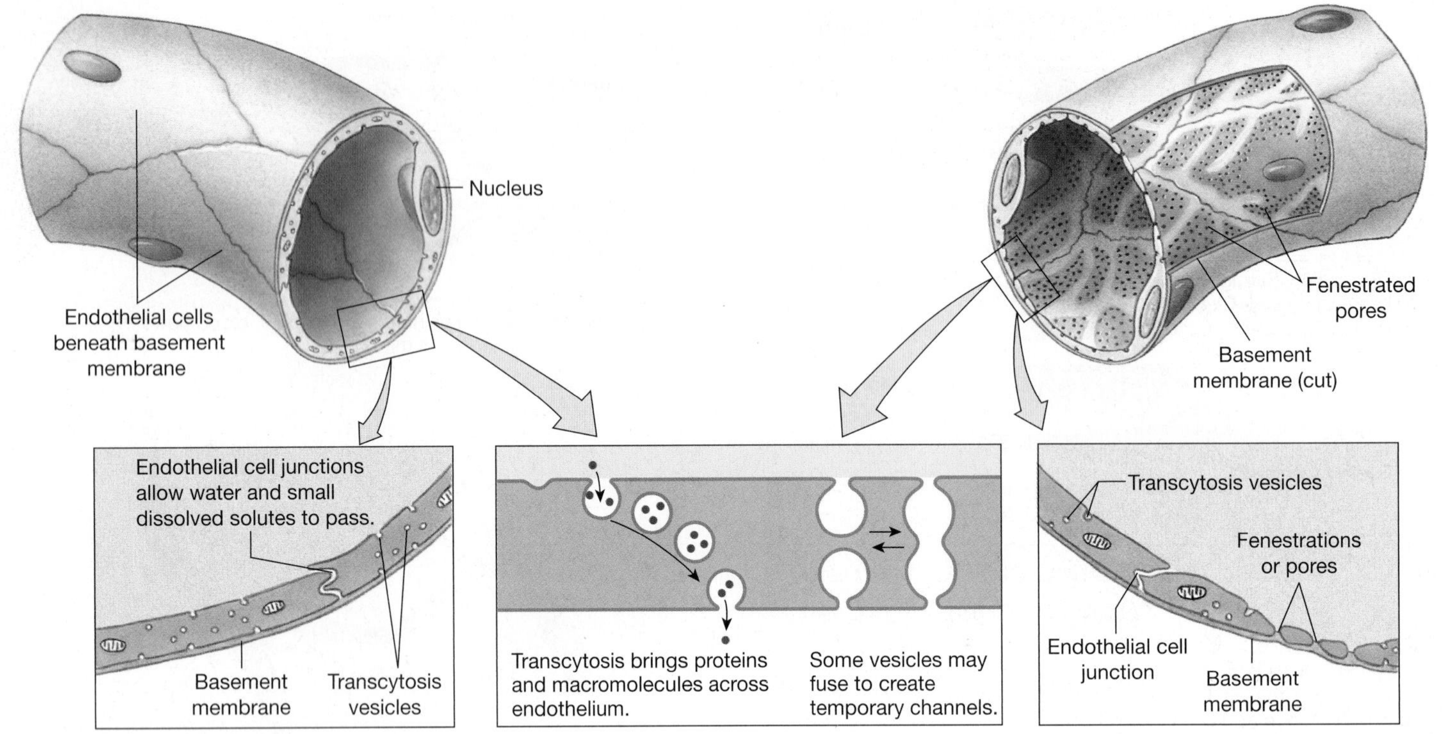

(a) Continuous capillaries have leaky junctions.

(b) Fenestrated capillaries have large pores.

● **FIGURE 15-17** ***The two types of capillaries***

What is total cross-sectional area? Imagine circles representing cross sections of all the capillaries placed edge to edge, and you have it. For the capillaries, those circles would cover an area much larger than the total cross-sectional areas of all the arteries and veins combined. Therefore, because total cross-sectional area of the capillaries is so large, the velocity of flow through them is low.

Figure 15-18 ● compares cross-sectional areas of different parts of the systemic circulation with the velocity of blood flow in each part. The fastest flow is in the relatively small-diameter arterial system. The slowest flow is in the capillaries and venules, which collectively have the largest cross-sectional area. The low velocity of flow through capillaries is a useful characteristic that allows enough time for diffusion to go to equilibrium [p. 136].

Most Capillary Exchange Takes Place by Diffusion and Transcytosis

Exchange between the plasma and interstitial fluid takes place either by movement between endothelial cells (the *paracellular pathway*) or by movement through the cells (*endothelial transport*). Smaller dissolved solutes and gases move by diffusion between or through the cells, depending on their lipid solubility [p. 139]. Larger solutes and proteins move mostly by vesicular transport [p. 152].

The diffusion rate for dissolved solutes is determined primarily by the concentration gradient between the plasma and the interstitial fluid. Oxygen and carbon dioxide diffuse freely across the thin endothelium. Their plasma concentrations reach equilibrium with the interstitial fluid and cells by the time blood reaches the venous end of the capillary. In capillaries with leaky cell junctions, most small dissolved solutes can diffuse freely between the cells or through the fenestrae.

In continuous capillaries, blood cells and most plasma proteins are unable to pass through the junctions between endothelial cells. However, we know that proteins do move from plasma to interstitial fluid and vice versa. In most capillaries, larger molecules (including selected proteins) are transported across the endothelium by *transcytosis* [p. 157]. The endothelial cell surface appears dotted with numerous *caveolae* and noncoated pits that become vesicles for transcytosis. It appears that in some capillaries, chains of vesicles fuse to create open channels that extend across the endothelial cell (Fig. 15-17).

Capillary Filtration and Absorption Take Place by Bulk Flow

A third form of capillary exchange is bulk flow into and out of the capillary. **Bulk flow** refers to the mass movement of fluid as the result of hydrostatic or osmotic pressure gradients. If the direction of bulk flow is into the capillary, the fluid movement is called **absorption**. If the direction of flow is out of the capillary, the fluid movement is known as **filtration**. Capillary filtration is caused by hydrostatic pressure that forces fluid out of the capillary through leaky cell junctions. As an analogy, think of garden "soaker" hoses whose perforated walls allow water to ooze out.

Most capillaries show a transition from net filtration at the arterial end to net absorption at the venous end. There are some exceptions to this rule, though. Capillaries in part of the kidney filter fluid along their entire length, for instance, and some capillaries in the intestine are only absorptive, picking up digested nutrients that have been transported into the interstitial fluid from the lumen of the intestine.

Two forces regulate bulk flow in the capillaries. One is hydrostatic pressure, the lateral pressure component of blood flow that pushes fluid out through the capillary pores [p. 472], and the other is osmotic pressure [p. 159]. These forces are sometimes called *Starling forces,* after the English physiologist E. H. Starling, who first described them (the same Starling as in the Frank-Starling law of the heart).

Osmotic pressure is determined by solute concentration of a compartment. The main solute difference between plasma and interstitial fluid is due to proteins, which are present in the plasma but mostly absent from interstitial fluid. The osmotic pressure created by the presence of these proteins is known as **colloid osmotic pressure** (π), also called *oncotic pressure*. Colloid osmotic pressure is *not* equivalent to the total osmotic pressure in a capillary. It is simply a measure of the osmotic pressure created by proteins. Because the capillary endothelium is freely permeable to ions and other solutes in the plasma and interstitial fluid, these other solutes do not contribute to the osmotic gradient.

Colloid osmotic pressure is higher in the plasma (π_{cap} = 25 mm Hg) than in the interstitial fluid (π_{IF} = 0 mm). Therefore, the osmotic gradient favors water movement by osmosis from the interstitial fluid into the plasma, represented by the red vertical arrows in Figure 15-19a ●. For the purposes of our discussion, colloid osmotic pressure is constant along the length of the capillary, at π_{cap} = 25 mm Hg.

Capillary hydrostatic pressure (P_{cap}), by contrast, decreases along the length of the capillary as energy is lost to friction. Average values for capillary hydrostatic pressure, shown in Figure 15-19a, are 32 mm Hg at the arterial end of a capillary and 15 mm Hg at the venous end. The hydrostatic pressure of the interstitial fluid (P_{IF}) is very low, and so we consider it to be essentially zero. This means that water movement due to hydrostatic pressure is directed out of the capillary, as denoted by the blue vertical arrows in Figure 15-19a, with the pressure gradient decreasing from the arterial end to the venous end.

Net fluid flow across the capillary is determined by the difference between the hydrostatic pressure gradient (ΔP) favoring filtration and the colloid osmotic pressure gradient favoring absorption:

$$\text{Filtration } (P_{out}) = \text{hydrostatic } \Delta P = P_{cap} - P_{IF}$$

$$\text{Absorption } (\pi_{in}) = \text{colloid osmotic } \Delta P = \pi_{IF} - \pi_{cap}$$

$$\text{Net pressure} = \text{hydrostatic } \Delta P + \text{colloid osmotic } \Delta P$$

$$= P_{out} + \pi_{in}$$

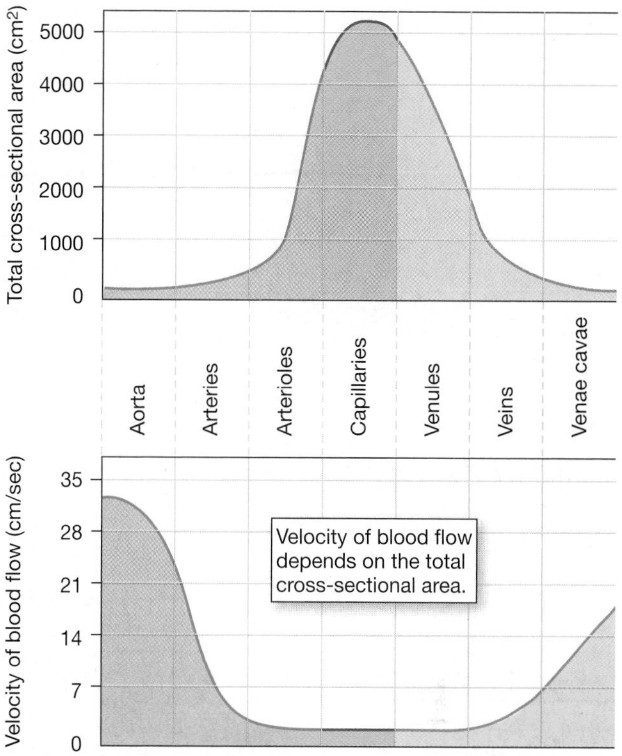

GRAPH QUESTION

(a) Is velocity directly proportional to or inversely proportional to cross-sectional area?

(b) What effect does changing only the cross-sectional area have on flow rate?

● **FIGURE 15-18** ***Velocity of flow depends on total cross-sectional area of the vessels.***

If we assume that the interstitial hydrostatic and colloid osmotic pressures are zero, as discussed above, then we see the following values at the arterial end of a capillary:

$$\text{Net pressure}_{\text{arterial end}} = (32 \text{ mm Hg} - 0) + (0 - 25 \text{ mm Hg})$$

$$= 32 - 25 \text{ mm Hg} = 7 \text{ mm Hg}$$

At the arterial end P_{out} is greater than π_{in}, so the net pressure is 7 mm Hg of filtration pressure. At the venous end, where capillary hydrostatic pressure is less:

$$\text{Net } P_{\text{venous end}} = (15 \text{ mm Hg} - 0) + (0 - 25 \text{ mm Hg})$$

$$= 15 - 25 \text{ mm Hg} = -10 \text{ mm Hg}$$

Here π_{in} is greater than P_{out}, and the net pressure is 10 mm Hg favoring absorption. (A negative net pressure indicates absorption.)

Fluid movement down the length of a capillary is shown in Figure 15-19a. At the arterial end there is net filtration, and at the venous end there is net absorption. If the point at which filtration equals absorption occurred in the middle of the capillary, there would be no net movement of fluid. All volume

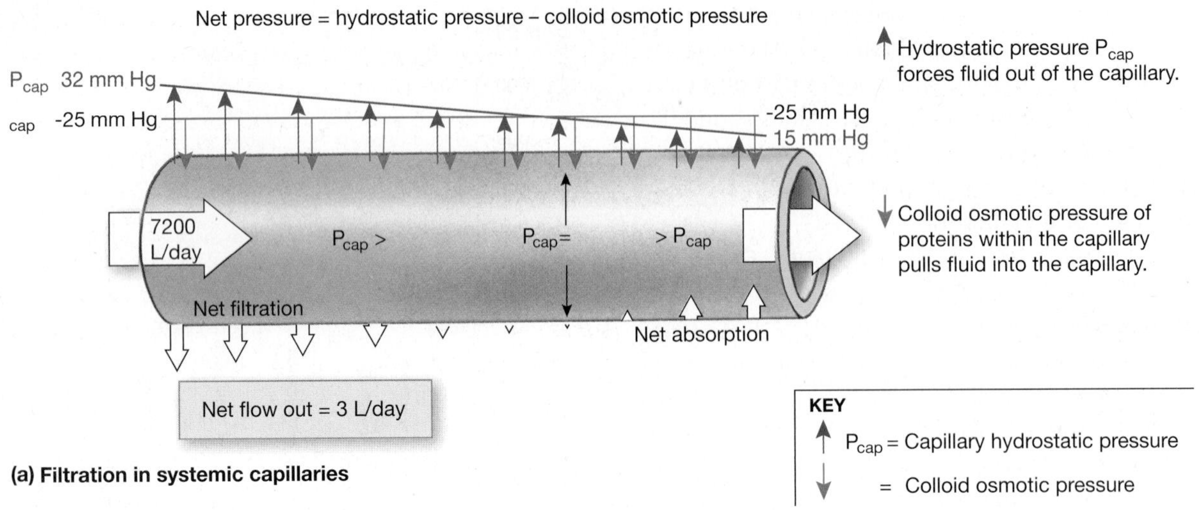

Net pressure = hydrostatic pressure – colloid osmotic pressure
Hydrostatic pressure P_{cap} forces fluid out of the capillary.
P_{cap} 32 mm Hg
cap -25 mm Hg
-25 mm Hg
15 mm Hg
7200 L/day
P_{cap} >
P_{cap}=
> P_{cap}
Colloid osmotic pressure of proteins within the capillary pulls fluid into the capillary.
Net filtration
Net absorption
Net flow out = 3 L/day
KEY
P_{cap} = Capillary hydrostatic pressure
= Colloid osmotic pressure

(a) Filtration in systemic capillaries

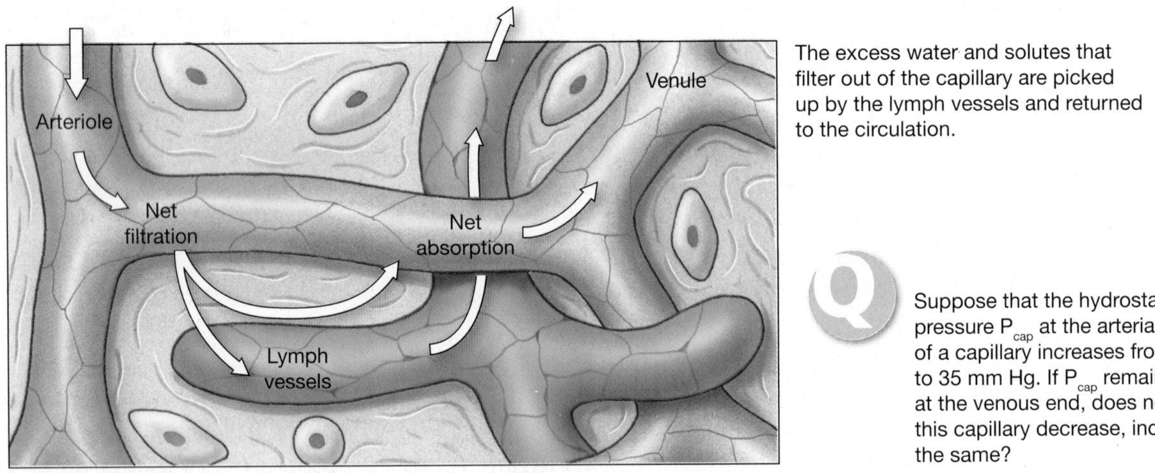

Venule
Arteriole
Net filtration
Net absorption
Lymph vessels
The excess water and solutes that filter out of the capillary are picked up by the lymph vessels and returned to the circulation.

(b) Relationship between capillaries and lymph vessels

Suppose that the hydrostatic pressure P_{cap} at the arterial end of a capillary increases from 32 mm Hg to 35 mm Hg. If P_{cap} remains 15 mm Hg at the venous end, does net filtration in this capillary decrease, increase, or stay the same?

● **FIGURE 15-19** ***Fluid exchange at a capillary.*** A net average of 3 L/day of fluid filters out of the capillaries.

that was filtered at the arterial end would be absorbed at the venous end. However, filtration is usually greater than absorption, resulting in bulk flow of fluid out of the capillary into the interstitial space.

By most estimates, that bulk flow amounts to about 3 liters per day, which is the equivalent of the entire plasma volume! If this filtered fluid could not be returned to the plasma, the blood would turn into a sludge of blood cells and proteins. Restoring fluid lost from the capillaries to the circulatory system is one of the functions of the lymphatic system, which we discuss next.

CONCEPT CHECK

11. A person with liver disease loses the ability to synthesize plasma proteins. What happens to the colloid osmotic pressure of his blood? What happens to the balance between filtration and absorption in his capillaries?
12. Why did this discussion refer to the colloid osmotic pressure of the plasma rather than the osmolarity of the plasma?

Answers: p. 545

THE LYMPHATIC SYSTEM

The vessels of the lymphatic system interact with three other physiological systems: the cardiovascular system, the digestive system, and the immune system. Functions of the lymphatic system include (1) returning fluid and proteins filtered out of the capillaries to the circulatory system, (2) picking up fat absorbed at the small intestine and transferring it to the circulatory system, and (3) serving as a filter to help capture and destroy foreign pathogens. In this discussion we focus on the role of the lymphatic system in fluid transport. We discuss the other two functions in connection with digestion (Ch. 21) and immunity (Ch. 24).

The lymphatic system allows the one-way movement of interstitial fluid from the tissues into the circulation. Blind-end lymph vessels (*lymph capillaries*) lie close to all blood capillaries except those in the kidney and central nervous system (Fig. 15-19b). The smallest lymph vessels are composed of a single layer of flattened endothelium that is even thinner than the capillary endothelium.

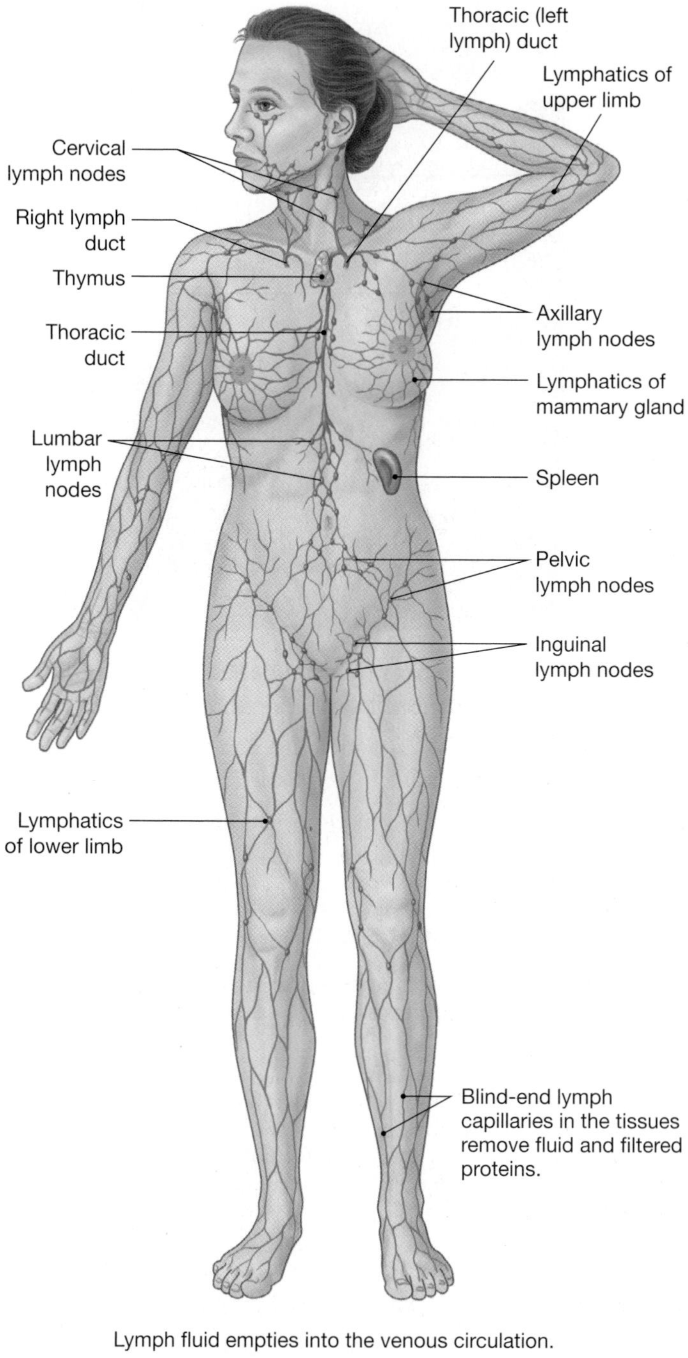
Thoracic (left lymph) duct
Lymphatics of upper limb
Cervical lymph nodes
Right lymph duct
Thymus
Thoracic duct
Axillary lymph nodes
Lymphatics of mammary gland
Lumbar lymph nodes
Spleen
Pelvic lymph nodes
Inguinal lymph nodes
Lymphatics of lower limb
Blind-end lymph capillaries in the tissues remove fluid and filtered proteins.
Lymph fluid empties into the venous circulation.

● **FIGURE 15-20** ***The lymphatic system.***

The walls of these tiny lymph vessels are anchored to the surrounding connective tissue by fibers that hold the thin-walled vessels open. Large gaps between cells allow fluid, interstitial proteins, and particulate matter such as bacteria to be swept into the lymph vessels, also called lymphatics, by bulk flow. Once inside the lymphatics, this clear fluid is called simply **lymph**.

Lymph vessels in the tissues join one another to form larger lymphatic vessels that progressively increase in size (Fig. 15-20 ●). These vessels have a system of semilunar valves, similar to valves in the venous circulation. The largest lymph ducts empty into the venous circulation just under the collarbones, where the left and right subclavian veins join the internal jugular veins. At intervals along the way, vessels enter **lymph nodes**, bean-shaped nodules of tissue with a fibrous outer capsule and an internal collection of immunologically active cells, including lymphocytes and macrophages.

The lymphatic system has no single pump like the heart. Lymph flow depends primarily on waves of contraction of smooth muscle in the walls of the larger lymph vessels. Flow is aided by contractile fibers in the endothelial cells, by the one-way valves, and by external compression created by skeletal muscles.

The skeletal muscle pump plays a significant role in lymph flow, as you know if you have ever injured a wrist or ankle. An immobilized limb frequently swells from the accumulation of fluid in the interstitial space, a condition known as **edema** [*oidema,* swelling]. Patients with edema in an injured limb are told to elevate the limb above the level of the heart so gravity assists lymph flow back to the blood.

An important reason for returning filtered fluid to the circulation is the recycling of plasma proteins. The body must maintain a low protein concentration in the interstitial fluid because colloid osmotic pressure is the only significant force that opposes capillary hydrostatic pressure. If proteins move from the plasma to the interstitial fluid, the osmotic pressure gradient that opposes filtration decreases. With less opposition to capillary hydrostatic pressure, additional fluid moves into the interstitial space.

Inflammation is an example of a situation in which the balance of colloid osmotic and hydrostatic pressures is disrupted. Histamine released in the inflammatory response makes capillary walls leakier and allows proteins to escape from the plasma into the interstitial fluid. The local swelling that accompanies a region of inflammation is an example of edema caused by redistribution of proteins from the plasma to the interstitial fluid.

15

Edema Results from Alterations in Capillary Exchange

Edema is a sign that normal exchange between the circulatory system and the lymphatics has been disrupted. Edema usually arises from one of two causes: (1) inadequate drainage of lymph or (2) blood capillary filtration that greatly exceeds capillary absorption.

Inadequate lymph drainage occurs with obstruction of the lymphatic system, particularly at the lymph nodes. Parasites, cancer, or fibrotic tissue growth caused by therapeutic radiation can block the movement of lymph through the system. For example, *elephantiasis* is a chronic condition marked by gross enlargement of the legs and lower appendages when parasites block the lymph vessels. Lymph drainage may also be impaired

RUNNING PROBLEM

Another few weeks go by, and Kurt again returns to Dr. Cortez for a checkup. Kurt's blood pressure is finally closer to the normal range and has been averaging 135/87. "But, Doc, can you give me something for this dry, hacking cough I've been having? I don't feel bad, but it's driving me nuts." Dr. Cortez explains that a dry cough is an occasional side effect of taking ACE inhibitors. "It is more of a nuisance than anything else, but let's change your medicine. I'd like to try you on a calcium channel blocker instead of the ACE inhibitor."

Question 4:
How do calcium channel blockers lower blood pressure?

if lymph nodes are removed during surgery, a common procedure in the diagnosis and treatment of cancer.

Factors that disrupt the normal balance between capillary filtration and absorption include:

1. *An increase in capillary hydrostatic pressure.* Increased hydrostatic pressure is usually indicative of elevated venous pressure. An increase in arterial pressure is generally not noticeable at the capillaries because of autoregulation of pressure in the arterioles.

   One common cause of increased venous pressure is *heart failure,* a condition in which one ventricle loses pumping power and can no longer pump all the blood sent to it by the other ventricle (see Ch. 14 Concept Check #30 on p. 500). For example, if the right ventricle begins to fail but the left ventricle maintains its cardiac output, blood accumulates in the systemic circulation. Blood pressure rises first in the right atrium, then in the veins and capillaries draining into the right side of the heart. When capillary hydrostatic pressure increases, filtration greatly exceeds absorption, leading to edema.
2. *A decrease in plasma protein concentration.* Plasma protein concentrations may decrease as a result of severe malnutrition or liver failure. The liver is the main site for plasma protein synthesis.
3. *An increase in interstitial proteins.* As discussed earlier, excessive leakage of proteins out of the blood decreases the colloid osmotic pressure gradient and increases net capillary filtration.

On occasion, changes in the balance between filtration and absorption help the body maintain homeostasis. For example, if arterial blood pressure falls, capillary hydrostatic pressure also decreases. This change increases fluid absorption. If blood pressure falls low enough, there is net absorption in the capillaries rather than net filtration. This passive mechanism helps maintain blood volume in situations in which blood pressure is very low, such as hemorrhage or severe dehydration.

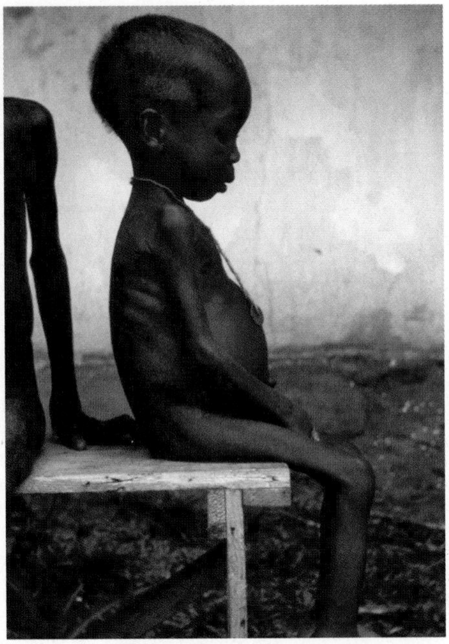

● **FIGURE 15-21** ***Ascites (abdominal edema) in a child with protein malnutrition.*** The African word for protein malnutrition is *kwashiorkor*.

CONCEPT CHECK

13. If the left ventricle fails to pump normally, blood backs up into what set of blood vessels? Where would you expect edema to occur?
14. Malnourished children who have inadequate protein in their diet often have grotesquely swollen bellies. This condition, which can be described as edema of the abdomen, is called *ascites* (Fig. 15-21 ●). Use the information you have just learned about capillary filtration to explain why malnutrition causes ascites.

Answers: p. 545

REGULATION OF BLOOD PRESSURE

The central nervous system coordinates the reflex control of blood pressure. The main integrating center is in the medulla oblongata. Because of the difficulty of studying neural networks in the brain, however, we still know relatively little about the nuclei, neurotransmitters, and interneurons of the **medullary cardiovascular control center**.

The Baroreceptor Reflex Controls Blood Pressure

The primary function of the cardiovascular control center is to maintain adequate blood flow to the brain and heart. Sensory input to this integrating center comes from a variety of peripheral sensory receptors. Stretch-sensitive mechanoreceptors known as **baroreceptors** are located in the walls of the carotid arteries and aorta (Fig. 15-22 ●), where they can

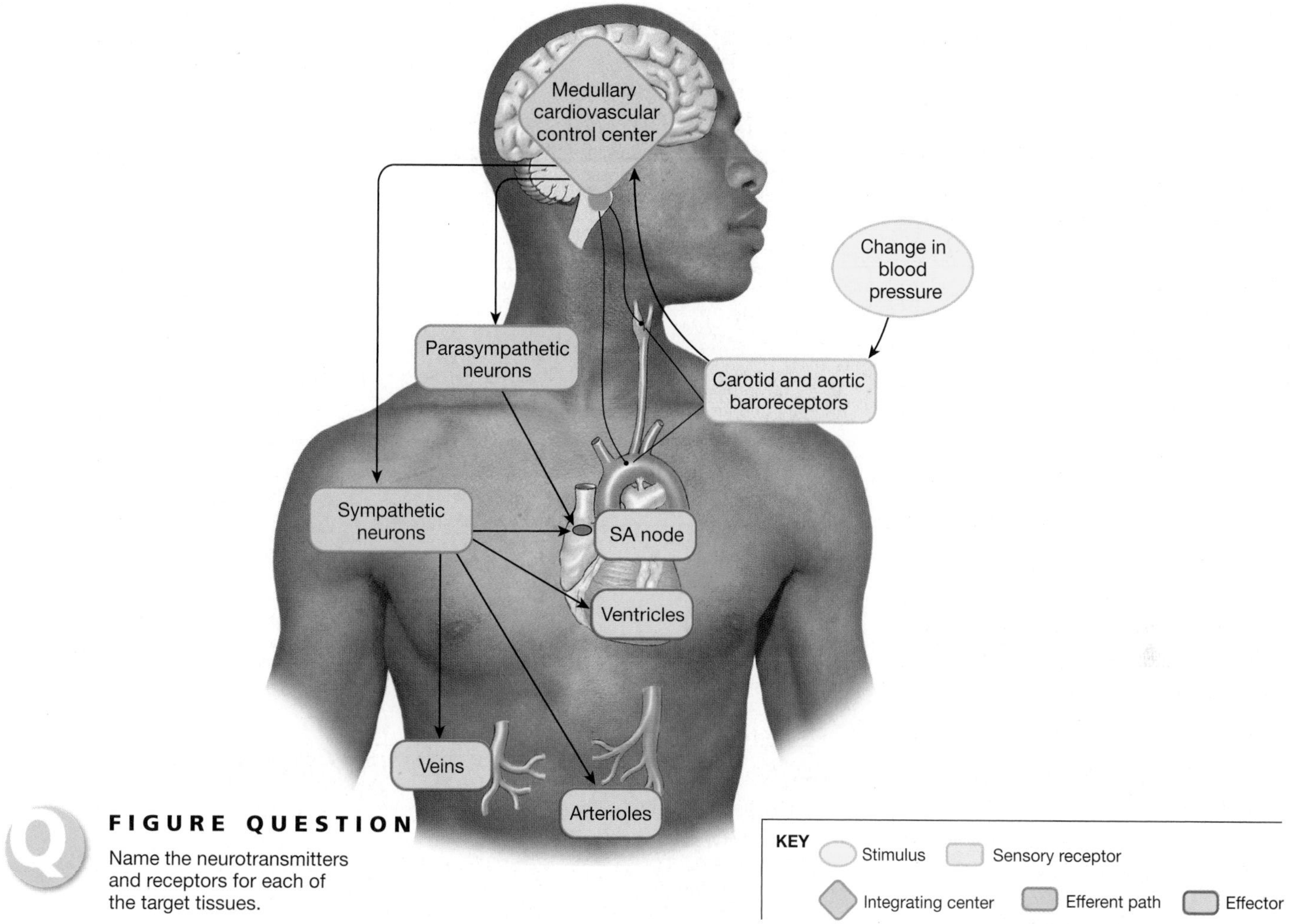

● **FIGURE 15-22** ***Components of the baroreceptor reflex***

monitor the pressure of blood flowing to the brain (carotid baroreceptors) and to the body (aortic baroreceptors). The carotid and aortic baroreceptors are tonically active stretch receptors that fire action potentials continuously at normal blood pressures.

The primary reflex pathway for homeostatic control of blood pressure is the **baroreceptor reflex**. When increased blood pressure in the arteries stretches the baroreceptor membrane, firing rate of the receptor increases. If blood pressure falls, the firing rate of the receptor decreases.

Action potentials from the baroreceptors travel to the medullary cardiovascular control center via sensory neurons. The cardiovascular control center integrates the sensory input and initiates an appropriate response. The response of the baroreceptor reflex is quite rapid: changes in cardiac output and peripheral resistance occur within two heartbeats of the stimulus.

Efferent output from the cardiovascular control center is carried via both sympathetic and parasympathetic autonomic neurons. Peripheral resistance is under tonic sympathetic control, with increased sympathetic discharge causing vasoconstriction.

Heart function is regulated by antagonistic control. Increased sympathetic activity increases heart rate at the SA node, shortens conduction time through the AV node, and enhances the force of myocardial contraction. Increased parasympathetic activity slows heart rate but has only a small effect on ventricular contraction.

The baroreceptor reflex is summarized in Figure 15-23 ●. Baroreceptors increase their firing rate as blood pressure increases, activating the medullary cardiovascular control center. In response, the cardiovascular control center increases parasympathetic activity and decreases sympathetic activity to slow down the heart. When heart rate falls, cardiac output falls. In the circulation, decreased sympathetic activity causes dilation of the arterioles, allowing more blood to flow out of the arteries. The combination of reduced cardiac output and decreased peripheral resistance lowers the mean arterial blood pressure.

Cardiovascular function can be modulated by input from peripheral receptors other than the baroreceptors. For example, arterial chemoreceptors activated by low blood oxygen levels increase cardiac output. The cardiovascular control center also has reciprocal communication with centers in the medulla that control breathing.

15

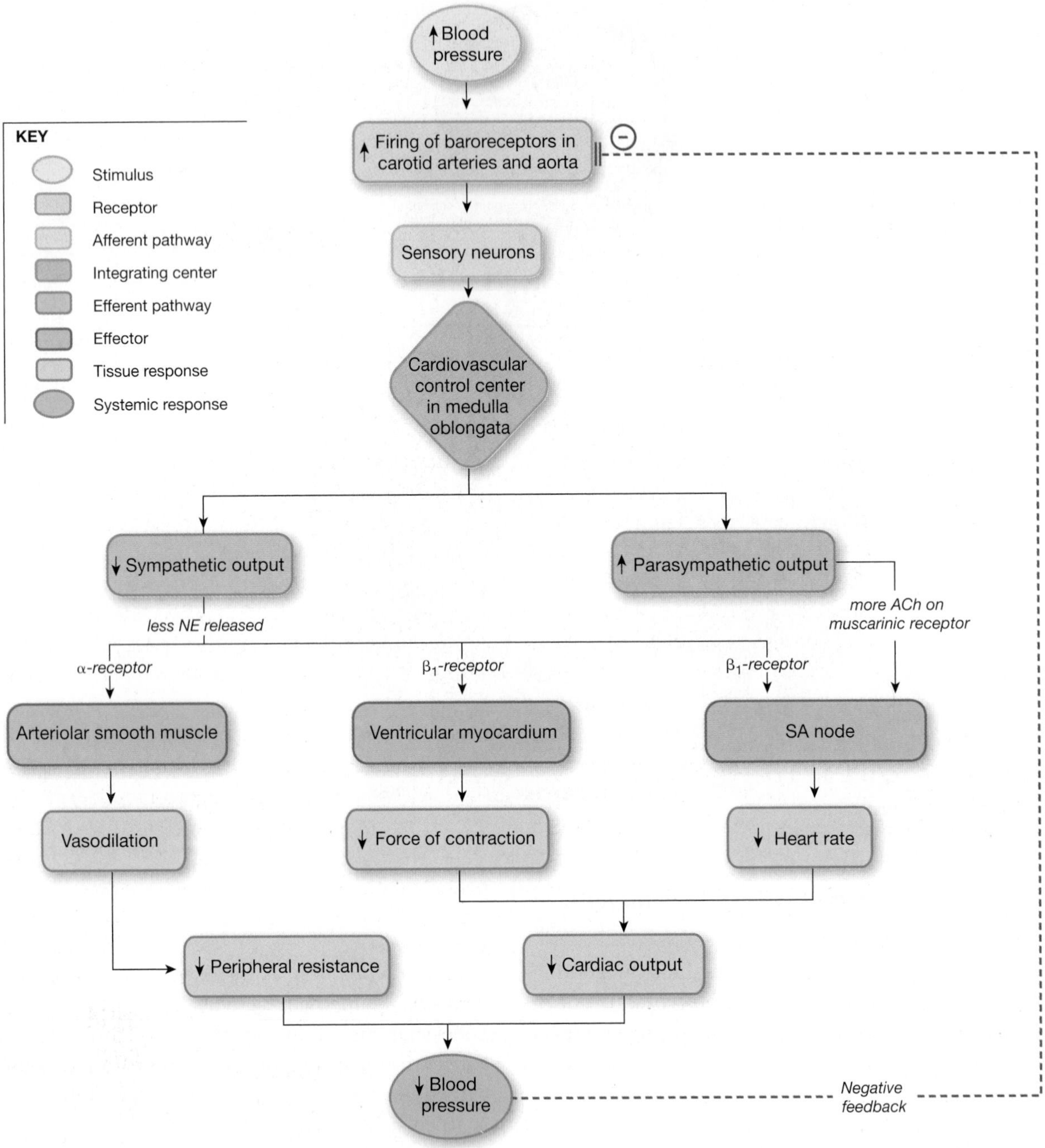
↑Blood pressure
↑ Firing of baroreceptors in carotid arteries and aorta
KEY
Stimulus
Receptor
Afferent pathway
Integrating center
Efferent pathway
Effector
Tissue response
Systemic response
Sensory neurons
Cardiovascular control center in medulla oblongata
↓ Sympathetic output
↑ Parasympathetic output
less NE released
more ACh on muscarinic receptor
α-receptor
β1-receptor
β1-receptor
Arteriolar smooth muscle
Ventricular myocardium
SA node
Vasodilation
↓ Force of contraction
↓ Heart rate
↓ Peripheral resistance
↓ Cardiac output
↓ Blood pressure
Negative feedback

● **FIGURE 15-23** ***The baroreceptor reflex: the response to increased blood pressure***

The integration of function between the respiratory and circulatory systems is adaptive. If tissues require more oxygen, it is supplied by the cardiovascular system working in tandem with the respiratory system. Consequently, increases in breathing rate are usually accompanied by increases in cardiac output.

Blood pressure is also subject to modulation by higher brain centers, such as the hypothalamus and cerebral cortex. The hypothalamus mediates vascular responses involved in body temperature regulation (see Ch. 22) and for the fight-or-flight response. Learned and emotional responses may originate in the cerebral cortex and be expressed by cardiovascular responses such as blushing and fainting.

One such reflex is *vasovagal syncope,* which may be triggered in some people by the sight of blood or a hypodermic needle. (Recall Anthony's experience at the beginning of this chapter). In this pathway, increased parasympathetic activity and decreased sympathetic activity slow heart rate and cause widespread vasodilation. Cardiac output and peripheral resistance both decrease, triggering a precipitous drop in blood pressure. With insufficient blood to the brain, the individual faints.

Regulation of blood pressure in the cardiovascular system is closely tied to regulation of body fluid balance by the kidneys. Certain hormones secreted from the heart act on the kidneys, while hormones secreted from the kidneys act on the heart and blood vessels. Together, the heart and kidneys play a major role in maintaining homeostasis of body fluids, the subject of Chapter 20. The overlap of these systems is an excellent example of the integration of organ system function.

CONCEPT CHECK

15. Baroreceptors have stretch-sensitive ion channels in their cell membrane. Increased pressure stretches the receptor cell membrane, opens the channels, and initiates action potentials. What ion probably flows through these channels and in which direction (into or out of the cell)? Answers: p. 545

Orthostatic Hypotension Triggers the Baroreceptor Reflex

The baroreceptor reflex functions every morning when you get out of bed. When you are lying flat, gravitational forces are distributed evenly up and down the length of your body, and blood is distributed evenly throughout the circulation. When you stand up, gravity causes blood to pool in the lower extremities. This pooling creates an instantaneous decrease in venous return. As a result, less blood is in the ventricles at the beginning of the next contraction. Cardiac output falls from 5 L/min to 3 L/min, causing arterial blood pressure to decrease. This decrease in blood pressure upon standing is known as *orthostatic hypotension* [*orthos*, upright + *statikos*, to stand].

Orthostatic hypotension normally triggers the baroreceptor reflex. The carotid and aortic baroreceptors respond to the fall in arterial blood pressure by decreasing their firing rate (Fig. 15-24 ●). Diminished sensory input into the cardiovascular control center increases sympathetic activity and decreases parasympathetic activity. As a result of autonomic changes, heart rate and force of contraction increase while arterioles and veins constrict. The combination of increased cardiac output and increased peripheral resistance increases mean arterial pressure and restores it to normal within two heartbeats. The skeletal muscle pump also contributes to the recovery by enhancing venous return when abdominal and leg muscles contract to maintain an upright position.

The baroreceptor reflex is not always effective, however. For example, during extended bed rest or in the zero-gravity conditions of space flights, blood from the lower extremities is distributed evenly throughout the body rather than pooled in the lower extremities. This even distribution raises arterial pressure, triggering the kidneys to excrete what is perceived as excess fluid. Over the course of three days, excretion of water leads to a 12% decrease in blood volume. When the person finally gets out of bed or returns to earth, gravity again causes blood to pool in the legs. Orthostatic hypotension occurs, and the baroreceptors attempt to compensate. In this instance, however, the cardiovascular system is unable to restore normal pressure because of the loss of blood volume. As a result, the individual may become dizzy or even faint from reduced delivery of oxygen to the brain.

CONCEPT CHECK

16. In the movie *Jurassic Park,* Dr. Ian Malcolm must flee from the *T. rex*. Draw a reflex map showing the cardiovascular response to his fight-or-flight situation. (*Hints:* What is the stimulus? Fear is integrated in the limbic system).

Answers: p. 545

CARDIOVASCULAR DISEASE

Disorders of the heart and blood vessels, such as heart attacks and strokes, play a role in more than half of all deaths in the United States. The American Heart Association predicted that in 2008 cardiovascular diseases will cost people in the United States more than $448.5 billion in medical expenses and lost wages. The prevalence of cardiovascular disease is reflected in the tremendous amount of research being done worldwide. The scientific investigations range from large-scale clinical studies that track cardiovascular disease in thousands of people, such as the Framingham (Massachusetts) Heart Study, to experiments at the cellular and molecular levels.

Much of the research at the cellular and molecular levels is designed to expand our understanding of both normal and abnormal function in the heart and blood vessels. Scientists are studying a virtual alphabet soup of transporters and regulators. Some of these molecules, such as adenosine, endothelin, vascular endothelial growth factor (VEGF), phospholamban, and nitric oxide, you have studied here and in Chapter 14.

As we increase our knowledge of cardiovascular function, we also begin to understand the actions of drugs that have been used for centuries. A classic example is the cardiac glycoside *digitalis* [p. 503], whose mechanism of action was explained when scientists discovered the role of Na^+-K^+-ATPase. It is a sobering thought to realize that for many therapeutic drugs, we know *what* they do without fully understanding *how* they do it.

Risk Factors Include Smoking and Obesity

As you learned in Chapter 1, conducting and interpreting research on humans is a complicated endeavor in part because of the difficulty of designing well-controlled experiments [p. 11]. The economic and social importance of cardiovascular disease (CVD) makes it the focus of many studies each year as researchers try to improve treatments and prediction algorithms. (An *algorithm* is a set of rules or a sequence of steps used to solve a problem). We can predict the likelihood that a person will develop cardiovascular disease during his or her lifetime by examining the various risk factors that the person possesses. The list of risk factors described here is the result of following the medical histories of thousands of people for many years in studies such as the Framingham Heart Study. As more data become available, additional risk factors may be added.

Risk factors are generally divided into those over which the person has no control and those that can be controlled.

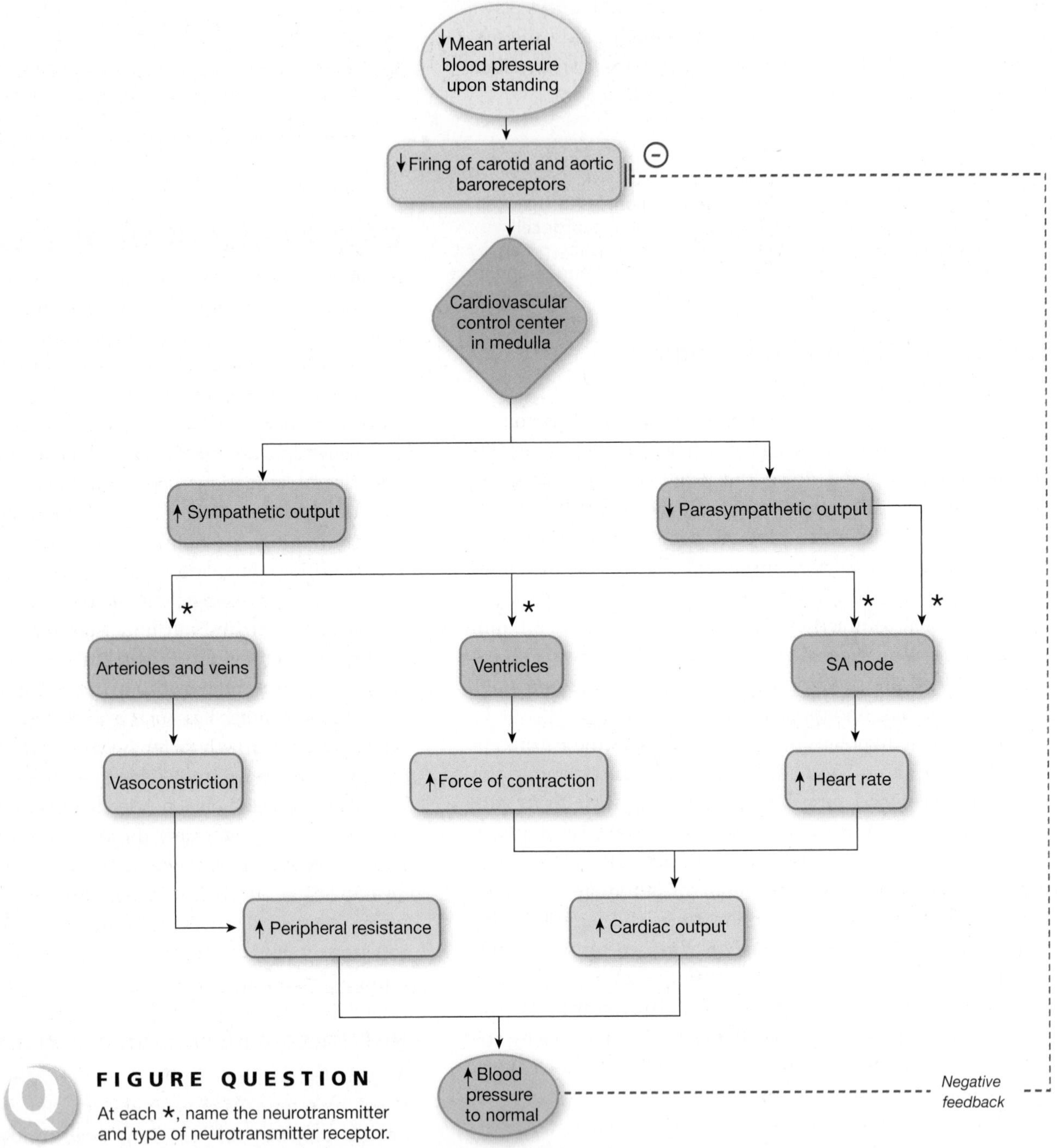

● **FIGURE 15-24** ***The baroreceptor reflex: the response to orthostatic hypotension***

Medical intervention is aimed at reducing risk from the controllable factors. The risk factors that cannot be controlled include sex, age, and a family history of early cardiovascular disease. As noted earlier in the chapter, *coronary heart disease* (CHD) is a form of cardiovascular disease in which the coronary arteries become blocked by cholesterol deposits and blood clots. Up until middle age, men have a 3–4 times higher risk of developing CHD than do women. After age 55, when most women have entered menopause, the death rate from CHD equalizes in men and women. In general, the risk of coronary heart disease increases as people age. Heredity also plays an important role. If a person has one or more close relatives with this condition, his or her risk is elevated.

Risk factors that can be controlled include cigarette smoking, obesity, sedentary lifestyle, and untreated hypertension. In the United States, smoking-related illnesses are the primary preventable cause of death, followed by conditions related to overweight and obesity. Physical inactivity and obesity have been steadily increasing in the United States since 1991, and currently nearly 70% of U.S. adults are either overweight or obese.

Two risk factors for cardiovascular disease—diabetes mellitus and elevated blood lipids—have both an uncontrollable

CLINICAL FOCUS

DIABETES AND CARDIOVASCULAR DISEASE

Having diabetes is one of the major risk factors for developing cardiovascular disease, and almost two-thirds of people with diabetes will die from cardiovascular problems. In diabetes, cells that cannot use glucose turn to fats and proteins for their energy. The body breaks down fat into fatty acids [p. 115] and dumps them into the blood. Plasma cholesterol levels are also elevated. When LDL-C remains in the blood, the excess is ingested by macrophages, starting a series of events that lead to atherosclerosis. Because of the pivotal role that LDL-C plays in atherosclerosis, many forms of therapy, ranging from dietary modification and exercise to drugs, are aimed at lowering LDL-C levels. Left untreated, blockage of small and medium-sized blood vessels in the lower extremities can lead to loss of sensation and *gangrene* (tissue death) in the feet. Atherosclerosis in larger vessels causes heart attacks and strokes. To learn more about diabetes and the increased risk of cardiovascular disease, visit the web sites of the American Diabetes Association (*www.diabetes.org*) and the American Heart Association (*www.americanheart.org*).

genetic component and a modifiable lifestyle component. Diabetes mellitus is a metabolic disorder that puts a person at risk for developing coronary heart disease by contributing to the development of **atherosclerosis** ("hardening of the arteries"), in which fatty deposits form inside arterial blood vessels. Elevated serum cholesterol and triglycerides also lead to atherosclerosis. The increasing prevalence of these risk factors has created an epidemic in the United States, with one in every 2.8 deaths in 2004 attributed to all forms of cardiovascular disease.

Atherosclerosis Is an Inflammatory Process

Coronary heart disease accounts for the majority of cardiovascular disease deaths and is the single largest killer of Americans, both men and women. Let's look at the underlying cause of this disease: atherosclerosis.

The role of elevated blood cholesterol in the development of atherosclerosis is well established. Cholesterol, like other lipids, is not very soluble in aqueous solutions, such as the plasma. Therefore, when cholesterol in the diet is absorbed from the digestive tract, it combines with lipoproteins to make it more soluble. (Chapters 21 and 22 discuss the details of cholesterol digestion, absorption, and metabolism). Multiple lipoproteins associate with cholesterol, but clinicians generally are concerned with two: those found in **high-density lipoprotein-cholesterol (HDL-C)** complexes and those found in **low-density lipoprotein-cholesterol (LDL-C)** complexes. HDL-C is the more desirable form of blood cholesterol because high levels of HDL are associated with lower risk of heart attacks. (Memory aid: "H" in HDL stands for "healthy.")

LDL-C is sometimes called "bad" cholesterol because elevated plasma LDL-C levels are associated with coronary heart disease. (Remember this by associating "L" with "lethal.") Normal levels of LDL-C are not bad, however, because LDL is necessary for cholesterol transport into cells. LDL-C's binding site—a protein called **apoB**—combines with an LDL receptor found in clathrin-coated pits on the cell membrane, and the receptor-LDL-C complex is brought into the cell by endocytosis [Fig. 5-21, p. 153]. The LDL receptor recycles to the cell membrane, and the endosome fuses with a lysosome. LDL-C's proteins are digested to amino acids, and the freed cholesterol is used to make cell membranes or steroid hormones.

Although LDL is needed for cellular uptake of cholesterol, excess levels of plasma LDL-C lead to atherosclerosis. Endothelial cells lining the arteries transport LDL-C into the extracellular space so that it accumulates just under the intima. There, macrophages ingest cholesterol and other lipids to become lipid-filled *foam cells* (Fig. 15-25b ●). Cytokines released by the macrophages promote smooth muscle cell division. This early-stage *lesion* [*laesio*, injury] is called a *fatty streak*. As the condition progresses, the lipid core grows, and smooth muscle cells reproduce, forming bulging *plaques* that protrude into the lumen of the artery. In the advanced stages of atherosclerosis, the plaques develop hard, calcified regions and fibrous collagen caps (Fig. 15-25c). The mechanism by which calcium carbonate is deposited is still being investigated.

Scientists once believed that the occlusion (blockage) of coronary blood vessels by large plaques that triggered blood clots was the primary cause of heart attacks, but that model has been revised. The new model indicates that blood clot formation on plaques is more dependent on the structure of a plaque than on its size. *Stable plaques* have thick fibrous caps that separate the lipid core from the blood and do not activate platelets. *Vulnerable plaques* have thin fibrous caps that are more likely to rupture, exposing collagen and activating platelets that initiate a blood clot (*thrombus*) (Fig. 15-25d). Atherosclerosis is now considered to be an inflammatory process in which macrophages release enzymes that convert stable plaques to vulnerable plaques.

If a clot blocks blood flow to the heart muscle, a heart attack (*myocardial infarction*) results. Blocked blood flow in a coronary artery cuts off the oxygen supply to myocardial cells supplied by that artery. The oxygen-starved cells must then rely on anaerobic metabolism [p. 109], which produces lactic acid (H^+). As ATP production declines, the contractile cells are unable to pump Ca^+ out of the cell. The combination of unusually high Ca^+ and H^+ concentrations in the cytosol closes gap junctions in the damaged cells. Closure electrically isolates the damaged cells so that they no longer contract, and it forces action potentials to find an alternate route from cell to cell. If the

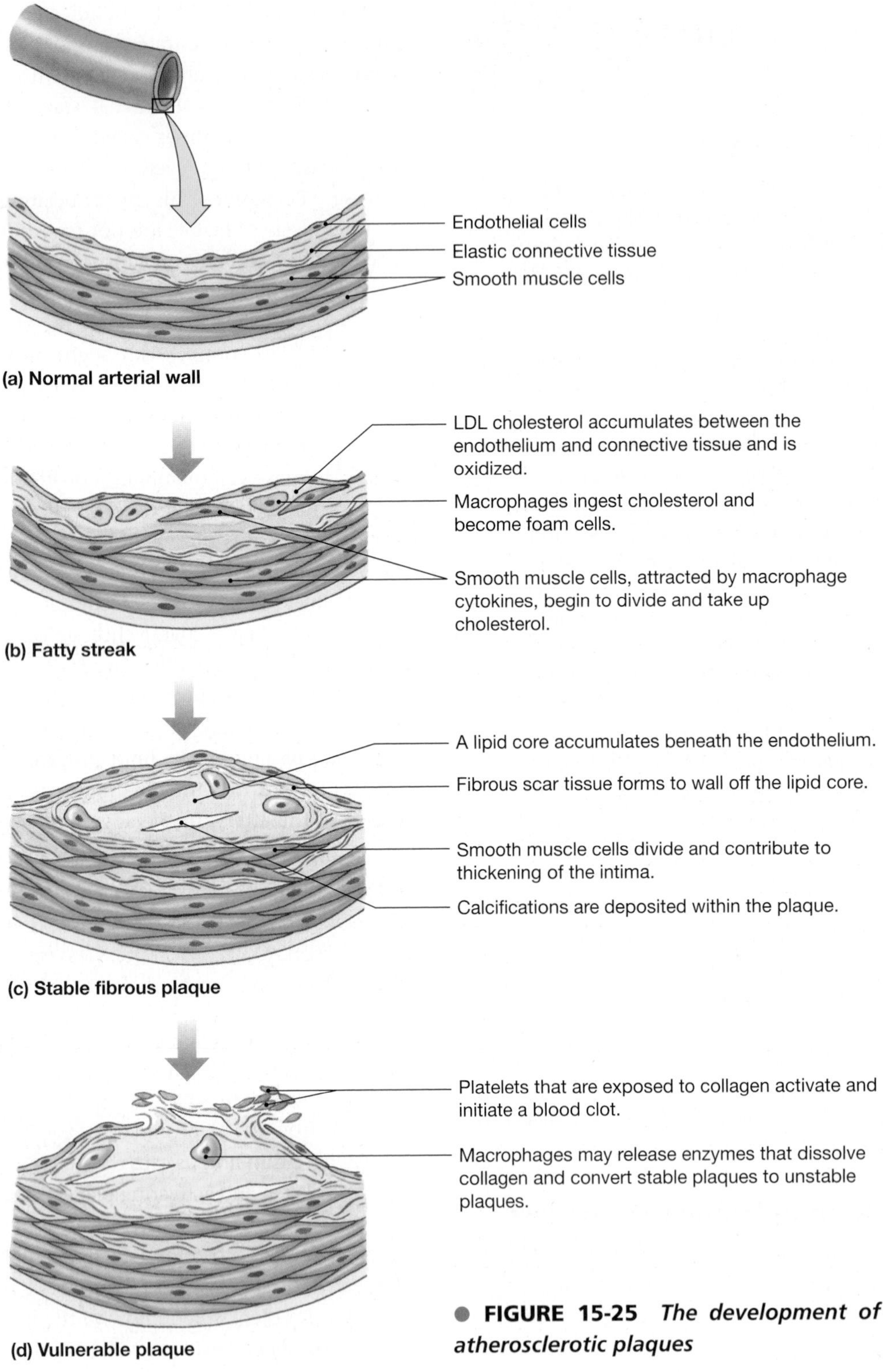
Endothelial cells
Elastic connective tissue
Smooth muscle cells
(a) Normal arterial wall
LDL cholesterol accumulates between the endothelium and connective tissue and is oxidized.
Macrophages ingest cholesterol and become foam cells.
Smooth muscle cells, attracted by macrophage cytokines, begin to divide and take up cholesterol.
(b) Fatty streak
A lipid core accumulates beneath the endothelium.
Fibrous scar tissue forms to wall off the lipid core.
Smooth muscle cells divide and contribute to thickening of the intima.
Calcifications are deposited within the plaque.
(c) Stable fibrous plaque
Platelets that are exposed to collagen activate and initiate a blood clot.
Macrophages may release enzymes that dissolve collagen and convert stable plaques to unstable plaques.
(d) Vulnerable plaque

● **FIGURE 15-25** ***The development of atherosclerotic plaques***

damaged area of myocardium is large, the disruption can lead to an irregular heartbeat (*arrhythmia*) and potentially result in cardiac arrest or death.

Hypertension Represents a Failure of Homeostasis

One controllable risk factor for cardiovascular disease is hypertension—chronically elevated blood pressure, with systolic pressures greater than 130–140 mm Hg or diastolic pressures greater than 80–90 mm Hg. Hypertension is a common disease in the United States and is one of the most common reasons for visits to physicians and for the use of prescription drugs. High blood pressure is associated with increasing risk of CVD: the risk doubles for each 20/10 mm Hg increase in blood pressure over a baseline value of 115/75 (Fig. 15-26 ●).

EMERGING CONCEPTS

INFLAMMATORY MARKERS FOR CARDIOVASCULAR DISEASE

In clinical studies, it is sometimes difficult to determine whether a factor that has a positive correlation with a disease functions in a cause-effect relationship or represents a simple association. For example, two factors associated with higher incidence of heart disease are C-reactive protein and homocysteine. *C-reactive protein* (CRP) is a molecule involved in the body's response to inflammation. In one study, women who had elevated blood CRP levels were more than twice as likely to have a serious cardiovascular problem as women with low CRP. Does this finding mean that CRP is causing cardiovascular disease? Or could it simply be a marker that can be used clinically to predict who is more likely to develop cardiovascular complications, such as a heart attack or stroke?

Similarly, elevated homocysteine levels are associated with an increased incidence of CVD. (*Homocysteine* is an amino acid that takes part in a complicated metabolic pathway that also requires folate and vitamin B_{12} as cofactors). Should physicians routinely measure homocysteine along with cholesterol? Currently there is little clinical evidence to show that reducing either CRP or homocysteine decreases a person's risk of developing CVD. If these two markers are not indicators for *modifiable* risk factors, should a patient's insurance be asked to pay for the tests used to detect them?

More than 90% of all patients with hypertension are considered to have *essential* (or *primary*) *hypertension,* with no clear-cut cause other than heredity. Cardiac output is usually normal in these people, and their elevated blood pressure appears to be associated with increased peripheral resistance. Some investigators have speculated that the increased resistance may be due to a lack of nitric oxide, the locally produced vasodilator formed by endothelial cells in the arterioles. In the remaining 5–10% of hypertensive cases, the cause is more apparent, and the hypertension is considered to be secondary to an underlying pathology. For instance, the cause might be an endocrine disorder that causes fluid retention.

A key feature of hypertension from all causes is adaptation of the carotid and aortic baroreceptors to higher pressure, with subsequent down-regulation of their activity. Without input from the baroreceptors, the cardiovascular control center interprets the high blood pressure as "normal," and no reflex reduction of pressure occurs.

Hypertension is a risk factor for atherosclerosis because high pressure in the arteries damages the endothelial lining of the vessels and promotes the formation of atherosclerotic

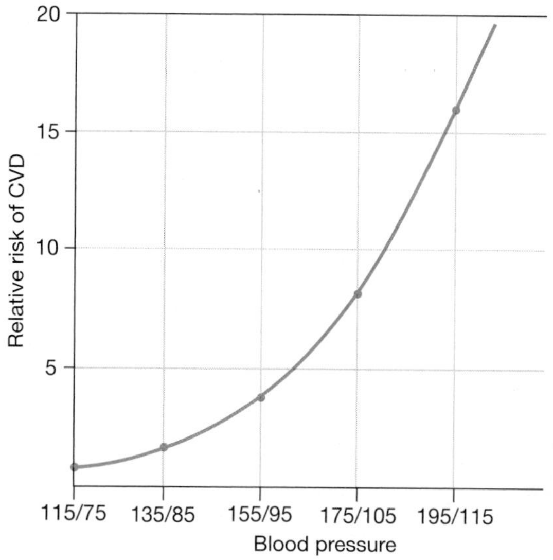

● **FIGURE 15-26** ***The risk of developing cardiovascular disease doubles with each 20/10 mm Hg increase in blood pressure.***

plaques. In addition, high arterial blood pressure puts additional strain on the heart by increasing afterload [p. 504]. When resistance in the arterioles is high, the myocardium must work harder to push the blood into the arteries.

Amazingly, stroke volume in hypertensive patients remains constant up to a mean blood pressure of about 200 mm Hg, despite the increasing amount of work that the ventricle must perform as blood pressure increases. The cardiac muscle of the left ventricle responds to chronic high systemic resistance in the same way that skeletal muscle responds to a weight-lifting routine. The heart muscle *hypertrophies,* increasing the size and strength of the muscle fibers.

However, if resistance remains high over time, the heart muscle cannot meet the work load and begins to fail: cardiac output by the left ventricle decreases. If cardiac output of the right heart remains normal while the output from the left side decreases, fluid collects in the lungs, creating *pulmonary edema.* At this point, a detrimental positive feedback loop begins. Oxygen exchange in the lungs diminishes because of the pulmonary edema, leading to less oxygen in the blood. Lack of oxygen for aerobic metabolism further weakens the heart, and its pumping effectiveness diminishes even more. Unless treated, this condition, known as *congestive heart failure,* eventually leads to death.

Many of the treatments for hypertension have their basis in the cardiovascular physiology you have learned. For example, calcium entry into vascular smooth muscle and cardiac muscle can be decreased by a class of drugs known as *calcium channel blockers.* These drugs bind to Ca^{+} channel proteins, making it less likely that the channels will open in response to depolarization. With less Ca^{2+} entry, vascular smooth muscle dilates, while in the heart the depolarization rate of the SA node and the force of contraction decrease. Vascular smooth

15

muscle is more sensitive than cardiac muscle to certain classes of calcium channel blockers, and it is possible to get vasodilation at drug doses that are low enough to have no effect on heart rate. Other tissues with Ca^+ channels, such as neurons, are only minimally affected by calcium channel blockers because their Ca^+ channels are of a different subtype.

Other drugs used to treat hypertension include diuretics, which decrease blood volume, and beta-blocking drugs that target β_1-receptors and decrease catecholamine stimulation of cardiac output. Two other groups of antihypertensive drugs, the ACE inhibitors and the angiotensin receptor blockers, act by decreasing the activity of angiotensin, a powerful vasoconstrictor substance. You will learn more about angiotensin later in the book, when you study the integrated control of blood pressure by the cardiovascular and renal systems. In the future, we may be seeing new treatments for hypertension that are based on other aspects of the molecular physiology of the heart and blood vessels.

RUNNING PROBLEM CONCLUSION

Essential Hypertension

Kurt remained on the calcium channel blocker and diuretic, and after several months his cough went away and his blood pressure stabilized at 130/85—a significant improvement. Kurt's new diet also brought his total blood cholesterol down below 200 mg/dL plasma. By improving two of his controllable risk factors, Kurt decreased his chances of having a heart attack. To learn more about hypertension and some of the therapies currently used to treat it, visit the web site of the American Heart Association (*www.americanheart.org*). Now check your understanding of this running problem by comparing your answers with the information in the summary table.

	QUESTION	FACTS	INTEGRATION AND ANALYSIS
1	Why are people with high blood pressure at greater risk for having a hemorrhagic (or bleeding) stroke?	High blood pressure exerts force on the walls of the blood vessels.	If an area of blood vessel wall is weakened or damaged, high blood pressure may cause that area to rupture, allowing blood to leak out of the vessel into the surrounding tissues.
2	What is the rationale for reducing salt intake and taking a diuretic to control hypertension?	Salt causes water retention. Diuretics increase renal fluid excretion.	Blood pressure increases if the circulating blood volume increases. By restricting salt in the diet, a person can decrease retention of fluid in the extracellular compartment, which includes the plasma. Diuretics also help decrease blood volume.
3	Why would blocking the action of a vasoconstrictor lower blood pressure?	Blood pressure is determined by cardiac output and peripheral resistance.	Resistance is inversely proportional to the radius of the blood vessels. Therefore, if blood vessels dilate as a result of blocking a vasoconstrictor, resistance and blood pressure decrease.
4	How do calcium channel blockers lower blood pressure?	Calcium entry from the extracellular fluid plays an important role in both smooth muscle and cardiac muscle contraction.	Blocking Ca^{2+} entry through Ca^{2+} channels decreases the force of cardiac contraction and decreases the contractility of vascular smooth muscle. Both of these effects lower blood pressure.

513 519 523 524 532 540

CHAPTER SUMMARY

Blood flow through the cardiovascular system is an excellent example of *mass flow* in the body. Cardiac contraction creates high pressure in the ventricles, and this pressure drives blood through the vessels of the systemic and pulmonary circuits, speeding up cell-to-cell *communication*. Resistance to flow is regulated by *local and reflex control mechanisms* that act on arteriolar smooth muscle and help match tissue perfusion to tissue needs. The *homeostatic* baroreceptor reflex monitors arterial pressure to ensure adequate perfusion of the brain and heart. Capillary *exchange of material* between the plasma and interstitial fluid *compartments* uses several transport mechanisms, including diffusion, transcytosis, and bulk flow.

1. Homeostatic regulation of the cardiovascular system is aimed at maintaining adequate blood flow to the brain and heart. (p. 513)
2. Total blood flow at any level of the circulation is equal to the cardiac output. (p. 514)

The Blood Vessels

iP Cardiovascular—Anatomy Review: Blood Vessel Structure & Function

3. Blood vessels are composed of layers of smooth muscle, elastic and fibrous connective tissue, and **endothelium**. (p. 514; Fig. 15-2)
4. **Vascular smooth muscle** maintains a state of muscle tone. (p. 514)
5. The walls of the aorta and major arteries are both stiff and springy. This property allows them to absorb energy and release it through elastic recoil. (p. 514)
6. **Metarterioles** regulate blood flow through capillaries and allow white blood cells to go directly from arterioles to the venous circulation. (p. 515; Fig. 15-3)
7. Capillaries and postcapillary **venules** are the site of exchange between blood and interstitial fluid. (p. 515)
8. Veins hold more than half of the blood in the circulatory system. Veins have thinner walls with less elastic tissue than arteries, so veins expand easily when they fill with blood. (p. 515)
9. **Angiogenesis** is the process by which new blood vessels grow and develop, especially after birth. (p. 516)

Blood Pressure

iP Cardiovascular: Measuring Blood Pressure

10. The ventricles create high pressure that is the driving force for blood flow. The aorta and arteries act as a pressure reservoir during ventricular relaxation. (p. 516; Fig. 15-4)
11. Blood pressure is highest in the arteries and decreases as blood flows through the circulatory system. At rest, average **systolic pressure** is 120 mm Hg, and average **diastolic pressure** is 80 mm Hg. (p. 516; Fig. 15-5)
12. Pressure created by the ventricles can be felt as a **pulse** in the arteries. **Pulse pressure** equals systolic pressure minus diastolic pressure. (p. 516)
13. Blood flow against gravity in the veins is assisted by one-way valves and by the respiratory and skeletal muscle pumps. (p. 516; Fig. 15-6)
14. Arterial blood pressure is indicative of the driving pressure for blood flow. **Mean arterial pressure** (MAP) is defined as diastolic pressure $+1/3$ (systolic pressure $-$ diastolic pressure). (p. 517)
15. Arterial blood pressure is usually measured with a sphygmomanometer. Blood squeezing through a compressed brachial artery makes **Korotkoff sounds**. (p. 518; Fig. 15-7)
16. Arterial pressure is a balance between cardiac output and the resistance to blood flow offered by the arterioles (**peripheral resistance**). (p. 519; Fig. 15-8)
17. If blood volume increases, blood pressure increases. If blood volume decreases, blood pressure decreases. (p. 520; Fig. 15-9)
18. Venous blood volume can be shifted to the arteries if arterial blood pressure falls. (p. 521; Fig. 15-10)

Resistance in the Arterioles

iP Cardiovascular: Factors That Affect Blood Pressure

19. The arterioles are the main site of variable resistance in the systemic circulation. A small change in the radius of an arteriole creates a large change in resistance: $R \propto 1/r^4$. (p. 522)
20. Arterioles regulate their own blood flow through **myogenic autoregulation**. Vasoconstriction increases the resistance offered by an arteriole and decreases the blood flow through the arteriole. (p. 523)
21. Arteriolar resistance is influenced by local control mechanisms that match tissue blood flow to the metabolic needs of the tissue. Vasodilator paracrines include nitric oxide, H^+, K^+, CO_2, prostaglandins, adenosine, and histamine. Low O_2 causes vasodilation. Endothelins are powerful vasoconstrictors. (p. 523; Tbl. 15-2)
22. **Active hyperemia** is a process in which increased blood flow accompanies increased metabolic activity. **Reactive hyperemia** is an increase in tissue blood flow following a period of low perfusion. (pp. 523–524; Fig. 15-11)
23. Most systemic arterioles are under tonic sympathetic control. Norepinephrine causes vasoconstriction. Decreased sympathetic stimulation causes vasodilation. (p. 524)
24. Epinephrine binds to arteriolar α-receptors and causes vasoconstriction. Epinephrine on β_2-receptors, found in the arterioles of the heart, liver, and skeletal muscle, causes vasodilation. (p. 524)

Distribution of Blood to the Tissues

25. Changing the resistance of the arterioles affects mean arterial pressure and alters blood flow through the arteriole. (p. 526; Fig. 15-15)
26. The flow through individual arterioles depends on their resistance. The higher the resistance in an arteriole, the lower the blood flow in that arteriole: $Flow_{arteriole} \propto 1/R_{arteriole}$. (p. 526)
27. Blood flow into individual capillaries can be regulated by **precapillary sphincters**. (p. 526; Fig. 15-16)

Exchange at the Capillaries

iP Cardiovascular: Autoregulation and Capillary Dynamics

28. Exchange of materials between the blood and the interstitial fluid occurs primarily by diffusion. (p. 528)

29. **Continuous capillaries** have leaky junctions between cells but also transport material using transcytosis. Continuous capillaries with tight junctions form the blood-brain barrier. (p. 527; Fig. 15-17)
30. **Fenestrated capillaries** have pores that allow large volumes of fluid to pass rapidly. (p. 527; Fig. 15-17)
31. The velocity of blood flow through the capillaries is slow, allowing diffusion to go to equilibrium. (p. 528; Fig. 15-18)
32. The mass movement of fluid between the blood and the interstitial fluid is **bulk flow**. Fluid movement is called **filtration** if the direction of flow is out of the capillary and **absorption** if the flow is directed into the capillary. (p. 528; Fig. 15-19)
33. The osmotic pressure difference between plasma and interstitial fluid due to the presence of plasma proteins is the **colloid osmotic pressure**. (p. 529)

The Lymphatic System

iP Fluids & Electrolytes: Electrolyte Homeostasis, Edema

34. About 3 liters of fluid filter out of the capillaries each day. The lymphatic system returns this fluid to the circulatory system. (p. 530; Fig. 15-20)
35. Lymph capillaries accumulate fluid, interstitial proteins, and particulate matter by bulk flow. Lymph flow depends on smooth muscle in vessel walls, one-way valves, and the skeletal muscle pump. (p. 531)
36. The condition in which excess fluid accumulates in the interstitial space is called **edema**. Factors that disrupt the normal balance between capillary filtration and absorption cause edema. (p. 531; Fig. 15-21)

Regulation of Blood Pressure

iP Cardiovascular: Blood Pressure Regulation

37. The reflex control of blood pressure resides in the medulla oblongata. **Baroreceptors** in the carotid artery and the aorta monitor arterial blood pressure and trigger the **baroreceptor reflex**. (pp. 532–533; Figs. 15-22, 15-23)
38. Efferent output from the medullary **cardiovascular control center** goes to the heart and arterioles. Increased sympathetic activity increases heart rate and force of contraction. Increased parasympathetic activity slows heart rate. Increased sympathetic discharge at the arterioles causes vasoconstriction. There is no significant parasympathetic control of arterioles. (p. 533)
39. Cardiovascular function can be modulated by input from higher brain centers and from the respiratory control center of the medulla. (p. 533)
40. The baroreceptor reflex functions each time a person stands up. The decrease in blood pressure upon standing is known as orthostatic hypotension. (p. 535; Fig. 15-24)

Cardiovascular Disease

41. **Cardiovascular disease** is the leading cause of death in the United States. Risk factors predict the likelihood that a person will develop cardiovascular disease during her or his lifetime. (p. 535)
42. **Atherosclerosis** is an inflammatory condition in which fatty deposits called plaques develop in arteries. If plaques are unstable, they may block the arteries by triggering blood clots. (p. 537; Fig. 15-25)
43. Hypertension is a significant risk factor for the development of cardiovascular disease. (p. 539; Fig. 15-26)

QUESTIONS

(Answers to the Review Questions begin on page A1).

THE PHYSIOLOGY PLACE

Access more review material online at **The Physiology Place** web site. There you'll find review questions, problem-solving activities, case studies, flashcards, and direct links to both *Interactive Physiology®* and *PhysioEx™* To access the site, go to *www.physiologyplace.com* and select *Human Physiology*, Fifth Edition.

LEVEL ONE REVIEWING FACTS AND TERMS

1. The first priority of blood pressure homeostasis is to maintain adequate perfusion to which two organs?
2. Match the types of systemic blood vessels with the terms that describe them. Each vessel type may have more than one match, and matching items may be used more than once.

(a) arterioles	1. store pressure generated by the heart
(b) arteries	2. have walls that are both stiff and elastic
(c) capillaries	3. carry low-oxygen blood
(d) veins	4. have thin walls of exchange epithelium
(e) venules	5. act as a volume reservoir
	6. their diameter can be altered by neural input
	7. blood flow slowest through these vessels
	8. have lowest blood pressure
	9. are the main site of variable resistance

3. List the four tissue components of blood vessel walls, in order from inner lining to outer covering. Briefly describe the importance of each tissue.
4. Blood flow to individual tissues is regulated by selective vasoconstriction and vasodilation of which vessels?
5. Aortic pressure reaches a typical high value of ________ (give both numeric value and units) during ________, or contraction of the heart. As the heart relaxes during the event called ________, aortic pressure declines to a typical low value of ________. This blood pressure reading would be written as ________/________.
6. The rapid pressure increase that occurs when the left ventricle pushes blood into the aorta can be felt as a pressure wave, or ________. What is the equation used to calculate the strength of this pressure wave?
7. List the factors that aid venous return to the heart.
8. What is hypertension, and why is it a threat to a person's health?
9. When measuring a person's blood pressure, at what point in the procedure are you likely to hear Korotkoff sounds?
10. List three paracrines that cause vasodilation. What is the source of each one? In addition to paracrines, list two other ways to control smooth muscle contraction in arterioles.

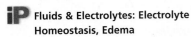

11. What is hyperemia? How does active hyperemia differ from reactive hyperemia?
12. Most systemic arterioles are innervated by the ________ branch of the nervous system. Increased sympathetic input will have what effect on arteriole diameter?
13. Match each event in the left column with all appropriate neurotransmitter(s) *and* receptor(s) from the list on the right.

(a) vasoconstriction of intestinal arterioles	1. norepinephrine
(b) vasodilation of coronary arterioles	2. epinephrine
(c) increased heart rate	3. acetylcholine
(d) decreased heart rate	4. β_1-receptor
(e) vasoconstriction of coronary arterioles	5. α-receptor
	6. β_2-receptor
	7. nicotinic receptor
	8. muscarinic receptor

14. Which organs receive more than two-thirds of the cardiac output at rest? Which organs have the highest flow of blood on a per unit weight basis?
15. By looking at the density of capillaries in a tissue, you can make assumptions about what property of the tissue? Which tissue has the lowest capillary density? Which tissue has the highest?
16. What type of transport is used to move each of the following substances across the capillary endothelium?
    (a) oxygen
    (b) proteins
    (c) glucose
    (d) water
17. With which three physiological systems do the vessels of the lymphatic system interact?
18. Define edema. List some ways in which it can arise.
19. Define the following terms and explain their significance to cardiovascular physiology.
    (a) perfusion
    (b) colloid osmotic pressure
    (c) vasoconstriction
    (d) angiogenesis
    (e) metarterioles
    (f) pericytes
20. The two major lipoprotein carriers of cholesterol are ________ and ________. Which type is bad when present in the body in elevated amounts?

LEVEL TWO REVIEWING CONCEPTS

21. **Concept map:** Map all the following factors that influence mean arterial pressure. You may add additional terms.

aorta	parasympathetic neuron
arteriole	peripheral resistance
baroreceptor	SA node
blood volume	sensory neuron
cardiac output	stroke volume
carotid artery	sympathetic neuron
contractility	vein
heart rate	venous return
medulla oblongata	ventricle

22. Compare and contrast the following sets of terms:
    (a) lymphatic capillaries and systemic capillaries
    (b) roles of the sympathetic and parasympathetic branches in blood pressure control
    (c) lymph and blood
    (d) continuous capillaries and fenestrated capillaries
    (e) hydrostatic pressure and colloid osmotic pressure in systemic capillaries
23. Calcium channel blockers prevent Ca^{2+} movement through Ca^{2+} channels. Explain two ways this action lowers blood pressure. Why are neurons and other cells unaffected by these drugs?
24. Define myogenic autoregulation. What mechanisms have been proposed to explain it?
25. Left ventricular failure may be accompanied by edema, shortness of breath, and increased venous pressure. Explain how these signs and symptoms develop.

LEVEL THREE PROBLEM SOLVING

26. Robert is a 52-year-old nonsmoker. He weighs 180 lbs and stands 5′9″ tall, and his blood pressure averaged 145/95 on three successive visits to his doctor's office. His father, grandfather, and uncle all had heart attacks in their early 50s, and his mother died of a stroke at the age of 71.
    (a) Identify Robert's risk factors for coronary heart disease.
    (b) Does Robert have hypertension? Explain.
    (c) Robert's doctor prescribes a drug called a beta blocker. Explain the mechanism by which a beta-receptor-blocking drug may help lower blood pressure.
27. The following figure is a schematic representation of the systemic circulation. Use it to help answer the following questions. (CO = cardiac output, MAP = mean arterial pressure).
    (a) If resistance in vessels 1 and 2 increases because of the presence of local paracrines but cardiac output is unchanged, what happens to MAP? What happens to flow through vessels 1 and 2? Through vessels 3 and 4?
    (b) Homeostatic compensation occurs within seconds. Draw a reflex map to explain the compensation (stimulus, receptor, and so on).
    (c) When vessel 1 constricts, what happens to the filtration pressure in the capillaries downstream from that arteriole?

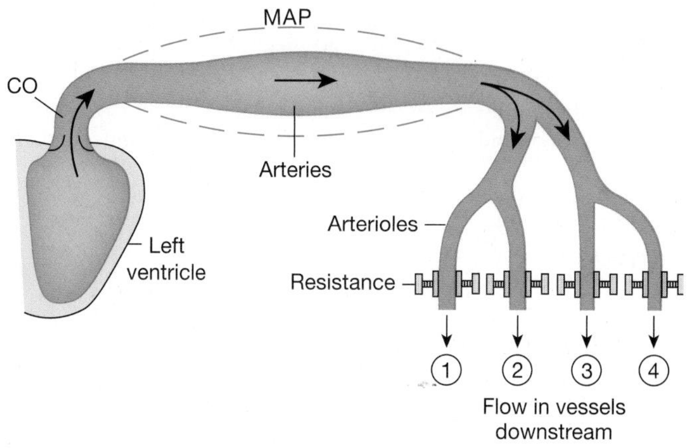

28. Draw a reflex map that explains Anthony's vasovagal syncope at the sight of blood. Include all the steps of the reflex, and explain whether pathways are being stimulated or inhibited.
29. A physiologist placed a section of excised arteriole in a perfusion chamber containing saline. When the oxygen content of the saline perfusing (flowing through) the arteriole was reduced, the arteriole dilated. In a follow-up experiment, she used an isolated piece of arteriolar smooth muscle that had been stripped away from the other layers of the arteriole wall. When the oxygen content of the saline was reduced as in the first experiment, the isolated muscle showed no response. What do these two experiments suggest about how low oxygen exerts local control over arterioles?
30. The following graphs are recordings of contractions in an isolated frog heart. The intact frog heart is innervated by sympathetic neurons that increase heart rate and by parasympathetic neurons that decrease heart rate. Based on these four graphs, what conclusion can you draw about the mechanism of action of atropine? (Atropine does not cross the cell membrane).

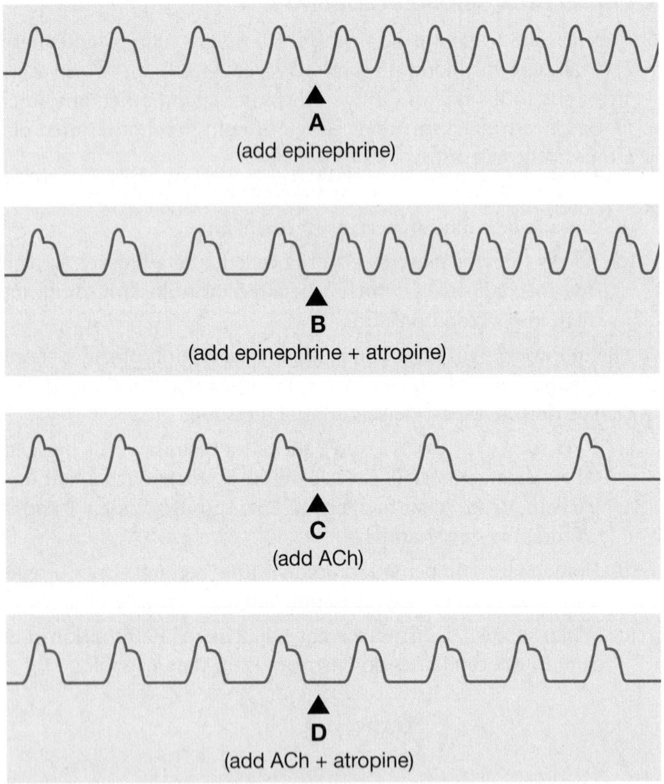
A
(add epinephrine)
B
(add epinephrine + atropine)
C
(add ACh)
D
(add ACh + atropine)

31. In advanced atherosclerosis, calcified plaques cause the normally elastic aorta and arteries to become stiff and noncompliant. (a) What effect does this change in the aorta have on afterload? (b) If cardiac output remains unchanged, what happens to peripheral resistance and mean arterial pressure?
32. During fetal development, most blood in the pulmonary artery bypasses the lungs and goes into the aorta by way of a channel called the *ductus arteriosus*. Normally this fetal bypass channel closes during the first day after birth, but each year about 4000 babies in the United States maintain a *patent* (open) ductus arteriosus and require surgery to close the channel.
    (a) Use this information to draw an anatomical diagram showing blood flow in an infant with a patent ductus arteriosus.
    (b) In the fetus, why does most blood bypass the lungs?
    (c) If the systemic side of the circulatory system is longer than the pulmonary side, which circuit has the greater resistance?
    (d) If flow is equal in the pulmonary and systemic circulations, which side of the heart must generate more pressure to overcome resistance?
    (e) Use your answer to (d) to figure out which way blood will flow through a patent ductus arteriosus.

LEVEL FOUR QUANTITATIVE PROBLEMS

33. Using the appropriate equation, mathematically explain what happens to blood flow if the *diameter* of a blood vessel increases from 2 mm to 4 mm.
34. Duplicate the calculations that led William Harvey to believe that blood circulated in a closed loop:
    (a) Take your resting pulse.
    (b) Assume that your heart at rest pumps 70 mL/beat, and that 1 mL of blood weighs one gram. Calculate how long it would take your heart to pump your weight in blood. (2.2 pounds = 1 kilogram)
35. Calculate the mean arterial pressure (MAP) and pulse pressure for a person with a blood pressure of 115/73.
36. According to the Fick principle, the oxygen consumption rate of an organ is equal to the blood flow through that organ times the amount of oxygen extracted from the blood as it flows through the organ:

$$\text{Oxygen consumption rate} = \text{blood flow} \times (\text{arterial oxygen content} - \text{venous oxygen content})$$

$$(\text{mL } O_2 \text{ consumed/min}) = (\text{mL blood/min} \times \text{mL } O_2/\text{mL blood})$$

A person has a total body oxygen consumption rate of 250 mL/min. The oxygen content of blood in his aorta is 200 mL O_2/L blood, the oxygen content of his pulmonary artery blood is 160 mL O_2/L blood. What is his cardiac output?

ANSWERS

Answers to Concept Check Questions

Page 517

1. Veins from the brain do not require valves because blood flow is aided by gravity.
2. The carotid wave would arrive slightly ahead of the wrist wave because the distance from heart to carotid artery is shorter.
3. Pressure of 130/95 has the higher pulse pressure (35 mm Hg).

Page 518

4. If heart rate increases, the relative time spent in diastole decreases. In that case, the contribution of systolic pressure to mean arterial pressure increases, and MAP increases.
5. Pulse pressure is 112 – 68 = 44 mm Hg. MAP is 68 + 1/3 (44) = 82.7 mm Hg.

Page 524

6. (d)
7. Extracellular K^+ dilates arterioles, which increases blood flow (see Tbl. 15-2).

Page 526

8. Epinephrine binding to myocardial β_1-receptors increases heart rate and force of contraction. Epinephrine binding to β_2-receptors on heart arterioles causes vasodilation.
9. α-Receptors have lower affinity for epinephrine than β_2-receptors, so the β_2-receptors dominate and arterioles dilate.

Page 526

10. (a) The kidney has the highest blood flow per unit weight. (b) The heart has the lowest total blood flow.

Page 530

11. Loss of plasma proteins will decrease colloid osmotic pressure. As a result, hydrostatic pressure will have a greater effect in the filtration-absorption balance, and filtration will increase.
12. Using osmotic pressure rather than osmolarity allows a direct comparison between absorption pressure and filtration pressure, both of which are expressed in mm Hg.

Page 532

13. If the left ventricle fails, blood backs up into the left atrium and pulmonary veins, and then into lung capillaries. Edema in the lungs is known as *pulmonary edema*.
14. Low-protein diets result in a low concentration of plasma proteins. Capillary absorption is reduced while filtration remains constant, resulting in edema and ascites.

Page 535

15. The most likely ion is Na^+ moving into the receptor cell.

Page 535

16. Stimulus: sight, sound, and smell of the *T. rex*. Receptors: eyes, ears, and nose. Integrating center: cerebral cortex, with descending pathways through the limbic system. Divergent pathways go to the cardiovascular control center, which increases sympathetic output to heart and arterioles. A second descending spinal pathway goes to the adrenal medulla, which releases epinephrine. Epinephrine on β_2-receptors of liver, heart, and skeletal muscle arterioles causes vasodilation of those arterioles. Norepinephrine onto α-receptors in other arterioles causes vasoconstriction. Both catecholamines increase heart rate and force of contraction.

Answers to Figure and Graph Questions

Page 000

Fig. 15-1: The pumps are arranged in series.

Page 525

Fig. 15-13: Sympathetic innervation and epinephrine increase heart rate and stroke volume; parasympathetic innervation decreases heart rate. Sympathetic input causes vasoconstriction but epinephrine causes vasodilation in selected arterioles. For paracrine factors that influence arteriolar diameter, see Table 15-2.

Page 526

Fig. 15-14: Blood flow through the lungs is 5 L/min.

Page 529

Fig. 15-18: (a) Velocity of flow is inversely proportional to area: as area increases, velocity decreases. (b) Changing only cross-sectional area has no effect on flow rate because flow rate is determined by cardiac output.

Page 530

Fig. 15-19: Net filtration will increase as a result of the increased hydrostatic pressure.

Page 533

Fig. 15-22: SA node: muscarinic cholinergic receptors for ACh and β_1-receptors for catecholamines. Ventricles: β_1-receptors for catecholamines. Arterioles and veins: α-receptors for norepinephrine.

Page 536

Fig. 15-24: Arterioles and veins: norepinephrine, α-receptors. Ventricles: norepinephrine, β_1-receptors. SA node: norepinephrine, β_1-receptors; and ACh, muscarinic receptors.

16

Blood

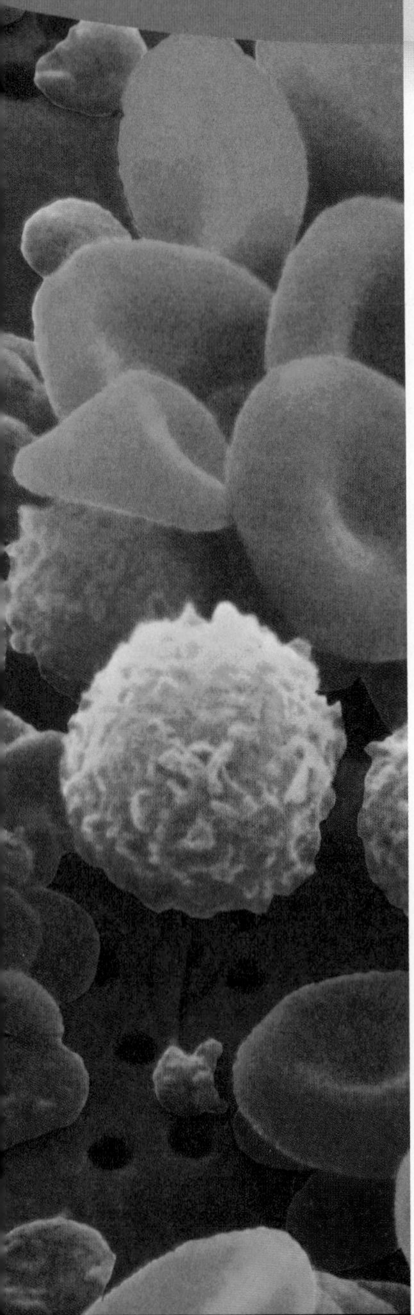

Red blood cells, white blood cells (yellow), and platelets (pink)

BACKGROUND BASICS

Protein structure: **31** Connective tissue: **80** Phagocytosis: **152** Second messenger cascade: **184** Viscosity and resistance: **473** Collagen: **80** Cell organelles: **63** Cytokines: **180**

Who would have thought the old man to have had so much blood in him?

—Macbeth, V, i, 42, *by William Shakespeare*

RUNNING PROBLEM

Blood Doping in Athletes

Athletes spend hundreds of hours training, trying to build their endurance. For Johann Muehlegg, a cross-country skier at the 2002 Salt Lake City Winter Olympics, it appeared that his training had paid off when he captured three gold medals. On the last day of the Games, however, Olympics officials expelled Muehlegg and stripped him of his gold medal in the 50-kilometer classical race. The reason? Muehlegg had tested positive for a performance-enhancing chemical that increased the oxygen-carrying capacity of his blood. Officials claimed Muehlegg's endurance in the grueling race was the result of blood doping, not training.

547 553 558 561 565

Blood, the fluid that circulates in the cardiovascular system, has occupied a prominent place throughout history as an almost mystical fluid. Humans undoubtedly had made the association between blood and life by the time they began to fashion tools and hunt animals. A wounded animal that lost blood would weaken and die if the blood loss was severe enough. The logical conclusion was that blood was necessary for existence. This observation eventually led to the term *lifeblood,* meaning anything essential for existence.

Ancient Chinese physicians linked blood to energy flow in the body. They wrote about the circulation of blood through the heart and blood vessels long before William Harvey described it in seventeenth-century Europe. In China, changes in blood flow were used as diagnostic clues to illness. Chinese physicians were expected to recognize some 50 variations in the pulse. Because blood was considered a vital fluid to be conserved and maintained, bleeding patients to cure disease was not a standard form of treatment.

In contrast, Western civilizations came to believe that disease-causing evil spirits circulated in the blood. The way to remove these spirits was to remove the blood containing them. Because blood was recognized as an essential fluid, however, bloodletting had to be done judiciously. Veins were opened with knives or sharp instruments (*venesection*), or blood-sucking leeches were applied to the skin. In ancient India, people believed that leeches could distinguish between healthy and infected blood.

There is no written evidence that venesection was practiced in ancient Egypt, but the work carried out by Galen of Pergamum in the second century A.D. influenced Western medicine for nearly 2000 years. This early Greek physician advocated bleeding as treatment for many disorders. The location, timing, and frequency of the bleeding depended on the condition, and the physician was instructed to remove enough blood to bring the patient to the point of fainting. Over the years, this practice undoubtedly killed more people than it cured.

What is even more remarkable is the fact that as late as 1923, an American medical textbook advocated bleeding for treating certain infectious diseases, such as pneumonia! Now that we better understand the importance of blood in the immune response, it is doubtful that modern medicine will ever again turn to blood removal as a nonspecific means of treating disease. It is still used, however, for selected *hematological disorders* [*haima,* blood].

PLASMA AND THE CELLULAR ELEMENTS OF BLOOD

What is this remarkable fluid that flows through the circulatory system? Blood makes up one-fourth of the extracellular fluid, the internal environment that bathes cells and acts as a buffer between cells and the external environment. Blood is the circulating portion of the extracellular fluid, responsible for carrying material from one part of the body to another.

Total blood volume in a 70-kg man is equal to about 7% of his total body weight, or 0.07×70 kg $= 4.9$ kg. Thus, if we assume that 1 kg of blood occupies a volume of 1 liter, a 70-kg man has about 5 liters of blood. Of this volume, about 2 liters is composed of blood cells, while the remaining 3 liters is composed of plasma, the fluid portion of the blood.

In this chapter we present an overview of the components of blood. We consider the functions of plasma, red blood cells, and platelets in this chapter but will reserve detailed discussion of hemoglobin for Chapter 18, and of white blood cells and blood types for Chapter 24.

Plasma Is Extracellular Matrix

Plasma is the fluid portion of the blood, within which cellular elements are suspended (Fig. 16-1 ●). Water is the main component of plasma, accounting for about 92% of its weight. Proteins account for another 7%. The remaining 1% is dissolved organic molecules (amino acids, glucose, lipids, and nitrogenous wastes), ions (Na^+, K^+, Cl^-, H^+, Ca^{2+}, and HCO_3^-), trace elements and vitamins, and dissolved oxygen (O_2) and carbon dioxide (CO_2).

Plasma is identical in composition to interstitial fluid except for the presence of **plasma proteins**. **Albumins** are the most prevalent type of protein in the plasma, making up about 60% of the total. Albumins and nine other proteins—including *globulins,* the clotting protein *fibrinogen,* and the iron-transporting protein *transferrin*—make up more than 90% of all plasma proteins. The liver makes most plasma proteins and secretes them into the blood. Some globulins, known as *immunoglobulins* or *antibodies,* are synthesized and secreted by specialized blood cells rather than by the liver.

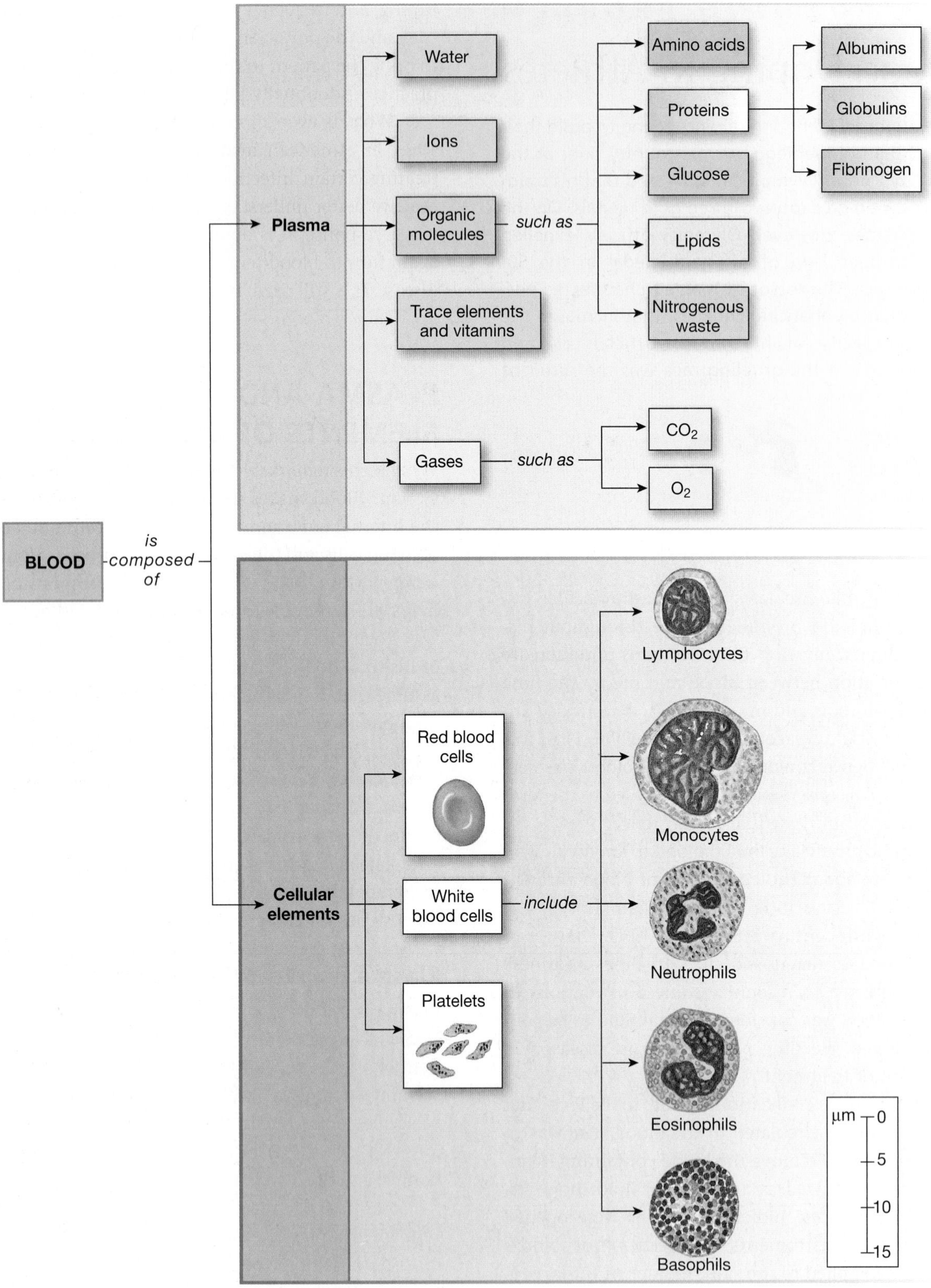

FIGURE 16-1 *Blood consists of plasma and cellular elements.*

TABLE 16-1 Functions of Plasma Proteins

NAME	SOURCE	FUNCTION
Albumins (multiple types)	Liver	Major contributors to colloid osmotic pressure of plasma; carriers for various substances
Globulins (multiple types)	Liver and lymphoid tissue	Clotting factors, enzymes, antibodies, carriers for various substances
Fibrinogen	Liver	Forms fibrin threads essential to blood clotting
Transferrin	Liver and other tissues	Iron transport

The presence of proteins in the plasma makes the osmotic pressure of the blood higher than that of the interstitial fluid. This osmotic gradient tends to pull water from the interstitial fluid into the capillaries, as you learned in Chapter 15 [p. 528].

Plasma proteins participate in many functions, including blood clotting and defense against foreign invaders. In addition, they act as carriers for steroid hormones, cholesterol, drugs, and certain ions such as iron (Fe^{2+}). Finally, some plasma proteins act as hormones or as extracellular enzymes. Table 16-1 ● summarizes the functions of plasma proteins.

Cellular Elements Include RBCs, WBCs, and Platelets

Three main cellular elements are found in blood (Fig. 16-1): **red blood cells** (RBCs), also called **erythrocytes** [*erythros,* red]; **white blood cells** (WBCs), also called **leukocytes** [*leukos,* white]; and **platelets** or *thrombocytes* [*thrombo-,* lump, clot]. White blood cells are the only fully functional cells in the circulation. Red blood cells have lost their nuclei by the time they enter the bloodstream, and platelets, which also lack a nucleus, are cell fragments that have split off a relatively large parent cell known as a **megakaryocyte** [*mega,* extremely large + *karyon,* kernel + *-cyte,* cell].

Red blood cells play a key role in transporting oxygen from lungs to tissues, and carbon dioxide from tissues to lungs. Platelets are instrumental in *coagulation,* the process by which blood clots prevent blood loss in damaged vessels. White blood cells play a key role in the body's immune responses, defending the body against foreign invaders, such as parasites, bacteria, and viruses. Although most white blood cells circulate through the body in the blood, their work is usually carried out in the tissues rather than in the circulatory system.

Blood contains five types of mature white blood cells: (1) **lymphocytes**, (2) **monocytes**, (3) **neutrophils**, (4) **eosinophils**, and (5) **basophils**. Monocytes that leave the circulation and enter the tissues develop into **macrophages**. Tissue basophils are called **mast cells**.

The types of white blood cells may be grouped according to common morphological or functional characteristics. Neutrophils, monocytes, and macrophages are collectively known as **phagocytes** because they can engulf and ingest foreign particles such as bacteria (phagocytosis) [p. 152]. Lymphocytes are sometimes called **immunocytes** because they are responsible for specific immune responses directed against invaders. Basophils, eosinophils, and neutrophils are called **granulocytes** because they contain cytoplasmic inclusions that give them a granular appearance.

CONCEPT CHECK

1. Name the five types of leukocytes.
2. Why do we say that erythrocytes and platelets are not fully functional cells?
3. On the basis of what you have learned about the origin and role of plasma proteins, explain why patients with advanced liver degeneration frequently suffer from edema [p. 531].

Answers: p. 567

BLOOD CELL PRODUCTION

Where do these different blood cells come from? They are all descendants of a single precursor cell type known as the *pluripotent hematopoietic stem cell* (Fig. 16-2 ●). This cell type is found primarily in **bone marrow**, a soft tissue that fills the hollow center of bones. Pluripotent stem cells have the remarkable ability to develop into many different cell types. As they specialize, they narrow their possible fates. First they become *uncommitted stem cells,* then *progenitor cells* that are committed to developing into one or perhaps two cell types. Progenitor cells differentiate into red blood cells, lymphocytes, other white blood cells, and megakaryocytes, the parent cells of platelets. It is estimated that only about one out of every 100,000 cells in the bone marrow is an uncommitted stem cell, making it difficult to isolate and study these cells.

In recent years scientists have been working to isolate and grow uncommitted hematopoietic stem cells to use as replacements in patients whose own stem cells have been killed by cancer chemotherapy. Originally scientists obtained these stem cells from bone marrow or peripheral blood. Now umbilical cord blood, collected at birth, has been found to be a rich source of hematopoietic stem cells that can be used for transplants in

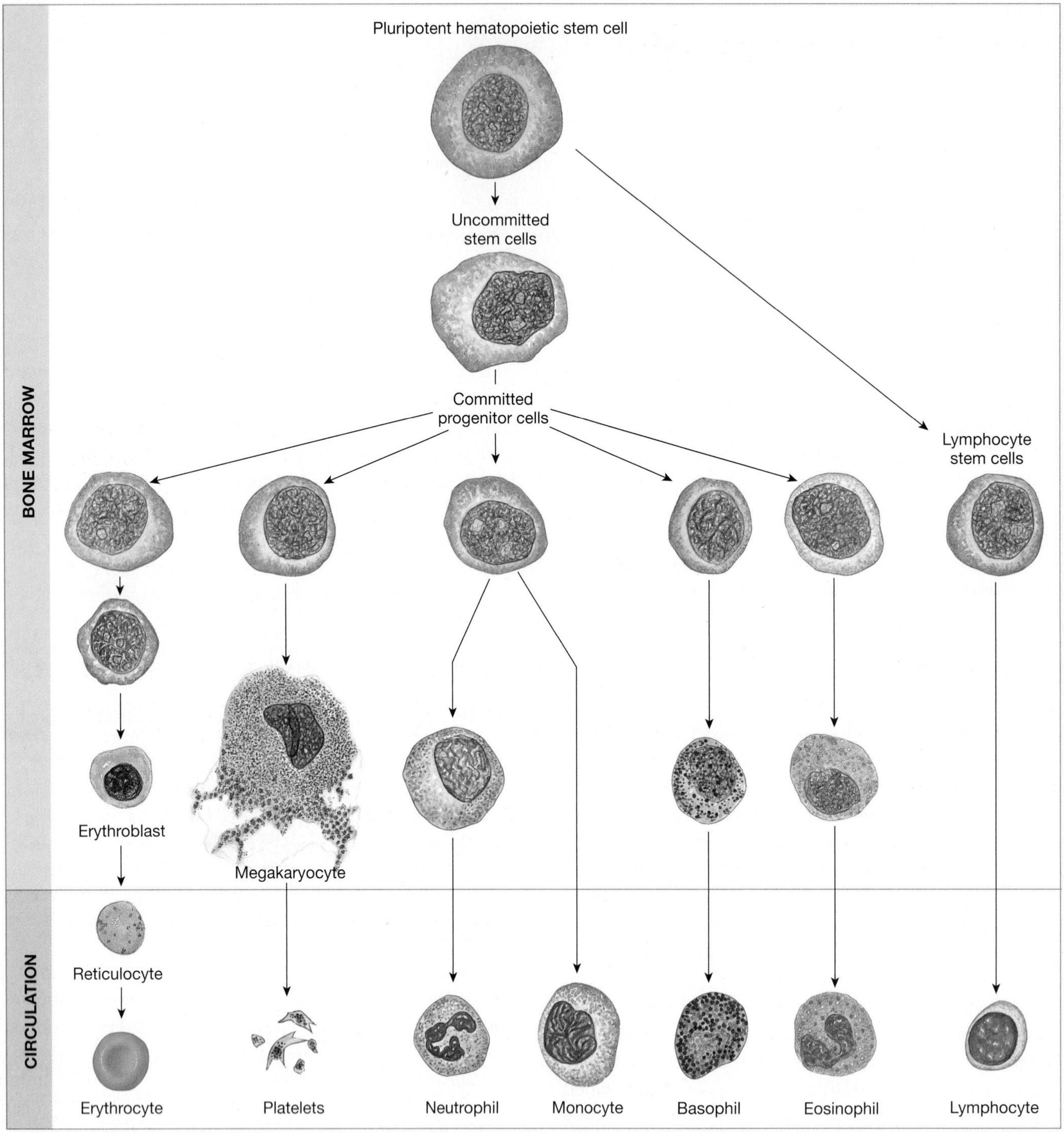

● **FIGURE 16-2** ***Hematopoiesis.*** Cells below the horizontal line are the predominant forms found circulating in the blood. Cells above the line are found mostly in the bone marrow.

patients with hematological diseases such as leukemia. Public and private cord blood banking programs are active in the United States and Europe, and the American National Marrow Donor Program Registry now includes genetic marker information from banked cord blood to help patients find stem cell matches. Currently researchers are working on techniques for culturing cord blood to increase the number of stem cells in each unit.

Blood Cells Are Produced in the Bone Marrow

Hematopoiesis [*haima,* blood + *poiesis,* formation], the synthesis of blood cells, begins early in embryonic development and continues throughout a person's life. In about the third week of fetal development, specialized cells in the yolk sac of the

TABLE 16-2 Cytokines Involved in Hematopoiesis

NAME	SITES OF PRODUCTION	INFLUENCES GROWTH OR DIFFERENTIATION OF
Erythropoietin (EPO)	Kidney cells primarily	Red blood cells
Thrombopoietin (TPO)	Liver primarily	Megakaryocytes
Colony-stimulating factors, interleukins, stem cell factor	Endothelium and fibroblasts of bone marrow, leukocytes	All types of blood cells; mobilizes hematopoietic stem cells

embryo form clusters. Some of these cell clusters are destined to become the endothelial lining of blood vessels, while others become blood cells. The common embryological origin of the endothelium and blood cells perhaps explains why many cytokines that control hematopoiesis are released by the vascular endothelium.

As the embryo develops, blood cell production spreads from the yolk sac to the liver, spleen, and bone marrow. By birth, the liver and spleen no longer produce blood cells. Hematopoiesis continues in the marrow of all the bones of the skeleton until age five. As the child continues to age, the active regions of marrow decrease. In adults, the only areas producing blood cells are the pelvis, spine, ribs, cranium, and proximal ends of long bones.

Active bone marrow is red because it contains **hemoglobin**, the oxygen-binding protein of red blood cells. Inactive marrow is yellow because of an abundance of adipocytes (fat cells). (You can see the difference between red and yellow marrow the next time you look at bony cuts of meat in the grocery store.) Although blood synthesis in adults is limited, the liver, spleen, and inactive (yellow) regions of marrow can resume blood cell production in times of need.

In the regions of marrow that are actively producing blood cells, about 25% of the developing cells are red blood cells, while 75% are destined to become white blood cells. The life span of white blood cells is considerably shorter than that of red blood cells, and so WBCs must be replaced more frequently. For example, neutrophils have a six-hour half-life, and the body must make more than *100 million* neutrophils each day in order to replace those that die. Red blood cells, on the other hand, live for nearly four months in the circulation.

Hematopoiesis Is Controlled by Cytokines

What controls the production and development of blood cells? The chemical factors known as cytokines are responsible. Cytokines are peptides or proteins released from one cell that affect the growth or activity of another cell [p. 180]. Chapter 7 describes how newly discovered hormones are identified by the word *factor,* and the same applies to cytokines. When first discovered, they are often called *factors* and given a modifier that describes their actions: growth factor, differentiating factor, trophic factor.

Some of the best-known cytokines in hematopoiesis are the *colony-stimulating factors,* molecules made by endothelial cells and white blood cells. Others are the **interleukins** [*inter-*, between + *leuko,* white], such as IL-3. The name *interleukin* was first given to cytokines released by one white blood cell to act on another white blood cell. Numbered interleukin names, such as interleukin-3, are given to cytokines once their amino acid sequences have been identified. Interleukins also play important roles in the immune system, as we discuss in Chapter 24.

Another hematopoietic cytokine is *erythropoietin,* which controls red blood cell synthesis. Erythropoietin is usually called a hormone, but technically it fits the definition of a cytokine because it is made on demand rather than stored in vesicles.

Table 16-2 ● lists a few of the many cytokines linked to hematopoiesis. The role cytokines play in blood cell production is so complicated that one review on this topic was titled "Regulation of hematopoiesis in a sea of chemokine family members with a plethora of redundant activities"!* Because of the complexity of the subject, we give only an overview of the key hematopoietic cytokines.

Colony-Stimulating Factors Regulate Leukopoiesis

Colony-stimulating factors (CSFs) were identified and named for their ability to stimulate the growth of leukocyte colonies in culture. These cytokines, made by endothelial cells, marrow fibroblasts, and white blood cells, regulate leukocyte production and development, or **leukopoiesis**. CSFs induce both cell division (mitosis) and cell maturation in stem cells. Once a leukocyte matures, it loses its ability to undergo mitosis.

One fascinating aspect of leukopoiesis is that production of new white blood cells is regulated in part by existing white blood cells. This form of control allows leukocyte development to be very specific and tailored to the body's needs. When the

*Broxmeyer, H. E. and C. H. Kim, *Experimental Hematology* 27(7): 1113–1123, 1999, July.

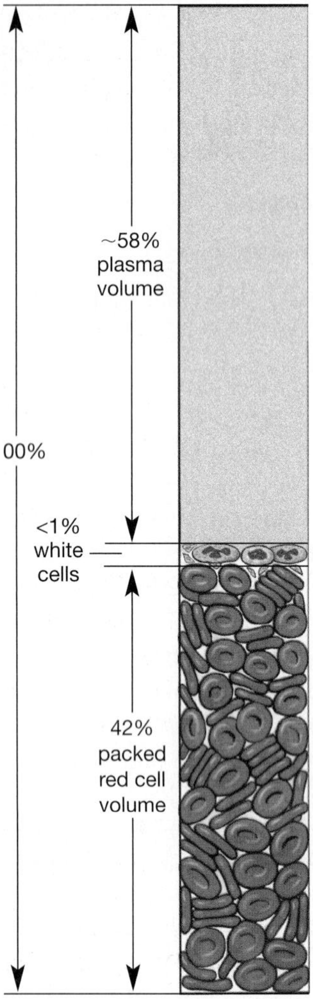

	MALES	FEMALES
Hematocrit	40%–54%	37%–47%
Hemoglobin (g Hb/dL* blood)	14–17	12–16
Red cell count (cells/μL)	$4.5–6.5 \times 10^6$	$3.9–5.6 \times 10^6$
Total white cell count (cells/μL)	$4–11 \times 10^3$	$4–11 \times 10^3$
Differential white cell count		
Neutrophils	50%–70%	50%–70%
Eosinophils	1%–4%	1%–4%
Basophils	<1%	<1%
Lymphocytes	20%–40%	20%–40%
Monocytes	2%–8%	2%–8%
Platelets (per μL)	$150–450 \times 10^3$	$150–450 \times 10^3$

*1 deciliter (dL) = 100 mL

● **FIGURE 16-3** ***The blood count.*** The table lists the normal ranges of values. **Hematocrit** is the percentage of total blood volume that is occupied by packed (centrifuged) red blood cells. The **hemoglobin** value reflects the oxygen-carrying capacity of red blood cells. In a **red cell count**, a machine counts erythrocytes as they stream through a beam of light. **Total white cell count** includes all types of leukocytes but does not distinguish between them. The **differential white cell count** presents estimates of the relative proportions of the five types of leukocytes in a thin blood smear stained with biological dyes. **Platelet count** is suggestive of the blood's ability to clot.

body's defense system is called on to fight off foreign invaders, both the absolute number of white blood cells and the relative proportions of the different types of white blood cells in the circulation change.

Clinicians often rely on a *differential white cell count* to help them arrive at a diagnosis (Fig. 16-3 ●). For example, a person with a bacterial infection usually has a high total number of white blood cells in the blood, with an increased percentage that are neutrophils. Cytokines released by active white blood cells fighting the bacterial infection stimulate the production of additional neutrophils and monocytes. A person with a viral infection may have a high, normal, or low total white cell count but often shows an increase in the percentage of lymphocytes. The complex process by which leukocyte production is matched to need is still not completely understood and is an active area of research.

Scientists are working to create a model for the control of leukopoiesis so that they can develop effective treatments for diseases characterized by either a lack or an excess of white blood cells. The *leukemias* are a group of diseases characterized by the abnormal growth and development of white blood cells. In *neutropenias* [*penia,* poverty], patients have too few white blood cells and are unable to fight off bacterial and viral infections. Researchers hope to find better treatments for both leukemias and neutropenias by unlocking the secrets of how the body regulates cell growth and division.

Thrombopoietin Regulates Platelet Production

Thrombopoietin (TPO) is a glycoprotein that regulates the growth and maturation of megakaryocytes, the parent cells of platelets. (Recall that *thrombocyte* is an alternative name for *platelet*). TPO is produced primarily in the liver but is also present in the kidney. This cytokine was first described in 1958, but its gene was not cloned until 1994. Within a year, TPO was widely available to researchers through the use of recombinant DNA techniques, and there has been an explosion of papers describing its effects on megakaryocytes and platelet production. Scientists still do not understand everything about the basic biology of thrombopoiesis, but TPO synthesis is a huge step forward in the search for answers.

Erythropoietin Regulates RBC Production

Red blood cell production (**erythropoiesis**) is controlled by the glycoprotein **erythropoietin (EPO)**, assisted by several cytokines. Erythropoietin is made primarily in the kidneys of adults. The stimulus for EPO synthesis and release is *hypoxia,* low oxygen levels in the tissues. Hypoxia stimulates production of a transcription factor called *hypoxia-inducible factor 1* (HIF-1), which turns on the EPO gene to increase EPO synthesis. This pathway, like other endocrine pathways, helps the body maintain homeostasis. By stimulating the synthesis of red blood cells, EPO puts more hemoglobin into the circulation to carry oxygen.

The existence of a hormone controlling red blood cell production was first suggested in the 1950s, but two decades passed before scientists succeeded in purifying the substance. One reason for the delay is that EPO is made on demand and not stored, as in an endocrine cell. It took scientists another nine years to identify the amino acid sequence of EPO and to isolate and clone the gene for it. However, an incredible leap was made after the EPO gene was isolated: only two years later, the hormone was produced by recombinant DNA technology and put into clinical use.

In recent years physicians have been able to prescribe not only genetically engineered EPO, such as epoetin, but also several colony-stimulating factors (sargramostim and filgrastim) that stimulate white blood cell synthesis. Cancer patients in whom hematopoiesis has been suppressed by chemotherapy have benefited from injections of these hematopoietic hormones, but in 2007 the Food and Drug Administration issued new dosing instructions and warnings about an increased risk of blood clots in patients taking erythropoiesis-stimulating agents. Scientists are currently monitoring the safety of CSFs to ensure that they do not increase the likelihood of developing hematological diseases.

CONCEPT CHECK

4. Name the cytokine(s) that regulates growth and maturation in (a) erythrocytes, (b) leukocytes, and (c) megakaryocytes.

Answers: p. 567

RED BLOOD CELLS

Erythrocytes are the most abundant cell type in the blood. A microliter of blood contains about 5 million red blood cells, compared with only 4000–11,000 white blood cells and 150,000–450,000 platelets. The primary function of red blood cells is to facilitate oxygen transport from the lungs to cells, and carbon dioxide transport from cells to lungs.

The ratio of red blood cells to plasma is indicated clinically by the **hematocrit** and is expressed as a percentage of the total blood volume (Fig. 16-3). Hematocrit is determined by drawing a blood sample into a narrow capillary tube and spinning it in a centrifuge so that the heavier red blood cells go to the bottom of the sealed tube, leaving the thin "buffy layer" of lighter white blood cells and platelets in the middle, and plasma on top.

The column of *packed red cells* is measured, and the hematocrit value is reported as a percentage of the total sample volume. The normal range of hematocrit is 40–54% for a man and 37–47% for a woman. This test provides a rapid and inexpensive way to estimate a person's red cell count because blood for a hematocrit can be collected by simply sticking a finger.

Mature RBCs Lack a Nucleus

In the bone marrow, committed progenitor cells differentiate through several stages into large, nucleated *erythroblasts*. As erythroblasts mature, the nucleus condenses and the cell shrinks in diameter from 20 μm to about 7 μm. In the last stage before maturation, the nucleus is pinched off and phagocytosed by bone marrow macrophages. At the same time, other membranous organelles (such as mitochondria) break down and disappear. The final immature cell form, called a *reticulocyte,* leaves the marrow and enters the circulation, where it matures into an erythrocyte in about 24 hours (Fig. 16-4c ●).

Mature mammalian red blood cells are biconcave disks, shaped much like jelly doughnuts with the filling squeezed out of the middle (Fig. 16-5a ● and 16-6b ●). They are simple membranous "bags" filled with enzymes and hemoglobin. Because red blood cells contain no mitochondria, they cannot carry out aerobic metabolism. Glycolysis is their primary source of ATP. Without a nucleus and endoplasmic reticulum to carry out protein synthesis, erythrocytes are unable to make new enzymes or to renew membrane components. This inability leads to an increasing loss of membrane flexibility, making older cells more fragile and likely to rupture.

The biconcave shape of the red blood cell is one of its most distinguishing features. The membrane is held in place by a complex cytoskeleton composed of filaments linked to

RUNNING PROBLEM

Blood doping to increase the oxygen-carrying capacity of the blood has been a problem in endurance sports for more than 30 years. The first sign that Muehlegg might be cheating by this method was the result of a simple blood test for hemoglobin and a hematocrit, taken several hours before his 50-kilometer race. Muehlegg's blood hemoglobin level registered above 17.5 g/dL. A repeat test was within acceptable limits, however, and Muehlegg was allowed to race.

Question 1:

What is the normal range for Muehlegg's hemoglobin (Fig. 16-3)?

Question 2:

Olympic officials also tested Muehlegg's hematocrit. With blood doping, would you expect a hematocrit value to be lower or higher than normal?

547 553 558 561 565

FOCUS ON . . . BONE MARROW

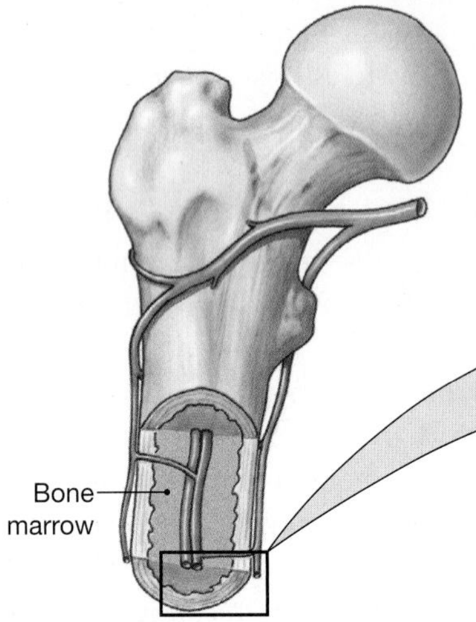
Bone marrow

(a) The bone marrow, hidden within the bones of the skeleton, is easily overlooked as a tissue, although collectively, it is nearly the size and weight of the liver!

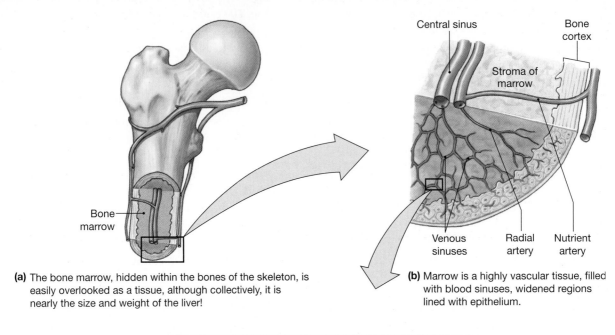

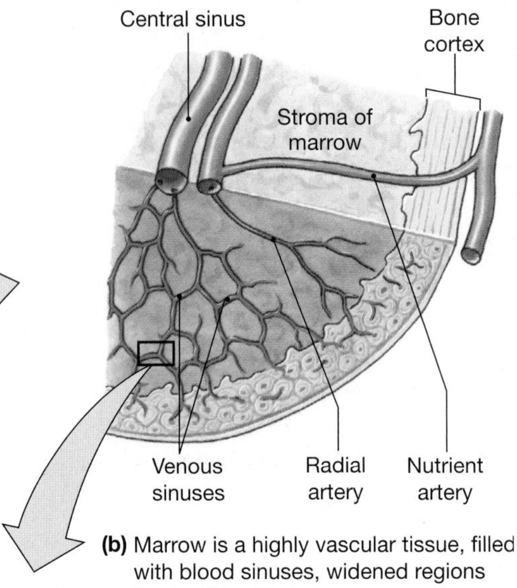
Central sinus
Bone cortex
Stroma of marrow
Venous sinuses
Radial artery
Nutrient artery

(b) Marrow is a highly vascular tissue, filled with blood sinuses, widened regions lined with epithelium.

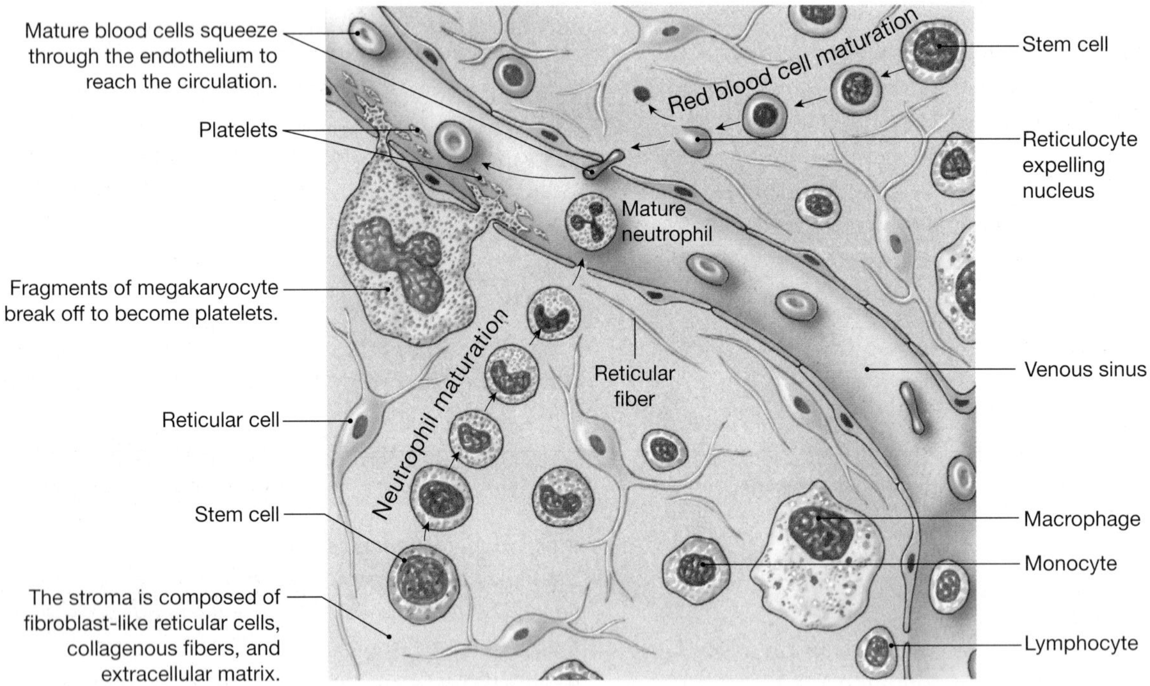
Mature blood cells squeeze through the endothelium to reach the circulation.
Platelets
Fragments of megakaryocyte break off to become platelets.
Reticular cell
Stem cell
The stroma is composed of fibroblast-like reticular cells, collagenous fibers, and extracellular matrix.
Red blood cell maturation
Mature neutrophil
Neutrophil maturation
Reticular fiber
Stem cell
Reticulocyte expelling nucleus
Venous sinus
Macrophage
Monocyte
Lymphocyte

(c) Bone marrow consists of blood cells in different stages of development and supporting tissue known as the **stroma** [mattress].

● **FIGURE 16-4**

transmembrane attachment proteins (Fig. 16-5c). Despite the cytoskeleton, red cells are remarkably flexible, like a partially filled water balloon that can compress into various shapes. This flexibility allows erythrocytes to change shape as they squeeze through the narrow capillaries of the circulation.

The disk-like structure of red blood cells also allows them to modify their shape in response to osmotic changes in the blood. An erythrocyte placed in a slightly hypotonic medium [p. 161] swells and forms a sphere without disruption of its membrane integrity (Fig. 16-6a). In hypertonic media, red

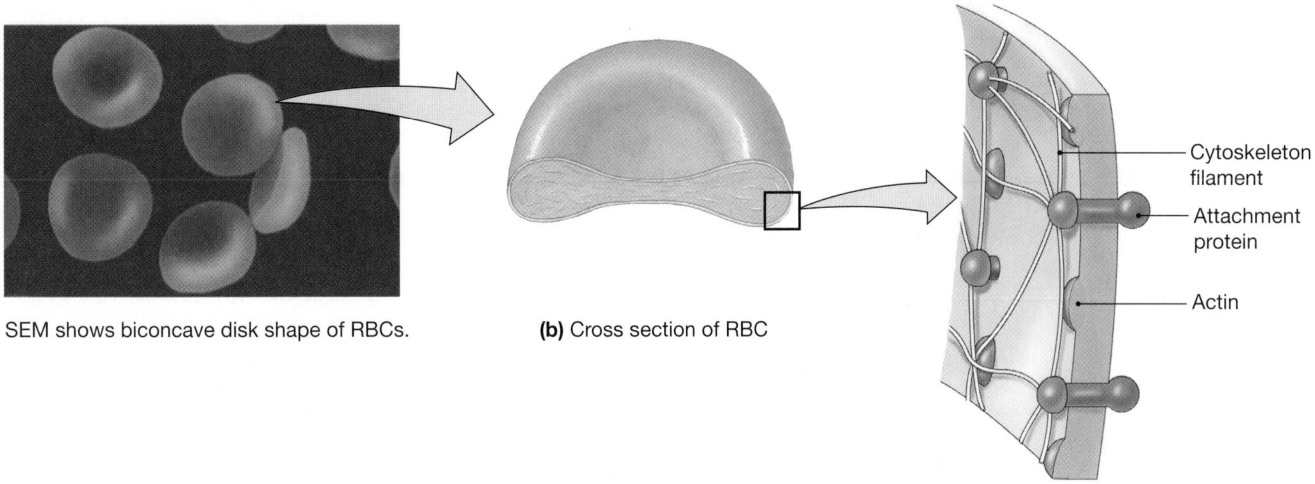
Cytoskeleton filament
Attachment protein
Actin

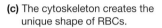

(a) SEM shows biconcave disk shape of RBCs.

(b) Cross section of RBC

(c) The cytoskeleton creates the unique shape of RBCs.

● **FIGURE 16-5** ***Red blood cells are shaped by their cytoskeleton.***

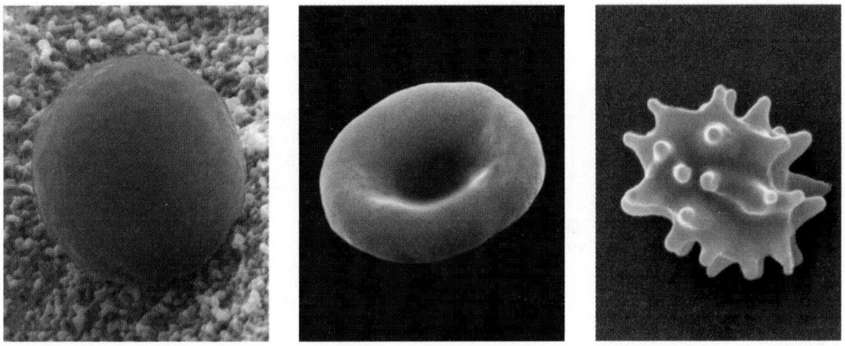

(a) **(b)** **(c)**

● **FIGURE 16-6** ***Osmotic changes to red blood cell shape.*** **(a)** Erythrocytes placed in a hypotonic medium swell and lose their characteristic biconcave disk shape, shown in **(b).** **(c)** Erythrocytes placed in a hypertonic medium shrink, but the rigid cytoskeleton remains intact, creating a spiky surface. These cells are said to be *crenated* [*crenatus,* a notch].

blood cells shrink up and develop a spiky surface when the membrane pulls tight against the cytoskeleton (Fig. 16-6c).

The **morphology** [*morphe,* form] of red blood cells can provide clues to the presence of disease. Sometimes the cells lose their flattened disk shape and become spherical (*spherocytosis*). In sickle cell anemia, the cells are shaped like a sickle or crescent moon. In some disease states, the size of red blood cells—the **mean red cell volume** (MCV)—may be either abnormally large or abnormally small. For example, red blood cells can be abnormally small in iron-deficiency anemia.

Hemoglobin Synthesis Requires Iron

Hemoglobin (Hb) is a tetramer comprising four globular protein chains (*globins*), each centered around an iron-containing *heme* group. We discuss the details of how hemoglobin transports oxygen in Chapter 18, but in this section we look at the process of hemoglobin synthesis and metabolism (Fig. 16-7 ●).

Hemoglobin synthesis requires an adequate supply of iron in the diet, from sources such as red meat, beans, spinach, and iron-fortified bread ①. Iron is absorbed in the small intestine by active transport ② (for details, see Chapter 21). It is transported in the blood by a carrier protein called **transferrin** ③. Developing red blood cells in the bone marrow use iron to make the heme group of hemoglobin ⑤. Excess iron in the body is stored, mostly in the liver, in the protein **ferritin** and its derivatives ④.

Excess iron in the body is toxic, and poisoning sometimes occurs in children when they ingest too many vitamin pills

CLINICAL FOCUS

DIABETES

HEMOGLOBIN AND HYPERGLYCEMIA

One of the goals of diabetes treatment is to keep blood glucose concentrations as close to normal as possible, but how can a clinician tell if a patient has been doing this? One way is to measure the patient's hemoglobin. Glucose in the plasma binds covalently to hemoglobin, producing a glycohemoglobin known as **hemoglobin A_{1C}** ("A-one-C"). The amount of hemoglobin A_{1C} in the plasma is directly related to hemoglobin's exposure to glucose over the preceding 8–12 weeks. By using this assay, a clinician can monitor long-term fluctuations in blood glucose levels and adjust a diabetic patient's therapy appropriately.

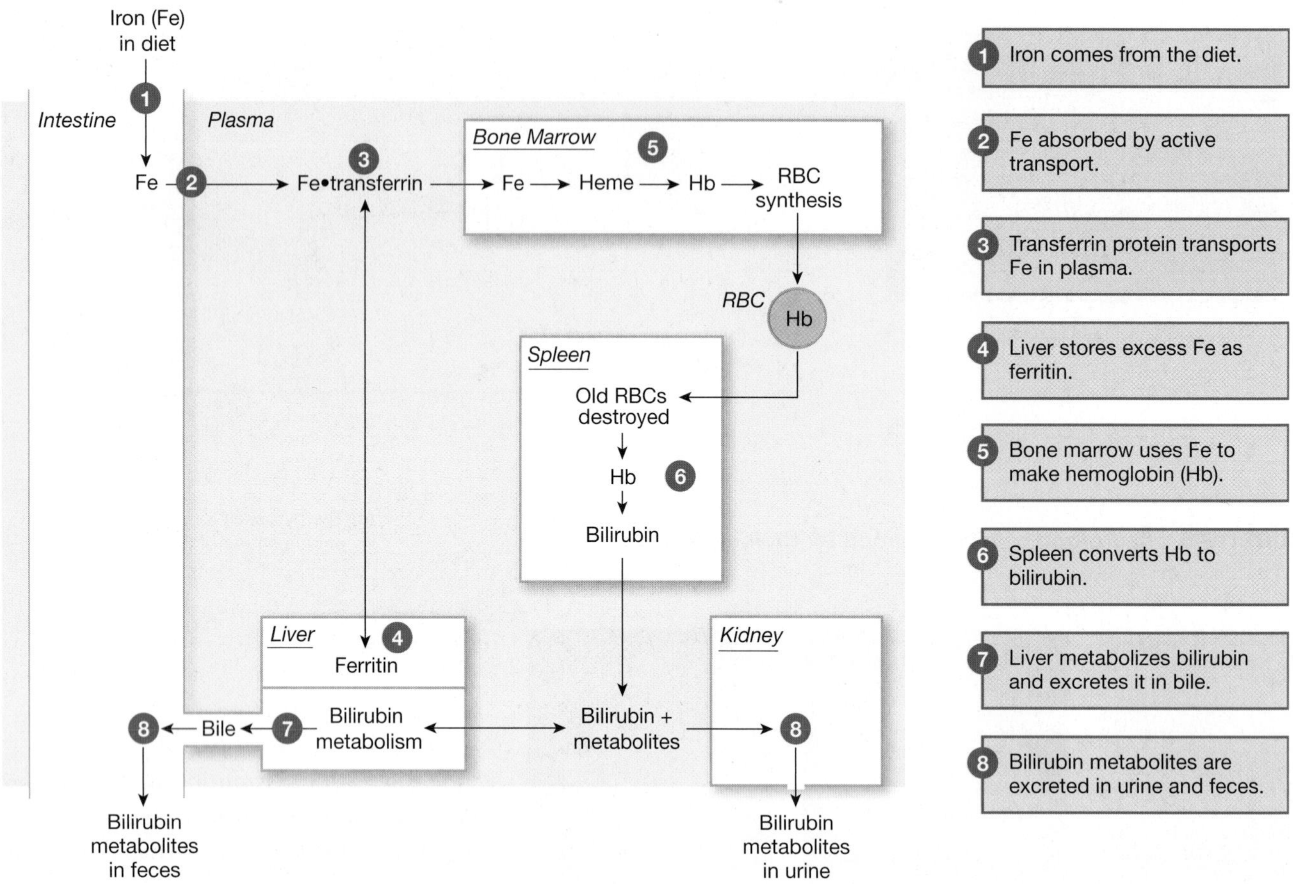
Iron (Fe)
in diet
Intestine
Plasma
Fe
Fe•transferrin
Bone Marrow
Fe → Heme → Hb → RBC synthesis
RBC
Hb
Spleen
Old RBCs destroyed
Hb
Bilirubin
Liver
Ferritin
Bilirubin metabolism
Bile
Bilirubin + metabolites
Kidney
Bilirubin metabolites in feces
Bilirubin metabolites in urine
1 Iron comes from the diet.
2 Fe absorbed by active transport.
3 Transferrin protein transports Fe in plasma.
4 Liver stores excess Fe as ferritin.
5 Bone marrow uses Fe to make hemoglobin (Hb).
6 Spleen converts Hb to bilirubin.
7 Liver metabolizes bilirubin and excretes it in bile.
8 Bilirubin metabolites are excreted in urine and feces.

● **FIGURE 16-7** ***Iron homeostasis and metabolism***

containing iron. Initial symptoms of iron toxicity are gastrointestinal pain, cramping, and internal bleeding, which occurs as iron corrodes the digestive epithelium. Subsequent problems include liver failure, which can be fatal.

RBCs Live About Four Months

Red blood cells in the circulation live for about 120 ± 20 days. Increasingly fragile older erythrocytes may rupture as they try to squeeze through narrow capillaries, or they may be engulfed by scavenging macrophages as they pass through the spleen (Fig. 16-7 ⑥).

Many components of hemoglobin are recycled. Amino acids from the globin chains are incorporated into new proteins, and some iron from the heme groups is reused in new heme groups. The spleen and liver convert remnants of the heme groups to a colored pigment called **bilirubin**. Bilirubin is carried by plasma albumin to the liver, where it is metabolized and incorporated into a secretion called **bile** (Fig. 16-7 ⑦). Bile is secreted into the digestive tract, and the bilirubin metabolites leave the body in the feces. Small amounts of other bilirubin metabolites are filtered from the blood in the kidneys, where they contribute to the yellow color of urine ⑧.

In some circumstances, bilirubin levels in the blood become elevated (*hyperbilirubinemia*). This condition, known as **jaundice**, causes the skin and whites of the eyes to take on a yellow cast. The accumulation of bilirubin can occur from several different causes. Newborns whose fetal hemoglobin is being broken down and replaced with adult hemoglobin are particularly susceptible to bilirubin toxicity, so doctors monitor babies for jaundice in the first weeks of life. Another common cause of jaundice is liver disease, in which the liver is unable to process or excrete bilirubin.

CONCEPT CHECK

5. Distinguish between (a) heme and hemoglobin, and (b) ferritin and transferrin.
6. Is bile an endocrine secretion or an exocrine secretion?

Answers: p. 567

RBC Disorders Decrease Oxygen Transport

Because hemoglobin plays a critical role in oxygen transport, the red blood cell count and hemoglobin content of the body are important. If hemoglobin content is too low—a condition known as **anemia**—the blood cannot transport enough oxygen to the tissues. People with anemia are usually tired and weak, especially during exercise. The major causes of anemia are summarized in Table 16-3 ●.

In the *hemolytic anemias* [*lysis,* rupture], the rate of red blood cell destruction exceeds the rate of red blood cell production. The hemolytic anemias are usually hereditary defects in which the body makes fragile cells. For example, in *hereditary spherocytosis,*

TABLE 16-3 Causes of Anemia

ACCELERATED RED BLOOD CELL LOSS
Blood loss: cells are normal in size and hemoglobin content but low in number
Hemolytic anemias: cells rupture at an abnormally high rate
Hereditary
Membrane defects (example: hereditary spherocytosis)
Enzyme defects
Abnormal hemoglobin (example: sickle cell anemia)
Acquired
Parasitic infections (example: malaria)
Drugs
Autoimmune reactions
DECREASED RED BLOOD CELL PRODUCTION
Defective red blood cell or hemoglobin synthesis in the bone marrow
Aplastic anemia: can be caused by certain drugs or radiation
Inadequate dietary intake of essential nutrients
Iron deficiency (iron is required for heme production)
Folic acid deficiency (folic acid is required for DNA synthesis)
Vitamin B_{12} deficiency (B_{12} is required for DNA synthesis): may be due to lack of intrinsic factor for B_{12} absorption.
Inadequate production of erythropoietin

the erythrocyte cytoskeleton does not link properly because of defective or deficient cytoskeletal proteins. Consequently, the cells are shaped more like spheres than like biconcave disks. This disruption in the cytoskeleton results in red blood cells that rupture easily and are unable to withstand osmotic changes as well as normal cells can. Several of the hemolytic anemias are acquired diseases, as indicated in Table 16-3.

Some anemias are the result of abnormal hemoglobin molecules. *Sickle cell disease* is a genetic defect in which glutamate, the sixth amino acid in the 146–amino acid beta chain of hemoglobin, is replaced by valine. The result is abnormal hemoglobin (a form referred to as *HbS*) that crystallizes when it gives up its oxygen. This crystallization pulls the red blood cells into a sickle shape, like a crescent moon (Fig. 16-8 ●). The sickled cells become tangled with other sickled cells as they pass through the smallest blood vessels, causing the cells to jam up and block blood flow to the tissues. This blockage creates tissue damage and pain from hypoxia.

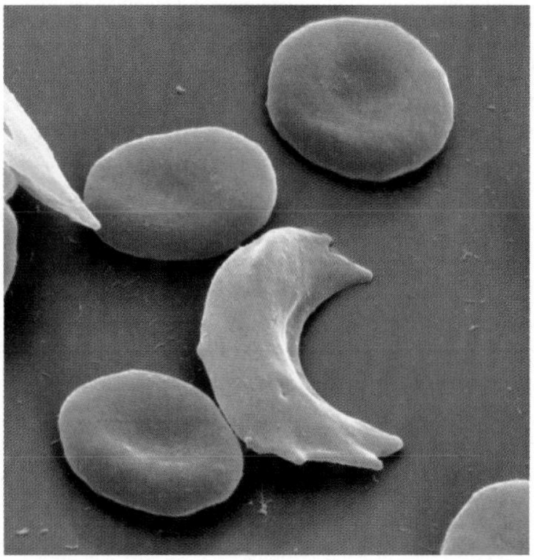

● **FIGURE 16-8** ***Sickled red blood cells***

One treatment for sickle cell disease is the administration of *hydroxyurea,* a compound that inhibits DNA synthesis. Hydroxyurea alters bone marrow function so that immature red blood cells produce the fetal form of hemoglobin (*HbF*) instead of adult hemoglobin. HbF interferes with the crystallization of hemoglobin, so that HbS no longer forms and the red blood cells no longer sickle. In addition, some studies show improvements in sickle cell symptoms before HbF levels increase. One theory of why this happens is based on the finding that hydroxyurea is metabolized to nitric oxide (NO), which causes vasodilation. Inhaled nitric oxide is now being tested as a treatment for sickle cell disease symptoms.

Other anemias result from the failure of the bone marrow to make adequate amounts of hemoglobin. One of the most common examples of an anemia that results from insufficient hemoglobin synthesis is *iron-deficiency anemia.* If iron loss by the body exceeds iron intake, the marrow does not have adequate iron to make heme groups, and hemoglobin synthesis slows. People with iron-deficiency anemia have either a low red blood cell count (reflected in a low hematocrit) or a low hemoglobin content in their blood. Their red blood cells are often smaller than usual (*microcytic* red blood cells), and the lower hemoglobin content may cause the cells to be paler than normal, in which case they are described as being *hypochromic* [*hypo-,* below normal; *chrom-,* color]. Women who menstruate are likely to suffer from iron-deficiency anemia because of iron loss in menstrual blood.

Although the anemias are common, it is also possible to have too many red blood cells. *Polycythemia vera* [*vera,* true] is a stem cell dysfunction that produces too many blood cells, white as well as red. These patients may have hematocrits as high as 60–70% (normal is 37–54%). The increased number of cells causes the blood to become more viscous and thus more resistant to flow through the circulatory system [p. 473].

In *relative polycythemia,* the person's red blood cell number is normal, but the hematocrit is elevated because of low plasma volume. This might occur with dehydration, for example. The

16

opposite problem can also occur. If an athlete overhydrates, the hematocrit may decrease temporarily because of increased plasma volume. In both of these situations, there is no actual pathology involving the red blood cells.

CONCEPT CHECK

7. A person who goes from sea level to a city that is 5000 feet above sea level begins to show an increased hematocrit within days. Draw the reflex pathway that links the hypoxia of high altitude to increased red blood cell production. Answers: p. 567

PLATELETS AND COAGULATION

Because of its fluid nature, blood flows freely throughout the circulatory system. However, if there is a break in the "piping" of the system, blood will be lost unless steps are taken. One of the challenges for the body is to plug holes in damaged blood vessels while still maintaining blood flow through the vessel.

It would be simple to block off a damaged blood vessel completely, like putting a barricade across a street full of potholes. However, just as shopkeepers on that street lose business if traffic is blocked, cells downstream from the point of injury die from lack of oxygen and nutrients if the vessel is completely blocked. The body's task is to allow blood flow through the vessel while simultaneously repairing the damaged wall.

This challenge is complicated by the fact that blood in the system is under pressure. If the repair "patch" is too weak, it is

RUNNING PROBLEM

In its earliest form, blood doping was accomplished by blood transfusions, which increased the athlete's oxygen-carrying capacity. One hallmark of a recent blood transfusion is elevated hemoglobin and hematocrit levels. Muehlegg claimed that his elevated hemoglobin was a result of his special diet and of dehydration from diarrhea he had suffered the night before.

Question 3:
Explain how diarrhea could cause a temporarily elevated hematocrit.

Question 4:
How might Muehlegg quickly reduce his hematocrit without removing red blood cells?

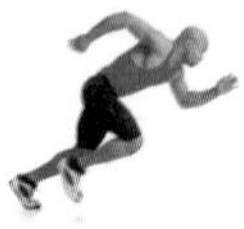

547 553 558 561 565

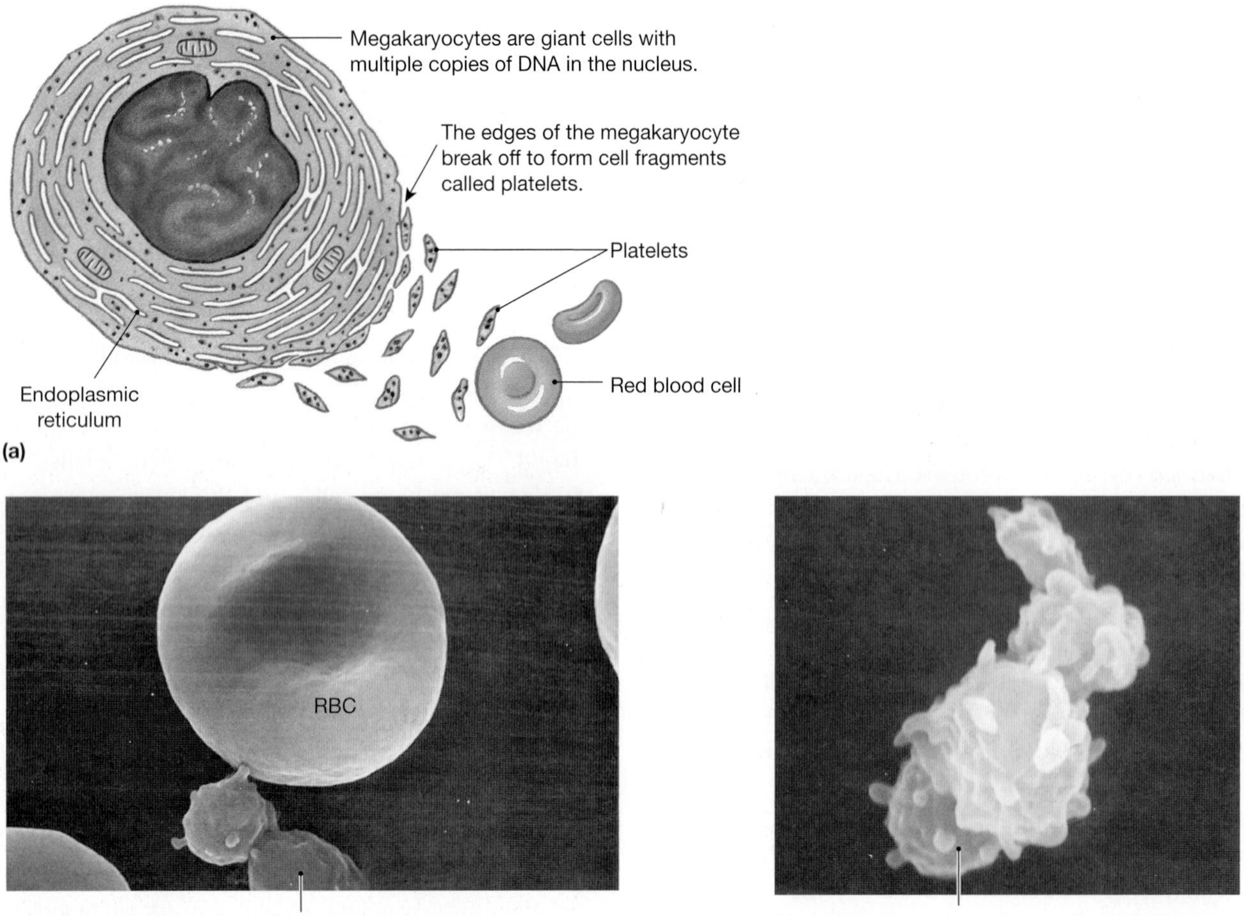
Megakaryocytes are giant cells with multiple copies of DNA in the nucleus.
The edges of the megakaryocyte break off to form cell fragments called platelets.
Platelets
Red blood cell
Endoplasmic reticulum
(a)
RBC

(b) Inactive platelets are small disk-like cell fragments.

(c) Activated platelets (shown enlarged) develop a spiky outer surface and adhere to each other.

● **FIGURE 16-9** ***Platelets form from megakaryocytes.***

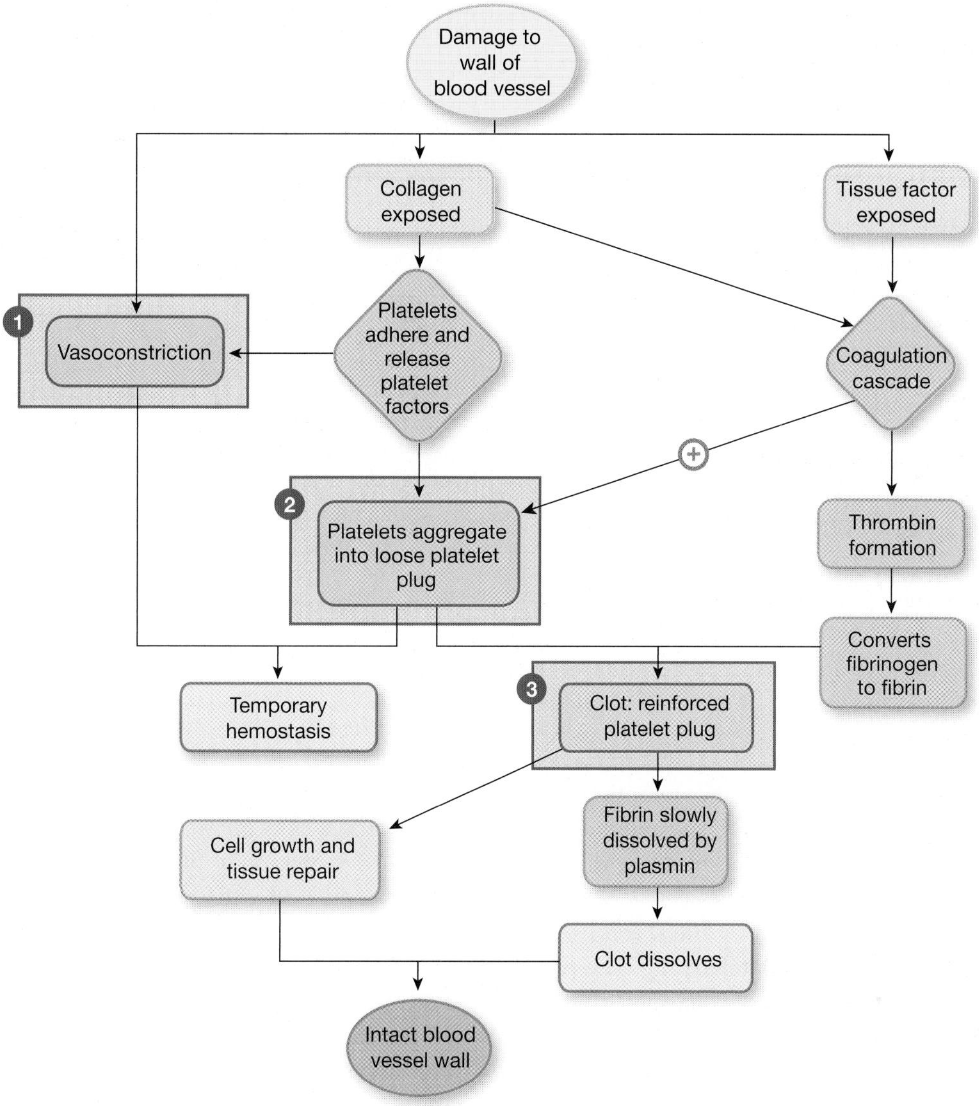

● **FIGURE 16-10** ***Overview of hemostasis and tissue repair***

blown out by the blood pressure. For this reason, stopping blood loss involves several steps. First, the pressure in the vessel must be decreased long enough to create a secure mechanical seal in the form of a blood clot. Once the clot is in place and blood loss has been stopped, the body's repair mechanisms can take over. Then, as the wound heals, enzymes gradually dissolve the clot while scavenger white blood cells ingest and destroy the debris.

Platelets Are Small Fragments of Cells

As noted earlier, platelets are cell fragments produced in the bone marrow from huge cells called megakaryocytes. Megakaryocytes develop their formidable size by undergoing mitosis up to seven times without undergoing nuclear or cytoplasmic division. The result is a *polyploid* cell with a lobed nucleus (Fig. 16-9a ●).

The outer edges of marrow megakaryocytes extend through the endothelium into the lumen of marrow blood sinuses, where the cytoplasmic extensions fragment into disk-like platelets (Fig. 16-4c). Platelets are smaller than red blood cells, are colorless, and have no nucleus. Their cytoplasm contains mitochondria, smooth endoplasmic reticulum, and many granules filled with clotting proteins and cytokines.

The typical life span of a platelet is about 10 days. Platelets are always present in the blood, but they are not active unless damage occurs to the walls of the circulatory system.

Hemostasis Prevents Blood Loss from Damaged Vessels

Hemostasis [*haima,* blood + *stasis,* stoppage] is the process of keeping blood within a damaged blood vessel. (The opposite of hemostasis is *hemorrhage* [*-rrhagia,* abnormal flow]). Hemostasis has three major steps: ① vasoconstriction, ② temporary blockage of a break by a platelet plug, and ③ blood coagulation, or formation of a clot that seals the hole until tissues are repaired.

Figure 16-10 ● gives an overview of hemostasis. The first step is immediate constriction of damaged vessels caused by

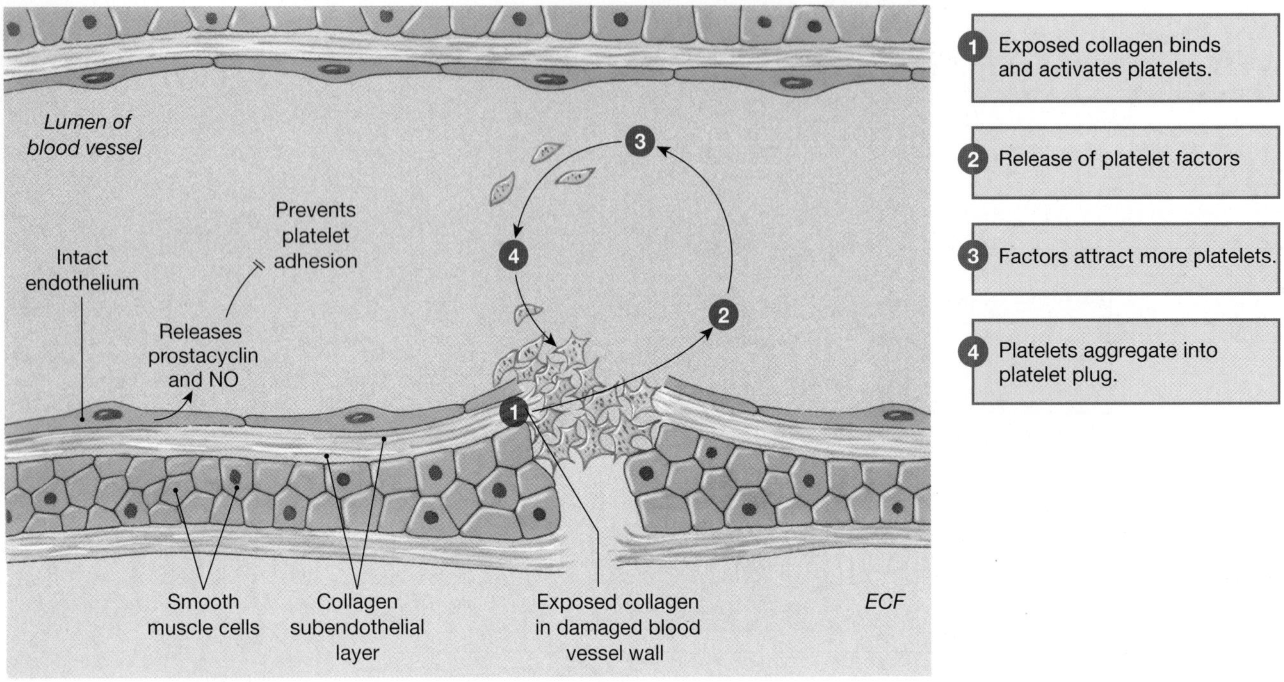

Lumen of blood vessel
Intact endothelium
Prevents platelet adhesion
Releases prostacyclin and NO
Smooth muscle cells
Collagen subendothelial layer
Exposed collagen in damaged blood vessel wall
ECF
1 Exposed collagen binds and activates platelets.
2 Release of platelet factors
3 Factors attract more platelets.
4 Platelets aggregate into platelet plug.

● **FIGURE 16-11** *Platelet plug formation*

vasoconstrictive paracrines released by the endothelium. Vasoconstriction temporarily decreases blood flow and pressure within the vessel. When you put pressure on a bleeding wound, you also decrease flow within the damaged vessel.

Vasoconstriction is rapidly followed by the second step, mechanical blockage of the hole by a **platelet plug**. The plug forms as platelets stick to the exposed collagen (**platelet adhesion**) and become activated, releasing cytokines into the area around the injury. Platelet factors reinforce local vasoconstriction and activate more platelets, which stick to one another (**platelet aggregation**) to form a loose platelet plug.

Simultaneously, exposed collagen and **tissue factor** (a protein-phospholipid mixture) initiate the third step, a series of reactions known as the **coagulation cascade**. The cascade is a series of enzymatic reactions that ends in the formation of a *fibrin* protein fiber mesh that stabilizes the platelet plug. The reinforced platelet plug is called a **clot**. Some chemical factors involved in the coagulation cascade also promote platelet adhesion and aggregation in the damaged region.

Eventually, as the damaged vessel repairs itself, the clot retracts and is slowly dissolved by the enzyme **plasmin**.

The body must maintain the proper balance during hemostasis. Too little hemostasis allows excessive bleeding; too much creates a **thrombus**, a blood clot that adheres to the undamaged wall of a blood vessel [*thrombos,* a clot or lump]. A large thrombus can block the lumen of the vessel and stop blood flow.

Hemostasis seems straightforward, but unanswered questions remain at the cellular and molecular levels. Because inappropriate blood clotting plays an important role in strokes and heart attacks, this area of research is very active. Research has led to the development and use of "clot busters," enzymes that can dissolve clots in arteries after heart attacks and strokes.

A detailed study of hemostasis involves many chemical factors, some of which play multiple roles and have multiple names. For this reason, learning about hemostasis can be especially challenging. For example, some factors participate in both platelet plug formation and coagulation, and one factor in the cascade activates enzymes for both clot formation and clot dissolution. Because of the complexity of the coagulation cascade, we discuss only a few aspects of hemostasis in additional detail.

Platelet Activation Begins the Clotting Process

When a blood vessel wall is first damaged, exposed collagen and chemicals from endothelial cells activate platelets (Fig. 16-10). Normally, the blood vessel's endothelium separates the collagenous matrix fibers from the circulating blood (Fig. 16-11 ●). But when the vessel is damaged, collagen is exposed, and platelets rapidly begin to adhere to it.

Platelets adhere to collagen with the help of *integrins,* membrane receptor proteins that are linked to the cytoskeleton [p. 188]. Binding activates platelets so that they release the contents of their intracellular granules, including *serotonin* (5-hydroxytryptamine), ADP, and **platelet-activating factor (PAF)**. PAF sets up a positive feedback loop by activating more platelets. It also initiates pathways that convert platelet membrane phospholipids into **thromboxane A_2** [p. 193]. Serotonin and thromboxane A_2 are vasoconstrictors. They also contribute to platelet aggregation, along with ADP and PAF

TABLE 16-4 Factors Involved in Platelet Function

CHEMICAL FACTOR	SOURCE	ACTIVATED BY OR RELEASED IN RESPONSE TO	ROLE IN PLATELET PLUG FORMATION	OTHER ROLES AND COMMENTS
Collagen	Subendothelial extracellular matrix	Injury exposes platelets to collagen	Binds platelets to begin platelet plug	N/A
von Willebrand factor (vWF)	Endothelium, megakaryocytes	Exposure to collagen	Links platelets to collagen	Deficiency or defect causes prolonged bleeding
Serotonin	Secretory vesicles of platelets	Platelet activation	Platelet aggregation	Vasoconstrictor
Adenosine diphosphate (ADP)	Platelet mitochondria	Platelet activation, thrombin	Platelet aggregation	N/A
Platelet-activating factor (PAF)	Platelets, neutrophils, monocytes	Platelet activation	Platelet aggregation	Plays role in inflammation; increases capillary permeability
Thromboxane A_2	Phospholipids in platelet membranes	Platelet-activating factor	Platelet aggregation	Vasoconstrictor; eicosanoid
Platelet-derived growth factor (PDGF)	Platelets	Platelet activation	N/A	Promotes wound healing by attracting fibroblasts and smooth muscle cells

(Table 16-4 ●). The net result is a growing platelet plug that seals the damaged vessel wall.

If platelet aggregation is a positive feedback event, what prevents the platelet plug from continuing to form and spreading beyond the site of injury to other areas of the vessel wall? The answer lies in the fact that platelets do not adhere to normal endothelium. Intact vascular endothelial cells convert their membrane lipids into **prostacyclin**, an eicosanoid [p. 31] that blocks platelet adhesion and aggregation (Fig. 16-11). Nitric oxide released by normal, intact endothelium also inhibits platelets from adhering. The combination of platelet attraction to the injury site and repulsion from the normal vessel wall creates a localized response that limits the platelet plug to the area of damage.

Coagulation Converts a Platelet Plug into a Clot

The third major step in hemostasis, coagulation, is a complex process in which fluid blood forms a gelatinous clot (see Fig. 16-10). Coagulation is divided into two pathways that eventually merge into one (Fig. 16-12 ●). An **intrinsic pathway** (yellow) begins with collagen exposure and involves proteins already present in the plasma. Collagen activates the first enzyme, factor XII, to begin the cascade. An **extrinsic pathway** (blue) starts when damaged tissues expose tissue factor, also called *tissue thromboplastin* or factor III. Tissue factor activates factor VII to begin the extrinsic pathway. The two pathways

RUNNING PROBLEM

After the 1984 Olympics Games, where U.S. cyclists reportedly suffered bad side effects following blood transfusions, the International Olympic Committee and other organizations banned blood doping. Then recombinant human EPO (rhEPO) became available in the late 1980s, and athletes started injecting the drug to increase their body's red blood cell production. Subsequently the biotechnology firm Amgen created a longer-acting derivative of EPO named darbepoietin. Athletes using rhEPO and darbepoietin hoped to escape detection by using these natural hormones, but sports organizations worked with scientists to develop methods for detection.

Question 5:

Endogenous EPO, rhEPO, and darbepoietin all induce red blood cell synthesis, but they can be distinguished from one another when a urine sample is tested by electrophoresis [p. 101]. Explain how three hormones made from the same gene can all be active yet different enough from one another to be detectable in the laboratory.

Question 6:

One hallmark of illegal EPO use is elevated reticulocytes in the blood. Why would this suggest greater-than-normal EPO activity?

547 553 558 561 565

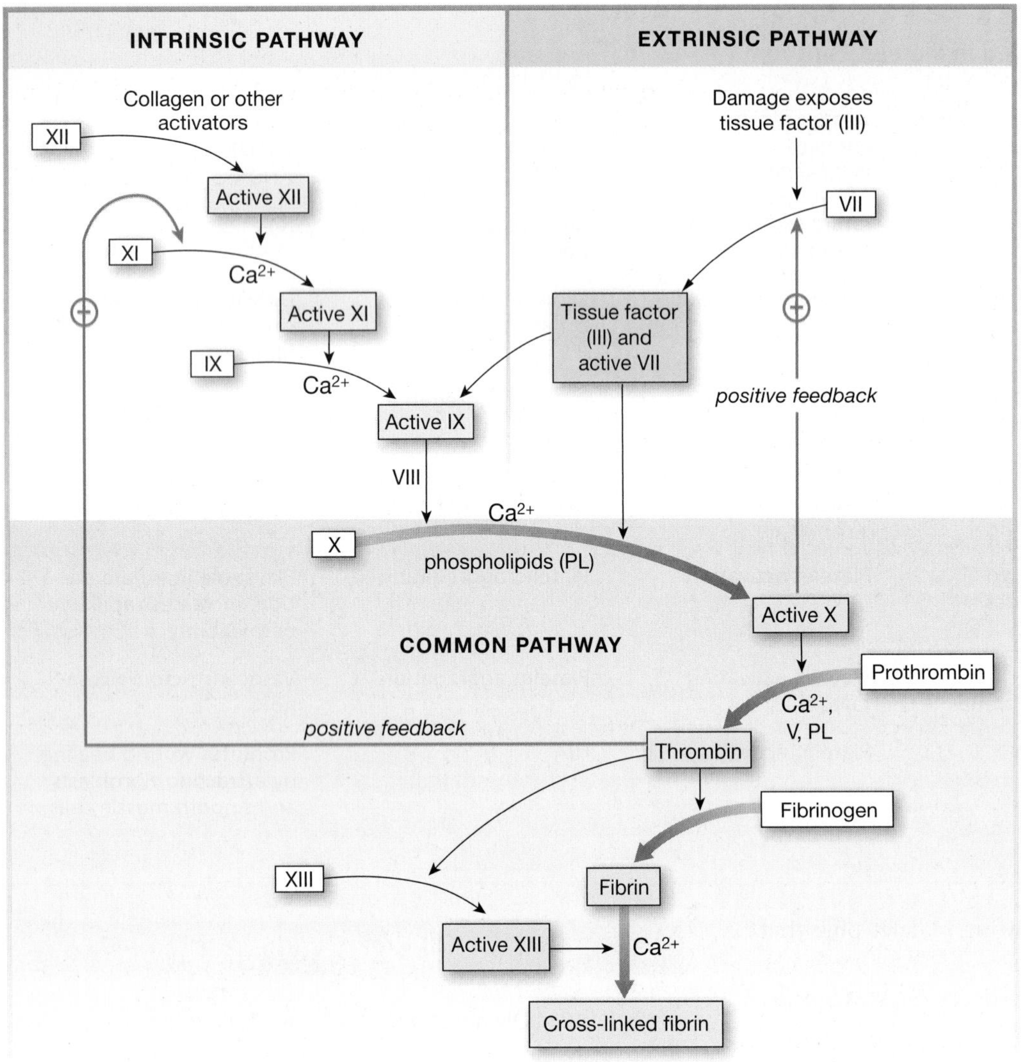
INTRINSIC PATHWAY
EXTRINSIC PATHWAY
Collagen or other activators
XII
Active XII
XI
Ca2+
Active XI
IX
Ca2+
Active IX
VIII
Damage exposes tissue factor (III)
VII
Tissue factor (III) and active VII
positive feedback
Ca2+
X
phospholipids (PL)
Active X
COMMON PATHWAY
Prothrombin
Ca2+, V, PL
positive feedback
Thrombin
Fibrinogen
XIII
Fibrin
Active XIII
Ca2+
Cross-linked fibrin

● **FIGURE 16-12** ***The coagulation cascade.*** Inactive plasma proteins are converted into active enzymes in each step of the pathway.

unite at the **common pathway** (green) to create **thrombin**, the enzyme that converts **fibrinogen** into insoluble **fibrin** polymers. These fibrin fibers become part of the clot.

Coagulation was initially regarded as a cascade similar to the second messenger cascades diagrammed in Chapter 6 [p. 185]. At each step an enzyme converts an inactive precursor into an active enzyme, often with the help of Ca^{2+}, membrane phospholipids, or additional factors. We now know, however, that the process is more than a simple cascade. Factors in the intrinsic and extrinsic pathways interact with each other, making coagulation a network rather than a simple cascade. In addition, several positive feedback loops sustain the cascade until one or more of the participating plasma proteins is completely consumed.

The end result of coagulation is the conversion of fibrinogen into fibrin, a reaction catalyzed by the enzyme thrombin (Fig. 16-13 ●). The fibrin fibers weave through the platelet plug and trap red blood cells within their mesh (Fig. 16-14 ●). Active factor XIII converts fibrin into a cross-linked polymer that stabilizes the clot.

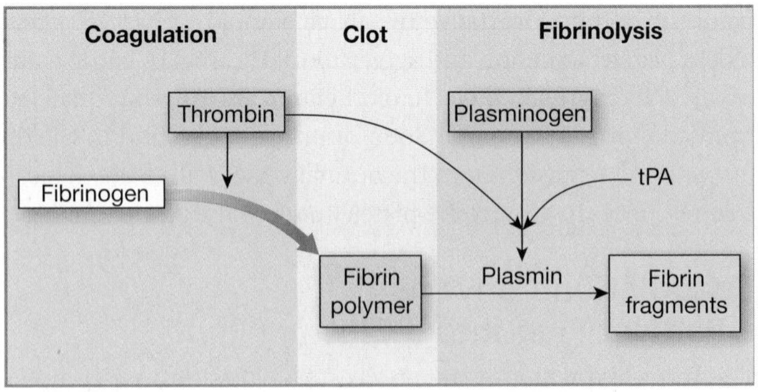
Coagulation
Clot
Fibrinolysis
Thrombin
Plasminogen
tPA
Fibrinogen
Fibrin polymer
Plasmin
Fibrin fragments

● **FIGURE 16-13** ***Coagulation and fibrinolysis***

As the clot forms, it incorporates plasmin molecules, the seeds of its own destruction. **Plasmin** is an enzyme created from plasminogen by thrombin and **tissue plasminogen activator (tPA)**. Plasmin breaks down fibrin polymers into fibrin fragments (Fig. 16-13). The dissolution of fibrin by plasmin is known as **fibrinolysis**. As the damaged vessel wall slowly repairs itself, fibrinolysis helps remove the clot.

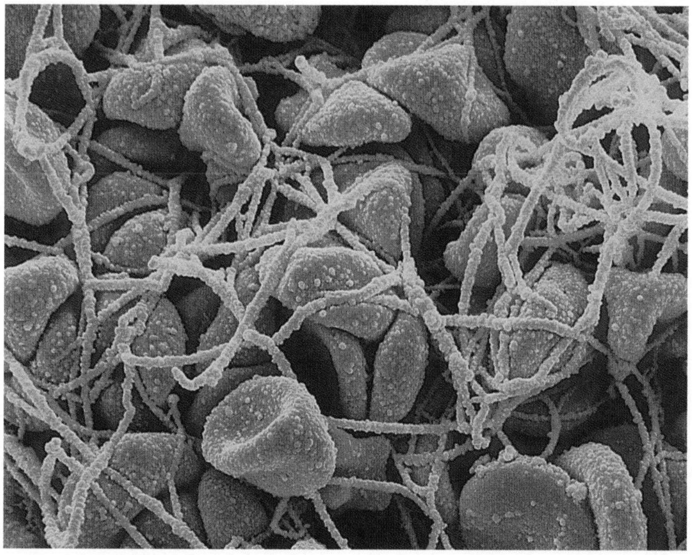

● **FIGURE 16-14** ***Red blood cells are trapped in the fibrin mesh of a clot.***

The large number of factors involved in coagulation and the fact that a single factor may have many different names can be confusing (Tbl. 16-5 ●). Scientists assigned numbers to the coagulation factors, but the factors are not numbered in the order in which they participate in the coagulation cascade. Instead, they are numbered according to the order in which they were discovered.

CONCEPT CHECK

8. In Figure 16-10, which box corresponds to the beginning of the intrinsic pathway of coagulation? Which corresponds to the beginning of the extrinsic pathway? To the beginning of the common pathway?

Answers: p. 567

Anticoagulants Prevent Coagulation

Once coagulation begins, what keeps it from continuing until the entire circulation has clotted? Two mechanisms limit the extent of blood clotting within a vessel: (1) inhibition of platelet adhesion and (2) inhibition of the coagulation cascade and fibrin production (Tbl. 16-6 ●). As mentioned earlier, factors such as prostacyclin in the blood vessel endothelium

TABLE 16-5 Factors Involved in Coagulation

CHEMICAL FACTOR	SOURCE	ACTIVATED BY OR RELEASED IN RESPONSE TO	ROLE IN COAGULATION	OTHER ROLES AND COMMENTS
Collagen	Subendothelial extracellular matrix	Injury that exposes collagen to plasma clotting factors	Starts intrinsic pathway	N/A
von Willebrand factor (vWF)	Endothelium, megakaryocytes	Exposure to collagen	Regulates level of factor VIII	Deficiency or defect causes prolonged bleeding
Kininogen and kallikrein	Liver and plasma	Cofactors normally present in plasma pathway	Cofactors for contact activation of intrinsic pathway	Mediate inflammatory response; enhance fibrinolysis
Tissue factor (tissue thromboplastin or factor III)	Most cells except platelets	Damage to tissue	Starts extrinsic pathway	N/A
Prothrombin and thrombin (factor II)	Liver and plasma	Platelet lipids, Ca^{2+}, and factor V	Fibrin production	N/A
Fibrinogen and fibrin (factor I)	Liver and plasma	Thrombin	Form insoluble fibers that stabilize platelet plug	N/A
Fibrin-stabilizing factor (XIII)	Liver, megakaryocytes	Platelets	Cross-links fibrin polymers to make stable mesh	N/A
Ca^{2+} (factor IV)	Plasma ions	N/A	Required for several steps of coagulation cascade	Never a limiting factor
Vitamin K	Diet	N/A	Needed for synthesis of factors II, VII, IX, X	N/A

TABLE 16-6 Endogenous Factors Involved in Fibrinolysis and Anticoagulation

CHEMICAL FACTOR	SOURCE	ACTIVATED BY OR RELEASED IN RESPONSE TO	ROLE IN ANTICOAGULATION OR FIBRINOLYSIS	OTHER ROLES AND COMMENTS
Plasminogen and plasmin	Liver and plasma	tPA and thrombin	Dissolves fibrin and fibrinogen	N/A
Tissue plasminogen activator (tPA)	Many tissues	Normally present; levels increase with stress, protein C	Activates plasminogen	Recombinant tPA used clinically to dissolve clots
Antithrombin III	Liver and plasma	N/A	Anticoagulant; blocks factors IX, X, XI, XII, thrombin, kallikrein	Facilitated by heparin; no effect on thrombin despite name
Prostacyclin (prostaglandin I, or PGI_2)	Endothelial cells	N/A	Blocks platelet aggregation	Vasodilator

and plasma ensure that the platelet plug is restricted to the area of damage (see left side of Fig. 16-11).

In addition, endothelial cells release chemicals known as **anticoagulants**, which prevent coagulation from taking place. Most act by blocking one or more of the reactions in the coagulation cascade. The body produces two anticoagulants, **heparin** and **antithrombin III**, which work together to block active factors IX, X, XI, and XII. **Protein C**, another anticoagulant in the body, inhibits clotting factors V and VIII.

Anticoagulant drugs may be prescribed for people who are in danger of forming small blood clots that could block off critical vessels in the brain, heart, or lungs. The family of *coumarin anticoagulants,* such as *warfarin* (Coumadin®), block the action of vitamin K, a cofactor [p. 41] in the synthesis of clotting factors II, VII, IX, and X. These anticoagulants were discovered when cattle that developed severe bleeding problems were found to have been eating spoiled sweet clover.

When blood samples are drawn into glass tubes, clotting takes place very rapidly unless the tube contains an anticoagulant. Several of the anticoagulants used for this purpose remove free Ca^{2+} from the plasma. Calcium is an essential clotting factor, so with no Ca^{2+}, no coagulation can occur. In the living body, however, plasma Ca^{2+} levels never decrease to levels that interfere with coagulation.

Acetylsalicylic acid (aspirin) is an agent that prevents platelet plug formation. It acts by inhibiting the COX enzymes [p. 193] that promote synthesis of the platelet activator thromboxane A_2. People who are at risk of developing small blood clots are sometimes told to take one aspirin every other day "to thin the blood." The aspirin does not actually make the blood less viscous, but it does prevent clots from forming by blocking platelet aggregation. Aspirin is now given routinely as emergency treatment for a suspected heart attack (see the Emerging Concepts box on Clot Busters).

Several inherited diseases affect the coagulation process. Patients with coagulation disorders bruise easily. In severe forms, spontaneous bleeding may occur throughout the body. Bleeding into the joints and muscles can be painful and disabling. If bleeding occurs in the brain, it can be fatal.

The best-known coagulation disorder is **hemophilia**, a name given to several diseases in which one of the factors in the coagulation cascade is either defective or lacking. Hemophilia A, a factor VIII deficiency, is the most common form, occurring in about 80% of all cases. This disease is a recessive sex-linked trait that usually affects only males.

EMERGING CONCEPTS

CLOT BUSTERS AND ANTIPLATELET AGENTS

The discovery of the factors controlling coagulation and fibrinolysis was an important step in developing treatments for heart attacks, more properly called *myocardial infarctions* (MIs), which occur when a coronary blood vessel is blocked by a clot (see the Chapter 15 Running Problem). Unless the blockage is removed promptly, the tissue will die or be severely damaged. One option for dissolving blood clots is to use fibrinolytic drugs—such as streptokinase (from bacteria) and tissue plasminogen activator (tPA)—to dissolve the clots. These drugs are now being combined with other agents that prevent further platelet plug and clot formation, such as antiplatelet agents, including some that are antagonists to platelet integrin receptors.

One exciting development in the treatment of hemophilia was a report on the first patients to be given gene therapy for hemophilia B, a deficiency in clotting factor IX. Patients injected with a virus engineered to carry the gene for factor IX started to produce some of the factor on their own, reducing their need for expensive injections of artificial factor IX. To learn more about these clinical trials and the latest treatments for hemophilia, visit the National Hemophilia Foundation web site at *www.hemophilia.org*.

RUNNING PROBLEM CONCLUSION

Blood Doping In Athletes

Johann Muehlegg's elevated hemoglobin and hematocrit prior to his 50-km race meant an automatic urine drug test following the race. At the time of the 2002 Olympics, athletes knew that there was a urine test for EPO, but they were not aware that the same test could detect darbepoietin. Both of Muehlegg's urine samples tested positive for darbepoietin, and he was stripped of his 50-km gold metal. The International Olympic Committee tested other athletes for rhEPO at the 2002 Salt Lake City Winter Olympics and had more than 100 positive results. Despite official prohibitions, blood doping in endurance sports remains a major problem.

Now check your understanding of the physiology behind blood doping by comparing your answers with the information in the following table.

	QUESTION	FACTS	INTEGRATION AND ANALYSIS
1	What is the normal range for Muehlegg's hemoglobin?	Normal hemoglobin range for males is 14–17 g/dL whole blood.	N/A
2	With blood doping, would you expect a hematocrit value to be lower or higher than normal?	Hematocrit is the percent of a blood sample volume that is packed red blood cells. A primary function of red blood cells is to carry oxygen.	Blood doping is done to increase oxygen-carrying capacity; therefore, the athlete would want more blood cells. This would mean a higher hematocrit.
3	Explain how diarrhea could cause a temporarily elevated hematocrit.	Diarrhea causes dehydration, which is loss of fluid volume. Plasma is the fluid component of blood.	If the total volume of red cells is unchanged but plasma volume decreases with dehydration, the hematocrit will increase.
4	How might Muehlegg quickly reduce his hematocrit without removing red blood cells?	$\text{Hematocrit} = \dfrac{\text{red cell volume}}{\text{red cell volume} + \text{plasma volume}}$	If plasma volume increases, hematocrit will decrease even though red cell volume does not change. By drinking fluids, Muehlegg could increase his plasma volume quickly.
5	Endogenous EPO, rhEPO, and darbepoietin all induce red blood cell synthesis but can be distinguished from one another by electrophoresis. Explain how three hormones made from the same gene can all be active yet different enough from one another to be detectable in the laboratory.	Activity depends on the protein binding to the receptor's binding site. Post-translational modification allows proteins from the same gene to be altered so that they are different from one another.	The three hormones have sites that bind to and activate the EPO receptor, but they have different sizes or charges that cause them to separate during electrophoresis. For example, the glycosylation pattern [p. 124] of rhEPO is different from the pattern in endogenous EPO.
6	One hallmark of illegal EPO use is elevated reticulocytes in the blood. Why would this suggest greater-than-normal EPO activity?	Reticulocytes are the final immature stage of red blood cell development. Maturation usually takes place in the marrow.	If red blood cell development becomes more rapid, more reticulocytes may be released into the blood before they have time to mature.

CHAPTER SUMMARY

Blood is an interesting tissue, with blood cells and cell fragments suspended in a liquid matrix—the plasma—that forms one of the two extracellular *compartments*. *Exchange* between the plasma and interstitial fluid takes place only in the capillaries. *Bulk flow* of blood through the body depends on the pressure gradient created by the heart. At the same time, high pressure in the blood vessels poses a danger should the wall of a vessel rupture. Collectively, the cellular and protein components of blood serve as a functional unit that provides protection against hemorrhage. Blood cells are also essential for oxygen transport and defense, as you will learn in later chapters.

Plasma and the Cellular Elements of Blood

1. Blood is the circulating portion of the extracellular fluid. (p. 547)
2. **Plasma** is composed mostly of water, with dissolved proteins, organic molecules, ions, and dissolved gases. (p. 547; Fig. 16-1)
3. The **plasma proteins** include **albumins**, **globulins**, and the clotting protein **fibrinogen**. They function in blood clotting, defense, and as hormones, enzymes, or carriers for different substances. (p. 547)
4. The cellular elements of blood are **red blood cells (erythrocytes)**, **white blood cells (leukocytes)**, and **platelets**. Platelets are fragments of cells called **megakaryocytes**. (p. 549; Fig. 16-1)
5. Blood contains five types of white blood cells: (1) **lymphocytes**, (2) **monocytes**, (3) **neutrophils**, (4) **eosinophils**, and (5) **basophils**. (p. 549; Fig. 16-1)

Blood Cell Production

6. All blood cells develop from a pluripotent hematopoietic stem cell. (p. 549; Fig. 16-2)
7. **Hematopoiesis** begins early in embryonic development and continues throughout a person's life. Most hematopoiesis takes place in the bone marrow. (p. 550; Fig. 16-4)
8. **Colony-stimulating factors** and other cytokines control white blood cell production. **Thrombopoietin** regulates the growth and maturation of megakaryocytes. Red blood cell production is regulated primarily by **erythropoietin**. (pp. 551–552)

Red Blood Cells

9. Mature mammalian red blood cells are biconcave disks lacking a nucleus. They contain hemoglobin, a red oxygen-carrying pigment. (p. 553; Fig. 16-5)
10. Hemoglobin synthesis requires iron in the diet. Iron is transported in the blood on **transferrin** and stored mostly in the liver, on **ferritin**. (p. 555; Fig. 16-7)
11. When hemoglobin is broken down, some heme groups are converted into **bilirubin**, which is incorporated into **bile** and excreted. Elevated bilirubin concentrations in the blood cause **jaundice**. (p. 556; Fig. 16-7)

Platelets and Coagulation

12. Platelets are cell fragments filled with granules containing clotting proteins and cytokines. Platelets are activated by damage to vascular endothelium. (p. 559; Fig. 16-9)
13. **Hemostasis** begins with vasoconstriction and the formation of a **platelet plug**. (p. 559; Fig. 16-10)
14. Exposed collagen triggers **platelet adhesion** and **platelet aggregation**. The platelet plug is converted into a clot when reinforced by **fibrin**. (p. 560; Fig. 16-10)
15. In the last step of the **coagulation cascade**, fibrin is made from **fibrinogen** through the action of **thrombin**. (p. 560; Fig. 16-12)
16. As the damaged vessel is repaired, **plasmin** trapped in the platelet plug dissolves fibrin (**fibrinolysis**) and breaks down the clot. (p. 562; Fig. 16-13)
17. Platelet plugs are restricted to the site of injury by **prostacyclin** in the membrane of intact vascular endothelium. **Anticoagulants** limit the extent of blood clotting within a vessel. (p. 563; Fig. 16-11)

QUESTIONS

(Answers to the Review Questions begin on page A1).

THE PHYSIOLOGY PLACE

Access more review material online at **The Physiology Place** web site. There you'll find review questions, problem-solving activities, case studies, flashcards, and direct links to both *Interactive Physiology*® and *PhysioEx*™. To access the site, go to *www.physiologyplace.com* and select *Human Physiology*, Fifth Edition.

LEVEL ONE REVIEWING FACTS AND TERMS

1. The fluid portion of the blood, called __________, is composed mainly of __________.
2. List the three types of plasma proteins. Name at least one function of each type. Which type is most prevalent in the body?
3. List the cellular elements found in blood, and name at least one function of each.
4. Blood cell production is called __________. When and where does it occur?
5. What role do colony-stimulating factors, cytokines, and interleukins play in blood cell production? How are these chemical signal molecules different? Give two examples of each.
6. List the technical terms for production of red blood cells, production of platelets, and production of white blood cells.
7. The hormone that directs red blood cell synthesis is called __________. Where is it produced, and what is the stimulus for its production?
8. How are the terms *hematocrit* and *packed red cells* related? What are normal hematocrit values for men and women?
9. Distinguish between an erythroblast and an erythrocyte. Give three distinct characteristics of erythrocytes.

10. Which chemical element in the diet is important for hemoglobin synthesis?
11. Define the following terms and explain their significance in hematology.
    (a) jaundice (c) transferrin
    (b) anemia (d) hemophilia
12. Chemicals that prevent blood clotting from occurring are called __________.

LEVEL TWO REVIEWING CONCEPTS

13. **Concept maps:** Combine each list of terms into a map. You may add other terms.

List 1	**List 2**	**List 3**
ADP	clot	bile
collagen	coagulation	bilirubin
integrins	fibrin	bone marrow
membrane	fibrinogen	erythropoietin
phospholipids	fibrinolysis	ferritin
platelet-activating factor	infarct	globin
platelet activation	plasmin	hematocrit
platelet adhesion	plasminogen	heme
platelet aggregation	polymer	hemoglobin
platelet plug	thrombin	intestine
positive feedback		iron
serotonin		liver
thromboxane A_2		reticulocyte
vasoconstriction		transferrin

14. Distinguish between the intrinsic, extrinsic, and common pathways of the coagulation cascade.
15. Once platelets are activated to aggregate, what factors halt their activity?

LEVEL THREE PROBLEM SOLVING

16. Rachel is undergoing chemotherapy for breast cancer. She has blood cell counts at regular intervals, with these results:

	Normal Count (cells/μL)	Patient Count 10 Days Post-Chemotherapy	Patient Count 20 Days Post-Chemotherapy
WBC	$4–11\times10^3$	2.6	4.9
RBC	$3.9–5.6\times12^6$	3.85	4.2
Platelets	$150–450\times10^3$	133	151

At the time of the 10-day test, Jen (the nurse) notes that Rachel, although pale and complaining of being tired, does not have any bruises on her skin. Jen tells Rachel to eat foods high in protein, take a multivitamin tablet containing iron, and stay home and away from crowds as much as possible. How are Jen's observations and recommendations related to the results of the 10-day and 20-day blood tests?

17. Hemochromatosis is an inherited condition in which the body overabsorbs iron, resulting in an elevated total body load of iron.
    (a) What plasma protein would you expect to be elevated in this disease?
    (b) Which organ(s) would you expect to show damage in this disease?
    (c) Can you think of a simple treatment that could decrease the body's overload of iron in hemochromatosis?
18. Erythropoietin (EPO) was first isolated from the urine of anemic patients who had high circulating levels of the hormone. Although these patients had high concentrations of EPO, they were unable to produce adequate amounts of hemoglobin or red cells. Give some possible reasons why the patients' EPO was unable to correct their anemia.

LEVEL FOUR QUANTITATIVE PROBLEMS

19. If we estimate that total blood volume is 7% of body weight, calculate the total blood volume in a 200-lb man and in a 130-lb woman (2.2 lb/kg). What are their plasma volumes if the man's hematocrit is 52% and the woman's hematocrit is 41%?
20. The total blood volume of an average person is 7% of total body weight. Using this figure and the fact that 1 kg of blood occupies a volume of about 1 liter, figure the total erythrocyte volume of a 50-kg woman with a hematocrit of 40%.

ANSWERS

Answers to Concept Check Questions

Page 549

1. The five types of leukocytes are lymphocytes, monocytes/macrophages, basophils/mast cells, neutrophils, and eosinophils.
2. Erythrocytes and platelets lack nuclei, which would make them unable to carry out protein synthesis.
3. Liver degeneration reduces the total plasma protein concentration, which reduces the osmotic pressure in the capillaries. This decease in osmotic pressure increases net capillary filtration, and edema results.

Page 553

4. (a) erythropoietin (EPO), (b) colony-stimulating factors (CSFs), (c) thrombopoietin (TPO).

Page 556

5. (a) Heme is an iron-containing subunit of a hemoglobin molecule. (b) Ferritin is the liver protein that stores iron. Transferrin is the plasma protein that transports iron in the blood.
6. Bile is an exocrine secretion because it is secreted into the intestine.

Page 558

7. Low atmospheric oxygen at high altitude → low arterial oxygen → sensed by kidney cells → secrete erythropoietin → acts on bone marrow → increased production of red blood cells.

Page 563

8. The intrinsic pathway starts at the gold "Collagen exposed" box, the extrinsic pathway starts at the gold "Tissue factor exposed" box, and the common pathway begins at the red "Coagulation cascade" diamond.

17

Mechanics of Breathing

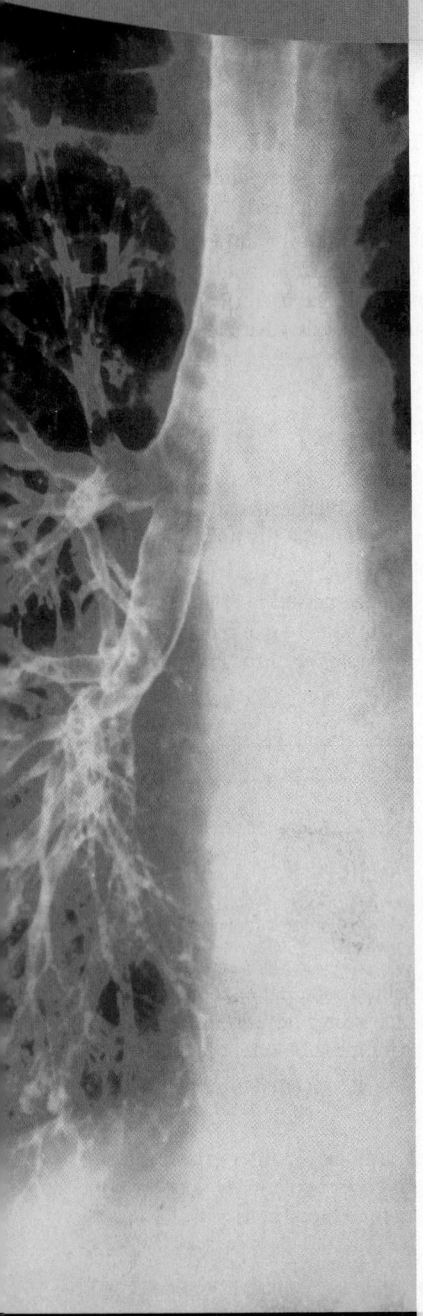

BACKGROUND BASICS

Ciliated and exchange epithelia: **74** Pressure, volume, flow, and resistance: **473** Pulmonary circulation: **471**
Hydrogen bonds and surface tension: **26** Autonomic and somatic motor neurons: **388** Velocity of flow: **475**

Colored x-ray of the lung showing the branching airways.

This being of mine, whatever it really is, consists of a little flesh, a little breath, and the part which governs.

—Marcus Aurelius Antoninus (C.E. 121–180)

RUNNING PROBLEM

Emphysema

You could hear her whistling, wheezing breathing preceding her down the hall. "Diagnosis: COPD," reads Edna Wilson's patient chart. COPD—chronic obstructive pulmonary disease—is the name given to diseases in which air exchange is impaired by narrowing of the lower airways. Most people with COPD have emphysema or chronic bronchitis or a combination of the two. Individuals in whom chronic bronchitis predominates are sometimes called "blue bloaters," owing to the bluish tinge of their skin (from low blood oxygen levels) and a tendency to be overweight. In contrast, patients with emphysema have been nicknamed "pink puffers." They tend to be thin, have normal (pink) skin coloration, and often breathe out through pursed lips, which helps open their airways. More than 12 million people in the United States have COPD. Its most common cause is smoking, and most people can avoid the disease simply by not smoking. Unfortunately, Edna has been a heavy smoker for 35 of her 47 years.

569 571 580 583 591 592

Imagine covering the playing surface of a racquetball court (about 75 m^2) with thin plastic wrap, then crumpling up the wrap and stuffing it into a 3-liter soft drink bottle. Impossible? Maybe so, if you use plastic wrap and a drink bottle. But the lungs of a 70-kg man have a gas exchange surface the size of that plastic wrap, compressed into a volume that is less than that of the bottle. This tremendous surface area for gas exchange is needed to supply the trillions of cells in the body with adequate amounts of oxygen.

Aerobic metabolism in cells depends on a steady supply of oxygen and nutrients from the environment, coupled with the removal of carbon dioxide. In very small aquatic animals, simple diffusion across the body surface meets these needs. Distance limits diffusion rate, however, so most multicelled animals require specialized respiratory organs associated with a circulatory system. Respiratory organs take a variety of forms, but all possess a large surface area compressed into a small space.

Besides needing a large exchange surface, humans and other terrestrial animals face an additional physiological challenge: dehydration. The exchange surface must be thin and moist to allow gases to pass from air into solution, and yet at the same time it must be protected from drying out as a result of exposure to air. Some terrestrial animals, such as the slug (a shell-less snail), meet the challenge of dehydration with behavioral adaptations that restrict them to humid environments and nighttime activities.

A more common solution is anatomical: an internalized respiratory epithelium. Human lungs are enclosed in the chest cavity to control their contact with the outside air. Internalization creates a humid environment for the exchange of gases with the blood and protects the delicate exchange surface from damage.

Internalized lungs create another challenge, however: how to move air between the atmosphere and an exchange surface deep within the body. Air flow requires a muscular pump to create pressure gradients. More complex respiratory systems therefore consist of two separate components: a muscle-driven pump and a thin, moist exchange surface. In humans, the pump is the musculoskeletal structure of the thorax [p. 54]. The lungs themselves consist of the exchange epithelium and associated blood vessels.

The four primary functions of the respiratory system are:

1. *Exchange of gases between the atmosphere and the blood.* The body brings in O_2 for distribution to the tissues and eliminates CO_2 waste produced by metabolism.
2. *Homeostatic regulation of body pH.* The lungs can alter body pH by selectively retaining or excreting CO_2.
3. *Protection from inhaled pathogens and irritating substances.* Like all other epithelia that contact the external environment, the respiratory epithelium is well supplied with defense mechanisms to trap and destroy potentially harmful substances before they can enter the body.
4. *Vocalization.* Air moving across the vocal cords creates vibrations used for speech, singing, and other forms of communication.

In addition to serving these functions, the respiratory system is also a significant source of water loss and heat loss from the body. These losses must be balanced using homeostatic compensations.

In this chapter you will learn how the respiratory system carries out these functions by exchanging air between the environment and the interior air spaces of the lungs. This exchange is the *bulk flow* of air, and it follows many of the same principles that govern the bulk flow of blood through the cardiovascular system:

1. Flow takes place from regions of higher pressure to regions of lower pressure.
2. A muscular pump creates pressure gradients.
3. Resistance to air flow is influenced primarily by the diameter of the tubes through which the air is flowing.

The primary difference between air flow in the respiratory system and blood flow in the circulatory system is that air is a less viscous, compressible mixture of gases while blood is a noncompressible liquid.

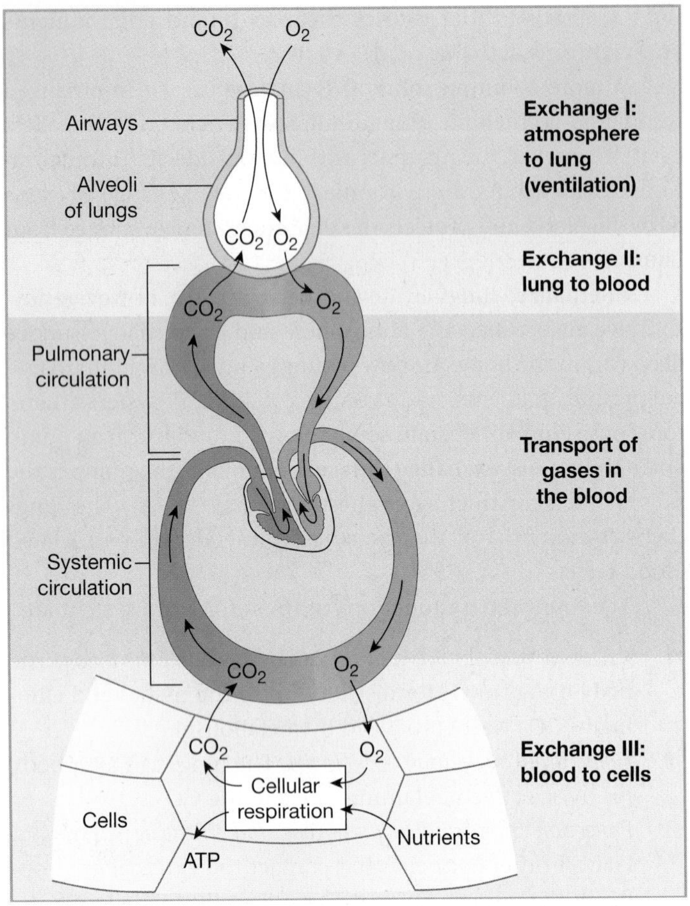

● **FIGURE 17-1** ***Overview of external and cellular respiration***

THE RESPIRATORY SYSTEM

The word *respiration* has several meanings in physiology (Fig. 17-1 ●). **Cellular respiration** refers to the intracellular reaction of oxygen with organic molecules to produce carbon dioxide, water, and energy in the form of ATP [p. 107]. **External respiration**, the topic of this chapter and the next, is the movement of gases between the environment and the body's cells. External respiration can be subdivided into four integrated processes, illustrated in Figure 17-1:

1. *The exchange of air between the atmosphere and the lungs.* This process is known as **ventilation**, or breathing. **Inspiration** (inhalation) is the movement of air into the lungs. **Expiration** (exhalation) is the movement of air out of the lungs. The mechanisms by which ventilation takes place are collectively called the *mechanics of breathing.*
2. *The exchange of O_2 and CO_2 between the lungs and the blood.*
3. *The transport of O_2 and CO_2 by the blood.*
4. *The exchange of gases between blood and the cells.*

External respiration requires the coordinated functioning of the respiratory and cardiovascular systems. The **respiratory system** consists of structures involved in ventilation and gas exchange (Fig. 17-2 ●):

1. The **conducting system** of passages, or **airways**, that lead from the external environment to the exchange surface of the lungs.
2. The **alveoli** (singular **alveolus**) [*alveus*, a concave vessel], a series of interconnected sacs and their associated *pulmonary capillaries.* These structures form the exchange surface, where oxygen moves from inhaled air to the blood, and carbon dioxide moves from the blood to air that is about to be exhaled.
3. The bones and muscles of the thorax (chest cavity) and abdomen that assist in ventilation.

The respiratory system can be divided into two parts. The **upper respiratory tract** consists of the mouth, nasal cavity, pharynx, and larynx. The **lower respiratory tract** consists of the trachea, two primary bronchi, their branches, and the lungs. The lower tract is also known as the *thoracic portion* of the respiratory system because it is enclosed in the thorax.

Bones and Muscles of the Thorax Surround the Lungs

The thorax is bounded by the bones of the spine and rib cage and their associated muscles. Together the bones and muscles are called the *thoracic cage*. The ribs and spine (the *chest wall*) form the sides and top of the cage. A dome-shaped sheet of skeletal muscle, the **diaphragm**, forms the floor (Fig. 17-2a).

Two sets of **intercostal muscles**, internal and external, connect the 12 pairs of ribs (Fig. 17-2b). Additional muscles, the **sternocleidomastoids** and the **scalenes**, run from the head and neck to the sternum and first two ribs.

Functionally, the thorax is a sealed container filled with three membranous bags, or sacs. One, the *pericardial sac,* contains the heart. The other two bags, the **pleural sacs**, each surround a lung [*pleura,* rib or side]. The esophagus and thoracic blood vessels and nerves pass between the pleural sacs (Fig. 17-2d).

Pleural Sacs Enclose the Lungs

The **lungs** (Fig. 17-2a, c) consist of light, spongy tissue whose volume is occupied mostly by air-filled spaces. These irregular cone-shaped organs nearly fill the thoracic cavity, with their bases resting on the curved diaphragm. Semi-rigid conducting airways—the bronchi—connect the lungs to the main airway, the trachea.

Each lung is surrounded by a double-walled pleural sac whose membranes line the inside of the thorax and cover the outer surface of the lungs (Fig. 17-3 ●). Each *pleural membrane,* or **pleura**, contains several layers of elastic connective tissue and numerous capillaries. The opposing layers of pleural membrane are held together by a thin film of **pleural fluid** whose total volume is only about 25–30 mL in a 70-kg man. The result is similar to an air-filled balloon (the lung) surrounded by a water-filled balloon (the pleural sac). Most illustrations

RUNNING PROBLEM

Edna has not been able to stop smoking, and her COPD is a combination of emphysema and bronchitis. Patients with chronic bronchitis have excessive mucus production and general inflammation of the entire respiratory tract. The mucus narrows the airways and makes breathing difficult.

Question 1:

What does narrowing of the airways do to the resistance airways offer to air flow? (Hint: The relationship between radius and resistance is the same for air flow in the respiratory system as it is for blood flow in the circulatory system. [p. 473])

569 571 580 583 591 592

exaggerate the volume of the pleural fluid, but you can appreciate its thinness if you imagine spreading 25 mL of water evenly over the surface of a 3-liter soft drink bottle.

Pleural fluid serves several purposes. First, it creates a moist, slippery surface so that the opposing membranes can slide across one another as the lungs move within the thorax. Second, it holds the lungs tight against the thoracic wall. To visualize this arrangement, think of two panes of glass stuck together by a thin film of water. You can slide the panes back and forth across each other, but you cannot pull them apart because of the cohesiveness of the water [p. 26]. A similar fluid bond between the two pleural membranes makes the lungs "stick" to the thoracic cage and holds them stretched in a partially inflated state, even at rest.

Airways Connect Lungs to the External Environment

Air enters the upper respiratory tract through the mouth and nose and passes into the **pharynx**, a common passageway for food, liquids, and air [*pharynx,* throat]. From the pharynx, air flows through the **larynx** into the **trachea**, or windpipe (Fig. 17-2a). The larynx contains the **vocal cords**, connective tissue bands that vibrate and tighten to create sound when air moves past them.

The trachea is a semiflexible tube held open by 15 to 20 C-shaped cartilage rings (Fig. 17-2e). It extends down into the thorax, where it branches (division 1) into a pair of **primary bronchi**, one *bronchus* to each lung. Within the lungs, the bronchi branch repeatedly (divisions 2–11) into progressively smaller bronchi (Fig. 17-2a, e). Like the trachea, the bronchi are semi-rigid tubes supported by cartilage.

In the lungs, the smallest bronchi branch to become **bronchioles**, small collapsible passageways with walls of smooth muscle. The bronchioles continue branching (divisions 12–23) until the *respiratory bronchioles* form a transition between the airways and the exchange epithelium of the lung.

The diameter of the airways becomes progressively smaller from the trachea to the bronchioles, but as the individual airways get narrower, their numbers increase geometrically (Fig. 17-4 ●). As a result, the total cross-sectional area increases with each division of the airways. Total cross-sectional area is lowest in the upper respiratory tract and greatest in the bronchioles, analogous to the increase in cross-sectional area that occurs from the aorta to the capillaries in the circulatory system [p. 475].

CONCEPT CHECK

1. What is the difference between cellular respiration and external respiration?
2. Name the components of the upper respiratory tract and those of the lower respiratory tract.
3. Based on the total cross-sectional area of different airways, where is the velocity of air flow highest and lowest?
4. Give two functions of pleural fluid.
5. Name the components (including muscles) of the thoracic cage. List the contents of the thorax.
6. Which air passages of the respiratory system are collapsible?

Answers: p. 595

The Airways Warm, Humidify, and Filter Inspired Air

During breathing, the upper airways and the bronchi do more than simply serve as passageways for air. They play an important role in conditioning air before it reaches the alveoli. Conditioning has three components:

1. *Warming* air to body temperature (37° C), so that core body temperature does not change and alveoli are not damaged by cold air;
2. *Adding water vapor* until the air reaches 100% humidity, so that the moist exchange epithelium does not dry out; and
3. *Filtering out foreign material,* so that viruses, bacteria, and inorganic particles do not reach the alveoli.

Inhaled air is warmed by the body's heat and moistened by water evaporating from the mucosal lining of the airways. Under normal circumstances, by the time air reaches the trachea, it has been conditioned to 100% humidity and 37° C. Breathing through the mouth is not nearly as effective at warming and moistening air as breathing through the nose. If you exercise outdoors in very cold weather, you may be familiar with the ache in your chest that results from breathing cold air through your mouth.

Air is filtered both in the trachea and in the bronchi. These airways are lined with ciliated epithelium that secretes

17

ANATOMY SUMMARY

THE LUNGS AND THORACIC CAVITY

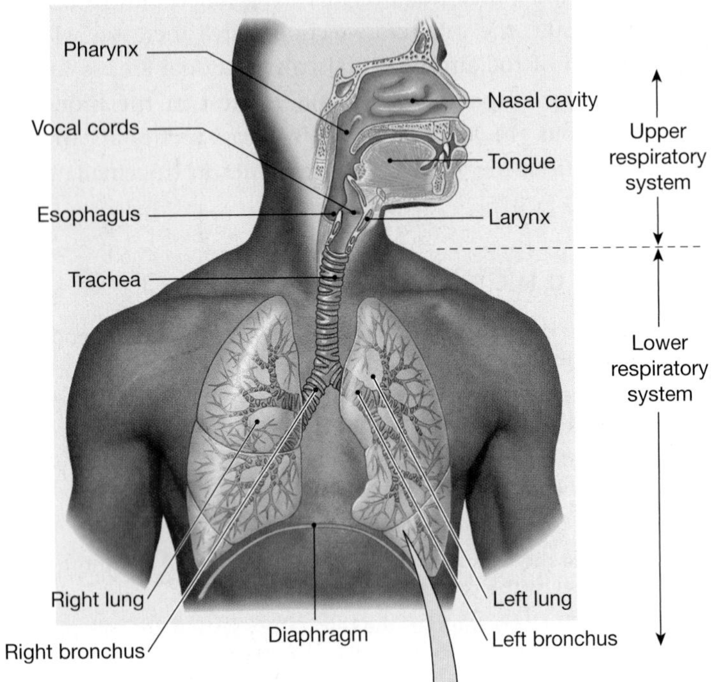

Pharynx
Nasal cavity
Vocal cords
Tongue
Esophagus
Larynx
Trachea
Upper respiratory system
Lower respiratory system
Right lung
Left lung
Right bronchus
Diaphragm
Left bronchus

(a) The respiratory system

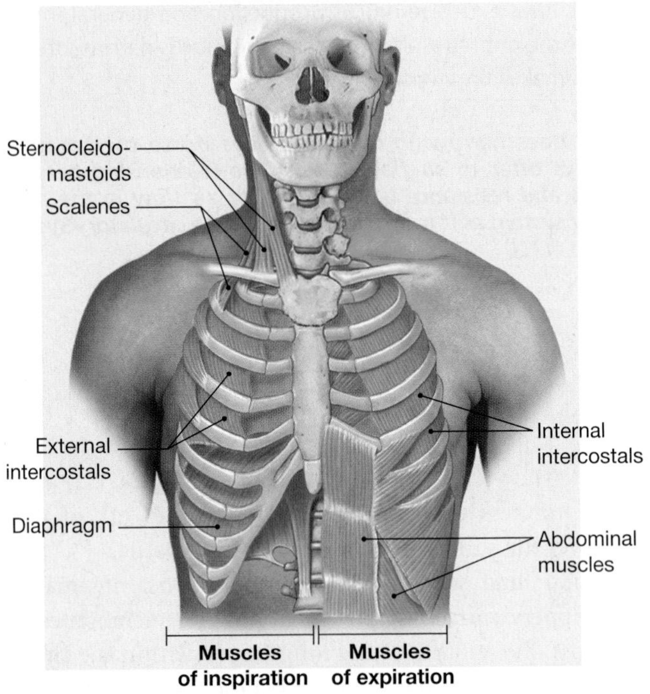

Sternocleido-mastoids
Scalenes
External intercostals
Internal intercostals
Diaphragm
Abdominal muscles
Muscles of inspiration
Muscles of expiration

(b) Muscles used for ventilation

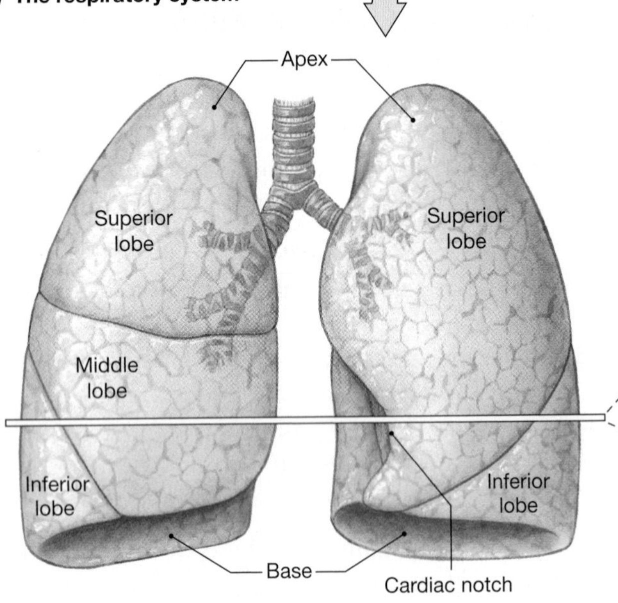

Apex
Superior lobe
Superior lobe
Middle lobe
Inferior lobe
Inferior lobe
Base
Cardiac notch

Right lung is divided into three lobes.

Left lung is divided into two lobes.

(c) External anatomy of lungs

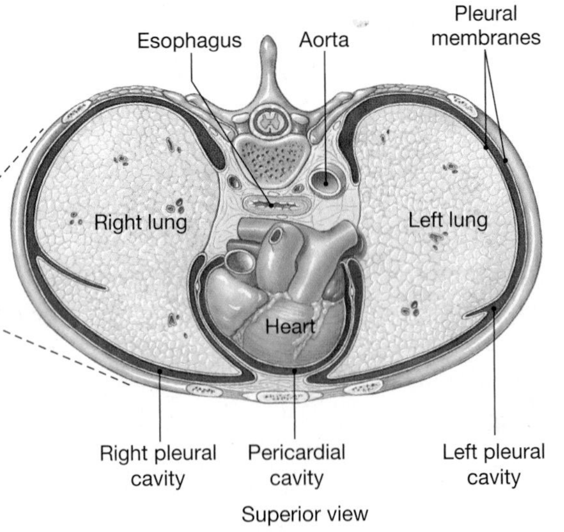

Esophagus
Aorta
Pleural membranes
Right lung
Left lung
Heart
Right pleural cavity
Pericardial cavity
Left pleural cavity
Superior view

(d) Sectional view of chest
Each lung is enclosed in two pleural membranes. The esophagus and aorta pass through the thorax between the pleural sacs.

FIGURE 17-2

THE BRONCHI AND ALVEOLI

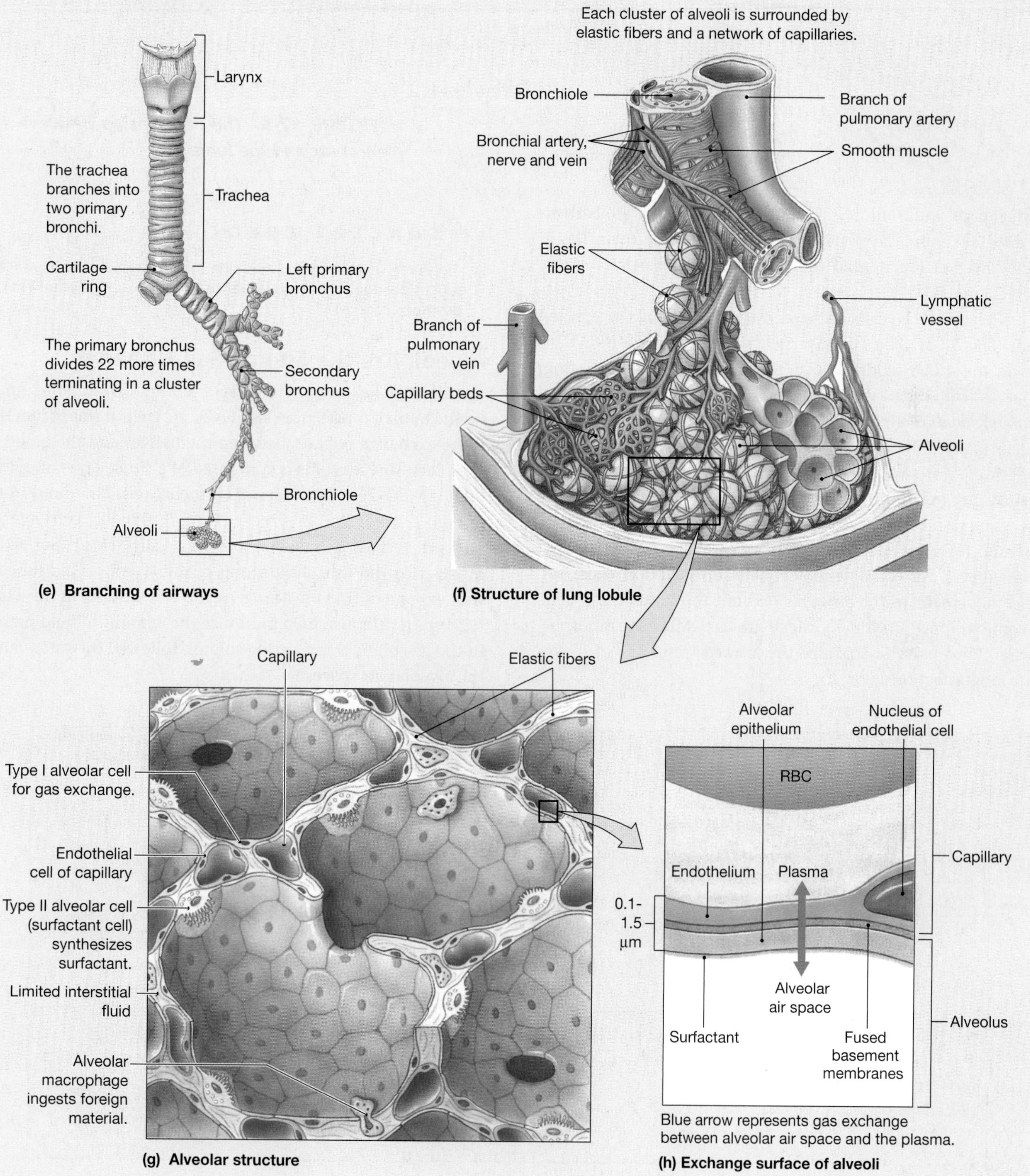

Larynx
Trachea
The trachea branches into two primary bronchi.
Cartilage ring
Left primary bronchus
The primary bronchus divides 22 more times terminating in a cluster of alveoli.
Secondary bronchus
Bronchiole
Alveoli
Each cluster of alveoli is surrounded by elastic fibers and a network of capillaries.
Bronchiole
Branch of pulmonary artery
Bronchial artery, nerve and vein
Smooth muscle
Elastic fibers
Lymphatic vessel
Branch of pulmonary vein
Capillary beds
Alveoli
Capillary
Elastic fibers
Type I alveolar cell for gas exchange.
Endothelial cell of capillary
Type II alveolar cell (surfactant cell) synthesizes surfactant.
Limited interstitial fluid
Alveolar macrophage ingests foreign material.
Alveolar epithelium
Nucleus of endothelial cell
RBC
Capillary
Endothelium
Plasma
0.1-1.5 µm
Alveolar air space
Alveolus
Surfactant
Fused basement membranes
Blue arrow represents gas exchange between alveolar air space and the plasma.

(e) Branching of airways

(f) Structure of lung lobule

(g) Alveolar structure

(h) Exchange surface of alveoli

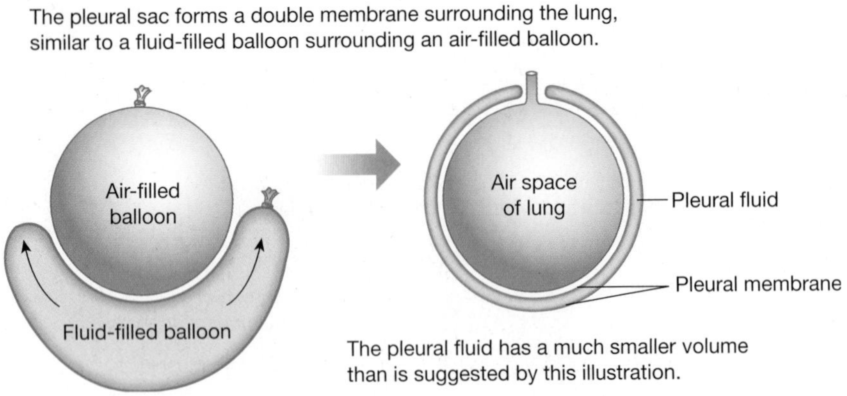
The pleural sac forms a double membrane surrounding the lung, similar to a fluid-filled balloon surrounding an air-filled balloon.
Air-filled balloon
Fluid-filled balloon
Air space of lung
Pleural fluid
Pleural membrane
The pleural fluid has a much smaller volume than is suggested by this illustration.

● **FIGURE 17-3** ***The relationship between the pleural sac and the lung***

both mucus and a dilute saline solution. The cilia are bathed in a watery saline layer (Fig. 17-5 ●). On top of them lies a sticky layer of mucus that traps most inhaled particles larger than 2 μm.

The mucus layer is secreted by *goblet cells* in the epithelium (Fig. 17-5). The cilia beat with an upward motion that moves the mucus continuously toward the pharynx, creating what is called the *mucociliary escalator*. Mucus contains *immunoglobulins* that can disable many pathogens. Once mucus reaches the pharynx, it can be spit out (*expectorated*) or swallowed. For swallowed mucus, stomach acid and enzymes destroy any remaining microorganisms.

Secretion of the watery saline layer beneath the mucus is essential for a functional mucociliary escalator. In the disease *cystic fibrosis,* for example, inadequate ion secretion decreases fluid movement in the airways. Without the saline layer, cilia become trapped in thick, sticky mucus. Mucus cannot be cleared, and bacteria colonize the airways, resulting in recurrent lung infections.

CONCEPT CHECK

7. Cigarette smoking paralyzes cilia in the airways and increases mucus production. Why would these effects cause smokers to develop a cough? Answers: p. 596

Alveoli Are the Site of Gas Exchange

The alveoli, clustered at the ends of terminal bronchioles, make up the bulk of lung tissue (Fig. 17-2f, g). Their primary function is the exchange of gases between themselves and the blood.

Each tiny alveolus is composed of a single layer of epithelium (Fig. 17-2g). Two types of epithelial cells are found in the alveoli. The smaller but thicker **type II alveolar cells** synthesize and secrete a chemical known as **surfactant.** Surfactant mixes with the thin fluid lining of the alveoli to aid lungs as they expand during breathing, as you will see later in this chapter. Type II cells also help minimize the amount of fluid present in the alveoli by transporting solutes, followed by water, out of the alveolar air space.

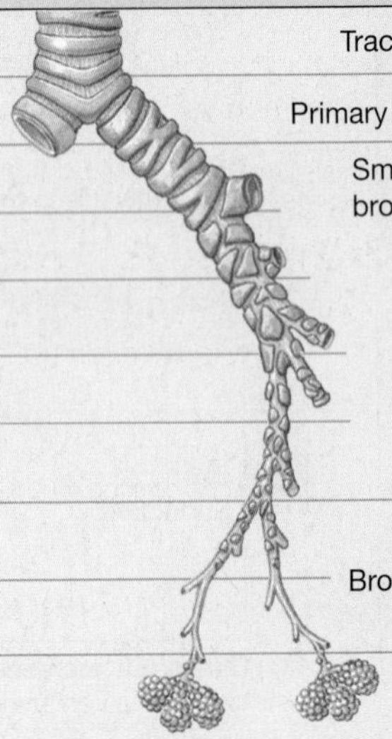

	Name	Division	Diameter (mm)	How many?	Cross-sectional area (cm^2)
Conducting system	Trachea	0	15-22	1	2.5
	Primary bronchi	1	10-15	2	↓
	Smaller bronchi ↓	2		4 ↓	
		3			
		4	1-10		
		5			
		6-11		1×10^4	↓
	Bronchioles	12-23	0.5-1	2×10^4 ↓ 8×10^7	100 ↓ 5×10^3
Exchange surface	Alveoli	24	0.3	$3\text{-}6 \times 10^8$	$>1 \times 10^6$

● **FIGURE 17-4** ***Branching of the airways***

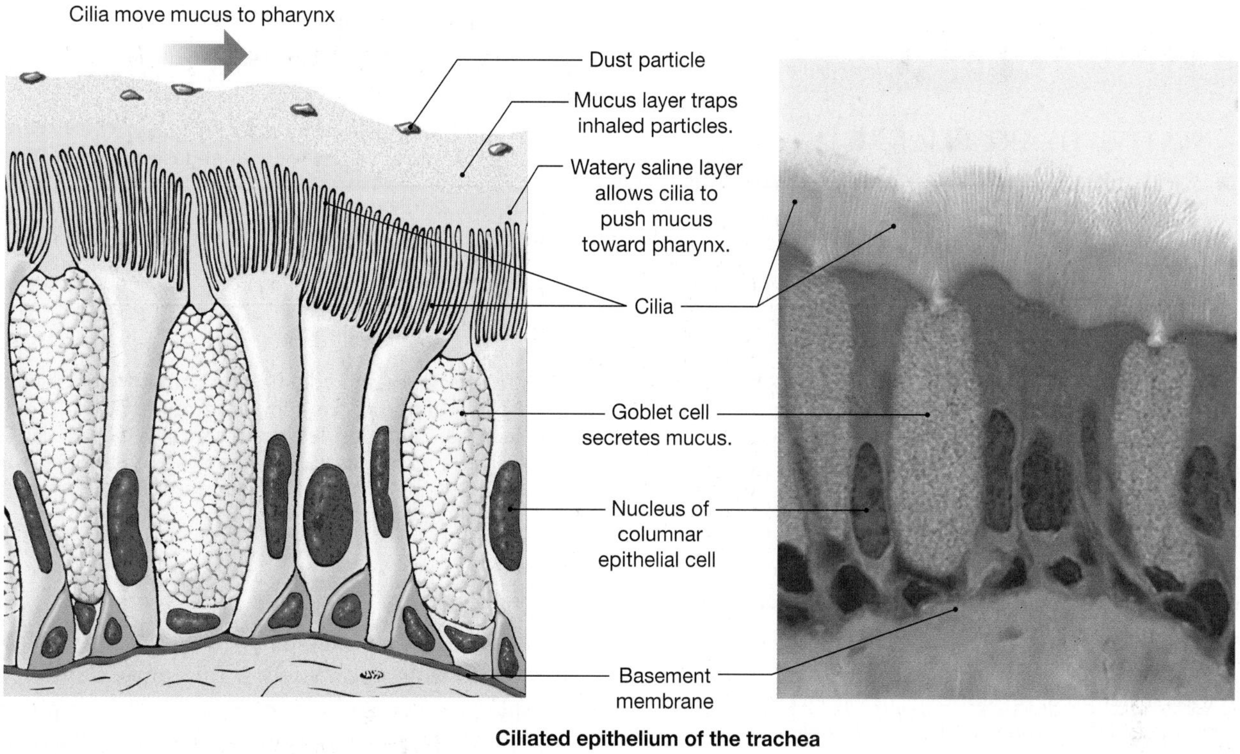

Cilia move mucus to pharynx
Dust particle
Mucus layer traps inhaled particles.
Watery saline layer allows cilia to push mucus toward pharynx.
Cilia
Goblet cell secretes mucus.
Nucleus of columnar epithelial cell
Basement membrane
Ciliated epithelium of the trachea

● **FIGURE 17-5** ***Ciliated respiratory epithelium.*** Cilia move the mucus layer toward the pharynx, removing trapped pathogens and particulate matter.

The larger **type I alveolar cells** occupy about 95% of the alveolar surface area and are very thin so that gases can diffuse rapidly through them (Fig. 17-2h). In much of the exchange area, a layer of basement membrane fuses the alveolar epithelium to the capillary endothelium. In the remaining area only a small amount of interstitial fluid is present.

The thin walls of the alveoli do not contain muscle because muscle fibers would block rapid gas exchange. As a result, lung tissue itself cannot contract. However, connective tissue between the alveolar epithelial cells contains many elastin and collagen fibers that create elastic recoil when lung tissue is stretched.

The close association of the alveoli with an extensive network of capillaries demonstrates the intimate link between the respiratory and cardiovascular systems. Blood vessels fill 80–90% of the space between alveoli, forming an almost continuous "sheet" of blood in close contact with the air-filled alveoli. The proximity of capillary blood to alveolar air is essential for the rapid exchange of gases.

Pulmonary Circulation Is High-Flow, Low-Pressure

The pulmonary circulation begins with the pulmonary trunk, which receives low-oxygen blood from the right ventricle. The pulmonary trunk divides into two pulmonary arteries, one to each lung [Fig. 14-1, p. 470]. Oxygenated blood from the lungs returns to the left atrium via the pulmonary veins.

At any given moment, the pulmonary circulation contains about 0.5 liter of blood, or 10% of total blood volume. About 75 mL of this amount is found in the capillaries, where gas exchange takes place, with the remainder in pulmonary arteries and veins. The rate of blood flow through the lungs is much higher than the rate in other tissues [p. 471] because the lungs receive the entire cardiac output of the right ventricle: 5 L/min. This means that as much blood flows through the lungs in one minute as flows through the entire rest of the body in the same amount of time!

Despite the high flow rate, pulmonary blood pressure is low. Pulmonary arterial pressure averages 25/8 mm Hg, much lower than the average systemic pressure of 120/80 mm Hg. The right ventricle does not have to pump as forcefully to create blood flow through the lungs because resistance of the pulmonary circulation is low. This low resistance can be attributed to the shorter total length of pulmonary blood vessels and to the distensibility and large total cross-sectional area of pulmonary arterioles.

Normally, the net hydrostatic pressure filtering fluid out of a pulmonary capillary into the interstitial space is low because of low mean blood pressure [p. 528]. The lymphatic system efficiently removes filtered fluid, and lung interstitial fluid volume is usually minimal. As a result, the distance between the alveolar air space and the capillary endothelium is short, and gases diffuse rapidly between them.

CLINICAL FOCUS

CONGESTIVE HEART FAILURE

When is a lung problem not a lung problem? The answer: when it's really a heart problem. Congestive heart failure (CHF) is an excellent example of the interrelationships among body systems, and demonstrates how disruptions in one system can have a domino effect in the others. The primary symptoms of heart failure are shortness of breath (*dyspnea*), wheezing during breathing, and sometimes a productive cough that may be pinkish from the presence of blood. Congestive heart failure arises when the right heart is a more effective pump than the left heart (see Ch. 14, Concept Check 30, p. 500). When blood accumulates in the pulmonary circulation, increased volume increases pulmonary blood pressure and capillary hydrostatic pressure. Capillary filtration exceeds the ability of the lymph system to drain interstitial fluid, resulting in pulmonary edema. Treatment of CHF includes increasing urinary output, which brings yet another organ system into the picture. By current estimates, about 5 million Americans suffer from CHF. To learn more about this condition, visit the American Heart Association website (*www.americanheart.org*) or MedlinePlus, published by the National Institutes of Health (*www.nlm.nih.gov/medlineplus/heartfailure.html*).

CONCEPT CHECK

8. Is blood flow through the pulmonary trunk greater than, less than, or equal to blood flow through the aorta?
9. A person has left ventricular failure but normal right ventricular function. As a result, blood pools in the pulmonary circulation, doubling pulmonary capillary hydrostatic pressure. What happens to net fluid flow across the walls of the pulmonary capillaries?
10. Calculate the mean pressure in a person whose pulmonary arterial pressure is 25/8 mm Hg. [p. 517]

Answers: p. 596

GAS LAWS

Respiratory air flow is very similar in many respects to blood flow in the cardiovascular system, even though blood is a noncompressible liquid and air is a compressible mixture of gases. In this book, blood pressure and environmental air pressure (**atmospheric pressure**) are both reported in millimeters of mercury (mm Hg). Respiratory physiologists sometimes report gas pressures in centimeters of water instead, where 1 mm Hg = 1.36 cm H_2O, or in kiloPascals (kPa), where 760 mm Hg = 101.325 kPa.

TABLE 17-1 Gas Laws

1. The total pressure of a mixture of gases is the sum of the pressures of the individual gases (Dalton's law).
2. Gases, singly or in a mixture, move from areas of higher pressure to areas of lower pressure.
3. If the volume of a container of gas changes, the pressure of the gas will change in an inverse manner: $P_1V_1 = P_2V_2$ (Boyle's law).
4. The pressure and volume of a container of gas are directly related to the temperature of the gas and the number of molecules in the container: PV = nRT, where n is the moles of gas, T is the absolute temperature, and R is the universal gas constant, 8.3145 J/mol K (Ideal Gas law).

At sea level, normal atmospheric pressure is 760 mm Hg. However, in this book we follow the convention of designating atmospheric pressure as 0 mm Hg. Because atmospheric pressure varies with altitude and because very few people live exactly at sea level, this convention allows us to compare pressure differences that occur during ventilation without correcting for altitude.

Table 17-1 ● summarizes the rules that govern the behavior of gases in air. These rules provide the basis for the exchange of air between the external environment and the alveoli. Chapter 18 discusses gas laws that govern the solubility of gases in solution.

Air Is a Mixture of Gases

The atmosphere surrounding the earth is a mixture of gases and water vapor. **Dalton's law** states that the total pressure exerted by a mixture of gases is the sum of the pressures exerted by the individual gases. For example, in dry air at an atmospheric pressure of 760 mm Hg, 78% of the total pressure is due to N_2, 21% to O_2, and so on (Tbl. 17-2 ●).

In respiratory physiology, we are concerned not only with total atmospheric pressure but also with the individual pressures of oxygen and carbon dioxide. The pressure of a single gas in a mixture is known as its **partial pressure** (P_{gas}). To find the partial pressure of any one gas in a sample of air, multiply the atmospheric pressure (P_{atm}) by the gas's relative contribution (%) to P_{atm}:

$$\text{Partial pressure of an atmospheric gas} = P_{atm} \times \%\text{ of gas in atmosphere}$$

$$\text{Partial pressure of oxygen} = 760 \text{ mm Hg} \times 21\%$$
$$P_{O_2} = 760 \times 0.21 = 160 \text{ mm Hg}$$

Thus, the partial pressure of oxygen (P_{O_2}) in dry air at sea level is 160 mm Hg. The pressure exerted by an individual gas is determined only by its relative abundance in the mixture and is independent of the molecular size or mass of the gas.

TABLE 17-2 Partial Pressures (P_{gas}) of Atmospheric Gases at 760 mm Hg

GAS AND ITS PERCENTAGE IN AIR	P_{GAS} IN DRY, 25° C AIR	P_{GAS} IN 25° C AIR, 100% HUMIDITY	P_{GAS} IN 37° C AIR, 100% HUMIDITY
Nitrogen (N_2) 78%	593 mm Hg	574 mm Hg	556 mm Hg
Oxygen (O_2) 21%	160 mm Hg	155 mm Hg	150 mm Hg
Carbon dioxide (CO_2) 0.033%	0.25 mm Hg	0.24 mm Hg	0.235 mm Hg
Water vapor	0 mm Hg	24 mm Hg	47 mm Hg

The partial pressures of gases in air vary slightly depending on how much water vapor is in the air because the pressure of water vapor "dilutes" the contribution of other gases to the total pressure. To calculate the partial pressure of a gas in humid air, you must first subtract the water vapor pressure from the total pressure. Table 17-2 compares the partial pressures of some gases in dry air and at 100% humidity.

CONCEPT CHECK

11. If nitrogen is 78% of atmospheric air, what is the partial pressure of nitrogen (P_{N_2}) in a sample of dry air that has an atmospheric pressure of 720 mm Hg?
12. The partial pressure of water vapor in inspired air is 47 mm Hg when inhaled air is fully humidified. If atmospheric pressure is 700 mm Hg and oxygen is 21% of the atmosphere at 0% humidity, what is the P_{O_2} of fully humidified air? Answers: p. 596

Gases Move Down Pressure Gradients

Air flow occurs whenever there is a pressure gradient. Bulk flow of air, like blood flow, is directed from areas of higher pressure to areas of lower pressure. Meteorologists predict the weather by knowing that areas of high atmospheric pressure move in to replace areas of low pressure. In ventilation, bulk flow of air down pressure gradients explains how air exchanges between the external environment and the lungs. Movement of the thorax during breathing creates alternating conditions of high and low pressure in the lungs.

Diffusion of gases down concentration (partial pressure) gradients applies to single gases. For example, oxygen moves from areas of higher oxygen partial pressure (P_{O_2}) to areas of lower oxygen partial pressure. Diffusion of individual gases is important in the alveoli-blood and blood-cell gas exchanges that we discuss in Chapter 18.

Boyle's Law Describes Pressure-Volume Relationships

The pressure exerted by a gas or mixture of gases in a sealed container is created by the collisions of moving gas molecules with the walls of the container and with each other. If the size of the container is reduced, the collisions between the gas molecules and the walls become more frequent, and the pressure rises. This relationship can be expressed by the equation

$$P_1V_1 = P_2V_2$$

where P represents pressure and V represents volume.

For example, start with a 1-liter container (V_1) of a gas whose pressure is 100 mm Hg (P_1), as shown in Figure 17-6 ●. What happens to the pressure of the gas when the lid of the container moves in to decrease the volume to 0.5 L? According to our equation,

$$P_1V_1 = P_2V_2$$

$$100 \text{ mm Hg} \times 1 \text{ L} = P_2 \times 0.5 \text{ L}$$

$$P_2 = 200 \text{ mm Hg}$$

This calculation tells us that if the volume is reduced by one-half, the pressure doubles. If the volume were to double, the pressure would be reduced by one-half. This relationship between pressure and volume was first noted by Robert Boyle in the 1600s and has been called **Boyle's law** of gases.

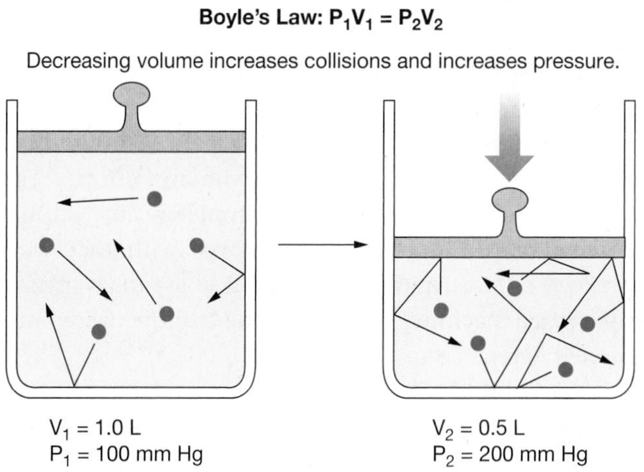

Boyle's Law: $P_1V_1 = P_2V_2$
Decreasing volume increases collisions and increases pressure.
V_1 = 1.0 L
P_1 = 100 mm Hg
V_2 = 0.5 L
P_2 = 200 mm Hg

● **FIGURE 17-6** ***Boyle's law.*** Boyle's law ($P_1V_1 = P_2V_2$) assumes that temperature and the number of gas molecules remain constant.

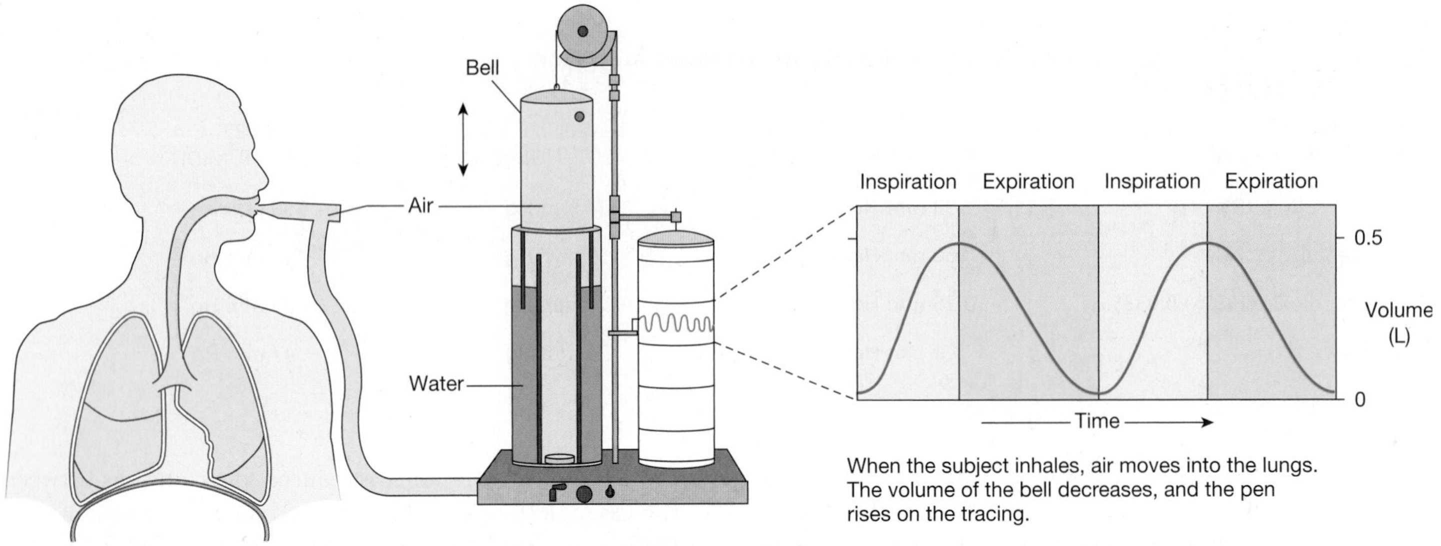
Bell
Air
Water
Inspiration
Expiration
Inspiration
Expiration
0.5
Volume (L)
0
Time
When the subject inhales, air moves into the lungs. The volume of the bell decreases, and the pen rises on the tracing.

● **FIGURE 17-7** ***A spirometer.*** The subject inserts a mouthpiece that is attached to an inverted bell filled with air or oxygen. The volume of the bell and the volume of the subject's respiratory tract create a closed system because the bell is suspended in water.

In the respiratory system, changes in the volume of the chest cavity during ventilation cause pressure gradients that create air flow. When chest volume increases, alveolar pressure falls, and air flows into the respiratory system. When the chest volume decreases, alveolar pressure increases, and air flows out into the atmosphere. This movement of air is bulk flow because the entire gas mixture is moving rather than merely one or two of the gas species contained in the air.

VENTILATION

The first exchange in respiratory physiology is ventilation, or breathing, the bulk flow exchange of air between the atmosphere and the alveoli (Fig. 17-1). A single **respiratory cycle** consists of an inspiration followed by an expiration.

Lung Volumes Change During Ventilation

Physiologists and clinicians assess a person's pulmonary function by measuring how much air the person moves during quiet breathing, then with maximum effort. These **pulmonary function tests** use a **spirometer**, an instrument that measures the volume of air moved with each breath (Fig. 17-7 ●). (Most spirometers in clinical use today are small computerized machines rather than the traditional spirometer illustrated here).

When a subject is attached to the traditional spirometer through a mouthpiece and the subject's nose is clipped closed, the subject's respiratory tract and the spirometer form a closed system. When the subject breathes in, air moves from the spirometer into the lungs, and the recording pen, which traces a graph on a rotating cylinder, moves up. When the subject exhales, air moves from the lungs back into the spirometer, and the pen moves down.

Lung Volumes The air moved during breathing can be divided into four lung volumes: (1) tidal volume, (2) inspiratory reserve volume, (3) expiratory reserve volume, and (4) residual volume. The numerical values used on the graph in Figure 17-8 ● represent average volumes for a 70-kg man. The volumes for women are typically less. Lung volumes vary considerably with age, sex, height, and weight, so clinicians use algorithms based on those parameters to predict lung volumes. (An *algorithm* is an equation or series of steps used to solve a problem).

Each of the following paragraphs begins with the instructions you would be given if you were being tested for these volumes.

"Breathe quietly." The volume of air that moves during a single inspiration or expiration is known as the **tidal volume** (V_T). Average tidal volume during quiet breathing is about 500 mL. (It is hard for subjects to breathe normally when they are thinking about their breathing, so the clinician may not give this instruction.)

"Now, at the end of a quiet inspiration, take in as much additional air as you possibly can." The additional volume you inspire above the tidal volume represents your **inspiratory reserve volume** (IRV). In a 70-kg man, this volume is about 3000 mL, a sixfold increase over the normal tidal volume.

"Now stop at the end of a normal exhalation, then exhale as much air as you possibly can." The amount of air forcefully exhaled after the end of a normal expiration is the **expiratory reserve volume** (ERV), which averages about 1100 mL.

The four lung volumes

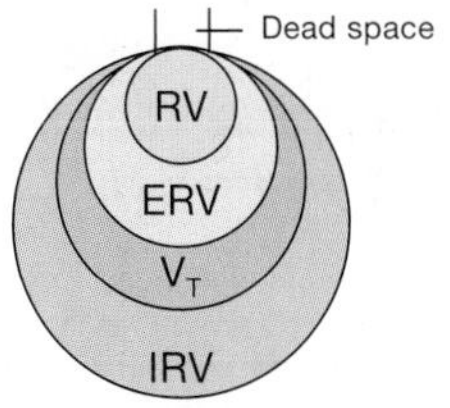

KEY

RV = Residual volume
ERV = Expiratory reserve volume
V_T = Tidal volume
IRV = Inspiratory reserve volume

Pulmonary volumes

		Males	Females	
Vital capacity	IRV	3000	1900	Inspiratory capacity
	V_T	500	500	
	ERV	1100	700	Functional residual capacity
Residual volume		1200	1100	
		5800 mL	4200 mL	

A spirometer tracing showing lung volumes and capacities.

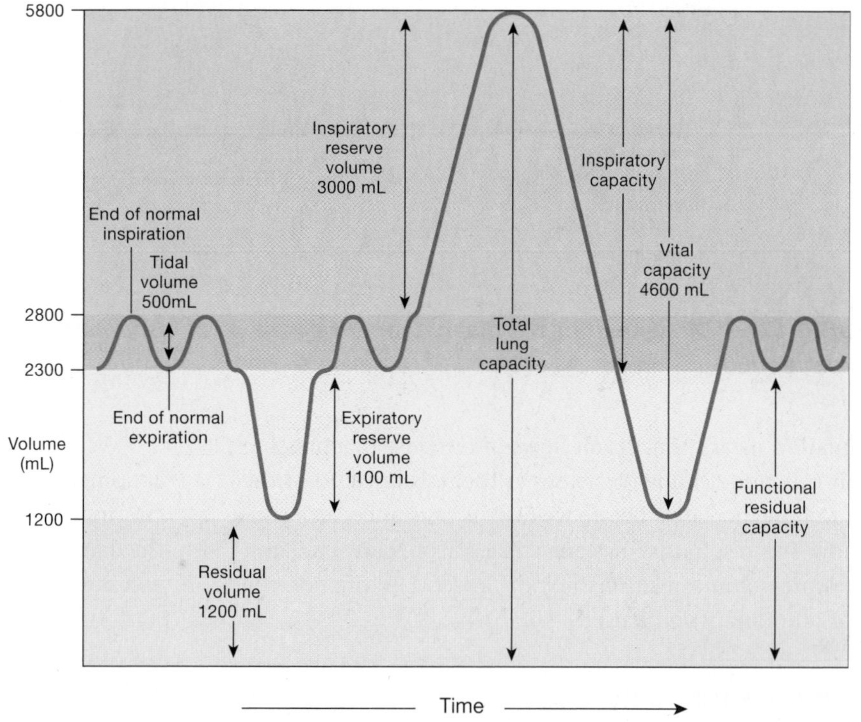

Capacities are sums of 2 or more volumes.

● **FIGURE 17-8** ***Lung volumes and capacities.*** Pulmonary volumes are given for a normal 70-kg man or a 50-kg woman, 28 years old.

The fourth volume cannot be measured directly. Even if you blow out as much air as you can, air still remains in the lungs and the airways. The volume of air in the respiratory system after maximal exhalation—about 1200 mL—is called the **residual volume** (RV). Most of this residual volume exists because the lungs are held stretched against the ribs by the pleural fluid.

Lung Capacities The sum of two or more lung volumes is called a **capacity**. The **vital capacity** (VC) is the sum of the inspiratory reserve volume, expiratory reserve volume, and tidal volume. Vital capacity represents the maximum amount of air that can be voluntarily moved into or out of the respiratory system with one breath. To measure vital capacity, you would instruct the person to take in as much air as possible, then blow it all out. Vital capacity decreases with age as muscles weaken and the lungs become less elastic.

Vital capacity plus the residual volume yields the **total lung capacity** (TLC). Other capacities of importance in pulmonary medicine include the **inspiratory capacity** (tidal volume + inspiratory reserve volume) and the **functional residual capacity** (expiratory reserve volume + residual volume).

CONCEPT CHECK

13. How are lung volumes related to lung capacities?
14. Which lung volume cannot be measured directly?
15. If vital capacity decreases with age but total lung capacity does not change, which lung volume must be changing? In which direction?
16. As inhaled air becomes humidified passing down the airways, what happens to the P_{O_2} of the air?

Answers: p. 596

During Ventilation, Air Flows Because of Pressure Gradients

Breathing is an active process that requires muscle contraction. Air flows into the lungs because of pressure gradients created by a pump, just as blood flows because of the pumping action of the heart. In the respiratory system, muscles of the thoracic cage and diaphragm function as the pump because most lung tissue is thin exchange epithelium. When these muscles contract, the lungs expand, held to the inside of the chest wall by the pleural fluid.

The primary muscles involved in quiet breathing (breathing at rest) are the diaphragm, the external intercostals, and the scalenes. During forced breathing, other muscles of the chest and abdomen may be recruited to assist. Examples of physiological situations in which breathing is forced include exercise, playing a wind instrument, and blowing up a balloon.

As we noted earlier in the chapter, air flow in the respiratory tract obeys the same rule as blood flow:

$$\text{Flow} \propto \Delta P/R$$

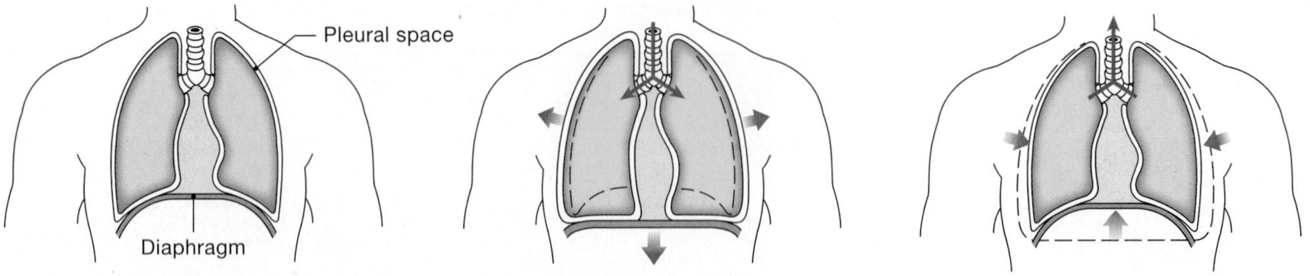

(a) At rest, diaphragm is relaxed.

(b) Diaphragm contracts, thoracic volume increases.

(c) Diaphragm relaxes, thoracic volume decreases.

● **FIGURE 17-9** ***Movement of the diaphragm during maximal inspiration and expiration***

This equation means that (1) air flows in response to a pressure gradient (ΔP) and (2) flow decreases as the resistance (R) of the system to flow increases. Before we discuss resistance, let's consider how the respiratory system creates a pressure gradient. The pressure-volume relationships of Boyle's law provide the basis for pulmonary ventilation.

CONCEPT CHECK

17. Compare the direction of air movement during one respiratory cycle with the direction of blood flow during one cardiac cycle.
18. Explain the relationship between the lungs, the pleural membranes, the pleural fluid, and the thoracic cage. Answers: p. 596

Inspiration Occurs When Alveolar Pressure Decreases

For air to move into the alveoli, pressure inside the lungs must become lower than atmospheric pressure. According to Boyle's law, an increase in volume will create a decrease in pressure. During inspiration, thoracic volume increases when certain skeletal muscles of the rib cage and diaphragm contract.

RUNNING PROBLEM

Edna's COPD began with chronic bronchitis and a morning cough that produced lots of mucus (*phlegm*). Cigarette smoke paralyzes the cilia that sweep debris and mucus out of the airways, and smoke irritation increases mucus production in the airway. Without functional cilia, mucus and debris pool in the airways, leading to a chronic cough. Eventually, smokers may begin to develop emphysema in addition to their bronchitis.

Question 2:
Why do people with chronic bronchitis have a higher-than-normal rate of respiratory infections?

569 571 580 583 591 592

When the diaphragm contracts, it drops down toward the abdomen. In quiet breathing, the diaphragm moves about 1.5 cm, increasing thoracic volume (Fig. 17-9 ●). Contraction of the diaphragm causes between 60% and 75% of the inspiratory volume change during normal quiet breathing.

Movement of the rib cage creates the remaining 25–40% of the volume change. During inhalation, the external intercostal and scalene muscles (see Fig. 17-2b) contract and pull the ribs

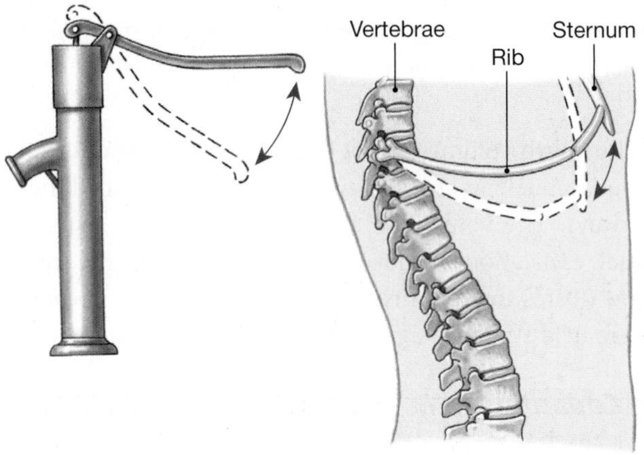

(a) "Pump handle" motion increases anterior-posterior dimension of rib cage.

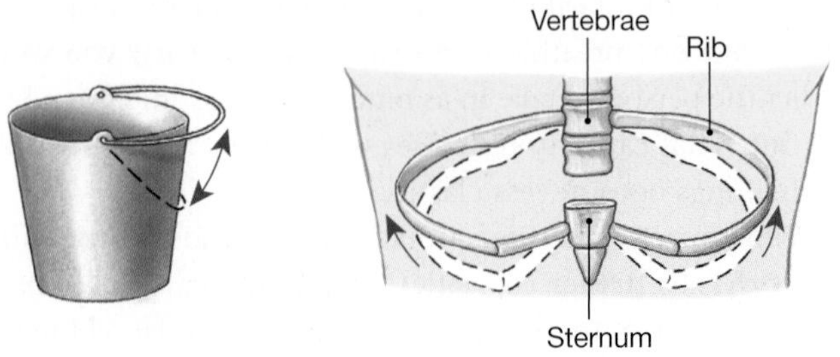

(b) "Bucket handle" motion increases lateral dimension of rib cage.

● **FIGURE 17-10** ***The dimensions of the thoracic cavity increase during inspiration.*** Movement of the handle on a hand pump is analogous to the lifting of the sternum and ribs. The bucket handle moving up and out is a good model for lateral rib movement during inspiration.

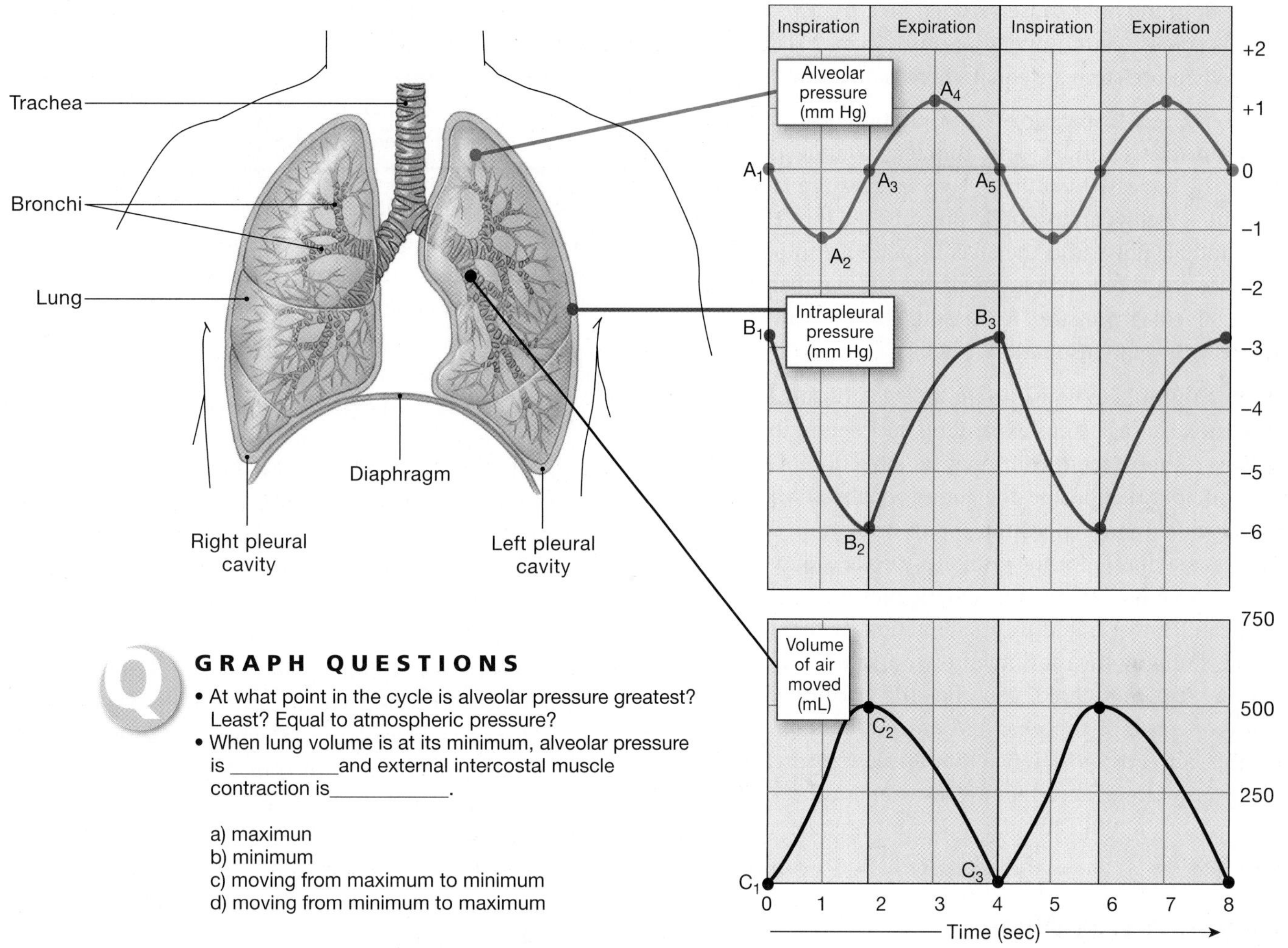

GRAPH QUESTIONS

- At what point in the cycle is alveolar pressure greatest? Least? Equal to atmospheric pressure?
- When lung volume is at its minimum, alveolar pressure is ___________and external intercostal muscle contraction is___________.

a) maximun
b) minimum
c) moving from maximum to minimum
d) moving from minimum to maximum

● **FIGURE 17-11** ***Pressure changes during quiet breathing.*** Normally expiration takes 2–3 times longer than inspiration (not shown to scale on this idealized graph).

upward and out. Rib movement during inspiration has been likened to a pump handle lifting up and away from the pump (the ribs moving up and away from the spine; Fig. 17-10a ●) and to the movement of a bucket handle as it lifts away from the side of a bucket (ribs moving outward in a lateral direction; Fig. 17-10b). The combination of these two movements broadens the rib cage in all directions. As thoracic volume increases, pressure decreases, and air flows into the lungs.

For many years, quiet breathing was attributed solely to the action of the diaphragm and the external intercostal muscles. It was thought that the scalenes and sternocleidomastoid muscles were active only during deep breathing. In recent years, however, studies have changed our understanding of how these accessory muscles contribute to quiet breathing. If an individual's scalenes are paralyzed, inspiration is achieved primarily by contraction of the diaphragm. Observation of patients with neuromuscular disorders has revealed that although the contracting diaphragm increases thoracic volume by moving toward the abdominal cavity, it also tends to pull the lower ribs inward, working against inspiration. In normal individuals, we know that the lower ribs move up and out during inspiration rather than inward. The fact that there is no up-and-out rib motion in patients with paralyzed scalenes tells us that normally the scalenes must be contributing to inspiration by lifting the sternum and upper ribs.

New evidence also downplays the role of the external intercostal muscles during quiet breathing. However, the external intercostals play an increasingly important role as respiratory activity increases. Because the exact contribution of external intercostals and scalenes varies depending on the type of breathing, we group these muscles together and simply call them the *inspiratory muscles.*

Now let's see how alveolar pressure (P_A) changes during a single inspiration. Follow the graphs in Figure 17-11 ● as you read through the process. Remember that atmospheric pressure is assigned a value of 0 mm Hg. Negative numbers designate subatmospheric pressures, and positive numbers denote higher-than-atmospheric pressures.

17

Time 0. In the brief pause between breaths, alveolar pressure is equal to atmospheric pressure (0 mm Hg at point A_1). When pressures are equal, there is no air flow.

Time 0–2 sec: Inspiration. As inspiration begins, inspiratory muscles contract, and thoracic volume increases. With the increase in volume, alveolar pressure falls about 1 mm Hg below atmospheric pressure (–1 mm Hg, point A_2), and air flows into the alveoli (point C_1 to point C_2). Because the thoracic volume changes faster than air can flow, alveolar pressure reaches its lowest value about halfway through inspiration (point A_2).

As air continues to flow into the alveoli, pressure increases until the thoracic cage stops expanding, just before the end of inspiration. Air movement continues for a fraction of a second longer, until pressure inside the lungs equalizes with atmospheric pressure (point A_3). At the end of inspiration, lung volume is at its maximum for the respiratory cycle (point C_2), and alveolar pressure is equal to atmospheric pressure.

You can demonstrate this phenomenon by taking a deep breath and stopping the movement of your chest at the end of inspiration. (Do not "hold your breath" because doing so closes the opening of the pharynx and prevents air flow.) If you do this correctly, you notice that air flow stops after you freeze the inspiratory movement. This exercise shows that at the end of inspiration, alveolar pressure is equal to atmospheric pressure.

Expiration Occurs When Alveolar Pressure Increases

At the end of inspiration, impulses from somatic motor neurons to the inspiratory muscles cease, and the muscles relax. Elastic recoil of the lungs and thoracic cage returns the diaphragm and rib cage to their original relaxed positions, just as a stretched elastic waistband recoils when released. Because expiration during quiet breathing involves passive elastic recoil rather than active muscle contraction, it is called **passive expiration**.

Time 2–4 sec: expiration. As lung and thoracic volumes decrease during expiration, air pressure in the lungs increases, reaching a maximum of about 1 mm Hg above atmospheric pressure (Fig. 17-11, point A_4). Alveolar pressure is now higher than atmospheric pressure, so air flow reverses and air moves out of the lungs.

Time 4 sec. At the end of expiration, air movement ceases when alveolar pressure is again equal to atmospheric pressure (point A_5). Lung volume reaches its minimum for the respiratory cycle (point C_3). At this point, the respiratory cycle has ended and is ready to begin again with the next breath.

The pressure differences shown in Figure 17-11 apply to quiet breathing. During exercise or forced heavy breathing, these values become proportionately larger. **Active expiration** occurs during voluntary exhalations and when ventilation exceeds 30–40 breaths per minute. (Normal resting ventilation rate is 12–20 breaths per minute for an adult.) Active expiration uses the internal intercostal muscles and the abdominal muscles (see Fig. 17-2b), which are not used during inspiration. These muscles are collectively called the *expiratory muscles*.

The internal intercostal muscles line the inside of the rib cage. When they contract, they pull the ribs inward, reducing the volume of the thoracic cavity. To feel this action, place your hands on your rib cage. Forcefully blow as much air out of your lungs as you can, noting the movement of your hands as you do so.

The internal and external intercostals function as antagonistic muscle groups [p. 408] to alter the position and volume of the rib cage during ventilation. The diaphragm, however, has no antagonistic muscles. Instead, abdominal muscles contract during active expiration to supplement the activity of the internal intercostals. Abdominal contraction pulls the lower rib cage inward and decreases abdominal volume, actions that displace the intestines and liver upward. The displaced viscera push the diaphragm up into the thoracic cavity and passively decrease chest volume even more. The action of abdominal muscles during forced expiration is why aerobics instructors tell you to blow air out as you lift your head and shoulders during abdominal "crunches." The active process of blowing air out helps contract the abdominals, the very muscles you are trying to strengthen.

Any neuromuscular disease that weakens skeletal muscles or damages their motor neurons can adversely affect ventilation. With decreased ventilation, less fresh air enters the lungs. In addition, loss of the ability to cough increases the risk of pneumonia and other infections. Examples of diseases that affect the motor control of ventilation include *myasthenia gravis* [p. 278], an illness in which acetylcholine receptors of the motor end plates of skeletal muscles are destroyed, and *polio* (poliomyelitis), a viral illness that paralyzes skeletal muscles.

CONCEPT CHECK

19. Scarlett O'Hara is trying to squeeze herself into a corset with an 18-inch waist. Will she be more successful by taking a deep breath and holding it or by blowing all the air out of her lungs? Why?
20. Why would loss of the ability to cough increase the risk of respiratory infections? (*Hint:* What does coughing do to mucus in the airways?)

Answers: p. 596

Intrapleural Pressure Changes During Ventilation

Ventilation requires that the lungs, which are unable to expand and contract on their own, move in association with the contraction and relaxation of the thorax. As we noted earlier in this chapter, the lungs are "stuck" to the thoracic cage by

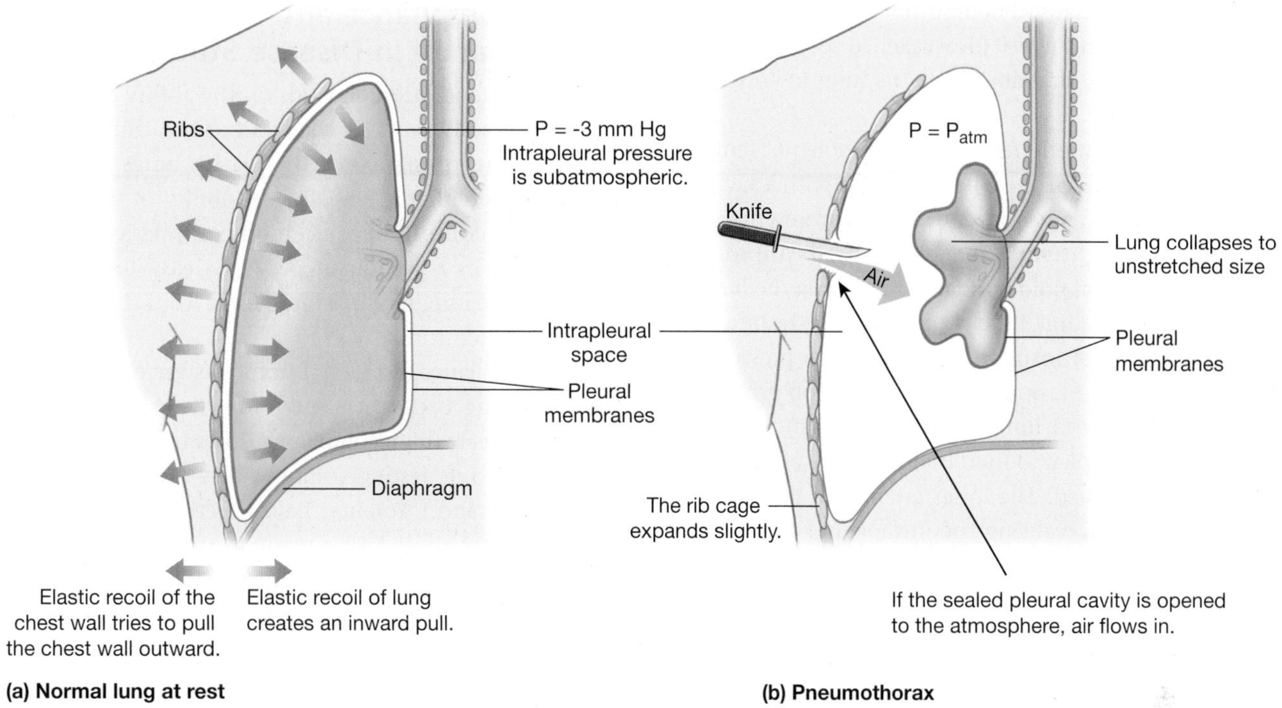

Ribs
P = -3 mm Hg
Intrapleural pressure
is subatmospheric.
Intrapleural
space
Pleural
membranes
Diaphragm
Elastic recoil of the chest wall tries to pull the chest wall outward.
Elastic recoil of lung creates an inward pull.
(a) Normal lung at rest
P = Patm
Knife
Air
Lung collapses to unstretched size
Pleural
membranes
The rib cage expands slightly.
If the sealed pleural cavity is opened to the atmosphere, air flows in.
(b) Pneumothorax

● **FIGURE 17-12** ***Subatmospheric pressure in the pleural cavity helps keep the lungs inflated.***

cohesive forces exerted by the fluid between the two pleural membranes. For this reason, when the thoracic cage moves, the lungs move with it.

The intrapleural pressure in the fluid between the pleural membranes is normally subatmospheric. This subatmospheric pressure arises during fetal development, when the thoracic cage with its associated pleural membrane grows more rapidly than the lung with its associated pleural membrane. The two pleural membranes are held together by the pleural fluid bond, so the elastic lungs are forced to stretch to conform to the larger volume of the thoracic cavity. At the same time, however, elastic recoil of the lungs creates an inwardly directed force that tries to pull the lungs away from the chest wall (Fig. 17-12a ●). The combination of the outward pull of the thoracic cage and inward recoil of the elastic lungs creates a subatmospheric intrapleural pressure of about −3 mm Hg.

You can create a similar situation by half-filling a syringe with water and capping it with a plugged-up needle. At this point, the pressure inside the barrel is equal to atmospheric pressure. Now hold the syringe barrel (the chest wall) in one hand while you try to withdraw the plunger (the elastic lung pulling away from the chest wall). As you pull on the plunger, the volume inside the barrel increases slightly, but the cohesive forces between the water molecules cause the water to resist expansion. The pressure in the barrel, which was initially equal to atmospheric pressure, decreases slightly as you pull on the plunger. If you release the plunger, it snaps back to its resting position, restoring atmospheric pressure inside the syringe.

What happens to subatmospheric intrapleural pressure if an opening is made between the sealed pleural cavity and the atmosphere? A knife thrust between the ribs, a broken rib that punctures the pleural membrane, or any other event that opens the pleural cavity to the atmosphere allows air to flow down its pressure gradient into the cavity, just as air enters when you break the seal on a vacuum-packed can.

Air in the pleural cavity breaks the fluid bond holding the lung to the chest wall. The chest wall expands outward while the elastic lung collapses to an unstretched state, like a deflated balloon (Fig. 17-12b). This condition, called **pneumothorax** [*pneuma,* air + *thorax,* chest], results in a collapsed lung that is

RUNNING PROBLEM

Emphysema is characterized by a loss of elastin, the elastic fibers that help the alveoli recoil during expiration. Elastin is destroyed by *elastase*, an enzyme released by alveolar macrophages, which must work overtime in smokers to rid the lungs of irritants. People with emphysema have more difficulty exhaling than inhaling. Their alveoli have lost elastic recoil, which makes expiration—normally a passive process—require conscious effort.

Question 3:

Name the muscles that patients with emphysema use to exhale actively.

569 571 580 583 591 592

unable to function normally. Pneumothorax can also occur spontaneously if a congenital *bleb* (or weakened section of lung tissue) ruptures, allowing air from inside the lung to enter the pleural cavity.

Correction of a pneumothorax has two components: removing as much air from the pleural cavity as possible with a suction pump, and sealing the hole to prevent more air from entering. Any air remaining in the cavity is gradually absorbed into the blood, restoring the pleural fluid bond and reinflating the lung.

Pressures in the pleural fluid vary during a respiratory cycle. At the beginning of inspiration, intrapleural pressure is about −3 mm Hg (Fig. 17-11, point B_1). As inspiration proceeds, the pleural membranes and lungs follow the expanding thoracic cage because of the pleural fluid bond, but the elastic lung tissue resists being stretched. The lungs attempt to pull farther away from the chest wall, causing the intrapleural pressure to become even more negative (Fig. 17-11, point B_2).

Because this process is difficult to visualize, return to the analogy of the water-filled syringe with the plugged-up needle. You can pull the plunger out a small distance without much effort, but the cohesiveness of the water makes it difficult to pull the plunger out any farther. The increased amount of work you do trying to pull the plunger out is paralleled by the work your inspiratory muscles must do when they contract during inspiration. The bigger the breath, the more work is required to stretch the elastic lung.

By the end of a quiet inspiration, when the lungs are fully expanded, intrapleural pressure falls to around −6 mm Hg (Fig. 17-11, point B_2). During exercise or other powerful inspirations, intrapleural pressure may reach −8 mm Hg or lower.

During expiration, the thoracic cage returns to its resting position. The lungs are released from their stretched position, and the intrapleural pressure returns to its normal value of about −3 mm Hg (point B_3). Notice that intrapleural pressure never equilibrates with atmospheric pressure because the pleural cavity is a closed compartment.

Pressure gradients required for air flow are created by the work of skeletal muscle contraction. Normally, about 3–5% of the body's energy expenditure is used for quiet breathing. During exercise, the energy required for breathing increases substantially. The two factors that have the greatest influence on the amount of work needed for breathing are the stretchability of the lungs and the resistance of the airways to air flow.

CONCEPT CHECK

21. A person has periodic spastic contractions of the diaphragm, otherwise known as hiccups. What happens to intrapleural and alveolar pressures when a person hiccups?
22. A stabbing victim is brought to the emergency room with a knife wound between the ribs on the left side of his chest. What has probably happened to his left lung? To his right lung? Why does the left side of his rib cage seem larger than the right side?

Answers: p. 596

Lung Compliance and Elastance May Change in Disease States

Adequate ventilation depends on the ability of the lungs to expand normally. Most of the work of breathing goes into overcoming the resistance of the elastic lungs and the thoracic cage to stretching. Clinically, the ability of the lung to stretch is called **compliance**. A high-compliance lung stretches easily, just as a compliant person is easy to persuade. A low-compliance lung requires more force from the inspiratory muscles to stretch it.

Compliance is different from **elastance** (elasticity), the ability to spring back after being stretched. The fact that a lung stretches easily (high compliance) does not necessarily mean that it returns to its resting volume when the stretching force is released (elastance). You may have experienced something like this with old gym shorts. After many washings the elastic waistband is easy to stretch (high compliance) but lacking in elastance, making it impossible for the shorts to stay up around your waist.

Analogous problems occur in the respiratory system. For example, as noted in the Running Problem, emphysema is a disease in which elastin fibers normally found in lung tissue are destroyed. Destruction of elastin results in lungs that exhibit high compliance and stretch easily during inspiration. However, these lungs also have decreased elastance, so they do not recoil to their resting position during expiration.

To understand the importance of elastic recoil to expiration, think of an inflated balloon and an inflated plastic bag. The balloon is similar to the normal lung. Its elastic walls squeeze on the air inside the balloon, thereby increasing the internal air pressure. When the neck of the balloon is opened to the atmosphere, elastic recoil causes air to flow out of the balloon. The inflated plastic bag, on the other hand, is like the lung of an individual with emphysema. It has high compliance and is easily inflated, but it has little elastic recoil. If the inflated plastic bag is opened to the atmosphere, most of the air remains inside the bag.

A decrease in lung compliance affects ventilation because more work must be expended to stretch a stiff lung. Pathological conditions in which compliance is reduced are called **restrictive lung diseases**. In these conditions, the energy expenditure required to stretch less-compliant lungs can far exceed the normal work of breathing. Two common causes of decreased compliance are inelastic scar tissue formed in *fibrotic lung diseases*, and inadequate alveolar production of surfactant, a chemical that facilitates lung expansion.

Pulmonary **fibrosis** is characterized by the development of stiff, fibrous scar tissue that restricts lung inflation. In *idiopathic* pulmonary fibrosis [*idios*, one's own], the cause is unknown. Other forms of fibrotic lung disease result from chronic inhalation of fine particulate matter, such as asbestos and silicon, that escapes the mucus lining the airways and reaches the alveoli. Wandering alveolar macrophages (see Fig. 17-2g) then ingest the inhaled particulate matter. If the particles are

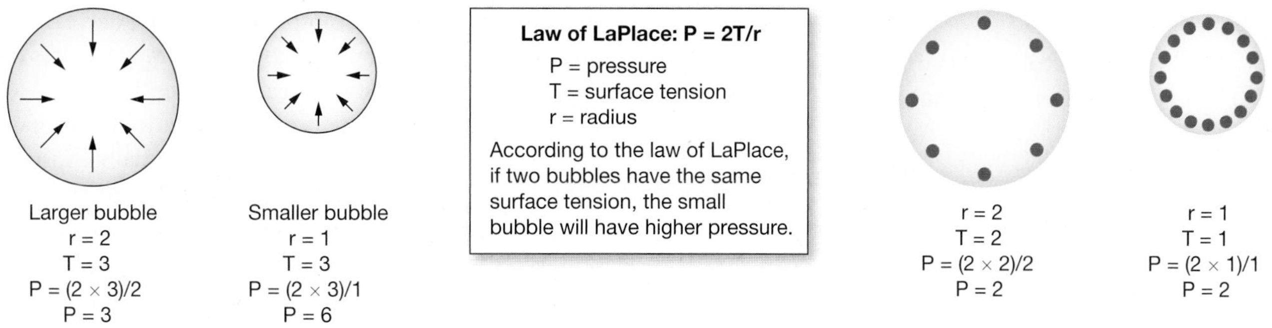
Larger bubble
r = 2
T = 3
P = (2 × 3)/2
P = 3
Smaller bubble
r = 1
T = 3
P = (2 × 3)/1
P = 6
Law of LaPlace: P = 2T/r
P = pressure
T = surface tension
r = radius
According to the law of LaPlace, if two bubbles have the same surface tension, the small bubble will have higher pressure.
r = 2
T = 2
P = (2 × 2)/2
P = 2
r = 1
T = 1
P = (2 × 1)/1
P = 2

(a) Pressure is greater in the smaller bubble.

(b) Surfactant reduces surface tension (T). Pressure is equalized in the large and small bubbles.

● **FIGURE 17-13** ***The law of LaPlace***

organic, the macrophages can digest them with lysosomal enzymes. However, if the particles cannot be digested or if they accumulate in large numbers, an inflammatory process ensues. The macrophages then secrete growth factors that stimulate fibroblasts in the lung's connective tissue to produce inelastic collagen. Pulmonary fibrosis cannot be reversed.

Surfactant Decreases the Work of Breathing

For years, physiologists assumed that elastin and other elastic fibers were the primary source of resistance to stretch in the lung. However, studies comparing the work required to expand air-filled and saline-filled lungs showed that air-filled lungs are much harder to inflate. From this result, researchers concluded that lung tissue itself contributes less to resistance than once thought. Some other property of the normal air-filled lung, a property not present in the saline-filled lung, must create most of the resistance to stretch.

This property is the surface tension [p. 27] created by the thin fluid layer between the alveolar cells and the air. At any air-fluid interface, the surface of the fluid is under tension, like a thin membrane being stretched. When the fluid is water, surface tension arises because of the hydrogen bonds between water molecules. The water molecules on the fluid's surface are attracted to other water molecules beside and beneath them but are not attracted to gases in the air at the air-fluid interface.

Alveolar surface tension is similar to the surface tension that exists in a spherical bubble. The surface tension created by the thin film of fluid is directed toward the center of the bubble and creates pressure in the interior of the bubble. The **law of LaPlace** is an expression of this pressure. It states that the pressure (P) inside a bubble formed by a fluid film is a function of two factors: the surface tension of the fluid (T) and the radius of the bubble (r). This relationship is expressed by the equation

$$P = 2T/r$$

Notice in Figure 17-13a ● that if two bubbles have different diameters but are formed by fluids with the same surface tension, the pressure inside the smaller bubble is greater than that inside the larger bubble.

How does this apply to the lung? In physiology, we can equate the bubble to a fluid-lined alveolus (although alveoli are not perfect spheres). The fluid lining all the alveoli creates surface tension. If the surface tension (T) of the fluid were the same in small and large alveoli, small alveoli would have higher inwardly directed pressure than larger alveoli, and increased resistance to stretch. As a result, more work would be needed to expand smaller alveoli.

Normally, however, our lungs secrete a surfactant that reduces surface tension. Surfactants ("*surf*ace *act*ive *agents*") are molecules that disrupt cohesive forces between water molecules by substituting themselves for water at the surface. For example, that product you add to your dishwasher to aid in the rinse cycle is a surfactant that keeps the rinse water from beading up on the dishes (and forming spots when the water beads dry). In the lungs, surfactant decreases surface tension of the alveolar fluid and thereby decreases resistance of the lung to stretch.

Surfactant is more concentrated in smaller alveoli, making their surface tension less than that in larger alveoli (Fig. 17-13b). Lower surface tension helps equalize the pressure among alveoli of different sizes and makes it easier to inflate the smaller alveoli. With lower surface tension, the work needed to expand the alveoli with each breath is greatly reduced. Human surfactant is a mixture containing proteins and phospholipids, such as *dipalmitoylphosphatidylcholine*, which are secreted into the alveolar air space by type II alveolar cells (see Fig. 17-2g).

Normally, surfactant synthesis begins about the twenty-fifth week of fetal development under the influence of various hormones. Production usually reaches adequate levels by the thirty-fourth week (about six weeks before normal delivery). Babies who are born prematurely without adequate concentrations of surfactant in their alveoli develop *newborn respiratory distress syndrome (NRDS)*. In addition to having "stiff" (low-compliance) lungs, NRDS babies also have alveoli that collapse each time they exhale. These infants must use a tremendous amount of energy to expand their collapsed lungs with each breath. Unless treatment is initiated rapidly, about 50% of these infants die. In the past, all physicians could do for NRDS

TABLE 17-3 Factors That Affect Airway Resistance

FACTOR	AFFECTED BY	MEDIATED BY
Length of the system	Constant; not a factor	
Viscosity of air	Usually constant; humidity and altitude may alter slightly	
Diameter of airways		
Upper airways	Physical obstruction	Mucus and other factors
Bronchioles	Bronchoconstriction	Parasympathetic neurons (muscarinic receptors), histamine, leukotrienes
	Bronchodilation	Carbon dioxide, epinephrine (β_2-receptors)

babies was administer oxygen. Today, however, the prognosis for NRDS babies is much better. Amniotic fluid can be sampled to assess whether or not the fetal lungs are producing adequate amounts of surfactant. If they are not, and if delivery cannot be delayed, NRDS babies can be treated with aerosol administration of artificial surfactant until the lungs mature enough to produce their own. The current treatment also includes artificial ventilation that forces air into the lungs (*positive-pressure ventilation*) and keeps the alveoli open.

Airway Diameter Determines Airway Resistance

The other factor besides compliance that influences the work of breathing is the resistance of the respiratory system to air flow. Resistance in the respiratory system is similar in many ways to resistance in the cardiovascular system [p. 473]. Three parameters contribute to resistance (R): the system's length (L), the viscosity of the substance flowing through the system (η), and the radius of the tubes in the system (r). As with flow in the cardiovascular system, Poiseuille's law relates these factors to one another:

$$R \propto L\eta/r^4$$

Because the length of the respiratory system is constant, we can ignore L in the equation. The viscosity of air is almost constant, although you may have noticed that it feels harder to breathe in a sauna filled with steam than in a room with normal humidity. Water droplets in the steam increase the viscosity of the steamy air, thereby increasing its resistance to flow. Viscosity also changes slightly with atmospheric pressure, decreasing as pressure decreases. A person at high altitude may feel less resistance to air flow than a person at sea level. Despite these exceptions, viscosity plays a very small role in resistance to air flow.

Because length and viscosity are essentially constant for the respiratory system, the radius (or diameter) of the airways becomes the primary determinant of airway resistance. Normally, however, the work needed to overcome resistance of the airways to air flow is much less than the work needed to overcome the resistance of the lungs and thoracic cage to stretch.

Nearly 90% of airway resistance normally can be attributed to the trachea and bronchi, rigid structures with the smallest total cross-sectional area. Because these structures are supported by cartilage and bone, their diameters normally do not change, and their resistance to air flow is constant. However, mucus accumulation from allergies or infections can dramatically increase resistance. If you have ever tried breathing through your nose when you have a cold, you can appreciate how the narrowing of an upper airway limits air flow!

The bronchioles normally do not contribute significantly to airway resistance because their total cross-sectional area is about 2000 times that of the trachea. Because the bronchioles are collapsible tubes, however, a decrease in their diameter can suddenly turn them into a significant source of airway resistance. **Bronchoconstriction** increases resistance to air flow and decreases the amount of fresh air that reaches the alveoli.

Bronchioles, like arterioles, are subject to reflex control by the nervous system and by hormones. However, most minute-to-minute changes in bronchiolar diameter occur in response to paracrines. Carbon dioxide in the airways is the primary paracrine that affects bronchiolar diameter. Increased CO_2 in expired air relaxes bronchiolar smooth muscle and causes **bronchodilation**.

Histamine is a paracrine that acts as a powerful bronchoconstrictor. This chemical is released by *mast cells* [p. 549] in response to either tissue damage or allergic reactions. In severe allergic reactions, large amounts of histamine may lead to widespread bronchoconstriction and difficult breathing. Immediate medical treatment in these patients is imperative.

The primary neural control of bronchioles comes from parasympathetic neurons that cause bronchoconstriction, a reflex designed to protect the lower respiratory tract from inhaled irritants. There is no significant sympathetic innervation of the bronchioles in humans. However, smooth muscle in the bronchioles is well supplied with β_2-receptors that respond to epinephrine. Stimulation of β_2-receptors relaxes airway smooth muscle and results in bronchodilation. This reflex is used therapeutically in the treatment of asthma and various allergic reactions characterized by histamine release and bronchoconstriction. Table 17-3 ● summarizes the factors that alter airway resistance.

CONCEPT CHECK

23. In a normal person, which contributes more to the work of breathing: airway resistance or lung and chest wall elastance?

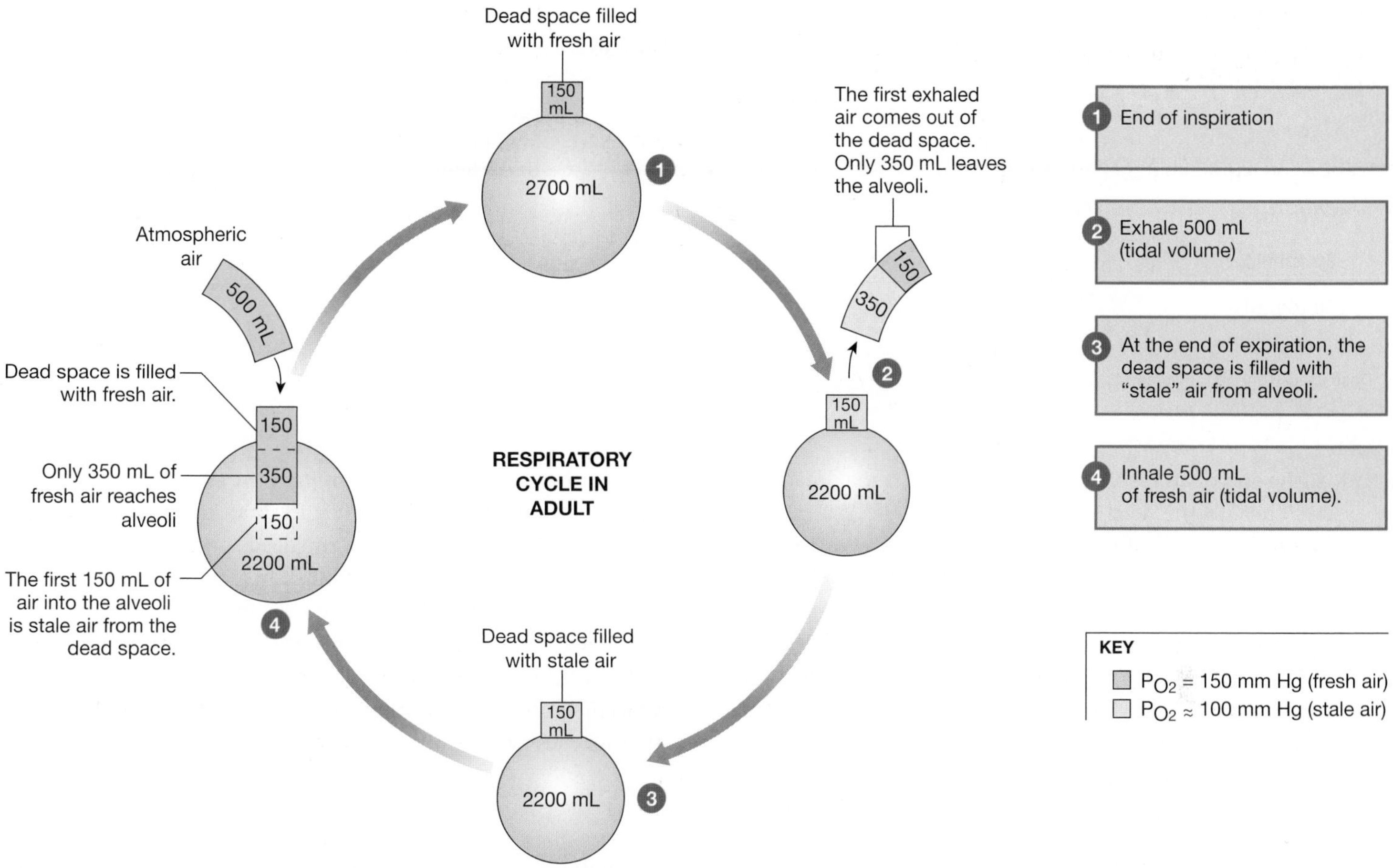
Dead space filled
with fresh air
150
mL
2700 mL
1
The first exhaled
air comes out of
the dead space.
Only 350 mL leaves
the alveoli.
150
350
2
150
mL
2200 mL
Atmospheric
air
500 mL
Dead space is filled
with fresh air.
150
350
150
2200 mL
Only 350 mL of
fresh air reaches
alveoli
The first 150 mL of
air into the alveoli
is stale air from the
dead space.
4
RESPIRATORY
CYCLE IN
ADULT
Dead space filled
with stale air
150
mL
2200 mL
3
1 End of inspiration
2 Exhale 500 mL
(tidal volume)
3 At the end of expiration, the
dead space is filled with
"stale" air from alveoli.
4 Inhale 500 mL
of fresh air (tidal volume).
KEY
PO2 = 150 mm Hg (fresh air)
PO2 ≈ 100 mm Hg (stale air)

● **FIGURE 17-14** ***Total pulmonary ventilation is greater than alveolar ventilation because of dead space.*** In this example, total pulmonary ventilation is 500 mL/breath × ventilation rate but alveolar ventilation is only 350 mL/breath × ventilation rate.

24. Coal miners who spend years inhaling fine coal dust have much of their alveolar surface area covered with scarlike tissue. What happens to their lung compliance as a result?
25. How does the work required for breathing change when surfactant is not present in the lungs?
26. A cancerous lung tumor has grown into the walls of a group of bronchioles, narrowing their lumens. What has happened to the resistance to air flow in these bronchioles?
27. Name the neurotransmitter and receptor for parasympathetic bronchoconstriction.

Answers: p. 596

Rate and Depth of Breathing Determine the Efficiency of Breathing

You may recall that the efficiency of the heart is measured by the cardiac output, which is calculated by multiplying heart rate by stroke volume. Likewise, we can estimate the effectiveness of ventilation by calculating **total pulmonary ventilation,** the volume of air moved into and out of the lungs each minute. Total pulmonary ventilation, also known as the *minute volume,* is calculated as follows:

Total pulmonary ventilation = ventilation rate × tidal volume

The normal ventilation rate for an adult is 12–20 breaths per minute. Using the average tidal volume (500 mL) and the slowest ventilation rate, we get:

Total pulmonary ventilation =
12 breaths/min × 500 mL/breath
= 6000 mL/min = 6 L/min

Total pulmonary ventilation represents the physical movement of air into and out of the respiratory tract, but is it a good indicator of how much fresh air reaches the alveolar exchange surface? Not necessarily.

Some air that enters the respiratory system does not reach the alveoli because part of every breath remains in the conducting airways, such as the trachea and bronchi. Because the conducting airways do not exchange gases with the blood, they are known as the **anatomic dead space.** Anatomic dead space averages about 150 mL.

To illustrate the difference between the total volume of air that enters the airways and the volume of fresh air that reaches the alveoli, let's consider a typical breath that moves 500 mL of air during a respiratory cycle (Fig. 17-14 ●).

TABLE 17-4 **Effects of Breathing Pattern on Alveolar Ventilation**

TIDAL VOLUME (mL)	VENTILATION RATE (BREATHS/MIN)	TOTAL PULMONARY VENTILATION (mL/MIN)	FRESH AIR TO ALVEOLI (mL) (TIDAL VOLUME − DEAD SPACE VOLUME*)	ALVEOLAR VENTILATION (mL/MIN)
500 (normal)	12 (normal)	6000	350	4200
300 (shallow)	20 (rapid)	6000	150	3000
750 (deep)	8 (slow)	6000	600	4800

*Dead space volume is assumed to be 150 mL.

1. At the end of an inspiration, lung volume is maximal, and fresh air fills the dead space.
2. The tidal volume of 500 mL is exhaled. However, the first portion of this 500 mL to exit the airways is the 150 mL of fresh air that had been in the dead space, followed by 350 mL of "stale" air from the alveoli. Thus even though 500 mL of air exited the alveoli, only 350 mL of that volume left the body. The remaining 150 mL of "stale" alveolar air stays in the dead space.
3. At the end of expiration, lung volume is at its minimum, and stale air from the most recent expiration fills the anatomic dead space.
4. With the next inspiration, 500 mL of fresh air enters the airways. The entering air returns the 150 mL of stale air in the anatomic dead space to the alveoli, followed by the first 350 mL of the fresh air. The last 150 mL of inspired fresh air again remains in the dead space and never reaches the alveoli.

Thus, although 500 mL of air entered the alveoli, only 350 mL of that volume was fresh air. The fresh air entering the alveoli equals the tidal volume minus the dead space volume.

Because a significant portion of inspired air never reaches an exchange surface, a more accurate indicator of ventilation efficiency is **alveolar ventilation**, the amount of fresh air that reaches the alveoli each minute. Alveolar ventilation is calculated by multiplying ventilation rate by the volume of fresh air that reaches the alveoli:

$$\text{Alveolar ventilation} = \text{ventilation rate} \times (\text{tidal volume} - \text{dead space})$$

Using the same ventilation rate and tidal volume as before, and a dead space of 150 mL, then

$$\text{Alveolar ventilation} = 12 \text{ breaths/min} \times (500 - 150 \text{ mL/breath}) = 4200 \text{ mL/min}$$

TABLE 17-5 **Types and Patterns of Ventilation**

NAME	DESCRIPTION	EXAMPLES
Eupnea	Normal quiet breathing	
Hyperpnea	Increased respiratory rate and/or volume in response to increased metabolism	Exercise
Hyperventilation	Increased respiratory rate and/or volume without increased metabolism	Emotional hyperventilation; blowing up a balloon
Hypoventilation	Decreased alveolar ventilation	Shallow breathing; asthma; restrictive lung disease
Tachypnea	Rapid breathing; usually increased respiratory rate with decreased depth	Panting
Dyspnea	Difficulty breathing (a subjective feeling sometimes described as "air hunger")	Various pathologies or hard exercise
Apnea	Cessation of breathing	Voluntary breath-holding; depression of CNS control centers

TABLE 17-6 Normal Ventilation Values in Pulmonary Medicine

Total pulmonary ventilation	6 L/min
Total alveolar ventilation	4.2 L/min
Maximum voluntary ventilation	125–170 L/min
Respiration rate	12–20 breaths/min

Thus, at 12 breaths per minute, the alveolar ventilation is 4.2 L/min. Although 6 L/min of fresh air enters the respiratory system, only 4.2 L reaches the alveoli.

Alveolar ventilation can be drastically affected by changes in the rate or depth of breathing. Table 17-4 ● shows that three people can have the same total pulmonary ventilation but dramatically different alveolar ventilation. **Maximum voluntary ventilation**, which involves breathing as deeply and quickly as possible, may increase total pulmonary ventilation to as much as 170 L/min. Table 17-5 ● describes various patterns of ventilation, and Table 17-6 ● gives normal ventilation values.

Gas Composition in the Alveoli Varies Little During Normal Breathing

How much can a change in alveolar ventilation affect the amount of fresh air and oxygen that reach the alveoli? Figure 17-15 ● shows how the partial pressures P_{O_2} and P_{CO_2} in the alveoli vary with hyper- and hypoventilation. As alveolar ventilation increases above normal levels during **hyperventilation**, alveolar P_{O_2} rises to about 120 mm Hg, and alveolar P_{CO_2} falls to around 20 mm Hg. During **hypoventilation**, when less fresh air enters the alveoli, alveolar P_{O_2} decreases and alveolar P_{CO_2} increases.

Although a dramatic change in alveolar ventilation pattern can affect gas partial pressures in the alveoli, the P_{O_2} and P_{CO_2} in the alveoli change surprisingly little during normal quiet breathing. Alveolar P_{O_2} is fairly constant at 100 mm Hg, and alveolar P_{CO_2} stays close to 40 mm Hg.

Intuitively, you might think that P_{O_2} would increase when fresh air first enters the alveoli, then decrease steadily as oxygen leaves to enter the blood. Instead, we find only very small swings in P_{O_2}. Why? The reasons are that (1) the amount of oxygen that enters the alveoli with each breath is roughly equal to the amount of oxygen that enters the blood, and (2) the amount of fresh air that enters the lungs with each breath is only a little more than 10% of the total lung volume at the end of inspiration.

CONCEPT CHECK

28. If a person increased his tidal volume, what would happen to his alveolar P_{O_2}?

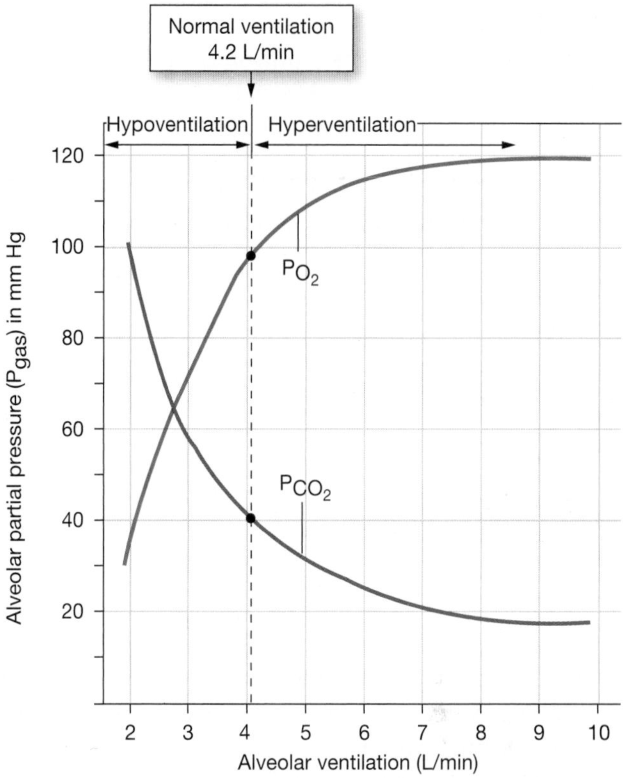

● **FIGURE 17-15** ***As alveolar ventilation increases, alveolar P_{O_2} increases and P_{CO_2} decreases.*** The opposite occurs as alveolar ventilation decreases.

29. If his breathing rate increased, what would happen to his alveolar P_{O_2}?

Answers: p. 596

Ventilation and Alveolar Blood Flow Are Matched

Moving oxygen from the atmosphere to the alveolar exchange surface is only the first step in external respiration. Next, gas exchange must occur across the alveolar-capillary interface. Finally, blood flow (*perfusion*) past the alveoli must be high enough to pick up the available oxygen. Matching the ventilation rate into groups of alveoli with blood flow past those alveoli is a two-part process involving local regulation of both air flow and blood flow.

Alterations in pulmonary blood flow depend almost exclusively on properties of the capillaries and on such local factors as the concentrations of oxygen and carbon dioxide in the lung tissue. Capillaries in the lungs are unusual because they are collapsible. If the pressure of blood flowing through the capillaries falls below a certain point, the capillaries close off, diverting blood to pulmonary capillary beds in which blood pressure is higher.

In a person at rest, some capillary beds in the apex (top) of the lung are closed off because of low hydrostatic pressure. Capillary beds at the base of the lung have higher hydrostatic pressure because of gravity and thus remain open. Consequently, blood flow is diverted toward the base of the

TABLE 17-7 Local Control of Arterioles and Bronchioles by Oxygen and Carbon Dioxide

GAS COMPOSITION	BRONCHIOLES	PULMONARY ARTERIOLES	SYSTEMIC ARTERIOLES
P_{CO_2} increases	Dilate	(Constrict)*	Dilate
P_{CO_2} decreases	Constrict	(Dilate)	Constrict
P_{O_2} increases	(Constrict)	(Dilate)	Constrict
P_{O_2} decreases	(Dilate)	Constrict	Dilate

*Parentheses indicate weak responses.

lung. During exercise, when blood pressure rises, the closed apical capillary beds open, ensuring that the increased cardiac output can be fully oxygenated as it passes through the lungs. The ability of the lungs to recruit additional capillary beds during exercise is an example of the reserve capacity of the body.

At the local level, the body attempts to match air flow and blood flow in each section of the lung by regulating the diameters of the arterioles and bronchioles. Bronchiolar diameter is mediated primarily by CO_2 levels in exhaled air passing through them (Tbl. 17-7 ●). An increase in the P_{CO_2} of expired air causes bronchioles to dilate. A decrease in the P_{CO_2} of expired air causes bronchioles to constrict.

Although there is some autonomic innervation of pulmonary arterioles, there is apparently little neural control of pulmonary blood flow. The resistance of pulmonary arterioles to blood flow is regulated primarily by the oxygen content of the interstitial fluid around the arteriole. If ventilation of alveoli in one area of the lung is diminished, as shown in Figure 17-16b ●, the P_{O_2} in that area decreases, and the arterioles respond by constricting, as shown in Figure 17-16c. This local vasoconstriction is adaptive because it diverts blood away from the underventilated region to better-ventilated parts of the lung.

Note that constriction of pulmonary arterioles in response to low P_{O_2} is the opposite of what occurs in the systemic circulation [p. 522]. In the systemic circulation, a decrease in the P_{O_2} of a tissue causes local arterioles to dilate, delivering more oxygen-carrying blood to those tissues that are consuming oxygen. In the lungs, blood is picking up oxygen, so it does not make sense to send more blood to an area with low tissue P_{O_2} due to poor ventilation.

Another important point must be noted here. Local control mechanisms are not effective regulators of air and blood flow under all circumstances. If blood flow is blocked in one pulmonary artery, or if air flow is blocked at the level of the

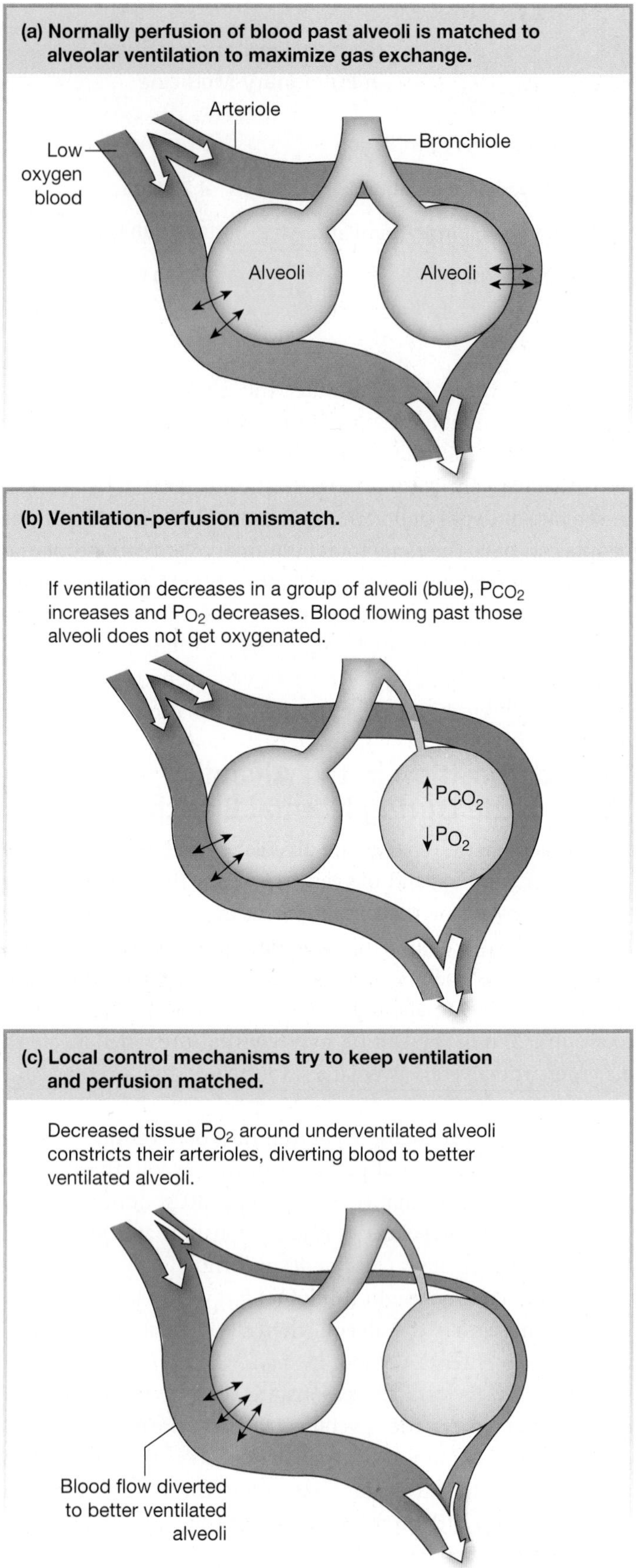
(a) Normally perfusion of blood past alveoli is matched to alveolar ventilation to maximize gas exchange.
Arteriole
Bronchiole
Low oxygen blood
Alveoli
Alveoli
(b) Ventilation-perfusion mismatch.
If ventilation decreases in a group of alveoli (blue), P_{CO_2} increases and P_{O_2} decreases. Blood flowing past those alveoli does not get oxygenated.
↑P_{CO_2}
↓P_{O_2}
(c) Local control mechanisms try to keep ventilation and perfusion matched.
Decreased tissue P_{O_2} around underventilated alveoli constricts their arterioles, diverting blood to better ventilated alveoli.
Blood flow diverted to better ventilated alveoli

● **FIGURE 17-16** ***Local control mechanisms attempt to match ventilation and perfusion.***

larger airways, local responses that shunt air or blood to other parts of the lung are ineffective because in these cases no part of the lung has normal ventilation or perfusion.

CONCEPT CHECK

30. If a lung tumor decreases blood flow in one small section of the lung to a minimum, what happens to P_{O_2} in the alveoli in that section and in the surrounding interstitial fluid? What happens to P_{CO_2} in that section? What is the compensatory response of the bronchioles in the affected section? Will the compensation bring ventilation in the affected section of the lung back to normal? Explain. Answers: p. 596

Auscultation and Spirometry Assess Pulmonary Function

Most pulmonary function tests are relatively simple to perform. Auscultation of breath sounds is an important diagnostic technique in pulmonary medicine, just as auscultation of heart sounds is an important technique in cardiovascular diagnosis [p. 497]. Breath sounds are more complicated to interpret than heart sounds, however, because breath sounds have a wider range of normal variation.

Normally, breath sounds are distributed evenly over the lungs and resemble a quiet "whoosh" made by flowing air. When air flow is reduced, such as in pneumothorax, breath sounds may be either diminished or absent. Abnormal sounds include various squeaks, pops, wheezes, and bubbling sounds caused by fluid and secretions in the airways or alveoli.

RUNNING PROBLEM

Edna has been experiencing shortness of breath while exercising, so her physician runs some tests, including measuring Edna's lung volumes with spirometry. Part of the test is a forced expiratory volume. With her lungs filled to their maximum with air, Edna is told to blow out as fast and as forcefully as she can. The volume of air that Edna expels in the first second of the test (the forced expiratory volume in one second, or FEV_1) is lower than normal because in COPD, airway resistance is increased. Another test the physician orders is a complete blood count (CBC). The results of this test show that Edna has higher-than-normal red blood cell count and hematocrit [p. 553].

Question 4:
When Edna fills her lungs maximally, the volume of air in her lungs is known as the _________ capacity. When she exhales all the air she can, the volume of air left in her lungs is the _________.

Question 5:
Why are Edna's RBC count and hematocrit increased? (Hint: Because of Edna's COPD, her arterial P_{O_2} is low.)

569 571 580 583 591 592

Inflammation of the pleural membrane results in a crackling or grating sound known as a *friction rub*. It is caused by swollen, inflamed pleural membranes rubbing against each other, and it disappears when fluid again separates them.

Diseases in which air flow is diminished because of increased airway resistance are known as **obstructive lung diseases**. When patients with obstructive lower airway diseases are asked to exhale forcefully, air whistling through the narrowed airways creates a wheezing sound that can be heard even without a stethoscope. Depending on the severity of the disease, the bronchioles may even collapse and close off before a forced expiration is completed, reducing both the amount and rate of air flow as measured by a spirometer.

Obstructive lung diseases include asthma, obstructive sleep apnea, emphysema, and chronic bronchitis. The latter two are sometimes called *chronic obstructive pulmonary disease* (COPD) because of their ongoing, or chronic, nature. *Obstructive sleep apnea* [*apnoia*, breathless] results from obstruction of the upper airway, often due to abnormal relaxation of the muscles of the pharynx and tongue that increases airway resistance during inspiration.

Asthma is an inflammatory condition, often associated with allergies, that is characterized by bronchoconstriction and airway edema. Asthma can be triggered by exercise (exercise-induced asthma) or by rapid changes in the temperature or humidity of inspired air. Asthmatic patients complain of "air hunger" and difficulty breathing (*dyspnea*). The severity of asthma attacks ranges from mild to life threatening. Studies of asthma at the cellular level show that a variety of chemical signals may be responsible for inducing asthmatic bronchoconstriction, including acetylcholine, histamine, substance P (a neuropeptide), and leukotrienes secreted by mast cells, macrophages, and eosinophils. *Leukotrienes* are lipid-like bronchoconstrictors that are released during the inflammatory response. Asthma is treated with inhaled and oral medications that include β_2-adrenergic agonists, anti-inflammatory drugs, and leukotriene antagonists.

CONCEPT CHECK

31. Restrictive lung diseases [p. 584] decrease lung compliance. How will inspiratory reserve volume change in patients with a restrictive lung disease?
32. Chronic obstructive lung disease causes patients to lose the ability to exhale fully. How does residual volume change in these patients? Answers: p. 596

This completes our discussion of the mechanics of ventilation. In the next chapter, we shift focus from the bulk flow of air to the diffusion and transport of oxygen and carbon dioxide as they travel between the air spaces of the alveoli and the cells of the body.

RUNNING PROBLEM CONCLUSION

Emphysema

Edna leaves the office with prescriptions for a mucus-thinning drug, a bronchodilator, and anti-inflammatory drugs to keep her airways as open as possible. She has agreed to try to stop smoking once more and also has a prescription and brochures for that. (See the Running Problem Conclusion for Chapter 11 on p. 401). Unfortunately, the lung changes that take place with COPD are not reversible, and Edna will require treatment for the rest of her life. According to the American Lung Association (*www.lungusa.org*), COPD is the fourth leading cause of death in the United States and costs more than $30 billion per year in direct medical costs and indirect costs such as lost wages.

In this running problem you learned about chronic obstructive pulmonary disease. Now check your understanding of the physiology in the problem by comparing your answers with those in the following table.

	QUESTION	FACTS	INTEGRATION AND ANALYSIS
1	What does narrowing of the airways do to the resistance airways offer to air flow?	The relationship between tube radius and resistance is the same for air flow as for blood flow: as radius decreases, resistance increases [p. 473].	When resistance increases, the body must use more energy to create air flow.
2	Why do people with chronic bronchitis have a higher-than-normal rate of respiratory infections?	Cigarette smoke paralyzes the cilia that sweep debris and mucus out of the airways. Without the action of cilia, mucus and trapped particles pool in the airways.	Bacteria trapped in the mucus can multiply and cause respiratory infections.
3	Name the muscles that patients with emphysema use to exhale actively.	Normal passive expiration depends on elastic recoil of muscles and elastic tissue in the lungs.	Forceful expiration involves the internal intercostal muscles and the abdominal muscles.
4	When Edna fills her lungs maximally, the volume of air in her lungs is known as the ________ capacity. When she exhales all the air she can, the volume of air left in her lungs is the ________.	The maximum volume of air in the lungs is the *total lung capacity.* Air left in the lungs after maximal exhalation is the *residual volume.*	N/A
5	Why are Edna's RBC count and hematocrit increased?	Because of Edna's COPD, her arterial P_{O_2} is low. The major stimulus for red blood cell synthesis is hypoxia.	Low arterial oxygen levels trigger EPO release, which increases the synthesis of red blood cells [p. 552]. More RBCs provide more binding sites for oxygen transport.

569 571 580 583 591 592

CHAPTER SUMMARY

Air flow into and out of the lungs is another example of the principle of *mass flow*. Like blood flow, air flow is bulk flow that requires a pump to create a pressure gradient and that encounters resistance, primarily from changes in the diameter of the tubes through which it flows. The *mechanical properties* of the pleural sacs and elastic recoil in the chest wall and lung tissue are essential for normal ventilation.

1. Aerobic metabolism in living cells consumes oxygen and produces carbon dioxide. (p. 569)
2. Gas exchange requires a large, thin, moist exchange surface; a pump to move air; and a circulatory system to transport gases to the cells. (p. 569)
3. Respiratory system functions include gas exchange, pH regulation, vocalization, and protection from foreign substances. (p. 569)

Respiratory System

iP Respiratory: Anatomy Review

4. **Cellular respiration** refers to cellular metabolism that consumes oxygen. **External respiration** is the exchange of gases between the atmosphere and cells of the body. It includes ventilation, gas exchange at the lung and cells, and transport of gases in the blood. **Ventilation** is the movement of air into and out of the lungs. (p. 570; Fig. 17-1)
5. The **respiratory system** consists of anatomical structures involved in ventilation and gas exchange. (p. 570)
6. The **upper respiratory tract** includes the mouth, nasal cavity, **pharynx**, and **larynx**. The **lower respiratory tract** includes the **trachea**, **bronchi**, **bronchioles**, and exchange surfaces of the **alveoli**. (p. 570; Fig. 17-2a)
7. The thoracic cage is bounded by the ribs, spine, and **diaphragm**. Two sets of **intercostal muscles** connect the ribs. (p. 570; Fig. 17-2b)
8. Each **lung** is contained within a double-walled **pleural sac** that contains a small quantity of **pleural fluid**. (p. 570; Figs. 17-2d, 17-3)
9. The two **primary bronchi** enter the lungs. Each primary bronchus divides into progressively smaller bronchi and finally into collapsible **bronchioles**. (p. 571; Figs. 17-2e, 17-4)
10. The upper respiratory system filters, warms, and humidifies inhaled air. (p. 571)
11. The alveoli consist mostly of thin-walled **type I alveolar cells** for gas exchange. **Type II alveolar cells** produce surfactant. A network of capillaries surrounds each alveolus. (pp. 574–575; Fig. 17-2f, g)
12. Blood flow through the lungs equals cardiac output. Resistance to blood flow in the pulmonary circulation is low. Pulmonary arterial pressure averages 25/8 mm Hg. (p. 575)

Gas Laws

iP Respiratory: Pulmonary Ventilation

13. The total pressure of a mixture of gases is the sum of the pressures of the individual gases in the mixture (**Dalton's law**). **Partial pressure** is the pressure contributed by a single gas in a mixture. (p. 576; Tbls. 17-1, 17-2)
14. Bulk flow of air occurs down pressure gradients, as does the movement of any individual gas making up the air. (p. 577)
15. **Boyle's law** states that as the volume available to a gas increases, the gas pressure decreases. The body creates pressure gradients by changing thoracic volume. (p. 577; Fig. 17-6)

Ventilation

iP Respiratory: Pulmonary Ventilation

16. A single **respiratory cycle** consists of an inspiration and an expiration. (p. 578)
17. **Tidal volume** is the amount of air taken in during a single normal inspiration. **Vital capacity** is tidal volume plus **expiratory** and **inspiratory reserve volumes**. Air volume in the lungs at the end of maximal expiration is the **residual volume**. (pp. 578–579; Fig. 17-8)
18. Air flow in the respiratory system is directly proportional to the pressure gradient, and inversely related to the resistance to air flow offered by the airways. (p. 579)
19. During **inspiration**, **alveolar pressure** decreases, and air flows into the lungs. Inspiration requires contraction of the inspiratory muscles and the diaphragm. (p. 580; Fig. 17-9)
20. **Expiration** is usually passive, resulting from elastic recoil of the lungs. (p. 582)
21. **Active expiration** requires contraction of the internal intercostal and abdominal muscles. (p. 582)
22. **Intrapleural pressures** are subatmospheric because the pleural cavity is a sealed compartment. (p. 583; Fig. 17-11)
23. **Compliance** is a measure of the ease with which the chest wall and lungs expand. Loss of compliance increases the work of breathing. **Elastance** is the ability of a stretched lung to return to its normal volume. (p. 584)
24. **Surfactant** decreases surface tension in the fluid lining the alveoli. Reduced surface tension prevents smaller alveoli from collapsing and also makes it easier to inflate the lungs. (p. 585; Fig. 17-13)
25. The diameter of the bronchioles determines how much resistance they offer to air flow. (p. 586)
26. Increased CO_2 in expired air dilates bronchioles. Parasympathetic neurons cause **bronchoconstriction** in response to irritant stimuli. There is no significant sympathetic innervation of bronchioles, but epinephrine causes **bronchodilation**. (p. 586; Tbl. 17-3)
27. **Total pulmonary ventilation** = tidal volume × ventilation rate. **Alveolar ventilation** = ventilation rate × (tidal volume − dead space volume). (pp. 587–588; Fig. 17-14)
28. Alveolar gas composition changes very little during a normal respiratory cycle. **Hyperventilation** increases alveolar P_{O_2} and decreases alveolar P_{CO_2}. **Hypoventilation** has the opposite effect. (p. 589; Fig. 17-15)
29. Local mechanisms match air flow and blood flow around the alveoli. Increased levels of CO_2 dilate bronchioles, and decreased O_2 constricts pulmonary arterioles. (p. 590; Fig. 17-16, Tbl. 17-7)

17

QUESTIONS

(Answers to the Review Questions begin on page A1.)

THE PHYSIOLOGY PLACE

Access more review material online at **The Physiology Place** web site. There you'll find review questions, problem-solving activities, case studies, flashcards, and direct links to both *Interactive Physiology*® and *PhysioEx*™. To access the site, go to *www.physiologyplace.com* and select *Human Physiology*, Fifth Edition.

LEVEL ONE REVIEWING FACTS AND TERMS

1. List four functions of the respiratory system.
2. Give two definitions for the word *respiration.*
3. Which sets of muscles are used for normal quiet inspiration? For normal quiet expiration? For active expiration? What kind(s) of muscles are the different respiratory muscles (skeletal, cardiac, or smooth)?
4. What is the function of pleural fluid?

5. Name the anatomical structures that an oxygen molecule passes on its way from the atmosphere to the blood.
6. Diagram the structure of an alveolus, and state the function of each part. How are capillaries associated with an alveolus?
7. Trace the path of the pulmonary circulation. About how much blood is found here at any given moment? What is a typical arterial blood pressure for the pulmonary circuit, and how does this pressure compare with that of the systemic circulation?
8. What happens to inspired air as it is conditioned during its passage through the airways?
9. During inspiration, most of the thoracic volume change is the result of movement of the ________.
10. Describe the changes in alveolar and intrapleural pressure during one respiratory cycle.
11. What is the function of surfactants in general? In the respiratory system?
12. Of the three factors that contribute to the resistance of air flow through a tube, which plays the largest role in changing resistance in the human respiratory system?
13. Match the following items with their correct effect on the bronchioles:

(a) histamine	1. bronchoconstriction
(b) epinephrine	2. bronchodilation
(c) acetylcholine	3. no effect
(d) increased P_{CO_2}	

14. Refer to the spirogram in the figure below:
    (a) Label tidal volume (V_T), inspiratory and expiratory reserve volumes (IRV and ERV), residual volume (RV), vital capacity (VC), total lung capacity (TLC).
    (b) What is the value of each of the volumes and capacities you labeled?
    (c) What is this person's ventilation rate?

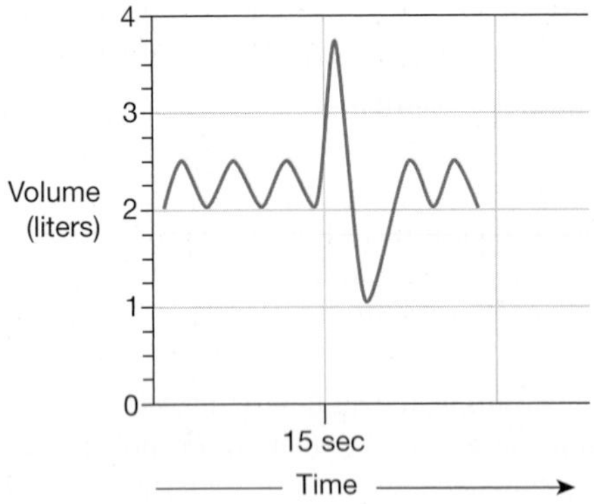

LEVEL TWO REVIEWING CONCEPTS

15. Compare and contrast the terms in each of the following sets:
    (a) compliance and elastance
    (b) inspiration, expiration, and ventilation
    (c) intrapleural pressure and alveolar pressure
    (d) total pulmonary ventilation and alveolar ventilation
    (e) type I and type II alveolar cells
    (f) pulmonary circulation and systemic circulation
16. List the major paracrines and neurotransmitters that cause bronchoconstriction and bronchodilation. What receptors do they act through? (muscarinic, nicotinic, α, β_1, β_2)
17. Compile the following terms into a map of ventilation. Use up arrows, down arrows, greater than symbols (>), and less than symbols (<) as modifiers. You may add additional terms.

abdominal muscles	
air flow	internal intercostals
contract	P_A
diaphragm	P_{atm}
expiratory muscles	$P_{intrapleural}$
external intercostals	quiet breathing
forced breathing	relax
in, out, from, to	scalenes
inspiratory muscles	

18. Decide whether each of the following parameters will increase, decrease, or not change in the situations given.
    (a) airway resistance with bronchodilation
    (b) intrapleural pressure during inspiration
    (c) air flow with bronchoconstriction
    (d) bronchiolar diameter with increased P_{CO_2}
    (e) tidal volume with decreased compliance
    (f) alveolar pressure during expiration
19. Define the following terms: pneumothorax, spirometer, auscultation, hypoventilation, bronchoconstriction, minute volume, partial pressure of a gas.
20. The cartoon coyote is blowing up a balloon in another attempt to catch the roadrunner. He first breathes in as much air as he can, then blows out all he can into the balloon.
    (a) The volume of air in the balloon is equal to the ________ ________ of the coyote's lungs. This volume can be measured directly by measuring the balloon volume or by adding which respiratory volumes together?
    (b) In 10 years, when the coyote is still chasing the roadrunner, will he still be able to put as much air into the balloon in one breath? Explain.
21. Match the descriptions on the right to the appropriate phase(s) of ventilation:

(a) inspiration	________ usually depend(s) on elastic recoil
(b) expiration	________ is/are easier when lung compliance decreases
(c) both inspiration and expiration	________ is/are driven mainly by positive intrapleural pressure generated by muscular contraction
(d) neither	________ is usually an active process requiring smooth muscle contraction

22. Draw and label a graph showing the P_{O_2} of air in the primary bronchi during one respiratory cycle. (*Hint:* What parameter goes on each axis?)
23. Lung compliance increases but chest wall compliance decreases as we age. In the absence of other changes, would the following parameters increase, decrease, or not change as compliance decreases?
    (a) work required for breathing
    (b) ease with which lungs inflate
    (c) lung elastance
    (d) airway resistance during inspiration

24. Will pulmonary surfactant increase, decrease, or not change the following?
    (a) work required for breathing
    (b) lung compliance
    (c) surface tension in the alveoli

LEVEL THREE PROBLEM SOLVING

25. Assume a normal female has a resting tidal volume of 400 mL, a respiratory rate of 13 breaths/min, and an anatomic dead space of 125 mL. When she exercises, which of the following scenarios would be most efficient for increasing her oxygen delivery to the lungs?
    (a) increase respiratory rate to 20 breaths/min but have no change in tidal volume
    (b) increase tidal volume to 550 mL but have no change in respiratory rate
    (c) increase tidal volume to 500 mL and respiratory rate to 15 breaths/min

    Which of these scenarios is most likely to occur during exercise in real life?
26. A 30-year-old computer programmer has had asthma for 15 years. When she lies down at night, she has spells of wheezing and coughing. Over the years, she has found that she can breathe better if she sleeps sitting nearly upright. Upon examination, her doctor finds that she has an enlarged thorax. Her lungs are overinflated on X-ray. Here are the results of her examination and pulmonary function tests. Use the normal values and abbreviations in Figure 17-8 to help answer the questions.

    Ventilation rate: 16 breaths/min

    Tidal volume: 600 mL

    ERV: 1000 mL

    RV: 3500 mL

    Inspiratory capacity: 1800 mL

    Vital capacity: 2800 mL

    Functional residual capacity: 4500 mL

    TLC: 6300 mL

    After she is given a bronchodilator, her vital capacity increased to 3650 mL.
    (a) What is her minute volume?
    (b) Explain the change in vital capacity with bronchodilators.
    (c) Which other values are abnormal? Can you explain why they might be, given her history and findings?

LEVEL FOUR QUANTITATIVE PROBLEMS

27. A container of gas with a movable piston has a volume of 500 mL and a pressure of 60 mm Hg. The piston is moved, and the new pressure is 150 mm Hg. What is the new volume of the container?
28. You have a mixture of gases in dry air, with an atmospheric pressure of 760 mm Hg. Calculate the partial pressure of each gas if the composition of the air is:
    (a) 21% oxygen, 78% nitrogen, 0.3% carbon dioxide
    (b) 40% oxygen, 13% nitrogen, 45% carbon dioxide, 2% hydrogen
    (c) 10% oxygen, 15% nitrogen, 1% argon, 25% carbon dioxide
29. Li is a tiny woman, with a tidal volume of 400 mL and a respiratory rate of 12 breaths per minute at rest. What is her total pulmonary ventilation? Just before a physiology exam, her ventilation increases to 18 breaths per minute from nervousness. Now what is her total pulmonary ventilation? Assuming her anatomic dead space is 120 mL, what is her alveolar ventilation in each case?
30. You collected the following data on your classmate Neelesh:

    Minute volume = 5004 mL/min

    Respiratory rate = 3 breaths/15 sec

    Vital capacity = 4800 mL

    Expiratory reserve volume = 1000 mL

    What are Neelesh's tidal volume and inspiratory reserve volume?
31. Use the figure below to help solve this problem. A spirometer with a volume of 1 liter (V_1) is filled with a mixture of oxygen and helium, with the helium concentration being 4 g/L (C_1). Helium does not move from the lungs into the blood or from the blood into the lungs. A subject is told to blow out all the air he possibly can. Once he finishes that exhalation, his lung volume is V_2. He then puts the spirometer tube in his mouth and breathes quietly for several breaths. At the end of that time, the helium is evenly dispersed in the spirometer and the subject's lungs. A measurement shows the new concentration of helium is 1.9 g/L. What was the subject's lung volume at the start of the experiment? (*Hint:* $C_1V_1 = C_2V_2$)

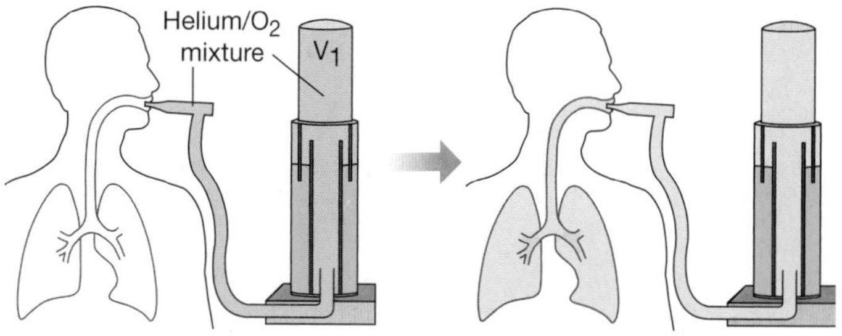

17

ANSWERS

Answers to Concept Check Questions

Page 571

1. Cellular respiration is intracellular and uses O_2 and organic substrates to produce ATP. External respiration is exchange and transport of gases between the atmosphere and cells.
2. Upper respiratory tract includes mouth, nasal cavity, pharynx, and larynx. Lower respiratory tract includes trachea, bronchi, bronchioles, and exchange surface of lungs.
3. Velocity is highest in the trachea and lowest in bronchioles.
4. Pleural fluid reduces friction and holds lungs tight against the chest wall.
5. The thoracic cage consists of rib cage with intercostal muscles, spinal (vertebral) column, and diaphragm. The thorax contains two lungs in pleural sacs, the heart and pericardial sac, esophagus, and major blood vessels.
6. The bronchioles are collapsible.

Page 574

7. If cilia cannot move mucus, the mucus collecting in the airways will trigger a cough reflex to clear the mucus out.

Page 576

8. Blood flow is approximately equal in pulmonary trunk and aorta. (Normally some venous blood leaving the bronchi, pleura, and part of the heart bypasses the pulmonary circulation and drains directly into the left side of the heart. This is called an anatomic shunt.)
9. Increased hydrostatic pressure causes greater net filtration out of capillaries and may result in pulmonary edema.
10. Mean pressure = 8 mm Hg + 1/3(25 − 8) mm Hg = 8 + 17/3 mm Hg = 13.7 mm Hg.

Page 577

11. 720 mm Hg × 0.78 = 562 mm Hg
12. 700 mm Hg − 47 mm Hg = 653 mm Hg × 21% = 137.1 mm Hg P_{O_2}

Page 579

13. Lung capacities are the sum of two or more lung volumes.
14. Residual volume cannot be measured directly.
15. If aging individuals have reduced vital capacity while total lung capacity does not change, then residual volume must increase.
16. As air becomes humidified, the P_{O_2} decreases.

Page 580

17. Air flow reverses direction during a respiratory cycle, but blood flows in a loop and never reverses direction.
18. See Figures 17-2d and 17-3. The lungs are enclosed in a pleural sac. One pleural membrane attaches to the lung, and the other lines the thoracic cage. Pleural fluid fills the pleural sac.

Page 582

19. Scarlett will be more successful if she exhales deeply, as this will decrease her thoracic volume and will pull her lower rib cage inward.
20. Inability to cough decreases the ability to expel the potentially harmful material trapped in airway mucus.

Page 584

21. A hiccup causes a rapid decrease in both intrapleural pressure and alveolar pressure.
22. The knife wound would collapse the left lung if the knife punctured the pleural membrane. Loss of adhesion between the lung and chest wall would release the inward pressure exerted on the chest wall, and the rib cage would expand outward. The right side would be unaffected as the right lung is contained in its own pleural sac.

Page 587

23. Normally, lung and chest wall elastance contribute more to the work of breathing.
24. Scar tissue reduces lung compliance.
25. Without surfactant, the work of breathing increases.
26. When bronchiolar diameter decreases, resistance increases.
27. Neurotransmitter is acetylcholine, and receptor is muscarinic.

Page 589

28. Increased tidal volume increases alveolar P_{O_2}.
29. Increased breathing rate increases alveolar P_{O_2}. Increasing breathing rate or tidal volume increases alveolar ventilation.

Page 591

30. P_{O_2} in alveoli in the affected section will increase because O_2 is not leaving the alveoli. P_{CO_2} will decrease because new CO_2 is not entering the alveoli from the blood. Bronchioles constrict when P_{CO_2} decreases (see Tbl. 17-7), shunting air to areas of the lung with better blood flow. This compensation cannot restore normal ventilation in this section of lung, and local control is insufficient to maintain homeostasis.

Page 591

31. Inspiratory reserve volume decreases.
32. Residual volume increases in patients who cannot fully exhale.

Answers to Graph Questions

Page 581

Fig. 17-11: Alveolar pressure is greatest in the middle of expiration and least in the middle of inspiration. It is equal to atmospheric pressure at the beginning and end of inspiration and expiration. When lung volume is at its minimum, alveolar pressure is (c) moving from maximum to minimum and external intercostal muscle contraction is (b) minimal.

18

Gas Exchange and Transport

BACKGROUND BASICS

Exchange epithelia: **74** pH and buffers: **38** Law of mass action: **102** Cerebrospinal fluid: **301** Simple diffusion: **136** Autonomic and somatic motor neurons: **388** Structure of the brain stem: **310** Red blood cells and hemoglobin: **553** Blood-brain barrier: **303**

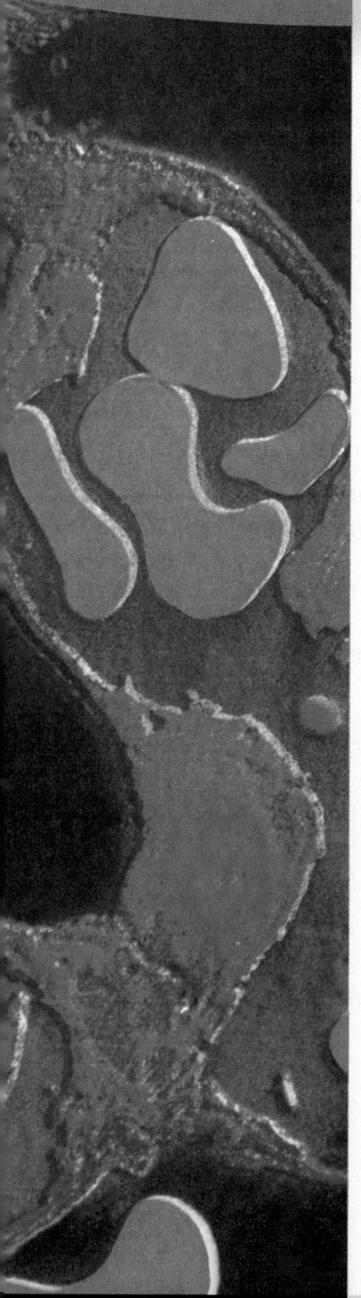

Alveolar capillaries (mauve) with red blood cells (red) surrounding alveolar space (black).

The successful ascent of Everest without supplementary oxygen is one of the great sagas of the 20th century.

—John B. West, *Climbing with O's*, NOVA Online (*www.pbs.org*)

RUNNING PROBLEM

High Altitude

In 1981 a group of 20 physiologists, physicians, and climbers, supported by 42 Sherpa assistants, formed the American Medical Research Expedition to Mt. Everest. The purpose of the expedition was to study human physiology at extreme altitudes, starting with the base camp at 5400 m (18,000 ft) and continuing on to the summit at 8850 m (over 29,000 ft). From the work of these scientists and others, we now have a good picture of the physiology of high-altitude acclimatization.

598 600 603 606 610 617 617

The book *Into Thin Air* by Jon Krakauer chronicles an ill-fated trek to the top of Mt. Everest. To reach the summit of Mt. Everest, climbers must pass through the "death zone" located at about 8000 meters (over 26,000 ft). Of the thousands of people who have attempted the summit, only about 2000 have been successful, and more than 185 have died. What are the physiological challenges of climbing Mt. Everest (8850 m or 29,035 ft), and why did it take so many years before humans successfully reached the top? The lack of oxygen at high altitude is part of the answer.

In the previous chapter we looked at the mechanics of breathing, the events that create bulk flow of air into and out of the lungs. In this chapter we focus on the two gases that are most significant to human physiology, oxygen and carbon dioxide, and look at how they move between alveolar air spaces and the cells of the body. The process can be divided into two components: the exchange of gases between compartments, which requires diffusion across cell membranes, and the transport of gases in the blood (Fig. 18-1 ●).

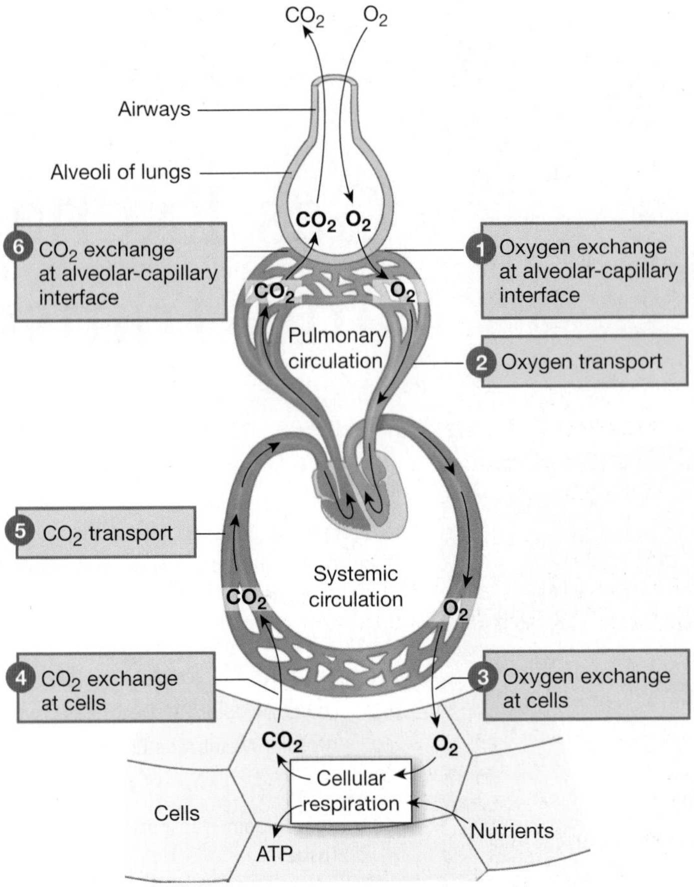

● **FIGURE 18-1** ***Oxygen and carbon dioxide move into and out of the blood at pulmonary and systemic capillaries.***

DIFFUSION AND SOLUBILITY OF GASES

The simple diffusion of oxygen and carbon dioxide across cell layers (between alveoli and pulmonary capillaries, or between systemic capillaries and cells) obeys the rules for simple diffusion across a membrane that are summarized in *Fick's law of diffusion* [p. 140]:

$$\text{Diffusion rate} \propto \frac{\text{surface area} \times \text{concentration gradient} \times \text{membrane permeability}}{\text{membrane thickness}}$$

If we assume that membrane permeability is constant, then three factors influence diffusion in the lungs:

1. *Surface area*. The rate of diffusion is directly proportional to the available surface area.
2. *Concentration gradient*. The rate of diffusion is directly proportional to the concentration gradient of the diffusing substance.
3. *Membrane thickness*. The rate of diffusion is inversely proportional to the thickness of the membrane.

From the general rules for diffusion, we can add a fourth influence: *diffusion distance*—diffusion is most rapid over short distances.

Under most circumstances, diffusion distance, surface area, and membrane thickness are constants in the body and are maximized to facilitate diffusion. Thus the most important factor for gas exchange in normal physiology is the concentration gradient.

When we think of concentrations in physiology, units such as moles per liter and milliosmoles per liter come to mind. However, respiratory physiologists commonly use *partial pressures* to express gas concentrations in solution. This measure allows direct comparison with partial pressures of the gases in air, which is important for establishing whether there is a concentration gradient between the alveoli and the blood.

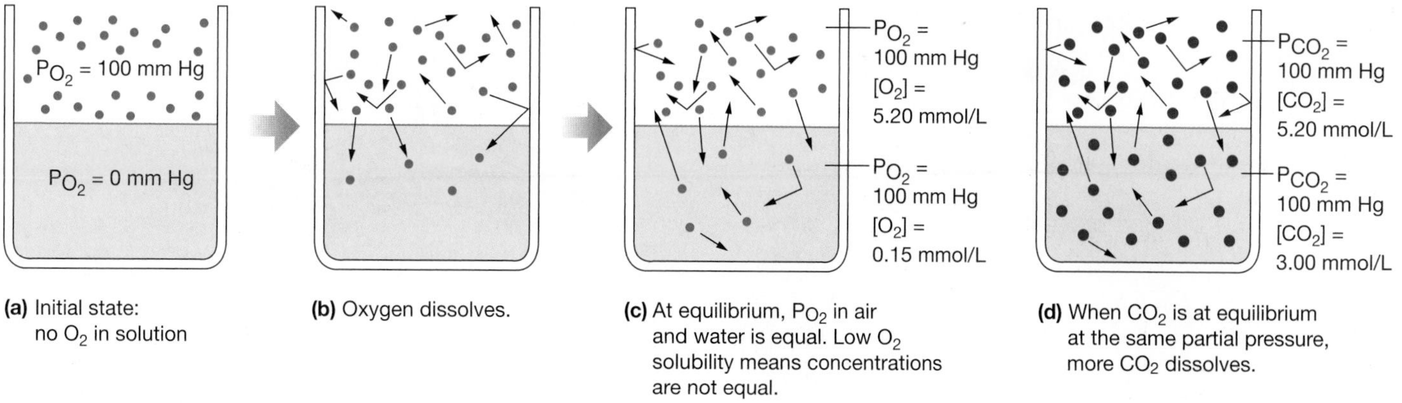
P_{O_2} = 100 mm Hg
P_{O_2} = 0 mm Hg
P_{O_2} = 100 mm Hg
$[O_2]$ = 5.20 mmol/L
P_{O_2} = 100 mm Hg
$[O_2]$ = 0.15 mmol/L
P_{CO_2} = 100 mm Hg
$[CO_2]$ = 5.20 mmol/L
P_{CO_2} = 100 mm Hg
$[CO_2]$ = 3.00 mmol/L
(a) Initial state: no O_2 in solution
(b) Oxygen dissolves.
(c) At equilibrium, P_{O_2} in air and water is equal. Low O_2 solubility means concentrations are not equal.
(d) When CO_2 is at equilibrium at the same partial pressure, more CO_2 dissolves.

● **FIGURE 18-2** ***Gases in solution.*** When temperature remains constant, the amount of a gas that dissolves in a liquid depends on both the solubility of the gas in the liquid and the partial pressure of the gas.

Dissolved Gas Depends on Pressure, Solubility, and Temperature

When a gas is placed in contact with water and there is a pressure gradient, the gas molecules move from one phase to the other. If gas pressure is higher in the water than in the gaseous phase, then gas molecules leave the water. If gas pressure is higher in the gaseous phase than in water, then the gas dissolves into the water.

The movement of gas molecules from air into a liquid is directly proportional to three factors: (1) the pressure gradient of the gas, (2) the solubility of the gas in the liquid, and (3) temperature. Because temperature is relatively constant in mammals, we will ignore its contribution in this discussion.

The ease with which a gas dissolves in a liquid is the **solubility** of the gas in that liquid. If a gas is very soluble, large numbers of gas molecules go into solution at a low gas partial pressure. With less soluble gases, even a high partial pressure may cause only a few molecules of the gas to dissolve in the liquid.

For example, consider a container of water exposed to air with a P_{O_2} of 100 mm Hg (Fig. 18-2a ●). Initially, the water has no oxygen dissolved in it (water P_{O_2} = 0 mm Hg). As the air stays in contact with the water, some of the moving oxygen molecules in the air diffuse into the water and dissolve (Fig. 18-2b). This process continues until equilibrium is reached. At equilibrium (Fig. 18-2c), the movement of oxygen from the air into the water is equal to the movement of oxygen from the water back into the air.

We refer to the concentration of oxygen dissolved in the water at any given P_{O_2} as the *partial pressure of the gas in solution.* In our example, therefore, if the air has a P_{O_2} of 100 mm Hg, at equilibrium the water also has a P_{O_2} of 100 mm Hg.

Note that this does *not* mean that the concentration of oxygen is the same in the air and in the water! The concentration of dissolved oxygen also depends on the *solubility* of oxygen in water. For example, when P_{O_2} is 100 mm Hg in both the air and the water, air contains 5.2 mmol O_2/L air, but water contains only 0.15 mmol O_2/L water (Fig. 18-2c). As you can see, oxygen is not very soluble in water and, by extension, in any aqueous solution. Its low solubility was a driving force for the evolution of oxygen-carrying molecules in the aqueous solution we call blood.

Now compare oxygen solubility with CO_2 solubility (Fig. 18-2d). Carbon dioxide is 20 times more soluble in water than oxygen is. At a P_{CO_2} of 100 mm Hg, the CO_2 concentration in air is 5.2 mmol CO_2/L air, and its concentration in water is 3.0 mmol/L water. So although P_{O_2} and P_{CO_2} are both 100 mm Hg in the water, the amount of each gas that dissolves in the water is very different.

CONCEPT CHECK

1. A saline solution is exposed to a mixture of nitrogen gas and hydrogen gas in which $P_{H_2} = P_{N_2}$. What information do you need to predict whether equal amounts of H_2 and N_2 dissolve in the solution?
2. If nitrogen is 78% of atmospheric air, what is the partial pressure of this gas when the dry atmospheric pressure is 720 mm Hg?
3. True or false? Plasma with a P_{O_2} of 40 mm Hg and a P_{CO_2} of 40 mm Hg has the same concentrations of oxygen and carbon dioxide.

Answers: p. 621

GAS EXCHANGE IN THE LUNGS AND TISSUES

The gas laws state that individual gases flow from regions of higher partial pressure to regions of lower partial pressure, and this rule governs the exchange of oxygen and carbon dioxide in the lungs and tissues.

Normal alveolar P_{O_2} is about 100 mm Hg (Fig. 18-3a ●). The P_{O_2} of systemic venous blood arriving at the lungs is 40 mm Hg. Oxygen therefore moves down its partial pressure (concentration) gradient from the alveoli into the capillaries.

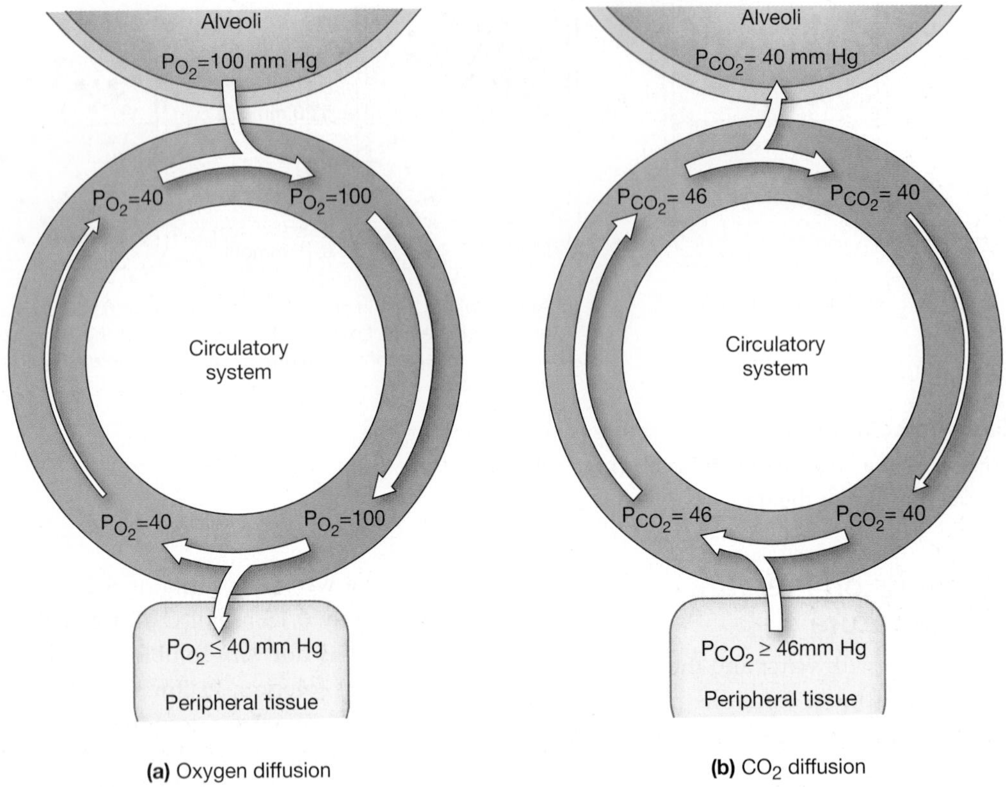

● **FIGURE 18-3** ***Gases diffuse down their partial pressure (concentration) gradients at alveoli and cells.***

Diffusion goes to equilibrium, and the P_{O_2} of arterial blood leaving the lungs is the same as in the alveoli: 100 mm Hg.

When arterial blood reaches tissue capillaries, the gradient is reversed. Cells are continuously using oxygen for oxidative phosphorylation. In the cells of a person at rest, intracellular P_{O_2} averages 40 mm Hg. Arterial blood arriving at the cells has a P_{O_2} of 100 mm Hg. Because P_{O_2} is lower in the cells, oxygen diffuses down its partial pressure gradient from plasma into cells. Once again, diffusion goes to equilibrium,

RUNNING PROBLEM

Hypoxia is the primary problem that people experience when ascending to high altitude. High altitude is considered anything above 1500 m (5000 ft), but most pathological responses to altitude occur above 2500 m (about 8000 ft). By one estimate, 25% of people arriving at 2590 m will experience some form of altitude sickness.

Question 1:

If water vapor contributes 47 mm Hg to the pressure of fully humidified air, what is the P_{O_2} of inspired air reaching the alveoli at 2500 m, where dry atmospheric pressure is 542 mm Hg? How does this value for P_{O_2} compare with that of fully humidified air at sea level?

598 600 603 606 610 617 617

and as a result venous blood has the same P_{O_2} as the cells it just passed.

Conversely, P_{CO_2} is higher in tissues than in systemic capillary blood because of CO_2 production during metabolism (Fig. 18-3b). Cellular P_{CO_2} in a person at rest is about 46 mm Hg, compared to an arterial plasma P_{CO_2} of 40 mm Hg. The gradient causes CO_2 to diffuse out of cells into the capillaries. Diffusion goes to equilibrium, and systemic venous blood averages a P_{CO_2} of 46 mm Hg.

At the pulmonary capillaries, the process reverses. Venous blood bringing waste CO_2 from the cells has a P_{CO_2} of 46 mm Hg. Alveolar P_{CO_2} is 40 mm Hg. Because P_{CO_2} is higher in the plasma, CO_2 moves from the capillaries into the alveoli. By the time blood leaves the alveoli, it has a P_{CO_2} of 40 mm Hg, identical to the P_{CO_2} of the alveoli (Fig. 18-3b). Table 18-1 ● summarizes the arterial and venous partial pressures just discussed.

TABLE 18-1 Normal Blood Values in Pulmonary Medicine

	ARTERIAL	VENOUS
P_{O_2}	95 mm Hg (85–100)	40 mm Hg
P_{CO_2}	40 mm Hg (35–45)	46 mm Hg
pH	7.4 (7.38–7.42)	7.37

TABLE 18-2 Classification of Hypoxias

TYPE	DEFINITION	TYPICAL CAUSES
Hypoxic hypoxia	Low arterial P_{O_2}	High altitude; alveolar hypoventilation; decreased lung diffusion capacity; abnormal ventilation-perfusion ratio
Anemic hypoxia	Decreased total amount of O_2 bound to hemoglobin	Blood loss; anemia (low [Hb] or altered HbO_2 binding); carbon monoxide poisoning
Ischemic hypoxia	Reduced blood flow	Heart failure (whole-body hypoxia); shock (peripheral hypoxia); thrombosis (hypoxia in a single organ)
Histotoxic hypoxia	Failure of cells to use O_2 because cells have been poisoned	Cyanide and other metabolic poisons

If the diffusion of gases between alveoli and blood is significantly impaired, *hypoxia* (a state of too little oxygen) results. Hypoxia frequently (but not always!) goes hand in hand with **hypercapnia**, elevated concentrations of carbon dioxide. These two conditions are clinical signs, not diseases, and clinicians must gather additional information to pinpoint their cause. Table 18-2 ● lists several types of hypoxia and some typical causes.

Three categories of problems result in low arterial oxygen content: (1) inadequate oxygen reaching the alveoli, (2) problems with oxygen exchange between alveoli and pulmonary capillaries, and (3) inadequate transport of oxygen in the blood. We consider these issues in the sections that follow.

CONCEPT CHECK

4. Cellular metabolism review: which of the following three metabolic pathways—glycolysis, the citric acid cycle, and the electron transport system—is *directly* associated with (a) O_2 consumption and with (b) CO_2 production?
5. Why doesn't the movement of oxygen from the alveoli to the plasma decrease the P_{O_2} of the alveoli?

Answers: p. 621

Lower Alveolar P_{O_2} Decreases Oxygen Uptake

The first requirement for adequate oxygen delivery to the tissues is adequate oxygen intake from the atmosphere, as reflected by the P_{O_2} of the alveoli. A decrease in alveolar P_{O_2} results in less oxygen entering the blood. There are two possible causes of low alveolar P_{O_2}: either (1) the inspired air has abnormally low oxygen content or (2) alveolar ventilation is inadequate.

The main factor that affects the oxygen content of inspired air is altitude. The partial pressure of oxygen in air decreases along with total atmospheric pressure as you move from sea level (where normal atmospheric pressure is 760 mm Hg) to higher altitudes. For example, Denver, 1609 m above sea level, has an atmospheric pressure of about 628 mm Hg. The P_{O_2} of dry air in Denver is 132 mm Hg, down from 160 mm Hg at sea level.

Unless a person is traveling, however, altitude remains constant. If alveolar P_{O_2} is low but the composition of inspired air is normal, then the problem lies with alveolar ventilation. Low alveolar ventilation is also known as *hypoventilation* and is characterized by lower-than-normal volumes of fresh air entering the alveoli. Pathological factors that cause alveolar hypoventilation (Fig. 18-4 ●) include decreased lung compliance

BIOTECHNOLOGY

THE PULSE OXIMETER

One important clinical indicator of the effectiveness of gas exchange in the lungs is the concentration of oxygen in arterial blood. Obtaining an arterial blood sample is difficult for the clinician and painful for the patient because it means finding an accessible artery. (Most blood is drawn from superficial veins rather than from arteries, which lie deeper within the body). Over the years, however, scientists have developed instruments that quickly and painlessly measure blood oxygen levels through the surface of the skin on a finger or earlobe. One such instrument, the *pulse oximeter*, clips onto the skin and in seconds gives a digital reading of arterial hemoglobin saturation. The oximeter works by measuring light absorbance of the tissue at two wavelengths. Another instrument, the *transcutaneous oxygen sensor*, measures dissolved oxygen using a variant of traditional gas-measuring electrodes. Both methods have limitations but are popular because they provide a rapid, noninvasive means of estimating arterial oxygen content.

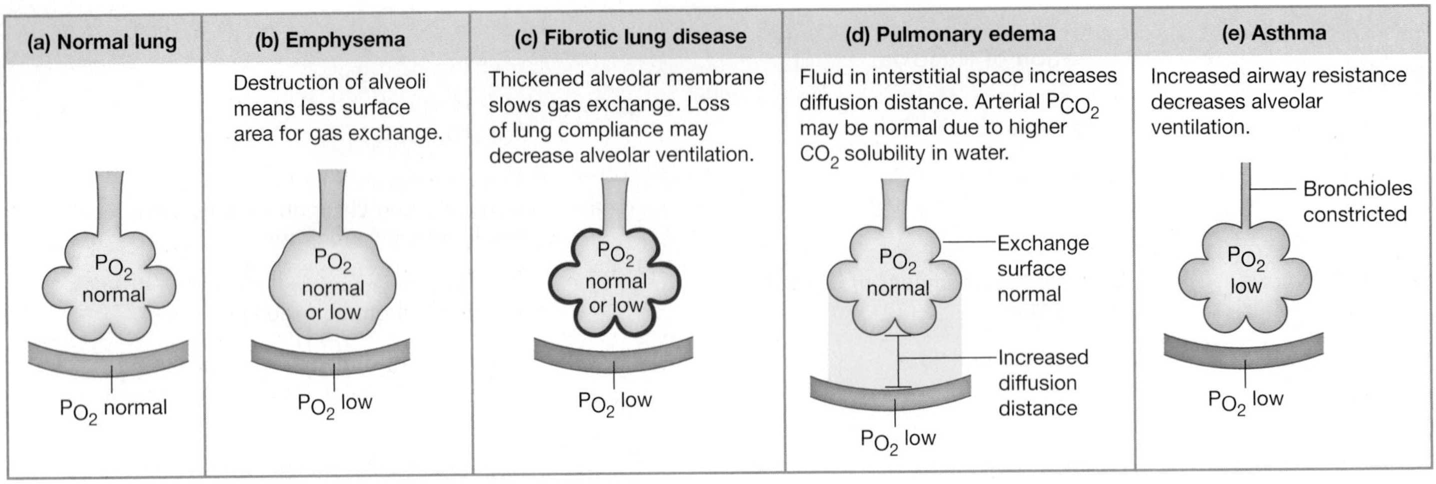

● **FIGURE 18-4** ***Pathological conditions that reduce alveolar ventilation and gas exchange***

(fibrosis; Fig. 18-4c), increased airway resistance (asthma; Fig. 18-4e), and overdoses of drugs (including alcohol) that depress the central nervous system and slow ventilation rate and depth.

CONCEPT CHECK

6. At the summit of Mt. Everest, an altitude of 8850 m, atmospheric pressure is only 250 mm Hg. What is the P_{O_2} of dry atmospheric air atop Everest? If water vapor added to inhaled air at the summit has a partial pressure of 47 mm Hg, what is the P_{O_2} of the inhaled air when it reaches the alveoli? Answers: p. 621

Alveolar Membrane Changes Alter Gas Exchange

In situations in which the composition of the air reaching the alveoli is normal but the P_{O_2} of arterial blood leaving the lungs is low, some aspect of the exchange process between alveoli and blood is defective. The transfer of oxygen from alveoli to blood requires diffusion across the barrier created by type I alveolar cells and by the capillary endothelium (Fig. 18-5 ●).

Normally, the diffusion distance is small because the cells are thin and there is little or no interstitial fluid between the two cell layers. In addition, both oxygen and carbon dioxide are soluble in both water and lipids. Gas exchange in the lungs is rapid, blood flow through pulmonary capillaries is slow, and diffusion reaches equilibrium in less than 1 second.

Pathological changes that adversely affect gas exchange include (1) a decrease in the amount of alveolar surface area available for gas exchange, (2) an increase in the thickness of the alveolar membrane, and (3) an increase in the diffusion distance between the alveolar air space and the blood.

Physical loss of alveolar surface area is dramatic in *emphysema*, a degenerative lung disease most often caused by cigarette smoking (Fig. 18-4b). The irritating effect of smoke in the alveoli activates alveolar macrophages that release elastase and other proteolytic enzymes. These enzymes destroy the elastic fibers of the lung [p. 80] and induce apoptosis of cells, breaking down the walls of the alveoli. The result is a high-compliance/low-elastic recoil lung with fewer and larger alveoli and less surface area for gas exchange.

Pathological changes in the alveolar membrane that alter its properties slow gas exchange. For example, in fibrotic lung diseases, scar tissue thickens the alveolar membrane (Fig. 18-4c). Diffusion of gases through this scar tissue is much slower than normal. However, because the lungs have a built-in reserve capacity, one-third of the exchange epithelium must be incapacitated before arterial P_{O_2} falls significantly.

The third pathological condition that decreases oxygen diffusion is excess fluid between the alveolar air space and the capillary. Fluid accumulation may occur inside the alveoli or in the interstitial compartment between the alveolar epithelium and the capillary (*edema*). In **pulmonary edema**, excessive interstitial fluid volume increases the diffusion distance between alveoli and capillaries (Fig. 18-4d). Normally, only small amounts of interstitial fluid are present in the lungs, the result of low pulmonary blood pressure and effective lymph drainage. However, if pulmonary blood pressure rises for some reason, such as left ventricular failure or mitral valve dysfunction, the normal filtration/reabsorption balance at the capillary is disrupted [Fig. 15-19, p. 530].

When capillary hydrostatic pressure increases, more fluid filters out of the capillary. If filtration increases too much, the lymphatics are unable to remove all the fluid, and excess accumulates in the pulmonary interstitial space, creating pulmonary edema. In severe cases, fluid even leaks across the alveolar membrane, collecting inside the alveoli.

Oxygen has low solubility in body fluids and takes longer to cross the increased diffusion distance present in pulmonary edema, resulting in decreased arterial P_{O_2}. Carbon dioxide, in contrast, is relatively soluble in body fluids, so the increased diffusion distance may not significantly affect carbon dioxide exchange. In some cases of pulmonary edema, arterial P_{O_2} is low but arterial P_{CO_2} is normal because of the different solubilities of the two gases.

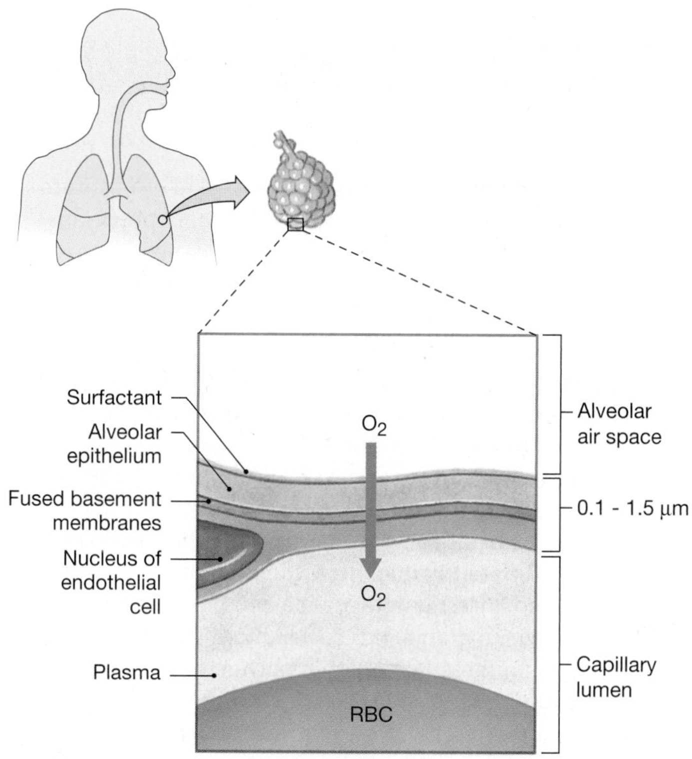

● **FIGURE 18-5** ***Oxygen diffuses across alveolar epithelial cells and capillary endothelial cells to enter the plasma.***

If the alveolar epithelium is damaged, such as from inflammation or inhaling toxic gases, or if edema exceeds the tissue's ability to retain it, fluid leaks from the interstitial space into the alveolar air space, flooding the alveoli. Normally the inside of the alveoli is a moist surface lined by a very thin (about 2 μm) layer of fluid with surfactant (see Fig. 18-5), but with alveolar flooding, this fluid layer can become much thicker and seriously impair gas exchange. If hypoxia due to alveolar fluid accumulation is severe and cannot be corrected by oxygen therapy, the condition may be called *adult respiratory distress syndrome* or ARDS.

CONCEPT CHECK

7. Why would left ventricular failure or mitral valve dysfunction cause elevated pulmonary blood pressure?
8. If alveolar ventilation increases, what happens to arterial P_{O_2}? To arterial P_{CO_2}? To venous P_{O_2} and P_{CO_2}? Explain your answers.

Answers: p. 621

GAS TRANSPORT IN THE BLOOD

Now that we have described gas exchange, we turn our attention to how oxygen and carbon dioxide are transported in the blood. The *law of mass action* [p. 102] plays an important role in this process. Changes in O_2 or CO_2 concentration disturb the equilibrium of reactions, shifting the balance between substrates and products.

RUNNING PROBLEM

Acute mountain sickness is the mildest illness caused by altitude hypoxia. The primary symptom is a headache that may be accompanied by dizziness, nausea, fatigue, or confusion. More severe illnesses are *high-altitude pulmonary edema* (HAPE) and *high-altitude cerebral edema*. HAPE is the major cause of death from altitude sickness. It is characterized by high pulmonary arterial pressure, extreme shortness of breath, and sometimes a productive cough yielding a pink, frothy fluid. Treatment is immediate relocation to lower altitude and administration of oxygen.

Question 2:
Why would someone with HAPE be short of breath?

Question 3:
Based on what you learned about the mechanisms for matching ventilation and perfusion in the lung [p. 589], can you explain why patients with HAPE have elevated pulmonary arterial blood pressure?

Hemoglobin Transports Most Oxygen to the Tissues

Oxygen is transported two ways in the blood: dissolved in the plasma and bound to hemoglobin (Hb). In other words:

$$\text{Total blood oxygen content} = \text{amount dissolved in plasma} + \text{amount bound to hemoglobin}$$

Hemoglobin, the oxygen-binding protein in red blood cells, binds reversibly to oxygen, as summarized in the equation

$$Hb + O_2 \rightleftharpoons HbO_2$$

In the pulmonary capillaries, where plasma P_{O_2} increases as oxygen diffuses in from the alveoli, hemoglobin binds oxygen. At the cells, where oxygen is being used and plasma P_{O_2} falls, hemoglobin gives up its oxygen. Because oxygen is only slightly soluble in aqueous solutions, we must have adequate amounts of hemoglobin in our blood to survive.

The importance of hemoglobin in oxygen transport is summarized in Figure 18-6 ●. More than 98% of the oxygen in a given volume of blood is bound to hemoglobin and transported inside red blood cells. The balance remains dissolved in plasma.

To understand just how low the solubility of oxygen is, consider the following example. In a situation in which blood has no hemoglobin, only 3 mL of O_2 dissolves in the plasma fraction of 1 liter of arterial blood (Fig. 18-7a ●). With a typical cardiac output of 5 L blood/min, about 15 mL of dissolved oxygen reaches the systemic tissues each minute. But oxygen consumption at rest is about 250 mL O_2/min, and that figure increases

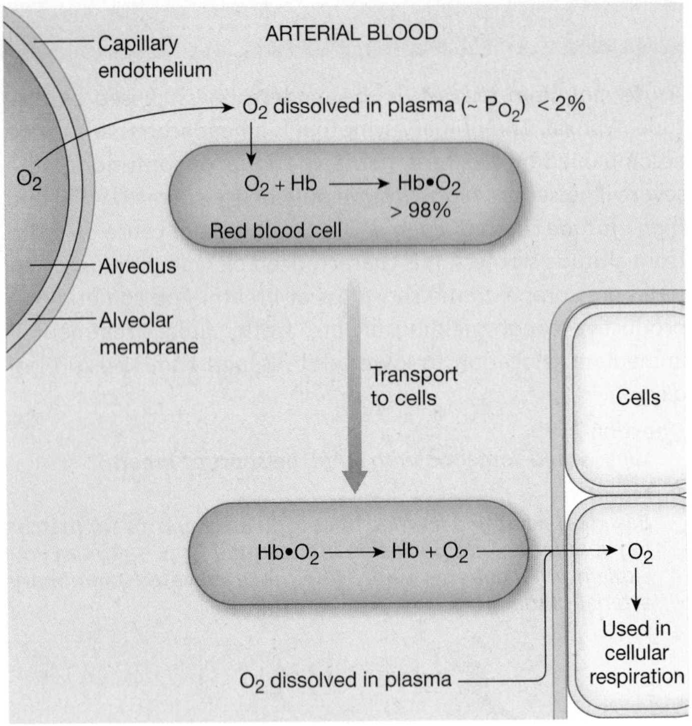

ARTERIAL BLOOD
Capillary endothelium
O_2 dissolved in plasma (~ P_{O_2}) < 2%
O_2
O_2 + Hb → Hb•O_2
> 98%
Red blood cell
Alveolus
Alveolar membrane
Transport to cells
Cells
Hb•O_2 → Hb + O_2 → O_2
Used in cellular respiration
O_2 dissolved in plasma

FIGURE QUESTION

How many cell membranes will O_2 cross in its passage between the airspace of the alveolus and binding to hemoglobin?

● **FIGURE 18-6** ***Summary of oxygen transport in the blood.*** More than 98% of the oxygen in blood is bound to hemoglobin in red blood cells, and less than 2% is dissolved in plasma.

dramatically with exercise, so the small amount dissolved in plasma cannot begin to meet the needs of the tissues. As a result, the body is dependent on oxygen carried by hemoglobin.

At normal hemoglobin levels, red blood cells carry about 197 mL O_2/L blood (Fig. 18-7b). Thus:

$$\text{Total arterial } O_2 \text{ carrying capacity} = 3 \text{ mL dissolved } O_2\text{/L blood} + 197 \text{ mL } HbO_2\text{/L blood} = 200 \text{ mL } O_2\text{/L blood}$$

If cardiac output remains 5 L/min, hemoglobin-assisted oxygen delivery to cells is almost 1000 mL/min, four times the oxygen consumption needed by the tissues at rest.

The amount of oxygen that binds to hemoglobin depends on two factors: (1) the P_{O_2} in the plasma surrounding the red blood cells and (2) the number of potential binding sites available in the red blood cells.

Plasma P_{O_2} is the primary factor determining how many of the available hemoglobin binding sites are occupied by oxygen. Figure 18-7c shows what happens to oxygen transport when alveolar and arterial P_{O_2} decrease. As you learned in previous sections, arterial P_{O_2} is established by (1) the composition of inspired air, (2) the alveolar ventilation rate, and (3) the efficiency of gas exchange from alveoli to blood.

EMERGING CONCEPTS

BLOOD SUBSTITUTES

Physiologists have been attempting to find a substitute for blood ever since 1878, when an intrepid physician named T. Gaillard Thomas transfused a patient with whole milk in place of blood. (It helped but the patient died anyway). Although milk seems an unlikely replacement for blood, it has two important properties: proteins to provide colloid osmotic pressure and molecules (emulsified lipids) capable of binding to oxygen. In the development of hemoglobin substitutes, oxygen transport is the most difficult property to mimic. A hemoglobin solution would seem to be the obvious answer, but hemoglobin that is not compartmentalized in red blood cells behaves differently than hemoglobin that is compartmentalized. Investigators are making progress by polymerizing hemoglobin into larger, more stable molecules and loading these hemoglobin polymers into phospholipid liposomes [p. 58]. Perfluorocarbon emulsions are also being tested as oxygen carriers. To learn more about this research, read "Physiological properties of blood substitutes," in *News in Physiological Sciences* 16(1): 38–41, 2001 Feb (*http://nips.physiology.org*).

The total number of oxygen-binding sites depends on the number of hemoglobin molecules in red blood cells. Clinically, this number can be estimated either by counting the red blood cells and quantifying the amount of hemoglobin per red blood cell (*mean corpuscular hemoglobin*) or by determining the blood hemoglobin content (g Hb/dL whole blood). Any pathological condition that decreases the amount of hemoglobin in the cells or the number of red blood cells adversely affects the blood's oxygen-transporting capacity.

People who have lost large amounts of blood need to replace hemoglobin for oxygen transport. A blood transfusion is the ideal replacement for blood loss, but in emergencies this is not always possible. Saline infusions can replace lost blood volume, but saline (like plasma) cannot transport sufficient quantities of oxygen to support cellular respiration. Faced with this problem, researchers are currently testing artificial oxygen carriers to replace hemoglobin. In times of large-scale disasters, these hemoglobin substitutes would eliminate the need to identify a patient's blood type before giving transfusions.

Hemoglobin Binds to Oxygen

Why is hemoglobin an effective oxygen carrier? The answer lies in its molecular structure. Hemoglobin is a large, complex protein whose quaternary structure has four globular protein chains, each of which is wrapped around an iron-containing

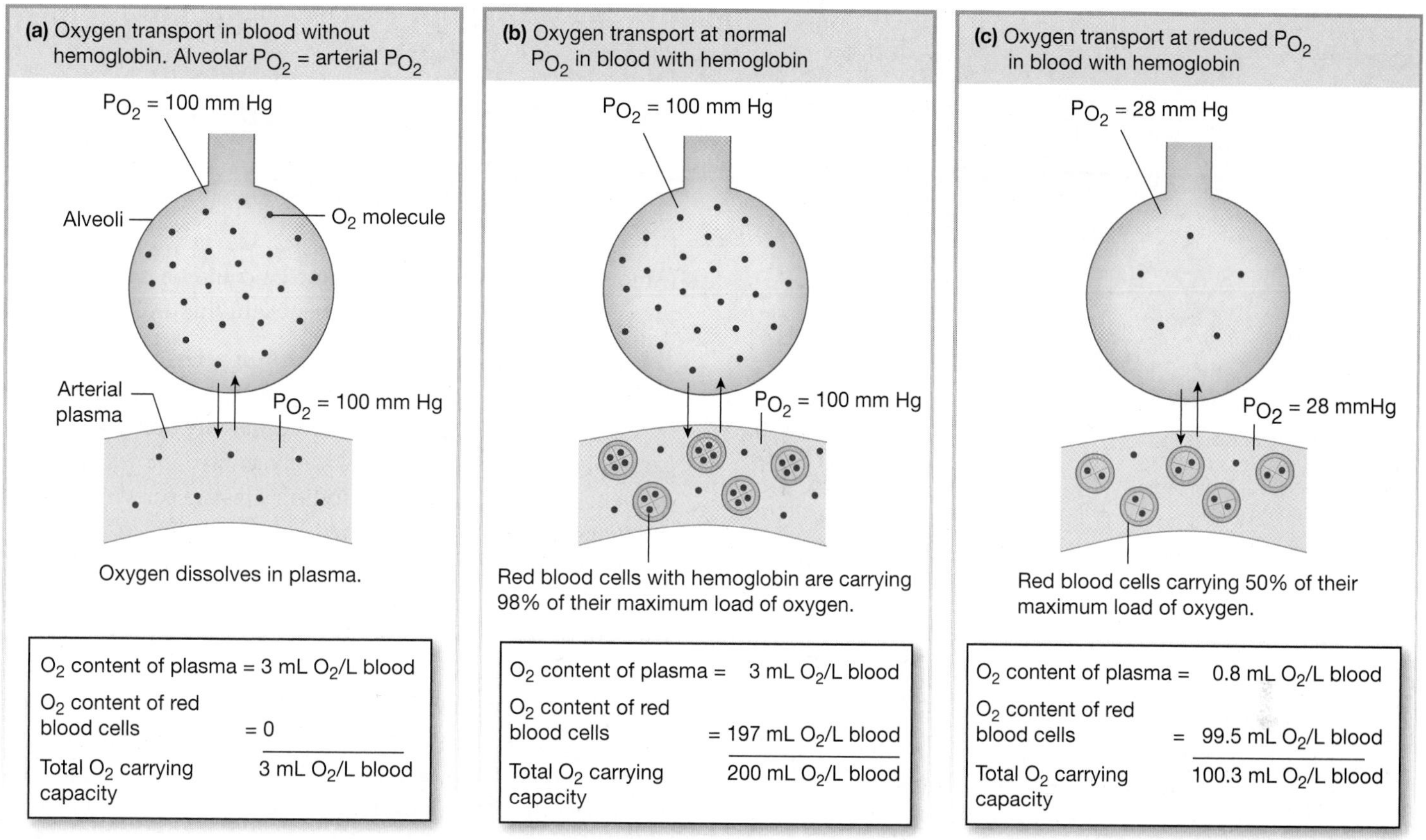

● **FIGURE 18-7** ***Hemoglobin increases oxygen transport by blood.***

heme group (Fig. 18-8a ●). The four heme groups in a hemoglobin molecule are identical. Each consists of a carbon-hydrogen-nitrogen *porphyrin ring* with an iron atom (Fe) in the center. About 70% of the iron in the body is found in the heme groups of hemoglobin.

The central iron atom of each heme group can bind reversibly with one oxygen molecule. Because there are four iron atoms per hemoglobin, each hemoglobin molecule has the potential to bind four oxygen molecules. The iron-oxygen interaction is a weak bond that can be easily broken without altering either the hemoglobin or the oxygen.

There are several forms of **globin** protein chains in hemoglobin. The most common forms are designated *alpha* (α), *beta* (β), *gamma* (γ), and *delta* (δ), depending on the structure of the chain. Most adult hemoglobin (designated *HbA*) has two alpha chains and two beta chains. However, a small portion of adult hemoglobin (about 2.5%) has two alpha chains and two delta chains (*HbA$_2$*).

The human fetus has a different isoform of hemoglobin that is adapted to attract oxygen from maternal blood in the placenta. *Fetal hemoglobin* (*HbF*) has two gamma chains in place of the two beta chains found in adult hemoglobin. Shortly after birth, fetal hemoglobin is replaced with the adult form as new red blood cells are made. We discuss the different binding properties of adult and fetal hemoglobin in the sections that follow.

Oxygen Binding Obeys the Law of Mass Action

Hemoglobin bound to oxygen is known as **oxyhemoglobin**, abbreviated HbO_2. (It would be more accurate to show the number of oxygen molecules carried on each hemoglobin molecule—$Hb(O_2)_{1-4}$—but we use the simpler abbreviation because the number of bound oxygen molecules varies from one hemoglobin molecule to another).

Oxygen-hemoglobin binding obeys the law of mass action:

$$Hb + O_2 \rightleftharpoons HbO_2$$

If oxygen concentration increases, this *oxygen-hemoglobin binding reaction* shifts to the right, and more oxygen binds to hemoglobin. If the concentration of oxygen decreases, the reaction shifts to the left, and hemoglobin releases some of its bound oxygen.

P_{O_2} Determines Oxygen-Hb Binding

Because of the law of mass action, the amount of oxygen bound to hemoglobin depends primarily on the P_{O_2} of plasma surrounding the red blood cells (Fig. 18-6). In the pulmonary capillaries, O_2 dissolved in the plasma diffuses into red blood cells, where it binds to hemoglobin. This removes dissolved O_2 from the plasma, causing more oxygen to diffuse in from the alveoli. The transfer of oxygen from alveolar air to plasma to

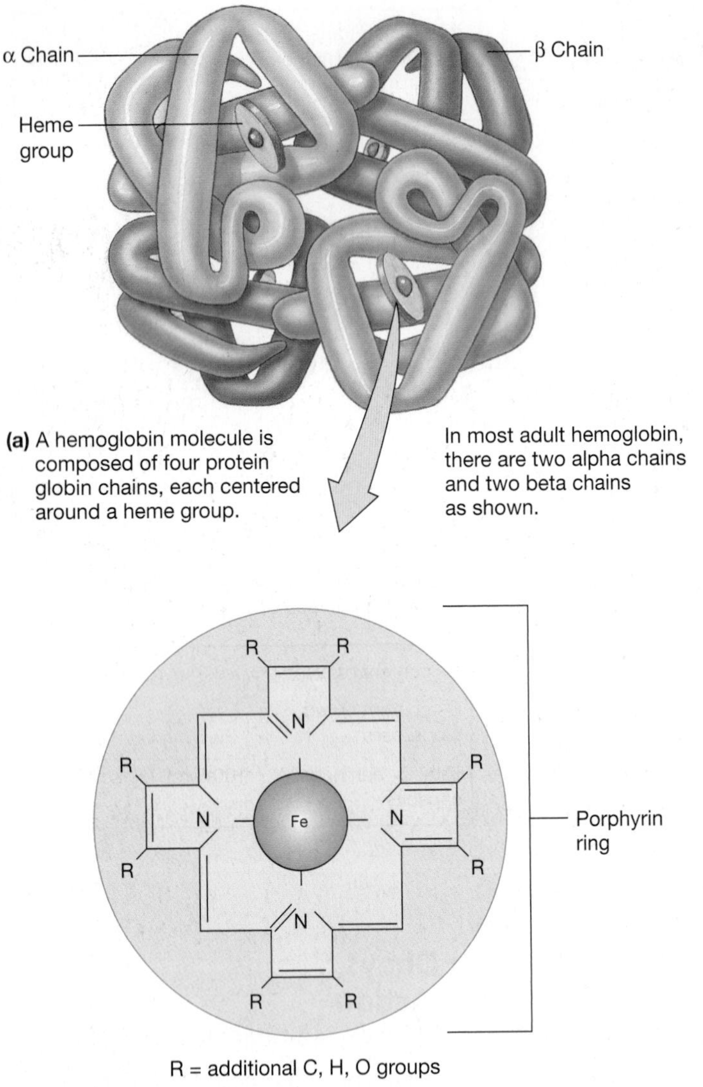
α Chain
Heme group
β Chain
In most adult hemoglobin, there are two alpha chains and two beta chains as shown.
R
N
Fe
Porphyrin ring
R = additional C, H, O groups

(a) A hemoglobin molecule is composed of four protein globin chains, each centered around a heme group.

(b) Each heme group consists of a porphyrin ring with an iron atom in the center.

● **FIGURE 18-8** ***Hemoglobin is a globular protein that contains iron.***

red blood cells and onto hemoglobin occurs so rapidly that blood in the pulmonary capillaries normally picks up as much oxygen as the P_{O_2} of the plasma and the number of red blood cells permit.

Once arterial blood reaches the tissues, the exchange process that took place in the lungs reverses. Dissolved oxygen diffuses out of systemic capillaries into cells, and the resultant decrease in plasma P_{O_2} disturbs the equilibrium of the oxygen-hemoglobin binding reaction by removing oxygen from the left side of the equation. The equilibrium shifts to the left according to the law of mass action, and the hemoglobin molecules release their oxygen stores, as represented in the bottom half of Figure 18-6.

Like oxygen loading at the lungs, this process of transferring oxygen to the body's cells takes place very rapidly and goes to equilibrium. The P_{O_2} of the cells determines how much oxygen is unloaded from hemoglobin. As cells increase their metabolic activity, their P_{O_2} decreases, and hemoglobin releases more oxygen to them.

Oxygen Binding Is Expressed as a Percentage

The amount of oxygen bound to hemoglobin at any given P_{O_2} is expressed as a percentage:

$$(\text{Amount of } O_2 \text{ bound/maximum that could be bound}) \times 100 = \text{percent saturation of hemoglobin}$$

The **percent saturation of hemoglobin** refers to the percentage of available binding sites that are bound to oxygen. If all binding sites of all hemoglobin molecules are occupied by oxygen molecules, the blood is 100% oxygenated, or *saturated* with oxygen. If half the available binding sites are carrying oxygen, the hemoglobin is 50% saturated, and so on.

The relationship between plasma P_{O_2} and percent saturation of hemoglobin can be explained with the following analogy. The hemoglobin molecules carrying oxygen are like students moving books from an old library to a new one. Each student (a hemoglobin molecule) can carry a maximum of four books (100% saturation). The librarian in charge controls how many books (O_2 molecules) each student will carry, just as plasma P_{O_2} determines the amount of oxygen that binds to hemoglobin.

At the same time, the total number of books being carried depends on the number of available students, just as the amount of oxygen delivered to the tissues depends on the number of available hemoglobin molecules. For example, if there are 100 students, and the librarian gives each of them four books (100% saturation), then 400 books are carried to the new library. If the librarian gives three books to each student (decreased plasma P_{O_2}), then only 300 books go to the new library, even though each student could carry four. (Students carrying only three of a possible four books correspond to 75%

RUNNING PROBLEM

In most people arriving at high altitude, normal physiological responses kick in to help acclimatize the body to the chronic hypoxia. Within two hours of arrival, hypoxia triggers the release of erythropoietin from the kidneys and liver. This hormone stimulates red blood cell production, and as a result, new erythrocytes appear in the blood within days.

Question 4:
How does adding erythrocytes to the blood help a person acclimatize to high altitude?

Question 5:
What does adding erythrocytes to the blood do to the viscosity of the blood? What effect will that change in viscosity have on blood flow?

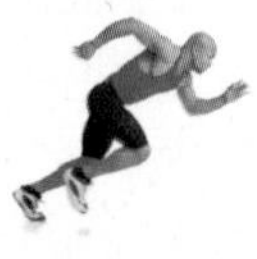

598 600 603 606 610 617 617

saturation of hemoglobin). If the librarian is handing out four books per student but only 50 students show up (fewer hemoglobin molecules), then only 200 books get to the new library, even though the students are taking the maximum number of books they can carry.

The physical relationship between P_{O_2} and how much oxygen binds to hemoglobin can be studied *in vitro*. Researchers expose samples of hemoglobin to various P_{O_2} levels and quantitatively determine the amount of oxygen that binds. **Oxyhemoglobin dissociation curves**, such as the one shown in Figure 18-9 ●, are the result of these *in vitro* binding studies.

The shape of the HbO_2 dissociation curve reflects the properties of the hemoglobin molecule and its affinity for oxygen. If you look at the curve, you find that at normal alveolar and arterial P_{O_2} (100 mm Hg), 98% of the hemoglobin is bound to oxygen. In other words, as blood passes through the lungs under normal conditions, hemoglobin picks up nearly the maximum amount of oxygen that it can carry.

Notice that the curve is nearly flat at P_{O_2} levels higher than 100 mm Hg (that is, the slope approaches zero). At P_{O_2} above 100 mm Hg, even large changes in P_{O_2} cause only minor changes in percent saturation. In fact, hemoglobin is not 100% saturated until the P_{O_2} reaches nearly 650 mm Hg, a partial pressure far higher than anything we encounter in everyday life.

The flattening of the dissociation curve at higher P_{O_2} also means that alveolar P_{O_2} can fall a good bit below 100 mm Hg without significantly lowering hemoglobin saturation. As long as P_{O_2} in the alveoli (and thus in the pulmonary capillaries) stays above 60 mm Hg, hemoglobin is more than 90% saturated and maintains near-normal levels of oxygen transport. However, once P_{O_2} falls below 60 mm Hg, the curve becomes steeper. The steep slope means that a small decrease in P_{O_2} causes a relatively large release of oxygen.

For example, if P_{O_2} falls from 100 mm Hg to 60 mm Hg, the percent saturation of hemoglobin goes from 98% to about 90%, a decrease of 8%. This is equivalent to a saturation change of 2% for each 10 mm Hg change. If P_{O_2} falls further, from 60 to 40 mm Hg, the percent saturation goes from 90% to 75%, a decrease of 7.5% for each 10 mm Hg. In the 40–20 mm Hg range, the curve is even steeper. Hemoglobin saturation declines from 75% to 35%, a change of 20% for each 10 mm Hg change.

What is the physiological significance of the shape of the dissociation curve? In blood leaving systemic capillaries with a P_{O_2} of 40 mm Hg (an average value for venous blood in a person at rest), hemoglobin is still 75% saturated, which means that at the cells it released only one-fourth of the oxygen it is capable of carrying. The oxygen that remains bound serves as a reservoir that cells can draw on if metabolism increases.

When metabolically active tissues use additional oxygen, their cellular P_{O_2} decreases, and hemoglobin releases additional oxygen at the cells. At a P_{O_2} of 20 mm Hg (an average value for exercising muscle), hemoglobin saturation falls to about 35%. With this 20 mm Hg decrease in P_{O_2} (40 mm Hg to 20 mm Hg), hemoglobin releases an additional 40% of the oxygen it is capable of carrying. This is another example of the built-in reserve capacity of the body.

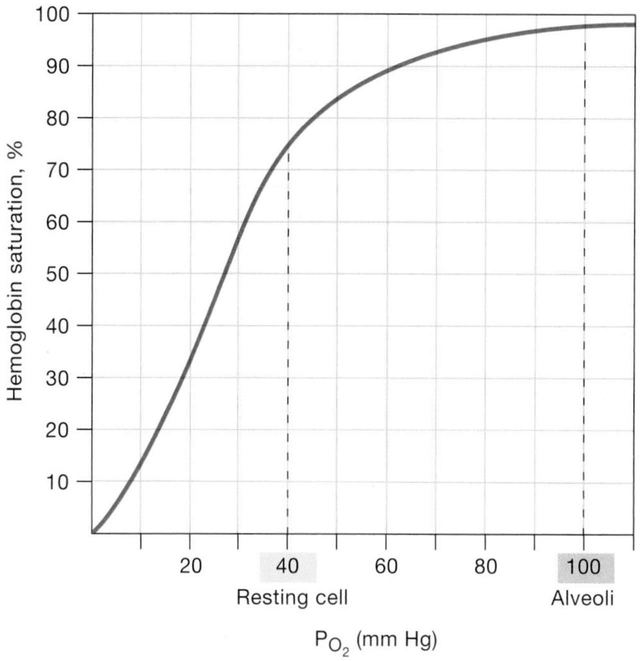

GRAPH QUESTIONS

(a) When the P_{O_2} is 20 mm Hg, what is the percent O_2 saturation of hemoglobin?

(b) At what P_{O_2} is hemoglobin 50% saturated with O_2?

● **FIGURE 18-9** ***The oxygen-hemoglobin dissociation curve***

Several Factors Affect Oxygen-Hb Binding

Any factor that changes the conformation of the hemoglobin protein may affect its ability to bind oxygen. In humans, physiological changes in plasma pH, P_{CO_2}, and temperature all alter the oxygen-binding affinity of hemoglobin. Changes in binding affinity are reflected by changes in the shape of the HbO_2 dissociation curve.

Increased temperature, increased P_{CO_2}, or decreased pH decrease the affinity of hemoglobin for oxygen and shift the oxygen-hemoglobin dissociation curve to the right (Fig. 18-10 ●). When these factors change in the opposite direction, binding affinity increases, and the curve shifts to the left. Notice that when the curve shifts in either direction, the changes are much more pronounced in the steep part of the curve. Physiologically, this means that oxygen binding at the lungs (in the 90–100 mm Hg P_{O_2} range) is not greatly affected, but oxygen delivery at the tissues (in the 20–40 mm Hg range) is significantly altered.

Let's examine one situation, the affinity shift that takes place when pH decreases from 7.4 (normal) to 7.2 (more acidic). (The normal range for blood pH is 7.38–7.42, but a pH of 7.2 is compatible with life). Look at the graph in Figure 18-10a. At a P_{O_2} of 40 mm Hg (equivalent to a resting cell) and

18

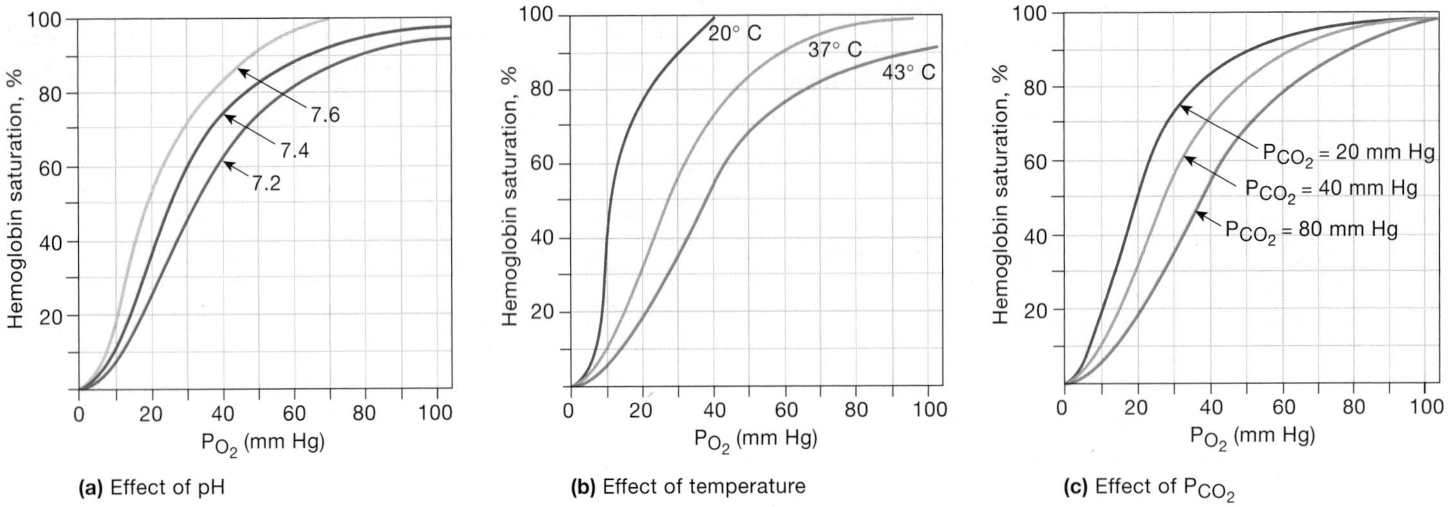

GRAPH QUESTIONS

(a) At a P_{O_2} of 20 mm Hg, how much more oxygen is released at an exercising muscle cell whose pH is 7.2 than at a cell with a pH of 7.4?

(b) What happens to oxygen release when the exercising muscle cell warms up?

● **FIGURE 18-10** ***Physical factors alter hemoglobin's affinity for oxygen.***

pH of 7.4, hemoglobin is about 75% saturated. At the same P_{O_2}, if the pH falls to 7.2, the percent saturation decreases to about 62%. This means that hemoglobin molecules release 13% more oxygen at pH 7.2 than they do at pH 7.4.

When does the body undergo shifts in blood pH? One situation is with maximal exertion that pushes cells into anaerobic metabolism. Anaerobic metabolism in exercising muscle fibers releases H^+ into the cytoplasm and extracellular fluid. As H^+ concentrations increase, pH falls, the affinity of hemoglobin for oxygen decreases, and the HbO_2 dissociation curve shifts to the right. More oxygen is released at the tissues as the blood becomes more acidic (pH decreases). A shift in the hemoglobin saturation curve that results from a change in pH is called the **Bohr effect**.

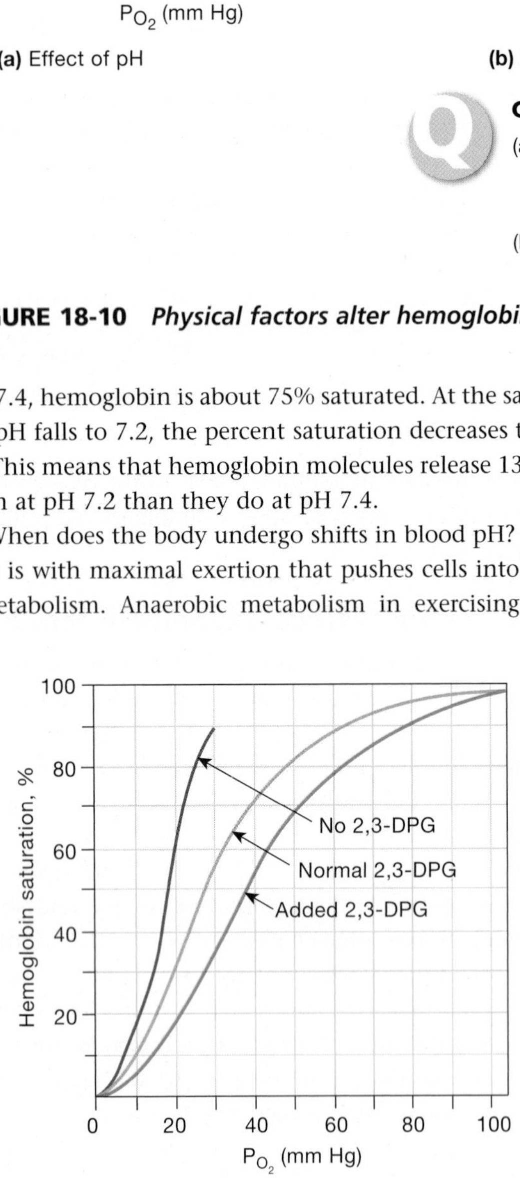

GRAPH QUESTION

Blood stored in blood banks loses its normal content of 2,3-DPG. Is this good or bad? Explain.

● **FIGURE 18-11** ***2,3-DPG decreases hemoglobin's affinity for oxygen.***

An additional factor that affects oxygen-hemoglobin binding is **2,3-diphosphoglycerate** (2,3-DPG; also called *2,3-bisphosphoglycerate* or 2,3-BPG), a compound made from an intermediate of the glycolysis pathway. **Chronic hypoxia** (extended periods of low oxygen) triggers an increase in 2,3-DPG production in red blood cells. Increased levels of 2,3-DPG lower the binding affinity of hemoglobin and shift the HbO_2 dissociation curve to the right (Fig. 18-11 ●). Ascent to high altitude and anemia are two situations that increase 2,3-DPG production.

Changes in hemoglobin's structure also change its oxygen-binding affinity. For example, fetal hemoglobin has gamma chain isoforms for two of its subunits. The presence of gamma chains enhances the ability of fetal hemoglobin to bind oxygen in the low-oxygen environment of the placenta. The altered binding affinity is reflected by the shape of the fetal HbO_2 dissociation curve, which differs from the shape of the adult curve (Fig. 18-12 ●). At any given placental P_{O_2}, oxygen released by maternal hemoglobin is picked up by the higher-affinity fetal hemoglobin for delivery to the developing fetus.

Figure 18-13 ● summarizes the factors that influence the total oxygen content of arterial blood.

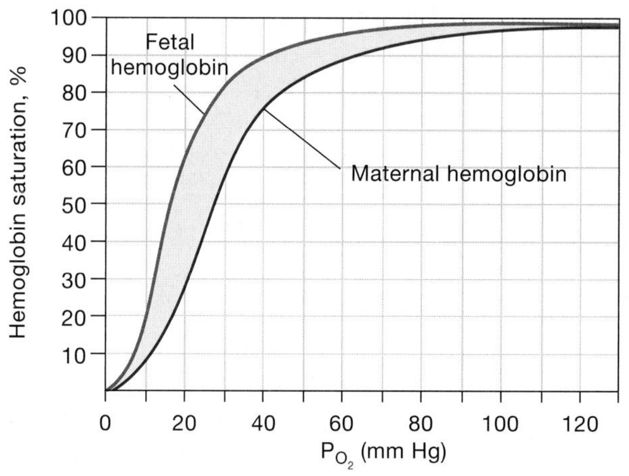

GRAPH QUESTIONS

(a) Because of incomplete gas exchange across the thick membranes of the placenta, hemoglobin in fetal blood leaving the placenta is 80% saturated with oxygen. What is the P_{O_2} of that placental blood?

(b) Blood in the vena cava of the fetus has a P_{O_2} around 10 mm Hg. What is the percent O_2 saturation of maternal hemoglobin at the same P_{O_2}?

● **FIGURE 18-12** ***Maternal and fetal hemoglobin have different oxygen-binding properties.***

CONCEPT CHECK

9. Can a person breathing 100% oxygen at sea level achieve 100% saturation of her hemoglobin?
10. What effect does hyperventilation have on the percent saturation of arterial hemoglobin? (Hint: See Fig. 17-15).
11. A muscle that is actively contracting may have a cellular P_{O_2} of 25 mm Hg. What happens to oxygen binding to hemoglobin at this low P_{O_2}? What is the P_{O_2} of the venous blood leaving the active muscle?

Answers: p. 621

Carbon Dioxide Is Transported in Three Ways

Gas transport in the blood includes carbon dioxide removal from the cells as well as oxygen delivery to cells, and hemoglobin also plays an important role in CO_2 transport. Carbon dioxide is a by-product of cellular respiration [p. 110]. It is more soluble in body fluids than oxygen is, but the cells produce far more CO_2 than can dissolve in the plasma. Only about 7% of the CO_2 carried by venous blood is dissolved in the blood. The remaining 93% diffuses into red blood cells, where 70% is converted to bicarbonate ion, as explained below, and 23% binds to hemoglobin (Hb·CO_2). Figure 18-14 ● summarizes these three mechanisms of carbon dioxide transport in the blood.

Why is removing CO_2 from the body so important? The reason is that elevated P_{CO_2} (*hypercapnia*) causes the pH disturbance known as *acidosis*. Extremes of pH interfere with hydrogen bonding of molecules and can denature proteins [p. 31]. Abnormally high P_{CO_2} levels also depress central nervous system function, causing confusion, coma, or even death. For these reasons, CO_2 is a potentially toxic waste product that must be removed by the lungs.

CO_2 and Bicarbonate Ions

As we just noted, about 70% of the CO_2 that enters the blood is transported to the lungs as bicarbonate ions (HCO_3^-) dissolved in the plasma. The conversion of CO_2 to HCO_3^- serves two purposes: (1) it provides an additional means of CO_2 transport from cells to lungs, and (2) HCO_3^- is available to act as a buffer for metabolic acids [p. 39], thereby helping stabilize the body's pH.

How does CO_2 turn into HCO_3^-? The rapid conversion depends on the presence of **carbonic anhydrase (CA)**, an

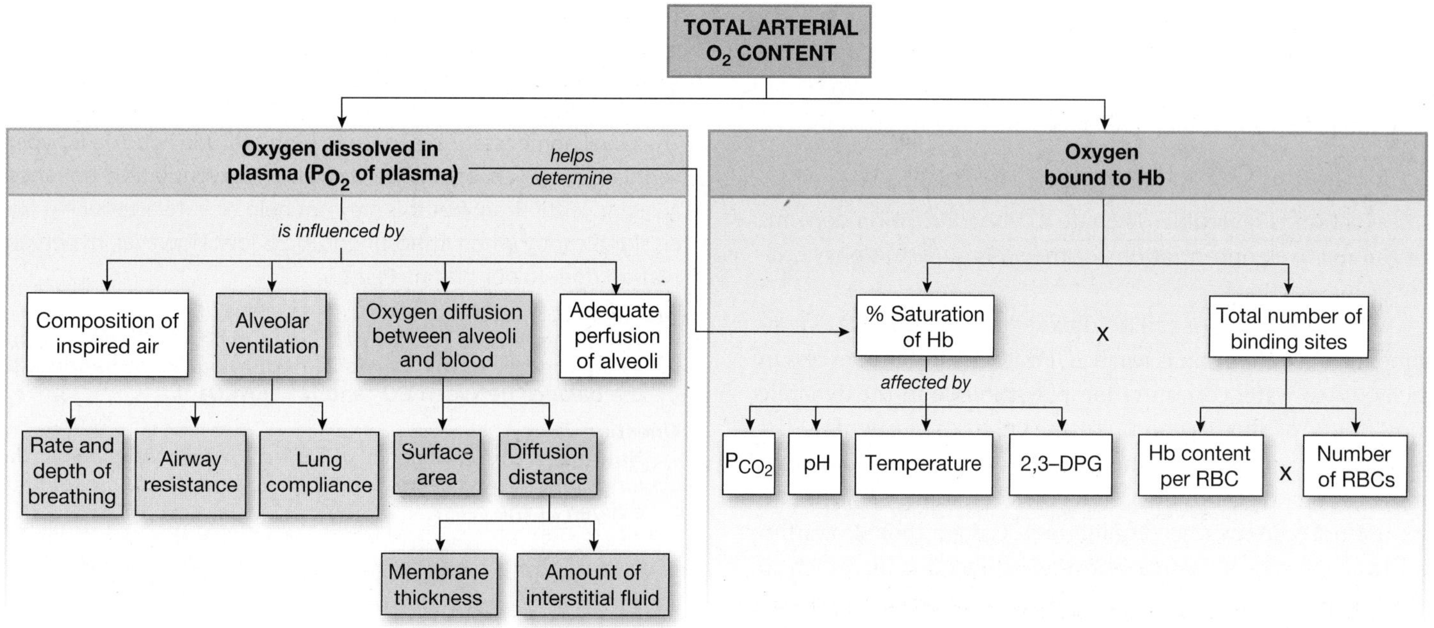

● **FIGURE 18-13** ***The total oxygen content of arterial blood depends on the amount of oxygen dissolved in plasma and bound to hemoglobin.***

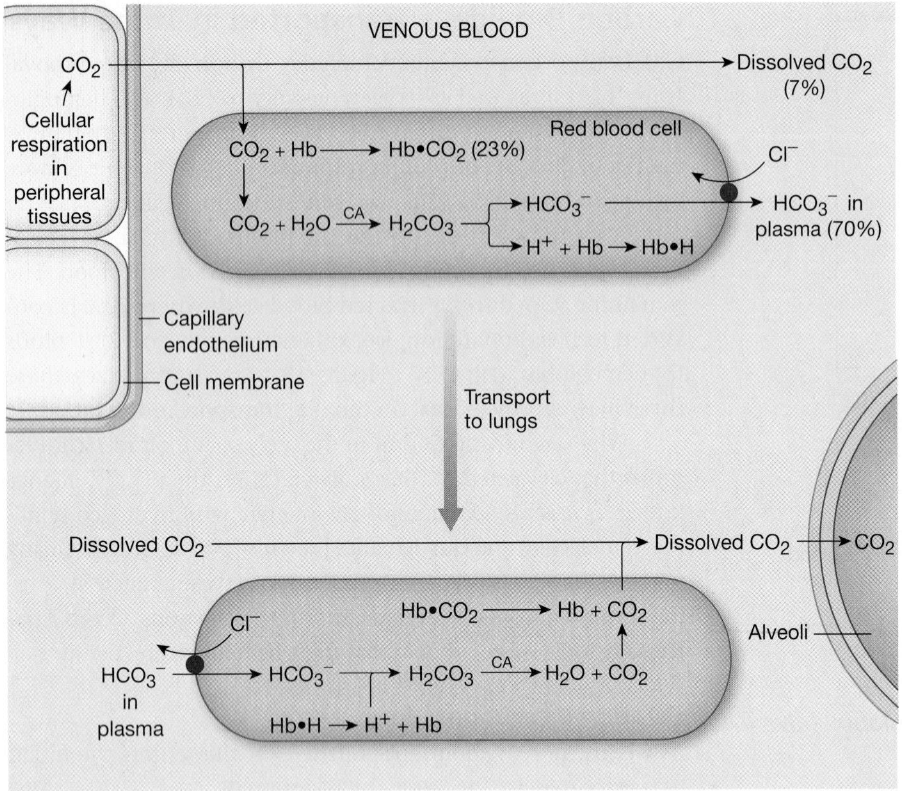

FIGURE 18-14 ***Carbon dioxide transport in the blood.*** CA = carbonic anhydrase.

enzyme found concentrated in red blood cells. Let's see how this happens. Dissolved CO_2 in the plasma diffuses into red blood cells, where it may react with water in the presence of carbonic anhydrase to form *carbonic acid* (H_2CO_3, top portion of Fig. 18-14). Carbonic acid then dissociates into a hydrogen ion and a bicarbonate ion:

$$CO_2 + H_2O \underset{}{\overset{\text{carbonic anhydrase}}{\rightleftharpoons}} \underset{\text{carbonic acid}}{H_2CO_3} \rightleftharpoons H^+ + HCO_3^-$$

Because the carbonic acid dissociates readily, we sometimes ignore the intermediate step and summarize the reaction as:

$$CO_2 + H_2O \rightleftharpoons H^+ + HCO_3^-$$

This reaction is reversible. The rate in either direction depends on the relative concentrations of the substrates and obeys the law of mass action.

The conversion of carbon dioxide to H^+ and HCO_3^- continues until equilibrium is reached. (Water is always in excess in the body, so water concentration plays no role in the dynamic equilibrium of this reaction). To keep the reaction going, the products (H^+ and HCO_3^-) must be removed from the cytoplasm of the red blood cell. If the product concentrations are kept low, the reaction cannot reach equilibrium. Carbon dioxide continues to move out of plasma into the red blood cells, which in turn allows more CO_2 to diffuse out of tissues into the blood.

Two separate mechanisms remove free H^+ and HCO_3^-. In the first, bicarbonate leaves the red blood cell on an antiport protein [p. 144]. This transport process, known as the **chloride shift**, exchanges HCO_3^- for Cl^-. The anion exchange maintains the cell's electrical neutrality. The transfer of HCO_3^- into the plasma makes this buffer available to moderate pH changes caused by the production of metabolic acids. Bicarbonate is the most important extracellular buffer in the body.

RUNNING PROBLEM

The usual homeostatic response to high-altitude hypoxia is hyperventilation, which begins on arrival. Hyperventilation enhances alveolar ventilation, but this may not help elevate arterial P_{O_2} levels significantly when atmospheric P_{O_2} is low. However, hyperventilation does lower plasma P_{CO_2}.

Question 6:

What happens to plasma pH during hyperventilation? (Hint: Apply the law of mass action to figure out what happens to the balance between CO_2 and H^+ + HCO_3^-).

Question 7:

How does this change in pH affect oxygen binding at the lungs when P_{O_2} is decreased? How does it affect unloading of oxygen at the cells?

598 600 603 606 610 617 617

Hemoglobin and H^+

The second mechanism removes free H^+ from the red blood cell cytoplasm. Hemoglobin within the red blood cell acts as a buffer and binds hydrogen ions in the reaction

$$H^+ + Hb \rightleftharpoons Hb \cdot H$$

Hemoglobin's buffering of H^+ is an important step that prevents large changes in the body's pH. If blood P_{CO_2} is elevated much above normal, the hemoglobin buffer cannot soak up all the H^+ produced from the reaction of CO_2 and water. In those cases, excess H^+ accumulates in the plasma, causing the condition known as **respiratory acidosis**. Additional information on the role of the respiratory system in maintaining pH homeostasis is found in Chapter 20.

Hemoglobin and CO_2

Although most carbon dioxide that enters red blood cells is converted to bicarbonate ions, about 23% of the CO_2 in venous blood binds directly to hemoglobin. At the cells, when oxygen leaves its binding sites on the hemoglobin molecule, CO_2 binds with free hemoglobin at exposed amino groups ($-NH_2$), forming **carbaminohemoglobin:**

$$CO_2 + Hb \rightleftharpoons Hb \cdot CO_2 \text{ (carbaminohemoglobin)}$$

The presence of CO_2 and H^+ facilitates formation of carbaminohemoglobin because both these factors decrease hemoglobin's binding affinity for oxygen (see Fig. 18-10).

CO_2 Removal at the Lungs

When venous blood reaches the lungs, the processes that took place in the systemic capillaries reverse (bottom portion of Fig. 18-14). The P_{CO_2} of the alveoli is lower than that of venous blood in the pulmonary capillaries. Therefore, CO_2 diffuses down its pressure gradient—in other words, out of plasma into the alveoli—and the plasma P_{CO_2} begins to fall.

The decrease in plasma P_{CO_2} allows dissolved CO_2 to diffuse out of the red blood cells. As CO_2 levels in the red blood cells decrease, the equilibrium of the CO_2-HCO_3^- reaction is disturbed, shifting toward production of more CO_2. Removal of CO_2 causes H^+ to leave the hemoglobin molecules, and the chloride shift reverses: Cl^- returns to the plasma in exchange for HCO_3^- moving back into the red blood cells. The HCO_3^- and newly released H^+ re-form into carbonic acid, which is then converted into water and CO_2. This CO_2 is then free to diffuse out of the red blood cell and into the alveoli.

Figure 18-15 ● shows the combined transport of CO_2 and O_2 in the blood. At the alveoli, O_2 diffuses down its pressure gradient, moving from the alveoli into the plasma and then from the plasma into the red blood cells. Hemoglobin binds to O_2, increasing the amount of oxygen that can be transported to the cells.

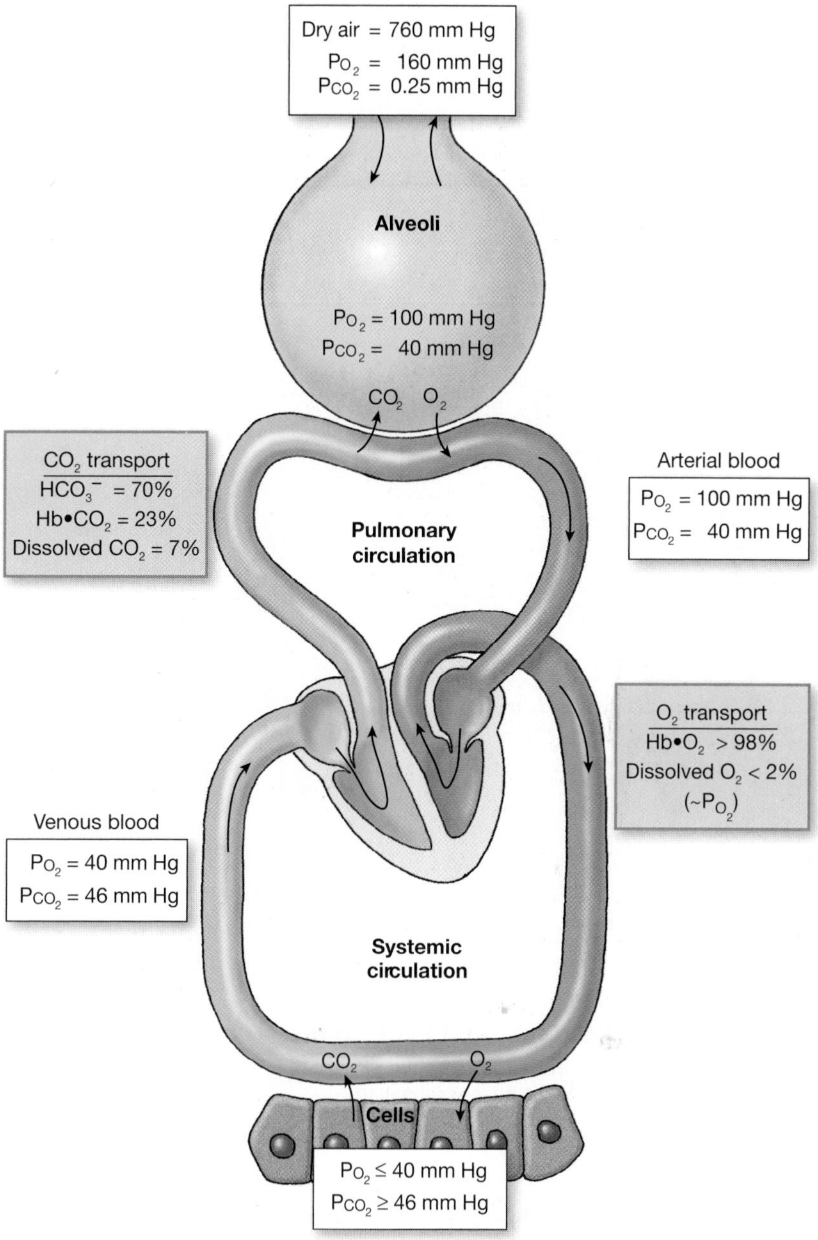

● **FIGURE 18-15** ***Summary of O_2 and CO_2 exchange and transport***

At the cells, the process reverses. Because P_{O_2} is lower in cells than in the arterial blood, O_2 diffuses from the plasma into the cells. The decrease in plasma P_{O_2} causes hemoglobin to release O_2, making additional oxygen available to enter cells.

Carbon dioxide from aerobic metabolism simultaneously leaves cells and enters the blood, dissolving in the plasma. From there, CO_2 enters red blood cells, where most is converted to HCO_3^- and H^+. The HCO_3^- is returned to the plasma in exchange for a Cl^- while the H^+ binds to hemoglobin. A fraction of the CO_2 that enters red blood cells also binds directly to hemoglobin. At the lungs, the process reverses as CO_2 diffuses out of the pulmonary capillaries and into the alveoli.

To understand fully how the respiratory system coordinates delivery of oxygen to the lungs with transport of oxygen

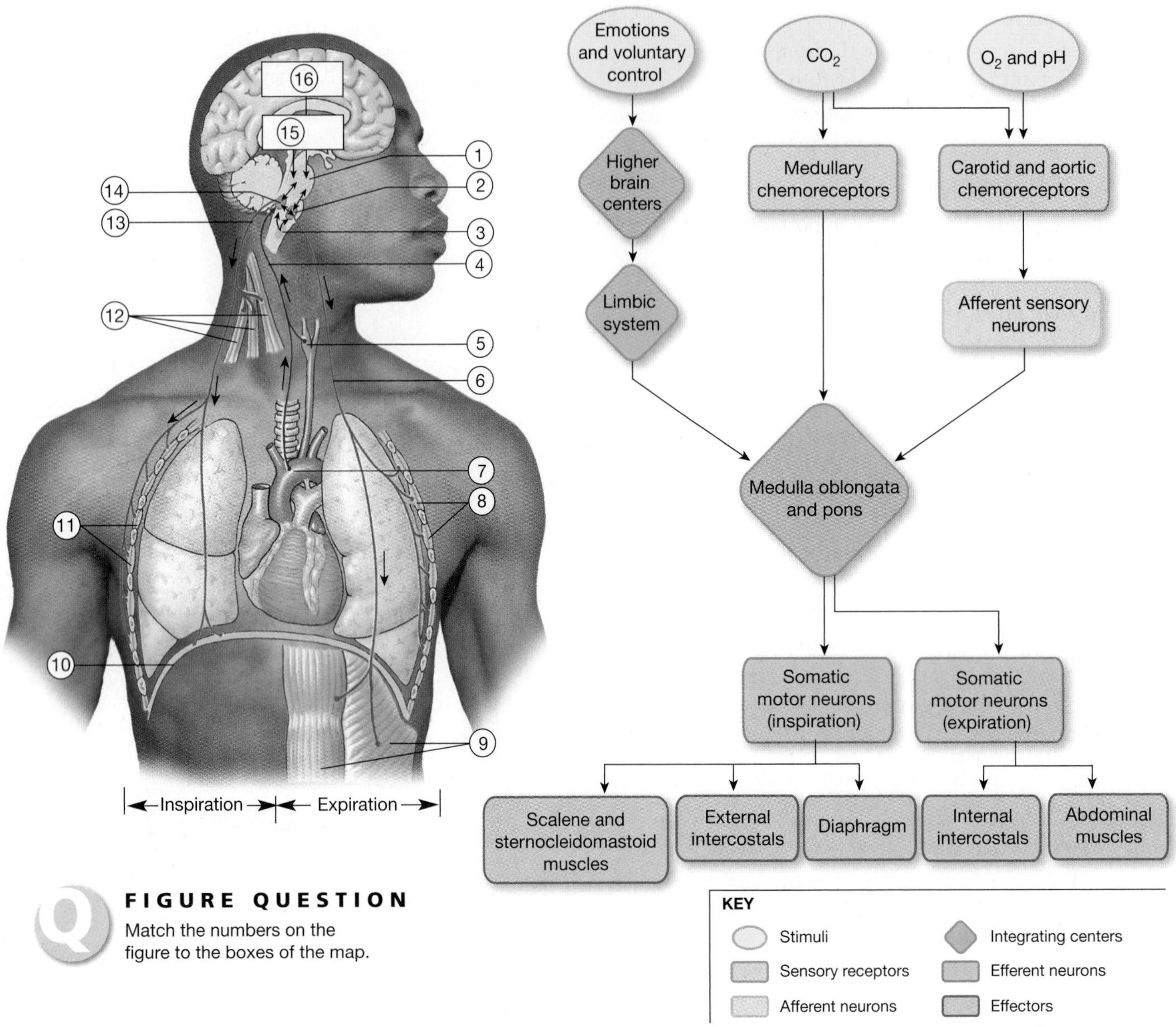

FIGURE QUESTION

Match the numbers on the figure to the boxes of the map.

● **FIGURE 18-16** ***The reflex control of ventilation.*** Chemoreceptors monitor blood gases and pH. Control networks in the brain stem regulate activity in somatic motor neurons leading to respiratory muscles.

in the circulation, we now consider the central nervous system control of ventilation.

CONCEPT CHECK

12. How would an obstruction of the airways affect alveolar ventilation, arterial P_{CO_2}, and the body's pH? Answers: p. 621

REGULATION OF VENTILATION

Breathing is a rhythmic process that usually occurs without conscious thought or awareness. In that respect, it resembles the rhythmic beating of the heart. However, skeletal muscles, unlike autorhythmic cardiac muscles, are not able to contract spontaneously. Instead, skeletal muscle contraction must be initiated by somatic motor neurons, which in turn are controlled by the central nervous system.

In the respiratory system, contraction of the diaphragm and other muscles is initiated by a spontaneously firing network of neurons in the brain stem (Fig. 18-16 ●). Breathing occurs automatically throughout a person's life but can also be controlled voluntarily, up to a point. Complicated synaptic interactions between neurons in the network create the rhythmic cycles of inspiration and expiration, influenced continuously by sensory input, especially that from chemoreceptors for CO_2,

O_2, and H^+. Ventilation pattern depends in large part on the levels of those three substances in the arterial blood and extracellular fluid.

The neural control of breathing is one of the few "black boxes" left in systems-level physiology. Although we know the major regions of the brain stem that are involved, the details remain elusive and controversial. The brain stem network that controls breathing behaves like a *central pattern generator* [p. 458], with intrinsic rhythmic activity that probably arises from *pacemaker neurons* with unstable membrane potentials.

Some of our understanding of how ventilation is controlled has come from observing patients with brain damage. Other information has come from animal experiments in which neural connections between major parts of the brain stem are severed, or sections of brain are studied in isolation. Research on CNS respiratory control is difficult because of the complexity of the neural network and its anatomical location, but in recent years scientists have developed better techniques for studying the system.

The details that follow represent a contemporary model for the control of ventilation. Although some parts of the model are well supported with experimental evidence, other aspects are still under investigation. This model states that:

1. Respiratory neurons in the medulla control inspiratory and expiratory muscles.
2. Neurons in the pons integrate sensory information and interact with medullary neurons to influence ventilation.
3. The rhythmic pattern of breathing arises from a neural network with spontaneously discharging neurons.
4. Ventilation is subject to continuous modulation by various chemoreceptor- and mechanoreceptor-linked reflexes and by higher brain centers.

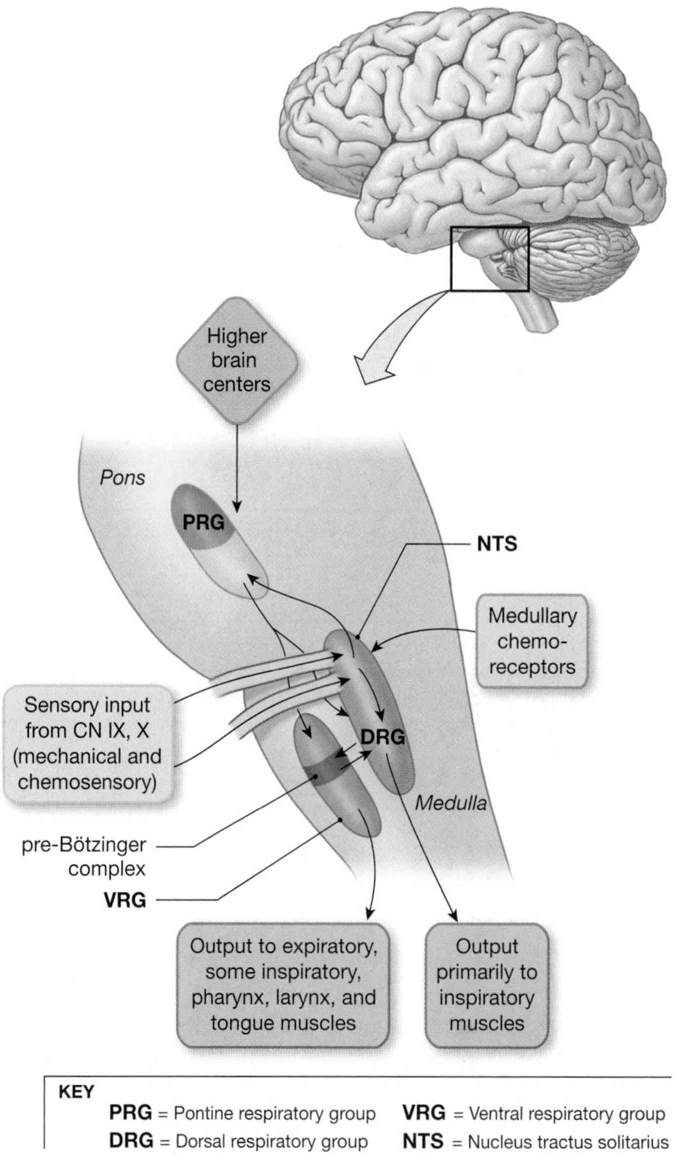

● **FIGURE 18-17** ***Neural networks in the brain stem control ventilation.***

Neurons in the Medulla Control Breathing

Classic descriptions of how the brain controls ventilation divided the brain stem into various control centers. More recent descriptions, however, are less specific about assigning function to particular "centers" and instead look at complex interactions between neurons in a network. We know that respiratory neurons are concentrated bilaterally in two areas of the medulla oblongata. Figure 18-17 ● shows these areas on the left side of the brain stem. One area called the **nucleus tractus solitarius** (NTS) contains the **dorsal respiratory group** (DRG) of neurons that control mostly muscles of inspiration. Output from the DRG goes via the **phrenic nerves** to the diaphragm and via the **intercostal nerves** to the intercostal muscles. In addition, the NTS receives sensory information from peripheral chemo- and mechanoreceptors through the *vagus* and *glossopharyngeal nerves* (cranial nerves X and IX; p. 310).

Respiratory neurons in the pons receive sensory information from the DRG and in turn influence the initiation and termination of inspiration. The **pontine respiratory groups** (previously called the pneumotaxic center) and other pontine neurons provide tonic input to the medullary networks to help coordinate a smooth respiratory rhythm.

The **ventral respiratory group** (VRG) of the medulla has multiple regions with different functions. One area known as the **pre-Bötzinger complex** contains spontaneously firing neurons that may act as the basic pacemaker for the respiratory rhythm. Other areas control muscles used for active expiration or for greater-than-normal inspiration, such as occurs during vigorous exercise. In addition, nerve fibers from the VRG innervate muscles of the larynx, pharynx, and tongue to keep the upper airways open during breathing. Inappropriate relaxation of these muscles during sleep contributes to

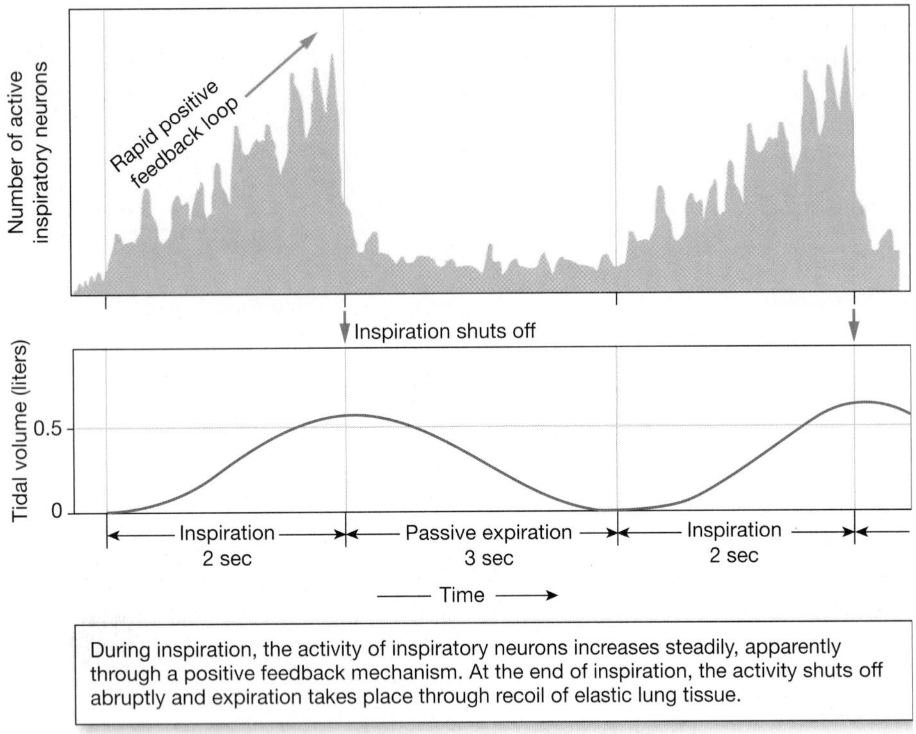
Number of active inspiratory neurons
Rapid positive feedback loop
Inspiration shuts off
Tidal volume (liters)
0.5
0
Inspiration 2 sec
Passive expiration 3 sec
Inspiration 2 sec
Time
During inspiration, the activity of inspiratory neurons increases steadily, apparently through a positive feedback mechanism. At the end of inspiration, the activity shuts off abruptly and expiration takes place through recoil of elastic lung tissue.

● **FIGURE 18-18** ***Neural activity cycles during quiet breathing***

GRAPH QUESTION

What is the ventilation rate of the person in this example?

obstructive sleep apnea, a sleeping disorder associated with snoring and excessive daytime sleepiness.

The integrated action of the respiratory control networks can be seen by monitoring electrical activity in the phrenic nerve and other motor nerves (Fig. 18-18 ●). During quiet breathing, a pacemaker initiates each cycle, and inspiratory neurons gradually increase stimulation of the inspiratory muscles. This increase is sometimes called *ramping* because of the shape of the graph of inspiratory neuron activity. A few inspiratory neurons fire to begin the ramp. The firing of these neurons recruits other inspiratory neurons to fire in an apparent positive feedback loop. As more neurons fire, more skeletal muscle fibers are recruited. The rib cage expands smoothly as the diaphragm contracts.

At the end of inspiration, the inspiratory neurons abruptly stop firing, and the respiratory muscles relax. Over the next few seconds, passive expiration occurs because of elastic recoil of the inspiratory muscles and elastic lung tissue. However, some motor neuron activity can be observed during passive expiration, suggesting that perhaps muscles in the upper airways contract to slow the flow of air out of the respiratory system.

Many neurons of the VRG remain inactive during quiet respiration. They function primarily during forced breathing, when inspiratory movements are exaggerated, and during active expiration. In forced breathing, increased activity of inspiratory neurons stimulates accessory muscles, such as the sternocleidomastoids. Contraction of these accessory muscles enhances expansion of the thorax by raising the sternum and upper ribs.

With active expiration, expiratory neurons from the VRG activate the internal intercostal and abdominal muscles. There seems to be some communication between inspiratory and expiratory neurons, as inspiratory neurons are inhibited during active expiration.

Carbon Dioxide, Oxygen, and pH Influence Ventilation

Sensory input from central and peripheral chemoreceptors modifies the rhythmicity of the control network to help maintain blood gas homeostasis. Carbon dioxide is the primary stimulus for changes in ventilation. Oxygen and plasma pH play lesser roles.

The chemoreceptors for oxygen and carbon dioxide are strategically associated with the arterial circulation. If too little oxygen is present in arterial blood destined for the brain and other tissues, the rate and depth of breathing increase. If the rate of CO_2 production by the cells exceeds the rate of CO_2 removal by the lungs, arterial P_{CO_2} increases, and ventilation is intensified to match CO_2 removal to production. These homeostatic reflexes operate constantly, keeping arterial P_{O_2} and P_{CO_2} within a narrow range.

Peripheral chemoreceptors located in the carotid and aortic arteries sense changes in the P_{O_2}, pH, and P_{CO_2} of the plasma (Fig. 18-16). These **carotid** and **aortic bodies** are close to the locations of the baroreceptors involved in reflex control of blood pressure [p. 533]. **Central chemoreceptors** in the brain respond to changes in the concentration of CO_2 in the cerebrospinal fluid. These central receptors lie on the ventral surface of the medulla, close to neurons involved in respiratory control.

Peripheral Chemoreceptors

When specialized **glomus cells** [*glomus*, a ball-shaped mass] in the carotid and aortic bodies are activated by a decrease in P_{O_2} or pH or by an increase in P_{CO_2}, they trigger a reflex increase in ventilation. Under most normal circumstances, oxygen is not an important factor in modulating ventilation because arterial P_{O_2} must fall to less than 60 mm Hg before ventilation is stimulated. This large decrease in P_{O_2} is equivalent to ascending to an altitude of 3000 m. (For reference, Denver is located at an altitude of 1609 m). However, any condition that reduces plasma pH or increases P_{CO_2} will activate the carotid and aortic glomus cells and increase ventilation.

The details of glomus cell function remain to be worked out, but the basic mechanism by which these chemoreceptors respond to low oxygen is similar to the mechanism you learned for insulin release by pancreatic beta cells [p. 171] or taste transduction in taste buds [p. 353].

In all three examples, a stimulus inactivates K^+ channels, causing the receptor cell to depolarize (Fig. 18-19 ●). Depolarization opens voltage-gated Ca^{2+} channels, and Ca^{2+} entry causes exocytosis of neurotransmitter onto the sensory neuron. In the carotid and aortic bodies, neurotransmitters initiate action potentials in sensory neurons leading to the brain stem respiratory networks, signaling them to increase ventilation.

Because the peripheral chemoreceptors respond only to dramatic changes in arterial P_{O_2}, arterial oxygen concentrations do not play a role in the everyday regulation of ventilation. However, unusual physiological conditions, such as ascending to high altitude, and pathological conditions, such as chronic obstructive pulmonary disease (COPD), can reduce arterial P_{O_2} to levels that are low enough to activate the peripheral chemoreceptors.

Central Chemoreceptors

The most important chemical controller of ventilation is carbon dioxide, mediated both through the peripheral chemoreceptors just discussed and through central chemoreceptors located in the medulla (Fig. 18-20 ●). These receptors set the respiratory pace, providing continuous input into the control network. When arterial P_{CO_2} increases, CO_2 crosses the blood-brain barrier and activates the central chemoreceptors. These receptors signal the control network to increase the rate and depth of ventilation, thereby enhancing alveolar ventilation and removing CO_2 from the blood (Fig. 18-21 ●).

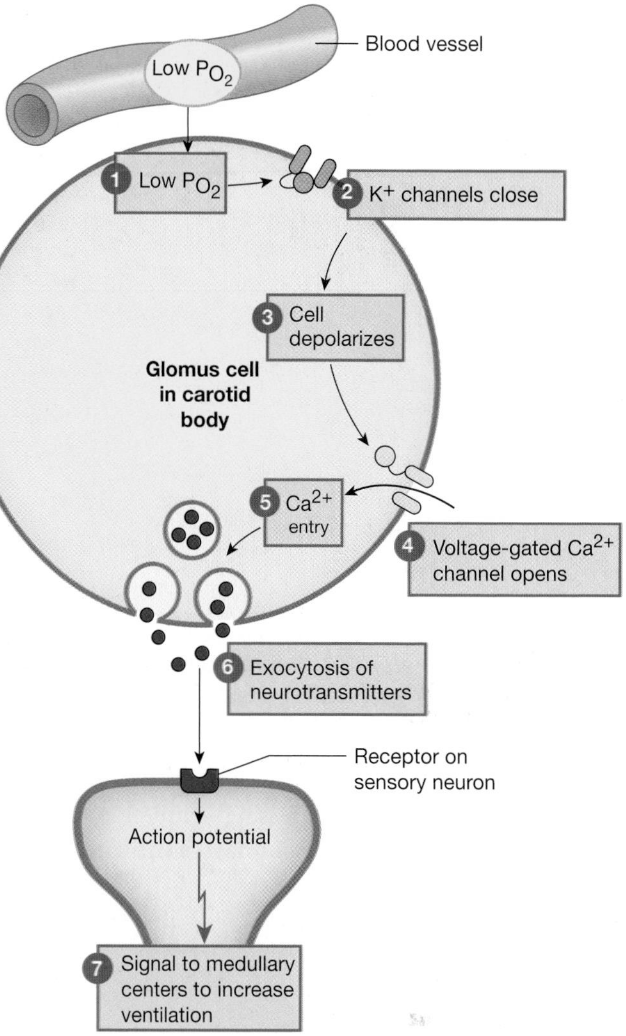

● **FIGURE 18-19** ***The carotid body oxygen sensor releases neurotransmitter when P_{O_2} decreases.***

Although we say that the central chemoreceptors monitor CO_2, they actually respond to pH changes in the cerebrospinal fluid (CSF). Carbon dioxide that diffuses across the blood-brain barrier into the CSF is converted to bicarbonate and H^+:

$$CO_2 + H_2O \rightleftharpoons H_2CO_3^- \rightleftharpoons H^+ + HCO_3^-$$

Experiments indicate that the H^+ produced by this reaction is what initiates the chemoreceptor reflex, rather than the increased level of CO_2.

Note, however, that pH changes in the plasma *do not* usually influence the central chemoreceptors directly. Although plasma P_{CO_2} enters the CSF readily, plasma H^+ crosses the blood-brain barrier very slowly and therefore has little direct effect on the central chemoreceptors.

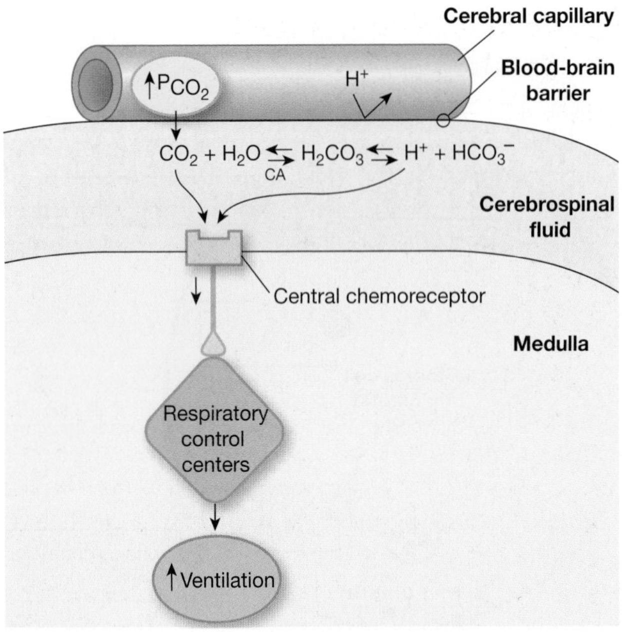

● **FIGURE 18-20** ***Central chemoreceptors monitor CO_2 in cerebrospinal fluid.*** CA = carbonic anhydrase.

When plasma P_{CO_2} increases, the chemoreceptors initially respond strongly by increasing ventilation. However, if P_{CO_2} remains elevated for several days, ventilation falls back toward normal rates as the chemoreceptor response adapts by mechanisms that are not clear. Fortunately for people with chronic lung diseases, the response of peripheral chemoreceptor to low arterial P_{O_2} remains intact over time, even though the central chemoreceptor response adapts to high P_{CO_2}.

In some situations, low P_{O_2} becomes the primary chemical stimulus for ventilation. For example, patients with severe chronic lung disease, such as COPD, have chronic hypercapnia and hypoxia. Their arterial P_{CO_2} may rise to 50–55 mm Hg (normal is 35–45) while their P_{O_2} falls to 45–50 mm Hg (normal 75–100). Because these levels are chronic, the chemoreceptor response adapts to the elevated P_{CO_2}. Most of the chemical stimulus for ventilation in this situation then comes from low P_{O_2}, sensed by the carotid and aortic chemoreceptors. If these patients are given too much oxygen, they may stop breathing because their chemical stimulus for ventilation is eliminated.

The central chemoreceptors respond to decreases in arterial P_{CO_2} as well as to increases. If alveolar P_{CO_2} falls, as it might during hyperventilation, plasma P_{CO_2} and cerebrospinal fluid P_{CO_2} follow suit. As a result, central chemoreceptor activity declines, and the control network slows the ventilation rate. When ventilation decreases, carbon dioxide begins to accumulate in alveoli and the plasma. Eventually, the arterial P_{CO_2} rises above the threshold level for the chemoreceptors. At that point, the receptors fire, and the control network again increases ventilation.

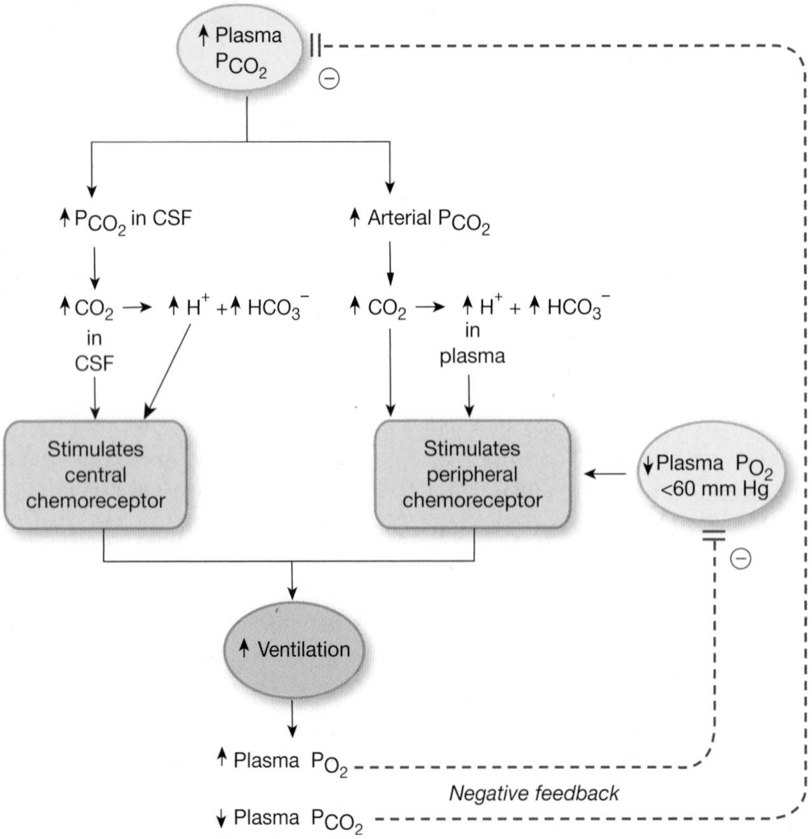

● **FIGURE 18-21** ***Chemoreceptor response to changes in plasma CO_2***

RUNNING PROBLEM

The hyperventilation response to hypoxia creates a peculiar breathing pattern called *periodic breathing*, in which the person goes through a 10–15-second period of breath-holding followed by a short period of hyperventilation. Periodic breathing occurs most often during sleep.

Question 8:

Based on your understanding of how the body controls ventilation, why do you think periodic breathing occurs most often during sleep?

598 600 603 606 610 617 617

Protective Reflexes Guard the Lungs

In addition to the chemoreceptor reflexes that help regulate ventilation, the body has protective reflexes that respond to physical injury or irritation of the respiratory tract and to overinflation of the lungs. The major protective reflex is *bronchoconstriction,* mediated through parasympathetic neurons that innervate bronchiolar smooth muscle. Inhaled particles or noxious gases stimulate **irritant receptors** in the airway mucosa. The irritant receptors send signals through sensory neurons to integrating centers in the CNS that trigger bronchoconstriction. Protective reflex responses also include coughing and sneezing.

The *Hering-Breuer inflation reflex* was first described in the late 1800s in anesthetized dogs. In these animals, if tidal volume exceeded a certain volume, stretch receptors in the lung signaled the brain stem to terminate inspiration. However, this reflex is difficult to demonstrate in adult humans and does not operate during quiet breathing and mild exertion. Studies on human infants, however, suggest that the Hering-Breuer inflation reflex may play a role in limiting their ventilation volumes.

Higher Brain Centers Affect Patterns of Ventilation

Conscious and unconscious thought processes also affect respiratory activities. Higher centers in the hypothalamus and cerebrum can alter the activity of the brain stem control network to change ventilation rate and depth. Voluntary control of ventilation falls into this category. Higher brain center control is not a *requirement* for ventilation, however. Even if the brain stem above the pons is severely damaged, essentially normal respiratory cycles continue.

Respiration can also be affected by stimulation of portions of the limbic system. For this reason, emotional and autonomic activities such as fear and excitement may affect the pace and depth of respiration. In some of these situations, the neural pathway goes directly to the somatic motor neurons, bypassing the control network in the brain stem.

Although we can temporarily alter our respiratory performance, we cannot override the chemoreceptor reflexes. Holding your breath is a good example. You can hold your breath voluntarily only until elevated P_{CO_2} in the blood and cerebrospinal fluid activates the chemoreceptor reflex, forcing you to inhale.

Small children having temper tantrums sometimes attempt to manipulate parents by threatening to hold their breath until they die. However, the chemoreceptor reflexes make it impossible for the children to carry out that threat. Extremely strong-willed children can continue holding their breath until they turn blue and pass out from hypoxia, but once they are unconscious, normal breathing automatically resumes.

Breathing is intimately linked to cardiovascular function. The integrating centers for both functions are located in the brain stem, and interneurons project between the two networks, allowing signaling back and forth. In Chapter 20 we examine the integration of cardiovascular, respiratory, and renal function as the three systems work together to maintain fluid and acid-base homeostasis. First, however, we examine the physiology of the kidneys in Chapter 19.

RUNNING PROBLEM CONCLUSION

High Altitude

On May 29, 1953, Edmund Hillary and Tenzing Norgay of the British Everest Expedition were the first humans to reach the summit of Mt. Everest. They carried supplemental oxygen with them, as it was believed that this feat was impossible without it. In 1978, however, Reinhold Messner and Peter Habeler achieved the "impossible." On May 8, they struggled to the summit using sheer willpower and no extra oxygen. In Messner's words, "I am nothing more than a single narrow gasping lung, floating over the mists and summits." Learn more about these Everest expeditions by doing a Google search for Hillary Everest or Messner Everest.

To learn more about different types of mountain sickness, see the International Society for Mountain Medicine (*www.ismmed.org/np_altitude_tutorial.htm*); "High altitude medicine," *American Family Physician* 1998 Apr. 15 (*www.aafp.org/afp/980415ap/harris.html*); and "High-altitude pulmonary edema" (*www.emedicine.com/MED/topic1956.htm*).

In this running problem you learned about normal and abnormal responses to high altitude. Check your understanding of the physiology behind this respiratory challenge by comparing your answers with the information in the following table.

RUNNING PROBLEM CONCLUSION *(continued)*

	QUESTION	FACTS	INTEGRATION AND ANALYSIS
1	What is the P_{O_2} of inspired air reaching the alveoli at 2500 m, where dry atmospheric pressure is 542 mm Hg? How does this value for P_{O_2} compare with the P_{O_2} value for fully humidified air at sea level?	Water vapor contributes a partial pressure of 47 mm Hg to fully humidified air. Oxygen is 21% of dry air. Normal atmospheric pressure at sea level is 760 mm Hg.	Correction for water vapor: $542 - 47 = 495$ mm Hg $\times$ 21% P_{O_2} = 104 mm Hg P_{O_2}. In humidified air at sea level, P_{O_2} = 150 mm Hg.
2	Why would someone with HAPE be short of breath?	Pulmonary edema increases the diffusion distance for oxygen.	Slower oxygen diffusion means less oxygen reaching the blood, which worsens the normal hypoxia of altitude.
3	Based on what you learned about mechanisms for matching ventilation and perfusion in the lung, can you explain why patients with HAPE have elevated pulmonary arterial blood pressure?	Low oxygen levels constrict pulmonary arterioles.	Constriction of pulmonary arterioles causes blood to collect in the pulmonary arteries behind the constriction. This increases pulmonary arterial blood pressure.
4	How does adding erythrocytes to the blood help a person acclimatize to high altitude?	98% of arterial oxygen is carried bound to hemoglobin.	Additional hemoglobin increases the oxygen-carrying capacity of the blood.
5	What does adding erythrocytes to the blood do to the viscosity of the blood? What effect will that change in viscosity have on blood flow?	Adding cells increases blood viscosity.	According to Poiseuille's law, increased viscosity increases resistance to flow, so blood flow will decrease.
6	What happens to plasma pH during hyperventilation?	Apply the law of mass action to the equation $CO_2 + H_2O \rightleftharpoons H^+ + HCO_3^-$	The amount of CO_2 in the plasma decreases during hyperventilation, which means the equation shifts to the left. This shift decreases H^+, which increases pH (alkalosis).
7	How does this change in pH affect oxygen binding at the lungs when P_{O_2} is decreased? How does it affect unloading of oxygen at the cells?	See Figure 18-10a.	The left shift of the curve means that, at any given P_{O_2}, more O_2 binds to hemoglobin. Less O_2 will unbind at the tissues for a given P_{O_2}, but P_{O_2} in the cells is probably lower than normal, and consequently there may be no change in unloading.
8	Why do you think periodic breathing occurs most often during sleep?	Periodic breathing alternates periods of breath-holding (apnea) and hyperventilation.	An awake person is more likely to make a conscious effort to breathe during the breath-holding spells, eliminating the cycle of periodic breathing.

598 600 603 606 610 617 617

CHAPTER SUMMARY

In this chapter, you learned why climbing Mt. Everest is such a respiratory challenge for the human body, and why people with emphysema experience the same respiratory challenges at sea level. The exchange and transport of oxygen and carbon dioxide in the body illustrate the *mass flow* of gases along concentration gradients. *Homeostasis* of these blood gases demonstrates *mass balance*: the concentration in the blood varies according to what enters or leaves at the lungs and tissues. The *law of mass action* governs the chemical reactions through which hemoglobin binds O_2, and carbonic anhydrase catalyzes the conversion of CO_2 and water to carbonic acid.

Diffusion and Solubility of Gases

1. Diffusion of O_2 and CO_2 is influenced by partial pressure gradients, surface area, membrane thickness, and diffusion distance. (p. 598)
2. The amount of a gas that dissolves in a liquid is proportional to the partial pressure of the gas and to the **solubility** of the gas in the liquid. Carbon dioxide is 20 times more soluble in aqueous solutions than oxygen is. (p. 599; Fig. 18-2)

Gas Exchange in the Lungs and Tissues

iP IP Respiratory: Gas Exchange

3. Normal alveolar and arterial P_{O_2} is about 100 mm Hg. Normal alveolar and arterial P_{CO_2} is about 40 mm Hg. (p. 599; Fig. 18-3)
4. Normal venous P_{O_2} is 40 mm Hg, and normal venous P_{CO_2} is 46 mm Hg. (p. 600; Fig. 18-3)
5. Both the composition of inspired air and the effectiveness of alveolar ventilation affect alveolar P_{O_2}. (p. 601)
6. Changes in alveolar surface area, in alveolar membrane thickness, and in interstitial distance between alveoli and pulmonary capillaries all affect gas exchange efficiency and arterial P_{O_2}. (p. 602; Fig. 18-4)

Gas Transport in the Blood

iP IP Respiratory: Gas Transport

7. Oxygen is transported both dissolved in plasma (<2%) and bound to hemoglobin (>98%). (p. 603; Fig. 18-6)
8. The P_{O_2} of plasma determines how much oxygen binds to hemoglobin. (p. 604; Fig. 18-9)
9. Oxygen-hemoglobin binding is influenced by pH, temperature, and **2,3-diphosphoglycerate** (2,3-DPG). (p. 607; Figs. 18-10, 18-11)
10. Venous blood carries 7% of its carbon dioxide dissolved in plasma, 23% as **carbaminohemoglobin**, and 70% as bicarbonate ion in the plasma. (p. 609; Fig. 18-14)
11. **Carbonic anhydrase** in red blood cells converts CO_2 to carbonic acid, which dissociates into H^+ and HCO_3^-. The H^+ then binds to hemoglobin, and HCO_3^- enters the plasma using the **chloride shift**. (p. 610)

Regulation of Ventilation

iP IP Respiratory: Control of Respiration

12. Respiratory control resides in networks of neurons in the medulla and pons, influenced by input from central and peripheral sensory receptors and higher brain centers. (p. 612)
13. The medullary **dorsal respiratory group** (DRG) contains mostly inspiratory neurons that control somatic motor neurons to the diaphragm. The **ventral respiratory group** (VRG) includes the **pre-Bötzinger complex** with its apparent pacemakers as well as neurons for inspiration and active expiration. (p. 613; Fig. 18-17)
14. **Peripheral chemoreceptors** in the carotid and aortic bodies monitor P_{O_2}, P_{CO_2}, and pH. P_{O_2} below 60 mm Hg triggers an increase in ventilation. (p. 615; Fig. 18-19)
15. Carbon dioxide is the primary stimulus for changes in ventilation. Chemoreceptors in the medulla and carotid bodies respond to changes in P_{CO_2}. (p. 615; Fig. 18-20)
16. Protective reflexes monitored by peripheral receptors prevent injury to the lungs from inhaled irritants. (p. 617)
17. Conscious and unconscious thought processes can affect respiratory activity. (p. 617)

QUESTIONS

(Answers to the Review Questions begin on page A1).

THE PHYSIOLOGY PLACE

Access more review material online at **The Physiology Place** web site. There you'll find review questions, problem-solving activities, case studies, flashcards, and direct links to both *Interactive Physiology®* and *PhysioEx™* To access the site, go to *http://www.physiologyplace.com* and select *Human Physiology*, Fifth Edition.

LEVEL ONE REVIEWING FACTS AND TERMS

1. List five factors that influence the diffusion of gases between alveolus and blood.
2. More than __________% of the oxygen in arterial blood is transported bound to hemoglobin. How is the remaining oxygen transported to the cells?
3. Name four factors that influence the amount of oxygen that binds to hemoglobin. Which of these four factors is the most important?
4. Describe the structure of a hemoglobin molecule. What chemical element is essential for hemoglobin synthesis?
5. The networks for control of ventilation are found in the __________ and __________ of the brain. What do the dorsal and ventral respiratory groups of neurons control? What is a central pattern generator?
6. Describe the chemoreceptors that influence ventilation. What chemical is the most important controller of ventilation?
7. Describe the protective reflexes of the respiratory system.
8. What causes the exchange of oxygen and carbon dioxide between alveoli and blood or between blood and cells?
9. List five possible physical changes that could result in less oxygen reaching the arterial blood.

LEVEL TWO REVIEWING CONCEPTS

10. Concept map: Construct a map of gas transport using the following terms. You may add additional terms.

alveoli	hemoglobin saturation
arterial blood	oxyhemoglobin
carbaminohemoglobin	P_{CO_2}
carbonic anhydrase	plasma
chloride shift	P_{O_2}
dissolved CO_2	pressure gradient
dissolved O_2	red blood cell
hemoglobin	venous blood

11. In respiratory physiology, it is customary to talk of the P_{O_2} of the plasma. Why is this not the most accurate way to describe the oxygen content of blood?
12. Compare and contrast the following pairs of concepts:
    (a) transport of O_2 and CO_2 in arterial blood
    (b) partial pressure and concentration of a gas dissolved in a liquid
13. Does HbO_2 binding increase, decrease, or not change with decreased pH?
14. Define hypoxia, COPD, and hypercapnia.
15. Why did oxygen-transporting molecules evolve in animals?
16. Draw and label the following graphs:
    (a) The effect of ventilation on arterial P_{O_2}
    (b) The effect of arterial P_{CO_2} on ventilation
17. As the P_{O_2} of plasma increases:
    (a) what happens to the amount of oxygen that dissolves in plasma?
    (b) what happens to the amount of oxygen that binds to hemoglobin?
18. If a person is anemic and has a lower-than-normal level of hemoglobin in her red blood cells, what is her arterial P_{O_2} compared to normal?
19. Create reflex pathways (stimulus, receptor, afferent path, and so on) for the chemical control of ventilation, starting with the following stimuli:
    (a) Increased arterial P_{CO_2} (b) Arterial P_{O_2} = 55 mm Hg
    Be as specific as possible regarding anatomical locations. Where known, include neurotransmitters and their receptors.

LEVEL THREE PROBLEM SOLVING

20. Marco tries to hide at the bottom of a swimming hole by breathing in and out through two feet of garden hose, which greatly increases his anatomic dead space. What happens to the following parameters in his arterial blood, and why?
    (a) P_{CO_2} (c) bicarbonate ion
    (b) P_{O_2} (d) pH
21. Which person carries more oxygen in his blood?
    (a) one with Hb of 15 g/dL and arterial P_{O_2} of 80 mm Hg
    (b) one with Hb of 12 g/dL and arterial P_{O_2} of 100 mm Hg
22. What would happen to each of the following parameters in a person suffering from pulmonary edema?
    (a) arterial P_{O_2}
    (b) arterial hemoglobin saturation
    (c) alveolar ventilation
23. In early research on the control of rhythmic breathing, scientists made the following observations. What hypotheses might the researchers have formulated from each observation?
    (a) *Observation.* If the brain stem is severed below the medulla, all respiratory movement ceases.
    (b) *Observation.* If the brain stem is severed above the level of the pons, ventilation is normal.
    (c) *Observation.* If the medulla is completely separated from the pons and higher brain centers, ventilation becomes irregular but a pattern of inspiration/expiration remains.
24. A hospitalized patient with severe chronic obstructive lung disease has a P_{CO_2} of 55 mm Hg and a P_{O_2} of 50 mm Hg. To elevate his blood oxygen, he is given pure oxygen through a nasal tube. The patient immediately stops breathing. Explain why this might occur.
25. You are a physiologist on a space flight to a distant planet. You find intelligent humanoid creatures inhabiting the planet, and they willingly submit to your tests. Some of the data you have collected are described below. The first graph below shows the oxygen dissociation curve for the oxygen-carrying molecule in the blood of the humanoid named Bzork. Bzork's normal alveolar P_{O_2} is 85 mm Hg. His normal cell P_{O_2} is 20 mm Hg, but it drops to 10 mm Hg with exercise.

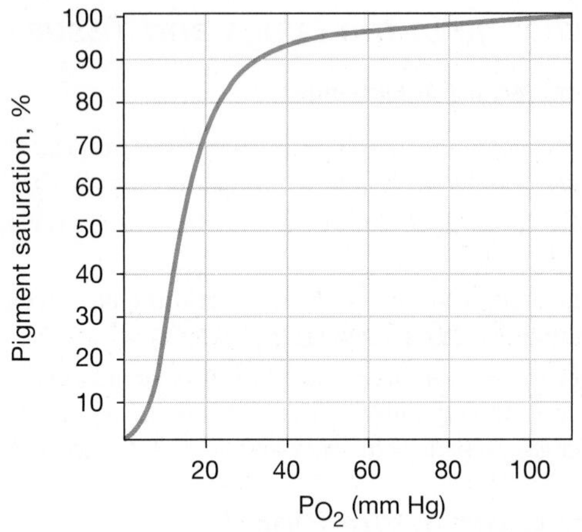

    (a) What is the percent saturation for Bzork's oxygen-carrying molecule in blood at the alveoli? In blood at an exercising cell?
    (b) Based on the graph above, what conclusions can you draw about Bzork's oxygen requirements during normal activity and during exercise?
26. The next experiment on Bzork involves his ventilatory response to different conditions. The data from that experiment are graphed below. Interpret the results of experiments A and C.

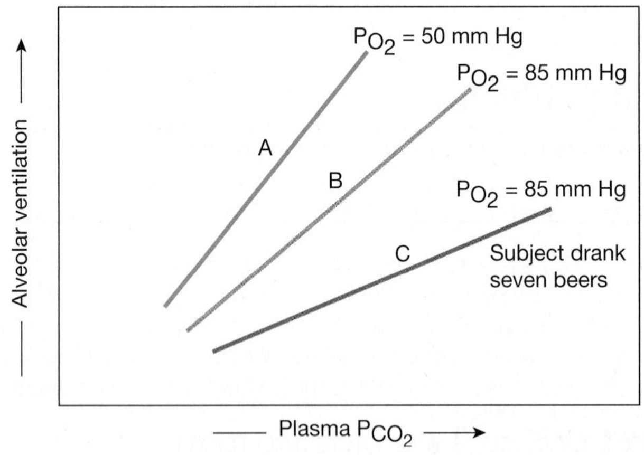

27. The alveolar epithelium is an absorptive epithelium and is able to transport ions from the fluid lining of alveoli into the interstitial space, creating an osmotic gradient for water to follow. Draw an alveolar epithelium and label apical and basolateral surfaces, the airspace, and interstitial fluid. Arrange the following proteins on the cell membrane so that the epithelium absorbs sodium and water: aquaporins, Na^+-K^+-ATPase, epithelial Na^+ channel (ENaC). (Remember: Na^+ concentrations are higher in the ECF than in the ICF).

LEVEL FOUR QUANTITATIVE PROBLEMS

28. You are given the following information on a patient.
    Blood volume = 5.2 liters
    Hematocrit = 47%

Hemoglobin concentration = 12 g/dL whole blood

Total amount of oxygen carried in blood = 1015 mL

Arterial plasma P_{O_2} = 100 mm Hg

You know that at a plasma P_{O_2} of 100 mm Hg, plasma contains 0.3 mL O_2/dL, and that hemoglobin is 98% saturated. Each hemoglobin molecule can bind to a maximum of four molecules of oxygen. Using this information, calculate the maximum oxygen-carrying capacity of hemoglobin (100% saturated). Units will be mL O_2/g Hb.

29. Adolph Fick, the nineteenth-century physiologist who derived Fick's law of diffusion, also developed the Fick equation that relates oxygen consumption, cardiac output, and blood oxygen content:

O_2 consumption = cardiac output × (arterial oxygen content − venous oxygen content)

A person has a cardiac output of 4.5 L/min, an arterial oxygen content of 105 mL O_2/L blood, and a vena cava oxygen content of 50 mL O_2/L blood. What is this person's oxygen consumption?

30. Describe what happens to the oxygen-hemoglobin dissociation curve in Figure 18-9 when blood hemoglobin falls from 15 g/dL blood to 10 g/dL blood.

ANSWERS

Answers to Concept Check Questions

Page 599

1. The other factor that affects how much of each gas dissolves in the saline solution is the solubility of the gas in that solution.
2. 720 mm Hg × 0.78 N_2 = 561.6 mm Hg
3. False. Plasma is essentially water, and Figure 18-2 shows that CO_2 is more soluble in water than O_2.

Page 601

4. (a) electron transport system (b) citric acid cycle
5. The P_{O_2} of the alveoli is constantly being replenished by fresh air. [p. 587]

Page 602

6. Air is 21% oxygen. Therefore, for dry air on Everest, P_{O_2} = 0.21 × 250 mm Hg = 53 mm Hg. Correction for P_{H_2O}: P_{O_2} = (250 mm Hg − 47 mm Hg) × 21% = (203 mm Hg) × 0.21 = 43 mm Hg.

Page 603

7. Blood pools in the lungs because the left heart is unable to pump all the blood coming into it from the lungs. Increased blood volume in the lungs increases pulmonary blood pressure.
8. When alveolar ventilation increases, arterial P_{O_2} increases because more fresh air enters the alveoli. Arterial P_{CO_2} decreases because the low P_{CO_2} of fresh air dilutes alveolar P_{CO_2}. The CO_2 pressure gradient between venous blood and the alveoli increases, causing more CO_2 to leave the blood. Venous P_{O_2} and P_{CO_2} do not change because these pressures are determined by oxygen consumption and CO_2 production in the cells.

Page 609

9. Yes. Hemoglobin reaches 100% saturation at 650 mm Hg. At sea level, atmospheric pressure is 760 mm Hg, and if the "atmosphere" is 100% oxygen, then P_{O_2} is 760 mm Hg.
10. The flatness at the top of the P_{O_2} curve tells you that hyperventilation causes only a minimal increase in percent saturation of arterial Hb.
11. As the P_{O_2} falls, more oxygen is released. The P_{O_2} of venous blood leaving the muscle is 25 mm Hg, same as the P_{O_2} of the muscle.

Page 612

12. An airway obstruction would decrease alveolar ventilation and increase arterial P_{CO_2}. Elevated arterial P_{CO_2} would increase the H^+ concentration in the arterial blood and decrease pH.

Answers to Figure and Graph Questions

Page 604

Fig. 18-6: O_2 crosses five cell membranes: two of the alveolar cell, two of the capillary endothelium, and one of the red blood cell.

Page 607

Fig. 18-9: (a) When P_{O_2} is 20 mm Hg, Hb saturation is 34%. (b) Hemoglobin is 50% saturated with oxygen at a P_{O_2} of 28 mm Hg.

Page 608

Fig. 18-10: (a) When pH falls from 7.4 to 7.2, Hb saturation decreases by 13%, from about 37% saturation to 24%. (b) When an exercising muscle cell warms up, Hb releases more oxygen.

Page 608

Fig. 18-11: Loss of 2,3-DPG is not good because then hemoglobin binds more tightly to oxygen at the P_{O_2} values found in cells.

Page 609

Fig. 18-12: (a) The P_{O_2} of placental blood is about 28 mm Hg. (b) At a P_{O_2} of 10 mm Hg, maternal blood is only about 8% saturated with oxygen.

Page 612

Fig. 18-16: 1. pons; 2. ventral respiratory group; 3. medullary chemoreceptor; 4. sensory neuron; 5. carotid chemoreceptor; 6. somatic motor neuron (expiration); 7. aortic chemoreceptor; 8. internal intercostals; 9. abdominal muscles; 10. diaphragm; 11. external intercostals; 12. scalenes and sternocleidomastoids; 13. somatic motor neuron (inspiration); 14. dorsal respiratory group; 15. limbic system; 16. higher brain centers (emotions and voluntary control)

Page 614

Fig. 18-18: One breath takes 5 seconds, so there are 12 breaths/min.

19

The Kidneys

Resin cast of ball-like glomerular capillaries with arterioles (orange).

BACKGROUND BASICS

Epithelial transport: **154** Mass balance: **133** Osmolarity and tonicity: **159** Filtration in capillaries: **528** Transcytosis: **157** Saturation: **45** Autoregulation of vascular resistance: **523** Transport across membranes: **141** pH and buffers: **38** Transporting epithelium: **77** Fenestrated capillaries: **527** Phosphocreatine: **420** Competition: **149**

Plasma undergoes modification to urine in the nephron.

—Arthur Grollman, in *Clinical Physiology: The Functional Pathology of Disease,* 1957

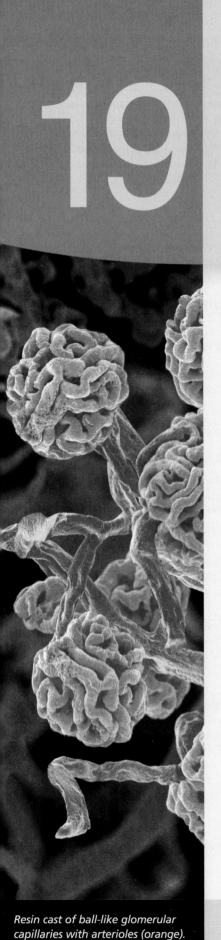

RUNNING PROBLEM

Gout

Michael Moustakakis, 43, had spent the last two days on the sofa, suffering from a relentless throbbing pain in his left big toe. When the pain began, Michael thought he had a mild sprain or perhaps the beginnings of arthritis. Then the pain intensified, and the toe joint became hot and red. Michael finally hobbled into his doctor's office, feeling a little silly about his problem. On hearing his symptoms and looking at the toe, the doctor seemed to know instantly what was wrong. "Looks to me like you have gout," said Dr. Garcia.

623 625 639 640 643 645

About C.E. 100, Aretaeus the Cappadocian wrote, "Diabetes is a wonderful affection, not very frequent among men, being a melting down of the flesh and limbs into urine. . . . The patients never stop making water [urinating], but the flow is incessant, as if from the opening of aqueducts." Physicians have known since ancient times that **urine**, the fluid waste produced by the kidneys, reflects the functioning of the body. To aid them in their diagnosis of illness, they even carried special flasks for the collection and inspection of patients' urine.

The first step in examining a urine sample is to determine its color. Is it dark yellow (concentrated), pale straw (dilute), red (indicating the presence of blood), or black (indicating the presence of hemoglobin metabolites)? One form of malaria was called *blackwater fever* because metabolized hemoglobin from the abnormal breakdown of red blood cells turned victims' urine black or dark red.

Physicians also inspected urine samples for clarity, froth (indicating abnormal presence of proteins), smell, and even taste. Physicians who did not want to taste the urine themselves would allow their students the "privilege" of tasting it for them. A physician without students might expose insects to the urine and study their reaction.

Probably the most famous example of using urine for diagnosis was the taste test for diabetes mellitus, historically known as the *honey-urine disease*. Diabetes is an endocrine disorder characterized by the presence of glucose in the urine. The urine of diabetics tasted sweet and attracted insects, making the diagnosis clear.

Today we have much more sophisticated tests for glucose in the urine, but the first step of a *urinalysis* is still to examine the color, clarity, and odor of the urine. In this chapter you will learn why we can tell so much about how the body is functioning by what is present in the urine.

FUNCTIONS OF THE KIDNEYS

If you ask people on the street, "What is the most important function of the kidney?" they are likely to say, "The removal of wastes." Actually, the most important function of the kidney is the homeostatic regulation of the water and ion content of the blood, also called *salt and water balance* or *fluid and electrolyte balance*. Waste removal is important, but disturbances in blood volume or ion levels cause serious medical problems before the accumulation of metabolic wastes reaches toxic levels.

The kidneys maintain normal blood concentrations of ions and water by balancing intake of those substances with their excretion in the urine, obeying the principle of *mass balance* [p. 133]. We can divide kidney function into six general areas:

1. **Regulation of extracellular fluid volume and blood pressure.** When extracellular fluid volume decreases, blood pressure also decreases [p. 520]. If ECF volume and blood pressure fall too low, the body cannot maintain adequate blood flow to the brain and other essential organs. The kidneys work in an integrated fashion with the cardiovascular system to ensure that blood pressure and tissue perfusion remain within an acceptable range.
2. **Regulation of osmolarity.** The body integrates kidney function with behavioral drives, such as thirst, to maintain blood osmolarity at a value close to 290 mOsM. We examine the reflex pathways for regulation of ECF volume and osmolarity in Chapter 20.
3. **Maintenance of ion balance.** The kidneys keep concentrations of key ions within a normal range by balancing dietary intake with urinary loss. Sodium (Na^+) is the major ion involved in the regulation of extracellular fluid volume and osmolarity. Potassium (K^+) and calcium (Ca^{2+}) concentrations are also closely regulated. We discuss renal control of sodium and potassium balance in Chapter 20 but defer the discussion of calcium until Chapter 22, when we look at all aspects of calcium homeostasis.
4. **Homeostatic regulation of pH.** The pH of plasma is normally kept within a narrow range [p. 38]. If extracellular fluid becomes too acidic, the kidneys remove H^+ and conserve bicarbonate ions (HCO_3^-), which act as a buffer [p. 39]. Conversely, when extracellular fluid becomes too alkaline, the kidneys remove HCO_3^- and conserve H^+. The kidneys play a significant role in pH homeostasis, but they do not correct pH disturbances as rapidly as the lungs do, as you will learn in Chapter 20.
5. **Excretion of wastes.** The kidneys remove metabolic waste products and foreign substances, such as drugs and environmental toxins. Metabolic wastes include creatinine from muscle metabolism [p. 420] and the nitrogenous wastes *urea* [p. 115] and *uric acid*. A metabolite of hemoglobin called *urobilinogen* gives urine its characteristic yellow color. Hormones are another endogenous substance

the kidneys clear from the blood. Examples of foreign substances that the kidneys actively remove include the artificial sweetener *saccharin* and the anion *benzoate,* part of the preservative *potassium benzoate,* which you ingest each time you drink a diet soft drink.

6. **Production of hormones.** Although the kidneys are not endocrine glands, they play important roles in three endocrine pathways. Kidney cells synthesize *erythropoietin,* the cytokine/hormone that regulates red blood cell synthesis [p. 552]. They also release *renin,* an enzyme that regulates the production of hormones involved in sodium balance and blood pressure homeostasis. Renal enzymes help convert vitamin D3 into a hormone that regulates Ca^{2+} balance.

The kidneys, like many other organs in the body, have a tremendous reserve capacity. By most estimates, you must lose nearly three-fourths of your kidney function before homeostasis begins to be affected. Many people function perfectly normally with only one kidney, including the one person in 1000 born with only one kidney (the other fails to develop during gestation) or those people who donate a kidney for transplantation.

CLINICAL FOCUS

URINARY TRACT INFECTIONS

Because of the shorter length of the female urethra and its proximity to bacteria leaving the large intestine, women are more prone than men to develop bacterial infections of the bladder and kidneys, or **urinary tract infections** (UTIs). The most common cause of UTIs is the bacterium *Escherichia coli*, a normal inhabitant of the human large intestine. *E. coli* is not harmful while restricted to the lumen of the large intestine, but it is pathogenic [*patho-*, disease + *-genic*, causing] if it gets into the urethra. The most common symptoms of a UTI are pain or burning during urination and increased frequency of urination. A urine sample from a patient with a UTI often contains many red and white blood cells, neither of which is commonly found in normal urine. UTIs are treated with antibiotics.

CONCEPT CHECK

1. Ion regulation is a key feature of kidney function. What happens to the resting membrane potential of a neuron if extracellular K^+ levels decrease? [p. 272]
2. What happens to the force of cardiac contraction if plasma Ca^{2+} levels decrease substantially? [p. 482]

Answers: p. 648

ANATOMY OF THE URINARY SYSTEM

The **urinary system** is composed of the kidneys and accessory structures (Fig. 19-1a ●). The study of kidney function is called **renal physiology**, from the Latin word *renes,* meaning "kidneys."

The Urinary System Consists of Kidneys, Ureters, Bladder, and Urethra

Let's begin by following the route a drop of water takes on its way from plasma to excretion in the urine. In the first step of urine production, water and solutes move from plasma into the hollow tubules (*nephrons*) that make up the bulk of the paired **kidneys.** These tubules modify the composition of the fluid as it passes through. The modified fluid leaves the kidney and passes into a hollow tube called a **ureter.** There are two ureters, one leading from each kidney to the **urinary bladder.** The bladder expands and fills with urine until, by reflex action, it contracts and expels urine through a single tube, the **urethra.**

The urethra in males exits the body through the shaft of the penis. In females, the urethral opening is found anterior to the openings of the vagina and anus. *Micturition,* or urination, is the process by which urine is excreted.

The kidneys are the site of urine formation. They lie on either side of the spine at the level of the eleventh and twelfth ribs, just above the waist (Fig. 19-1b). Although they are below the diaphragm, they are technically outside the abdominal cavity, sandwiched between the membranous **peritoneum**, which lines the abdomen, and the bones and muscles of the back. Because of their location behind the peritoneal cavity, the kidneys are sometimes described as being *retroperitoneal* [*retro-,* behind].

The concave surface of each kidney faces the spine. The renal blood vessels, nerves, lymphatics, and ureters all emerge from this surface. **Renal arteries**, which branch off the abdominal aorta, supply blood to the kidneys. **Renal veins** carry blood from the kidneys to the inferior vena cava.

At any given time, the kidneys receive 20–25% of the cardiac output, even though they constitute only 0.4% of total body weight (4.5–6 ounces each). This high rate of blood flow through the kidneys is critical to renal function.

The Nephron Is the Functional Unit of the Kidney

A cross section through a kidney shows that the interior is arranged in two layers: an outer **cortex** and inner **medulla** (Fig. 19-1c). The layers are formed by the organized arrangement of microscopic tubules called **nephrons.** About 80% of the nephrons in a kidney are almost completely contained within the cortex (*cortical* nephrons), but the other 20%—called *juxtamedullary* nephrons [*juxta-,* beside]—dip down into the medulla (Fig. 19-1i, h).

The nephron is the functional unit of the kidney. (A *functional unit* is the smallest structure that can perform all the functions of an organ.) Each of the 1 million nephrons in a kidney is divided into sections (Fig. 19-1j), and each section is closely associated with specialized blood vessels (Fig. 19-1g, h).

Vascular Elements of the Kidney Blood enters the kidney through the renal artery before flowing into smaller arteries and then into arterioles in the cortex (Fig. 19-1d, e). At this point, the arrangement of blood vessels turns into a portal system, one of three in the body [p. 232]. Blood flows from the **afferent arteriole** into a ball-like network of capillaries known as the **glomerulus** [*glomus*, a ball-shaped mass; plural *glomeruli*] (Fig. 19-1f).

Blood leaving the glomerulus flows into an **efferent arteriole**, then into a second set of capillaries, the **peritubular capillaries** [*peri-*, around] that surround the tubule (Fig. 19-1g). In juxtamedullary nephrons, the long peritubular capillaries that dip into the medulla are called the **vasa recta** (Fig. 19-1h). Finally, renal capillaries join to form venules and small veins, conducting blood out of the kidney through the renal vein.

The function of the renal portal system is first to filter fluid out of the blood and into the lumen of the nephron at the glomerular capillaries, then to *reabsorb* fluid from the tubule back into the blood at the peritubular capillaries. The forces behind fluid movement in the renal portal system are similar to those that govern filtration of water and molecules out of systemic capillaries in other tissues.

CONCEPT CHECK

3. If net filtration out of glomerular capillaries occurs, then you know that capillary hydrostatic pressure must be (*greater than/less than/equal to*) capillary colloid osmotic pressure. [p. 528]
4. If net reabsorption into peritubular capillaries occurs, then capillary hydrostatic pressure must be (*greater than/less than/equal to*) the capillary colloid osmotic pressure. Answers: p. 648

Tubular Elements of the Kidney The nephron begins with a hollow, ball-like structure called **Bowman's capsule** that surrounds the glomerulus (Fig. 19-1j). The endothelium of the glomerulus is fused to the epithelium of Bowman's capsule so that fluid filtering out of the capillaries passes directly into the lumen of the tubule. The combination of glomerulus and Bowman's capsule is called the **renal corpuscle.**

From Bowman's capsule, filtered fluid flows into the **proximal tubule** [*proximal*, close or near], then into the **loop of Henle**, a hairpin-shaped segment that dips down toward the medulla and then back up. The loop of Henle is divided into two limbs, a thin **descending limb** and an **ascending limb** with thin and thick segments. The fluid then passes into the **distal tubule** [*distal*, distant or far]. The distal tubules of up to eight nephrons drain into a single larger tube called the **collecting duct.** (The distal tubule and its collecting duct together form the **distal nephron.**) Collecting ducts pass from the cortex through the medulla and drain into the **renal pelvis** (Fig. 19-1c). From the renal pelvis, the filtered and modified fluid, now called **urine,** flows into the ureter on its way to excretion.

Notice in Figure 19-1g how the nephron twists and folds back on itself so that the final part of the ascending limb of the loop of Henle passes between the afferent and efferent arterioles. This region is known as the **juxtaglomerular apparatus.** The proximity of the ascending limb and the arterioles allows paracrine communication between the two structures, a key feature of kidney autoregulation. Because the twisted configuration of the nephron makes it difficult to follow fluid flow, we unfold the nephron in many of the remaining figures in this chapter so that fluid flows from left to right across the figure, as in Figure 19-1j.

OVERVIEW OF KIDNEY FUNCTION

Imagine drinking a 12-ounce soft drink every three minutes around the clock: by the end of 24 hours, you would have consumed the equivalent of 90 two-liter bottles. The thought of putting 180 liters of liquid into your intestinal tract is staggering, but that is how much plasma moves into the nephrons every day! But because the average volume of urine leaving the kidneys is only 1.5 L/day, more than 99% of the fluid that enters nephrons must find its way back into the blood, or the body would rapidly dehydrate.

Kidneys Filter, Reabsorb, and Secrete

Three basic processes take place in the nephron: filtration, reabsorption, and secretion (Fig. 19-2). **Filtration** is the movement of fluid from blood into the lumen of the nephron. Filtration takes place only in the renal corpuscle, where the walls of glomerular capillaries and Bowman's capsule are modified to allow bulk flow of fluid.

RUNNING PROBLEM

Gout is a metabolic disease characterized by high blood concentrations of uric acid (*hyperuricemia*). If uric acid concentrations reach a critical level (7.5–8 mg/dL), monosodium urate precipitates out of solution and forms crystals in peripheral joints, particularly in the feet, ankles, and knees. These crystals trigger an inflammatory reaction and cause periodic attacks of excruciating pain. Uric acid crystals may also form kidney stones in the renal pelvis.

Question 1:
Trace the route followed by these kidney stones when they are excreted.

Question 2:
Name the anion formed when uric acid dissociates.

623 625 639 640 643 645

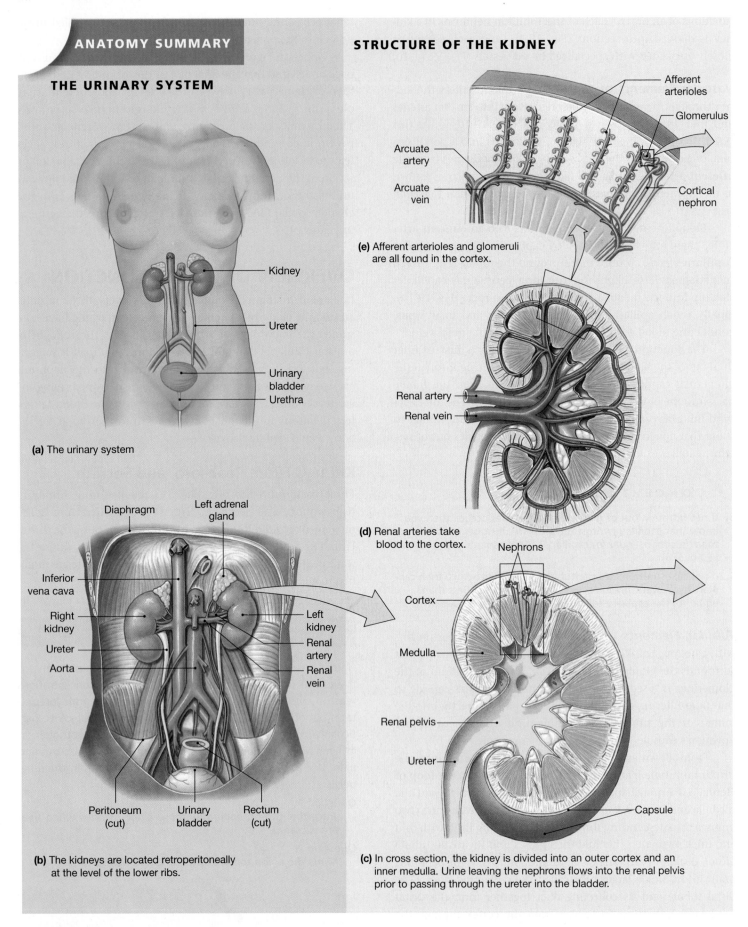

ANATOMY SUMMARY

THE URINARY SYSTEM

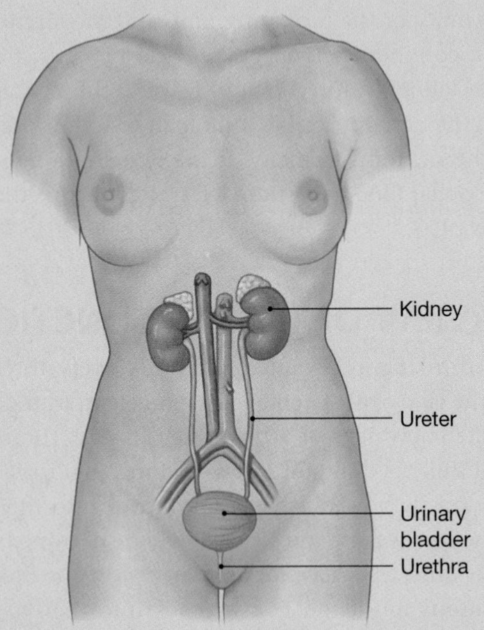
Kidney
Ureter
Urinary bladder
Urethra

(a) The urinary system

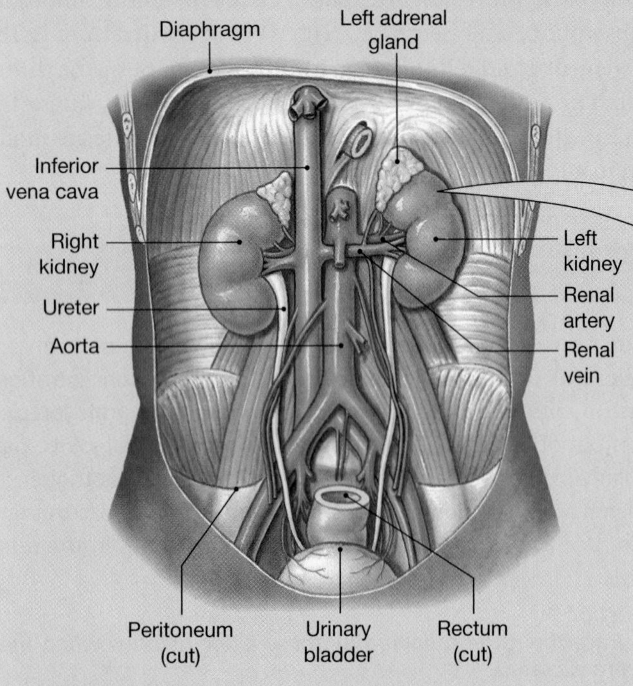
Diaphragm
Left adrenal gland
Inferior vena cava
Right kidney
Ureter
Aorta
Left kidney
Renal artery
Renal vein
Peritoneum (cut)
Urinary bladder
Rectum (cut)

(b) The kidneys are located retroperitoneally at the level of the lower ribs.

STRUCTURE OF THE KIDNEY

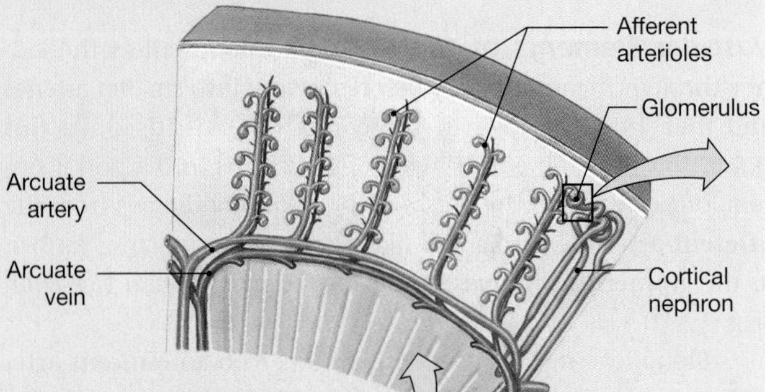
Afferent arterioles
Glomerulus
Arcuate artery
Arcuate vein
Cortical nephron

(e) Afferent arterioles and glomeruli are all found in the cortex.

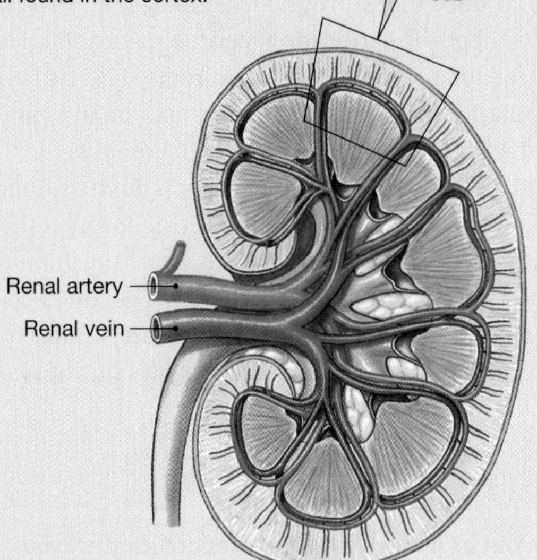
Renal artery
Renal vein

(d) Renal arteries take blood to the cortex.

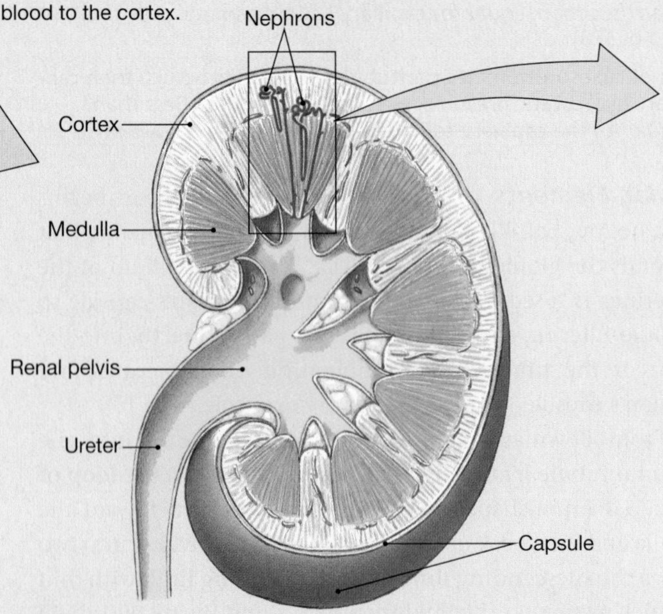
Nephrons
Cortex
Medulla
Renal pelvis
Ureter
Capsule

(c) In cross section, the kidney is divided into an outer cortex and an inner medulla. Urine leaving the nephrons flows into the renal pelvis prior to passing through the ureter into the bladder.

FIGURE 19-1

STRUCTURE OF THE NEPHRON

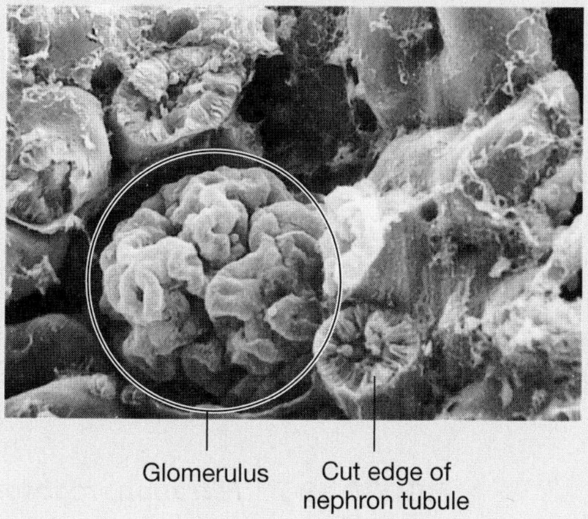
Glomerulus
Cut edge of nephron tubule

(f) The capillaries of the glomerulus form a ball-like mass.

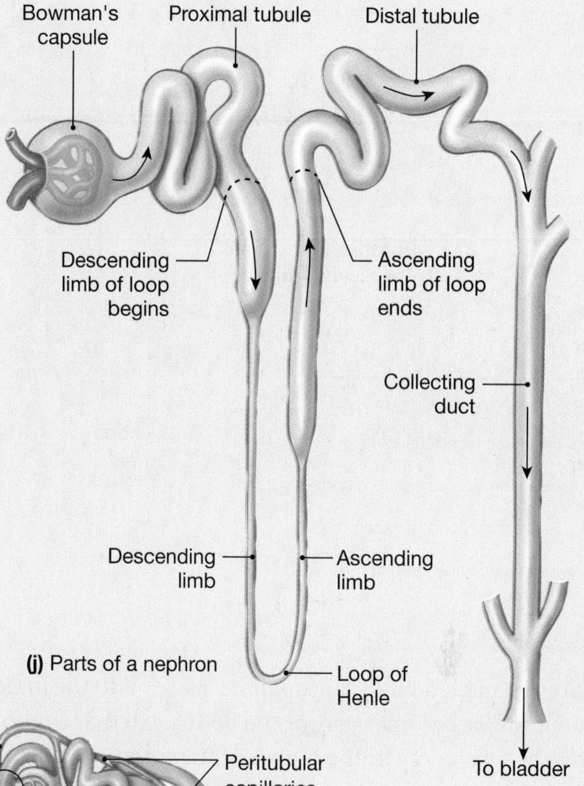
Bowman's capsule
Proximal tubule
Distal tubule
Descending limb of loop begins
Ascending limb of loop ends
Collecting duct
Descending limb
Ascending limb
Loop of Henle
To bladder

(j) Parts of a nephron

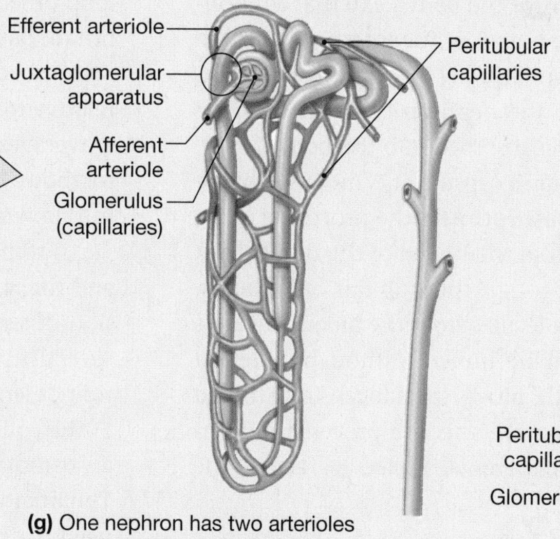
Efferent arteriole
Juxtaglomerular apparatus
Afferent arteriole
Glomerulus (capillaries)
Peritubular capillaries

(g) One nephron has two arterioles and two sets of capillaries.

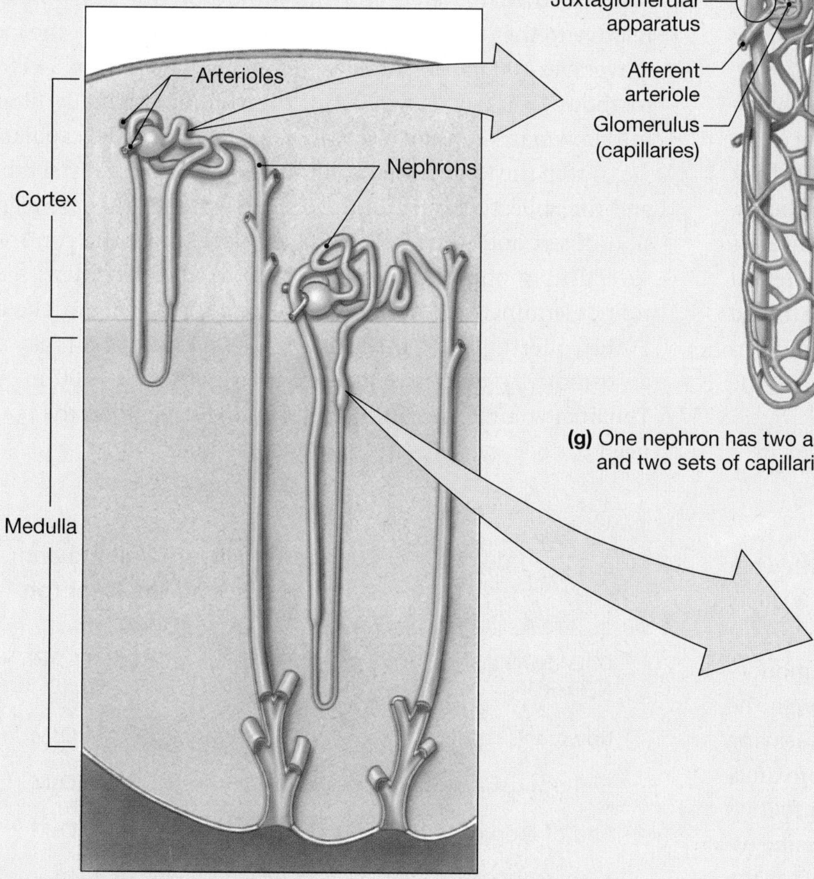
Arterioles
Nephrons
Cortex
Medulla

(i) Some nephrons dip deep into the medulla.

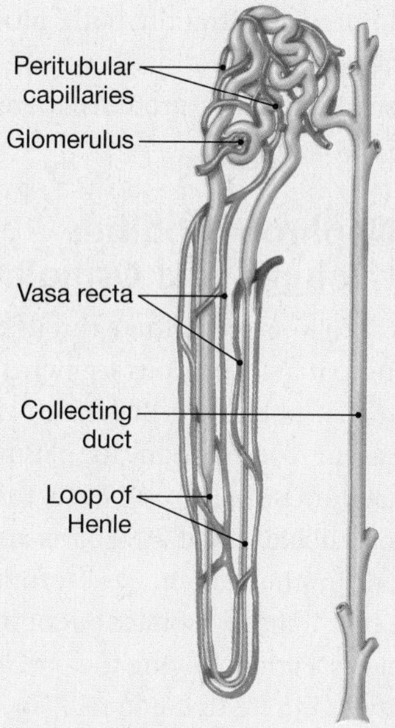
Peritubular capillaries
Glomerulus
Vasa recta
Collecting duct
Loop of Henle

(h) Juxtamedullary nephron with vasa recta

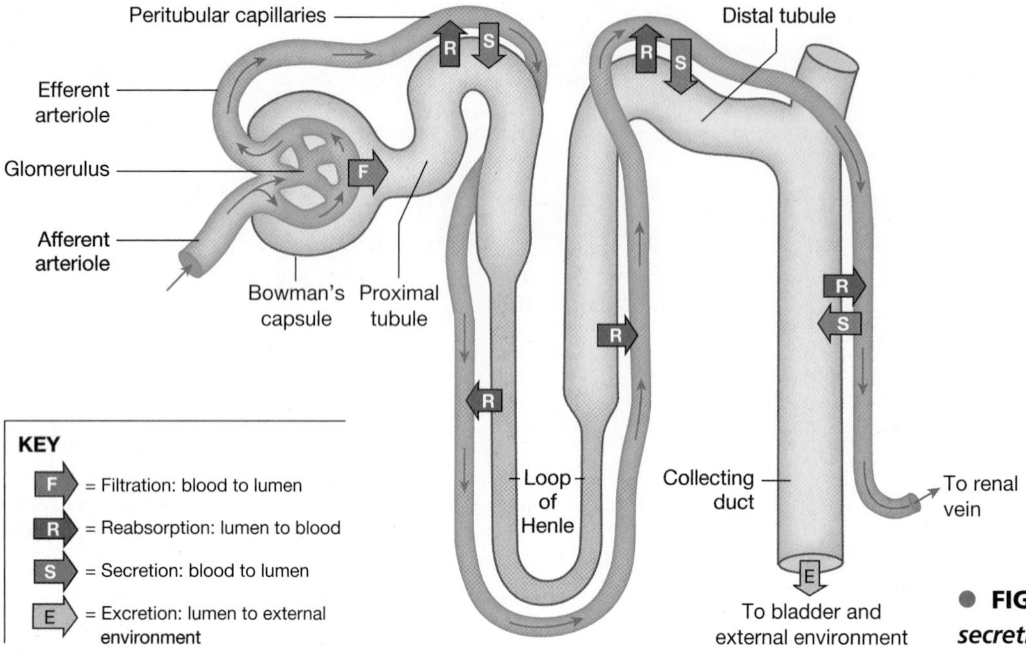
Peritubular capillaries
Distal tubule
Efferent arteriole
Glomerulus
Afferent arteriole
Bowman's capsule
Proximal tubule
Loop of Henle
Collecting duct
To renal vein
To bladder and external environment
KEY
F = Filtration: blood to lumen
R = Reabsorption: lumen to blood
S = Secretion: blood to lumen
E = Excretion: lumen to external environment

● **FIGURE 19-2** ***Filtration, reabsorption, secretion, and excretion***

Once the filtered fluid, called *filtrate*, passes into the lumen of the nephron, it becomes part of the body's external environment, just as substances in the lumen of the intestinal tract are part of the external environment [Fig. 1-2, p. 3]. For this reason, anything that filters into the nephron is destined for removal in the urine unless it is reabsorbed into the body.

After filtrate leaves Bowman's capsule, it is modified by reabsorption and secretion. **Reabsorption** is the process of moving substances in the filtrate from the lumen of the tubule back into the blood flowing through peritubular capillaries. **Secretion** removes selected molecules from the blood and adds them to the filtrate in the tubule lumen. Although secretion and glomerular filtration both move substances from blood into the tubule, secretion is a more selective process that usually uses membrane proteins to move molecules across the tubule epithelium.

The Nephron Modifies Fluid Volume and Osmolarity

Now let's follow some filtrate through the nephron to learn what happens to it in the various segments (Tbl. 19-1 ●). The 180 liters of fluid that filters into Bowman's capsule each day are almost identical in composition to plasma and nearly isosmotic—about 300 mOsM [p. 159]. As this filtrate flows through the proximal tubule, about 70% of its volume is reabsorbed, leaving 54 liters in the lumen. Reabsorption occurs when proximal tubule cells transport solutes out of the lumen, and water follows by osmosis. Filtrate leaving the proximal tubule has the same osmolarity as filtrate that entered. For this reason, we say that the primary function of the proximal tubule is the *bulk reabsorption of isosmotic fluid.*

After leaving the proximal tubule, filtrate passes into the loop of Henle, the primary site for creating dilute urine. As the filtrate passes through the loop, proportionately more solute is reabsorbed than water, and the filtrate becomes hyposmotic relative to the plasma. By the time filtrate flows out of the loop, it averages 100 mOsM, and its volume has fallen from 54 L/day to about 18 L/day. Now 90% of the volume originally filtered into Bowman's capsule has been reabsorbed into the capillaries.

From the loop of Henle, filtrate passes into the distal tubule and the collecting duct. In these two segments, the fine regulation of salt and water balance takes place under the control of several hormones. Reabsorption and (to a lesser extent) secretion determine the final composition of the filtrate. By the end of the collecting duct, the filtrate has a volume of 1.5 L/day and an osmolarity that can range from 50 mOsM to 1200 mOsM. The final volume and osmolarity of urine depend on the body's need to conserve or excrete water and solute.

Table 19-1 Changes in Filtrate Volume and Osmolarity Along the Nephron

LOCATION IN NEPHRON	VOLUME OF FLUID	OSMOLARITY OF FLUID
Bowman's capsule	180 L/day	300 mOsM
End of proximal tubule	54 L/day	300 mOsM
End of loop of Henle	18 L/day	100 mOsM
End of collecting duct (final urine)	1.5 L/day (average)	50–1200 mOsM

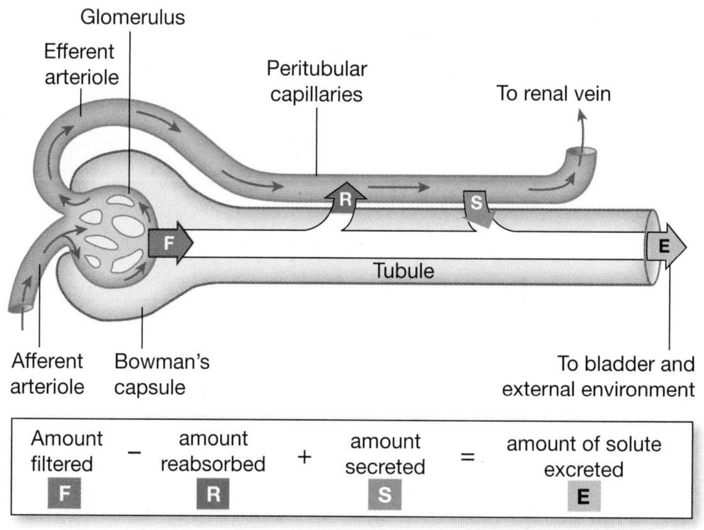

● **FIGURE 19-3** ***The urinary excretion of a substance depends on its filtration, reabsorption, and secretion.***

A word of caution here: it is very easy to confuse *secretion* with *excretion*. Try to remember the origins of the two prefixes. *Se-* means *apart,* as in to separate something from its source. In the nephron, secreted solutes are moved from plasma to tubule lumen. *Ex-* means *out,* or *away,* as in out of or away from the body. Excretion refers to the removal of a substance from the body. Besides the kidneys, other organs that carry out excretory processes include the lungs (CO_2) and intestines (undigested food, bilirubin).

Figure 19-2 summarizes filtration, reabsorption, secretion, and excretion. Filtration takes place in the renal corpuscle as fluid moves from the capillaries of the glomerulus into Bowman's capsule. Reabsorption and secretion occur along the remainder of the tubule, transferring materials between the lumen and the peritubular capillaries. The quantity and composition of the substances being reabsorbed and secreted vary in different segments of the nephron. Filtrate that remains in the lumen at the end of the nephron is excreted as urine.

The amount of any substance excreted in the urine reflects how that substance was handled during its passage through the nephron (Fig. 19-3 ●). The amount excreted is equal to the amount filtered into the tubule, minus the amount reabsorbed into the blood, plus the amount secreted into the tubule lumen:

$$\text{Amount excreted} = \text{amount filtered} - \text{amount reabsorbed} + \text{amount secreted}$$

This equation is a useful way to think about renal handling of solutes. In the following sections, we look in more detail at the important processes of filtration, reabsorption, secretion, and excretion.

CONCEPT CHECK

5. Name one way in which filtration and secretion are alike. Name one way in which they differ.
6. A water molecule enters the renal corpuscle from the blood and ends up in the urine. Name all the anatomical structures that the molecule passes through on its trip to the outside world.
7. What would happen to the body if filtration continued at a normal rate but reabsorption dropped to half the normal rate?

Answers: p. 649

FILTRATION

The filtration of plasma into the kidney tubule is the first step in urine formation. This relatively nonspecific process creates a filtrate whose composition is like that of plasma minus most of the plasma proteins. Under normal conditions, blood cells remain in the capillary, so that the filtrate is composed only of water and dissolved solutes.

When you visualize plasma filtering out of the glomerular capillaries, it is easy to imagine that all the plasma in the capillary moves into Bowman's capsule. However, filtration of all the plasma would leave behind a sludge of blood cells and proteins that could not flow out of the glomerulus. Instead, only about one-fifth of the plasma that flows through the kidneys filters into the nephrons. The remaining four-fifths of the plasma, along with most plasma proteins and blood cells, flows into the peritubular capillaries (Fig. 19-4 ●). The percentage of total plasma volume that filters into the tubule is called the **filtration fraction.**

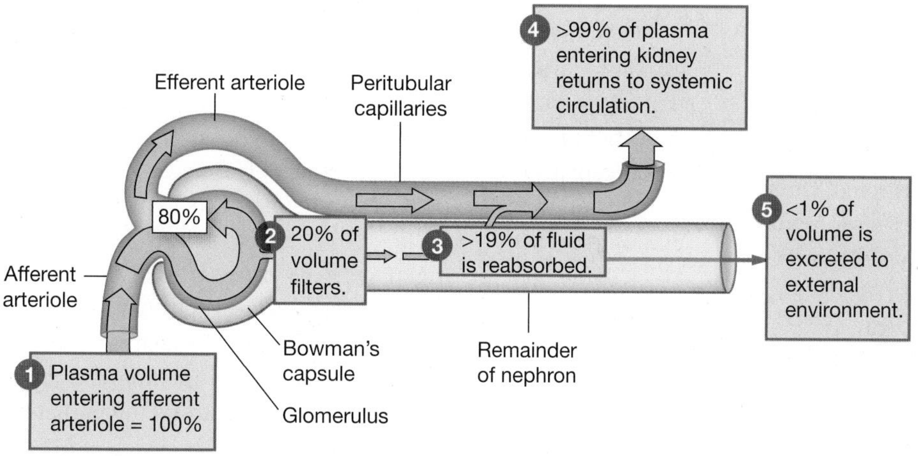

● **FIGURE 19-4** ***The filtration fraction.*** Only 20% of the plasma that passes through the glomerulus is filtered. Less than 1% of filtered fluid is eventually excreted.

19

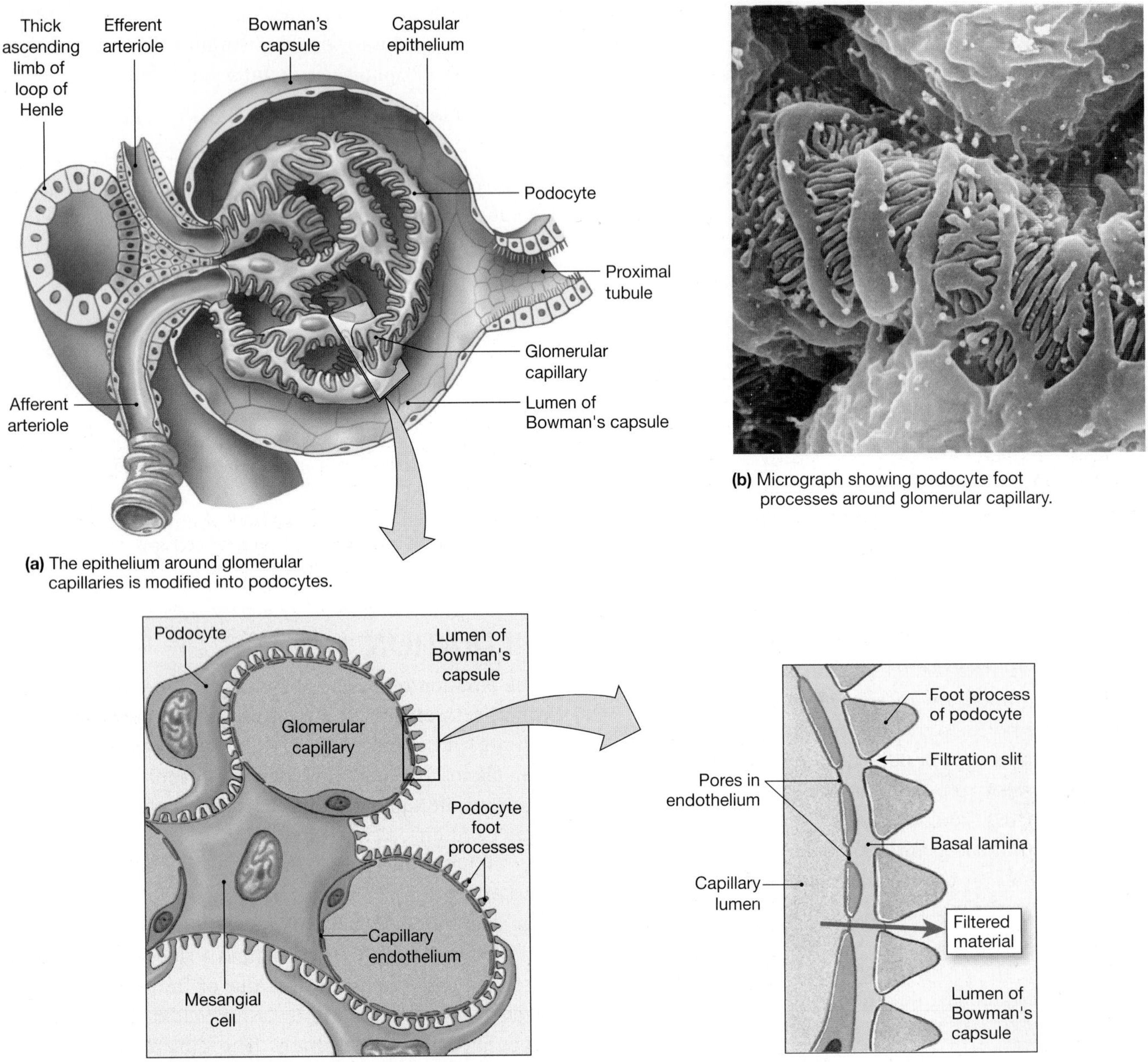

(a) The epithelium around glomerular capillaries is modified into podocytes.

(b) Micrograph showing podocyte foot processes around glomerular capillary.

(c) Podocyte foot processes surround each capillary, leaving slits through which filtration takes place.

(d) Filtered substances pass through endothelial pores and filtration slits.

● **FIGURE 19-5** ***The renal corpuscle.*** The glomerular capillary endothelium, basal lamina, and Bowman's capsule epithelium create a three-layer filtration barrier.

The Renal Corpuscle Contains Filtration Barriers

Filtration takes place in the renal corpuscle (Fig. 19-5 ●), which consists of the glomerular capillaries surrounded by Bowman's capsule. Substances leaving the plasma must pass through three *filtration barriers* before entering the tubule lumen: the glomerular capillary endothelium, a basal lamina (basement membrane), and the epithelium of Bowman's capsule (Fig. 19-5d). The details of how these filtration barriers function are still under investigation.

The first barrier is the capillary endothelium. Glomerular capillaries are *fenestrated capillaries* [p. 527] with large pores that allow most components of the plasma to filter through the endothelium. The pores are small enough, however, to prevent blood cells from leaving the capillary. The negatively charged proteins on the pore surfaces also help repel negatively charged plasma proteins.

Glomerular **mesangial cells** lie between and around the glomerular capillaries (Fig. 19-5c). Mesangial cells have cytoplasmic bundles of actin-like filaments that enable them to contract and alter blood flow through the capillaries. In addition, mesangial cells secrete cytokines associated with immune and inflammatory processes. Disruptions of mesangial cell function have been linked to several disease processes in the kidney.

The second filtration barrier is the **basal lamina**, an acellular layer of extracellular matrix that separates the capillary endothelium from the epithelial lining of Bowman's capsule (Fig. 19-5d). The basal lamina consists of negatively charged glycoproteins, collagen, and other proteins. The lamina acts like a coarse sieve, excluding most plasma proteins from the fluid that filters through it.

The third filtration barrier is the epithelium of Bowman's capsule. The portion of the capsule epithelium that surrounds each glomerular capillary consists of specialized cells called **podocytes** [*podos*, foot] (Fig. 19-5c). Podocytes have long cytoplasmic extensions called **foot processes** that extend from the main cell body (Fig. 19-5a, b). These processes wrap around the glomerular capillaries and interlace with one another, leaving narrow **filtration slits** closed by a semiporous membrane. The filtration slit membrane contains several unique proteins, including *nephrin* and *podocin*. These proteins were discovered by investigators looking for the gene mutations responsible for two congenital kidney diseases. In these diseases, where nephrin or podocin are absent or abnormal, proteins leak across the glomerular filtration barrier into the urine.

Capillary Pressure Causes Filtration

What drives filtration across the walls of the glomerular capillaries? The process is similar in many ways to filtration of fluid out of systemic capillaries [p. 528] and is influenced by these three pressures:

1. The *hydrostatic pressure* (P_H) of blood flowing through the glomerular capillaries forces fluid through the leaky endothelium. Capillary blood pressure averages 55 mm Hg and favors filtration into Bowman's capsule. Although pressure declines along the length of the capillaries, it remains higher than the opposing pressures. Consequently, filtration takes place along nearly the entire length of the glomerular capillaries.
2. The *colloid osmotic pressure* (π) inside glomerular capillaries is higher than that of the fluid in Bowman's capsule. This pressure gradient is due to the presence of proteins in the plasma. The osmotic pressure gradient averages 30 mm Hg and favors fluid movement back into the capillaries.
3. Bowman's capsule is an enclosed space (unlike the interstitial fluid), and so the presence of fluid in the capsule creates a hydrostatic *fluid pressure* (P_{fluid}) that opposes fluid movement into the capsule. Fluid filtering out of the capillaries must displace the fluid already in the capsule lumen. Hydrostatic fluid pressure in the capsule averages 15 mm Hg, opposing filtration.

The three pressures—capillary blood pressure, capillary colloid osmotic pressure, and capsule fluid pressure—that influence glomerular filtration are summarized in Figure 19-6 ●. The

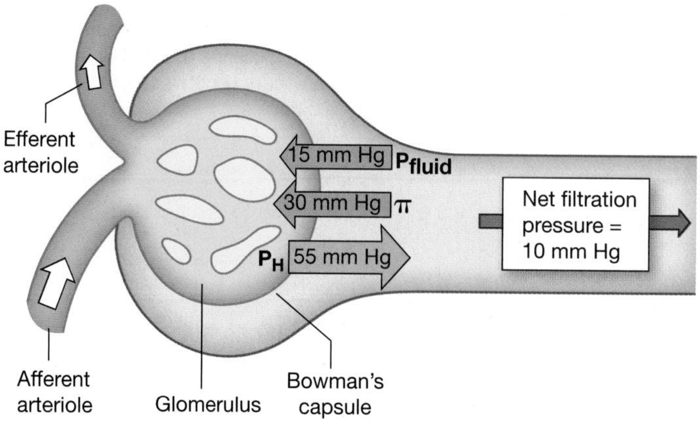

P_H	−	π	−	P_{fluid}	= net filtration pressure
55	−	30	−	15	= 10mm Hg

KEY

P_H = Hydrostatic pressure (blood pressure)
π = Colloid osmotic pressure gradient due to proteins in plasma but not in Bowman's capsule
P_{fluid} = Fluid pressure created by fluid in Bowman's capsule

● **FIGURE 19-6** ***Filtration pressure in the renal corpuscle depends on hydrostatic pressure, and is opposed by colloid osmotic pressure and capsule fluid pressure.***

EMERGING CONCEPTS

DIABETES

DIABETIC NEPHROPATHY

End-stage renal failure, in which kidney function has deteriorated beyond recovery, is a life-threatening complication in 30–40% of people with type 1 diabetes and in 10–20% of those with type 2 diabetes. As with many other complications of diabetes, the exact causes of renal failure are not clear. Diabetic nephropathy usually begins with an increase in glomerular filtration. This is followed by the appearance of proteins in the urine (*proteinuria*), an indication that the normal filtration barrier has been altered. In later stages, filtration rates decline. This stage is associated with thickening of the glomerular basal lamina and changes in both podocytes and mesangial cells. Abnormal proliferation of mesangial cells compresses the glomerular capillaries and impedes blood flow, contributing to the decrease in glomerular filtration. At this point, patients must have their kidney function supplemented by dialysis, and eventually they may need a kidney transplant.

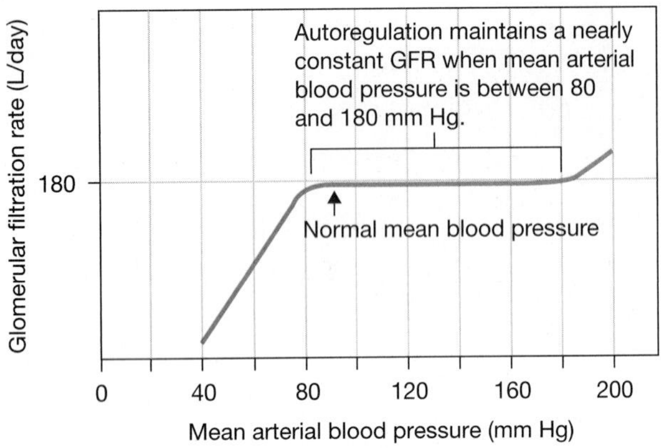

● **FIGURE 19-7** ***Autoregulation of glomerular filtration rate takes place over a wide range of blood pressures.***

net driving force is 10 mm Hg in the direction favoring filtration. Although this pressure may not seem very high, when combined with the very leaky nature of the fenestrated capillaries, it results in rapid fluid filtration into the tubules.

The volume of fluid that filters into Bowman's capsule per unit time is the **glomerular filtration rate (GFR).** Average GFR is 125 mL/min, or 180 L/day, an incredible rate considering that total plasma volume is only about 3 liters. This rate means that the kidneys filter the entire plasma volume 60 times a day, or 2.5 times every hour. If most of the filtrate were not reabsorbed during its passage through the nephron, we would run out of plasma in only 24 minutes of filtration!

GFR is influenced by two factors: the net filtration pressure just described and the filtration coefficient. Filtration pressure is determined primarily by renal blood flow and blood pressure. The **filtration coefficient** has two components: the surface area of the glomerular capillaries available for filtration and the permeability of interface between the capillary and Bowman's capsule. In this respect, glomerular filtration is similar to gas exchange at the alveoli, where the rate of gas exchange depends on partial pressure differences, the surface area of the alveoli, and the permeability of the alveolar membrane.

GFR Is Relatively Constant

Blood pressure provides the hydrostatic pressure that drives glomerular filtration. Therefore, it might seem reasonable to assume that if blood pressure increased, GFR would increase, and if blood pressure fell, GFR would decrease. That is not usually the case, however. Instead, GFR is remarkably constant over a wide range of blood pressures. As long as mean arterial blood pressure remains between 80 mm Hg and 180 mm Hg, GFR averages 180 L/day (Fig. 19-7 ●).

GFR is controlled primarily by regulation of blood flow through the renal arterioles (Fig. 19-8 ●). If the overall resistance

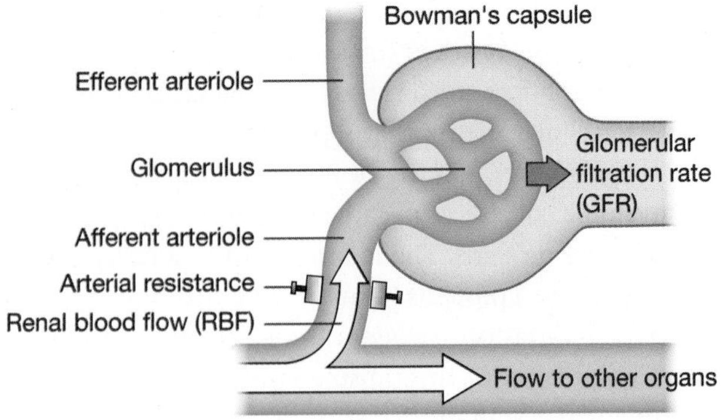

(a) Renal blood flow and GFR change if resistance in the arterioles changes.

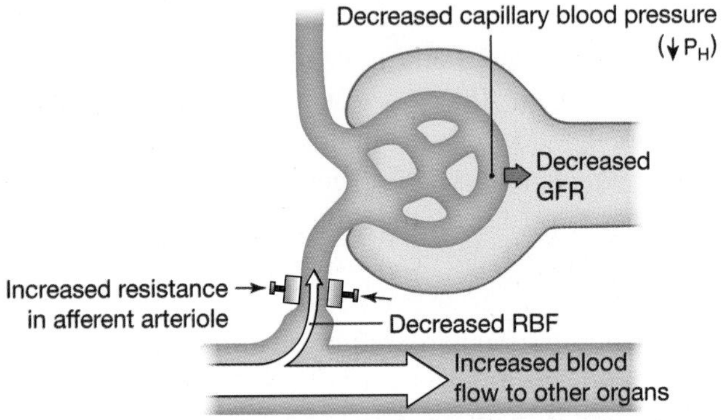

(b) Vasoconstriction of the afferent arteriole increases resistance and decreases renal blood flow, capillary blood pressure (P_H), and GFR.

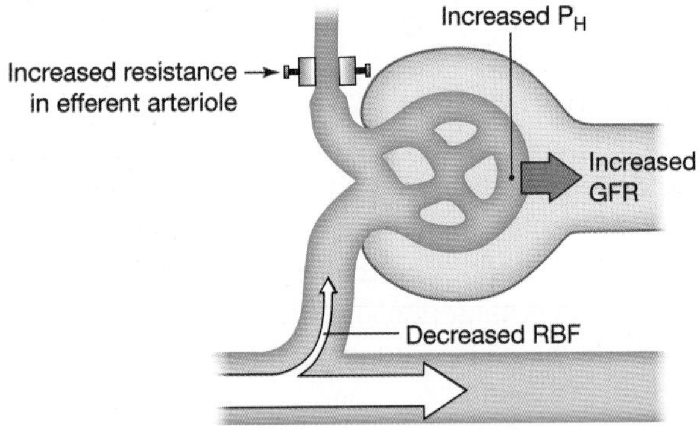

(c) Increased resistance of efferent arteriole decreases renal blood flow but increases P_H and GFR.

FIGURE QUESTION

What happens to capillary blood pressure, GFR, and RBF when the afferent arteriole dilates?

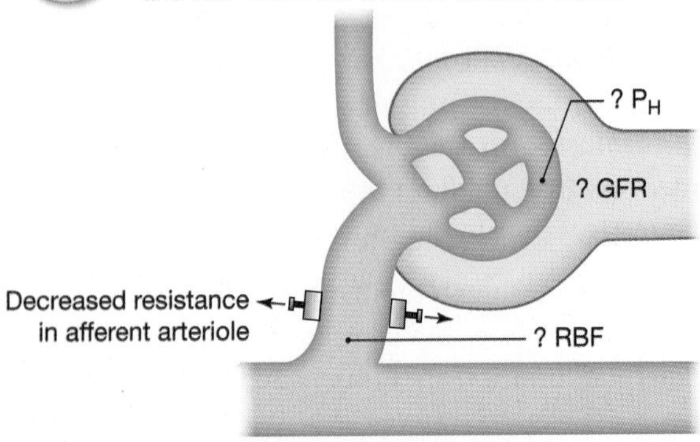

● **FIGURE 19-8** ***Resistance changes in renal arterioles alter renal blood flow and GFR.***

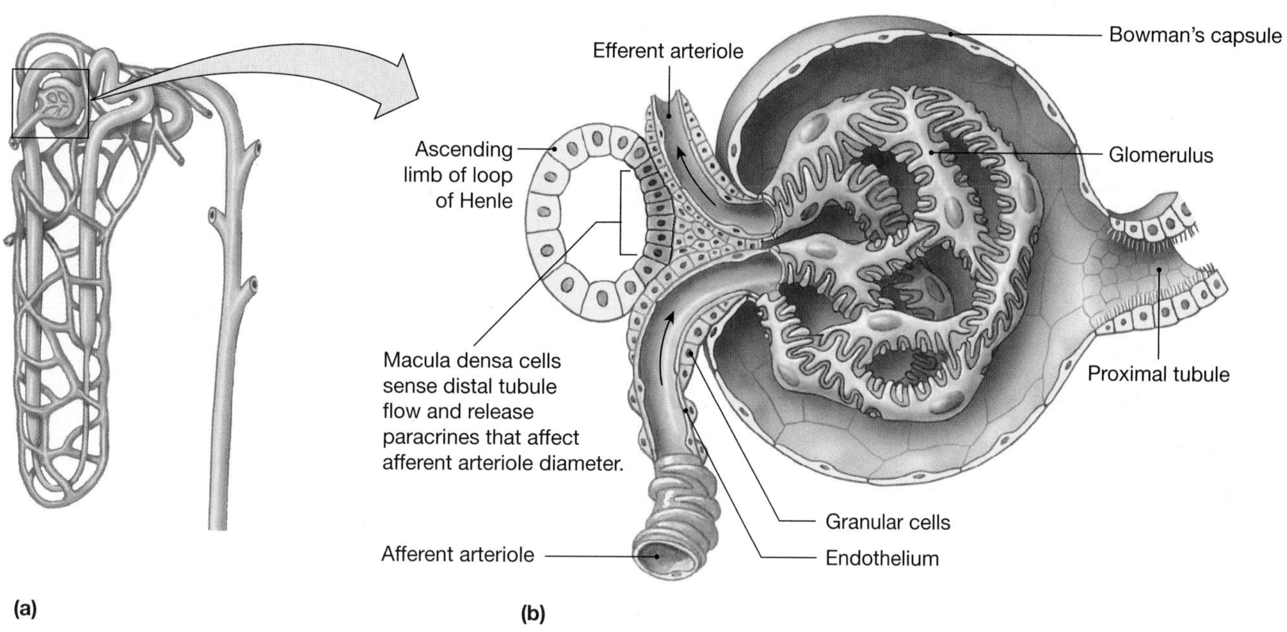

● **FIGURE 19-9** ***The juxtaglomerular apparatus consists of macula densa and granular cells.***

of the renal arterioles increases, renal blood flow decreases, and blood is diverted to other organs [Fig. 15-15, p. 527]. The effect of increased resistance on GFR, however, depends on *where* the resistance change takes place.

If resistance increases in the *afferent* arteriole (Fig. 19-8b), hydrostatic pressure decreases on the glomerular side of the constriction. This translates into a decrease in GFR. If resistance increases in the *efferent* arteriole, blood "dams up" in front of the constriction, and hydrostatic pressure in the glomerular capillaries increases (Fig. 19-8c). Increased glomerular pressure increases GFR. The opposite changes occur with decreased resistance in the afferent or efferent arterioles. Most regulation occurs at the afferent arteriole.

CONCEPT CHECK

8. Why is the osmotic pressure of plasma in efferent arterioles higher than that in afferent arterioles?
9. If a hypertensive person's blood pressure is 143/107 mm Hg and mean arterial pressure is diastolic pressure + ⅓ the pulse pressure, what is this person's mean arterial pressure? What is this person's GFR according to Figure 19-7? Answers: p. 649

GFR Is Subject to Autoregulation

Autoregulation of glomerular filtration rate is a local control process in which the kidney maintains a relatively constant GFR in the face of normal fluctuations in blood pressure. One important function of GFR autoregulation is to protect the filtration barriers from high blood pressures that might damage them. We do not completely understand the autoregulation process, but several mechanisms are at work. The **myogenic response** is the intrinsic ability of vascular smooth muscle to respond to pressure changes. **Tubuloglomerular feedback** is a paracrine signaling mechanism through which changes in fluid flow through the loop of Henle influence GFR.

Myogenic Response The myogenic response of afferent arterioles is similar to autoregulation in other systemic arterioles. When smooth muscle in the arteriole wall stretches because of increased blood pressure, stretch-sensitive ion channels open, and the muscle cells depolarize. Depolarization opens voltage-gated Ca^{2+} channels, and the vascular smooth muscle contracts [p. 523]. Vasoconstriction increases resistance to flow, and so blood flow through the arteriole diminishes. The decrease in blood flow decreases filtration pressure in the glomerulus.

If blood pressure decreases, the tonic level of arteriolar contraction disappears, and the arteriole becomes maximally dilated. However, vasodilation is not as effective at maintaining GFR as vasoconstriction because normally the afferent arteriole is fairly relaxed. Consequently, when mean blood pressure drops below 80 mm Hg, GFR decreases. This decrease is adaptive in the sense that if less plasma is filtered, the potential for fluid loss in the urine is decreased. In other words, a decrease in GFR helps the body conserve blood volume.

Tubuloglomerular Feedback Tubuloglomerular feedback is a local control pathway in which fluid flow through the tubule influences GFR. The twisted configuration of the nephron, as shown in Figure 19-9a ●, causes the final portion of the ascending limb of the loop of Henle to pass between the afferent and efferent arterioles. The tubule and arteriolar walls are modified in the regions where they contact each other and together form the juxtaglomerular apparatus.

19

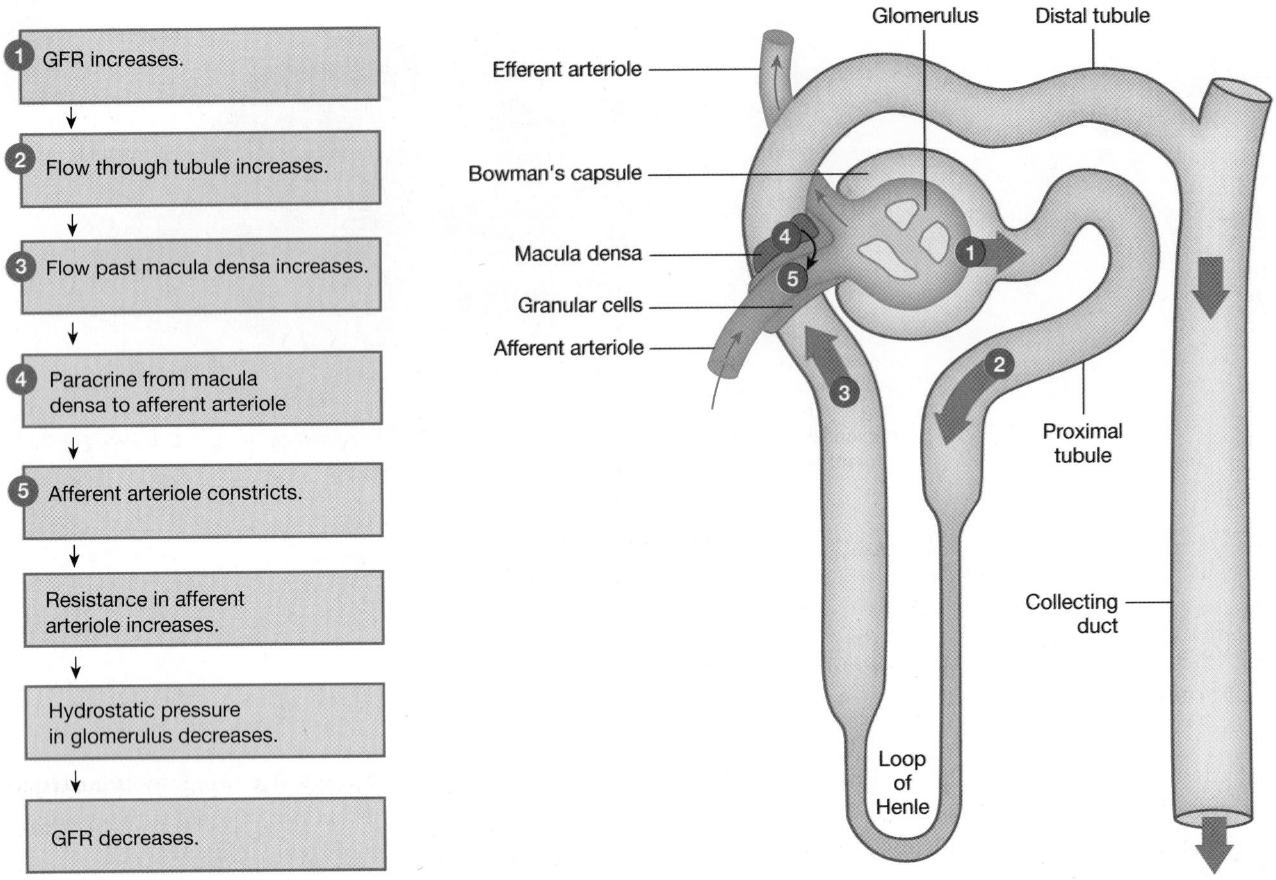
1 GFR increases.
2 Flow through tubule increases.
3 Flow past macula densa increases.
4 Paracrine from macula densa to afferent arteriole
5 Afferent arteriole constricts.
Resistance in afferent arteriole increases.
Hydrostatic pressure in glomerulus decreases.
GFR decreases.
Glomerulus
Distal tubule
Efferent arteriole
Bowman's capsule
Macula densa
Granular cells
Afferent arteriole
Proximal tubule
Collecting duct
Loop of Henle

● **FIGURE 19-10** ***Tubuloglomerular feedback helps GFR autoregulation.***

The modified portion of the tubule epithelium is a plaque of cells called the **macula densa** (Fig. 19-9b). The adjacent wall of the afferent arteriole has specialized smooth muscle cells called **granular cells** (also known as *juxtaglomerular cells* or *JG cells*). The granular cells secrete *renin*, an enzyme involved in salt and water balance. When NaCl delivery past the macula densa increases as a result of increased GFR, the macula densa cells send a paracrine message to the neighboring afferent arteriole (Fig. 19-10 ●). The afferent arteriole constricts, increasing resistance and decreasing GFR.

Experimental evidence indicates that the macula densa cells transport NaCl, and that increases in salt transport initiate tubuloglomerular feedback. The paracrine signaling between the macula densa and the afferent arteriole is complex, and the details are still controversial. Experiments show that several paracrine signals, including ATP, adenosine, and nitric oxide, pass from the macula densa to the arteriole.

Hormones and Autonomic Neurons Also Influence GFR

Although local mechanisms within the kidney attempt to maintain a constant GFR, the importance of the kidneys in systemic blood pressure homeostasis means that integrating centers outside the kidney can override local controls. Hormones and the autonomic nervous system alter glomerular filtration rate in two ways: by changing resistance in the arterioles and by altering the filtration coefficient.

Neural control of GFR is mediated by sympathetic neurons that innervate both the afferent and efferent arterioles. Sympathetic innervation of α-receptors on vascular smooth muscle causes vasoconstriction [p. 524]. If sympathetic activity is moderate, there is little effect on GFR. If systemic blood pressure drops sharply, however, as occurs with hemorrhage or severe dehydration, sympathetically induced vasoconstriction of the arterioles decreases GFR and renal blood flow. This is an adaptive response that helps conserve fluid volume.

A variety of hormones also influence arteriolar resistance. Among the most important are *angiotensin II,* a potent vasoconstrictor, and prostaglandins, which act as vasodilators. These same hormones may affect the filtration coefficient by acting on podocytes or mesangial cells. Podocytes change the size of the glomerular filtration slits. If the slits widen, more surface area is available for filtration, and GFR increases. Contraction of mesangial cells apparently changes the glomerular capillary surface area available for filtration. We still have much to learn about these processes, and physiologists are actively investigating them.

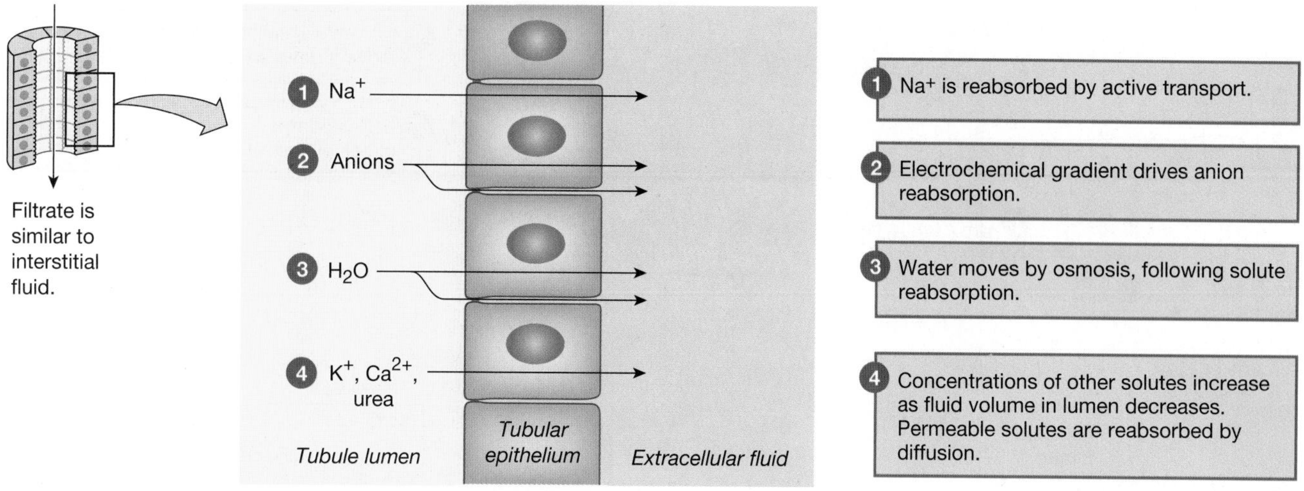

Filtrate is similar to interstitial fluid.
1 Na+
2 Anions
3 H2O
4 K+, Ca2+, urea
Tubule lumen
Tubular epithelium
Extracellular fluid
1 Na+ is reabsorbed by active transport.
2 Electrochemical gradient drives anion reabsorption.
3 Water moves by osmosis, following solute reabsorption.
4 Concentrations of other solutes increase as fluid volume in lumen decreases. Permeable solutes are reabsorbed by diffusion.

● **FIGURE 19-11** ***Principles governing the tubular reabsorption of solutes and water.*** Some solutes and water move into and then out of epithelial cells (transcellular or epithelial transport); other solutes move through junctions between epithelial cells (the paracellular pathway). Membrane transporters are not shown in this illustration.

CONCEPT CHECK

10. If systemic blood pressure remains constant but the afferent arteriole of a nephron constricts, what happens to renal blood flow and GFR in that nephron?
11. A person with cirrhosis of the liver has lower-than-normal levels of plasma proteins and consequently a higher-than-normal GFR. Explain why a decrease in plasma protein concentration causes an increase in GFR.

Answers: p. 649

REABSORPTION

Each day, 180 liters of filtered fluid pass from the glomerular capillaries into the tubules, yet only about 1.5 liters are excreted in the urine. Thus more than 99% of the fluid entering the tubules must be reabsorbed into the blood as filtrate moves through the nephrons. Most of this reabsorption takes place in the proximal tubule, with a smaller amount of reabsorption in the distal segments of the nephrons. Regulated reabsorption in the distal nephron allows the kidneys to return ions and water to the plasma selectively—as needed to maintain homeostasis.

One question you might be asking is, "Why bother to filter 180 L/day and then reabsorb 99% of it? Why not simply filter and excrete the 1% that needs to be eliminated?" There are two reasons. First, many foreign substances are filtered into the tubule but not reabsorbed into the blood. The high daily filtration rate helps clear such substances from the plasma very rapidly.

Second, filtering ions and water into the tubule simplifies their regulation. If a portion of filtrate that reaches the distal nephron is not needed to maintain homeostasis, it passes into the urine. With a high GFR, this excretion can occur quite rapidly. However, if the ions and water are needed, they are reabsorbed.

Reabsorption May Be Active or Passive

Reabsorption of water and solutes from the tubule lumen to the extracellular fluid depends on active transport. The filtrate flowing out of Bowman's capsule into the proximal tubule has the same solute concentrations as extracellular fluid. To move solute out of the lumen, the tubule cells must therefore use active transport to create concentration or electrochemical gradients. Water osmotically follows solutes as they are reabsorbed.

Figure 19-11 ● is an overview of reabsorption. Active transport of Na^+ from the tubule lumen to the extracellular fluid creates a transepithelial electrical gradient in which the lumen is more negative than the ECF. Anions then follow the positively charged Na^+ out of the lumen. The net movement of Na^+ and anions from lumen to ECF dilutes the luminal fluid and increases the concentration of the ECF, so water leaves the tubule by osmosis.

The loss of volume from the lumen increases the concentration of solutes (including K^+, Ca^{2+}, and urea) left behind in the filtrate: an unchanged amount of solute in a smaller volume increases concentration. Once luminal solute concentrations are higher than solute concentrations in the extracellular fluid, the solutes diffuse out of the lumen if the epithelium of the tubule is permeable to them.

Reabsorption involves both **epithelial transport** (also called *transcellular transport*), in which substances cross both the apical and basolateral membranes of the tubule epithelial cell [p. 77], and the **paracellular pathway**, in which substances pass through the junction between two adjacent cells. Which route a solute takes depends on the permeability of the epithelial junctions and on the electrochemical gradient for the solute. For solutes that move through the epithelial cells, their

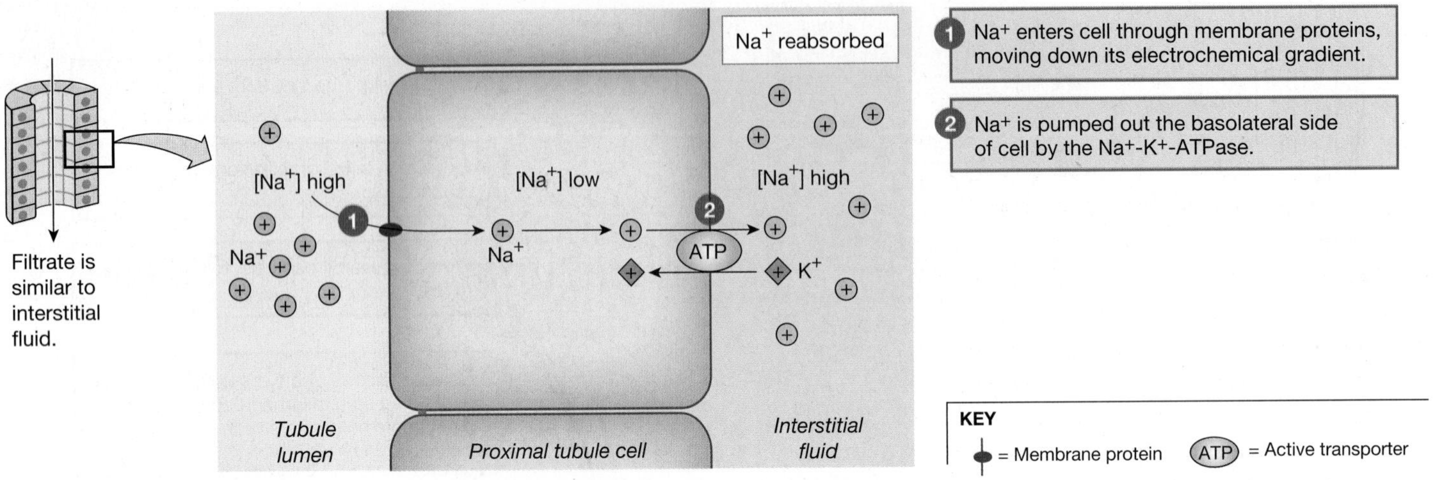

● **FIGURE 19-12** ***Sodium reabsorption in the proximal tubule***

concentration or electrochemical gradients determine their transport mechanisms. Solutes moving down their gradient use open leak channels or facilitated diffusion carriers to cross the cell membrane. Molecules that need to be pushed against their gradient are moved by either primary or secondary active transport. Sodium is directly or indirectly involved in many instances of both passive and active transport.

Active Transport of Sodium The active transport of Na^+ is the primary driving force for most renal reabsorption. As noted earlier, filtrate entering the proximal tubule is similar in ion composition to plasma, with a higher Na^+ concentration than is found in cells. Thus Na^+ in the filtrate can enter tubule cells passively by moving down its electrochemical gradient (Fig. 19-12 ●). Apical movement of Na^+ uses a variety of symport and antiport transport proteins [p. 144] or open leak channels. In the proximal tubule, the NHE Na^+-H^+ antiporter plays a major role in Na^+ reabsorption. Once inside a tubule cell, Na^+ is actively transported out across the basolateral membrane by Na^+-K^+-ATPase. The end result is Na^+ reabsorption across the tubule epithelium.

Secondary Active Transport: Symport with Sodium
Sodium-linked secondary active transport in the nephron is responsible for the reabsorption of many substances, including glucose, amino acids, ions, and various organic metabolites. Figure 19-13 ● shows one example: Na^+-dependent glucose reabsorption across the proximal tubule epithelium [Fig. 5-15, p. 149]. The apical membrane contains the Na^+-glucose cotransporter (SGLT) that brings glucose into the cytoplasm against its concentration gradient by harnessing the energy of Na^+ moving down its electrochemical gradient. On the basolateral side of the cell, Na^+ is pumped out by the Na^+-K^+-ATPase while glucose diffuses out with the aid of a facilitated diffusion

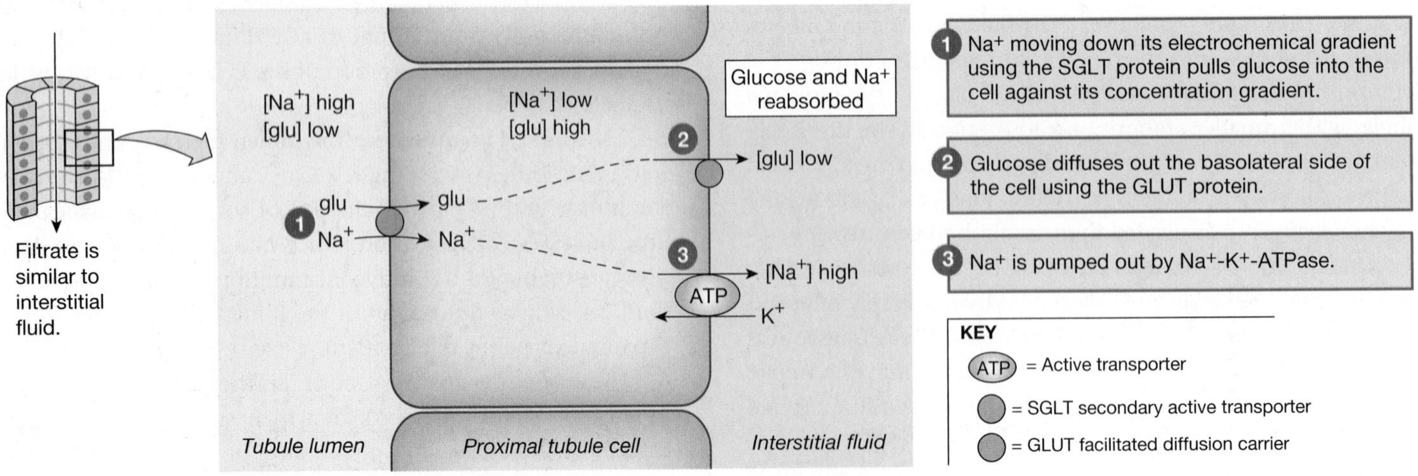

● **FIGURE 19-13** ***Sodium-linked glucose reabsorption in the proximal tubule.*** Amino acids, other organic metabolites, and some ions are also absorbed by Na^+-dependent cotransport.

GLUT transporter. The same basic pattern holds for many other molecules absorbed by Na^+-dependent transport: an apical symport protein and a basolateral facilitated diffusion carrier.

Passive Reabsorption: Urea The nitrogenous waste product urea has no active transporters in the proximal tubule but can move across the epithelium by diffusion if there is a urea concentration gradient. Initially, urea concentrations in the filtrate and extracellular fluid are equal. However, the active transport of Na^+ and other solutes in the proximal tubule creates a urea concentration gradient by the following process.

When Na^+ and other solutes are reabsorbed from the proximal tubule, the transfer of osmotically active particles makes the extracellular fluid more concentrated than the filtrate remaining in the lumen (see Fig. 19-11). In response to the osmotic gradient, water moves by osmosis across the epithelium. Up to this point, no urea molecules have moved out of the lumen because there has been no urea concentration gradient. Now, however, when water leaves the lumen, the filtrate concentration of urea increases because the same amount of urea is contained in a smaller volume. Once a concentration gradient for urea exists, urea uses facilitated diffusion transporters to move out of the lumen into the extracellular fluid.

Transcytosis: Plasma Proteins Filtration of plasma at the glomerulus normally leaves most plasma proteins in the blood, but some smaller protein hormones and enzymes can pass through the filtration barrier. Most filtered proteins are reabsorbed in the proximal tubule, with the result that normally only trace amounts of protein appear in urine.

Small as they are, filtered proteins are too large to be reabsorbed by carriers or through channels. Instead they enter proximal tubule cells by receptor-mediated endocytosis [p. 153] at the apical membrane. Once in the cells, the proteins may be digested and released as amino acids or delivered intact to the extracellular fluid via transcytosis [p. 157].

Recently scientists have discovered a membrane-bound receptor protein in coated pits on the surface of proximal tubule cells and some other tissues in the body. The protein is a member of the LDL-receptor family [p. 154] and has been named *megalin*. Megalin appears to be responsible for filtered protein reabsorption and may also play a role in cellular uptake of carrier-bound steroid hormones and lipid-soluble vitamins.

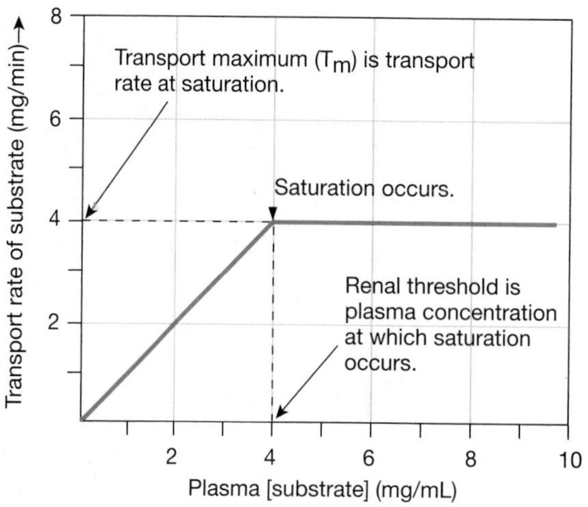

GRAPH QUESTION

What is the transport rate at the following plasma substrate concentrations: 3 mg/mL, 5 mg/mL, 8 mg/mL? At what plasma substrate concentration is the transport rate 2 mg/min?

● **FIGURE 19-14** ***Saturation of mediated transport.*** The transport rate of a substance is proportional to the plasma concentration of the substance, up to the point at which transporters become saturated. Once saturation occurs, transport rate reaches a maximum. The plasma concentration of substrate at which the transport maximum occurs is called the renal threshold.

Renal Transport Can Reach Saturation

Most transport in the nephron uses membrane proteins and exhibits the three characteristics of mediated transport: saturation, specificity, and competition [p. 148].

Saturation refers to the maximum rate of transport that occurs when all available carriers are occupied by (are saturated with) substrate. At substrate concentrations below the saturation point, transport rate is directly related to substrate concentration (Fig. 19-14 ●). At substrate concentrations equal to or

BIOTECHNOLOGY

ARTIFICIAL KIDNEYS

Many people with severe renal disease depend on *dialysis*, a medical procedure that either supplements or completely replaces their kidney function. Imagine trying to make a machine or develop a procedure that performs the functions of the kidney. What would it have to do? Dialysis is based on diffusion through a semipermeable membrane. Solutes and water pass from a patient's extracellular fluid across the membrane into a dialysis fluid. *Hemodialysis* routes blood from the arm past a membrane in an external dialysis machine. This technique requires attachment to the machine for 3–5 hours three days a week and is used for more severe cases of renal failure. *Peritoneal dialysis* is also called *continuous ambulatory peritoneal dialysis* (CAPD) because it takes place while the patient moves about during daily activities. In CAPD, dialysis fluid is injected into the peritoneal cavity, where it accumulates waste products from the blood for 4–6 hours before being drained out. For more information about dialysis, see the web site for the National Institute of Diabetes and Digestive and Kidney Diseases (*www.niddk.nih.gov*) and search for *dialysis*.

19

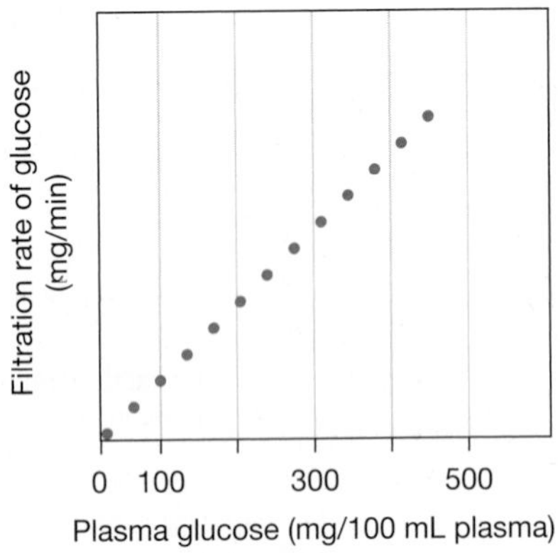

(a) Filtration of glucose is proportional to the plasma concentration.

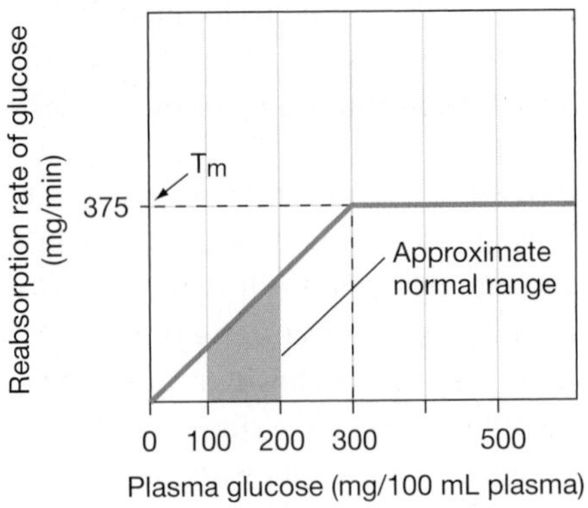

(b) Reabsorption of glucose is proportional to plasma concentration until the transport maximum (T_m) is reached.

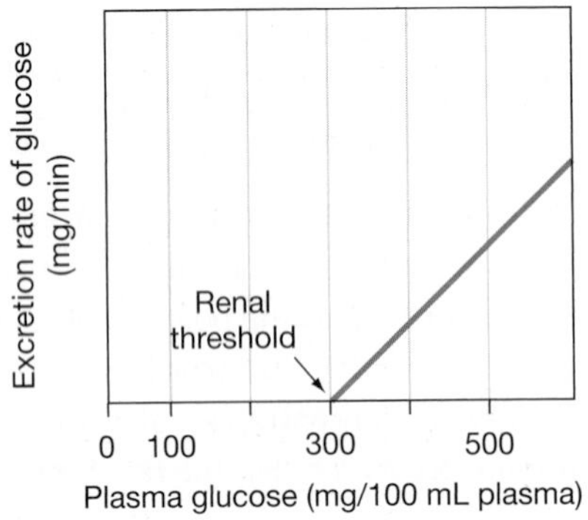

(c) Glucose excretion is zero until the renal threshold is reached.

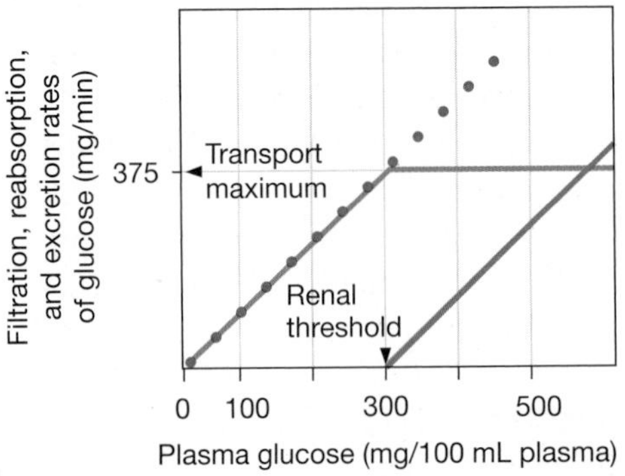

(d) Composite graph shows the relationship between filtration, reabsorption, and excretion of glucose.

● **FIGURE 19-15** ***Glucose handling by the nephron***

above the saturation point, transport occurs at a maximum rate. The transport rate at saturation is the **transport maximum**, or $\mathbf{T_m}$ [p. 151].

Glucose reabsorption in the nephron is an excellent example of the consequences of saturation. At normal plasma glucose concentrations, all glucose that enters the nephron is reabsorbed before it reaches the end of the proximal tubule. The tubule epithelium is well supplied with carriers to capture glucose as the filtrate flows past.

But what happens if blood glucose concentrations become excessive, as they do in diabetes mellitus? In that case, glucose is filtered faster than the carriers can reabsorb it. The carriers become saturated and are unable to reabsorb all the glucose that flows through the tubule. As a result, some glucose escapes reabsorption and is excreted in the urine.

Consider the following analogy. Assume that the carriers are like seats on a train at Disney World. Instead of boarding the stationary train from a stationary platform, passengers step onto a moving sidewalk that rolls them past the train. As the passengers see an open seat, they grab it. However, if more people are allowed onto the moving sidewalk than there are seats in the train, some people will not find seats. And because the sidewalk is moving people past the train toward an exit, they cannot wait for the next train. Instead, they end up being transported out the exit.

Glucose molecules entering Bowman's capsule in the filtrate are like passengers stepping onto the moving sidewalk. To be reabsorbed, each glucose molecule must bind to a transporter as the filtrate flows through the proximal tubule. If only a few glucose molecules enter the tubule at a time, each one can find a free transporter and be reabsorbed, just as a small number of people on the moving sidewalk all find seats on the train. However, if glucose molecules filter into the tubule faster than the glucose carriers can transport them, some glucose remains in the lumen and is excreted in the urine.

Figure 19-15 ● is a graphic representation of glucose handling by the kidney. Figure 19-15a shows that the filtration rate of glucose from plasma into Bowman's capsule is proportional to the plasma concentration of glucose. Because filtration does not exhibit saturation, the graph continues infinitely in a straight line: the filtrate glucose concentration is always equal to the plasma glucose concentration.

Figure 19-15b plots the reabsorption rate of glucose in the proximal tubule against the plasma concentration of glucose. Reabsorption exhibits a maximum transport rate (T_m) when the carriers reach saturation.

Figure 19-15c plots the excretion rate of glucose in relation to the plasma concentration of glucose. When plasma glucose concentrations are low enough that 100% of the filtered glucose is reabsorbed, no glucose is excreted. Once the carriers reach saturation, glucose excretion begins. The plasma concentration at which glucose first appears in the urine is called the **renal threshold** for glucose.

Figure 19-15d is a composite graph that compares filtration, reabsorption, and excretion of glucose. Recall from our earlier discussion that

$$\text{Amount excreted} = \text{amount filtered} - \text{amount reabsorbed} + \text{amount secreted}$$

For glucose, which is not secreted, the equation can be rewritten as

$$\text{Glucose excreted} = \text{glucose filtered} - \text{glucose reabsorbed}$$

Under normal conditions, all filtered glucose is reabsorbed. In other words, filtration is equal to reabsorption.

Notice in Figure 19-15d that the lines representing filtration and reabsorption are identical up to the plasma glucose concentration that equals the renal threshold. If filtration equals reabsorption, the algebraic difference between the two is zero, and there is no excretion. Once the renal threshold is reached, filtration begins to exceed reabsorption. Notice on the graph that the filtration and reabsorption lines diverge at this point. The difference between the filtration line and the reabsorption line represents the excretion rate:

$$\text{Excretion} = \underset{\text{(increasing)}}{\text{filtration}} - \underset{\text{(constant)}}{\text{reabsorption}}$$

Excretion of glucose in the urine is called **glucosuria** or **glycosuria** [*-uria,* in the urine] and usually indicates an elevated blood glucose concentration. Rarely, glucose appears in the urine even though the blood glucose concentrations are normal. This situation is due to a genetic disorder in which the nephron does not make enough carriers.

Peritubular Capillary Pressures Favor Reabsorption

The reabsorption we have just discussed refers to the movement of solutes and water from the tubule lumen to the interstitial fluid. How does that reabsorbed fluid then get into the capillary? The answer is that the driving force for reabsorption from the interstitial fluid into the capillaries is the low hydrostatic pressure that exists along the entire length of the peritubular capillaries. This low pressure favors reabsorption.

RUNNING PROBLEM

Uric acid, the molecule that causes gout, is a normal product of purine metabolism. Increased uric acid production may be associated with cell and tissue breakdown, or it may occur as a result of inherited enzyme defects. Plasma urate, the anionic form of uric acid, filters freely into Bowman's capsule but is almost totally reabsorbed in the first part of the proximal tubule. The middle section of the proximal tubule then secretes about half of the reabsorbed urate back into the lumen, and the terminal section of the proximal tubule again reabsorbs some of it. The end result is net secretion.

Question 3:
Purines are part of which category of biomolecules? Using that information, explain why uric acid levels in the blood go up when cell breakdown increases.

Question 4:
Based on what you have learned about uric acid and urate, predict two ways a person may develop hyperuricemia.

623 625 639 640 643 645

The peritubular capillaries have an average hydrostatic pressure of 10 mm Hg (in contrast to the glomerular capillaries, where hydrostatic pressure averages 55 mm Hg). Colloid osmotic pressure, which favors movement of fluid into the capillaries, is 30 mm Hg. As a result, the pressure gradient in peritubular capillaries is 20 mm Hg, favoring the absorption of fluid into the capillaries. Fluid that is reabsorbed passes from the capillaries to the venous circulation and returns to the heart.

SECRETION

Secretion is the transfer of molecules from extracellular fluid into the lumen of the nephron (see Fig. 19-2). Secretion, like reabsorption, depends mostly on membrane transport systems. The secretion of K^+ and H^+ by the nephron is important in the homeostatic regulation of those ions, as we discuss in Chapter 20. In addition, many organic compounds are secreted. These compounds include both metabolites produced in the body and substances brought into the body.

Secretion enables the nephron to enhance excretion of a substance. If a substance is filtered and not reabsorbed, it is excreted very efficiently. If, however, the substance is filtered into the tubule, not reabsorbed, *and* then more of it is secreted into the tubule from the peritubular capillaries, excretion is even more efficient.

Secretion is an active process because it requires moving substrates against their concentration gradients. Most organic compounds are transported across the tubule epithelium into the lumen by secondary active transport.

Competition Decreases Penicillin Secretion

An interesting and important example of an organic molecule secreted by the nephron is the antibiotic *penicillin*. Many people today take antibiotics for granted, but until the early decades of the twentieth century, infections were a leading cause of death.

In 1928, Alexander Fleming discovered a substance in the bread mold *Penicillium* that retarded the growth of bacteria. But the antibiotic was difficult to isolate, so it did not become available for clinical use until the late 1930s. During World War II, penicillin made a major difference in the number of deaths and amputations caused by infected wounds. The only means of producing penicillin, however, was to isolate it from bread mold, and supplies were limited.

Demand for the drug was heightened by the fact that kidney tubules secrete penicillin. Renal secretion is so efficient at clearing foreign molecules from the blood that within three to four hours after a dose of penicillin has been administered, about 80% has been excreted in the urine. During the war, the drug was in such short supply that it was common procedure to collect the urine from patients being treated with penicillin so that the antibiotic could be isolated and reused.

This solution was not satisfactory, however, and so researchers looked for a way to slow penicillin secretion. They hoped to find a molecule that could compete with penicillin for the organic anion transporter responsible for secretion [p. 149]. That way, when presented with both drugs, the carrier would bind preferentially to the competitor and secrete it, leaving penicillin behind in the blood. A synthetic compound named *probenecid* was the answer. When probenecid is administered concurrently with penicillin, the transporter removes probenecid preferentially, prolonging the activity of penicillin in the body. Once mass-produced synthetic penicillin became available and supply was no longer a problem, the medical use of probenecid declined.

EXCRETION

Urine output is the result of all the processes that take place in the kidney. By the time fluid reaches the end of the nephron, it bears little resemblance to the filtrate that started in Bowman's capsule. Glucose, amino acids, and useful metabolites are gone, having been reabsorbed into the blood, and organic wastes are more concentrated. The concentrations of ions and water in the urine are highly variable, depending on the state of the body.

Although excretion tells us what the body is eliminating, excretion by itself cannot tell us the details of renal function. Recall that for any substance,

$$\text{Excretion} = \text{filtration} - \text{reabsorption} + \text{secretion}$$

Simply looking at the excretion rate of a substance tells us nothing about how the kidney handled that substance. The excretion rate of a substance depends on (1) its filtration rate and (2) whether the substance is reabsorbed, secreted, or both as it passes through the tubule.

Renal handling of a substance and GFR are often of clinical interest. For example, clinicians use information about a person's glomerular filtration rate as an indicator of overall kidney function. And pharmaceutical companies developing drugs must provide the Food and Drug Administration with complete information on how the human kidney handles each new compound.

But how can investigators dealing with living humans assess filtration, reabsorption, and secretion at the level of the individual nephron? They have no way to do this directly because the kidneys are not easily accessible and the nephrons are microscopic. Scientists therefore had to develop a technique that would allow them to assess renal function using only analysis of the urine and blood. From their work came the concept of clearance.

Clearance Is a Noninvasive Way to Measure GFR

Clearance of a solute is the rate at which that solute disappears from the body by excretion or by metabolism [p. 133]. For any solute that is cleared only by renal excretion, clearance is expressed as the volume of plasma passing through the kidneys that has been totally cleared of that solute in a given period of time. Because this is such an indirect way to think of excretion (how much blood has been cleared of *X* rather than how much *X* has been excreted), clearance is often a very difficult concept for students.

RUNNING PROBLEM

Michael found it amazing that a metabolic problem could lead to pain in his big toe. "How do we treat gout?" he asked. Dr. Garcia explained that the treatment includes anti-inflammatory agents, lots of water, and avoidance of alcohol, which can trigger gout attacks. "In addition, I would like to put you on a uricosuric agent, like probenecid, which will enhance renal excretion of urate," replied Dr. Garcia. "By enhancing excretion, we can reduce uric acid levels in your blood and thus provide relief." Michael agreed to try these measures.

Question 5:

Urate is reabsorbed by some proximal tubule cells and secreted by others using membrane transporters, one on the apical membrane and one on the basolateral membrane. Could the same transporters be used by cells that reabsorb urate and cells that secrete it? Defend your reasoning.

Question 6:

Uricosuric agents, like urate, are organic acids. Given this fact, explain how uricosuric agents might enhance excretion of urate.

Before we jump into the mathematical expression of clearance, let's look at an example that shows how clearance relates to kidney function. For our example, we use **inulin**, a polysaccharide isolated from the tuberous roots of a variety of plants. (Inulin is not the same as *insulin,* the protein hormone that regulates glucose metabolism.) Scientists discovered from experiments with isolated nephrons that inulin injected into the plasma filters freely into the nephron. As it passes through the kidney tubule, inulin is neither reabsorbed nor secreted. In other words, 100% of the inulin that filters into the tubule is excreted.

How does this relate to clearance? To answer this question, take a look at Figure 19-16 ●, which assumes that 100% of a filtered volume of plasma is reabsorbed. (This is not too far off the actual value, which is more than 99%.) Inulin has been injected so that its plasma concentration is 4 inulin molecules per 100 mL plasma. If GFR is 100 mL plasma filtered per minute, we can calculate the filtration rate, or *filtered load,* of inulin using the equation

$$\text{Filtered load of } X = [X]_{\text{plasma}} \times \text{GFR}$$

$$\begin{aligned}\text{Filtered load of inulin} &= (4 \text{ inulin}/100 \text{ mL plasma}) \\ &\quad \times 100 \text{ mL plasma filtered/min} \\ &= 4 \text{ inulin/min}\end{aligned}$$

As the filtered inulin and the filtered plasma pass along the nephron, all the plasma is reabsorbed, but all the inulin remains in the tubule. The reabsorbed plasma contains no inulin, so we say it has been totally *cleared* of inulin. The *inulin clearance* therefore is 100 mL of plasma cleared/min. At the same time, the excretion rate of inulin is 4 inulin molecules excreted per minute.

What good is this information? For one thing, we can use it to calculate the glomerular filtration rate. Notice from Figure 19-16 that inulin clearance (100 mL plasma cleared/min) is equal to the GFR (100 mL plasma filtered/min). Thus, *for any substance that is freely filtered but neither reabsorbed nor secreted, its clearance is equal to GFR.*

Now let's show mathematically that inulin clearance is equal to GFR. We already know that

$$\text{Filtered load of } X = [X]_{\text{plasma}} \times \text{GFR} \qquad (1)$$

We also know that 100% of the inulin that filters into the tubule is excreted. In other words:

$$\text{Filtered load of inulin} = \text{excretion rate of inulin} \qquad (2)$$

Because of this equality, we can substitute excretion rate for filtered load in equation (1) by using algebra (if A = B and A = C, then B = C):

$$\text{Excretion rate of inulin} = [\text{inulin}]_{\text{plasma}} \times \text{GFR} \qquad (3)$$

This equation can be rearranged to read

$$\text{GFR} = \frac{\text{excretion rate of inulin}}{[\text{inulin}]_{\text{plasma}}} \qquad (4)$$

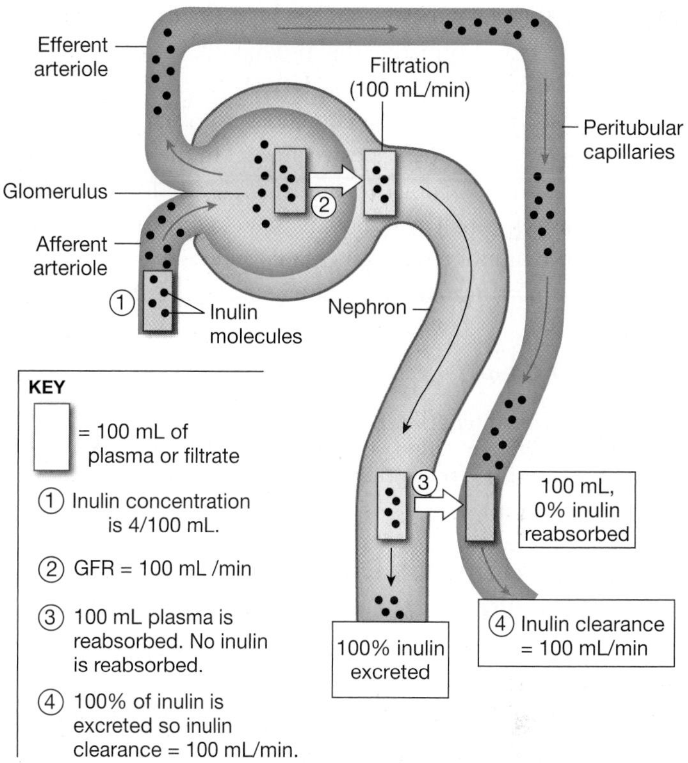

● **FIGURE 19-16** ***Inulin clearance is equal to GFR.***

It turns out that the right side of this equation is identical to the clearance equation for inulin. Thus the general equation for the clearance of any substance X (mL plasma cleared/min) is

$$\text{Clearance rate of } X = \frac{\text{excretion rate of } X \text{ (mg/min)}}{[X]_{\text{plasma}} \text{ (mg/mL plasma)}} \qquad (5)$$

For inulin:

$$\text{Inulin clearance} = \frac{\text{excretion rate of inulin}}{[\text{inulin}]_{\text{plasma}}} \qquad (6)$$

The right sides of equations (4) and (6) are identical, so by using algebra again, we can say that:

$$\text{GFR} = \text{inulin clearance} \qquad (7)$$

So why is this important? For one thing, you have just learned how we can measure GFR in a living human by taking only blood and urine samples. Try the example in Concept Check 12 to see if you understand the preceding discussion.

Inulin is not practical for routine clinical applications because it does not occur naturally in the body and must be administered by continuous intravenous infusion. As a result, inulin use is restricted to research. Unfortunately, no substance that occurs naturally in the human body is handled by the kidney exactly the way inulin is handled.

In clinical settings, physicians use creatinine to estimate GFR. **Creatinine** is a breakdown product of phosphocreatine, an energy-storage compound found primarily in muscles [p. 420]. It is constantly produced by the body and need not be administered. Normally, the production and breakdown rates of phosphocreatine are relatively constant, and the plasma concentration of creatinine does not vary much.

Although creatinine is always present in the plasma and is easy to measure, it is not the perfect molecule for estimating GFR because a small amount is secreted into the urine. However, the amount secreted is small enough that, in most people, *creatinine clearance* is routinely used to estimate GFR.

CONCEPT CHECK

12. If plasma creatinine = 1.8 mg/100 mL plasma, urine creatinine = 1.5 mg/mL urine, and urine volume is 1100 mL in 24 hours, what is the creatinine clearance? What is GFR?

Answers: p. 649

Clearance Helps Us Determine Renal Handling

Once we know a person's GFR, we can determine how the kidney handles any solute by measuring the solute's plasma concentration and its excretion rate. If we assume that the solute is freely filtered at the glomerulus, we know from equation (1) that

$$\text{Filtered load of } X = [X]_{plasma} \times \text{GFR}$$

By comparing the filtered load of the solute with its excretion rate, we can tell how the nephron handled that substance (Tbl. 19-2 ●). For example, if less of the substance appears in the urine than was filtered, net reabsorption occurred (excreted = filtered − reabsorbed). If more of the substance appears in the urine than was filtered, there must have been net secretion of the substance into the lumen (excreted = filtered − secreted). If the same amount of the substance is filtered and excreted, then the substance is handled like inulin—neither reabsorbed nor secreted.

Suppose that glucose is present in the plasma at 100 mg glucose/dL plasma, and GFR is calculated from creatinine clearance to be 125 mL plasma/min. For these values, equation (1) tells us that

$$\text{Filtered load of glucose} = (100 \text{ mg glucose}/100 \text{ mL plasma}) \times 125 \text{ mL plasma/min}$$

$$\text{Filtered load of glucose} = 125 \text{ mg glucose/min}$$

There is no glucose in this person's urine, however: glucose excretion is zero. Because glucose was filtered at a rate of 125 mg/min but excreted at a rate of 0 mg/min, it must have been totally reabsorbed.

Clearance values can also be used to determine how the nephron handles a filtered solute. In this method, researchers calculate creatinine or inulin clearance, then compare the clearance of the solute being investigated with the creatinine or inulin clearance (Tbl. 19-2). If clearance of the solute is less than the inulin clearance, the solute has been reabsorbed. If the clearance of the solute is higher than the inulin clearance, additional solute has been secreted into the urine. More plasma was cleared of the solute than was filtered, so the additional solute must have been removed from the plasma by secretion.

Table 19-2 Renal Handling of Solutes

For any molecule *X* that is freely filtered at the glomerulus:	Renal handling of *X* is:
Filtration is greater than excretion	Net reabsorption of *X*
Excretion is greater than filtration	Net secretion of *X*
Filtration and excretion are the same	No net reabsorption or secretion
Clearance of *X* is less than inulin clearance	Net reabsorption of *X*
Clearance of *X* is equal to inulin clearance	*X* is neither reabsorbed nor secreted.
Clearance of *X* is greater than inulin clearance	Net secretion of *X*

Figure 19-17 ● shows clearance of three molecules: glucose, urea, and penicillin. All solutes have the same concentration in the blood entering the glomerulus: 4 molecules/100 mL plasma. GFR is 100 mL/min, and we assume for simplicity that the entire 100 mL of plasma filtered into the tubule is reabsorbed.

For any solute, its clearance reflects how the kidney tubule handles it. For example, 100% of the glucose that filters is reabsorbed, and glucose clearance is zero (Fig. 19-17a, ③ and ④). On the other hand, urea is partially reabsorbed; four molecules filter, but only two are reabsorbed (Fig. 19-17b, ③). Consequently, urea clearance is 50 mL plasma per minute ④. Urea and glucose clearance are both less than the inulin clearance of 100 mL/min, which tells you that urea and glucose have been reabsorbed.

Penicillin is filtered but not reabsorbed, and additional penicillin molecules are secreted from plasma in the peritubular capillaries (Fig. 19-17c, ③). In this example, an extra 50 mL of plasma have been cleared of penicillin in addition to the original 100 mL that filtered. The penicillin clearance therefore is 150 mL plasma per minute ④. Penicillin clearance is greater than the inulin clearance of 100 mL/min, which tells you that net secretion of penicillin occurs.

Note that a comparison of clearance values tells you only the *net* handling of the solute. It does not tell you if a molecule is both reabsorbed and secreted. For example, nearly all K^+ filtered is reabsorbed in the proximal tubule and loop of Henle, and then a small amount is secreted back into the tubule lumen at the distal nephron. On the basis of K^+ clearance, it appears that only reabsorption occurred.

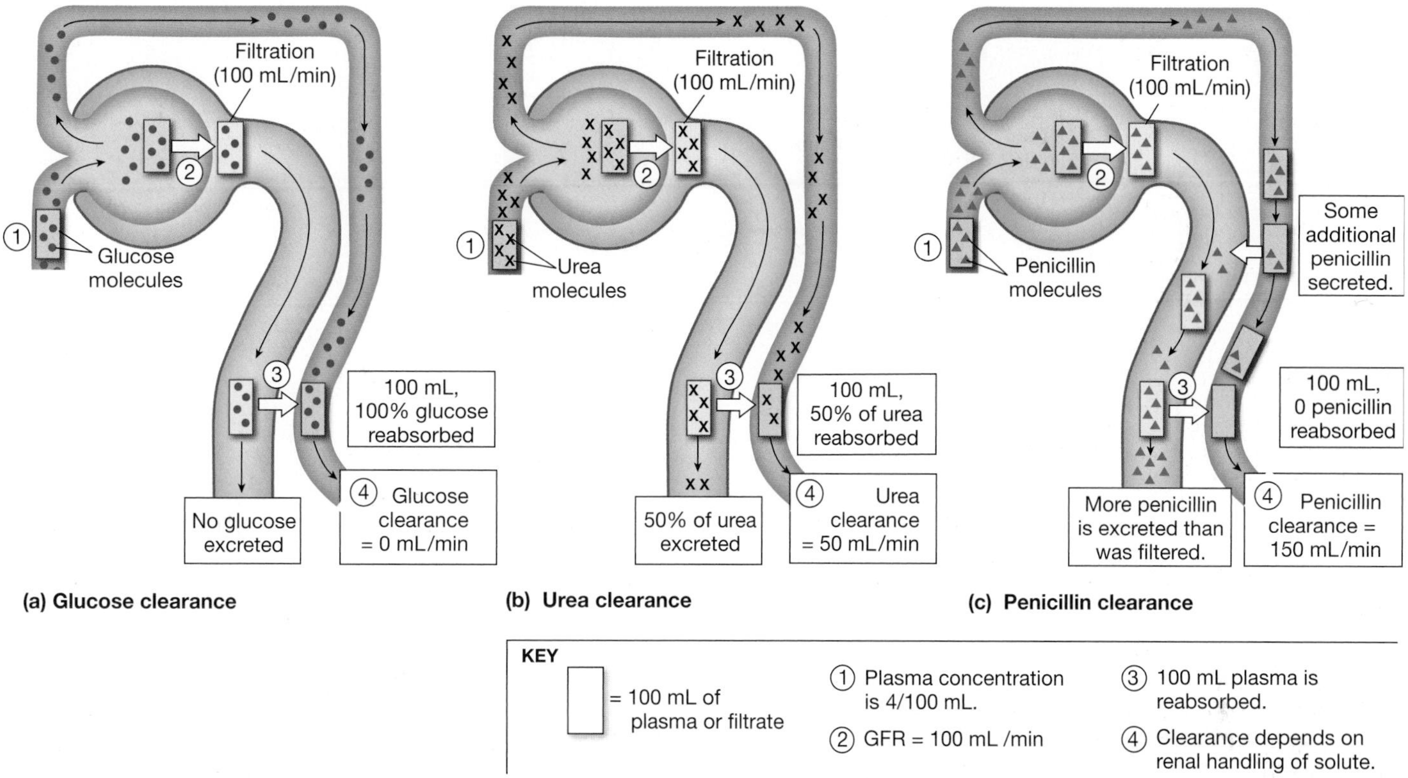

● **FIGURE 19-17** ***The relationship between clearance and excretion.*** The figure represents the events taking place in one minute. For simplicity, 100% of the filtered volume is assumed to be reabsorbed.

Clearance calculations are relatively simple because all you need to know are the urine excretion rates and the plasma concentrations for any solute of interest, and both values are easily obtained. If you also know either inulin or creatinine clearance, then you can determine the renal handling of any compound.

MICTURITION

Once filtrate leaves the collecting ducts, it can no longer be modified, and its composition does not change. The filtrate, now called urine, flows into the renal pelvis and then down the *ureter* to the bladder with the help of rhythmic smooth muscle contractions. The bladder is a hollow organ whose walls contain well-developed layers of smooth muscle. In the bladder, urine is stored until released in the process known as urination, voiding, or more formally, **micturition** [*micturire*, to desire to urinate].

The bladder can expand to hold a volume of about 500 mL. The neck of the bladder is continuous with the *urethra,* a single tube through which urine passes to reach the external environment. The opening between the bladder and urethra is closed by two rings of muscle called *sphincters* (Fig. 19-18a ●).

RUNNING PROBLEM

Three weeks later, Michael was back in Dr. Garcia's office. The anti-inflammatory drugs and probenecid had eliminated the pain in his toe, but last night he had gone to the hospital with a very painful kidney stone. "We'll have to wait until the analysis comes back," said Dr. Garcia, "but I will guess that it is a uric acid stone. Did you drink as much water as I told you to?" Sheepishly, Michael admitted that he had good intentions but could never find the time at work to drink much water. "You have to drink enough water while on this drug to produce 3 liters or more of urine a day. That's more than three quarts. Otherwise, you may end up with another uric acid kidney stone." Michael remembered how painful the kidney stone was and agreed that this time he would follow instructions to the letter.

Question 7:

Explain why not drinking enough water while taking uricosuric agents may cause uric acid crystals to form kidney stones in the urinary tract.

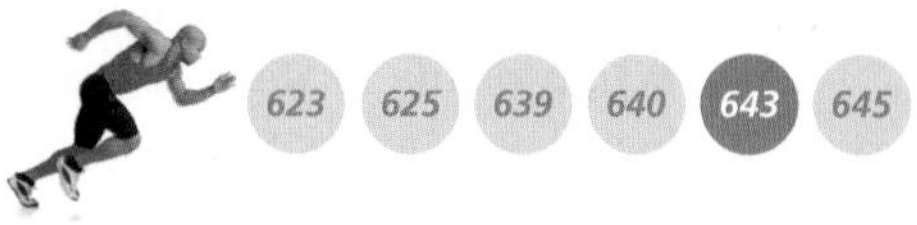

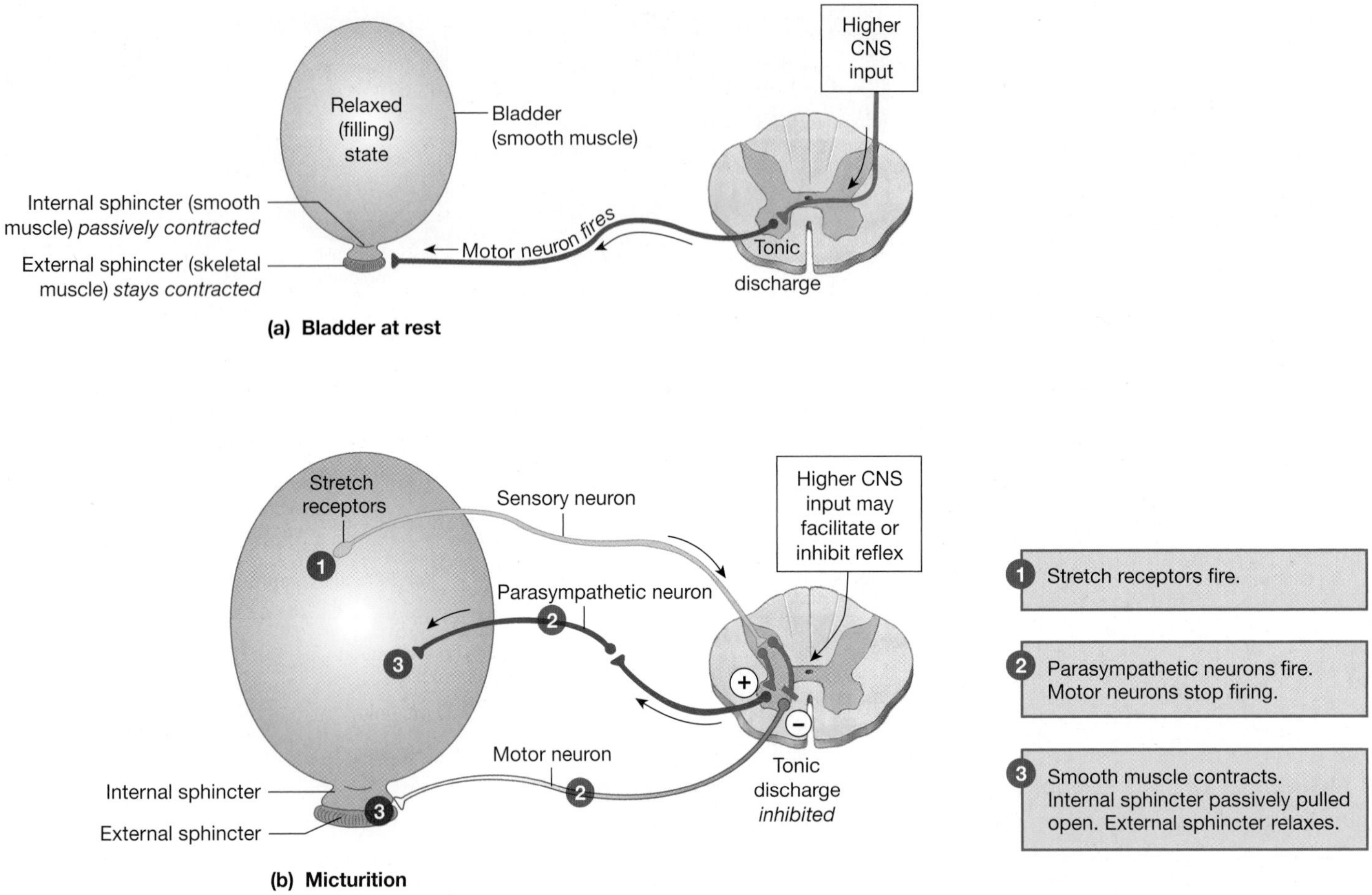

● **FIGURE 19-18** ***Micturition is a spinal reflex subject to higher brain control.***

The **internal sphincter** is a continuation of the bladder wall and consists of smooth muscle. Its normal tone keeps it contracted. The **external sphincter** is a ring of skeletal muscle controlled by somatic motor neurons. Tonic stimulation from the central nervous system maintains contraction of the external sphincter except during urination.

Micturition is a simple spinal reflex that is subject to both conscious and unconscious control from higher brain centers. As the bladder fills with urine and its walls expand, stretch receptors send signals via sensory neurons to the spinal cord (Fig. 19-18b). There the information is integrated and transferred to two sets of neurons. The stimulus of a full bladder excites parasympathetic neurons leading to the smooth muscle in the bladder wall. The smooth muscle contracts, increasing the pressure on the bladder contents. Simultaneously, somatic motor neurons leading to the external sphincter are inhibited.

Contraction of the bladder occurs in a wave that pushes urine downward toward the urethra. Pressure exerted by the urine forces the internal sphincter open while the external sphincter relaxes. Urine passes into the urethra and out of the body, aided by gravity.

This simple micturition reflex occurs primarily in infants who have not yet been toilet trained. A person who has been toilet trained acquires a learned reflex that keeps the micturition reflex inhibited until she or he consciously desires to urinate. The learned reflex involves additional sensory fibers in the bladder that signal the degree of fullness. Centers in the brain stem and cerebral cortex receive that information and override the basic micturition reflex by directly inhibiting the parasympathetic fibers and by reinforcing contraction of the external sphincter. When an appropriate time to urinate arrives, those same centers remove the inhibition and facilitate the reflex by inhibiting contraction of the external sphincter.

In addition to conscious control of urination, various subconscious factors can affect the micturition reflex. "Bashful bladder" is a condition in which a person is unable to urinate in the presence of other people despite the conscious intent to do so. The sound of running water facilitates micturition and is often used to help patients urinate if the urethra is irritated from insertion of a *catheter,* a tube inserted into the bladder to drain it passively.

RUNNING PROBLEM CONCLUSION

Gout

In this running problem, you learned that gout, which often presents as a debilitating pain in the big toe, is a metabolic problem whose cause and treatment can be linked to kidney function. Urate handling by the kidney is a complex process because urate is both secreted and reabsorbed in different segments of the proximal tubule. Scientists have now identified three different but related transport proteins that are involved in the process: the *organic anion transporter* (OAT), an antiporter that exchanges two anions in an electrically neutral exchange; *urate transporter* 1 (URAT1), which is also an anion exchanger but with high specificity for urate; and *urate transporter* (UAT), an electrogenic uniport urate transporter. The arrangement of these transport proteins on the polarized cell membrane determines whether the cell reabsorbs or secretes urate.

Gout is one of the oldest known diseases and for many years was considered a "rich man's" disease caused by too much rich food and drink. Thomas Jefferson and Benjamin Franklin both suffered from gout. To learn more about its causes, symptoms, and treatments, go to the Mayo Clinic's health information pages (*www.mayoclinic.com*) and search for *gout*. Check your understanding of this running problem by comparing your answers against the information in the summary table.

	QUESTION	FACTS	INTEGRATION AND ANALYSIS
1	Trace the route followed by kidney stones when they are excreted.	Kidney stones often form in the renal pelvis.	From the renal pelvis, a stone passes down the ureter, into the urinary bladder, then into the urethra and out of the body.
2	Name the anion formed when uric acid dissociates.	The suffix *–ate* is used to identify the anion of organic acids [p. 108].	The anion of uric acid is urate.
3	Purines are part of which category of biomolecules? Using that information, explain why uric acid levels in the blood go up when cell breakdown increases.	Purines include adenine and guanine, which are components of DNA, RNA, and ATP [p. 34]. When a cell dies, nuclear DNA and other chemical components are broken down.	Degradation of the cell's DNA, RNA, and ATP increases purine production, which in turn increases uric acid production.
4	Based on what you have learned about uric acid and urate, predict two ways a person may develop hyperuricemia.	Hyperuricemia is a disturbance of mass balance. Uric acid is made from purines. Urate is filtered by the kidneys with net secretion.	Hyperuricemia results either from overproduction of uric acid or from a defect in the renal excretion of urate.
5	Could the same transporters be used by cells that reabsorb urate and cells that secrete it? Defend your reasoning.	Some transporters move substrates in one direction only but others are reversible. Assume one urate transporter brings urate into the cell and another takes it out.	You could use the same two transporters if you reverse their positions on the apical and basolateral membranes. Cells reabsorbing urate would bring it in on the apical side and move it out on the basolateral. Cells secreting urate would reverse this pattern.
6	Uricosuric agents, like urate, are organic acids. With that information, explain how uricosuric agents might enhance excretion of urate.	Mediated transport exhibits competition, in which related molecules compete for one transporter. Usually, one molecule binds preferentially and therefore inhibits transport of the second molecule [p. 149].	Uricosuric agents are organic anions, so they may compete with urate for the proximal tubule organic anion transporter. Preferential binding of the uricosuric agents would block urate access to the OAT, leaving urate in the lumen and increasing its excretion.
7	Explain why not drinking enough water while taking uricosuric agents may cause uric acid stones to form in the urinary tract.	Uric acid stones form when uric acid concentrations exceed a critical level and crystals precipitate.	If a person drinks large volumes of water, the excess water will be excreted by the kidneys. Large amounts of water dilute the urine, thereby preventing the high concentrations of uric acid needed for stone formation.

623 625 639 640 643 645

CHAPTER SUMMARY

The urinary system, like the lungs, uses the principle of *mass balance* to maintain homeostasis. The components of urine are constantly changing and reflect the kidney's functions of regulating ions and water and removing wastes.

One of the body's three *portal systems*—each of which includes two capillary beds—is found in the kidney. Filtration occurs in the first capillary bed and reabsorption in the second. The *pressure-flow-resistance* relationship you encountered in the cardiovascular and pulmonary systems also plays a role in glomerular filtration and urinary excretion.

Compartmentation is illustrated by the movement of water and solutes between the internal and external environments as filtrate is modified along the nephron. Reabsorption and secretion of solutes depend on *molecular interactions* and on the *movement of molecules across membranes* of the tubule cells.

Functions of the Kidneys

1. The kidneys regulate extracellular fluid volume, blood pressure, and osmolarity; maintain ion balance; regulate pH; excrete wastes and foreign substances; and participate in endocrine pathways. (p. 623)

Anatomy of the Urinary System

iP Urinary System: Glomerular Filtration

2. The **urinary system** is composed of two kidneys, two ureters, a bladder, and a urethra. (p. 624; Fig. 19-1a)
3. Each **kidney** has about 1 million microscopic **nephrons.** In cross section, a kidney is arranged into an outer **cortex** and inner **medulla.** (p. 624; Fig. 19-1c)
4. Renal blood flow goes from **afferent arteriole** to **glomerulus** to **efferent arteriole** to **peritubular capillaries.** The **vasa recta** capillaries dip into the medulla. (p. 625; Fig. 19-1g-i)
5. Fluid filters from the glomerulus into **Bowman's capsule.** From there, it flows through the **proximal tubule, loop of Henle, distal tubule**, and **collecting duct**, then drains into the **renal pelvis. Urine** flows through the **ureter** to the **urinary bladder.** (p. 625; Fig. 19-1b, c, j)

Overview of Kidney Function

6. **Filtration** is the movement of fluid from plasma into Bowman's capsule. **Reabsorption** is the movement of filtered materials from tubule to blood. **Secretion** is the movement of selected molecules from blood to tubule. (pp. 625, 628; Fig. 19-2)
7. Average urine volume is 1.5 L/day. Osmolarity varies between 50 and 1200 mOsM. (p. 628; Tbl. 19-1)
8. The amount of a solute excreted equals the amount filtered minus the amount reabsorbed plus the amount secreted. (p. 629; Fig. 19-3)

Filtration

iP Urinary System: Glomerular Filtration

9. One-fifth of renal plasma flow filters into the tubule lumen. The percentage of total plasma volume that filters is called the **filtration fraction.** (pp. 629–630; Fig. 19-4)
10. Bowman's capsule epithelium has specialized cells called **podocytes** that wrap around the glomerular capillaries and create **filtration slits. Mesangial cells** are associated with the glomerular capillaries. (pp. 630–631; Fig. 19-5a, c)
11. Filtered solutes must pass first through glomerular capillary endothelium, then through a **basal lamina,** and finally through Bowman's capsule epithelium before reaching the lumen of Bowman's capsule. (p. 631; Fig. 19-5d)
12. Filtration allows most components of plasma to enter the tubule but excludes blood cells and most plasma proteins. (p. 631)
13. Hydrostatic pressure in glomerular capillaries averages 55 mm Hg, favoring filtration. Opposing filtration are colloid osmotic pressure of 30 mm Hg and hydrostatic capsule fluid pressure averaging 15 mm Hg. The net driving force is 10 mm Hg, favoring filtration. (p. 631; Fig. 19-6)
14. The **glomerular filtration rate** (**GFR**) is the amount of fluid that filters into Bowman's capsule per unit time. Average GFR is 125 mL/min, or 180 L/day. (p. 631)
15. Hydrostatic pressure in glomerular capillaries can be altered by changing resistance in the afferent and efferent arterioles. (p. 633; Fig. 19-8)
16. Autoregulation of glomerular filtration is accomplished by a **myogenic response** of vascular smooth muscle in response to pressure changes and by **tubuloglomerular feedback.** When fluid flow through the distal tubule increases, the **macula densa** cells send a paracrine signal to the afferent arteriole, which constricts. (pp. 633–634; Fig. 19-10)
17. Reflex control of GFR is mediated through systemic signals, such as hormones, and through the autonomic nervous system. (p. 634)

Reabsorption

iP Urinary System: Early Filtrate Processing

18. Most reabsorption takes place in the proximal tubule. Finely regulated reabsorption takes place in the more distal segments of the nephron. (p. 635)
19. The active transport of Na^+ and other solutes creates concentration gradients for passive reabsorption of urea and other solutes. (p. 635; Fig. 19-11)
20. Most reabsorption involves transepithelial transport, but some solutes and water are reabsorbed by the paracellular pathway. (p. 635)
21. Glucose, amino acids, ions, and various organic metabolites are reabsorbed by Na^+-linked secondary active transport. (p. 636; Fig. 19-13)
22. Most renal transport is mediated by membrane proteins and exhibits saturation, specificity, and competition. The **transport maximum T_m** is the transport rate at saturation. (p. 638; Fig. 19-14)
23. The **renal threshold** is the plasma concentration at which a substance first appears in the urine. (p. 639; Fig. 19-14)
24. Peritubular capillaries reabsorb fluid along their entire length. (p. 639)

Secretion

25. Secretion enhances excretion by removing solutes from the peritubular capillaries. K^+, H^+, and a variety of organic compounds are secreted. (p. 639)
26. Molecules that compete for renal carriers slow the secretion of a molecule. (p. 640)

Excretion

27. The excretion rate of a solute depends on (1) its filtered load and (2) whether it is reabsorbed or secreted as it passes through the nephron. (p. 640)
28. **Clearance** describes how many milliliters of plasma passing through the kidneys have been totally cleared of a solute in a given period of time. (p. 640)
29. **Inulin** clearance is equal to GFR. In clinical settings, **creatinine** is used to measure GFR. (p. 641; Fig. 19-16)
30. Clearance can be used to determine how the nephron handles a solute filtered into it. (p. 642; Fig. 19-17)

Micturition

31. The external sphincter of the bladder is skeletal muscle that is tonically contracted except during urination. (p. 643; Fig. 19-18)
32. Micturition is a simple spinal reflex subject to conscious and unconscious control. (p. 644)
33. Parasympathetic neurons cause contraction of the smooth muscle in the bladder wall. Somatic motor neurons leading to the external sphincter are simultaneously inhibited. (p. 644)

QUESTIONS

(Answers to the Review Questions begin on page A1.)

THE PHYSIOLOGY PLACE

Access more review material online at **The Physiology Place** web site. There you'll find review questions, problem-solving activities, case studies, flashcards, and direct links to both *Interactive Physiology®* and *PhysioEx™*. To access the site, go to *www.physiologyplace.com* and select *Human Physiology*, Fifth Edition.

LEVEL ONE REVIEWING FACTS AND TERMS

1. List and explain the significance of the five characteristics of urine that can be found by physical examination.
2. List and explain the six major kidney functions.
3. At any given time, what percentage of cardiac output goes to the kidneys?
4. List the major structures of the urinary system in their anatomical sequence, from the kidneys to the urine leaving the body. Describe the function of each structure.
5. Arrange the following structures in the order that a drop of water entering the nephron would encounter them:
   (a) afferent arteriole
   (b) Bowman's capsule
   (c) collecting duct
   (d) distal tubule
   (e) glomerulus
   (f) loop of Henle
   (g) proximal tubule
   (h) renal pelvis
6. Name the three filtration barriers that solutes must cross as they move from plasma to the lumen of Bowman's capsule. What components of blood are usually excluded by these layers?
7. What force(s) promote(s) glomerular filtration? What force(s) oppose(s) it? What is meant by the term *net driving force*?
8. What does the abbreviation GFR stand for? What is a typical numerical value for GFR in milliliters per minute? In liters per day?
9. Identify the following structures, then explain their significance in renal physiology:
   (a) juxtaglomerular apparatus
   (b) macula densa
   (c) mesangial cell
   (d) podocyte
   (e) sphincters in the bladder
   (f) renal cortex
10. In which segment of the nephron does most reabsorption take place? When a molecule or ion is reabsorbed from the lumen of the nephron, where does it go? If a solute is filtered and not reabsorbed from the tubule, where does it go?
11. Match each of the following ions or molecules with its primary mode(s) of transport across the kidney epithelium.

(a) Na^+	1. transcytosis
(b) glucose	2. primary active transport
(c) urea	3. secondary active transport
(d) plasma proteins	4. facilitated diffusion
(e) water	5. movement through open channels
	6. simple diffusion through the phospholipid bilayer

12. List three solutes secreted into the tubule lumen.
13. What solute that is normally present in the body is used to estimate GFR in humans?
14. What is micturition?

LEVEL TWO REVIEWING CONCEPTS

15. Map the following terms. You may add additional terms if you like.

α-receptor	glomerulus
afferent arteriole	JG cells
autoregulation	macula densa
basal lamina	mesangial cell
Bowman's capsule	myogenic autoregulation
capillary blood pressure	norepinephrine
capsule fluid pressure	paracrine
colloid osmotic pressure	plasma proteins
efferent arteriole	podocyte
endothelium	resistance
epithelium	vasoconstriction
GFR	

19

16. Define, compare, and contrast the items in the following sets of terms:
    (a) filtration, secretion, and excretion
    (b) saturation, transport maximum, and renal threshold
    (c) probenecid, creatinine, inulin, and penicillin
    (d) clearance, excretion, and glomerular filtration rate
17. What are the advantages of a kidney that filters a large volume of fluid and then reabsorbs 99% of it?
18. If the afferent arteriole of a nephron constricts, what happens to GFR in that nephron? If the efferent arteriole of a nephron constricts, what happens to GFR in that nephron? Assume that no autoregulation takes place.
19. Diagram the micturition reflex. How is this reflex altered by toilet training? How do higher brain centers influence micturition?
20. Antimuscarinic drugs are the accepted treatment for an overactive bladder. Explain why they work for this condition.

LEVEL THREE PROBLEM SOLVING

21. You have been asked to study kidney function in a new species of rodent found in the Amazonian jungle. You isolate some nephrons and expose them to inulin. The following graph shows the results of your studies. (a) How is the rodent nephron handling inulin? Is inulin filtered? Is it excreted? Is there net inulin reabsorption? Is there net secretion? (b) On the graph, accurately draw a line indicating the net reabsorption or secretion. (*Hint:* excretion = filtration − reabsorption + secretion)

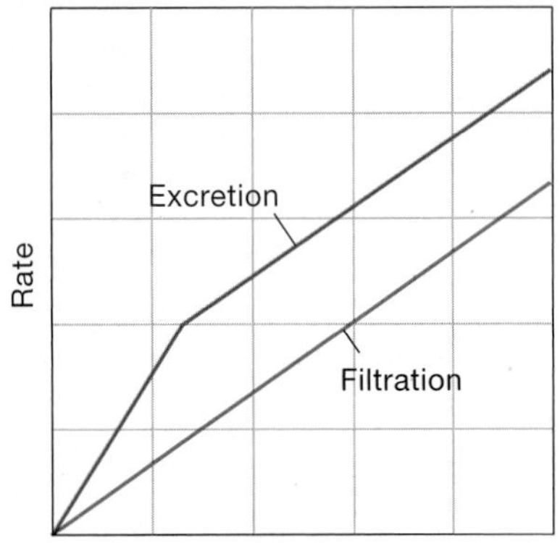

22. Draw a section of renal tubule epithelium showing three cells joined by cell junctions. Label the apical and basolateral membranes, the tubule lumen, and the extracellular fluid. Use the following written description of proximal tubule processes to draw a model cell.

    The proximal tubule cells contain carbonic anhydrase, which promotes the conversion of CO_2 and water to carbonic acid. Carbonic acid then dissociates to H^+ and HCO_3^-. Sodium is reabsorbed by an apical Na^+- H^+ antiporter and a basolateral Na^+- K^+-ATPase. Chloride is passively reabsorbed by movement through the paracellular pathway. Bicarbonate produced in the cytoplasm leaves the cell on a basolateral Na^+- HCO_3^- symporter.
23. Read the box on hemodialysis on p. 637 and see if you can create a model system that would work for dialysis. Draw two compartments (one to represent blood and one to represent dialysis fluid) separated by a semipermeable membrane. In the blood compartment, list normal extracellular fluid solutes and their concentrations (see the table with normal values of blood components inside the back cover of this book). What will happen to the concentrations of these solutes during kidney failure? Which of these solutes should you put in the dialysis fluid, and what should their concentrations be? (*Hint:* Do you want diffusion into the dialysis fluid, out of the dialysis fluid, or no net movement?) How would you change the dialysis fluid if the patient was retaining too much water?

LEVEL FOUR QUANTITATIVE PROBLEMS

24. Darlene weighs 50 kg. Assume that her total blood volume is 8% of her body weight, that her heart pumps her total blood volume once a minute, and that her renal blood flow is 25% of her cardiac output. Calculate the volume of blood that flows through Darlene's kidneys each minute.
25. Dwight was competing for a spot on the Olympic equestrian team. As his horse, Nitro, cleared a jump, the footing gave way, causing the horse to somersault, landing on Dwight and crushing him. The doctors feared kidney damage and ran several tests. Dwight's serum creatinine level was 2 mg/100 mL. His 24-hour urine specimen had a volume of 1 L and a creatinine concentration of 20 mg/mL. A second specimen taken over the next 24 hours had the same serum creatinine value and urine volume, but a urine creatinine concentration of 4 mg/ml. How many milligrams of creatinine are in each specimen? What is Dwight's creatinine clearance in each test? What is his GFR? Evaluate these results and comment on Dwight's kidney function.
26. You are a physiologist taking part in an archeological expedition to search for Atlantis. One of the deep-sea submersibles has come back with a mermaid, and you are taking a series of samples from her. You have determined that her GFR is 250 mL/min and that her kidneys reabsorb glucose with a transport maximum of 50 mg/min. What is her renal threshold for glucose? When her plasma concentration of glucose is 15 mg/mL, what is its glucose clearance?

ANSWERS

Answers to Concept Check Questions

Page 624

1. If extracellular K^+ decreases, more K^+ leaves the neuron, and the membrane potential hyperpolarizes (becomes more negative, increases).
2. If plasma Ca^{2+} decreases, the force of contraction decreases.

Page 625

3. When net filtration out of the glomerular capillaries occurs, the capillary hydrostatic pressure must be *greater than* the capillary colloid osmotic pressure.
4. When net reabsorption into the peritubular capillaries occurs, the capillary hydrostatic pressure must be *less than* the capillary colloid osmotic pressure.

Page 629

5. Filtration and secretion both represent movement from the extracellular fluid into the lumen. Filtration takes place only at Bowman's capsule; secretion takes place all along the rest of the tubule.
6. Glomerulus → Bowman's capsule → proximal tubule → loop of Henle → distal tubule → collecting duct → renal pelvis → ureter → urinary bladder → urethra.
7. If reabsorption decreases to half the normal rate, the body would run out of plasma in under an hour.

Page 633

8. Osmotic pressure is higher in efferent arterioles because fluid volume is decreased there, leaving the same amount of protein in a smaller volume.
9. This person's mean arterial pressure is 119 mm Hg. This person's GFR is 180 L/day.

Page 635

10. If the afferent arteriole constricts, the resistance in that arteriole increases, and blood flow through that arteriole is diverted to lower-resistance arterioles. GFR will decrease in the nephron whose arteriole constricted.
11. The primary driving force for GFR is blood pressure opposed by fluid pressure in Bowman's capsule and colloid osmotic pressure due to plasma proteins (Fig. 19-6). With fewer plasma proteins, the plasma has lower-than-normal colloid osmotic pressure. With less colloid osmotic pressure opposing GFR, GFR increases.

Page 642

12. Creatinine clearance = creatinine excretion rate/$[\text{creatinine}]_{\text{plasma}}$ = (1.5 mg creatinine/mL urine $\times$ 1.1 L urine/day)/1.8 mg creatinine/100 mL plasma. Creatinine clearance is about 92 L/day, and GFR is equal to creatinine clearance.

Answers to Figure and Graph Questions

Page 632

Fig. 19-8: Capillary blood pressure, GFR, and renal blood flow all increase.

Page 637

Fig. 19-14: The transport rate at 3 mg/mL is 3 mg/min; at 5 and 8 mg/mL, it is 4 mg/min. The transport rate is 2 mg/min at a plasma concentration of 2 mg/mL.

20 Integrative Physiology II: Fluid and Electrolyte Balance

Computer analysis of microarray data showing gene expression.

BACKGROUND BASICS

pH and buffers: **38** Control of blood pressure: **533** CO_2 excretion by lungs: **614** Membrane recycling: **153** Peptide hormones: **221** Membrane transport: **141** Carbonic anhydrase: **610** Osmolarity and tonicity: **159** Posterior pituitary hormones: **228** Body fluid compartments: **4** Steroid hormones: **222** Polarized epithelial cells: **155** Second messenger systems: **184** Glomerular filtration rate: **631** Protein structure: **31**

At a 10% loss of body fluid, the patient will show signs of confusion, distress, and hallucinations and at 20%, death will occur.

—Poul Astrup, in ***Salt and Water in Culture and Medicine***, 1993

RUNNING PROBLEM

Hyponatremia

Lauren was competing in her first ironman-distance triathlon, a 140.6-mile race consisting of 2.4 miles of swimming, 112 miles of cycling, and 26.2 miles of running. At mile 22 of the run, approximately 16 hours after starting the race, she collapsed. After being admitted to the medical tent, Lauren complained of nausea, a headache, and general fatigue. The medical staff noted that Lauren's face and clothing were covered in white crystals. When they weighed her and compared that value with her pre-race weight recorded at registration, they realized Lauren had gained 2 kg during the race.

651 653 667 669 675 681

The American businesswoman in Tokyo finished her workout and stopped at the snack bar of the fitness club to ask for a sports drink. The attendant handed her a bottle labeled "Pocari Sweat®." Although the thought of drinking sweat is not very appealing, the physiological basis for the name is sound.

During exercise, the body secretes sweat, a dilute solution of water and ions, particularly Na^+, K^+, and Cl^-. To maintain homeostasis, the body must replace any substances it has lost to the external environment. For this reason, the replacement fluid a person consumes after exercise should resemble sweat.

In this chapter, we explore how humans maintain salt and water balance, also known as fluid and electrolyte balance. The homeostatic control mechanisms for fluid and electrolyte balance in the body are aimed at maintaining four parameters: fluid volume, osmolarity, the concentrations of individual ions, and pH.

FLUID AND ELECTROLYTE HOMEOSTASIS

The human body is in a state of constant flux. Over the course of a day we ingest about 2 liters of fluid that contains 6–15 grams of NaCl. In addition, we take in varying amounts of other electrolytes, including K^+, H^+, Ca^{2+}, HCO_3^-, and phosphate ions (HPO_4^{2-}). The body's task is to maintain *mass balance* [p. 133]: what comes in must be excreted if the body does not need it.

The body has several routes for excreting ions and water. The kidneys are the primary route for water loss and for removal of many ions. Under normal conditions, small amounts of both water and ions are lost in the feces and sweat as well. In addition, the lungs lose water and help remove H^+ and HCO_3^- by excreting CO_2.

Although physiological mechanisms that maintain fluid and electrolyte balance are important, behavioral mechanisms also play an essential role. *Thirst* is critical because drinking is the only normal way to replace lost water. *Salt appetite* is a behavior that leads people and animals to seek and ingest salt (sodium chloride, NaCl).

Why are we concerned with homeostasis of these substances? Water and Na^+ are associated with extracellular fluid volume and osmolarity. Disturbances in K^+ balance can cause serious problems with cardiac and muscle function by disrupting the membrane potential of excitable cells. Ca^{2+} is involved in a variety of body processes, from exocytosis and muscle contraction to bone formation and blood clotting, and H^+ and HCO_3^- are the ions whose balance determines body pH.

ECF Osmolarity Affects Cell Volume

Why is maintaining osmolarity so important to the body? The answer lies in the fact that water crosses most cell membranes freely. If the osmolarity of the extracellular fluid changes, water moves into or out of cells and changes intracellular volume. If ECF osmolarity decreases as a result of excess water intake, water moves into the cells and they swell. If ECF osmolarity increases as a result of salt intake, water moves out of the cells and they shrink. Cell volume is so important that many cells have independent mechanisms for maintaining it.

For example, renal tubule cells in the medulla of the kidney are constantly exposed to high extracellular fluid osmolarity, yet these cells maintain normal cell volume. They do so by synthesizing organic solutes as needed to make their intracellular osmolarity match that of the medullary interstitial fluid. The organic solutes used to raise intracellular osmolarity include sugar alcohols and certain amino acids. Other cells in the body regulate their volume by changing their ionic composition.

In a few instances, changes in cell volume are believed to act as signals that initiate certain cellular responses. For example, swelling of liver cells activates protein and glycogen synthesis, and shrinkage of these cells causes protein and glycogen breakdown. In many cases, however, inappropriate changes in cell volume—either shrinking or swelling—impair cell function. The brain, encased in the rigid skull, is particularly vulnerable to damage from swelling. In general, maintenance of ECF osmolarity within a normal range is essential to maintain cell volume homeostasis.

Multiple Systems Integrate Fluid and Electrolyte Balance

The process of fluid and electrolyte balance is truly integrative because it involves the respiratory and cardiovascular systems in addition to renal and behavioral responses. Adjustments made by the lungs and cardiovascular system are primarily

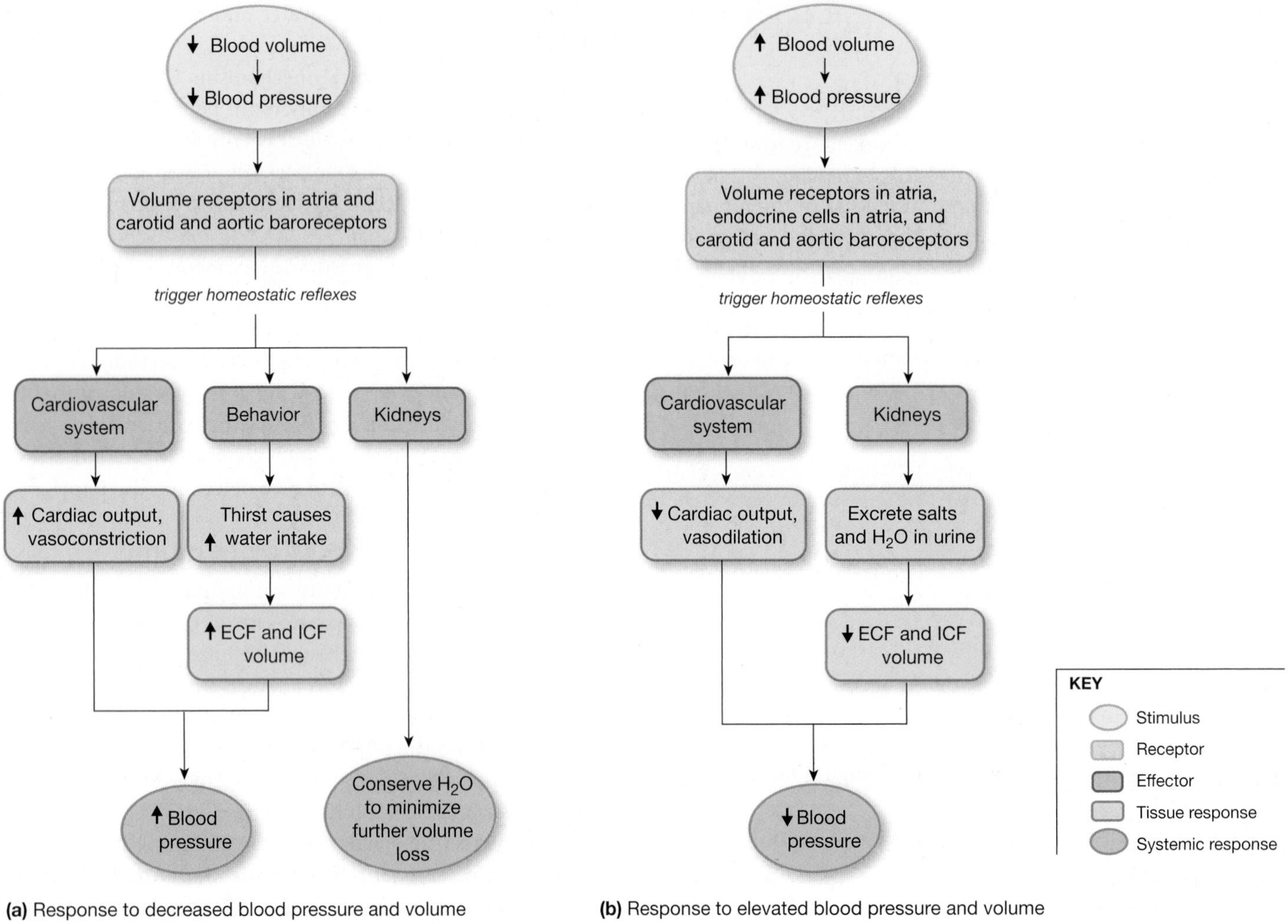

● **FIGURE 20-1** ***The body's integrated responses to changes in blood volume and blood pressure***

under neural control and can be made quite rapidly. Homeostatic compensation by the kidneys occurs more slowly because the kidneys are primarily under endocrine and neuroendocrine control. For example, small changes in blood pressure that result from increases or decreases in blood volume are quickly corrected by the cardiovascular control center in the brain [p. 533]. If volume changes are persistent or of large magnitude, the kidneys step in to help maintain homeostasis.

Figure 20-1 ● summarizes the integrated response of the body to changes in blood volume and blood pressure. Signals from carotid and aortic baroreceptors and atrial volume receptors initiate a quick neural response mediated through the cardiovascular control center and a slower response elicited from the kidneys. In addition, low blood pressure stimulates thirst. In both situations, renal function integrates with the cardiovascular system to keep blood pressure within a normal range.

Because of the overlap in their functions, a change made by one system—whether renal or cardiovascular—is likely to have consequences that affect the other. Endocrine pathways initiated by the kidneys have direct effects on the cardiovascular system, for instance, and hormones released by myocardial cells act on the kidneys. Sympathetic pathways from the cardiovascular control center affect not only cardiac output and vasoconstriction but also glomerular filtration and hormone release by the kidneys.

In this way the maintenance of blood pressure, blood volume, and ECF osmolarity forms a network of interwoven control pathways. This integration of function in multiple systems is one of the more difficult concepts in physiology but it is also one of the most exciting areas of medicine and physiological research.

WATER BALANCE

Water is the most abundant molecule in the body, constituting about 50% of total body weight in females ages 17 to 39, and 60% of total body weight in males of the same age group. A 60-kg (132-lb) woman contains about 30 liters of body water, and the "standard" 70-kg man contains about 42 liters. Two-thirds of his water (about 28 liters) is inside the cells, about

3 liters are in the plasma, and the remaining 11 liters are in the interstitial fluid [Fig. 5-25, p. 158].

Daily Water Intake and Excretion Are Balanced

To maintain a constant volume of water in the body, we must take in the same amount of water that we excrete: intake must equal output. There are multiple avenues for daily water gain and loss (Fig. 20-2 ●). On average, an adult ingests a little more than 2 liters of water in food and drink in a day. Normal metabolism, especially aerobic respiration (glucose + $O_2 \rightarrow CO_2$ + H_2O), adds about 0.3 liter of water, bringing the total daily intake to approximately 2.5 liters.

Notice that the only means by which water normally enters the body from the external environment is by absorption through the digestive tract. Unlike some animals, we cannot absorb significant amounts of water directly through our skin. If fluids must be rapidly replaced or an individual is unable to eat and drink, fluid can be added directly to the plasma by means of **intravenous (IV) injection,** a medical procedure.

Most water is lost from the body in the urine, which has a daily volume of about 1.5 liters (Fig. 20-2). A small volume of water (about 100 mL) is lost in the feces. Additionally, water leaves the body through **insensible water loss.** This water loss, called *insensible* because we are not normally aware of it, occurs across the skin surface and during the exhalation of humidified air. Even though the human epidermis is modified with an outer layer of keratin to reduce evaporative water loss in a terrestrial environment [p. 86], we still lose about 900 mL of water insensibly each day. Thus the 2.5 liters of water we take in are balanced by the 2.5 liters that leave the body. Only water loss in the urine can be regulated.

Although urine is normally the major route of water loss, in certain situations other routes of water loss can become significant. Excessive sweating is one example. Another way in which water is lost is through *diarrhea,* a condition that can pose a major threat to the maintenance of water balance, particularly in infants.

Pathological water loss disrupts homeostasis in two ways. Volume depletion of the extracellular compartment decreases blood pressure. If blood pressure cannot be maintained through homeostatic compensations, the tissues do not get adequate oxygen. Also, if the fluid lost is hyposmotic to the body (as is the case in excessive sweating), the solutes left behind in the body raise osmolarity, potentially disrupting cell function.

Normally, water balance takes place automatically. Salty food makes us thirsty. Drinking 42 ounces of a soft drink means an extra trip to the bathroom. Salt and water balance is a subtle process that we are only peripherally aware of, like breathing and the beating of the heart.

Now that we have discussed *why* regulation of osmolarity is important, let's see *how* the body accomplishes that goal.

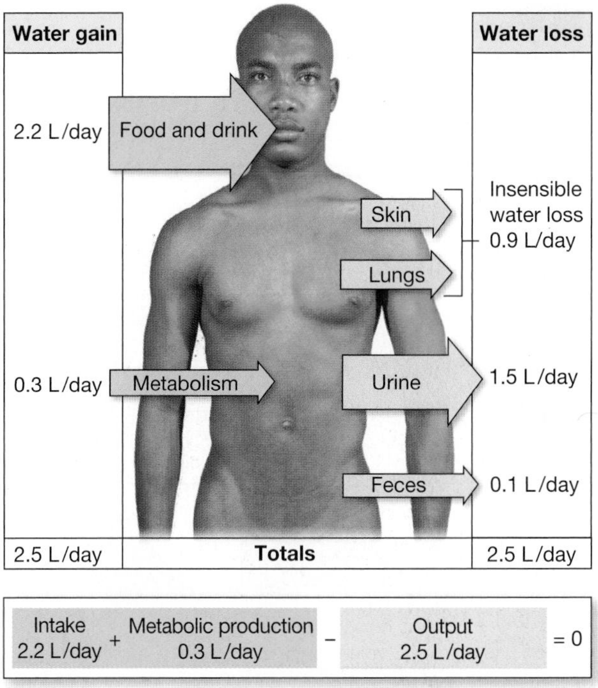

● **FIGURE 20-2** ***Water balance in the body***

The Kidneys Conserve Water

Figure 20-3 ● summarizes the role of the kidneys in water balance. The mug represents the body, and its hollow handle represents the kidneys, where body fluid filters into the nephrons and then may or may not be reabsorbed into the body. Some solutes and water leave the body in the urine, but the volume that leaves can be regulated, as indicated at the bottom of the handle.

The normal range for fluid volume in the mug lies between the dashed line and the open top. Fluid in the mug enters the handle (equivalent to being filtered into the kidney)

RUNNING PROBLEM

The medical staff was concerned with Lauren's large weight increase during the race. They asked her to recall what she ate and drank during the race. Lauren reported that to avoid getting dehydrated in the warm weather, she had drunk large quantities of water in addition to sports gel and sports drinks containing carbohydrates and electrolytes.

Question 1:
Name the two major body fluid compartments and give the major ions in each compartment.

Question 2:
Based on Lauren's history, give a reason for why her weight increased during the race.

651 653 667 669 675 681

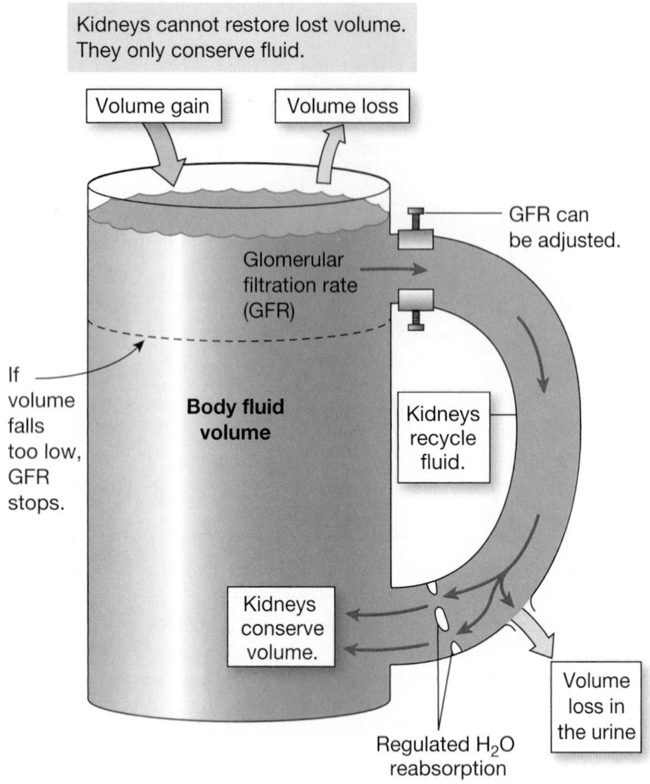
Kidneys cannot restore lost volume. They only conserve fluid.
Volume gain
Volume loss
GFR can be adjusted.
Glomerular filtration rate (GFR)
If volume falls too low, GFR stops.
Body fluid volume
Kidneys recycle fluid.
Kidneys conserve volume.
Volume loss in the urine
Regulated H_2O reabsorption

● **FIGURE 20-3** ***The kidneys conserve volume but cannot replace lost volume.***

and cycles back into the body of the mug to maintain the mug's volume. If fluid is added to the mug and threatens to overflow, the extra fluid is allowed to drain out of the handle (comparable to excess water excreted in urine). If a small volume is lost from the mug, fluid still flows through the handle, but fluid loss from the handle is turned off to prevent additional fluid loss.

The only way to replace lost fluid is to add water from a source outside the mug. Translating this model to the body underscores the fact that *the kidneys cannot replenish lost water: all they can do is conserve it.* And as shown in the mug model, if fluid loss is severe and volume falls below the dashed line, fluid no longer flows into the handle, just as a major decrease in blood volume and blood pressure shuts down renal filtration.

The Renal Medulla Creates Concentrated Urine

The concentration, or osmolarity, of urine is a measure of how much water is excreted by the kidneys. When maintenance of homeostasis requires eliminating excess water, the kidneys produce copious amounts of dilute urine with an osmolarity as low as 50 mOsM. Removal of excess water in urine is known as **diuresis** [*diourein,* to pass in urine]. (For this reason drugs that promote the excretion of urine are called *diuretics.*) When the kidneys are conserving water, the urine becomes quite concentrated, up to four times as concentrated as the blood (1200 mOsM versus the blood's 300 mOsM).

The kidneys control urine concentration by varying the amounts of water and Na^+ reabsorbed in the distal nephron (distal tubule and collecting duct). To produce dilute urine, the kidney must reabsorb solute without allowing water to follow by osmosis. This means that the apical tubule cell membranes must not be permeable to water. On the other hand, if urine is to become concentrated, the nephron must be able to reabsorb water but leave solute in the tubule lumen.

Mechanistically, it seems simple enough to create an epithelium that transports solutes but is impermeable to water (dilute urine)—simply remove all water pores on the apical cell membrane. But mechanistically it seems much more difficult to create concentrated urine. How can the kidney reabsorb water without first reabsorbing solute? At one time, scientists speculated that water was actively transported on carriers, just as Na^+ and other ions are. However, once scientists developed micropuncture techniques for sampling fluid inside kidney tubules, they discovered that water is reabsorbed only by osmosis through water pores (*aquaporins*).

The mechanism for absorbing water without solute turned out to be simple: make the collecting duct cells and interstitial fluid more concentrated than the fluid flowing into the tubule. Then, if the tubule cells have water pores, water can be absorbed from the lumen without first reabsorbing solute. This is indeed the situation in the kidney. Through an unusual arrangement of blood vessels and renal tubules, which we discuss later, the renal medulla maintains a high osmotic concentration in its cells and interstitial fluid. This high *medullary interstitial osmolarity* allows urine to be concentrated as it flows through the collecting duct.

Let's follow some filtered fluid through a nephron to see where these changes in osmolarity take place (Fig. 20-4 ●). The renal cortex has an interstitial osmolarity of about 300 mOsM but moving into the medulla, the interstitial osmolarity steadily increases until it reaches about 1200 mOsM where the collecting ducts empty into the renal pelvis [Fig. 19-1c, p. 626]. Recall from Chapter 19 that reabsorption in the proximal tubule is isosmotic [p. 628], and filtrate entering the loop of Henle has an osmolarity of about 300 mOsM (Fig. 20-4 ①).

Fluid leaving the loop of Henle, however, is hyposmotic, with an osmolarity of around 100 mOsM. This hyposmotic fluid is created when cells in the thick portion of the ascending limb of the loop transport Na^+, K^+, and Cl^- out of the tubule lumen (Fig. 20-4 ②). These cells are unusual because their apical surface (facing the tubule lumen) is impermeable to water. For this reason, when these cells transport solute out of the lumen, water cannot follow, decreasing the concentration of the tubule fluid. The loop of Henle is the primary site where the kidney creates hyposmotic fluid.

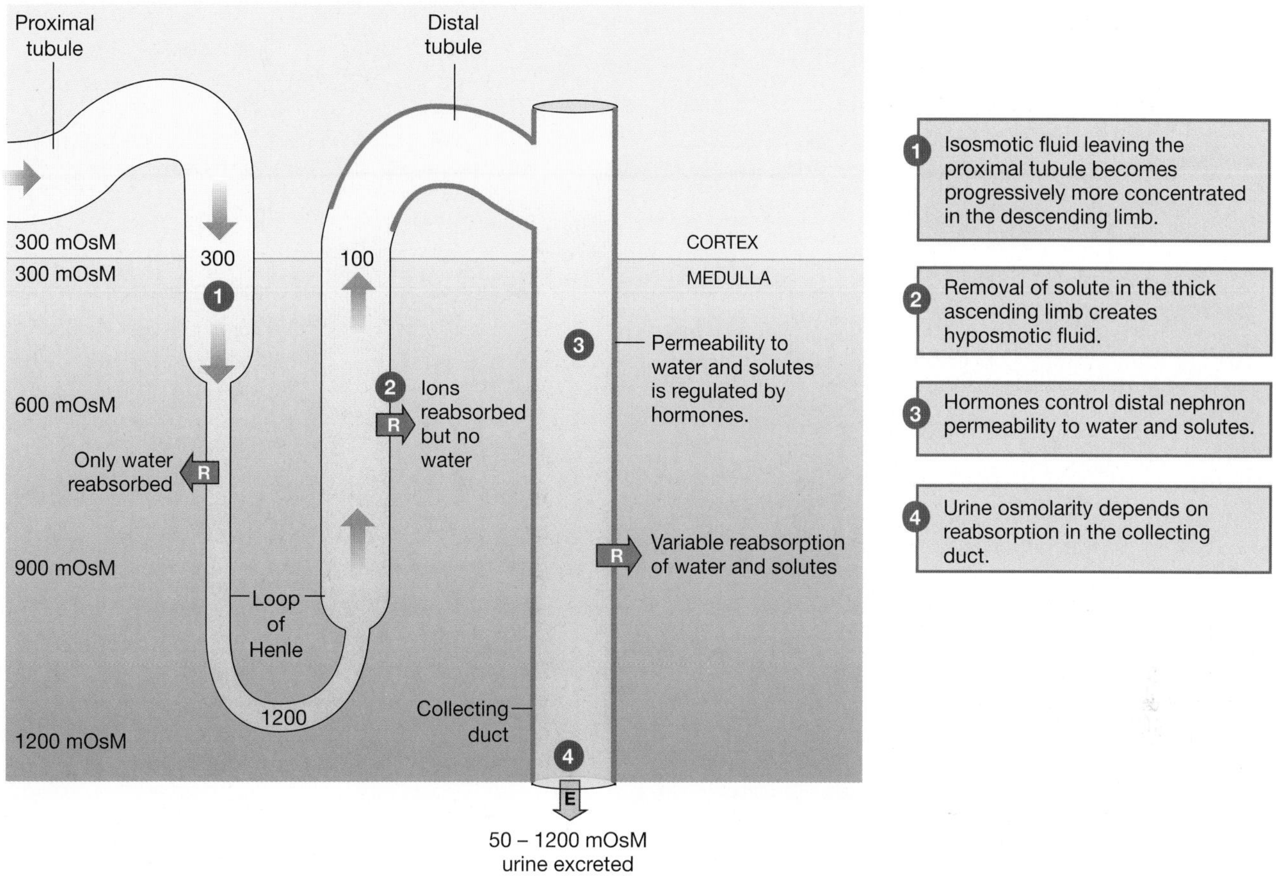
Proximal tubule
Distal tubule
300 mOsM
300 mOsM
300
100
CORTEX
MEDULLA
600 mOsM
Only water reabsorbed
Ions reabsorbed but no water
Permeability to water and solutes is regulated by hormones.
900 mOsM
Loop of Henle
Variable reabsorption of water and solutes
1200
1200 mOsM
Collecting duct
50 – 1200 mOsM urine excreted
Isosmotic fluid leaving the proximal tubule becomes progressively more concentrated in the descending limb.
Removal of solute in the thick ascending limb creates hyposmotic fluid.
Hormones control distal nephron permeability to water and solutes.
Urine osmolarity depends on reabsorption in the collecting duct.

● **FIGURE 20-4** *Osmolarity changes as filtrate flows through the nephron.*

Once hyposmotic fluid leaves the loop of Henle, it passes into the distal nephron. Here the water permeability of the tubule cells is variable and under hormonal control (Fig. 20-4 ③). When the apical membrane of distal nephron cells is not permeable to water, water cannot leave the tubule, and the filtrate remains dilute. A small amount of additional solute can be reabsorbed as fluid passes along the collecting duct, making the filtrate even more dilute. When this happens, the concentration of urine can be as low as 50 mOsM (Fig. 20-4 ④).

On the other hand, when the body needs to conserve water by reabsorbing it, the tubule epithelium in the distal nephron must become permeable to water. The cells accomplish this by inserting water pores into their apical membranes. Once water can enter the cells, osmosis draws water out of the less-concentrated lumen and into the more concentrated interstitial fluid. At maximal water permeability, removal of water from the tubule leaves behind concentrated urine with an osmolarity that can be as high as 1200 mOsM (Fig. 20-4 ④).

Water reabsorption in the kidneys conserves water and can decrease body osmolarity to some degree when coupled with excretion of solute in the urine. But remember that the kidney's homeostatic mechanisms can do nothing to restore lost fluid volume. Only the ingestion or infusion of water can replace water that has been lost.

Vasopressin Controls Water Reabsorption

How do the distal tubule and collecting duct cells alter their permeability to water? The process involves adding or removing

CLINICAL FOCUS

DIABETES

OSMOTIC DIURESIS

The primary sign of diabetes mellitus is an elevated blood glucose concentration. In untreated diabetics, if blood glucose levels exceed the renal threshold for glucose reabsorption [p. 639], glucose is excreted in the urine. This may not seem like a big deal, but any additional nonreabsorbable solute that remains in the lumen forces additional water to be excreted, causing *osmotic diuresis*. Suppose, for example, that the nephrons must excrete 300 milliosmoles of NaCl. If the urine is maximally concentrated at 1200 mOsM, the NaCl is excreted in a volume of 0.25 L. However, if the NaCl is joined by 300 milliosmoles of glucose that must be excreted, the volume of urine doubles, to 0.5 L. Osmotic diuresis in untreated diabetics (primarily type 1) causes *polyuria* (excessive urination) and *polydipsia* (excessive thirst) [*dipsios,* thirsty] as a result of dehydration and high plasma osmolarity.

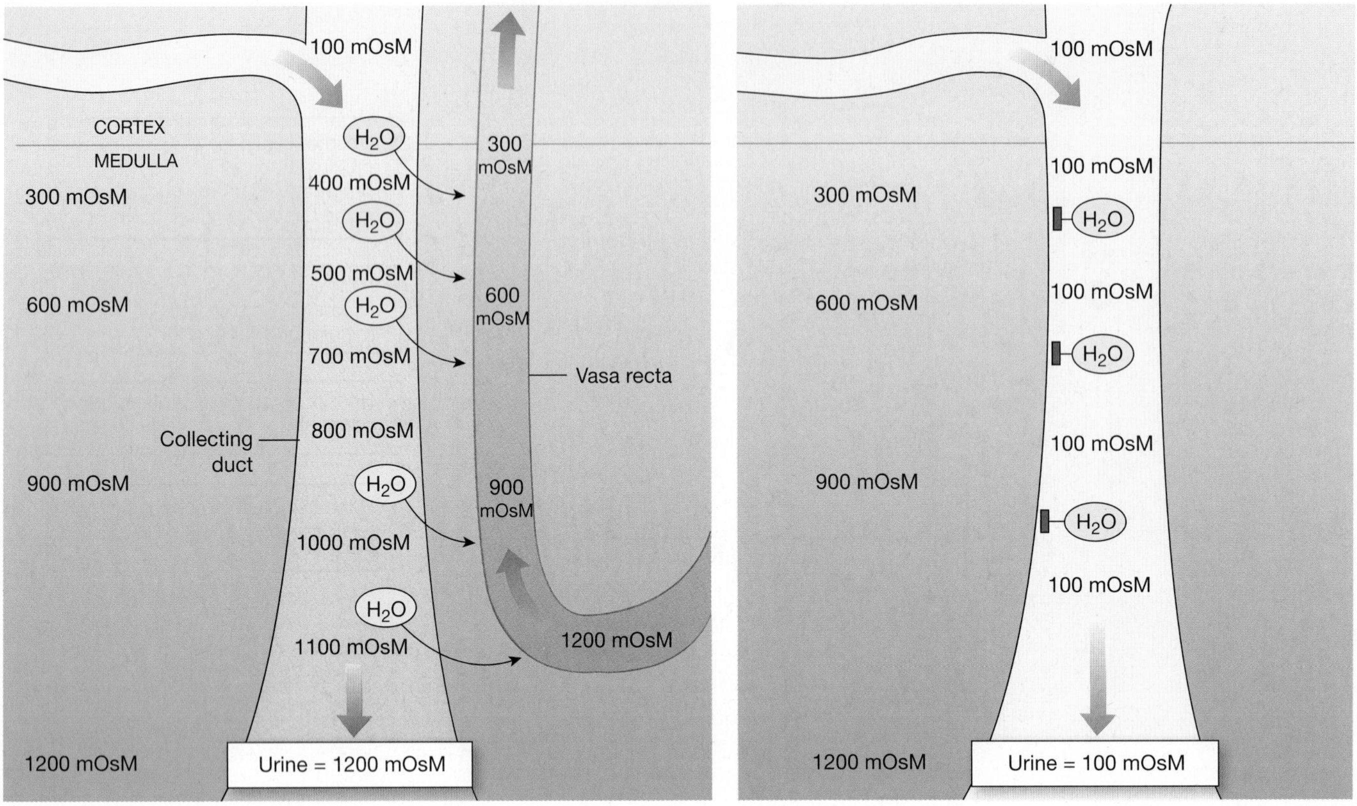
100 mOsM
CORTEX
MEDULLA
300 mOsM
600 mOsM
900 mOsM
1200 mOsM
H_2O
400 mOsM
500 mOsM
700 mOsM
800 mOsM
1000 mOsM
1100 mOsM
300 mOsM
600 mOsM
900 mOsM
1200 mOsM
Vasa recta
Collecting duct
Urine = 1200 mOsM
100 mOsM
300 mOsM
600 mOsM
900 mOsM
1200 mOsM
Urine = 100 mOsM

(a) With maximal vasopressin, the collecting duct is freely permeable to water. Water leaves by osmosis and is carried away by the vasa recta capillaries. Urine is concentrated.

(b) In the absence of vasopressin, the collecting duct is impermeable to water and the urine is dilute.

● **FIGURE 20-5** ***Vasopressin makes the collecting duct permeable to water.***

water pores in the apical membrane under the direction of the posterior pituitary hormone **vasopressin** [p. 229]. Because vasopressin causes the body to retain water, it is also known as *antidiuretic hormone (ADH).*

When vasopressin acts on target cells, water pores are inserted into the apical membrane, allowing water to move out of the lumen by osmosis (Fig. 20-5a ●). The water moves by osmosis because solute concentration in the cells and interstitial fluid of the renal medulla is higher than that of fluid in the tubule. In the absence of vasopressin, the collecting duct is impermeable to water (Fig. 20-5b). Although a concentration gradient is present across the epithelium, water remains in the tubule, producing dilute urine.

The water permeability of the collecting duct is not an all-or-none phenomenon, as the previous paragraph might suggest. Permeability is variable, depending on how much vasopressin is present. The graded effect of vasopressin allows the body to match urine concentration closely to the body's needs.

Vasopressin and Aquaporins Most membranes in the body are freely permeable to water. What makes the cells of the distal nephron different? The answer lies with the *water pores* found in these cells. Water pores are **aquaporins,** a family of membrane channels with at least 10 different isoforms that occur in mammalian tissues. The kidney has multiple isoforms of aquaporins, including *aquaporin-2* (AQP2), the water channel regulated by vasopressin.

AQP2 in a collecting duct cell may be found in two locations: on the apical membrane facing the tubule lumen and in the membrane of cytoplasmic storage vesicles (Fig. 20-6 ●). (Two other isoforms of aquaporins are present in the basolateral membrane, but they are not regulated by vasopressin.) When vasopressin levels (and, consequently, collecting duct water permeability) are low, the collecting duct cell has few water pores in its apical membrane and stores its AQP2 water pores in cytoplasmic storage vesicles.

When vasopressin from the posterior pituitary arrives at its target, it binds to its *V2 receptor* on the basolateral side of the cell (step 1 in Fig. 20-6). Binding activates a G-protein/cAMP second messenger system [p. 186]. Subsequent phosphorylation of intracellular proteins causes the AQP2 vesicles to move to the apical membrane and fuse with it. Exocytosis inserts the AQP2 water pores into the apical membrane. Now the cell is permeable to water. This process, in which parts of the cell membrane are alternately added

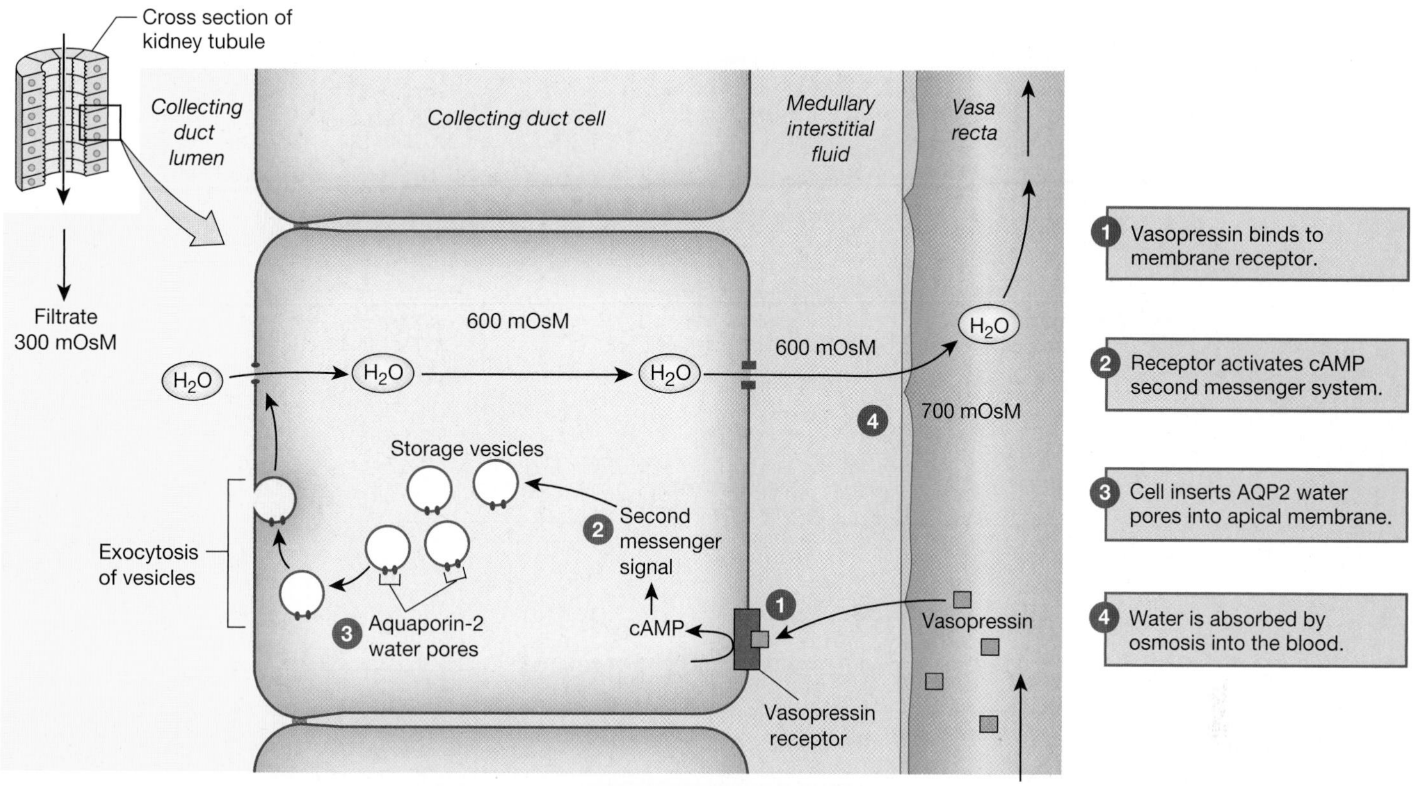
Cross section of kidney tubule
Collecting duct lumen
Collecting duct cell
Medullary interstitial fluid
Vasa recta
Filtrate 300 mOsM
600 mOsM
600 mOsM
700 mOsM
H2O
Storage vesicles
Second messenger signal
cAMP
Exocytosis of vesicles
Aquaporin-2 water pores
Vasopressin
Vasopressin receptor
1 Vasopressin binds to membrane receptor.
2 Receptor activates cAMP second messenger system.
3 Cell inserts AQP2 water pores into apical membrane.
4 Water is absorbed by osmosis into the blood.

● **FIGURE 20-6** ***Vasopressin causes insertion of water pores into the apical membrane.***

by exocytosis and withdrawn by endocytosis, is known as **membrane recycling** (Fig. 5-21, p. 153).

CONCEPT CHECK

1. Does the apical membrane of a collecting duct cell have more water pores when vasopressin is present or when it is absent?
2. If vasopressin secretion is suppressed, will urine be dilute or concentrated?

Answers: p. 684

Blood Volume and Osmolarity Activate Osmoreceptors

What stimuli control vasopressin secretion? There are three: plasma osmolarity, blood volume, and blood pressure (Fig. 20-7 ●). The most potent stimulus for vasopressin release is an increase in plasma osmolarity. Osmolarity is monitored by **osmoreceptors,** stretch-sensitive neurons that increase their firing rate as osmolarity increases. Our current model indicates that when the osmoreceptors shrink, nonspecific cation channels linked to actin filaments open, depolarizing the cell.

The primary osmoreceptors for vasopressin release are in the hypothalamus. When plasma osmolarity is below the threshold value of 280 mOsM, the osmoreceptors do not fire, and vasopressin release from the pituitary ceases (Fig. 20-8 ●). If plasma osmolarity rises above 280 mOsM, the osmoreceptors stimulate release of vasopressin.

Decreases in blood pressure and blood volume are less powerful stimuli for vasopressin release. The primary receptors for decreased volume are stretch-sensitive receptors in the atria. Blood pressure is monitored by the same carotid and aortic baroreceptors that initiate cardiovascular responses [p. 533]. When blood pressure or blood volume is low, these receptors signal the hypothalamus to secrete vasopressin and conserve fluid.

In adults, vasopressin secretion also shows a circadian rhythm, with increased secretion during the overnight hours. As a result of this increase, less urine is produced overnight than during the day, and the first urine excreted in the morning is more concentrated. One theory for the cause of bedwetting, or **nocturnal enuresis,** in children is that these children have a developmental delay in the normal pattern of increased vasopressin secretion at night. With less vasopressin, the children's urine output stays elevated, causing the bladder to fill to its maximum capacity and empty spontaneously during sleep. Many of these children can be successfully treated with a nasal spray of *desmopressin,* a vasopressin derivative, administered at bedtime.

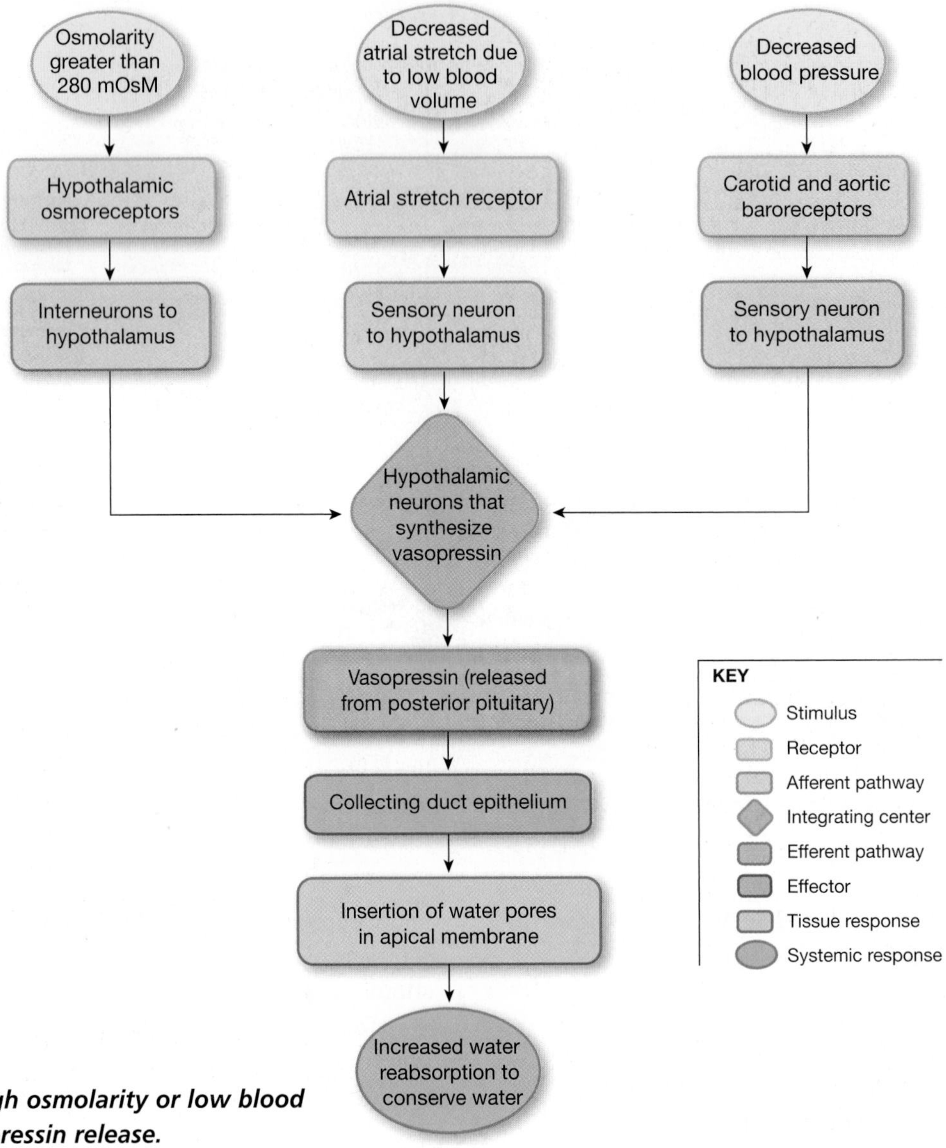

● **FIGURE 20-7** ***High osmolarity or low blood pressure cause vasopressin release.***

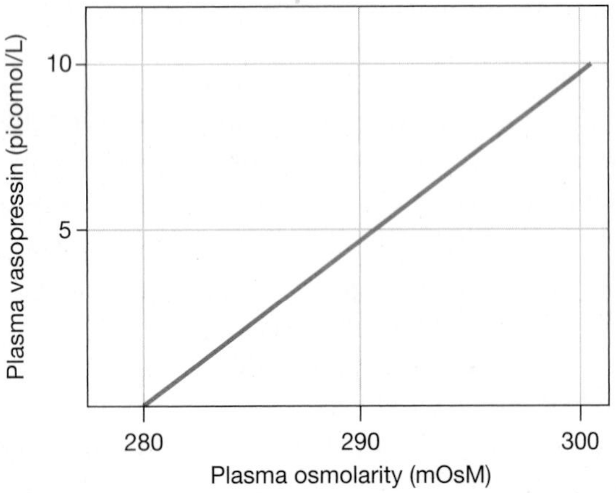

● **FIGURE 20-8** ***The effect of plasma osmolarity on vasopressin secretion from the posterior pituitary***

CONCEPT CHECK

3. A scientist monitoring the activity of osmoreceptors notices that infusion of hyperosmotic saline (NaCl) causes increased firing of the osmoreceptors. Infusion of hyperosmotic urea (a penetrating solute) [p. 161] had no effect on the firing rate. If osmoreceptors fire only when cell volume decreases, explain why hyperosmotic urea did not affect them.
4. If vasopressin increases water reabsorption by the blood vessels of a nephron, would vasopressin secretion be increased or decreased with dehydration?
5. Experiments suggest that there are peripheral osmoreceptors in the lumen of the upper digestive tract and in the hepatic portal vein [Fig. 14-1, p. 470]. What is the adaptive significance of osmoreceptors in these locations? Answers: p. 684

FIGURE 20-9 ***A countercurrent heat exchanger***

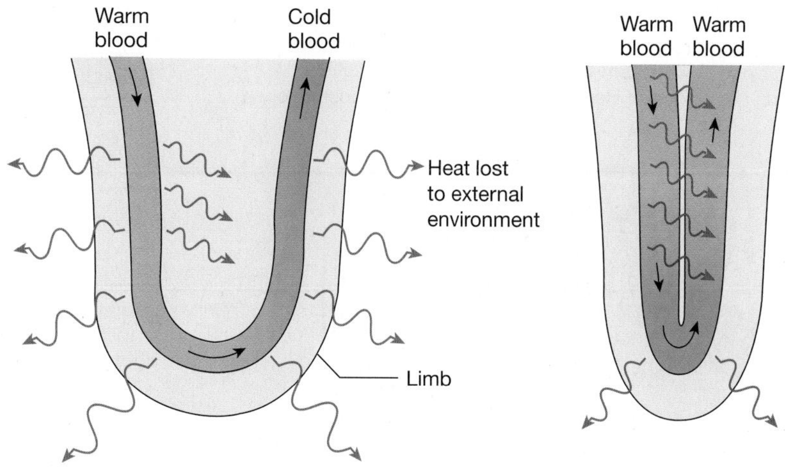

(a) If blood vessels are not close to each other, heat is dissipated to the external environment.

(b) Countercurrent heat exchanger allows warm blood entering the limb to transfer heat directly to blood flowing back into the body.

The Loop of Henle Is a Countercurrent Multiplier

Vasopressin is the signal for water reabsorption out of the nephron tubule, but the key to the kidney's ability to produce concentrated urine is the high osmolarity of the medullary *interstitium* (interstitial fluid compartment of the kidney). Without it, there would be no concentration gradient for osmotic movement of water out of the collecting duct. What creates this high ECF osmolarity? And why isn't the interstitial fluid osmolarity reduced as water is reabsorbed from the collecting duct and descending limb of the loop of Henle (see Fig. 20-4)? The answers to these questions lie in the anatomical arrangement of the loop of Henle and its associated blood vessels, the vasa recta. Together, these structures form a *countercurrent exchange system*.

Countercurrent Exchange Systems **Countercurrent exchange systems** require arterial and venous blood vessels that pass very close to each other, with their fluid flow moving in opposite directions (the name *countercurrent* reflects the fact that the two flows run *counter to* each other). This anatomical arrangement allows the passive transfer of heat or molecules from one vessel to the other. Because the countercurrent heat exchanger is easier to understand, we first examine how it works and then apply the same principle to the kidney.

The countercurrent heat exchanger in mammals and birds evolved to reduce heat loss from flippers, tails, and other limbs that are poorly insulated and have a high surface-area-to-volume ratio. Without a heat exchanger, warm blood flowing from the body core into the limb would easily lose heat to the surrounding environment (Fig. 20-9a ●). With a countercurrent heat exchanger, warm arterial blood entering the limb transfers its heat to cooler venous blood flowing from the tip of the limb back into the body (Fig. 20-9b). This arrangement reduces the amount of heat lost to the external environment.

The countercurrent exchange system of the kidney—the loop of Henle—works on the same principle, except that it transfers water and solutes instead of heat. However, because the kidney forms a closed system, the solutes are not lost to the environment. Instead, the solutes concentrate in the interstitium. This process is aided by active transport of solutes out of the ascending limb, which makes the ECF osmolarity even greater. A countercurrent exchange system in which exchange is enhanced by active transport of solutes is called a **countercurrent multiplier**.

The Renal Countercurrent Multiplier An overview of the countercurrent multiplier system in the renal medulla is shown in Figure 20-10a ●. The system has two components: loops of Henle that leave the cortex, dip down into the more concentrated environment of the medulla, then ascend into the cortex again, and the peritubular capillaries known as the **vasa recta**. These capillaries, like the loop of Henle, dip down into the medulla and then go back up to the cortex, also forming hairpin loops.

Although textbooks traditionally show a single nephron with a single loop of capillary (as we do in Fig. 20-10a), each kidney has thousands of collecting ducts and loops of Henle packed between thousands of vasa recta capillaries, blurring the direct association between a nephron and its vascular supply. Functionally, blood flow in the vasa recta moves in the opposite direction from filtrate flow in the loops of Henle, as shown in Figure 20-10a.

Let's follow some fluid as it moves through the loop. Isosmotic filtrate from the proximal tubule first flows into the descending limb of the loop of Henle. The descending limb is permeable to water but does not transport ions. As the loop dips into the medulla, water moves by osmosis from the descending limb into the progressively more

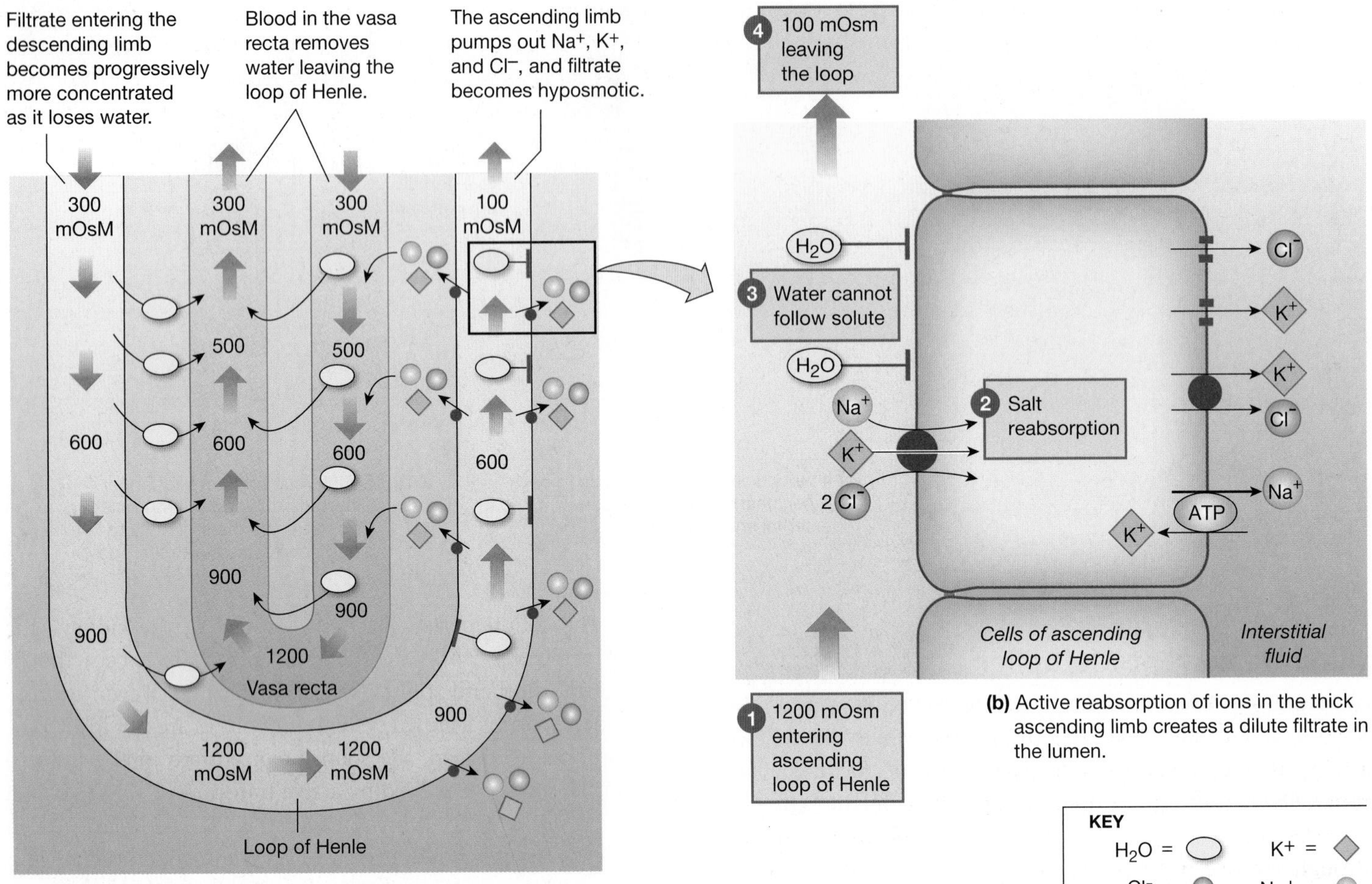

(a) Countercurrent exchange in the medulla of the kidney

(b) Active reabsorption of ions in the thick ascending limb creates a dilute filtrate in the lumen.

● **FIGURE 20-10** ***Countercurrent exchange in the medulla of the kidney.***
The thick ascending limb of the loop of Henle transports salt to create dilute urine.

concentrated interstitial fluid, leaving solutes behind in the tubule lumen.

The filtrate becomes progressively more concentrated as it moves deeper into the medulla. At the tips of the longest loops of Henle, the filtrate reaches a concentration of 1200 mOsM. Filtrate in shorter loops (which do not extend into the most concentrated regions of the medulla) does not reach such a high concentration.

When the fluid flow reverses direction and enters the ascending limb of the loop, the properties of the tubule epithelium change. The tubule epithelium in this segment of the nephron is impermeable to water while actively transporting Na^+, K^+ and Cl^- out of the tubule into the interstitial fluid. The loss of solute from the lumen causes the filtrate osmolarity to decrease steadily, from 1200 mOsM at the bottom of the loop to 100 mOsM at the point where the ascending limb leaves the medulla and enters the cortex. The net result of the countercurrent multiplier in the kidney is to produce hyperosmotic interstitial fluid in the medulla and hyposmotic filtrate leaving the loop of Henle.

Normally, about 25% of all Na^+ and K^+ reabsorption takes place in the ascending limb of the loop. Some transporters responsible for active ion reabsorption in the thick portion of the ascending limb are shown in Figure 20-10b. The *NKCC symporter* uses energy stored in the Na^+ concentration gradient to transport Na^+, K^+, and 2 Cl^- from the lumen into the epithelial cells of the ascending limb. The Na^+-K^+-ATPase removes Na^+ from the cells on the basolateral side of the epithelium, while K^+ and Cl^- leave the cells together on a cotransport protein or through open channels. NKCC-mediated transport can be inhibited by drugs known as "loop diuretics," such as furosemide (Lasix).

CONCEPT CHECK

6. Explain why patients taking a loop diuretic that inhibits solute reabsorption excrete greater-than-normal volumes of urine.
7. Loop diuretics that inhibit the NKCC symporter are sometimes called "potassium-wasting" diuretics. Explain why people who are on loop diuretics must increase their dietary K^+ intake.

Answers: p. 684

The Vasa Recta Removes Water It is easy to see how transport of solute out of the ascending limb of the loop of Henle dilutes the filtrate and helps concentrate the interstitial fluid in the medulla. Still, why doesn't the water leaving the descending limb of the loop (see Fig. 20-10a) *dilute* the interstitial fluid of the medulla? The answer lies in the close anatomical association of the loop of Henle and the peritubular capillaries of the vasa recta.

Water or solutes that leave the tubule move into the vasa recta if an osmotic or concentration gradient exists between the medullary interstitium and the blood in the vasa recta. For example, assume that at the point at which the vasa recta enter the medulla, the blood in the vasa recta is 300 mOsM, isosmotic with the cortex. As the blood flows deeper into the medulla, it loses water and picks up solutes transported out of the ascending limb of the loop of Henle, carrying these solutes farther into the medulla. By the time the blood reaches the bottom of the vasa recta loop, it has a high osmolarity, similar to that of the surrounding interstitial fluid (1200 mOsM).

Then, as blood in the vasa recta flows back toward the cortex, the high plasma osmolarity attracts the water that is being lost from the descending limb, as Figure 20-10a shows. The movement of this water into the vasa recta decreases the osmolarity of the blood while simultaneously preventing the water from diluting the concentrated medullary interstitial fluid.

The end result of this arrangement is that blood flowing through the vasa recta removes the water reabsorbed from the loop of Henle. Without the vasa recta, water moving out of the descending limb of the loop of Henle would eventually dilute the medullary interstitium. The vasa recta thus play an important part in keeping the medullary solute concentration high.

Urea Increases the Osmolarity of the Medullary Interstitium The high solute concentration in the medullary interstitium is only partly due to NaCl. Nearly half the solute in this compartment is urea. Where does this urea come from? For many years scientists thought urea crossed cell membranes only by passive transport. However, in recent years researchers have learned that membrane transporters for urea are present in the collecting duct and loops of Henle. One family of transporters consists of facilitated diffusion carriers, and the other family has Na^+-dependent secondary active transporters. These urea transporters help concentrate urea in the medullary interstitium, where it contributes to the high interstitial osmolarity.

SODIUM BALANCE AND ECF VOLUME

With an average American diet, we ingest a lot of NaCl—about 9 grams per day. This is about 2 teaspoons of salt, or 155 milliosmoles of Na^+ and 155 milliosmoles of Cl^-. Let's see what would happen to our bodies if the kidneys could not get rid of this Na^+. (Remember from Chapter 19 that Cl^- follows the electrical gradient created by Na^+ transport [p. 635].)

Our normal plasma Na^+ concentration, measured from a venous blood sample, is 135–145 milliosmoles Na^+ per liter of plasma. Because Na^+ distributes freely between plasma and interstitial fluid, this value also represents our ECF Na^+ concentration. If we add 155 milliosmoles of Na^+ to the ECF, how much water would we have to add to keep the ECF Na^+ concentration at 140 mOsM? One form of an equation asking this question is

$$155 \text{ mosmol}/x \text{ liters} = 140 \text{ mosmol/liter}$$

$$x = 1.1 \text{ liters}$$

We would have to add more than a liter of water to the ECF to compensate for the addition of the Na^+. Normal ECF volume is about 14 liters, and so that increase in volume would represent about an 8% gain! Imagine what that volume increase would do to blood pressure.

Suppose, however, that instead of adding water to keep plasma concentrations constant, we add the NaCl but don't drink any water. What happens to osmolarity now? If we assume that normal total body osmolarity is 300 mOsM and that the volume of fluid in the body is 42 L, the addition of 155 milliosmoles of Na^+ and 155 milliosmoles of Cl^- would increase total body osmolarity to 307 mOsM*—a substantial increase. In addition, because NaCl is a nonpenetrating solute, it would stay in the ECF. Higher osmolarity in the ECF would draw water from the cells, shrinking them and disrupting normal cell function.

Fortunately, our homeostatic mechanisms usually maintain mass balance: anything extra that comes into the body is excreted. Figure 20-11 ● shows a generalized homeostatic pathway for sodium balance in response to salt ingestion. Here's how it works:

The addition of NaCl to the body raises osmolarity. This stimulus triggers two responses: vasopressin secretion and thirst. Vasopressin release causes the kidneys to conserve water (by reabsorbing water from the filtrate) and concentrate the urine. Thirst prompts us to drink water or other fluids. The increased fluid intake decreases osmolarity, but the combination of salt and water intake increases both ECF volume and blood pressure. These increases then trigger another series of control pathways, which bring ECF volume, blood pressure, and total-body osmolarity back into the normal range by excreting extra salt and water.

The kidneys are responsible for most Na^+ excretion, and normally only a small amount of Na^+ leaves the body in feces and perspiration. However, in situations such as vomiting, diarrhea, and heavy sweating, we may lose significant amounts of Na^+ and Cl^- through nonrenal routes.

*(155 mosmol Na^+ + 155 mosmol Cl^-)/42 L = 7.4 mosmol/L added; 300 mosmol/L initial + 7.4 mosmol/L added = 307 mOsM final

● **FIGURE 20-11** ***Homeostatic responses to salt ingestion***

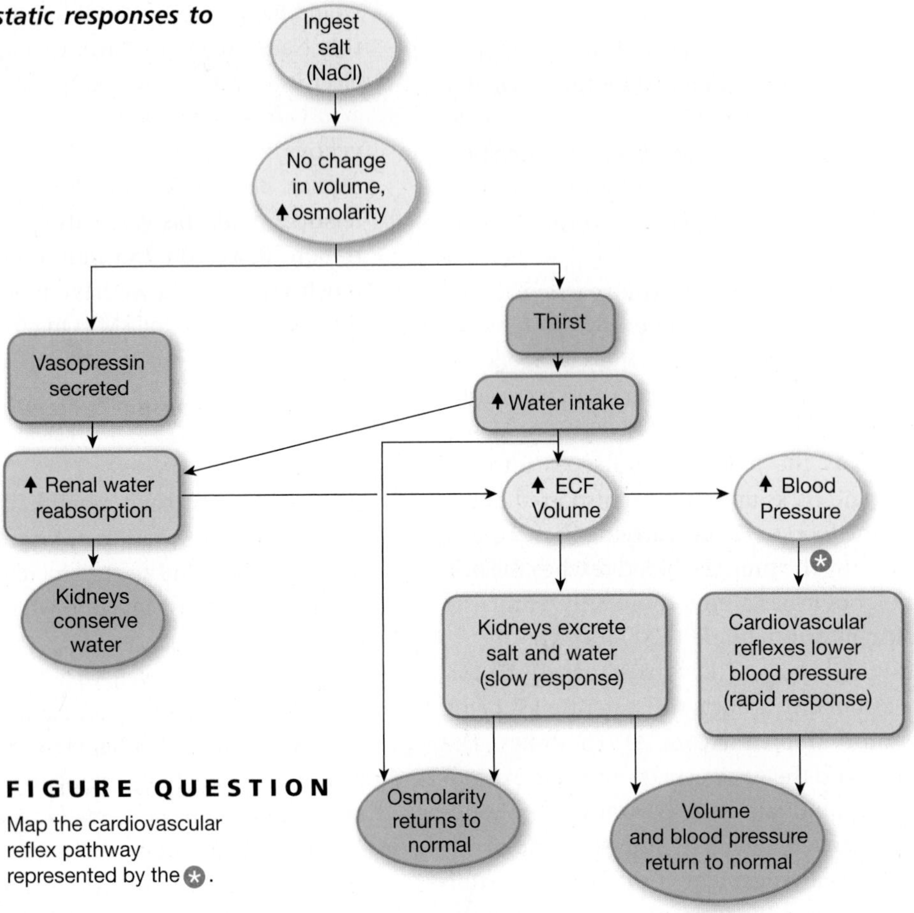

FIGURE QUESTION

Map the cardiovascular reflex pathway represented by the ✪.

Although we speak of ingesting and losing salt (NaCl), only renal Na^+ absorption is regulated. And actually, the stimuli that set the Na^+ balance pathway in motion are more closely tied to blood volume and blood pressure than to Na^+ levels. Chloride movement usually follows Na^+ movement, either indirectly via the electrochemical gradient created by Na^+ transport or directly via membrane transporters such as the NKCC transporter of the loop of Henle or the Na^+-Cl^- symporter of the distal tubule.

Aldosterone Controls Sodium Balance

The regulation of blood Na^+ levels takes place through one of the most complicated endocrine pathways of the body. The reabsorption of Na^+ in the distal tubules and collecting ducts of the kidney is regulated by the steroid hormone **aldosterone**: the more aldosterone, the more Na^+ reabsorption. Because one target of aldosterone is increased activity of the Na^+-K^+-ATPase, aldosterone also causes K^+ secretion.

Aldosterone is a steroid hormone synthesized in the adrenal cortex, the outer portion of the adrenal gland that sits atop each kidney [p. 394]. Like other steroid hormones, aldosterone is secreted into the blood and transported on a protein carrier to its target.

The primary site of aldosterone action is the last third of the distal tubule and the portion of the collecting duct that runs through the kidney cortex (the *cortical collecting duct*). The primary target of aldosterone is **principal cells,** or **P cells** (Fig. 20-12 ●). Principal cells are arranged much like other polarized transporting epithelial cells, with Na^+-K^+-ATPase pumps on the basolateral membrane, and various channels and transporters on the apical membrane [p. 155]. In principal cells, the apical membranes contain leak channels for Na^+ (called ENaC, for epithelial Na^+ channel) and for K^+ (called ROMK, for renal outer medulla K^+ channel).

Aldosterone enters P cells by simple diffusion. Once inside, it combines with a cytoplasmic receptor (Fig. 20-12 ①). In the early response phase, apical Na^+ and K^+ channels increase their open time under the influence of an as-yet-unidentified signal molecule. As intracellular Na^+ levels rise, the Na^+-K^+-ATPase speeds up, transporting cytoplasmic Na^+ into the ECF and bringing K^+ from the ECF into the P cell. The net result is a rapid increase in Na^+ reabsorption and K^+ secretion that does not require the synthesis of new channel or ATPase proteins. In the slower phase of aldosterone action, newly synthesized channels and pumps are inserted into epithelial cell membranes (Fig. 20-12 ④).

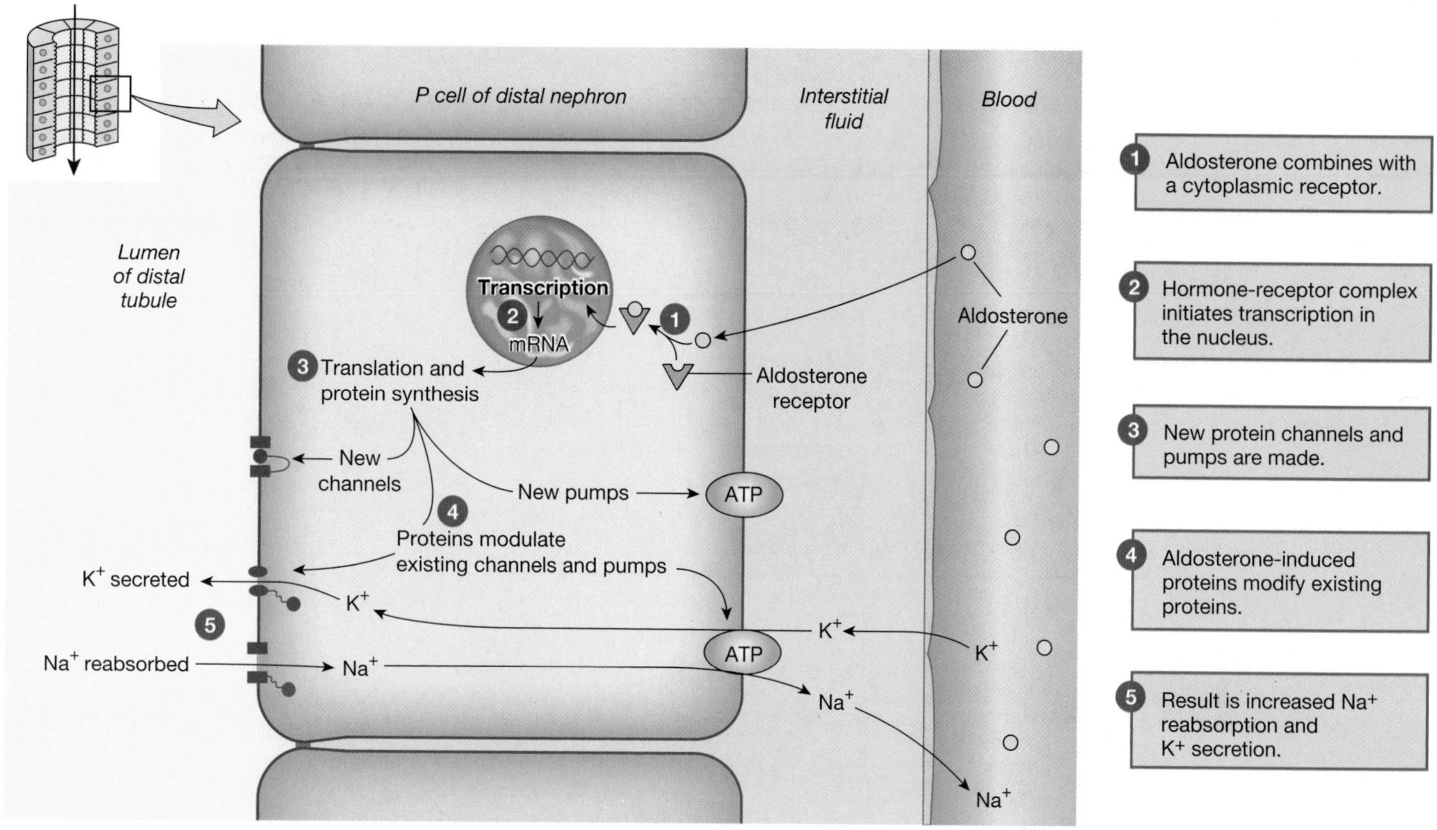
P cell of distal nephron
Interstitial fluid
Blood
Lumen of distal tubule
Transcription
mRNA
Translation and protein synthesis
Aldosterone
Aldosterone receptor
New channels
New pumps
ATP
Proteins modulate existing channels and pumps
K+ secreted
K+
Na+ reabsorbed
Na+
1 Aldosterone combines with a cytoplasmic receptor.
2 Hormone-receptor complex initiates transcription in the nucleus.
3 New protein channels and pumps are made.
4 Aldosterone-induced proteins modify existing proteins.
5 Result is increased Na+ reabsorption and K+ secretion.

FIGURE 20-12 *Aldosterone acts on principal cells.*

Note that Na^+ and water reabsorption are separately regulated in the distal nephron. Water does not automatically follow Na^+ reabsorption: vasopressin must be present to make the distal-nephron epithelium permeable to water. In contrast, Na^+ reabsorption in the proximal tubule is automatically followed by water reabsorption because the proximal tubule epithelium is always freely permeable to water.

CONCEPT CHECK

8. In Figure 20-12, what force(s) cause(s) Na^+ and K^+ to cross the apical membrane?
9. If a person experiences hyperkalemia, what happens to resting membrane potential and the excitability of neurons and the myocardium?

Answers: p. 685

Low Blood Pressure Stimulates Aldosterone Secretion

What controls physiological aldosterone secretion from the adrenal cortex? There are two primary stimuli: increased extracellular K^+ concentration and decreased blood pressure. Elevated K^+ concentrations act directly on the adrenal cortex in a reflex that protects the body from hyperkalemia. Decreased blood pressure initiates a complex pathway that results in release of a hormone, **angiotensin II,** that stimulates aldosterone secretion in most situations.

Two additional factors modulate aldosterone release in pathological states: an increase in ECF osmolarity acts directly on adrenal cortex cells to inhibit aldosterone secretion during dehydration, and an abnormally large (10–20 mEq/L) decrease in plasma Na^+ can directly stimulate aldosterone secretion.

The Renin-Angiotensin-Aldosterone Pathway Angiotensin II (ANG II) is the usual signal controlling aldosterone release from the adrenal cortex. ANG II is one component of the **renin-angiotensin-aldosterone system (RAAS),** a complex, multistep pathway for maintaining blood pressure. The RAAS pathway begins when juxtaglomerular granular cells in the afferent arterioles of a nephron [p. 634] secrete an enzyme called **renin** (Fig. 20-13). Renin converts an inactive plasma protein, **angiotensinogen,** into **angiotensin I (ANG I).** (The suffix *-ogen* indicates an inactive precursor.) When ANG I in the blood encounters an enzyme called **angiotensin-converting enzyme (ACE),** ANG I is converted into ANG II.

This conversion was originally thought to take place only in the lungs, but ACE is now known to occur on the endothelium of blood vessels throughout the body. When ANG II in the blood reaches the adrenal gland, it causes synthesis and release of aldosterone. Finally, at the distal nephron, aldosterone initiates a series of intracellular reactions that cause the tubule to reabsorb Na^+.

20

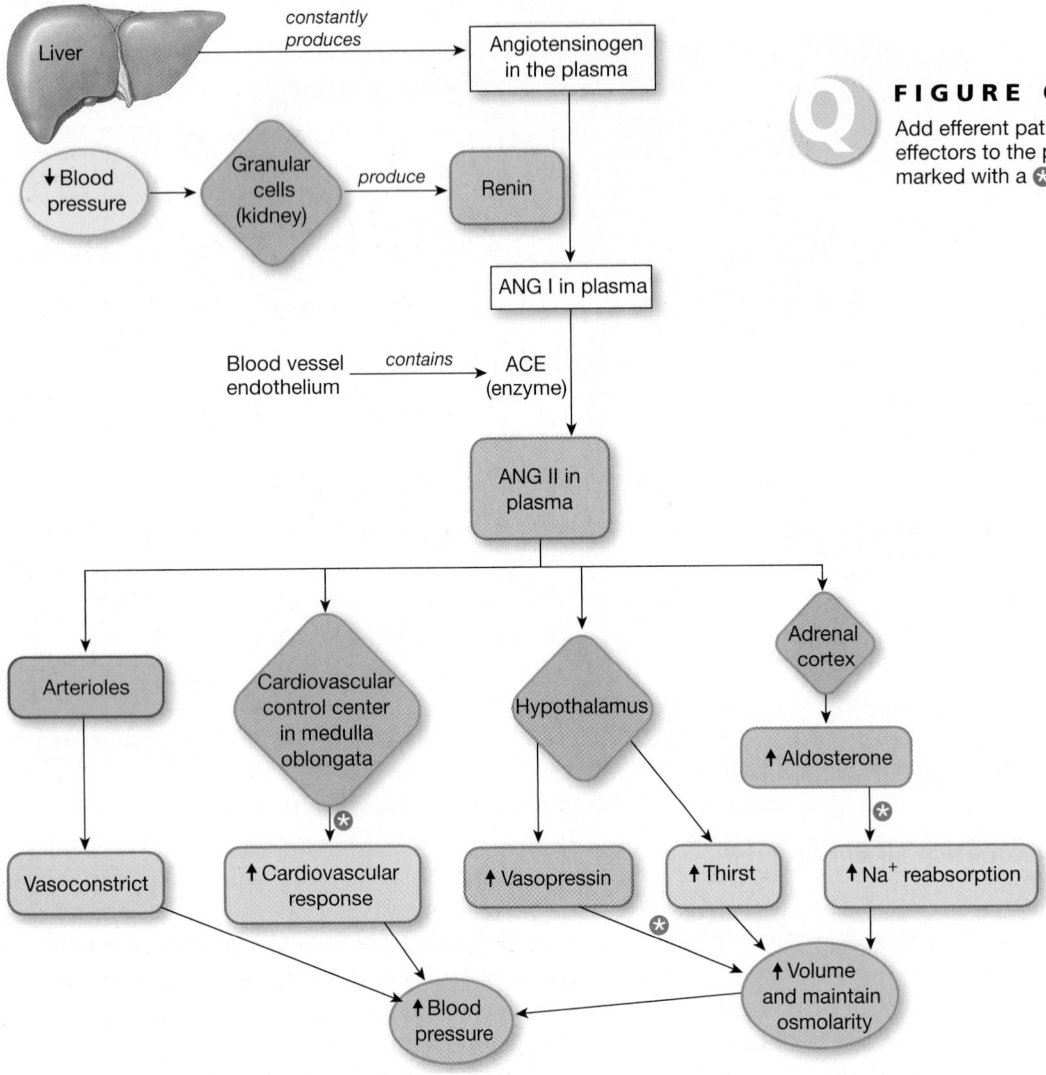

FIGURE QUESTION

Add efferent pathways and/or effectors to the pathways marked with a ✪.

● **FIGURE 20-13** ***The renin-angiotensin-aldosterone system (RAAS).*** This map outlines the control of aldosterone secretion as well as the blood pressure-raising effects of ANG II.

The stimuli that begin the RAAS pathway are all related either directly or indirectly to low blood pressure (Fig. 20-14 ●):

1. The *granular cells* are directly sensitive to blood pressure. They respond to low blood pressure in renal arterioles by secreting renin.
2. *Sympathetic neurons,* activated by the cardiovascular control center when blood pressure decreases, terminate on the granular cells and stimulate renin secretion.
3. *Paracrine feedback*—from the macula densa in the distal tubule to the granular cells—stimulates renin release [p. 633]. When fluid flow through the distal tubule is relatively high, the macula densa cells release paracrines, which inhibit renin release. When fluid flow in the distal tubule decreases, macula densa cells signal the granular cells to secrete renin.

Sodium reabsorption does not directly raise low blood pressure, but retention of Na^+ increases osmolarity, which stimulates thirst. Fluid intake when the person drinks more water increases ECF volume (see Fig. 20-11). When blood volume increases, blood pressure also increases.

The effects of the RAAS pathway are not limited to aldosterone release, however. Angiotensin II is a remarkable hormone with additional effects directed at raising blood pressure. These actions make ANG II an important hormone in its own right, not merely an intermediate step in the aldosterone control pathway.

ANG II Has Many Effects

Angiotensin II has significant effects on fluid balance and blood pressure beyond stimulating aldosterone secretion, underscoring the integrated functions of the renal and cardiovascular systems. ANG II increases blood pressure both directly and indirectly through four additional pathways (Fig. 20-13):

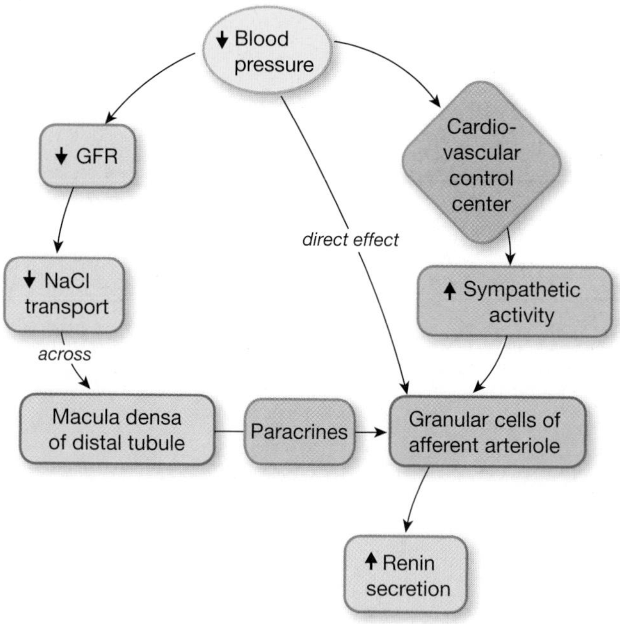

● **FIGURE 20-14** ***Decreased blood pressure stimulates renin secretion.***

1. *ANG II increases vasopressin secretion.* ANG II receptors in the hypothalamus initiate this reflex. Fluid retention in the kidney under the influence of vasopressin helps conserve blood volume, thereby maintaining blood pressure.
2. *ANG II stimulates thirst.* Fluid ingestion is a behavioral response that expands blood volume and raises blood pressure.
3. *ANG II is one of the most potent vasoconstrictors* known in humans. Vasoconstriction causes blood pressure to increase without a change in blood volume.
4. *Activation of ANG II receptors in the cardiovascular control center increases sympathetic output to the heart and blood vessels.* Sympathetic stimulation increases cardiac output and vasoconstriction, both of which increase blood pressure.

Once these blood-pressure-raising effects of ANG II became known, it was not surprising that pharmaceutical companies started looking for drugs to block ANG II. Their research produced a new class of antihypertensive drugs called *ACE inhibitors.* These drugs block the ACE-mediated conversion of ANG I to ANG II, thereby helping to relax blood vessels and lower blood pressure. Less ANG II also means less aldosterone release, a decrease in Na^+ reabsorption and, ultimately, a decrease in ECF volume. All these responses contribute to lowering blood pressure.

However, the ACE inhibitors are not without side effects. ACE inactivates a cytokine called *bradykinin.* When ACE is inhibited by drugs, bradykinin levels increase, and in some patients this creates a dry, hacking cough. One solution was the development of drugs called *angiotensin receptor blockers (ARBs)* that block the blood-pressure-raising effects of ANG II at target cells by binding to *AT_1 receptors.* Recently another new class of drugs, *direct renin inhibitors*, was approved. Direct renin inhibitors decrease the plasma activity of renin, which in turn blocks production of ANG I and inhibits the entire RAAS pathway.

CONCEPT CHECK

10. A man comes to the doctor with high blood pressure. Tests show that he also has elevated plasma renin levels and atherosclerotic plaques that have nearly blocked blood flow through his renal arteries. How does decreased blood flow in his renal arteries cause elevated renin levels?
11. Describe the pathways through which elevated renin causes high blood pressure in the man mentioned in Concept Check 10.

Answers: p. 685

ANP Promotes Na^+ and Water Excretion

Once it was known that aldosterone and vasopressin increase Na^+ and water reabsorption, scientists speculated that other hormones might cause Na^+ loss, or **natriuresis** [*natrium,* sodium + *ourein,* to urinate] and water loss (diuresis) in the urine. If found, these hormones might be used clinically to lower blood volume and blood pressure in patients with essential hypertension [p. 539]. During years of searching, however, evidence for the other hormones was not forthcoming.

Then, in 1981, a group of Canadian researchers found that injections of homogenized rat atria caused rapid but short-lived excretion of Na^+ and water in the rats' urine. They hoped they had found the missing hormone, one whose activity would complement that of aldosterone and vasopressin. As it turned out, they had discovered the first *natriuretic peptide* (NP), one member of a family of hormones that appear to be endogenous RAAS antagonists.

Atrial natriuretic peptide (ANP; also known as *atriopeptin*) is a peptide hormone produced in specialized myocardial cells in the atria of the heart. It is synthesized as part of a large prohormone that is cleaved into several active hormone fragments [p. 221]. A related hormone, **brain natriuretic peptide** (BNP), is synthesized by ventricular myocardial cells and certain brain neurons. Both natriuretic peptides are released by the heart when myocardial cells stretch more than normal, as would occur with increased blood volume. The peptides bind to membrane receptors that work through a cGMP second messenger system.

At the systemic level, natriuretic peptides enhance Na^+ and water excretion, but the exact mechanisms by which they do so are not clear (Fig. 20-15 ●). The NPs increase GFR and directly decrease NaCl and water reabsorption in the collecting duct. The cellular mechanism by which NPs affect tubular reabsorption is not clear.

Natriuretic peptides also act indirectly to increase Na^+ and water excretion by inhibiting the release of renin, aldosterone, and vasopressin (Fig. 20-15), actions that reinforce the natriuretic-diuretic effect. In addition, natriuretic peptides act directly on

● **FIGURE 20-15** ***Natriuretic peptides promote salt and water excretion.***

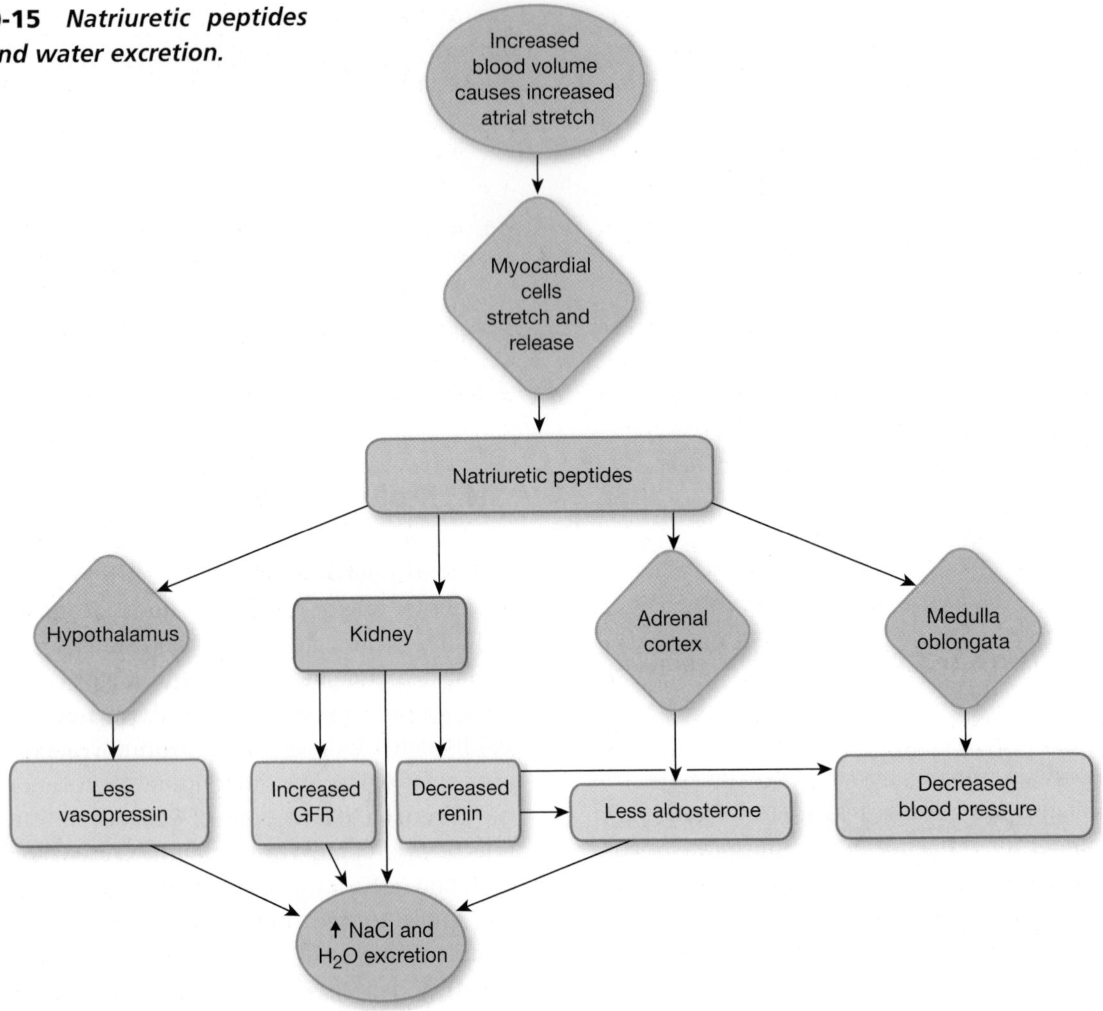

the cardiovascular control center of the medulla to lower blood pressure.

Brain natriuretic peptide (BNP) is now recognized as an important biological marker for heart failure because production of this substance increases with ventricular dilation and increased ventricular pressure. According to one estimate in 2004, more than 70% of U.S. hospitals test for BNP levels to assist in the diagnosis of ventricular failure. This peptide has also been shown to be an independent predictor of heart failure and sudden death from cardiac arrhythmias.

POTASSIUM BALANCE

Aldosterone (but not other factors in the RAAS pathway) also plays a critical role in potassium homeostasis. Only about 2% of the body's K^+ load is in the ECF, but regulatory mechanisms keep plasma K^+ concentrations within a narrow range (3.5–5 meq/L). Under normal conditions, mass balance matches K^+ excretion to K^+ ingestion. If intake exceeds excretion and plasma K^+ goes up, aldosterone is released into the blood through the direct effect of hyperkalemia on the adrenal cortex. Aldosterone acting on distal-nephron P cells keeps the cells' apical ion channels open longer and speeds up the Na^+-K^+-ATPase, enhancing renal excretion of K^+.

The regulation of body potassium levels is essential to maintaining a state of well-being. As you learned in Chapter 8, changes in extracellular K^+ concentration affect the resting membrane potential of all cells [Fig. 8-19, p. 273]. If plasma (and ECF) K^+ concentrations decrease (hypokalemia), the concentration gradient between the cell and the ECF becomes larger, more K^+ leaves the cell, and the resting membrane potential becomes more negative. If ECF K^+ concentrations increase (hyperkalemia), the concentration gradient decreases and more K^+ remains in the cell, depolarizing it. (Remember that when plasma K^+ concentrations change, anions such as Cl^- are also added to or subtracted from the ECF in a 1:1 ratio, maintaining overall electrical neutrality.)

Because of the effect of plasma K^+ on excitable tissues, such as the heart, clinicians are always concerned about keeping plasma K^+ within its normal range. If K^+ falls below 3 meq/L or rises above 6 meq/L, the excitable tissues of muscle and nerve begin to show altered function. For example, hypokalemia causes muscle weakness because it is more difficult for hyperpolarized neurons and muscles to fire action potentials. The danger in this condition lies in the failure of respiratory muscles and the heart. Fortunately, skeletal muscle weakness is usually significant enough to lead patients to seek treatment before cardiac problems occur. Mild hypokalemia may be corrected by oral intake of K^+ supplements and K^+-rich foods, such as orange juice and bananas.

Hyperkalemia is a more dangerous potassium disturbance because in this case depolarization of excitable tissues makes them more excitable initially. Subsequently, the cells are unable to repolarize fully and actually become *less* excitable. In this state, they have action potentials that are either smaller than normal or nonexistent. Cardiac muscle excitability affected by changes in plasma K^+ can lead to life-threatening cardiac arrhythmias.

Disturbances in K^+ balance may result from kidney disease, eating disorders, loss of K^+ in diarrhea, or the use of certain types of diuretics that prevent the kidneys from fully reabsorbing K^+. Inappropriate correction of dehydration can also create K^+ imbalance. Consider a golfer playing a round of golf when the temperature was above 100° F. He was aware of the risk of dehydration, so he drank lots of water to replace fluid lost through sweating. The replacement of lost sweat with pure water kept his ECF volume normal but dropped his total blood osmolarity and his K^+ and Na^+ concentrations. He was unable to finish the round of golf because of muscle weakness, and he required medical attention that included ion replacement therapy. A more suitable replacement fluid would have been one of the sports drinks that include salt and K^+.

Potassium balance is also closely tied to acid-base balance, as you will learn in the final section of this chapter. Correction of a pH disturbance requires close attention to plasma K^+ levels. Similarly, correction of K^+ imbalance may alter body pH.

RUNNING PROBLEM

The medical staff analyzed Lauren's blood for electrolyte concentrations. Her serum Na^+ concentration was 124 mEq/L. The normal range is 135–145 mEq/L. Lauren's diagnosis was **hyponatremia** [*hypo-*, below + *natri-*, sodium + *-emia*, blood], defined as a serum Na^+ concentration below 135 mEq/L. Hyponatremia induced by the consumption of large quantities of low-sodium or sodium-free fluid, which is what happened in Lauren's case, is sometimes called *dilutional hyponatremia*.

Question 3:
Which body fluid compartment is being diluted in dilutional hyponatremia?

Question 4:
One way to estimate body osmolarity is to double the plasma Na^+ concentration. Estimate Lauren's osmolarity and explain what effect the dilutional hyponatremia has on her cells.

Question 5:
In dilutional hyponatremia, the medical personnel are most concerned about which organ or tissue?

651 653 667 669 675 681

BEHAVIORAL MECHANISMS IN SALT AND WATER BALANCE

Although neural, neuroendocrine, and endocrine reflexes play key roles in salt and water homeostasis, behavioral responses are critical in restoring the normal state, especially when ECF volume decreases or osmolarity increases. Drinking water is normally the only way to restore lost water, and eating salt is the only way to raise the body's Na^+ content. Both behaviors are essential for normal salt and water balance. Clinicians must recognize the absence of these behaviors in patients who are unconscious or otherwise unable to obey behavioral urges, and must adjust treatment accordingly. The study of the biological basis for behaviors, including drinking and eating, is a field known as *physiological psychology*.

Drinking Replaces Fluid Loss

Thirst is one of the most powerful urges known in humans. In 1952, the Swedish physiologist Bengt Andersson showed that stimulating certain regions of the hypothalamus triggered drinking behavior. This discovery led to the identification of hypothalamic osmoreceptors that initiate drinking when body osmolarity rises above 280 mOsM. This is an example of a behavior initiated by an internal stimulus.

It is interesting to note that although increased osmolarity triggers thirst, the act of drinking is sufficient to relieve thirst. The ingested water need not be absorbed in order for thirst to be quenched. As-yet-unidentified receptors in the mouth and pharynx (*oropharynx receptors*) respond to cold water by decreasing thirst and decreasing vasopressin release even though plasma osmolarity remains high. This oropharynx reflex is one reason surgery patients are allowed to suck on ice chips: the ice alleviates their thirst without putting significant amounts of fluid into the digestive system.

A similar reflex exists in camels. When led to water, they drink just enough to replenish their water deficit. Oropharynx receptors apparently act as a feedforward "metering" system that helps prevent wide swings in osmolarity by matching water intake to water need.

In humans, cultural rituals complicate the thirst reflex. For example, we may drink during social events, whether or not we are thirsty. As a result, our bodies must be capable of eliminating fluid ingested in excess of our physiological needs.

CONCEPT CHECK

12. Incorporate the thirst reflex into Figure 20-7. Answers: p. 685

Low Na^+ Stimulates Salt Appetite

Thirst is not the only urge associated with fluid balance. **Salt appetite** is a craving for salty foods that occurs when plasma Na^+ concentrations drop. It can be observed in deer and cattle attracted to salt blocks or naturally occurring salt licks. In humans,

Volume \ Osmolarity	Decrease	No change	Increase
Increase	Drinking large amount of water	Ingestion of isotonic saline	Ingestion of hypertonic saline
No change	Replacement of sweat loss with plain water	Normal volume and osmolarity	Eating salt without drinking water
Decrease	Incomplete compensation for dehydration	Hemorrhage	Dehydration (e.g., sweat loss or diarrhea)

● **FIGURE 20-16** ***Disturbances in volume and osmolarity***

salt appetite is linked to aldosterone and angiotensin, hormones that regulate Na^+ balance. The centers for salt appetite are in the hypothalamus close to the center for thirst.

Avoidance Behaviors Help Prevent Dehydration

Other behaviors play a role in fluid balance by preventing or promoting dehydration. Desert animals avoid the heat of the day and become active only at night, when environmental temperatures fall and humidity rises. Humans, especially now that we have air conditioning, are not always so wise.

The midday nap, or *siesta,* is a cultural adaptation in tropical countries that keeps people indoors during the hottest part of the day, thereby helping prevent dehydration and overheating. In the United States, we have abandoned this civilized custom and are active continuously during daylight hours, even when the temperature soars during summer in the South and Southwest. Fortunately, our homeostatic mechanisms usually keep us out of trouble.

INTEGRATED CONTROL OF VOLUME AND OSMOLARITY

The body uses an integrated response to correct disruptions of salt and water balance. The cardiovascular system responds to changes in blood volume, and the kidneys respond to changes in blood volume or osmolarity. Maintaining homeostasis throughout the day is a continuous process in which the amounts of salt and water in the body shift, according to whether you just drank a soft drink or sweated through an aerobics class.

In that respect, maintaining fluid balance is like driving a car down the highway and making small adjustments to keep the car in the center of the lane. However, just as exciting movies feature wild car chases, not sedate driving, the exciting part of fluid homeostasis is the body's response to crisis situations, such as severe dehydration or hemorrhage. In this section we examine challenges to salt and water balance.

Osmolarity and Volume Can Change Independently

Normally, volume and osmolarity are homeostatically maintained within an acceptable range. Under some circumstances, however, fluid loss exceeds fluid gain or vice versa, and the body goes out of balance. Common pathways for fluid loss include excessive sweating, vomiting, diarrhea, and hemorrhage. All of these situations may require medical intervention. In contrast, fluid gain is seldom a medical emergency, unless it is addition of water that decreases osmolarity below an acceptable range.

Volume and osmolarity of the ECF can each have three possible states: normal, increased, or decreased. The relation of volume and osmolarity changes can be represented by the matrix in Figure 20-16 ●. The center box represents the normal state, and the surrounding boxes represent the most common examples of the variations from normal.

In all cases, the appropriate homeostatic compensation for the change acts according to the principle of mass balance: whatever fluid and solute were added to the body must be removed, or whatever was lost must be replaced. However, perfect compensation is not always possible. Let's begin at the upper right corner of Figure 20-16 and move right to left across each row.

1. *Increased volume, increased osmolarity.* A state of increased volume and increased osmolarity might occur if you ate salty food and drank liquids at the same time, such as popcorn and a soft drink at the movies. The net result could be ingestion of hypertonic saline that increases ECF volume and osmolarity. The appropriate homeostatic response is excretion of hypertonic urine. For homeostasis to be maintained, the osmolarity and volume of the urinary output must match the salt and water input from the popcorn and soft drink.
2. *Increased volume, no change in osmolarity.* Moving one cell to the left in the top row, we see that if the proportion of salt and water in ingested food is equivalent to an isotonic NaCl solution, volume increases but osmolarity does not change. The appropriate response is excretion of isotonic urine whose volume equals that of the ingested fluid.
3. *Increased volume, decreased osmolarity.* This situation would occur if you drank pure water without ingesting any solute. The goal here would be to excrete very dilute urine to maximize water loss while conserving salts. However, because our kidneys cannot excrete pure water, there is always some loss of solute in the urine. In this situation,

urinary output cannot exactly match input, and so compensation is imperfect.

4. *No change in volume, increased osmolarity.* This disturbance (middle row, right cell) might occur if you ate salted popcorn without drinking anything. The ingestion of salt without water increases ECF osmolarity and causes some water to shift from cells to the ECF. The homeostatic response is intense thirst, which prompts ingestion of water to dilute the added solute. The kidneys help by creating highly concentrated urine of minimal volume, conserving water while removing excess NaCl. Once water is ingested, the disturbance becomes that described in situation 1 or situation 2.
5. *No change in volume, decreased osmolarity.* This scenario (middle row, left cell) might occur when a person who is dehydrated replaces lost fluid with pure water, like the golfer described earlier. The decreased volume resulting from the dehydration is corrected, but the replacement fluid has no solutes to replace those lost. Consequently, a new imbalance is created.

   This situation led to the development of electrolyte-containing sports beverages. If people working out in hot weather replace lost sweat with pure water, they may restore volume but run the risk of diluting plasma K^+ and Na^+ concentrations to dangerously low levels (*hypokalemia* and *hyponatremia,* respectively).
6. *Decreased volume, increased osmolarity.* Dehydration is a common cause of this disturbance (bottom row, right cell). Dehydration has multiple causes. During prolonged heavy exercise, water loss from the lungs can double while sweat loss may increase from 0.1 liter to as much as 5 liters! Because the fluid secreted by sweat glands is hyposmotic, the fluid left behind in the body becomes hyperosmotic.

   Diarrhea [*diarhein,* to flow through], excessively watery feces, is a pathological condition involving major water and solute loss, this time from the digestive tract. In both sweating and diarrhea, if too much fluid is lost from the circulatory system, blood volume decreases to the point that the heart can no longer pump blood effectively to the brain. In addition, cell shrinkage caused by increased osmolarity disrupts cell function.
7. *Decreased volume, no change in osmolarity.* This situation (bottom row, middle cell) occurs with hemorrhage. Blood loss represents the loss of isosmotic fluid from the extracellular compartment, similar to scooping a cup of seawater out of a large bucketful. If a blood transfusion is not immediately available, the best replacement solution is one that is isosmotic and remains in the ECF, such as isotonic NaCl.
8. *Decreased volume, decreased osmolarity.* This situation (bottom row, left cell) might also result from incomplete compensation of dehydration, but it is uncommon.

RUNNING PROBLEM

During exercise in the heat, sweating rate and sweat composition are quite variable among athletes and depend partly on how acclimatized the individual is to the heat. Sweat fluid losses can range from less than 0.6 L/h to more than 2.5 L/h, and sweat Na^+ concentrations can range from less than 20 mEq/L to more than 90 mEq/L. The white salt crystals noted on Lauren's face and clothing suggest that she is a "salty sweater" who probably lost a large amount of salt during the race. Follow-up testing revealed that Lauren's sweat Na^+ concentration was 70 mEq/L.

Question 6:

Assuming a sweating rate of 1 L/hr, how much Na^+ did Lauren lose during the 16-hour race?

Question 7:

Total body water for a 60-kg female is approximately 30 L, and her ECF volume is 10 L. Based on the information given in the problem so far, calculate how much fluid Lauren probably ingested during the race.

651 653 667 669 675 681

Dehydration Triggers Homeostatic Responses

To understand the body's integrated response to changes in volume and osmolarity, you must first have a clear idea of which pathways become active in response to various stimuli. Table 20-1 ● is a summary of the many pathways involved in the homeostasis of salt and water balance. For details of individual pathways, refer to the figures cited in Table 20-1.

The homeostatic response to severe dehydration is an excellent example of how the body works to maintain blood volume and cell volume in the face of decreased volume and increased osmolarity. It also illustrates the role of neural and endocrine integrating centers. In severe dehydration, the adrenal cortex receives two opposing signals. One says, "Secrete aldosterone"; the other says, "Do not secrete aldosterone." The body has multiple mechanisms for dealing with diminished blood volume, but high ECF osmolarity causes cells to shrink and presents a more immediate threat to well-being. Thus, faced with decreased volume and increased osmolarity, the adrenal cortex does not secrete aldosterone. (If secreted, aldosterone would cause Na^+ reabsorption, which could worsen the already-high osmolarity associated with dehydration.)

In severe dehydration, compensatory mechanisms are aimed at restoring normal blood pressure, ECF volume, and osmolarity by (1) conserving fluid to prevent additional loss, (2) triggering cardiovascular reflexes to increase blood pressure, and (3) stimulating thirst so that normal fluid volume and osmolarity can be restored. Figure 20-17 ● maps the interwoven nature of these responses. This figure is complex and intimidating at first glance, so let's discuss it step by step.

TABLE 20-1 Responses Triggered by Changes in Volume, Blood Pressure, and Osmolarity

STIMULUS	ORGAN OR TISSUE INVOLVED	RESPONSE(S)	FIGURE(S)
DECREASED BLOOD PRESSURE/VOLUME			
Direct effects			
	Granular cells	Renin secretion	20-13
	Glomerulus	Decreased GFR	19-7, 20-14
Reflexes			
Carotid and aortic baroreceptors	Cardiovascular control center	Increased sympathetic output, decreased parasympathetic output	15-24, 20-14
Carotid and aortic volume receptors	Hypothalamus	Thirst stimulation	20-1a
Carotid and aortic volume receptors	Hypothalamus	Vasopressin secretion	20-7
Atrial volume receptors	Hypothalamus	Thirst stimulation	20-1a
Atrial volume receptors	Hypothalamus	Vasopressin secretion	20-7
INCREASED BLOOD PRESSURE			
Direct effects			
	Glomerulus	Increased GFR (transient)	19-8, 19-10
	Myocardial cells	Natriuretic peptide secretion	20-15
Reflexes			
Carotid and aortic baroreceptors	Cardiovascular control center	Decreased sympathetic output, increased parasympathetic output	15-23
Carotid and aortic baroreceptors	Hypothalamus	Thirst inhibition	
Carotid and aortic baroreceptors	Hypothalamus	Vasopressin inhibition	
Atrial baroreceptors	Hypothalamus	Thirst inhibition	
Atrial baroreceptors	Hypothalamus	Vasopressin inhibition	
INCREASED OSMOLARITY			
Direct effects			
Pathological dehydration	Adrenal cortex	Decreased aldosterone secretion	20-17
Reflexes			
Osmoreceptors	Hypothalamus	Thirst stimulation	20-11
Osmoreceptors	Hypothalamus	Vasopressin secretion	20-7
DECREASED OSMOLARITY			
Direct effects			
Pathological hyponatremia	Adrenal cortex	Increased aldosterone secretion	
Reflexes			
Osmoreceptors	Hypothalamus	Decreased vasopressin secretion	

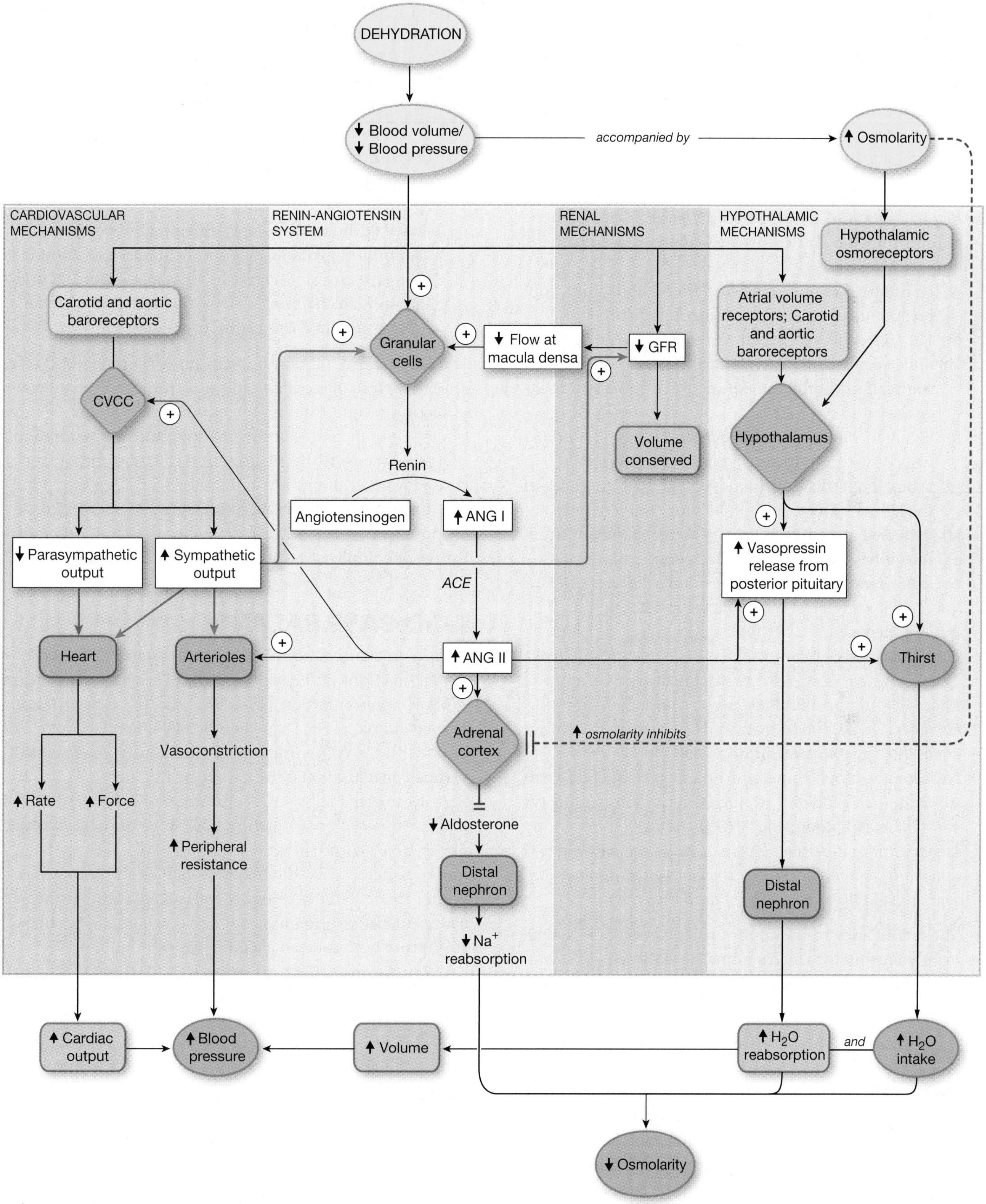

● **FIGURE 20-17** ***Homeostatic compensation for severe dehydration***

At the top of the map (in yellow) are the two stimuli caused by dehydration: decreased blood volume/pressure, and increased osmolarity. Decreased ECF volume causes decreased blood pressure. Blood pressure acts both directly and as a stimulus for several reflex pathways that are mediated through the carotid and aortic baroreceptors and the pressure-sensitive granular cells. Decreased volume is sensed by the atrial volume receptors.

1. *The carotid and aortic baroreceptors signal the cardiovascular control center (CVCC) to raise blood pressure.* Sympathetic output from the CVCC increases while parasympathetic output decreases.
   (a) Heart rate goes up as control of the SA node shifts from predominantly parasympathetic to sympathetic.
   (b) The force of ventricular contraction also increases under sympathetic stimulation. The increased force of contraction combines with increased heart rate to increase cardiac output.
   (c) Simultaneously, sympathetic input causes arteriolar vasoconstriction, increasing peripheral resistance.
   (d) Sympathetic vasoconstriction of afferent arterioles in the kidneys decreases GFR, helping conserve fluid.
   (e) Increased sympathetic activity at the granular cells of the kidneys increases renin secretion.
2. *Decreased peripheral blood pressure directly decreases GFR.* A lower GFR conserves ECF volume by filtering less fluid into the nephron.
3. *Paracrine feedback causes the granular cells to release renin.* Decreased fluid flow past the macula densa as a result of lower GFR triggers renin release.
4. *Granular cells respond to decreased blood pressure by releasing renin.* The combination of decreased blood pressure, increased sympathetic input onto granular cells, and signals from the macula densa stimulates renin release and ensures increased production ANG II.
5. *Decreased blood pressure, decreased blood volume, increased osmolarity, and increased ANG II production all stimulate vasopressin and the thirst centers of the hypothalamus.*

The redundancy in the control pathways ensures that all four main compensatory mechanisms are activated: cardiovascular responses, ANG II, vasopressin, and thirst.

1. *Cardiovascular responses* combine increased cardiac output and increased peripheral resistance to raise blood pressure. Note, however, that this increase in blood pressure does *not necessarily* mean that blood pressure returns to normal. If dehydration is severe, compensation may be incomplete, and blood pressure may remain below normal.
2. *Angiotensin II* has a variety of effects aimed at raising blood pressure, including stimulation of thirst, vasopressin release, direct vasoconstriction, and reinforcement of cardiovascular control center output. ANG II also reaches the adrenal cortex and attempts to stimulate aldosterone release. In dehydration, however, Na^+ reabsorption worsens the already-high osmolarity. Consequently, high osmolarity at the adrenal cortex directly inhibits aldosterone release, blocking the action of ANG II. The RAAS pathway in dehydration produces the beneficial blood-pressure-enhancing effects of ANG II while avoiding the detrimental effects of Na^+ reabsorption. This is a beautiful example of integrated function.
3. *Vasopressin* increases the water permeability of the renal collecting ducts, allowing water reabsorption to conserve fluid. Without fluid replacement, however, vasopressin cannot bring volume and osmolarity back to normal.
4. *Oral (or intravenous) intake of water* in response to thirst is the only mechanism for replacing lost fluid volume and for restoring ECF osmolarity to normal.

The net result of all four mechanisms is (1) restoration of volume by water conservation and fluid intake, (2) maintenance of blood pressure through increased blood volume, increased cardiac output, and vasoconstriction, and (3) restoration of normal osmolarity by decreased Na^+ reabsorption and increased water reabsorption and intake.

Using the pathways listed in Table 20-1 and Figure 20-17 as a model, try to create reflex maps for the seven other disturbances of volume and osmolarity shown in Figure 20-16.

ACID-BASE BALANCE

Acid-base balance (also called pH homeostasis) is one of the essential functions of the body. The pH of a solution is a measure of its H^+ concentration [p. 38]. The H^+ concentration of normal arterial plasma sample is 0.00004 meq/L, minute compared with the concentrations of other ions. (For example, the plasma concentration of Na^+ is about 135 meq/L.)

Because the body's H^+ concentration is so low, it is commonly expressed on a logarithmic pH scale of 0–14, in which a pH of 7.0 is neutral (neither acidic nor basic). If the pH of a solution is below 7.0, the solution has an H^+ concentration greater than 1×10^{-7} M and is considered acidic. If the pH is above 7.0, the solution has an H^+ concentration lower than 1×10^{-7} M and is considered alkaline (basic).

The normal pH of the body is 7.40, slightly alkaline. A change of 1 pH unit represents a 10-fold change in H^+ concentration. To review the concept of pH and the logarithmic scale on which it is based, see Appendix B.

pH Changes Can Denature Proteins

The normal pH range of plasma is 7.38–7.42. Extracellular pH usually reflects intracellular pH, and vice versa. Because monitoring intracellular conditions is difficult, plasma values are used clinically as an indicator of ECF and whole body pH. Body fluids that are "outside" the body's internal environment, such as those in the lumen of the gastrointestinal tract or kidney tubule, can have a pH that far exceeds the normal range. Acidic secretions in the stomach, for instance, may create a gastric pH as low as 1, and the pH of urine varies between 4.5 and 8.5, depending on the body's need to excrete H^+ or HCO_3^-.

The concentration of H^+ in the body is closely regulated. Intracellular proteins, such as enzymes and membrane channels, are particularly sensitive to pH because the function of these proteins depends on their three-dimensional shape [p. 31]. Changes in H^+ concentration alter the tertiary structure of proteins by interacting with hydrogen bonds in the molecules, disrupting the proteins' three-dimensional structures and activities.

Abnormal pH may significantly affect the activity of the nervous system. If pH is too low—the condition known as **acidosis**—neurons become less excitable and CNS depression results. Patients become confused and disoriented, then slip into a coma. If CNS depression progresses, the respiratory centers cease to function, causing death.

If pH is too high—the condition known as **alkalosis**—neurons become hyperexcitable, firing action potentials at the slightest signal. This condition shows up first as sensory changes, such as numbness or tingling, then as muscle twitches. If alkalosis is severe, muscle twitches turn into sustained contractions (*tetanus*) that paralyze respiratory muscles.

Disturbances of acid-base balance are associated with disturbances in K^+ balance. This is partly due to a renal transporter that moves K^+ and H^+ ions in an antiport fashion. In acidosis, the kidneys excrete H^+ and reabsorb K^+ using an *H^+-K^+-ATPase*. In alkalosis, the kidneys reabsorb H^+ and excrete K^+. Potassium imbalance usually shows up as disturbances in excitable tissues, especially the heart.

Acids and Bases in the Body Come from Many Sources

In day-to-day functioning, the body is challenged by intake and production of acids more than bases. Hydrogen ions come both from food and from internal metabolism. Maintaining mass balance requires that acid intake and production be balanced by acid excretion. Hydrogen balance in the body is summarized in Figure 20-18 ●.

Acid Input Many metabolic intermediates and foods are organic acids that ionize and contribute H^+ to body fluids.* Examples of organic acids include amino acids, fatty acids, intermediates in the citric acid cycle, and lactic acid produced by anaerobic metabolism. Metabolic production of organic acids each day creates a significant amount of H^+ that must be excreted to maintain mass balance.

Under extraordinary circumstances, metabolic organic acid production can increase significantly and create a crisis. For example, severe anaerobic conditions, such as circulatory collapse, produce so much lactic acid that normal homeostatic mechanisms cannot keep pace, resulting in a state of *lactic acidosis*. In diabetes mellitus, abnormal metabolism of fats and amino acids creates strong acids known as **ketoacids**. These acids cause a state of metabolic acidosis known as *ketoacidosis*.

*The anion forms of many organic acids end with the suffix *–ate,* such as pyruvate and lactate.

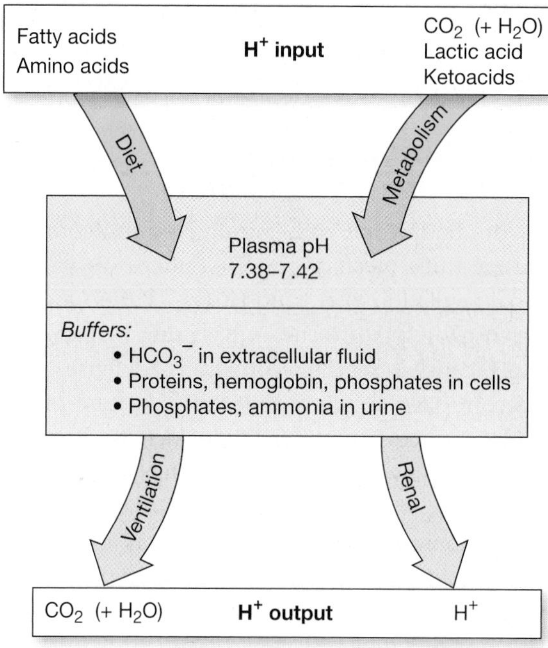

● **FIGURE 20-18** ***Hydrogen ion and pH balance in the body***

The biggest source of acid on a daily basis is the production of CO_2 during aerobic respiration. Carbon dioxide is not an acid because it does not contain any hydrogen atoms. However, CO_2 from respiration combines with water to form carbonic acid (H_2CO_3), which dissociates into H^+ and HCO_3^-:

$$CO_2 + H_2O \rightleftharpoons H_2CO_3 \rightleftharpoons H^+ + HCO_3^-$$

This reaction takes place in all cells and in the plasma, but at a slow rate. However, in certain cells of the body, the reaction proceeds very rapidly because of the presence of large amounts of *carbonic anhydrase* [p. 610]. This enzyme catalyzes the conversion of CO_2 and H_2O to H_2CO_3.

The production of H^+ from CO_2 and H_2O is the single biggest source of acid input under normal conditions. By some estimates, CO_2 from resting metabolism produces 12,500 meq of H^+ each day. If this amount of acid were placed in a volume of water equal to the plasma volume, it would create an H^+ concentration of 4167 meq/L, over one hundred million (10^8) times as concentrated as the normal plasma H^+ concentration of 0.00004 meq/L!

These numbers show that CO_2 from aerobic respiration has the potential to affect pH in the body dramatically. Fortunately, homeostatic mechanisms normally prevent CO_2 from accumulating in the body.

Base Input Acid-base physiology focuses on acids for good reasons. First, our diet and metabolism have few significant sources of bases. Some fruits and vegetables contain anions that metabolize to HCO_3^-, but the influence of these foods is far outweighed by the contribution of acidic fruits, amino acids, and

20

fatty acids. Second, acid-base disturbances due to excess acid are more common than those due to excess base. For these reasons, the body expends far more resources removing excess acid.

pH Homeostasis Depends on Buffers, Lungs, and Kidneys

How does the body cope with minute-to-minute changes in pH? There are three mechanisms: (1) buffers, (2) ventilation, and (3) renal regulation of H^+ and HCO_3^-. Buffers are the first line of defense, always present and waiting to prevent wide swings in pH. Ventilation, the second line of defense, is a rapid, reflexively controlled response that can take care of 75% of most pH disturbances. The final line of defense lies with the kidneys. They are slower than buffers or the lungs but are very effective at coping with any remaining pH disturbance under normal conditions. These three mechanisms help the body balance acid so effectively that normal body pH varies only slightly. Let's take a closer look at each of them.

Buffer Systems Include Proteins, Phosphate Ions, and HCO_3^-

A buffer is a molecule that moderates but does not prevent changes in pH by combining with or releasing H^+ [p. 39]. In the absence of buffers, the addition of acid to a solution causes a sharp change in pH. In the presence of a buffer, the pH change is moderated or may even be unnoticeable. Because acid production is the major challenge to pH homeostasis, most physiological buffers combine with H^+.

Buffers are found both within cells and in the plasma. Intracellular buffers include cellular proteins, phosphate ions (HPO_4^{2-}), and hemoglobin. As we have seen, hemoglobin in red blood cells buffers the H^+ produced by the reaction of CO_2 with H_2O [Fig. 18-14, p. 610].

Each H^+ ion buffered by hemoglobin leaves a matching bicarbonate ion inside the red blood cell. This HCO_3^- can then leave the red blood cell by exchanging with plasma Cl^-, the *chloride shift* described in Chapter 18 [p. 610].

The large amounts of plasma bicarbonate produced from metabolic CO_2 create the most important extracellular buffer system of the body. Plasma HCO_3^- concentration averages 24 meq/L, which is approximately 600,000 times as concentrated as plasma H^+. Although H^+ and HCO_3^- are created in a 1:1 ratio from CO_2 and H_2O, intracellular buffering of H^+ by hemoglobin is a major reason the two ions do not appear in the plasma in the same concentration. The HCO_3^- in plasma can then buffer H^+ from nonrespiratory sources, such as metabolism.

The relationship between CO_2, HCO_3^-, and H^+ in the plasma is expressed by the equation we just looked at:

$$CO_2 + H_2O \rightleftharpoons \underset{\text{carbonic acid}}{H_2CO_3} \rightleftharpoons H^+ + HCO_3^- \qquad (1)$$

According to the law of mass action, any change in the amount of CO_2, H^+, or HCO_3^- in the reaction solution causes the reaction to shift until a new equilibrium is reached. (Water is always in excess in the body and does not contribute to the reaction equilibrium.) For example, if CO_2 increases (red), the equation shifts to the right, creating one additional H^+ and one additional HCO_3^- from each CO_2 and water:

$$\uparrow CO_2 + H_2O \rightarrow H_2CO_3 \rightarrow \uparrow H^+ + \uparrow HCO_3^- \qquad (2)$$

Once a new equilibrium is reached, both H^+ and HCO_3^- levels have increased. The addition of H^+ makes the solution more acidic and therefore lowers its pH. In this reaction, it does not matter that a HCO_3^- buffer molecule has also been produced because HCO_3^- acts as a buffer only when it binds to H^+ and becomes carbonic acid.

Now suppose H^+ (red) is added to the plasma from some metabolic source, such as lactic acid:

$$CO_2 + H_2O \rightleftharpoons H_2CO_3 \rightleftharpoons \uparrow H^+ + HCO_3^- \qquad (3)$$

In this case, plasma HCO_3^- *can* act as a buffer by combining with some of the added H^+ until the reaction reaches a new equilibrium state. The increase in H^+ shifts the equation to the left:

$$CO_2 + H_2O \leftarrow H_2CO_3 \leftarrow \uparrow H^+ + HCO_3^- \qquad (4)$$

Converting some of the added H^+ and bicarbonate buffer to carbonic acid means that at equilibrium, H^+ is still elevated, but not as much as it was initially. The concentration of HCO_3^- is decreased because some has been used as a buffer. The buffered H^+ is converted to CO_2 and H_2O, increasing the amounts of both. At equilibrium, the reaction looks like this:

$$\uparrow CO_2 + \uparrow H_2O \rightleftharpoons H_2CO_3 \rightleftharpoons \uparrow H^+ + \downarrow HCO_3^- \qquad (5)$$

The law of mass action is a useful way to think about the relationship between changes in the concentrations of H^+, HCO_3^-, and CO_2, as long as you remember certain qualifications. First, a change in HCO_3^- concentration (as indicated in reaction 5) may not show up clinically as a HCO_3^- concentration outside the normal range. This is because HCO_3^- is 600,000 times more concentrated in the plasma than H^+ is. If both H^+ and HCO_3^- are added to the plasma, you may observe changes in pH (but not in HCO_3^- concentration), because so much HCO_3^- was present initially. Both H^+ and HCO_3^- experience an *absolute* increase in concentration, but because so many HCO_3^- were in the plasma to begin with, the *relative increase* in HCO_3^- goes unnoticed.

As an analogy, think of two football teams playing in a stadium packed with 80,000 fans. If 10 more players (H^+) run out onto the field, everyone notices. But if 10 people (HCO_3^-) come into the stands at the same time, no one pays any attention because there were already so many people watching the game that 10 more make no significant difference.

The second qualification for the law of mass action is that when the reaction shifts to the left and increases plasma CO_2, a nearly instantaneous increase in ventilation takes place (in a normal person). If extra CO_2 is ventilated off, arterial P_{CO_2} may remain normal or even fall below normal as a result of hyperventilation.

● **FIGURE 20-19** ***The reflex pathway for respiratory compensation of metabolic acidosis***

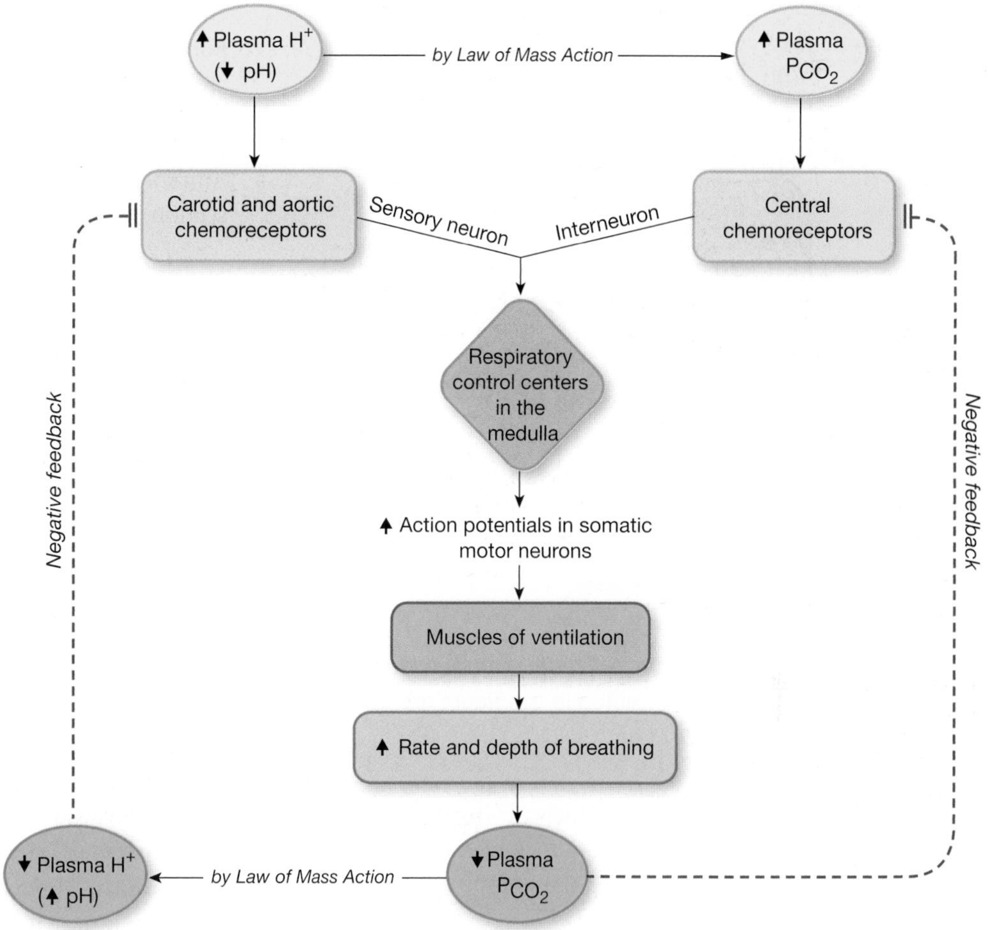

Ventilation Can Compensate for pH Disturbances

The increase in ventilation just described is a *respiratory compensation* for acidosis. Ventilation and acid-base status are intimately linked, as shown by the equation

$$CO_2 + H_2O \rightleftharpoons H_2CO_3 \rightleftharpoons H^+ + HCO_3^-$$

Changes in ventilation can correct disturbances in acid-base balance, but they can also cause them. Because of the dynamic equilibrium between CO_2 and H^+, any change in plasma P_{CO_2} affects both H^+ and HCO_3^- content of the blood.

For example, if a person hypoventilates and P_{CO_2} increases (red), the equation shifts to the right. More carbonic acid is formed, and H^+ goes up, creating a more acidotic state:

$$\uparrow CO_2 + H_2O \rightarrow H_2CO_3 \rightarrow \ \uparrow H^+ + \ \uparrow HCO_3^- \qquad (6)$$

On the other hand, if a person hyperventilates, blowing off CO_2 and thereby decreasing the plasma P_{CO_2} (red), the equation shifts to the left, which means that H^+ combines with HCO_3^- and becomes carbonic acid, thereby decreasing the H^+ concentration and so raising the pH:

$$\downarrow CO_2 + H_2O \leftarrow H_2CO_3 \leftarrow \ \downarrow H^+ + \ \downarrow HCO_3^- \qquad (7)$$

In these two examples, you can see that a change in P_{CO_2} affects the H^+ concentration and therefore the pH of the plasma. The body uses ventilation as a method for adjusting pH only if a stimulus associated with pH triggers the reflex response. Two stimuli can do so: H^+ and CO_2.

Ventilation is affected directly by plasma H^+ levels through carotid and aortic chemoreceptors (Fig. 20-19 ●). These chemoreceptors are located in the aorta and carotid arteries along with the oxygen sensors and blood pressure sensors we discussed previously [p. 532]. An increase in plasma H^+

RUNNING PROBLEM

The human body attempts to maintain fluid and sodium balance via several hormonal mechanisms. During exercise sessions, increased sympathetic output causes increased production of aldosterone and vasopressin, which promote the retention of Na^+ and water by the kidneys.

Question 8:
What would you expect to happen to vasopressin and aldosterone production in response to dilutional hyponatremia?

20

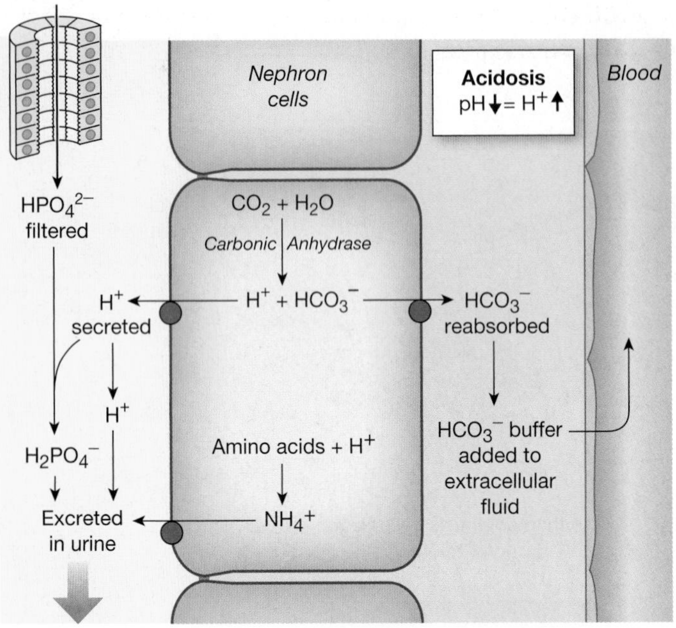

● **FIGURE 20-20** ***Overview of renal compensation for acidosis.*** The transporters represented in this figure are depicted in greater detail in Figures 20-21 and 20-22.

stimulates the chemoreceptors, which in turn signal the medullary respiratory control centers to increase ventilation. Increased alveolar ventilation allows the lungs to excrete more CO_2 and convert H^+ to carbonic acid.

The central chemoreceptors of the medulla oblongata cannot respond directly to changes in plasma pH because H^+ does not cross the blood-brain barrier. However, changes in pH change P_{CO_2}, and CO_2 stimulates the central chemoreceptors [Fig. 18-19, p. 615]. Dual control of ventilation through the central and peripheral chemoreceptors helps the body respond rapidly to changes in either pH or plasma CO_2.

CONCEPT CHECK

13. Name the muscles of ventilation that might be involved in the reflex represented in Figure 20-19.
14. In equation 6, the amount of HCO_3^- present is increased at equilibrium. Why doesn't this HCO_3^- act as a buffer and prevent acidosis from occurring?

Answers: p. 685

Kidneys Use Ammonia and Phosphate Buffers

The kidneys take care of the 25% of compensation that the lungs cannot handle. They alter pH two ways: (1) directly, by excreting or reabsorbing H^+ and (2) indirectly, by changing the rate at which HCO_3^- buffer is reabsorbed or excreted.

In acidosis, the kidney secretes H^+ into the tubule lumen using direct and indirect active transport (Fig. 20-20 ●). Ammonia from amino acids and phosphate ions (HPO_4^{2-}) in the kidney act as buffers, trapping large amounts of H^+ as NH_4^+ and $H_2PO_4^-$ and allowing more H^+ to be excreted. Phosphate ions are present in filtrate and combine with H^+ secreted into the nephron lumen:

$$HPO_4^{2-} + H^+ \rightleftharpoons H_2PO_4^-$$

Ammonia is made from amino acids, as described in the next section.

Even with these buffers, urine can become quite acidic, down to a pH of about 4.5. While H^+ is being excreted, the kidneys make new HCO_3^- from CO_2 and H_2O. The HCO_3^- is reabsorbed into the blood to act as a buffer and increase pH.

In alkalosis, the kidney reverses the general process just described for acidosis, excreting HCO_3^- and reabsorbing H^+ in an effort to bring pH back into the normal range. Renal compensations are slower than respiratory compensations, and their effect on pH may not be noticed for 24–48 hours. However, once activated, renal compensations effectively handle all but severe acid-base disturbances.

The cellular mechanisms for renal handling of H^+ and HCO_3^- resemble transport processes in other epithelia. However, these mechanisms involve some membrane transporters that you have not encountered before:

1. The **apical Na^+-H^+ exchanger (NHE)** is an indirect active transporter that brings Na^+ into the epithelial cell in exchange for moving H^+ against its concentration gradient into the lumen. This transporter is also active in proximal tubule Na^+ reabsorption.
2. The **basolateral Na^+-HCO_3^- symport** moves Na^+ and HCO_3^- out of the epithelial cell and into the interstitial fluid. This indirect active transporter couples the energy of HCO_3^- diffusing down its concentration gradient to the uphill movement of Na^+ from the cell to the ECF.
3. The **H^+-ATPase** uses energy from ATP to acidify the urine, pushing H^+ against its concentration gradient into the lumen of the distal nephron.
4. The **H^+-K^+-ATPase** puts H^+ into the urine in exchange for reabsorbed K^+. This exchange contributes to the potassium imbalance that sometimes accompanies acid-base disturbances.
5. A **Na^+-NH_4^+ antiport** moves NH_4^+ from the cell to the lumen in exchange for Na^+.

In addition to these transporters, the renal tubule also uses the ubiquitous Na^+-K^+-ATPase and the same HCO_3^--Cl^- antiport protein that is responsible for the chloride shift in red blood cells.

The Proximal Tubule Secretes H^+ and Reabsorbs HCO_3^-

The amount of bicarbonate ion the kidneys filter each day is equivalent to the bicarbonate in a pound of baking soda ($NaHCO_3$)! Most of this HCO_3^- must be reabsorbed to maintain the body's buffer capacity. The proximal tubule reabsorbs most

● **FIGURE 20-21** ***Proximal tubule H^+ secretion and the reabsorption of filtered HCO_3^-***

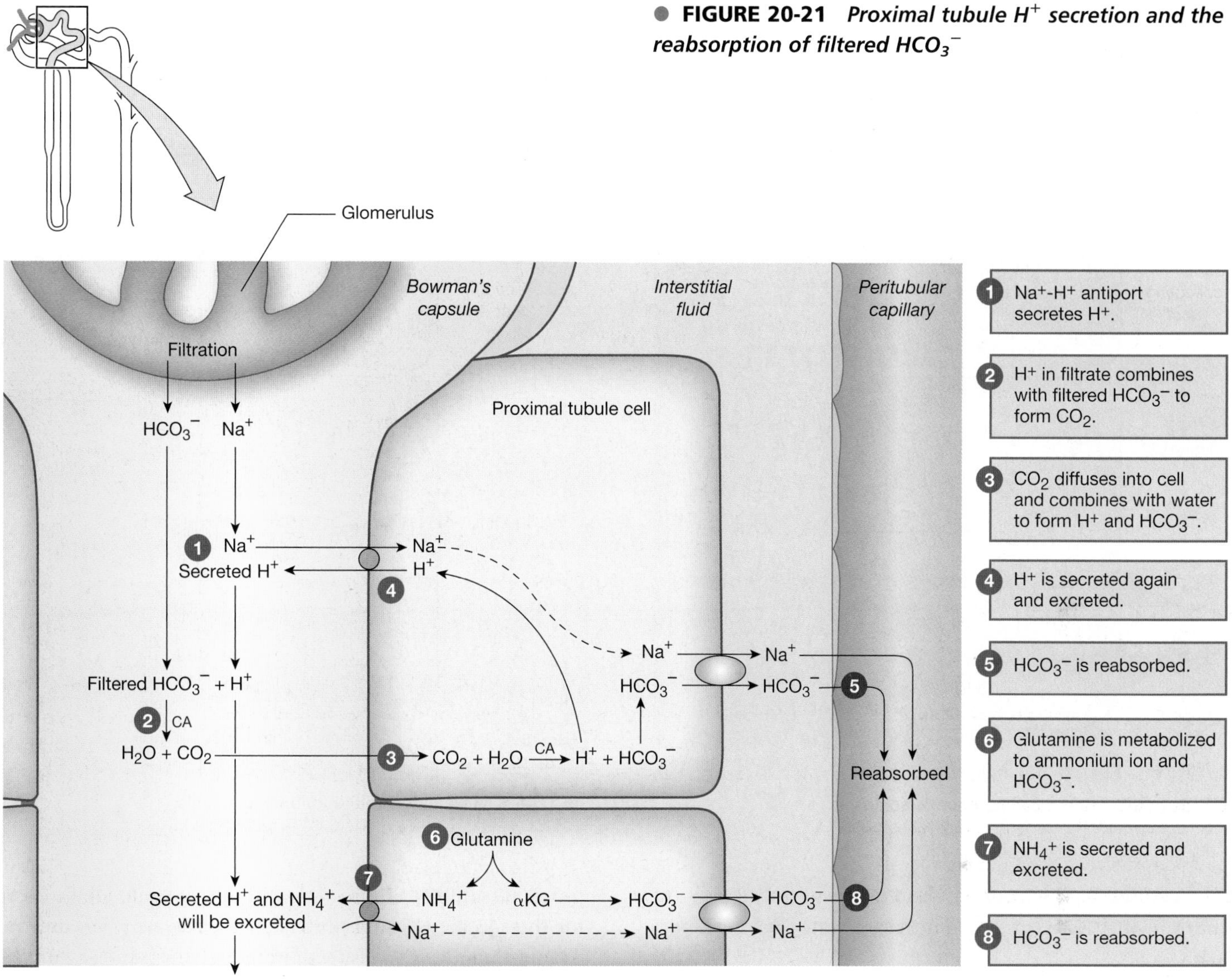

filtered HCO_3^- by indirect methods because there is no apical membrane transporter to bring HCO_3^- into the tubule cell.

Figure 20-21 ● shows the two pathways by which bicarbonate is reabsorbed in the proximal tubule. (The numbers in the following lists correspond to the steps shown in the figure.) By following this illustration, you will see how the transporters listed in the previous section function together.

The first pathway converts filtered HCO_3^- into CO_2, then back into HCO_3^-, which is reabsorbed:

1. H^+ is secreted from the proximal tubule cell into the lumen in exchange for filtered Na^+, which moves from the lumen into the tubule cell.
2. The secreted H^+ combines with filtered HCO_3^- to form CO_2 in the lumen. This reaction is facilitated by carbonic anhydrase that is bound to the luminal membrane of the tubule cells.
3. This newly formed CO_2 diffuses into the tubule cell and combines with water to form H_2CO_3, which dissociates to H^+ and HCO_3^- in the cytoplasm.
4. The H^+ created in step 3 is secreted, replacing the H^+ that combined with filtered HCO_3^- in step 2.
5. The HCO_3^- created in step 3 is transported out of the cell on the basolateral side by the HCO_3^--Na^+ symporter.

The net result of this process is reabsorption of filtered Na^+ and HCO_3^- and secretion of H^+.

A second way to reabsorb bicarbonate and excrete H^+ comes from metabolism of the amino acid glutamine:

6. Glutamine in the proximal tubule cell loses its two amino groups, which become ammonia (NH_3). The ammonia buffers H^+ to become ammonium ion.
7. The ammonium ion is transported into the lumen in exchange for Na^+.
8. The α-ketoglutarate (αKG) molecule made from deamination of glutamine is metabolized further to HCO_3^-, which is transported into the blood along with Na^+.

This pathway also reabsorbs filtered Na^+ and HCO_3^- and secretes H^+, but buffered this time by ammonia. The net result

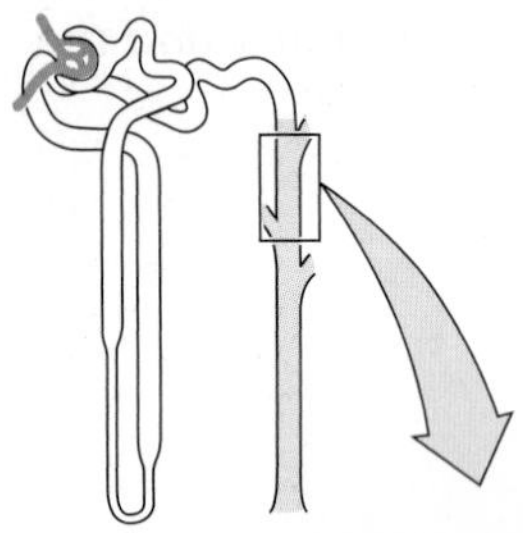

● **FIGURE 20-22** ***Role of intercalated cells in acidosis and alkalosis.*** Intercalated cells in the collecting duct secrete or reabsorb H^+ and HCO_3^- according to the needs of the body.

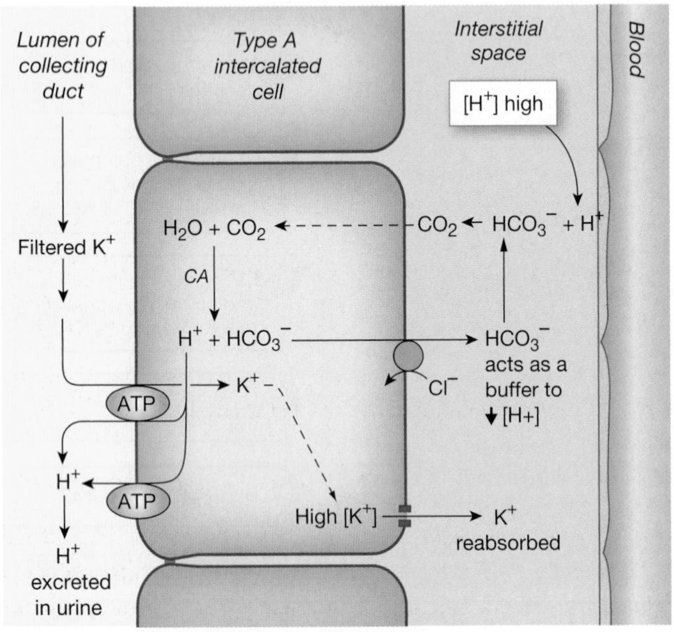

(a) Type A intercalated cell function in acidosis.
H^+ is excreted; HCO_3^- and K^+ are reabsorbed.

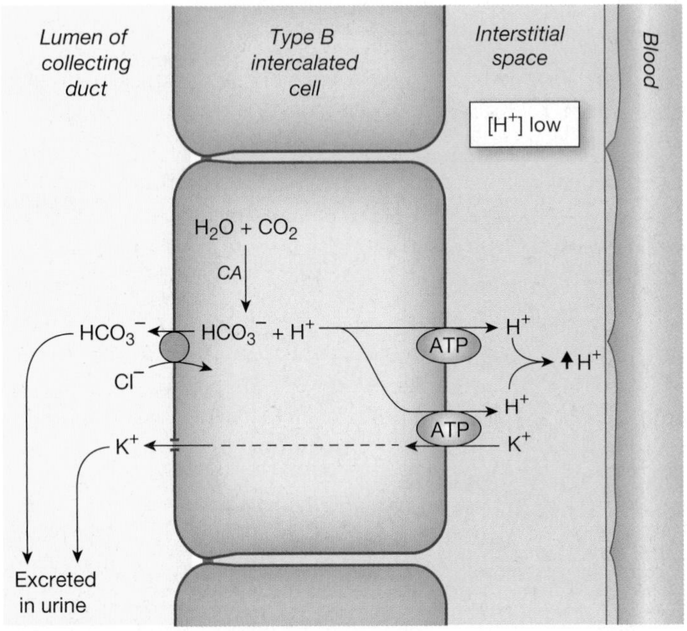

(b) Type B intercalated cell function in alkalosis.
HCO_3^- and K^+ are excreted; H^+ is reabsorbed.

of both pathways is secretion of acid (H^+) and reabsorption of buffer in the form of sodium bicarbonate—baking soda, $NaHCO_3$.

The Distal Nephron Controls Acid Excretion

The distal nephron plays a significant role in the fine regulation of acid-base balance. The **intercalated cells** (or **I cells**) interspersed among the principal cells are responsible for acid-base regulation.

Intercalated cells are characterized by high concentrations of carbonic anhydrase in their cytoplasm. This enzyme allows them to rapidly convert CO_2 and water into H^+ and HCO_3^-. The H^+ ions are pumped out of the intercalated cell either by the H^+-ATPase or by an ATPase that exchanges one H^+ for one K^+. Bicarbonate leaves the cell by means of the HCO_3^--Cl^- antiport exchanger.

There are two types of intercalated cells, and their transporters are found on different faces of the epithelial cell. During periods of acidosis, type A intercalated cells secrete H^+ and reabsorb bicarbonate. During periods of alkalosis, type B intercalated cells secrete HCO_3^- and reabsorb H^+.

Fig. 20-22a ● shows how type A intercalated cells work during acidosis, secreting H^+ and reabsorbing HCO_3^-. The process is similar to H^+ secretion in the proximal tubule except for the specific H^+ transporters. The distal nephron uses H^+-ATPase and H^+-K^+-ATPase rather than the Na^+-H^+ antiport protein found in the proximal tubule.

During alkalosis, when the H^+ concentration of the body is too low, H^+ is reabsorbed and HCO_3^- buffer is excreted in the urine (Fig. 20-22b). Once again, the ions are produced by the dissociation of H_2CO_3 formed from H_2O and CO_2. Hydrogen ions are reabsorbed into the ECF on the basolateral side of the nephron cell while HCO_3^- is secreted into the lumen. The polarity of the two types of I cells is reversed, with the same transport processes taking place, but on the opposite sides of the cell.

The H^+-K^+-ATPase of the distal nephron helps create parallel disturbances of acid-base balance and K^+ balance. In acidosis, when plasma H^+ is high, the kidney secretes H^+ and reabsorbs K^+. For this reason, acidosis is often accompanied by hyperkalemia. (Other nonrenal events also contribute to elevated ECF K^+ concentrations in acidosis.) The reverse is true for alkalosis, when blood H^+ levels are low. The mechanism that allows the distal nephron to reabsorb H^+ simultaneously causes it to secrete K^+, with the result that alkalosis goes hand in hand with hypokalemia.

CONCEPT CHECK

15. Why is ATP required for H^+ secretion by the H^+-K^+ transporter but not for the Na^+-H^+ exchanger?
16. In hypokalemia, the intercalated cells of the distal nephron reabsorb K^+ from the tubule lumen. What happens to blood pH as a result? Answers: p. 685

Acid-Base Disturbances May Be Respiratory or Metabolic

The three compensatory mechanisms (buffers, ventilation, and renal excretion) take care of most variations in plasma pH. But under some circumstances, the production or loss of H^+ or HCO_3^- is so extreme that compensatory mechanisms fail to maintain pH homeostasis. In these states, the pH of the blood moves out of the normal range of 7.38–7.42. If the body fails to keep pH between 7.00 and 7.70, acidosis or alkalosis can be fatal.

Acid-base problems are classified both by the direction of the pH change (acidosis or alkalosis) and by the underlying cause (metabolic or respiratory). As you learned earlier, changes in P_{CO_2} resulting from hyper- or hypoventilation cause pH to shift. These disturbances are said to be of respiratory origin. If the pH problem arises from acids or bases of non-CO_2 origin, the problem is said to be a metabolic problem.

Note that by the time an acid-base disturbance becomes evident as a change in plasma pH, the body's buffers are ineffectual. The loss of buffering ability leaves the body with only two options: respiratory compensation or renal compensation. And if the problem is of respiratory origin, only one homeostatic compensation is available—the kidneys. If the problem is of metabolic origin, both respiratory and renal mechanisms can compensate.

The combination of an initial pH disturbance and the resultant compensatory changes is one factor that makes analysis of acid-base disorders in the clinical setting so difficult. In this book we concentrate on simple scenarios with a single underlying cause. Changes that occur in the four simple acid-base disturbances are listed in Table 20-2 ●.

TABLE 20-2 Plasma P_{CO_2}, Ions, and pH in Acid-Base Disturbances

DISTURBANCE	P_{CO_2}	H^+	PH	HCO_3^-
Acidosis				
Respiratory	↑	↑	↓	↑
Metabolic	Normal* or ↓	↑	↓	↓
Alkalosis				
Respiratory	↓	↓	↑	↓
Metabolic	Normal* or ↑	↓	↑	↑

* These values are different from what you would expect from the law of mass action because almost instantaneous respiratory compensation keeps P_{CO_2} from changing significantly.

Respiratory Acidosis A state of respiratory acidosis occurs when alveolar hypoventilation results in CO_2 retention and elevated plasma P_{CO_2}. Some situations in which this occurs are respiratory depression due to drugs (including alcohol), increased airway resistance in asthma, impaired gas exchange in fibrosis or severe pneumonia, and muscle weakness in muscular dystrophy and other muscle diseases. The most common cause of respiratory acidosis is *chronic obstructive pulmonary disease* (COPD), such as emphysema, in which inadequate gas exchange is compounded by loss of alveolar exchange area.

No matter what the cause of respiratory acidosis, plasma CO_2 levels increase (red), leading to elevated H^+ and HCO_3^-:

$$\uparrow CO_2 + H_2O \rightarrow H_2CO_3 \rightarrow \uparrow H^+ + \uparrow HCO_3^- \qquad (8)$$

The hallmark of respiratory acidosis is decreased pH and elevated bicarbonate levels (Tbl. 20-2). Because the problem is of respiratory origin, the body cannot carry out respiratory compensation. (However, depending on the problem, mechanical ventilation can be used to assist breathing.)

Any compensation for respiratory acidosis must occur through renal mechanisms that excrete H^+ and reabsorb HCO_3^-. The excretion of H^+ raises plasma pH. Reabsorption of HCO_3^- provides additional buffer that combines with H^+, lowering the H^+ concentration and therefore raising the pH.

In chronic obstructive pulmonary disease, renal compensation mechanisms for acidosis can moderate the pH change, but they may not be able to return the pH to its normal range. If you look at pH and HCO_3^- levels in patients with compensated respiratory acidosis, you find that both those values are higher than they were when the acidosis was at its worst.

Metabolic Acidosis Metabolic acidosis is a disturbance of mass balance that occurs when the dietary and metabolic input of H^+ exceeds H^+ excretion. Metabolic causes of acidosis include lactic acidosis, which is a result of anaerobic metabolism, and ketoacidosis, which results from excessive breakdown of fats or certain amino acids. The metabolic pathway that produces ketoacids in diabetes mellitus is described in Chapter 21. Ingested substances that cause metabolic acidosis include methanol, aspirin, and ethylene glycol (antifreeze).

Metabolic acidosis is expressed by the equation

$$\uparrow CO_2 + H_2O \leftarrow H_2CO_3 \leftarrow \uparrow H^+ + \downarrow HCO_3^- \quad (9)$$

Hydrogen ion concentration increases (red) because of the H^+ contributed by the metabolic acids. This increase shifts the equilibrium represented in the equation to the left, increasing CO_2 levels and using up HCO_3^- buffer.

Metabolic acidosis can also occur if the body loses HCO_3^-. The most common cause of bicarbonate loss is diarrhea, during which HCO_3^- is lost from the intestines. The pancreas produces HCO_3^- from CO_2 and H_2O by a mechanism similar to the renal mechanism illustrated in Figure 20-20. The H^+ made at the same time is released into the blood. Normally, the HCO_3^- is released into the small intestine, then reabsorbed into the blood, buffering the H^+. However, if a person is experiencing diarrhea, HCO_3^- is not reabsorbed, and a state of acidosis may result.

Whether HCO_3^- concentration is elevated or decreased is an important criterion for distinguishing metabolic acidosis from respiratory acidosis (Tbl. 20-2).

You would think from looking at equation 9 that metabolic acidosis would be accompanied by elevated P_{CO_2}. However, unless the individual also has a lung disease, respiratory compensation takes place almost instantaneously. Both elevated CO_2 and elevated H^+ stimulate ventilation through the pathways described earlier. As a result, P_{CO_2} decreases to normal or even below-normal levels via hyperventilation.

Uncompensated metabolic acidosis is rarely seen clinically. Actually, a common sign of metabolic acidosis is hyperventilation, evidence of respiratory compensation occurring in response to the acidosis.

The renal compensations discussed for respiratory acidosis also take place in metabolic acidosis: secretion of H^+ and reabsorption of HCO_3^-. Renal compensations take several days to reach full effectiveness, and so they are not usually seen in recent-onset (acute) disturbances.

Respiratory Alkalosis States of alkalosis are much less common than acidotic conditions. Respiratory alkalosis occurs as a result of hyperventilation, when alveolar ventilation increases without a matching increase in metabolic CO_2 production. Consequently, plasma P_{CO_2} falls (red), and alkalosis results when the equation shifts to the left:

$$\downarrow CO_2 + H_2O \leftarrow H_2CO_3 \leftarrow \downarrow H^+ + \downarrow HCO_3^- \quad (10)$$

The decrease in CO_2 shifts the equilibrium to the left, and both plasma H^+ and plasma HCO_3^- decrease. Low plasma HCO_3^- levels in alkalosis indicate a respiratory disorder.

The primary clinical cause of respiratory alkalosis is excessive artificial ventilation. Fortunately, this condition is easily corrected by adjusting the ventilator. The most common physiological cause of respiratory alkalosis is hysterical hyperventilation caused by anxiety. When this is the cause, the neurological symptoms caused by alkalosis can be partially reversed by having the patient breathe into a paper bag. In doing so, the patient rebreathes exhaled CO_2, a process that raises arterial P_{CO_2} and corrects the problem.

Because this alkalosis has respiratory cause, the only compensation available to the body is renal. Filtered bicarbonate, which if reabsorbed could act as a buffer and increase pH even more, is not reabsorbed in the proximal tubule and is secreted in the distal nephron. The combination of HCO_3^- excretion and H^+ reabsorption in the distal nephron decreases the body's HCO_3^- and increases its H^+, both of which help correct the alkalosis.

Metabolic Alkalosis Metabolic alkalosis has two common causes: excessive vomiting of acidic stomach contents and excessive ingestion of bicarbonate-containing antacids. In both cases, the resulting alkalosis reduces H^+ concentration (red):

$$\downarrow CO_2 + H_2O \rightarrow H_2CO_3 \rightarrow \downarrow H^+ + \uparrow HCO_3^- \quad (11)$$

The decrease in H^+ shifts the equilibrium to the right, meaning that carbon dioxide (P_{CO_2}) decreases and HCO_3^- goes up.

Just as in metabolic acidosis, respiratory compensation for metabolic alkalosis is rapid. The increase in pH and drop in P_{CO_2} depress ventilation. Less CO_2 is blown off, raising the P_{CO_2} and creating more H^+ and HCO_3^-. This respiratory compensation helps correct the pH problem but elevates HCO_3^- levels even more. However, the compensation is limited because hypoventilation causes hypoxia. Once the arterial P_{O_2} drops below 60 mm Hg, hypoventilation ceases.

The renal response to metabolic alkalosis is the same as that for respiratory alkalosis: HCO_3^- is excreted and H^+ is reabsorbed.

This chapter has used fluid balance and acid-base balance to illustrate functional integration in the cardiovascular, respiratory, and renal systems. Changes in body fluid volume, reflected by changes in blood pressure, trigger both cardiovascular and renal homeostatic responses. Disturbances of acid-base balance are met with compensatory responses from both the respiratory and renal systems. Because of the interwoven responsibilities of these three systems, a disturbance in one system is likely to cause disturbances in the other two. Recognition of this fact is an important aspect of treatment for many clinical conditions.

RUNNING PROBLEM CONCLUSION

Hyponatremia

In acute cases of dilutional hyponatremia such as Lauren's, the treatment goal is to correct the body's depleted Na^+ load and raise the plasma osmolarity to reduce cerebral swelling. The physicians in the emergency medical tent started a slow intravenous drip of 3% saline and restricted Lauren's oral fluid intake. Over the course of several hours, the combination of Na^+ intake and excretion of dilute urine returned Lauren's plasma Na^+ to normal levels.

Hyponatremia has numerous causes, including inappropriate secretion of antidiuretic hormone (a condition known as SIADH, which stands for syndrome of inappropriate antidiuretic hormone secretion). To learn more about medical causes of hyponatremia, Google *hyponatremia*. To learn more about exercise-associated hyponatremia, visit the Gatorade Sports Science Institute at *www.gssiweb.com.* (This problem was developed by Matt Panke while he was a kinesiology graduate student at the University of Texas.)

	QUESTION	FACTS	INTEGRATION AND ANALYSIS
1	Name the two major body fluid compartments and give the major ions in each compartment.	The major compartments are the intracellular fluid (ICF) and extracellular fluid (ECF) compartments. The primary ICF ion is K^+, and the major ECF ions are Na^+ and Cl^-.	N/A*
2	Based on Lauren's history, give a reason for why her weight increased during the race.	Lauren reported drinking lots of water and sports drinks. One liter of pure water has a mass of 1 kg.	Lauren's fluid intake was greater than her fluid loss from sweating. A 2-kg increase in body weight means she drank an excess of about 2 L.
3	Which body fluid compartment is being diluted in dilutional hyponatremia?	Ingested water distributes itself throughout the ECF and ICF. Sodium is one of the major extracellular cations.	Lauren consumed a large amount of Na-free fluid and therefore diluted her Na^+ stores. However, the body compartments are in osmotic equilibrium so both ECF and ICF have lower osmolarities.
4	One way to estimate osmolarity is to double the plasma Na^+ concentration. Estimate Lauren's osmolarity and explain what effect the dilutional hyponatremia has on her cells.	Lauren's plasma Na^+ is 124 mEq/L. For Na^+, 1 mEq = 1 milliosmole. Doubling this value tells you that Lauren's estimated plasma osmolarity is 248 mOsM. Water distributes to maintain osmotic equilibrium.	At the start of the race, Lauren's cells were at 280 mOsM. The water she ingested distributed to maintain osmotic equilibrium, so water entered the ICF from the ECF, resulting in cell swelling.
5	In dilutional hyponatremia, the medical personnel are most concerned about which organ or tissue?	All cells in Lauren's body swell as a result of excess water ingestion. The brain is encased in the rigid skull.	The bony skull restricts the swelling of brain tissue, causing neurological symptoms, including confusion, headache, and loss of coordination. With lower Na^+ concentrations, death can result.
6	Assuming a sweating rate of 1.0 L/hr, how much Na^+ did Lauren lose during the 16-hour race?	1.0 L sweat lost/hr × 16 hr × 70 mEq Na^+/L sweat = 1120 mEq Na^+ lost during the 16-hour race.	N/A*
7	Total body water for a 60-kg female is approximately 30 L, and her ECF volume is 10 L. Based on the information given so far, how much fluid did Lauren ingest during the race?	From the sweating rate given in question 6, you know that Lauren lost 16 liters of sweat during the race. You also know that she gained 2 kg in weight. One liter of water weighs 1 kg.	Lauren must have ingested at least 18 liters of fluid. You have no information on other routes of fluid loss, such as urine and insensible water lost during breathing.
8	What would you expect to happen to vasopressin and aldosterone production in response to dilutional hyponatremia?	Vasopressin secretion is inhibited by a decrease in osmolarity. The usual stimuli for renin or aldosterone release are low blood pressure and hyperkalemia.	Vasopressin secretion decreases with hyponatremia. The usual stimuli for aldosterone secretion are absent, but a pathological decrease in plasma Na^+ of 10 mEq/L can stimulate the adrenal cortex to secrete aldosterone. Thus, Lauren's plasma Na^+ may be low enough to increase her aldosterone secretion.

*N/A = not applicable

651 653 667 669 675 681

CHAPTER SUMMARY

Homeostasis of body fluid volume, electrolytes, and pH follows the principle of *mass balance:* to maintain constant amount of a substance in the body, any intake or production must be offset by metabolism or excretion. The *control systems* that regulate these parameters are among the most complicated reflexes of the body because of the overlapping functions of the kidneys, lungs, and cardiovascular system. At the cellular level, however, the *movement of molecules across membranes* follows familiar patterns, as transfer of water and solutes from one *compartment* to another depends on osmosis, diffusion, and protein-mediated transport.

Fluid and Electrolyte Homeostasis

1. The renal, respiratory, and cardiovascular systems control fluid and electrolyte balance. Behaviors such as drinking also play an important role. (p. 651; Fig. 20-1)
2. Pulmonary and cardiovascular compensations are more rapid than renal compensation. (p. 652)

Water Balance

iP Urinary: Early Filtrate Processing

3. Most water intake comes from food and drink. The largest water loss is 1.5 liters/day in urine. Smaller amounts are lost in feces, by evaporation from skin, and in exhaled humidified air. (p. 653; Fig. 20-2)
4. Renal water reabsorption conserves water but cannot restore water lost from the body. (p. 654; Fig. 20-3)
5. To produce dilute urine, the nephron must reabsorb solute without reabsorbing water. To concentrate urine, the nephron must reabsorb water without reabsorbing solute. (p. 654)
6. Filtrate leaving the ascending limb of the loop of Henle is dilute. The final concentration of urine depends on the water permeability of the collecting duct. (p. 654; Fig. 20-4)
7. The hypothalamic hormone **vasopressin** controls collecting duct permeability to water in a graded fashion. When vasopressin is absent, water permeability is nearly zero. (p. 656; Fig. 20-5)
8. Vasopressin causes distal nephron cells to insert **aquaporin** water pores in their apical membrane. (p. 656; Fig. 20-6)
9. An increase in ECF osmolarity or a decrease in blood pressure stimulates vasopressin release from the posterior pituitary. Osmolarity is monitored by hypothalamic **osmoreceptors.** Blood pressure and blood volume are sensed by receptors in the carotid and aortic bodies, and in the atria, respectively. (p. 657; Figs. 20-7, 20-8)
10. The loop of Henle is a **countercurrent multiplier** that creates high osmolarity in the medullary interstitial fluid by actively transporting Na^+, Cl^-, and K^+ out of the nephron. This high medullary osmolarity is necessary for formation of concentrated urine as filtrate flows through the collecting duct. (pp. 659–660; Figs. 20-9, 20-10)
11. The **vasa recta** capillaries carry away water leaving the nephron tubule so that the water does not dilute the medullary interstitium. (p. 661; Fig. 20-10)
12. Urea contributes to the high osmolarity in the renal medulla. (p. 661)

Sodium Balance and ECF Volume

iP Urinary: Late Filtrate Processing

13. The total amount of Na^+ in the body is a primary determinant of ECF volume. (p. 661; Fig. 20-11)
14. The steroid hormone **aldosterone** increases Na^+ reabsorption and K^+ secretion. (p. 662; Fig. 20-12)
15. Aldosterone acts on **principal cells** (P cells) of the distal nephron. This hormone enhances Na^+-K^+-ATPase activity and increases open time of Na^+ and K^+ leak channels. It also stimulates the synthesis of new pumps and channels. (p. 662; Fig. 20-12)
16. Aldosterone secretion can be controlled directly at the adrenal cortex. Increased ECF K^+ stimulates aldosterone secretion, but increased ECF osmolarity inhibits it. (p. 663; Tbl. 20-1)
17. Aldosterone secretion is also stimulated by **angiotensin II.** Granular cells in the kidney secrete **renin**, which converts **angiotensinogen** in the blood to **angiotensin I. Angiotensin-converting enzyme (ACE)** converts ANG I to ANG II. (pp. 663–664; Fig. 20-13)
18. The stimuli for the release of renin are related either directly or indirectly to low blood pressure. (p. 664; Fig. 20-14)
19. ANG II has additional effects that raise blood pressure, including increased vasopressin secretion, stimulation of thirst, vasoconstriction, and activation of the cardiovascular control center. (pp. 664–665; Fig. 20-13)
20. **Atrial natriuretic peptide** (ANP) and **brain natriuretic peptide** (BNP) enhance Na^+ excretion and urinary water loss by increasing GFR, inhibiting tubular reabsorption of NaCl, and inhibiting the release of renin, aldosterone, and vasopressin. (p. 665; Fig. 20-15)

Potassium Balance

21. Potassium homeostasis keeps plasma K^+ concentrations in a narrow range. **Hyperkalemia** and **hypokalemia** cause problems with excitable tissues, especially the heart. (p. 666)

Behavioral Mechanisms in Salt and Water Balance

22. Thirst is triggered by hypothalamic osmoreceptors and relieved by drinking. (p. 667)
23. **Salt appetite** is triggered by aldosterone and angiotensin. (p. 667)

Integrated Control of Volume and Osmolarity

iP Fluids & Electrolytes: Water Homeostasis

24. Homeostatic compensations for changes in salt and water balance follow the law of mass balance. Fluid and solute added to the body must be removed, and fluid and solute lost from the body must be replaced. However, perfect compensation is not always possible. (pp. 668–669; Fig. 20-17; Tbl. 20-2)

Acid-Base Balance

iP Fluids & Electrolytes: Acid/Base Homeostasis

25. The body's pH is closely regulated because pH affects intracellular proteins, such as enzymes and membrane channels. (p. 672)
26. Acid intake from foods and acid production by the body's metabolic processes are the biggest challenge to body pH. The most

significant source of acid is CO_2 from respiration, which combines with water to form carbonic acid (H_2CO_3). (p. 673; Fig. 20-18)

27. The body copes with changes in pH by using buffers, ventilation, and renal secretion or reabsorption of H^+ and HCO_3^-. (p. 674; Fig. 20-18)
28. Bicarbonate produced from CO_2 is the most important extracellular buffer of the body. Bicarbonate buffers organic acids produced by metabolism. (p. 674)
29. Ventilation can correct disturbances in acid-base balance because changes in plasma P_{CO_2} affect both the H^+ content and the HCO_3^- content of the blood. An increase in P_{CO_2} stimulates central chemoreceptors. An increase in plasma H^+ stimulates carotid and aortic chemoreceptors. Increased ventilation excretes CO_2 and decreases plasma H^+. (p. 675; Fig. 20-19)
30. In **acidosis**, the kidneys secrete H^+ and reabsorb HCO_3^-. (p. 676; Figs. 20-20, 20-21, 20-22a)
31. In **alkalosis**, the kidneys secrete HCO_3^- and reabsorb H^+. (p. 676; Fig. 20-22b)
32. **Intercalated cells** in the collecting duct are responsible for the fine regulation of acid-base balance. (p. 678; Fig. 20-22)

QUESTIONS

(Answers to the Review Questions begin on page A1.)

THE PHYSIOLOGY PLACE

Access more review material online at **The Physiology Place** web site. There you'll find review questions, problem-solving activities, case studies, flashcards, and direct links to both *Interactive Physiology®* and *PhysioEx™*. To access the site, go to *www.physiologyplace.com* and select *Human Physiology*, Fifth Edition.

LEVEL ONE REVIEWING FACTS AND TERMS

1. What is an electrolyte? Name five electrolytes whose concentrations must be regulated by the body.
2. List five organs and four hormones important in maintaining fluid and electrolyte balance.
3. Compare the routes by which water enters the body with the routes by which the body loses water.
4. List the receptors that regulate osmolarity, blood volume, blood pressure, ventilation, and pH. Where are they located, what stimulates them, and what compensatory mechanisms are triggered by them?
5. How do the two limbs of the loop of Henle differ in their permeability to water? What makes this difference in permeability possible?
6. Which ion is a primary determinant of ECF volume? Which ion is the determinant of extracellular pH?
7. What happens to the resting membrane potential of excitable cells when plasma K^+ concentrations decrease? Which organ is most likely to be affected by changes in K^+ concentration?
8. Appetite for what two substances is important in regulating fluid volume and osmolarity?
9. Write out the words for the following abbreviations: ADH, ANP, ACE, ANG II, JG apparatus, P cell, I cell.
10. Make a list of all the different membrane transporters in the kidney. For each transporter, tell (a) which section(s) of the nephron contain(s) the transporter; (b) whether the transporter is on the apical membrane only, on the basolateral membrane only, or on both; (c) whether it participates in reabsorption only, in secretion only, or in both.
11. List and briefly explain three reasons why monitoring and regulating ECF pH are important. What three mechanisms does the body use to cope with changing pH?
12. Which is more likely to accumulate in the body, acids or bases? List some sources of each.
13. What is a buffer? List three intracellular buffers. Name the primary extracellular buffer.
14. Name two ways the kidneys alter plasma pH. Which compounds serve as urinary buffers?
15. Write the equation that shows how CO_2 is related to pH. What enzyme increases the rate of this reaction? Name two cell types that possess high concentrations of this enzyme.
16. When ventilation increases, what happens to arterial P_{CO_2}? To plasma pH? To plasma H^+ concentration?

LEVEL TWO REVIEWING CONCEPTS

17. Concept map: Map the homeostatic reflexes that occur in response to each of the following situations:
    (a) decreased blood volume, normal blood osmolarity
    (b) increased blood volume, increased blood osmolarity
    (c) normal blood volume, increased blood osmolarity
18. Figures 20-19 and 20-20 show the respiratory and renal compensations for acidosis. Draw similar maps for alkalosis.
19. Explain how the loop of Henle and vasa recta work together to create dilute renal filtrate.
20. Diagram the mechanism by which vasopressin alters the composition of urine.
21. Make a table that specifies the following for each substance listed: hormone or enzyme? steroid or peptide? produced by which cell or tissue? target cell or tissue? target has what response?
    (a) ANP
    (b) aldosterone
    (c) renin
    (d) ANG II
    (e) vasopressin
    (f) angiotensin-converting enzyme
22. Name the four main compensatory mechanisms for restoring low blood pressure to normal. Why do you think there are so many homeostatic pathways for raising low blood pressure?
23. Compare and contrast the terms in each set:
    (a) principal cells and intercalated cells
    (b) renin, ANG II, aldosterone, ACE
    (c) respiratory acidosis and metabolic acidosis, including causes and compensations
    (d) water reabsorption in proximal tubule, distal tubule, and ascending limb of the loop of Henle
    (e) respiratory alkalosis and metabolic alkalosis, including causes and compensations

24. The interstitial fluid in contact with the basolateral side of collecting duct cells has an extremely high osmolarity, and yet the cells do not shrivel up. How can they maintain normal cell volume in the face of such high ECF osmolarity?

LEVEL THREE PROBLEM SOLVING

25. A 45-year-old man visiting from out of town arrives at the emergency room having an asthma attack caused by pollen.
    (a) Blood drawn before treatment showed the following: HCO_3^- = 30 meq/L (normal: 24), P_{CO_2} = 70 mm Hg, pH = 7.24. What is the man's acid-base state? Is this an acute or a chronic situation?
    (b) The man was treated and made a complete recovery. Over the next ten years he continued to smoke a pack of cigarettes a day, and a year ago his family doctor diagnosed chronic obstructive pulmonary disease (emphysema). The man's most recent blood test showed the following: HCO_3^- = 45 meq/L, P_{CO_2} = 85 mm Hg, pH = 7.34. What is the man's acid-base state now? Is this an acute or a chronic situation?
    (c) Explain why in his second illness his plasma bicarbonate level and P_{CO_2} are higher than in the first illness but his pH is closer to normal.
26. The U.S. Food and Drug Administration recently approved a new class of drugs called *vasopressin receptor antagonists*. Predict the effect these drugs would have on renal function and describe some clinical situations or diseases in which these drugs might be useful.
27. Karen has bulimia, in which she induces vomiting to avoid weight gain. When the doctor sees her, her weight is 89 lb and her respiration rate is 6 breaths/min (normal 12). Her blood HCO_3^- is 62 meq/L (normal: 24–29), arterial blood pH is 7.61, and P_{CO_2} is 61 mm Hg.
    (a) What is her acid-base condition called?
    (b) Explain why her plasma bicarbonate level is so high.
    (c) Why is she hypoventilating? What effect does this have on the pH and total oxygen content of her blood? Explain your answers.
28. Hannah, a 31-year-old woman, decided to have colonic irrigation, a procedure during which large volumes of distilled water were infused into her rectum. During the treatment she absorbed 3000 mL of water. About 12 hours later, her roommate found her in convulsions and took her to the emergency room. Her blood pressure was 140/90, her plasma Na^+ concentration was 106 meq/L (normal: 135 meq/L), and her plasma osmolarity was 270 mOsM. In a concept map or flow chart, diagram all the homeostatic responses her body was using to attempt compensation for the changes in blood pressure and osmolarity.

LEVEL FOUR QUANTITATIVE PROBLEMS

29. The **Henderson-Hasselbalch equation** is a mathematical expression of the relationship between pH, HCO_3^- concentration, and dissolved CO_2 concentration. One variant of the equation uses P_{CO_2} instead of dissolved CO_2 concentration:

$$pH = 6.1 + \log \frac{[HCO_3^-]}{0.03 \times P_{CO_2}}$$

    (a) If arterial blood has a P_{CO_2} of 40 mm Hg and its HCO_3^- concentration is 24 mM, what is its pH? (Use a log table or calculator with a logarithmic function capability.)
    (b) What is the pH of venous blood with the same HCO_3^- concentration but a P_{CO_2} of 46 mm Hg?
30. In extreme dehydration, urine can reach a concentration of 1400 mOsM. If the minimum amount of waste solute that a person must excrete daily is about 600 milliosmoles, what is the minimum urine volume that is excreted in one day?
31. Hyperglycemia in a diabetic patient leads to osmotic diuresis and dehydration. Given the following information, answer the questions.

    Plasma glucose = 400 mg/dL
    Normal urine flow = 1 L per day
    GFR = 130 mL/min
    Normal urine osmolarity = 300 mOsM
    Glucose T_m = 400 mg/min
    Molecular mass of glucose = 180 daltons
    Renal plasma flow = 500 mL/min

    (a) How much glucose filters into the nephron each minute?
    (b) How much glucose is reabsorbed each minute?
    (c) How much glucose is excreted in the urine each day?
    (d) Assuming that dehydration causes maximal vasopressin secretion and allows the urine to concentrate to 1200 mOsM, how much additional urine does this diabetic patient excrete in a day?

ANSWERS

Answers to Concept Check Questions

Page 657

1. Apical membranes have more water pores when vasopressin is present.
2. If vasopressin secretion is suppressed, the urine is dilute.

Page 658

3. Hyperosmotic NaCl is hypertonic and causes the osmoreceptors to shrink, but hyperosmotic urea is hypotonic and causes them to swell. Because only cell shrinkage causes firing, osmoreceptors exposed to urea do not fire.
4. Because vasopressin enhances water reabsorption, vasopressin levels would increase with dehydration.
5. Osmoreceptors in the lumen of the digestive tract and hepatic portal vein would sense high-osmolarity food or drink that has been ingested and absorbed, before it is in the general circulation. This would allow an anticipatory, or feed-forward, secretion of vasopressin to conserve body water.

Page 660

6. Solutes that remain in the lumen when the NKCC symporter is inhibited force water to remain in the lumen with them because urine can be concentrated only to 1200 mOsM. Thus each 12 milliosmoles of un-reabsorbed solute "holds" an additional 10 mL of water in the urine.

7. Diuretics that inhibit the NKCC symporter leave K^+ in the tubule lumen, where it is likely to be excreted, thus increasing urinary K^+ loss.

Page 663

8. Na^+ and K^+ are moving down their electrochemical gradients.
9. In hyperkalemia, resting membrane potential depolarizes. Excitable tissues fire one action potential but are unable to repolarize to fire a second one.

Page 665

10. Atherosclerotic plaques block blood flow, which decreases GFR and decreases pressure in the afferent arteriole. Both events are stimuli for renin release.
11. Renin secretion begins a cascade that produces ANG II. This powerful hormone then causes vasoconstriction, acts on the medullary cardiovascular control center to increase blood pressure, increases production of vasopressin and aldosterone, and increases thirst, resulting in drinking and an increased fluid volume in the body. All these responses may contribute to increased blood pressure.

Page 667

12. On the left side of Figure 20-7, interneurons also lead from hypothalamic osmoreceptors to the hypothalamic thirst centers.

Page 676

13. The muscles of ventilation involved are the diaphragm, the external intercostals, and the scalenes.
14. The bicarbonate level increases as the reaction shifts to the right as a result of added CO_2. Once a new equilibrium state is achieved, bicarbonate cannot act as a buffer because the system is at equilibrium.

Page 679

15. In the distal nephron, both K^+ and H^+ are being moved against their concentration gradients, which requires ATP. In the proximal tubule, Na^+ is moving down its concentration gradient, providing the energy to push H^+ against its gradient.
16. When intercalated cells reabsorb K^+, they secrete H^+, and therefore blood pH increases.

Q Answers to Figure Questions

Page 662

Figure 20-11: See Figure 15-22, p. 000.

Page 664

Figure 20-13: See Figure 15-23, p. 000, for the cardiovascular pathway, Figure 20-12 for the effector cell involved in aldosterone action, and Figure 20-6 for the effector cell involved in vasopressin action.

21

The Digestive System

BACKGROUND BASICS

Biomolecules: **28** Micelles: **58** Smooth muscle: **432** Lymphatics: **530** Secondary active transport: **147** Cell junctions: **72** Renal Na^+ transport: **636** Positive feedback: **203** Microvilli: **66** Endocrine and exocrine glands: **79** Transporting and secretory epithelia: **74** Apical and basolateral surfaces: **77** Enzymes: **100** Protein synthesis and storage: **117** Acidification of urine: **678** Exocytosis and transcytosis: **154** Portal systems: **232, 471**

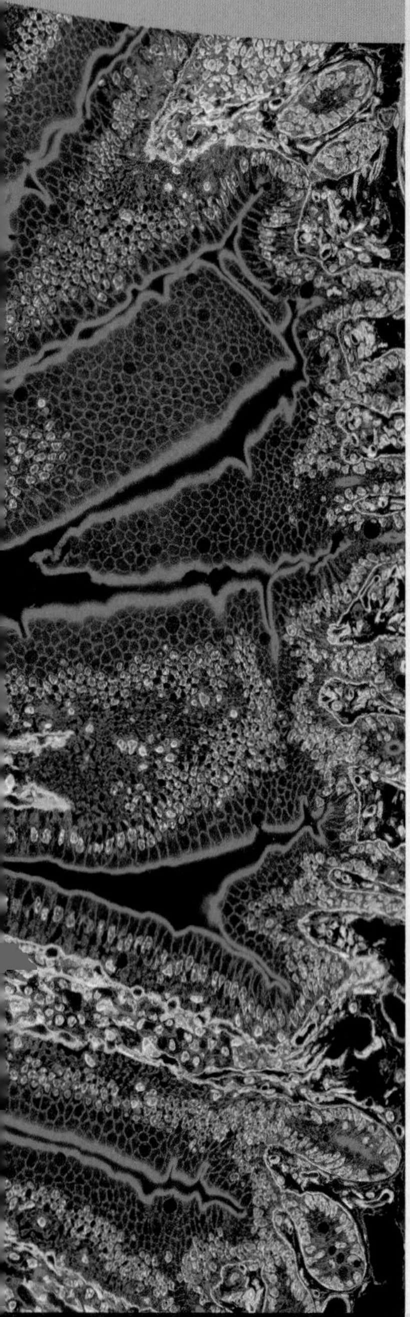

Cross-section of intestinal villi (outlined in red).

Give me a good digestion, Lord, and also something to digest.

—Anonymous, *A Pilgrim's Grace*

RUNNING PROBLEM

Peptic Ulcers

Your stomach is one of the most hostile environments on earth. Bathed in acid strong enough to digest iron nails, its walls protected by a sticky mucus, and constantly churning, the stomach was once thought to be uninhabitable by any life form. However, scientists have discovered a remarkable organism that actually thrives in the stomach's formidable environment. This hardy bacterium, called *Helicobacter pylori*, has evolved a set of defenses that allowed it to escape detection until 1982. But *H. pylori* is not merely a silent passenger in the stomach: it is associated with many cases of peptic ulcers worldwide. Proper drug treatment kills *H. pylori* and allows ulcers in the stomach and duodenum to heal. That is good news to Tonya Berry, whose physician has just informed her that he thinks she has a peptic ulcer. "I thought it was stress," Tonya said.

687 692 697 700 717 719

A shotgun wound to the stomach seems an unlikely beginning to the scientific study of digestive processes. But in 1822 at Fort Mackinac, a young Canadian trapper named Alexis St. Martin narrowly escaped death when a gun discharged three feet from him, tearing open his chest and abdomen and leaving a hole in his stomach wall. U.S. Army surgeon William Beaumont attended to St. Martin and nursed him back to health over the next two years.

The gaping wound over the stomach failed to heal properly, leaving a *fistula,* or opening, into the lumen. St. Martin was destitute and unable to care for himself, so Beaumont "retained St. Martin in his family for the special purpose of making physiological experiments." In a legal document, St. Martin even agreed to "obey, suffer, and comply with all reasonable and proper experiments of the said William [Beaumont] in relation to . . . the exhibiting . . . of his said stomach and the power and properties . . . and states of the contents thereof."

Beaumont's observations on digestion and on the state of St. Martin's stomach under various conditions created a sensation. In 1832, just before Beaumont's observations were published, the nature of gastric juice [*gaster*, stomach] and digestion in the stomach was a subject of much debate. Beaumont's careful observations went far toward solving the mystery. Like physicians of old who tasted urine when making a diagnosis, Beaumont tasted the mucous lining of the stomach and the gastric juices. He described them both as "saltish," but mucus was not at all acidic, and gastric fluid was very acidic. Beaumont collected copious amounts of gastric fluid through the fistula, and in controlled experiments he confirmed that gastric fluid digested meat, using a combination of hydrochloric acid and another active factor now known to be the enzyme pepsin.

These observations and others about motility and digestion in the stomach became the foundation of what we know about digestive physiology. Although research today is conducted more at the cellular and molecular level, researchers still create surgical fistulas in experimental animals to observe and sample the contents of the digestive tract.

Why is the digestive system—also referred to as the **gastrointestinal system** [*intestinus,* internal]—of such great interest? The reason is that gastrointestinal diseases today account for nearly one-tenth of the money spent on health care. Many of these conditions, such as heartburn, indigestion, gas, and constipation, are troublesome rather than major health risks, but their significance should not be underestimated. Go into any drugstore and look at the number of over-the-counter medications for digestive disorders to get a feel for the impact digestive diseases have on our society. In this chapter we examine the gastrointestinal system and the remarkable way in which it transforms the food we eat into nutrients for the body's use.

DIGESTIVE FUNCTION AND PROCESSES

The **gastrointestinal tract**, or **GI tract**, is a long tube passing through the body. The tube has muscular walls lined with epithelium and is closed off by a skeletal-muscle sphincter at each end. Because the GI tract opens to the outside world, the lumen and its contents are actually part of the external environment. (Think of a hole passing through the center of a bead.) [Fig. 1-2, p. 3] The primary function of the GI tract is to move nutrients, water, and electrolytes from the external environment into the body's internal environment.

The food we eat is mostly in the form of macromolecules, such as proteins and complex carbohydrates, so our digestive systems must secrete powerful enzymes to digest food into molecules that are small enough to be absorbed into the body. At the same time, however, these enzymes must not digest the cells of the GI tract itself (*autodigestion*). If protective mechanisms against autodigestion fail, we may develop raw patches known as *peptic ulcers* [*peptos,* digested] on the walls of the GI tract.

Another challenge the digestive system faces daily is mass balance: matching fluid input with output (Fig. 21-1 ●). People ingest about 2 liters of fluid a day. In addition, exocrine glands and cells secrete 7 liters or so of enzymes, mucus, electrolytes, and water into the lumen of the GI tract. That volume of secreted fluid is the equivalent of one-sixth of the body's total body water (42 liters), or more than twice the plasma volume of 3 liters, and it must be reabsorbed or the body would rapidly dehydrate. Normally reabsorption is very efficient, and only

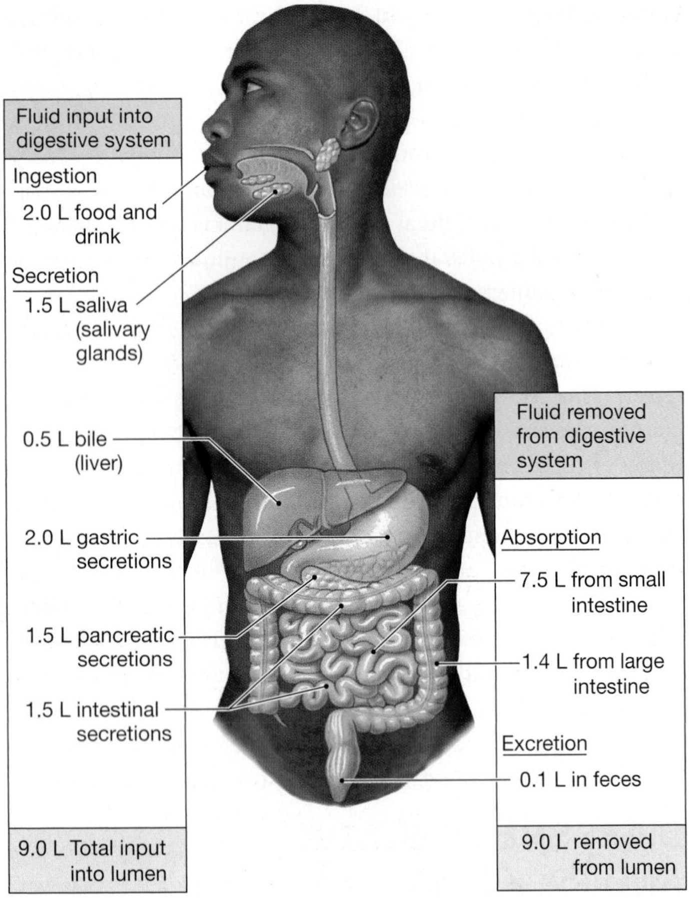
Fluid input into digestive system
Ingestion
2.0 L food and drink
Secretion
1.5 L saliva (salivary glands)
0.5 L bile (liver)
2.0 L gastric secretions
1.5 L pancreatic secretions
1.5 L intestinal secretions
9.0 L Total input into lumen
Fluid removed from digestive system
Absorption
7.5 L from small intestine
1.4 L from large intestine
Excretion
0.1 L in feces
9.0 L removed from lumen

● **FIGURE 21-1** ***To maintain homeostasis, the volume of fluid entering the GI tract lumen by intake or secretion must equal the volume leaving the lumen.***

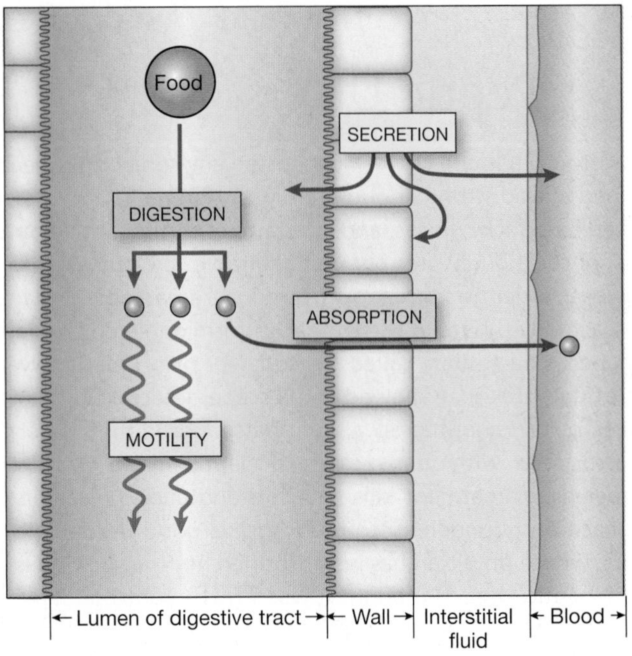
Food
SECRETION
DIGESTION
ABSORPTION
MOTILITY
Lumen of digestive tract
Wall
Interstitial fluid
Blood

● **FIGURE 21-2** ***Four basic processes of the digestive system.*** The four digestive system processes are *digestion* of food into smaller units; *absorption* of substances from the lumen into the ECF; *motility*, the movement of materials through the GI tract; and *secretion* of substances from epithelial cells into the lumen or ECF.

about 100 mL of fluid is lost in the feces. However, vomiting and diarrhea (excessively watery feces) can become an emergency when GI secretions that would normally be reabsorbed are lost to the environment. In severe cases, this fluid loss can deplete extracellular fluid volume to the point that the circulatory system is unable to maintain adequate blood pressure.

A final challenge the digestive system faces is repelling foreign invaders. It is counterintuitive, but the largest area of contact between the internal environment and the outside world is in the lumen of the digestive system. As a result, the GI tract, with a total surface area about the size of a tennis court, faces daily conflict between the need to absorb water and nutrients, and the need to keep bacteria, viruses, and other pathogens from entering the body. To this end, the transporting epithelium of the GI tract is assisted by an array of physiological defense mechanisms, including mucus, digestive enzymes, acid, and the largest collection of lymphoid tissue in the body, the **gut-associated lymphoid tissue** (GALT). By one estimate, 80% of all lymphocytes [p. 549] in the body are found in the small intestine.

The human body meets these sometimes conflicting physiological challenges by coordinating the four basic processes of the digestive system: digestion, absorption, motility, and secretion (Fig. 21-2 ●). **Digestion** is the chemical and mechanical breakdown of foods into smaller units that can be taken across the intestinal epithelium into the body. **Absorption** is the active or passive transfer of substances from the lumen of the GI tract to the extracellular fluid. **Motility** [*movere,* move + *tillis,* characterized by] is movement of material in the GI tract as a result of muscle contraction. **Secretion** refers to both the transepithelial transfer of water and ions from the ECF to the digestive tract lumen and the release of substances synthesized by GI epithelial cells.

Scientists used to believe that nutrient absorption was not regulated and that "what you eat is what you get." Now, however, evidence indicates that some nutrient absorption changes in response to long-term environmental changes. In contrast, motility and secretion are continuously regulated to maximize the availability of absorbable material. Motility is regulated because if food moves through the system too rapidly, there is not enough time for everything in the lumen to be digested and absorbed. Secretion is regulated because if digestive enzymes are not secreted in adequate amounts, food in the GI tract cannot be broken down into an absorbable form.

When digested nutrients have been absorbed and have reached the body's cells, cellular metabolism directs their use or storage (see Chapter 22). Some of the same chemical signal molecules that alter digestive motility and secretion also participate in the control of metabolism, providing an integrating link between the two steps.

ANATOMY OF THE DIGESTIVE SYSTEM

The digestive system begins with the oral cavity (mouth and pharynx), which serves as a receptacle for food (Fig. 21-3a ●). In the oral cavity the first stages of digestion begin with chewing and the secretion of saliva by three pairs of **salivary glands:** *sublingual glands* under the tongue, *submandibular glands* under the mandible (jawbone), and *parotid glands* lying near the hinge of the jaw.

Once swallowed, food moves into the GI tract. At intervals along the tract, rings of smooth muscle function as sphincters to separate the tube into segments with distinct functions. Food moves through the tract propelled by waves of muscle contraction. Along the way, secretions are added to the food by secretory epithelium, the liver, and the pancreas, creating a soupy mixture known as **chyme.**

Digestion takes place primarily in the lumen of the tube. The products of digestion are absorbed across the epithelium and pass into the extracellular compartment. From there, they move into the blood or lymph for distribution throughout the body. Any waste remaining in the lumen at the end of the GI tract leaves the body through the opening known as the *anus*.

CONCEPT CHECK

1. Define digestion.
2. What is the difference between digestion and metabolism [p. 105]?
3. What is the difference between absorption and secretion?

Answers: p. 723

The Digestive System Is a Tube

When you swallow a piece of food, it passes into the **esophagus**, a narrow tube that travels through the thorax to the abdomen (Fig. 21-3a). The esophageal walls are skeletal muscle initially but transition to smooth muscle about two-thirds of the way down the length. Just below the diaphragm, the esophagus ends at the **stomach**, a baglike organ that can hold as much as 2 liters of food and fluid when fully (if uncomfortably) expanded.

The stomach is divided into three sections: the upper **fundus**, the central **body**, and the lower **antrum** (Fig. 21-3b). The stomach continues digestion that began in the mouth by mixing food with acid and enzymes to create chyme. The **pylorus** [gatekeeper] or opening between the stomach and the **small intestine** is guarded by the **pyloric valve.** This thickened band of smooth muscle relaxes to allow only small amounts of chyme into the small intestine at any one time. In this way, the stomach acts as an intermediary between the behavioral act of eating and the physiological events of digestion and absorption in the intestine. Integrated signals and feedback loops between the intestine and stomach regulate the rate at which chyme enters the duodenum, ensuring that the intestine is not overwhelmed with more than it can digest and absorb.

Most digestion takes place in the small intestine, which is also divided into three sections: the **duodenum** (the first 25 cm), **jejunum**, and **ileum** (the latter two together are about 260 cm long). Digestion is carried out by intestinal enzymes, aided by exocrine secretions from two *accessory glandular organs:* the pancreas and the liver (Fig. 21-3a). Secretions from these two organs enter the initial section of the duodenum through ducts. A tonically contracted sphincter (the *sphincter of Oddi*) keeps pancreatic fluid and bile from entering the small intestine except during a meal.

Digestion is essentially completed in the small intestine, and nearly all digested nutrients and secreted fluids are absorbed there, leaving about 1.5 liters of chyme per day to pass into the **large intestine** (Fig. 21-3a). In the **colon**—the proximal section of the large intestine—watery chyme is converted into semisolid **feces** [*faeces,* dregs] as water and electrolytes are absorbed out of the chyme and into the ECF.

When feces are propelled into the terminal section of the large intestine, known as the **rectum**, distension of the rectal wall triggers a *defecation reflex*. Feces leave the GI tract through the **anus**, with its **external anal sphincter** of skeletal muscle, which is under voluntary control. The portion of the GI tract running from the stomach to the anus is collectively called the **gut.**

In a living person, the digestive system from mouth to anus is about 450 cm (nearly 15 ft) long! Of this length, 395 cm (about 13 ft) consists of the large and small intestines. Try to imagine 13 feet of rope ranging from 1 to 3 inches in diameter all coiled up inside your abdomen from the belly button down. The tight arrangement of the abdominal organs helps explain why you feel the need to loosen your belt after consuming a large meal.

Measurements of intestinal length made during autopsies are nearly double those given here because after death, the longitudinal muscles of the intestinal tract relax. This relaxation accounts for the wide variation in intestinal length you may encounter in different references.

The GI Tract Wall Has Four Layers

The basic structure of the gastrointestinal wall is similar in the stomach and intestines, although variations exist from one section of the GI tract to another (Fig. 21-3c, d, e). The wall consists of four layers: (1) an inner *mucosa* facing the lumen, (2) a layer known as the *submucosa,* (3) layers of smooth muscle known collectively as the *muscularis externa,* and (4) a covering of connective tissue called the *serosa*.

ANATOMY SUMMARY

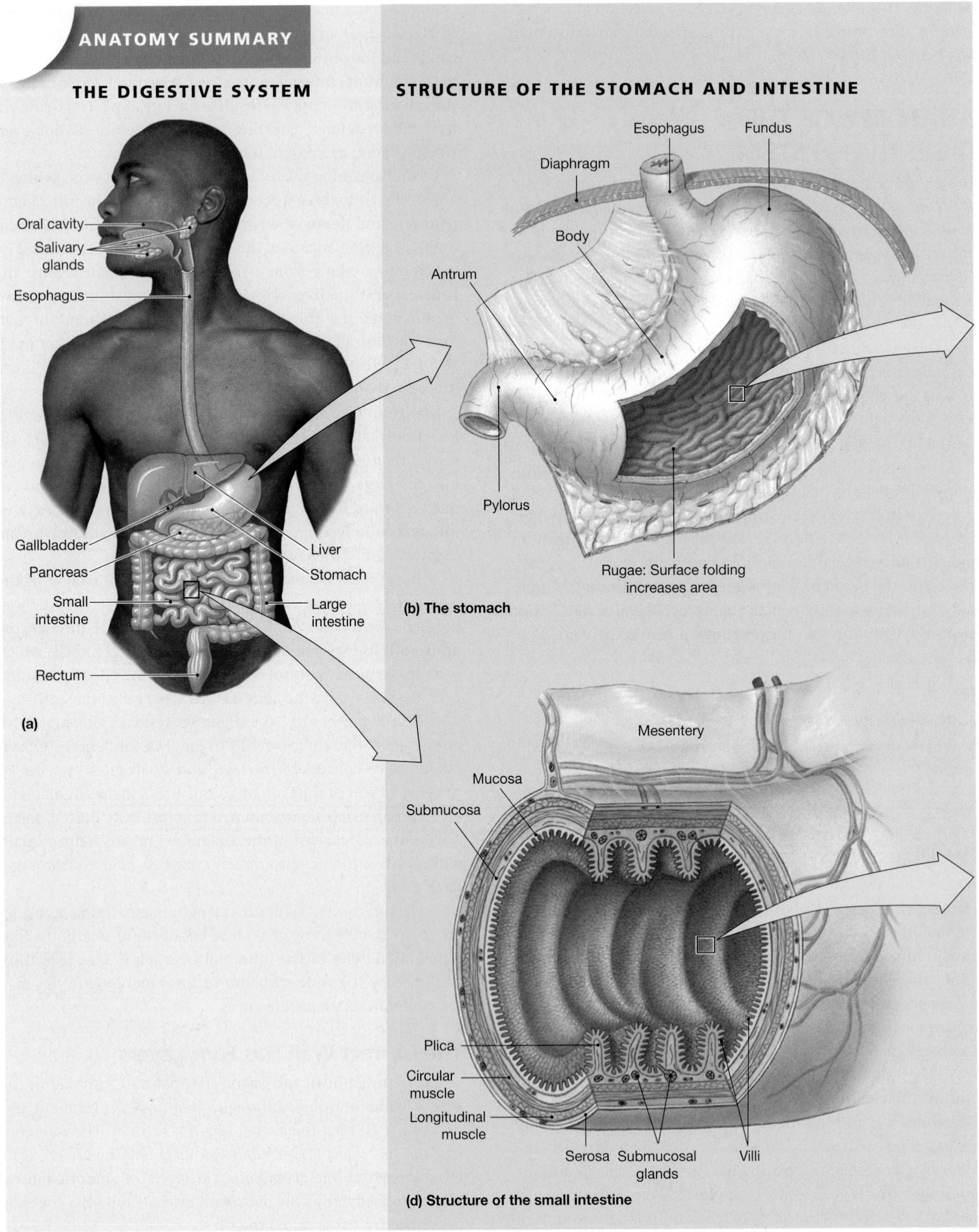
THE DIGESTIVE SYSTEM
Oral cavity
Salivary glands
Esophagus
Gallbladder
Pancreas
Small intestine
Rectum
Liver
Stomach
Large intestine
(a)
STRUCTURE OF THE STOMACH AND INTESTINE
Esophagus
Fundus
Diaphragm
Body
Antrum
Pylorus
Rugae: Surface folding increases area
(b) The stomach
Mesentery
Mucosa
Submucosa
Plica
Circular muscle
Longitudinal muscle
Serosa
Submucosal glands
Villi
(d) Structure of the small intestine

● **FIGURE 21-3**

SECTIONAL VIEWS OF THE STOMACH AND INTESTINE

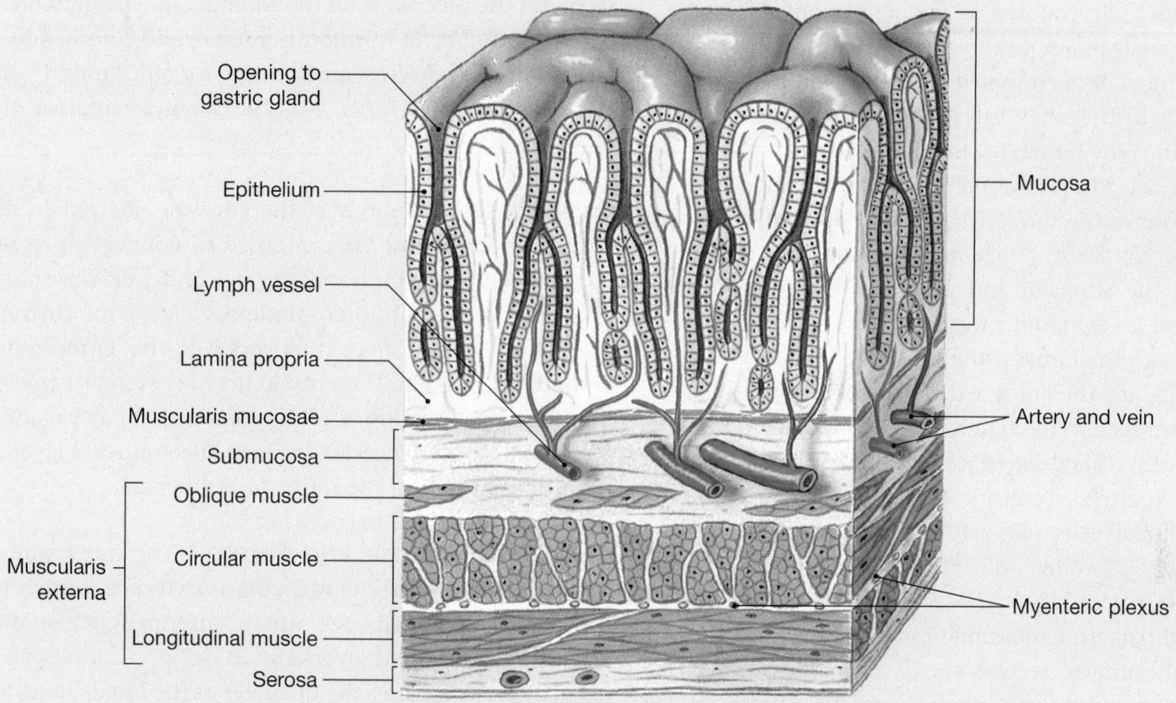
Opening to gastric gland
Epithelium
Lymph vessel
Lamina propria
Muscularis mucosae
Submucosa
Oblique muscle
Muscularis externa
Circular muscle
Longitudinal muscle
Serosa
Mucosa
Artery and vein
Myenteric plexus

(c) In the stomach, surface area is increased by invaginations called gastric glands.

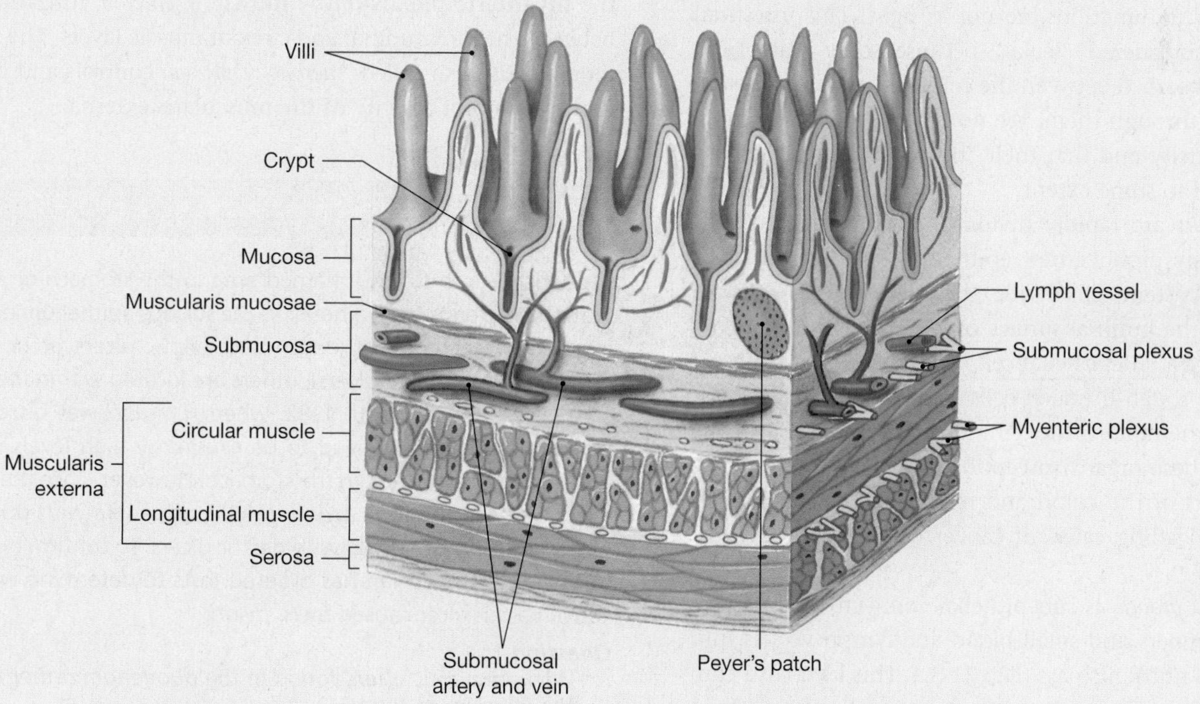
Villi
Crypt
Mucosa
Muscularis mucosae
Submucosa
Muscularis externa
Circular muscle
Longitudinal muscle
Serosa
Lymph vessel
Submucosal plexus
Myenteric plexus
Submucosal artery and vein
Peyer's patch

(e) Intestinal surface area is enhanced by fingerlike villi and invaginations called crypts.

Mucosa The **mucosa**, the inner lining of the gastrointestinal tract, is created from (1) a single layer of epithelial cells; (2) the **lamina propria**, subepithelial connective tissue that holds the epithelium in place; and (3) the **muscularis mucosae**, a thin layer of smooth muscle. Several structural modifications increase the amount of mucosal surface area to enhance absorption.

First, the entire wall is crumpled into folds: *rugae* in the stomach, and *plicae* in the small intestine. The intestinal mucosa also projects into the lumen in small fingerlike extensions known as **villi** (Fig. 21-3d). Additional surface area is added by tubular invaginations of the surface that extend down into the supporting connective tissue. These invaginations are called **gastric glands** in the stomach and **crypts** in the intestine. Some of the deepest invaginations form secretory **submucosal glands** that open into the lumen through ducts.

Epithelial cells are the most variable feature of the GI tract, changing from section to section. The cells include transporting epithelial cells (called *enterocytes* in the small intestine), endocrine and exocrine secretory cells, and stem cells. Transporting epithelial cells move ions and water into the lumen, and absorb ions, water, and nutrients into the ECF. At the *mucosal* (apical) surface [p. 77], secretory cells release enzymes, mucus, and paracrine molecules into the lumen. At the *serosal* (basolateral) surface, secretory cells secrete hormones into the blood or paracrine messengers into the interstitial fluid, where they act on neighboring cells.

The cell-to-cell junctions that tie GI epithelial cells together vary [p. 72]. In the stomach and colon, the junctions form a tight barrier so that little can pass between the cells. In the small intestine, junctions are not as tight. This intestinal epithelium is considered "leaky" because some water and solutes can be absorbed between the cells (the *paracellular pathway*) instead of through them. We now know that these junctions have plasticity and that their "tightness" and selectivity can be regulated to some extent.

GI *stem cells* are rapidly dividing, undifferentiated cells that continuously produce new epithelium in the crypts and gastric glands. As stem cells divide, the newly formed cells are pushed toward the luminal surface of the epithelium. The average life span of a GI epithelial cell is only a few days, a good indicator of the rough life such cells lead. As with other types of epithelium, the rapid turnover and cell division rate in the GI tract make these organs susceptible to developing cancers. In 2005, cancers of the colon and rectum (colorectal cancer) were the third leading cause of cancer deaths in the United States.

The *lamina propria* is subepithelial connective tissue that contains nerve fibers and small blood and lymph vessels into which absorbed nutrients pass (Fig. 21-3c). This layer also contains wandering immune cells, such as macrophages and lymphocytes, patrolling for invaders that enter through breaks in the epithelium. In the intestine, collections of lymphoid tissue adjoining the epithelium form small *nodules* and larger **Peyer's patches** that create visible bumps in the mucosa (Fig. 21-3e). These lymphoid aggregations are a major part of the gut-associated lymphoid tissue (GALT).

The third region of the mucosa, the *muscularis mucosae*, separates the mucosa from the submucosa. The muscularis mucosae is a thin layer of smooth muscle, and contraction of this layer alters the effective surface area for absorption by moving the villi back and forth, like the waving tentacles of a sea anemone.

Submucosa The layer of the gut wall adjacent to the mucosa, the **submucosa**, is composed of connective tissue with larger blood and lymph vessels (Fig. 21-3c, e). The submucosa also contains the **submucosal plexus** [*plexus,* interwoven], one of the two major nerve networks of the **enteric nervous system** [p. 249]. The enteric nervous system helps coordinate digestive function, and the submucosal plexus (also called *Meissner's plexus*) innervates cells in the epithelial layer as well as smooth muscle of the muscularis mucosae.

Muscularis Externa and Serosa The outer wall of the gastrointestinal tract, the **muscularis externa**, consists primarily of two layers of smooth muscle: an inner circular layer and an outer longitudinal layer (Fig. 21-3d, e). Contraction of the circular layer decreases the diameter of the lumen, and contraction of the longitudinal layer shortens the tube. The stomach has an incomplete third layer of oblique muscle between the circular muscles and the submucosa (Fig. 21-3c).

The second nerve network of the enteric nervous system, the **myenteric plexus** [*myo-,* muscle + *enteron,* intestine], lies between the longitudinal and circular muscle layers. The myenteric plexus (also called *Auerbach's plexus*) controls and coordinates the motor activity of the muscularis externa.

RUNNING PROBLEM

A peptic ulcer is a raw, inflamed area in the stomach or duodenum that extends from a break in the surface epithelium past the muscularis mucosae. Although most peptic ulcers occur in the duodenum (duodenal ulcers), others are located within the stomach (gastric ulcers). Until 1982, when *H. pylori* was discovered, peptic ulcers were believed to be caused by high levels of acid and enzyme production in the stomach. However, since the 1980s, scientists have found *H. pylori* in 90% of people with duodenal ulcers and 70% of people with gastric ulcers. To confirm his suspicions, Tonya's physician has ordered tests to determine whether Tonya has an ulcer caused by *H. pylori.*

Question 1:
Why are peptic ulcers found in the duodenum rather than in the jejunum or ileum?

687 692 697 700 717 719

The outer covering of the entire digestive tract, the **serosa,** is a connective tissue membrane that is a continuation of the **peritoneal membrane** (*peritoneum*) lining the abdominal cavity [p. 54]. The peritoneum also forms sheets of **mesentery** that hold the intestines in place so that they do not become tangled as they move.

Now let's take a brief look at the four processes of motility, secretion, digestion, and absorption. Gastrointestinal physiology is a rapidly expanding field, and this textbook does not attempt to be all inclusive. Instead, it focuses on selected broad aspects of digestive physiology.

CONCEPT CHECK

4. Is the lumen of the digestive tract on the apical or basolateral side of the intestinal epithelium? On the serosal or mucosal side?
5. Name the structures a piece of food passes through as it travels from mouth to anus.
6. Why is the digestive system associated with the largest collection of lymphoid tissue in the body?

Answers: p. 723

MOTILITY

Motility in the gastrointestinal tract serves two purposes: moving food from the mouth to the anus and mechanically mixing food to break it into uniformly small particles. This mixing maximizes exposure of the particles to digestive enzymes by increasing their surface area. Gastrointestinal motility is determined by the properties of the tract's smooth muscle and modified by chemical input from nerves, hormones, and paracrine signals.

GI Smooth Muscle Contracts Spontaneously

Most of the gastrointestinal tract is composed of single-unit smooth muscle, with groups of cells electrically connected by gap junctions [p. 72] to create contracting segments. Different regions exhibit different types of contraction. **Tonic contractions** that are sustained for minutes or hours occur in some smooth muscle sphincters and in the anterior portion of the stomach. **Phasic contractions,** with contraction-relaxation cycles lasting only a few seconds, occur in the posterior region of the stomach and in the small intestine.

Cycles of smooth muscle contraction and relaxation are associated with spontaneous cycles of depolarization and repolarization known as **slow wave potentials** (or simply *slow waves*). Slow wave potentials differ from myocardial pacemaker potentials in that the former have a much slower rate (3–12 waves/min GI versus 60–90 waves/min myocardial) and do not reach threshold with each cycle (Fig. 21-4 ●). A slow wave that does not reach threshold does not cause a contraction in the muscle fiber.

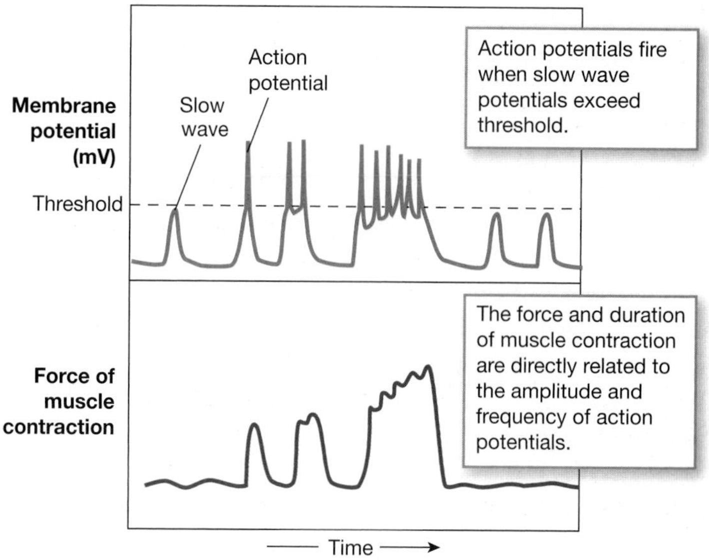

● **FIGURE 21-4** ***Slow waves are spontaneous depolarizations in GI smooth muscle.***

When a slow wave potential does reach threshold, voltage-gated Ca^{2+} channels in the muscle fiber open, Ca^{2+} enters, and the cell fires one or more action potentials. The depolarization phase of the action potential, like that in myocardial autorhythmic cells, is the result of Ca^{2+} entry into the cell. In addition, Ca^{2+} entry initiates muscle contraction [p. 435].

Contraction of smooth muscle, like that of cardiac muscle, is graded according to the amount of Ca^{2+} that enters the fiber. The longer the duration of the slow wave, the more action potentials fire, and the greater the contraction force in the muscle. Similarly, the longer the duration of the slow wave, the longer the duration of contraction. Both amplitude and duration can be modified by neurotransmitters, hormones, or paracrine molecules.

Slow wave frequency varies by region of the digestive tract, ranging from 3 waves/min in the stomach to 12 waves/min in the duodenum. Current research indicates that slow waves originate in a network of cells called the **interstitial cells of Cajal** (named for the Spanish neuroanatomist Santiago Ramón y Cajal), or ICCs. These modified smooth muscle cells lie between smooth muscle layers and the intrinsic nerve plexuses, and they may act as an intermediary between the neurons and smooth muscle.

It appears that ICCs function as the pacemakers for slow wave activity in different regions of the GI tract. Slow waves that begin spontaneously in ICCs spread to adjacent smooth muscle layers through gap junctions. Just as in the cardiac conducting system, the fastest pacemaker in a group of ICCs sets the pace for the entire group [p. 485]. The observation that ICCs seem to coordinate GI motility now has researchers working to establish a link between ICCs and functional bowel disorders, such as irritable bowel syndrome and chronic constipation.

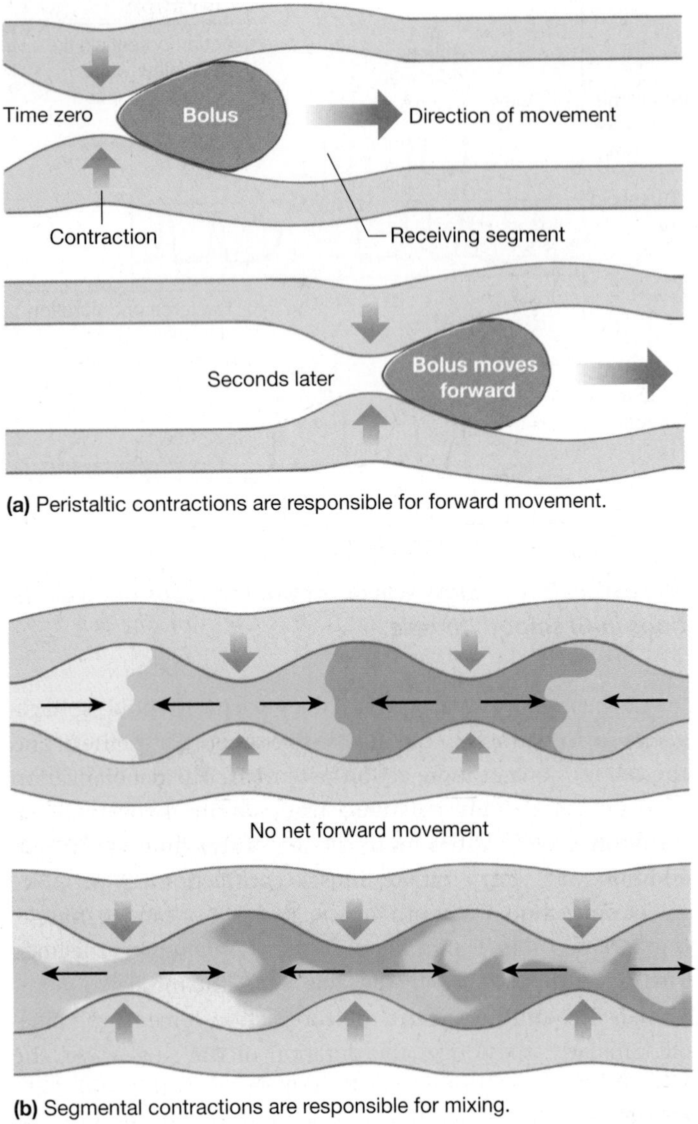
Time zero
Bolus
Direction of movement
Contraction
Receiving segment
Seconds later
Bolus moves forward
(a) Peristaltic contractions are responsible for forward movement.
No net forward movement
(b) Segmental contractions are responsible for mixing.

● **FIGURE 21-5** ***Peristaltic and segmental contractions in the GI tract***

GI Smooth Muscle Exhibits Different Patterns of Contraction

Muscle contractions in the gastrointestinal tract occur in three general patterns. Between meals, when the tract is largely empty, a series of contractions begins in the stomach and passes slowly from section to section, each taking about 90 minutes to reach the large intestine. This pattern, known as the **migrating motor complex**, is a "housekeeping" function that sweeps food remnants and bacteria out of the upper GI tract and into the large intestine.

Muscle contractions during and following a meal fall into one of two other patterns. **Peristalsis** [*peri-*, surrounding + *stalsis*, contraction] is progressive waves of contraction that move from one section of the GI tract to the next, just like the human "waves" that ripple around a football stadium or basketball arena. In peristalsis, circular muscles contract just behind a mass, or **bolus**, of food. This contraction pushes the bolus forward into a *receiving segment,* where the circular muscles are relaxed (Fig. 21-5a ●). The receiving segment then contracts, continuing the forward movement. Peristaltic contractions push a bolus forward at speeds between 2 and 25 cm/sec.

Peristalsis occurs mainly in the esophagus, where it propels material from pharynx to stomach. Peristalsis contributes to food mixing in the stomach, but in normal digestion intestinal peristaltic waves are limited to short distances. Hormones, paracrine signals, and the autonomic nervous system influence peristalsis in all regions of the GI tract.

In **segmental contractions,** short (1–5 cm) segments of intestine alternately contract and relax (Fig. 21-5b). In the contracting segments, circular muscles contract while longitudinal muscles relax. These contractions may occur randomly along the intestine or at regular intervals. Alternating segmental contractions churn the intestinal contents, mixing them and keeping them in contact with the absorptive epithelium. When segments contract sequentially, in an oral-to-aboral direction [*ab-*, away], digesting material is propelled short distances.

Motility disorders are among the more common gastrointestinal problems. They range from esophageal spasms and delayed gastric (stomach) emptying to constipation and diarrhea. *Irritable bowel syndrome* is a chronic functional disorder characterized by altered bowel habits and abdominal pain.

CONCEPT CHECK

7. Why are some sphincters of the digestive system tonically contracted?
Answers: p. 723

CLINICAL FOCUS

DIABETES

DELAYED GASTRIC EMPTYING

Diabetes mellitus has an impact on almost every organ system. The digestive tract is not exempt. One problem that plagues more than a third of all diabetics is *gastroparesis,* also called delayed gastric emptying. In these patients, the migrating motor complex is absent between meals, and the stomach empties very slowly after meals. Many patients suffer nausea and vomiting as a result. The causes of diabetic gastroparesis are unclear, but recent studies of animal models and human patients show loss or dysfunction of the interstitial cells of Cajal, which serve as pacemakers and a link between GI smooth muscle and the enteric and autonomic nervous systems. Adopting the cardiac model of an external pacemaker, scientists are now testing an implantable gastric pacemaker to promote gastric motility in diabetic patients with severe gastroparesis.

SECRETION

In a typical day, 9 liters of fluid pass through the lumen of an adult's gastrointestinal tract—equal to the contents of three 3-liter soft drink bottles! Only about 2 liters of that volume enter the GI system through the mouth. The remaining 7 liters of fluid come from body water secreted along with enzymes and mucus (see Fig. 21-1). About half the secreted fluid comes from accessory organs and glands such as the salivary glands, pancreas, and liver. The remaining 3.5 liters are secreted by epithelial cells of the digestive tract itself.

The Digestive System Secretes Ions and Water

A large portion of the 7 liters of fluid secreted by the digestive system each day is composed of water and ions, particularly Na^+, K^+, Cl^-, HCO_3^-, and H^+. The ions are first secreted into the lumen of the tract, then reabsorbed. Water follows osmotic gradients created by the transfer of solutes from one side of the epithelium to the other. Water moves through the epithelial cells via membrane channels or between cells (the paracellular pathway).

Gastrointestinal epithelial cells, like those in the kidney, have distinct apical and basolateral membranes. Each cell surface contains proteins for active transport, facilitated diffusion, and ion movement through open channels. The arrangement of channels and transporters on the apical and basolateral membranes determines the net movement of solutes across the epithelium. In addition, Na^+ may move through leaky junctions between cells in some parts of the digestive tract.

Many of the membrane transporters of the GI tract are similar to those of the renal tubule. The basolateral membrane contains the ubiquitous Na^+-K^+-ATPase. Cotransporters include the Na^+-K^+-$2Cl^-$ symporter (NKCC), Cl^--HCO_3^- exchangers, the Na^+-H^+ exchanger (NHE), and H^+-K^+-ATPase. Ion channels include Na^+, K^+, and Cl^- channels, such as the gated Cl^- channel known as the **cystic fibrosis transmembrane conductance regulator**, or **CFTR chloride channel.** Defects in CFTR channel structure or function lead to the disease *cystic fibrosis* (see the Chapter 5 Running Problem).

The sections that follow describe our current models of how cells arrange these membrane proteins to create acid secretion by the stomach, bicarbonate secretion by the pancreas and duodenum, and isotonic NaCl secretion by the intestines.

Acid Secretion **Parietal cells** deep in the gastric glands secrete hydrochloric acid into the lumen of the stomach. Acid secretion in the stomach averages 1–3 liters per day and can create a luminal pH as low as 1. The cytoplasmic pH of the parietal cells is about 7.2, which means the cells are pumping H^+ against a gradient that is 2.5 *million* times more concentrated in the lumen.

The parietal cell pathway for acid secretion is depicted in Figure 21-6 ●. The process begins when H^+ from water inside the parietal cell is pumped into the stomach lumen by an H^+-K^+-ATPase in exchange for K^+ entering the cell. Cl^- then follows H^+ through an open chloride channel, resulting in net secretion of HCl by the cell. (The molecular identity of this chloride channel is uncertain.) While acid is being secreted into the lumen, bicarbonate made from CO_2 and the OH^- from water is absorbed into the blood. The buffering action of HCO_3^- makes blood leaving the stomach less acidic, creating the "*alkaline tide*" that can be measured as a meal is being digested.

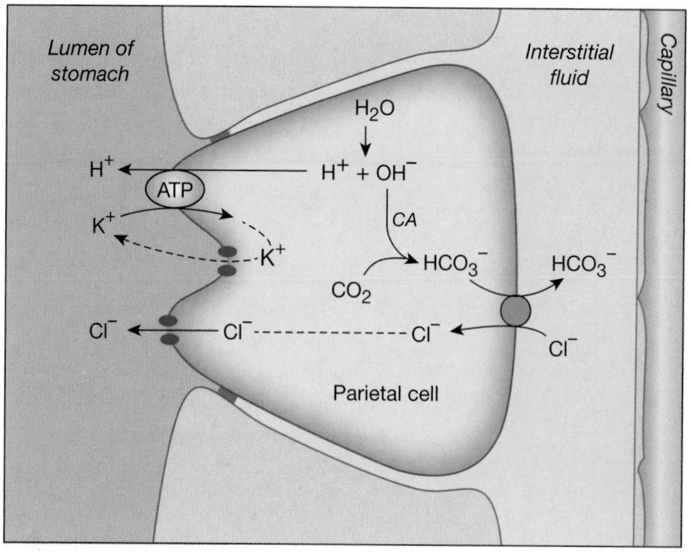

● **FIGURE 21-6** ***Parietal cells secrete hydrochloric acid into the lumen of the stomach.***

Bicarbonate Secretion Bicarbonate secretion into the duodenum neutralizes acid entering from the stomach. A small amount of bicarbonate is secreted by duodenal cells, but most comes from the pancreas, which secretes a watery solution of $NaHCO_3$. The exocrine portion of the pancreas consists of lobules called **acini** [*acinus,* grape or berry] that open into ducts whose lumens are part of the body's external environment (Fig. 21-7 ●). The *acinar cells* secrete digestive enzymes, and the duct cells secrete the $NaHCO_3$ solution. The pancreas also secretes hormones from *islet cells* tucked among the acinar cells.

Bicarbonate production requires high levels of the enzyme *carbonic anhydrase,* levels similar to those found in renal tubule cells and red blood cells [pp. 610, 673]. Bicarbonate produced from CO_2 and water is secreted by an apical Cl^--HCO_3^- exchanger (Fig. 21-8 ●). Chloride enters the cell on a basolateral NKCC cotransporter and leaves via an apical CFTR channel. Luminal Cl^- then re-enters the cell in exchange for HCO_3^- entering the lumen. Hydrogen ions produced along with bicarbonate leave the cell on basolateral Na^+-H^+ exchangers. The H^+ thus reabsorbed into the intestinal circulation helps balance HCO_3^- put into the blood when parietal cells secrete H^+ into the stomach (see Fig. 21-6).

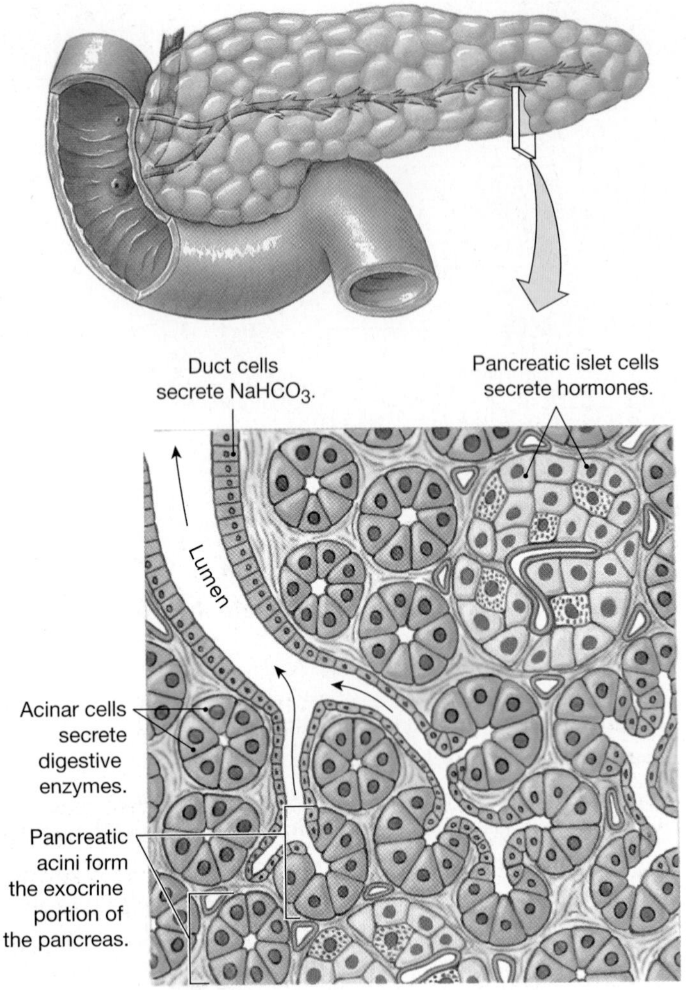

● **FIGURE 21-7** ***Anatomy of the exocrine and endocrine pancreas.*** The secretions of the exocrine pancreas enter the digestive tract through ducts. Hormones from the endocrine islet cells enter the blood.

Sodium and water movement in these tissues is a passive process, driven by electrochemical and osmotic gradients. The net movement of negative ions from the ECF to the lumen attracts Na^+, which moves down its electrochemical gradient through leaky junctions between the cells. The secretion of Na^+ and HCO_3^- into the lumen creates an osmotic gradient, and water follows by osmosis. The net result is secretion of a watery sodium bicarbonate solution.

In cystic fibrosis, an inherited defect causes the CFTR channel to be defective or absent. As a result, secretion of Cl^- and fluid ceases, but goblet cells [p. 79] continue to secrete mucus, resulting in thickened mucus. In the digestive system, the thick mucus clogs small pancreatic ducts and prevents digestive enzyme secretion into the intestine. In airways of the respiratory system, where the CFTR channel is also found, failure to secrete fluid clogs the mucociliary escalator [p. 574] with thick mucus, leading to recurrent lung infections.

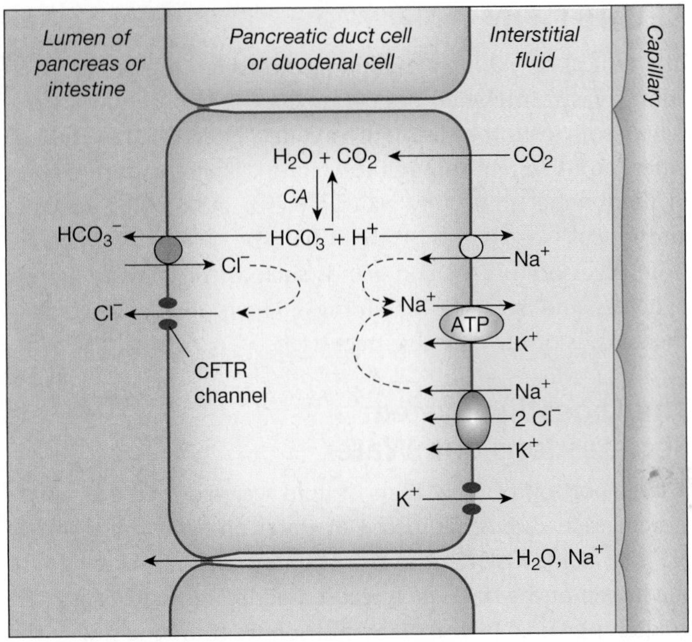

● **FIGURE 21-8** ***Bicarbonate secretion in the pancreas and duodnum.*** Cells that produce bicarbonate have high concentrations of carbonic anhydrase (CA).

NaCl Secretion Crypt cells in the small intestine and colon secrete an isotonic NaCl solution that mixes with mucus secreted by goblet cells to help lubricate the contents of the gut. The active step is Cl^- secretion similar to that just described for pancreatic cells (Fig. 21-9 ●). Chloride from the ECF enters cells via NKCC transporters, then exits into the lumen via apical CFTR channels. Na^+ and water follow along the paracellular pathway, with the end result being secretion of isotonic saline solution.

Digestive Enzymes Are Secreted into the Lumen

Digestive enzymes are secreted either by exocrine glands (salivary glands and the pancreas) or by epithelial cells in the mucosa of the stomach and small intestine. Enzymes are proteins, which means they are synthesized on the rough endoplasmic reticulum, packaged by the Golgi complex into secretory vesicles, and then stored in the cell until needed. On demand, they are released by exocytosis [p. 154]. Many intestinal enzymes are not released free into the lumen but remain bound to the apical membranes of intestinal cells, anchored by transmembrane protein "stalks" or lipid anchors [p. 59].

Some digestive enzymes are secreted in an inactive *proenzyme* form known collectively as *zymogens*. Zymogens must be activated in the GI lumen before they can carry out digestion [p. 41]. This late activation allows enzymes to be stockpiled in the cells that make them without damaging those cells. Zymogen names often have the suffix *–ogen* added to the enzyme name, such as *pepsinogen*.

● **FIGURE 21-9** ***Cl⁻ secretion by intestinal and colonic crypt cells.*** Chloride enters cells by indirect active transport and leaves the apical side through a CFTR channel. Sodium and water follow passively by the paracellular pathway.

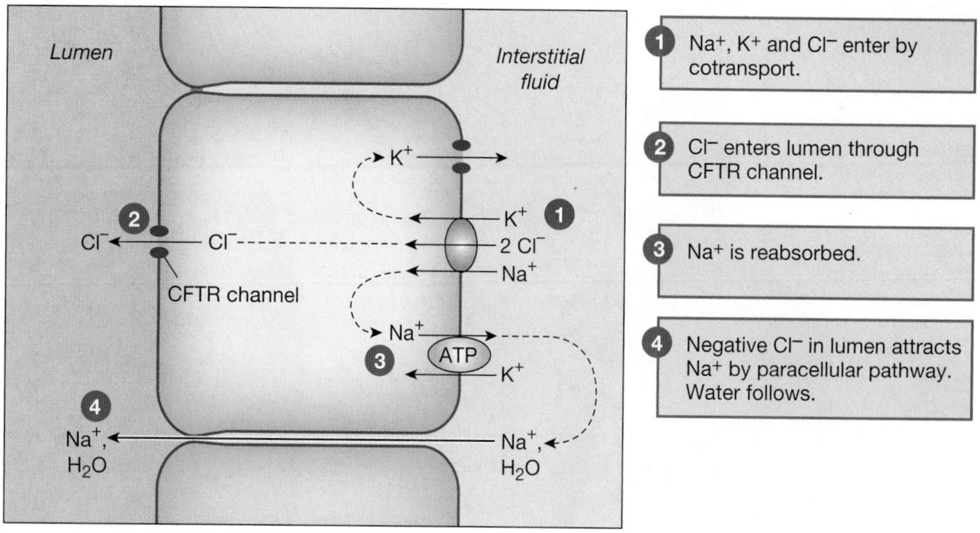
Lumen
Interstitial fluid
K+
K+
2 Cl−
Na+
Cl−
Cl−
CFTR channel
Na+
ATP
K+
Na+,
H2O
Na+,
H2O
1 Na+, K+ and Cl− enter by cotransport.
2 Cl− enters lumen through CFTR channel.
3 Na+ is reabsorbed.
4 Negative Cl− in lumen attracts Na+ by paracellular pathway. Water follows.

The control pathways for enzyme release vary but include a variety of neural, hormonal, and paracrine signals. Usually, stimulation of parasympathetic neurons in the vagus nerve enhances enzyme secretion.

Specialized Cells Secrete Mucus

Mucus is a viscous secretion composed primarily of glycoproteins collectively called **mucins**. The primary functions of mucus are to form a protective coating over the GI mucosa and to lubricate the contents of the gut. Mucus is made in specialized exocrine cells called *mucous cells* in the stomach and *goblet cells* in the intestine [Fig. 3-27, p. 79]. Goblet cells make up between 10% and 24% of the intestinal cell population. The salivary glands also secrete mucus from specialized cells.

The signals for mucus release include parasympathetic innervation, a variety of neuropeptides found in the enteric nervous system, and cytokines from immunocytes. Parasitic infections and inflammatory processes in the gut also cause substantial increases in mucus output as the body attempts to fortify its protective barrier.

Saliva Is an Exocrine Secretion

Saliva is a complex hyposmotic fluid secreted by the salivary glands of the oral cavity. The components of saliva include water, ions, mucus, and proteins such as enzymes and immunoglobulins. At resting flow rates, saliva is slightly acidic, with a pH of 6–7.

The ionic composition of saliva is determined in two epithelial transport steps. The salivary glands are exocrine glands, with a secretory epithelium (the *acinus*) that opens to the outside environment through a duct [Fig. 3-28, p. 79]. Fluid secreted by the acinar cells resembles extracellular fluid in its ionic composition. As this fluid passes through the duct on its way to the oral cavity, epithelial cells along the duct reabsorb Na^+ and secrete K^+ until the ion ratio in the duct fluid is more like that of intracellular fluid (high K^+ and low Na^+). The duct cells have very low water permeability, and the net removal of solute from the secreted fluid results in saliva that is hyposmotic to plasma.

Salivation is controlled by the autonomic nervous system. Parasympathetic innervation is the primary stimulus for secretion of saliva, but there is also some sympathetic innervation to the glands. In ancient China, a person suspected of a crime was sometimes given a mouthful of dry rice to chew during questioning. If he could produce enough saliva to moisten the rice and swallow it, he went free. If his nervous state dried up his salivary reflex, however, he was pronounced guilty. Recent research has confirmed that stress, such as that associated with lying or anxiety from being questioned, decreases salivary secretion.

RUNNING PROBLEM

Protein digestion in the stomach releases large amounts of urea, the nitrogenous breakdown product of amino acids. *Helicobacter pylori* exploits this sea of urea as protection against the acidic environment of the stomach. The outer membrane of *H. pylori* is studded with ureases, enzymes that convert urea into carbon dioxide and ammonia, which is a base. The first test Tonya undergoes is a urea breath test. In this test she drinks a urea solution that is made with either ^{14}C or ^{13}C instead of the carbon isotope that usually occurs in nature. After a few minutes her exhaled breath is collected and sent to a laboratory for analysis.

Question 2:
What is the most common isotope of carbon in nature? (Hint: See the periodic table inside the back cover.)

Question 3:
How does the conversion of urea into ammonia protect **H. pylori** ***from the hostile environment of the stomach?***

Question 4:
What component of Tonya's exhaled breath does this test measure? What result of her breath analysis would suggest that she has an **H. pylori** ***infection?***

687 692 697 700 717 719

21

FOCUS ON . . . THE LIVER

(a) The liver is the largest of the internal organs, weighing about 1.5 kg (3.3 lb) in an adult. It lies just under the diaphragm, toward the right side of the body.

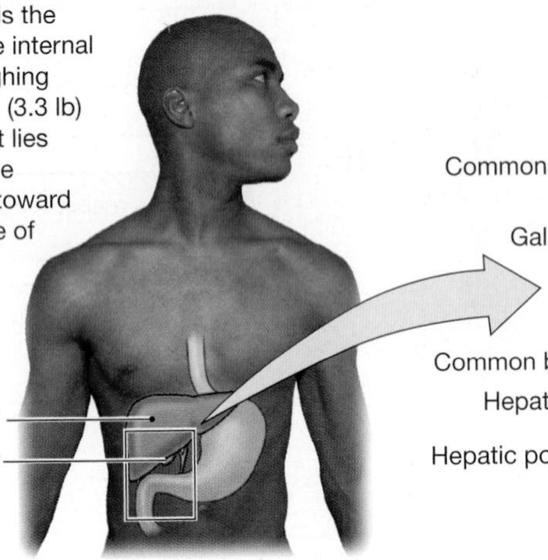

Liver
Gallbladder

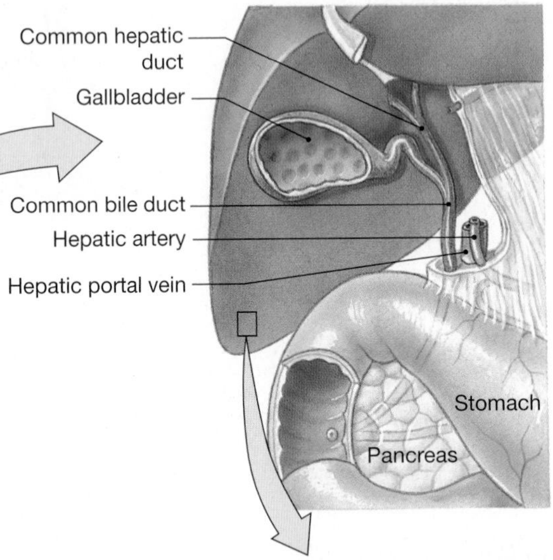

Common hepatic duct
Gallbladder
Common bile duct
Hepatic artery
Hepatic portal vein
Stomach
Pancreas

(b) Blood flow into the liver comes from two sources. Oxygenated blood containing metabolites from peripheral tissues reaches the liver via the hepatic artery. Blood coming to the liver through the hepatic portal vein is rich in absorbed nutrients from the gastrointestinal tract (Fig. 21-30) and contains hemoglobin breakdown products from the spleen. Blood leaves the liver in the hepatic vein (not shown). Bile synthesized in the liver is secreted into the **common hepatic duct** for storage in the gallbladder. From there, it is secreted into the lumen of the intestine through the **common bile duct**.

(c) The hepatocytes of the liver are organized into irregular hexagonal units called lobules. Each lobule is centered around a central vein that drains blood into the hepatic vein. Along its periphery, a lobule is associated with branches of the hepatic portal vein and hepatic artery. These vessels branch among the hepatocytes, forming **sinusoids** into which the blood flows. About 70% of the surface area of each hepatocyte faces the sinusoids, maximizing the exchange between the blood and the cells. Roughly 15% of the hepatocyte membrane faces the **bile canaliculi**, small channels into which bile is secreted. The canaliculi coalesce into bile ductules that run through the liver alongside the portal veins.

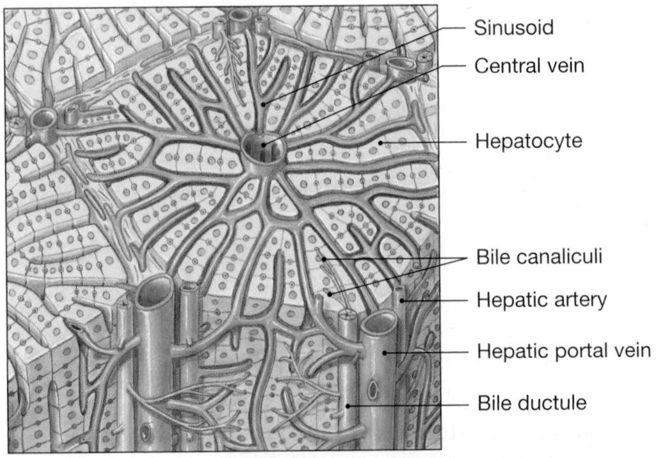

Sinusoid
Central vein
Hepatocyte
Bile canaliculi
Hepatic artery
Hepatic portal vein
Bile ductule

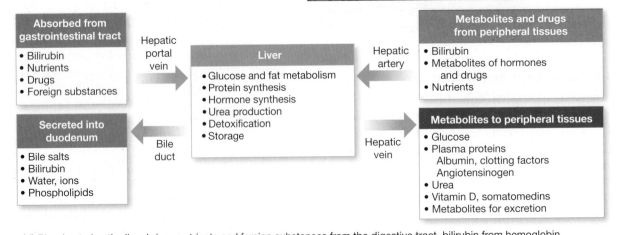

Absorbed from gastrointestinal tract
- Bilirubin
- Nutrients
- Drugs
- Foreign substances

→ Hepatic portal vein →

Liver
- Glucose and fat metabolism
- Protein synthesis
- Hormone synthesis
- Urea production
- Detoxification
- Storage

← Hepatic artery ←

Metabolites and drugs from peripheral tissues
- Bilirubin
- Metabolites of hormones and drugs
- Nutrients

← Bile duct ←

Secreted into duodenum
- Bile salts
- Bilirubin
- Water, ions
- Phospholipids

→ Hepatic vein →

Metabolites to peripheral tissues
- Glucose
- Plasma proteins
  Albumin, clotting factors
  Angiotensinogen
- Urea
- Vitamin D, somatomedins
- Metabolites for excretion

(d) Blood entering the liver brings nutrients and foreign substances from the digestive tract, bilirubin from hemoglobin breakdown, and metabolites from peripheral tissues of the body. In turn, the liver excretes some of these in the bile and stores or metabolizes others. Some of the liver's products are wastes to be excreted by the kidney; others are essential nutrients, such as glucose. In addition, the liver synthesizes an assortment of plasma proteins.

● **FIGURE 21-10**

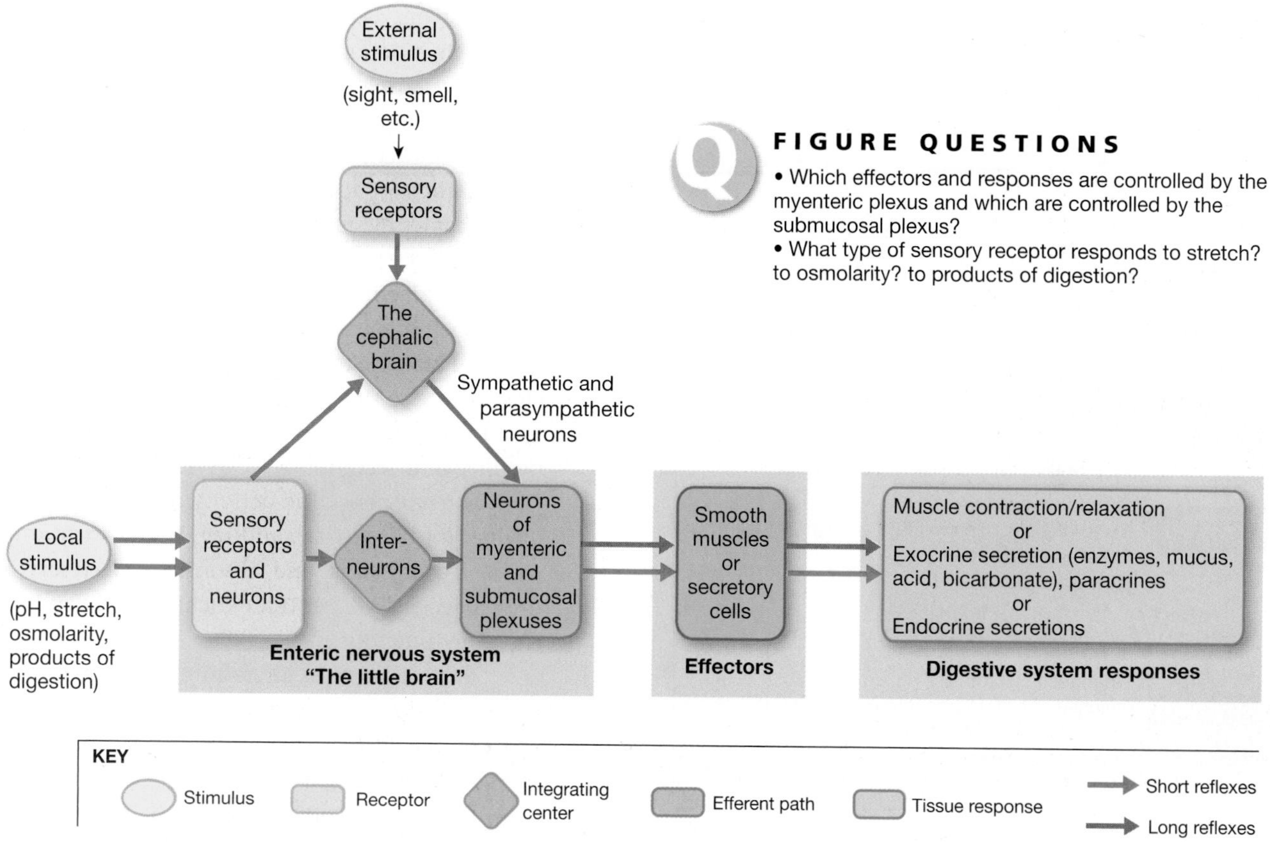

FIGURE QUESTIONS

- Which effectors and responses are controlled by the myenteric plexus and which are controlled by the submucosal plexus?
- What type of sensory receptor responds to stretch? to osmolarity? to products of digestion?

● **FIGURE 21-11** ***Integration of long and short reflexes in the digestive system.*** Long reflexes are integrated in the CNS. Some long reflexes originate outside the GI tract, but others originate in the enteric nervous system. Short reflexes originate in the enteric nervous system and are carried out entirely within the wall of the gut.

The Liver Secretes Bile

Bile is a nonenzymatic solution secreted from **hepatocytes,** or liver cells (see Focus on the Liver, Fig. 21-10 ●). The key components of bile are (1) **bile salts,** which facilitate enzymatic fat digestion, (2) *bile pigments,* such as bilirubin, which are the waste products of hemoglobin degradation, and (3) *cholesterol,* which is excreted in the feces. Drugs and other xenobiotics are cleared from the blood by hepatic processing and are also excreted in bile. Bile salts, which act as detergents to solubilize fats during digestion, are made from steroid **bile acids** combined with amino acids.

Bile is secreted into hepatic ducts that lead to the **gallbladder,** which stores and concentrates the bile solution. During a meal, contraction of the gallbladder sends bile into the duodenum through the **common bile duct,** along with a watery solution of bicarbonate and digestive enzymes from the pancreas.

REGULATION OF GI FUNCTION

The digestive system has remarkably complex regulation of motility and secretion. The various control mechanisms, with neural, endocrine, and local components, include the following:

1. **Long reflexes integrated in the CNS.** A classic neural reflex begins with a stimulus transmitted along a sensory neuron to the CNS, where the stimulus is integrated and acted on. In the digestive system, some classic reflexes originate with sensory receptors in the GI tract, but others originate outside the digestive system (gray arrows in Fig. 21-11 ●). No matter where they originate, digestive reflexes integrated in the CNS are called **long reflexes.**

   Long reflexes that originate completely outside the digestive system include feedforward reflexes [p. 204] and emotional reflexes. These reflexes are called **cephalic reflexes** because they originate in the cephalic brain [*cephalicus,* head]. *Feedforward reflexes* begin with stimuli such as the sight, smell, sound, or thought of food, and they prepare the digestive system for food that the brain is anticipating. For example, if you are hungry and smell dinner cooking, your mouth waters and your stomach growls.

   The influence of emotions on the GI tract illustrates another reflexive link between the brain and the digestive system. GI responses to emotions range from traveler's constipation to "butterflies in the stomach" to psychologically induced diarrhea. Fight-or-flight reactions also influence GI function.

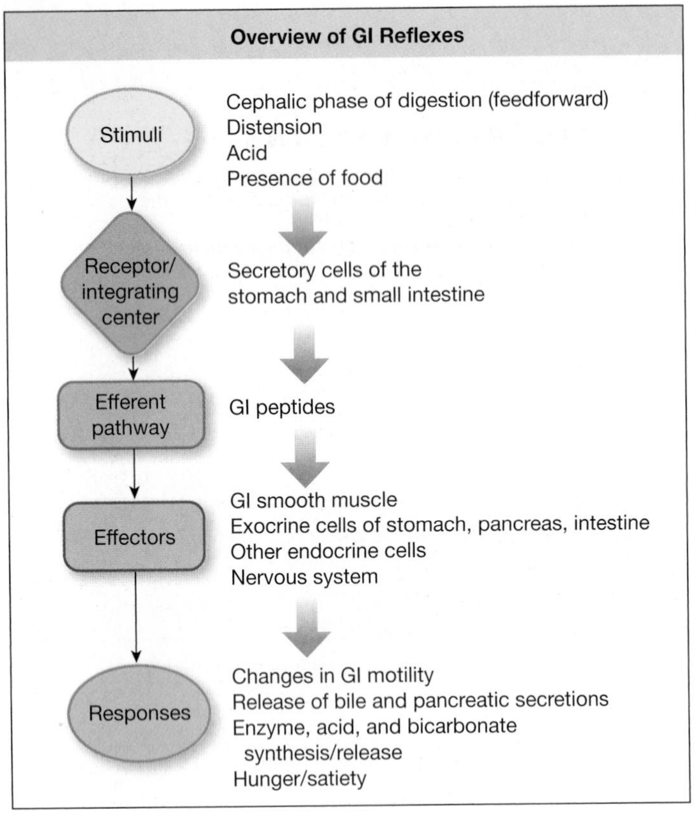
Overview of GI Reflexes
Stimuli
Cephalic phase of digestion (feedforward)
Distension
Acid
Presence of food
Receptor/integrating center
Secretory cells of the stomach and small intestine
Efferent pathway
GI peptides
Effectors
GI smooth muscle
Exocrine cells of stomach, pancreas, intestine
Other endocrine cells
Nervous system
Responses
Changes in GI motility
Release of bile and pancreatic secretions
Enzyme, acid, and bicarbonate synthesis/release
Hunger/satiety

● **FIGURE 21-12** *Reflexes involving GI peptides*

In long reflexes, the smooth muscle and glands of the GI tract are under autonomic control. In general, we say that parasympathetic neurons to the GI tract, carried mostly in the vagus nerve, are excitatory and enhance GI functions. Sympathetic neurons usually inhibit GI function.

2. **Short reflexes integrated in the enteric nervous system.** Neural control of the GI tract does not rely strictly on the CNS. Instead, the enteric nerve plexus in the gut wall acts as a "little brain," allowing local reflexes to begin, be integrated, and end completely in the GI tract (red arrows in Fig. 21-11). Reflexes that originate within the enteric nervous system (ENS) and are integrated there without outside input are called **short reflexes.** Although the ENS can work in isolation, it also coordinates function with autonomic neurons bringing signals from the CNS.

   The processes controlled by the enteric nervous system are related to motility, secretion, and growth. The submucosal plexus contains sensory neurons that receive signals from the lumen of the gut. The ENS network integrates the sensory information, then initiates responses through submucosal neurons that control secretion by GI epithelial cells and myenteric neurons that influence motility.

3. **Reflexes involving GI peptides.** Peptides secreted by cells of the digestive tract may act as hormones or paracrine signals. Some of the peptide signal molecules involved in digestive regulation were first identified in other body systems. Because their names have nothing to do with their function in the gastrointestinal system, learning the terminology can be a challenge.

   GI hormones, like all hormones, are secreted into the blood. They act on the GI tract, on accessory organs such as the pancreas, and on more distant targets, such as the brain. Paracrine molecules are secreted either into the lumen of the GI tract or into the extracellular fluid. Luminal paracrine signals combine with receptors on the apical membrane of the luminal epithelium to elicit a response. Paracrine molecules in the ECF act locally, on cells close to where they were secreted.

   In the digestive system, GI peptides excite or inhibit motility and secretion (Fig. 21-12 ●). Motility effects include altered peristaltic activity, contraction of the gallbladder for bile release, and regulated gastric emptying to maximize digestion and absorption. Secretory processes influenced by GI peptides include both endocrine and exocrine functions.

   Some of the most interesting pathways for GI peptides involve the brain. For example, in experimental studies the GI hormone cholecystokinin (CCK) was found to enhance *satiety,* the feeling that hunger has been satisfied. However, these findings are complicated by the fact that CCK is also manufactured by neurons and functions as a neurotransmitter in the brain. Another GI peptide, *ghrelin,* is secreted by the stomach and acts on the brain to increase food intake. We discuss peptides and appetite further in Chapter 22.

The Enteric Nervous System Can Act Independently

The ENS was first recognized more than a century ago, when scientists noted that an increase in GI intraluminal pressure

RUNNING PROBLEM

Tonya also undergoes endoscopy, a procedure in which a fiberoptic scope is inserted into her esophagus and maneuvered into her stomach. Small pincers attached to the end of the scope pluck a piece of her stomach lining, which is sent to the pathology laboratory for study. During the procedure, Tonya is awake but groggy from a tranquilizer. That afternoon she feels fine, but her stomach hurts. She chews an antacid tablet for relief.

Question 5:

Some antacids contain sodium bicarbonate ($NaHCO_3$), while many others contain aluminum hydroxide ($Al(OH)_3$). Antacids act as buffers that help neutralize hydrochloric acid (HCl) secreted by the stomach. For both types of antacids, write the chemical equation showing how antacids buffer hydrochloric acid.

687 692 697 700 717 719

caused a reflex wave of peristaltic contraction to sweep along sections of isolated intestine removed from the body. What they observed was the ability of the ENS to carry out a reflex independent of control by the CNS.

In this respect, the ENS is much like the nerve networks of jellyfish and sea anemones (phylum Cnidaria) introduced in Chapter 9 [p. 297]. You might have seen sea anemones being fed at an aquarium. As a piece of shrimp or fish drifts close to the tentacles, they begin to wave, picking up chemical "odors" through the water. Once the food contacts the tentacles, it is directed toward the mouth, passed from one tentacle to another until it disappears into the digestive cavity.

This purposeful reflex is accomplished without a brain, eyes, or a nose. The anemone's nervous system consists of a network composed of sensory neurons, interneurons, and efferent neurons that control the muscles and secretory cells of the anemone's body. The neurons of the network are linked in a way that allows them to integrate information and act on it. In the same way that an anemone captures its food, the ENS receives stimuli and acts on them. For this reason, the ENS is able to function autonomously, independent of efferent signals from the CNS.

Anatomically and functionally, the ENS shares many features with the CNS:

1. *Intrinsic neurons.* The **intrinsic neurons** of the two nerve plexuses of the digestive tract are those neurons that lie completely within the wall of the gut, just as interneurons are completely contained within the CNS. Autonomic neurons that bring signals from the CNS to the digestive system are called **extrinsic neurons.**
2. *Neurotransmitters and neuromodulators.* ENS neurons release more than 30 neurotransmitters and neuromodulators, most of which are identical to molecules found in the brain. These neurotransmitters are sometimes called *nonadrenergic, noncholinergic* to distinguish them from the traditional autonomic neurotransmitters norepinephrine and acetylcholine. Among the best known neurotransmitters and neuromodulators are serotonin, vasoactive intestinal peptide, and nitric oxide.
3. *Glial support cells.* The glial cells of neurons within the ENS are more similar to astroglia of the brain than to Schwann cells of the peripheral nervous system.
4. *Diffusion barrier.* The capillaries that surround ganglia in the ENS are not very permeable and create a diffusion barrier that is similar to the blood-brain barrier of cerebral blood vessels.
5. *Integrating center.* As noted earlier, reflexes that originate in the GI tract can be integrated and acted on without neural signals leaving the ENS. For this reason, the neuron network of the ENS is its own integrating center, much like the brain and spinal cord.

It was once thought that if we could explain how the ENS integrates simple behaviors, we could use the system as a model for CNS function. But studying ENS function is difficult because enteric reflexes have no discrete command center. Instead, in an interesting twist, GI physiologists are applying information gleaned from studies of the brain and spinal cord to investigate ENS function. The complex interactions between the enteric and central nervous systems, the endocrine system, and the immune system promise to provide scientists with questions to investigate for many years to come.

EMERGING CONCEPTS

TASTE RECEPTORS IN THE GUT

Scientists have known for years that the GI tract has the ability to sense and respond specifically and differentially to the composition of a meal. Fats and proteins do not stimulate the same endocrine and exocrine responses as a meal of pure carbohydrate. But how does the gut "know" what's in a meal? Traditional sensory receptors, such as osmoreceptors and stretch receptors, are not tuned to respond to biomolecules. New research indicates that epithelial cells in the gut, especially some of the endocrine cells, express the same G protein–coupled receptors and the taste-linked G protein gustducin as taste buds [p. 352]. Researchers using knockout mice and cultured cell lines are now trying to establish the functional link between gut "taste receptors" and physiological responses to food.

GI Peptides Include Hormones, Neuropeptides, and Cytokines

The hormones of the gastrointestinal tract occupy an interesting place in the history of endocrinology. In 1902, two Canadian physiologists, W. M. Bayliss and E. H. Starling, discovered that acidic chyme entering the small intestine from the stomach caused the release of pancreatic juices even when all nerves to the pancreas were cut. Because the only communication remaining between intestine and pancreas was the blood supply that ran between them, Bayliss and Starling postulated the existence of some blood-borne (*humoral*) factor released by the intestine.

When duodenal extracts applied directly to the pancreas stimulated secretion, they knew they were dealing with a chemical produced by the duodenum. They named the substance *secretin*. Starling further proposed that the general name *hormone,* from the Greek word meaning "I excite," be given to all humoral agents that act at a site distant from their release.

In 1905, J.S. Edkins postulated the existence of a gastric hormone that stimulated gastric acid secretion. It took more than 30 years for researchers to isolate a relatively pure extract of the gastric hormone, and it was 1964 before the hormone, named *gastrin,* was finally purified.

Why was research on the digestive hormones so slow to develop? A major reason is that GI hormones are secreted by isolated endocrine cells scattered among other cells of the mucosal epithelium. At one time, the only way to obtain these hormones was to make a crude extract of the entire epithelium, a procedure that also liberated digestive enzymes and paracrine molecules made in adjacent cells. For this reason, it was very difficult to tell if the physiological effect elicited by the extract came from one hormone, from more than one hormone, or from a paracrine signal such as histamine.

Although researchers have now sequenced more than 30 peptides from the GI mucosa, only some of them are widely accepted as hormones. A few peptides have well-defined paracrine effects, but most fall into a long list of candidate hormones. In addition, we know of nonpeptide regulatory molecules, such as histamine, that function as paracrine signals. Because of the uncertainty associated with the field, we restrict our focus to the major regulatory molecules.

The gastrointestinal hormones are usually divided into three families. All the members of a family have similar amino acid sequences, and in some cases there is overlap in their ability to bind to receptors.

1. The *gastrin family* includes the hormones **gastrin** and **cholecystokinin** (CCK), plus several variants of each. Their structural similarity means that both gastrin and CCK can bind to and activate the CCKB receptor found on parietal cells.
2. The *secretin family* includes **secretin**; **vasoactive intestinal peptide** (VIP), a neurocrine [p. 180] molecule; and **GIP**, a hormone known originally as *gastric inhibitory peptide* because it inhibited gastric acid secretion in early experiments. Subsequent studies, however, indicated that GIP administered in lower physiological doses does not block acid secretion. Researchers proposed a new name with the same initials—**glucose-dependent insulinotropic peptide**—that more accurately describes the hormone's action: it stimulates insulin release in response to glucose in the intestinal lumen. However, for the most part *gastric inhibitory peptide* has remained the preferred name.

Another member of the secretin family is the hormone **glucagon-like peptide 1** (GLP-1), which also plays an important role in glucose homeostasis. We discuss GIP and GLP-1 further in Chapter 22.

TABLE 21-1 The Digestive Hormones

	STIMULUS FOR RELEASE	PRIMARY TARGET(S)	PRIMARY EFFECT(S)	OTHER INFORMATION
STOMACH				
Gastrin	Peptides and amino acids; neural reflexes	ECL cells and parietal cells	Stimulates gastric acid secretion and mucosal growth.	Somatostatin inhibits release.
INTESTINE				
Cholecystokinin (CCK)	Fatty acids and some amino acids	Gallbladder, pancreas, stomach	Stimulates gallbladder contraction and pancreatic enzyme secretion. Inhibits gastric emptying and acid secretion.	Promotes satiety. Some effects may be due to CCK as a neurotransmitter.
Secretin	Acid in small intestine	Pancreas, stomach	Stimulates bicarbonate secretion. Inhibits gastric emptying and acid secretion.	
Motilin	Fasting: periodic release every 1.5–2 hours	Gastric and intestinal smooth muscle	Stimulates migrating motor complex.	Inhibited by eating a meal.
Gastric inhibitory peptide (GIP)	Glucose, fatty acids, and amino acids in small intestine	Beta cells of pancreas	Stimulates insulin release (feedforward mechanism). Inhibits gastric emptying and acid secretion.	
Glucagon-like peptide 1 (GLP-1)	Mixed meal that includes carbohydrates or fats in the lumen	Endocrine pancreas	Stimulates insulin release. Inhibits glucagon release and gastric function.	Promotes satiety.

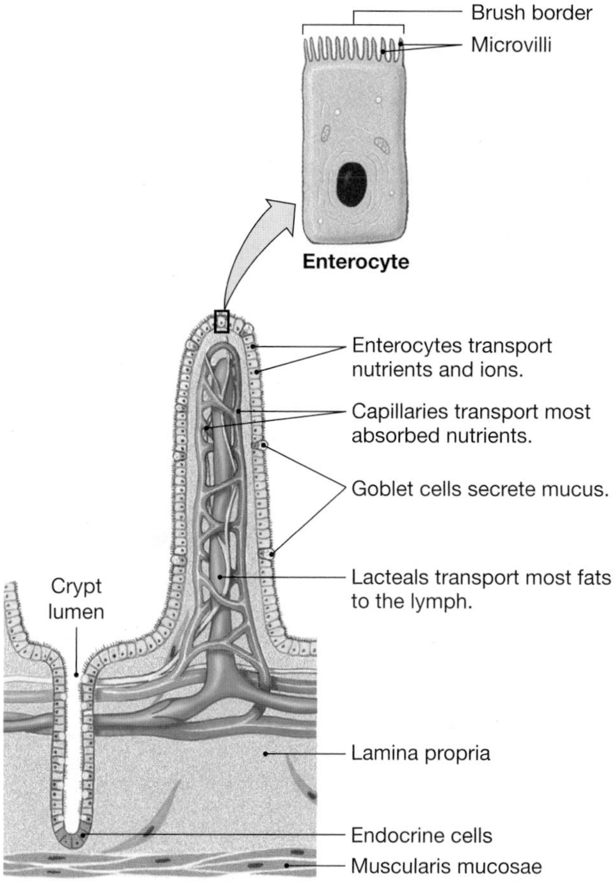

● **FIGURE 21-13** ***A villus and a crypt in the small intestine.*** Villi and crypts increase the effective surface area of the small intestine. Stem cells in the crypts produce new epithelial cells to replace those that die or are damaged.

3. The third family of peptides contains those that do not fit into the other two families. The primary member of this group is the hormone **motilin.**

The sources, targets, and effects of some GI hormones are summarized in Table 21-1 ●.

DIGESTION AND ABSORPTION

The GI system digests macromolecules into absorbable units using a combination of mechanical and enzymatic breakdown. Chewing and churning create smaller pieces of food with more surface area exposed to digestive enzymes. Bile, the complex chemical mixture secreted by the liver, serves a similar purpose by dispersing lipids (more commonly called *fats* in digestive physiology) as fine droplets with greater surface area.

The pH at which different digestive enzymes function best [p. 101] reflects the location where they are most active. Enzymes that act in the stomach work well at acidic pH, and those secreted into the small intestine work best at alkaline pH.

Most absorption takes place in the small intestine, with additional absorption of water and ions in the large intestine.

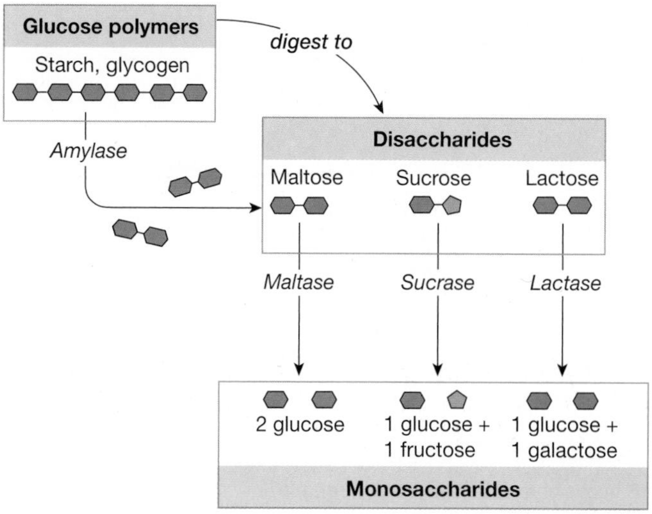

● **FIGURE 21-14** ***Carbohydrates break down into monosaccharides.***

The surface area of the intestine is greatly increased by the presence of fingerlike villi (see Fig. 21-3d, e) and by the **brush border** on the luminal surface of enterocytes, created from numerous microvilli on each cell (Fig. 21-13 ●). Absorption of nutrients and ions across the GI epithelium, like secretion, uses many of the same transport proteins as the kidney tubule. Once absorbed, most nutrients enter capillaries within the villi. The exception is fats, which mostly enter lymph vessels called **lacteals.**

Digestion and absorption are not directly regulated except in a few instances. Instead, they are influenced primarily by motility and secretion in the digestive tract, the two processes that in turn are regulated by hormones, the nervous system, and local control mechanisms.

Carbohydrates Are Absorbed as Monosaccharides

About half the calories the average American ingests are in the form of carbohydrates, mainly *starch* and *sucrose* (table sugar). Other dietary carbohydrates include the glucose polymers *glycogen* and *cellulose,* disaccharides such as *lactose* and *maltose,* and the monosaccharides *glucose* and *fructose* [Fig. 2-7, p. 29].

Intestinal carbohydrate transport is restricted to monosaccharides, which means that all complex carbohydrates and disaccharides must be digested if they are to be absorbed. We are unable to digest cellulose because we lack the necessary enzymes. As a result, the cellulose in plant matter becomes what is known as dietary *fiber* or *roughage* and is excreted undigested. Similarly, *sucralose* (Splenda®), the artificial sweetener made from sucrose, cannot be digested because chlorine atoms substituted for three hydroxyl groups block enzymatic digestion of the sugar derivative.

The complex carbohydrates we can digest are starch and glycogen (Fig. 21-14 ●). The enzyme **amylase** breaks long glucose

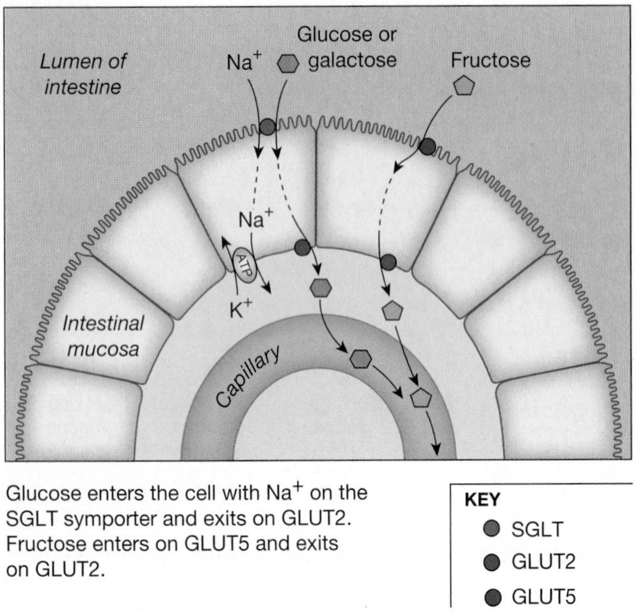

● **FIGURE 21-15** ***Carbohydrate absorption in the small intestine***

polymers into smaller glucose chains and into the disaccharide maltose. Maltose and other disaccharides are broken down by intestinal brush-border enzymes known as **disaccharidases** (maltase, sucrase, and lactase). The end products of carbohydrate digestion are glucose, galactose, and fructose.

Intestinal glucose and galactose absorption uses transporters identical to those found in the renal proximal tubule: the apical Na^+-glucose SGLT symporter and the basolateral GLUT2 transporter (Fig. 21-15 ●). These transporters move galactose as well as glucose. Fructose absorption, however, is not Na^+-dependent. Fructose moves across the apical membrane by facilitated diffusion on the GLUT5 transporter and across the basolateral membrane by GLUT2 [p. 146].

If glucose is the major metabolic substrate for aerobic respiration, why don't enterocytes use the glucose they absorb for their own metabolism? How can these cells keep intracellular glucose concentrations high so that facilitated diffusion moves glucose into the extracellular space? The metabolism of enterocytes (and proximal tubule cells) apparently differs from that of most other cells in that these transporting cells do not use glucose as their preferred energy source. Current studies indicate that these cells use the amino acid glutamine as their main source of energy, thus allowing absorbed glucose to pass unchanged into the bloodstream.

Proteins Are Digested into Small Peptides and Amino Acids

Unlike carbohydrates, which are ingested in forms ranging from simple to complex, most ingested proteins are polypeptides or larger [Fig. 2-9, p. 31]. Not all proteins are equally digestible by humans, however. Plant proteins are the least digestible. Among the most digestible is egg protein, 85–90% of which is in a form that can be digested and absorbed. Surprisingly, between 30% and 60% of the protein found in the intestinal lumen comes not from ingested food but from the sloughing of dead cells and from protein secretions such as enzymes and mucus.

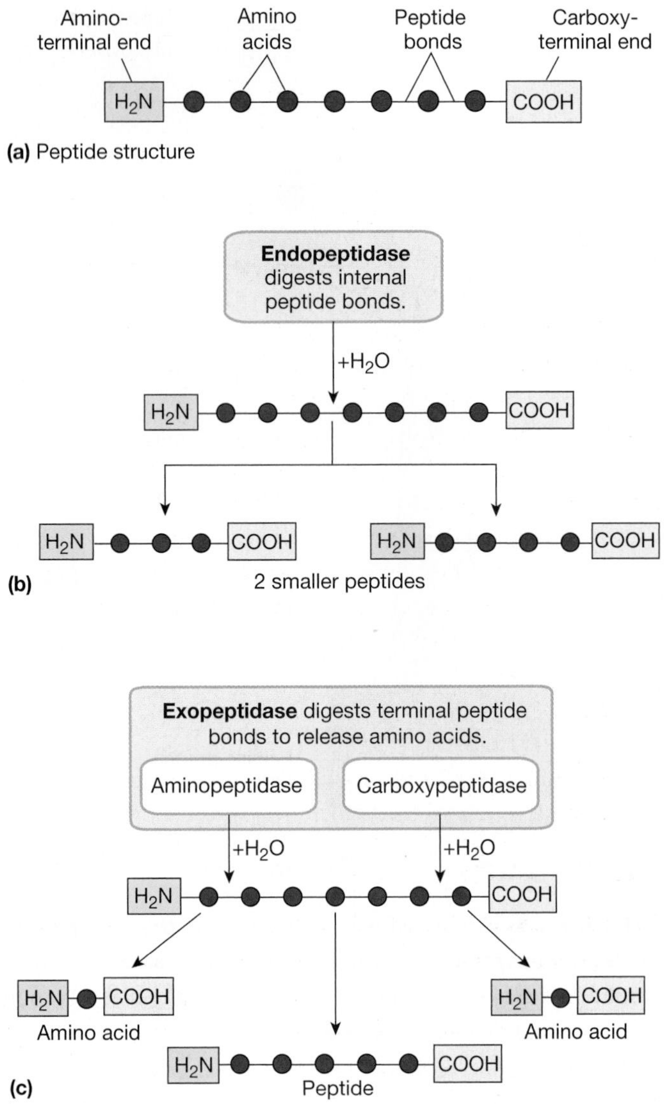

● **FIGURE 21-16** ***Enzymes for protein digestion.*** Endopeptidases include pepsin in the stomach, and trypsin and chymotrypsin, which act in the small intestine.

The enzymes for protein digestion are classified into two broad groups: endopeptidases and exopeptidases. **Endopeptidases,** more commonly called *proteases,* attack peptide bonds in the interior of the amino acid chain and break a long peptide chain into smaller fragments (Fig. 21-16b ●). Proteases are secreted as inactive proenzymes from epithelial cells in the stomach, intestine, and pancreas and are activated in the GI tract lumen. Examples of proteases include **pepsin** secreted in the stomach, and **trypsin** and **chymotrypsin** secreted by the pancreas.

Exopeptidases release single amino acids from peptides by chopping them off the ends, one at a time (Fig. 21-16c). The most important digestive exopeptidases are two isozymes of *carboxypeptidase* secreted by the pancreas. *Aminopeptidases* play a lesser role in digestion.

The primary products of protein digestion are free amino acids, dipeptides, and tripeptides, all of which can be absorbed. Amino acid structure is so variable that multiple amino acid transport systems are found in the intestine. Most free amino acids are carried by Na^+-dependent cotransport proteins similar to those in the proximal tubule of the kidney (Fig. 21-17 ●). A few amino acid transporters are H^+-dependent.

Dipeptides and tripeptides are carried into the mucosal cell on the oligopeptide transporter *PepT1* that uses H^+-dependent cotransport (Fig. 21-17). Once inside the epithelial cell, the *oligopeptides* [*oligos*, little] have two possible fates. Most are digested by cytoplasmic peptidases into amino acids, which are then transported across the basolateral membrane and into the circulation. Those oligopeptides that are not digested are transported intact across the basolateral membrane on an H^+-dependent exchanger. The transport system that moves oligopeptides also is responsible for intestinal uptake of certain drugs, including beta-lactam antibiotics, angiotensin-converting enzyme inhibitors, and thrombin inhibitors.

Some Larger Peptides Can Be Absorbed Intact

Some peptides larger than three amino acids are absorbed by transcytosis [p. 157] after binding to membrane receptors on the luminal surface of the intestine. The discovery that ingested proteins can be absorbed as small peptides has implications in medicine because these peptides may act as *antigens,* substances that stimulate antibody formation and result in allergic reactions. Consequently, the intestinal absorption of peptides may be a significant factor in the development of food allergies and food intolerances.

In newborns, peptide absorption takes place primarily in intestinal crypt cells (see Fig. 21-13). At birth, intestinal villi are very small, so the crypts are well exposed to the luminal contents. As the villi grow and the crypts have less access to chyme, the high peptide absorption rates present at birth decline steadily. If parents delay feeding the infant allergy-inducing peptides, the gut has a chance to mature, lessening the likelihood of antibody formation.

One of the most common antigens responsible for food allergies is gluten, a component of wheat. The incidence of childhood gluten allergies has decreased since the 1970s, when parents were cautioned not to feed infants gluten-based cereals until they were several months old.

In another medical application, pharmaceutical companies have developed undigestible peptide drugs that can be given orally instead of by injection. Probably the best-known example is DDAVP (1-deamino-8-D-arginine vasopressin), the synthetic analog of vasopressin. If the natural hormone vasopressin is ingested, it is digested rather than absorbed intact. By changing the structure of the hormone slightly, scientists created a synthetic peptide that has the same activity but is absorbed without being digested.

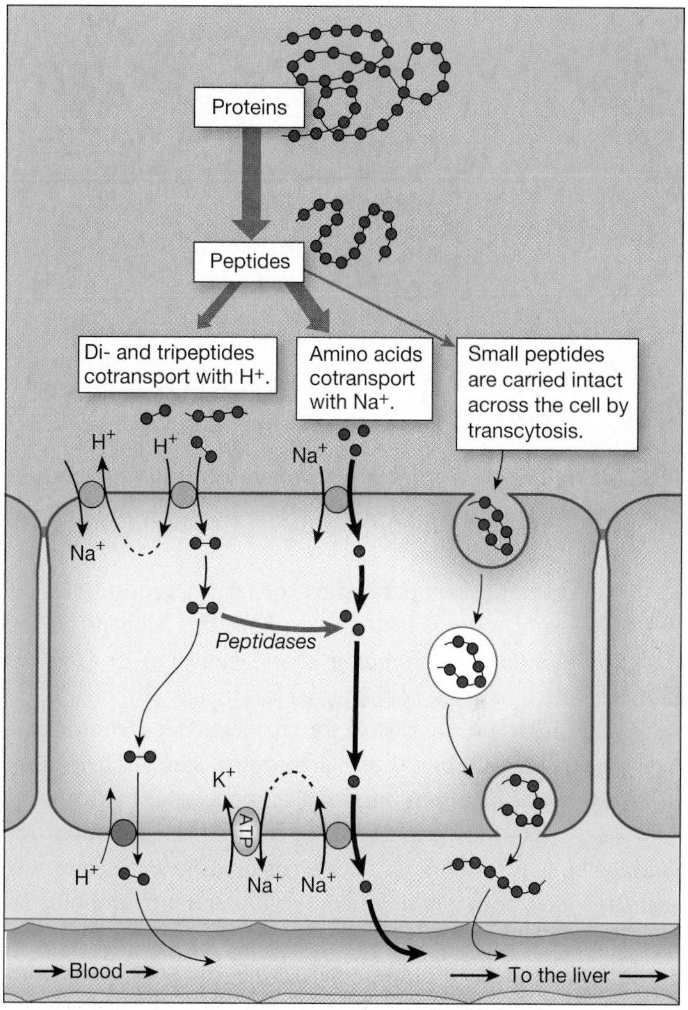

● **FIGURE 21-17** ***Peptide absorption.*** After digestion, proteins are absorbed mostly as free amino acids. A few di- and tripeptides are absorbed. Some peptides larger than tripeptides can be absorbed by transcytosis.

Bile Salts Facilitate Fat Digestion

Fats and related molecules in the Western diet include triglycerides, cholesterol, phospholipids, long-chain fatty acids, and the fat-soluble vitamins [Fig. 2-8, p. 30]. Nearly 90% of our fat calories come from triglycerides because they are the primary form of lipid in both plants and animals.

Enzymatic fat digestion is carried out by **lipases,** enzymes that remove two fatty acids from each triglyceride molecule. The result is one monoglyceride and two free fatty acids (Fig. 21-18 ●). Phospholipids are digested by pancreatic *phospholipase.* Free cholesterol need not be digested before being absorbed.

21

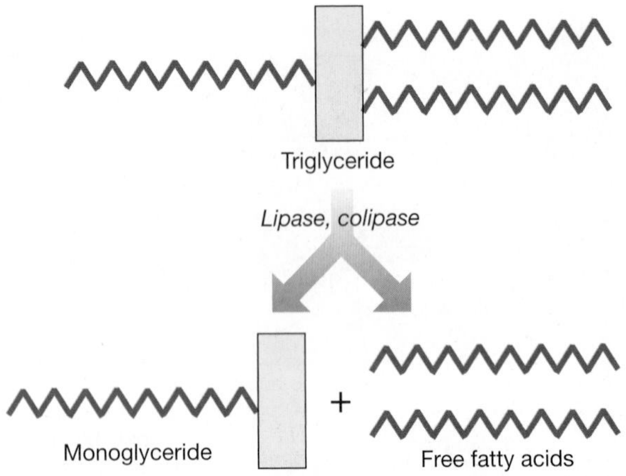

● **FIGURE 21-18** ***Triglycerides digest into monoglycerides and free fatty acids.***

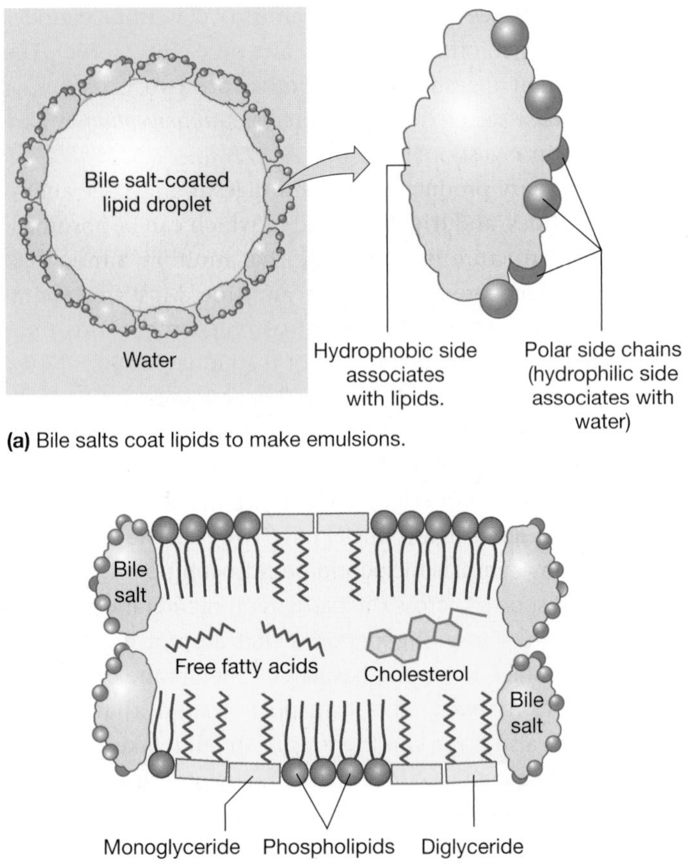

(a) Bile salts coat lipids to make emulsions.

(b) Micelles are small disks with bile salts, phospholipids, fatty acids, cholesterol, and mono- and diglycerides.

● **FIGURE 21-19** ***Bile salts emulsify fats.***

Fat digestion is complicated by the fact that most lipids are not particularly water soluble. As a result, the aqueous chyme leaving the stomach contains a coarse emulsion of large fat droplets, which have less surface area than smaller particles. To increase the surface area available for enzymatic fat digestion, the liver secretes bile salts into the small intestine. Bile salts help break down the coarse emulsion into smaller, more stable particles.

Bile salts, like phospholipids of cell membranes, are *amphipathic* [*amphi-*, on both sides + *pathos*, experience], meaning that they have both a hydrophobic region and a hydrophilic region (Fig. 21-19a ●). The hydrophobic regions of bile salts associate with the surface of lipid droplets while the polar side chains interact with water, creating a stable emulsion of small, water-soluble fat droplets. You can see a similar emulsion when you shake a bottle of salad dressing to combine the oil and aqueous layers.

The bile salt coating of the intestinal emulsion complicates digestion, however, because lipase is unable to penetrate the bile salts. For this reason fat digestion also requires **colipase**, a protein cofactor secreted by the pancreas. Colipase displaces some bile salts, allowing lipase access to fats inside the bile salt coating (Fig. 21-20 ② ●). As enzymatic and mechanical digestion proceed, fatty acids, bile salts, monoglycerides, phospholipids, and cholesterol form small disk-shaped **micelles** (Fig. 21-19b) [p. 58]. Micelles then enter the unstirred aqueous layer close to the absorptive cells (*enterocytes*) lining the small intestine lumen.

Because fats are lipophilic, many are absorbed primarily by simple diffusion. Fatty acids and monoglycerides move out of their micelles and diffuse across the apical membrane into the epithelial cells (Fig. 21-20 ③a). Initially scientists believed that cholesterol also diffused across the enterocyte membrane, but the discovery of a drug called *ezetimibe* that inhibits cholesterol absorption suggested that transport proteins were involved. Experiments now indicate that cholesterol is transported across the apical membrane on specific, energy-dependent membrane transporters, including one named *NPC1L1*, the protein that is inhibited by ezetimibe (Fig. 21-20 ③b).

Once monoglycerides and fatty acids are inside the enterocytes, they move to the smooth endoplasmic reticulum, where they recombine into triglycerides (Fig. 21-20 ④). The triglycerides then join cholesterol and proteins to form large droplets called **chylomicrons**. Because of their size, chylomicrons must be packaged into secretory vesicles and leave the cell by exocytosis.

The large size of chylomicrons also prevents them from crossing the basement membrane to enter capillaries (Fig. 21-20 ⑤). Instead, chylomicrons are absorbed into *lacteals*, the lymph vessels of the villi (see Fig. 21-13). Chylomicrons pass through the lymphatic system and finally enter the venous blood just before it flows into the heart [p. 531]. Some shorter fatty acids (10 or fewer carbons) are not assembled into chylomicrons. These fatty acids can therefore cross the capillary basement membrane and go directly into the blood.

Nucleic Acids Are Digested into Bases and Monosaccharides

The nucleic acid polymers DNA and RNA are only a very small part of most diets. They are digested by pancreatic and intestinal enzymes, first into their component nucleotides and then into nitrogenous bases and monosaccharides [Fig. 2-11, p. 33]. The bases are absorbed by active transport, and the

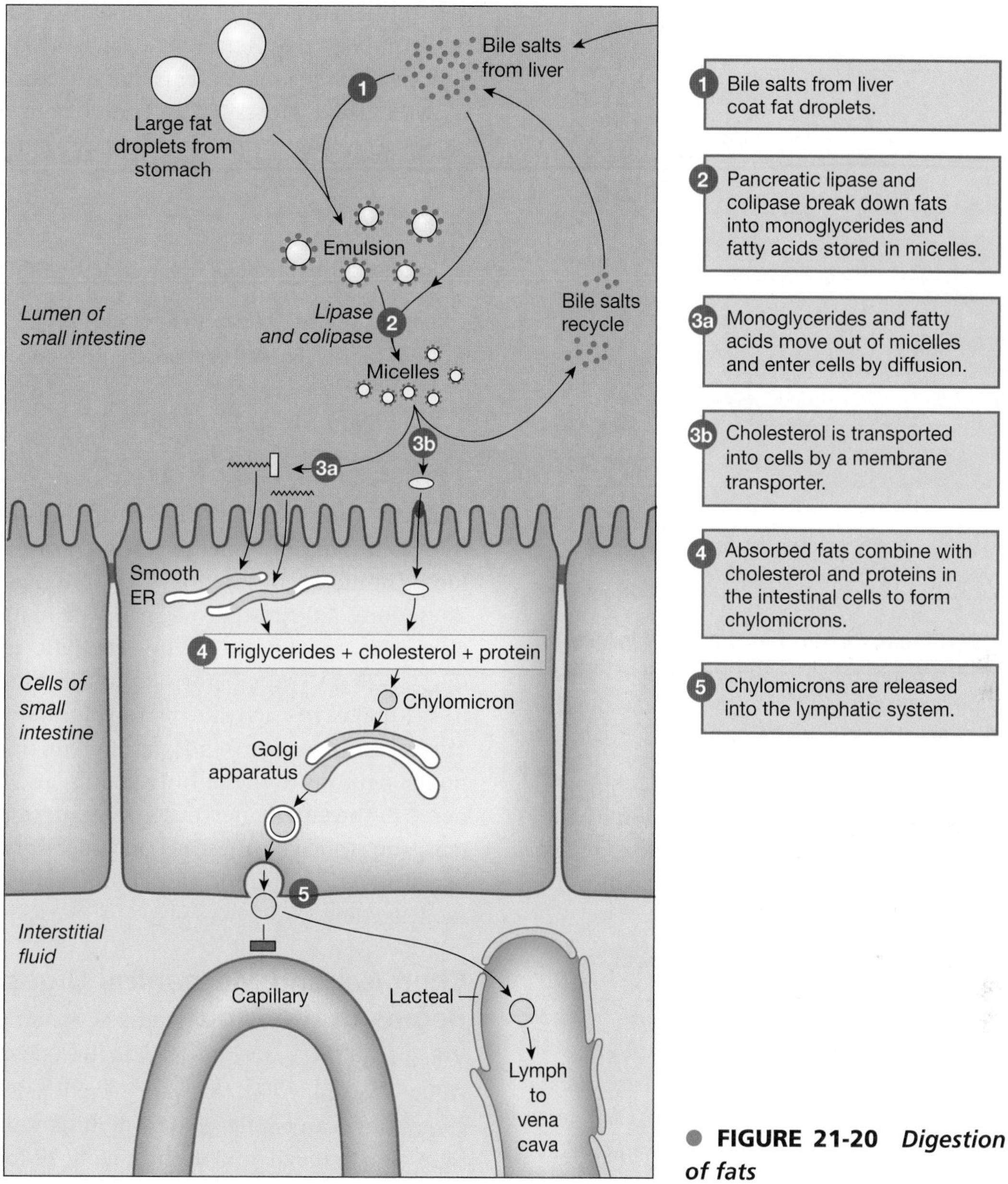
Bile salts from liver
Large fat droplets from stomach
Emulsion
Lumen of small intestine
Lipase and colipase
Micelles
Bile salts recycle
1
2
3a
3b
Smooth ER
4 Triglycerides + cholesterol + protein
Chylomicron
Cells of small intestine
Golgi apparatus
5
Interstitial fluid
Capillary
Lacteal
Lymph to vena cava
1 Bile salts from liver coat fat droplets.
2 Pancreatic lipase and colipase break down fats into monoglycerides and fatty acids stored in micelles.
3a Monoglycerides and fatty acids move out of micelles and enter cells by diffusion.
3b Cholesterol is transported into cells by a membrane transporter.
4 Absorbed fats combine with cholesterol and proteins in the intestinal cells to form chylomicrons.
5 Chylomicrons are released into the lymphatic system.

● **FIGURE 21-20** ***Digestion and absorption of fats***

monosaccharides are absorbed by facilitated diffusion and secondary active transport like other simple sugars.

The Intestine Absorbs Vitamins and Minerals

In general, the fat-soluble vitamins (A, D, E, and K) are absorbed in the small intestine along with fats—one reason that health professionals are concerned about excessive consumption of "fake fats," such as Olestra, that are not absorbed. The water-soluble vitamins (C and most B vitamins) are absorbed by mediated transport. The major exception is **vitamin B_{12}**, also known as *cobalamin*. This vitamin is made by bacteria, but we obtain most of our dietary supply from seafood, meat, and milk products. The intestinal transporter for B_{12} is found only in the ileum and recognizes B_{12} only when the vitamin is complexed with a protein called **intrinsic factor**, secreted by the stomach.

Mineral absorption usually occurs by active transport. Iron and calcium are two of the few substances whose intestinal absorption is actively regulated. For both minerals, a decrease in body concentrations of the mineral leads to enhanced uptake at the intestine.

Iron is ingested as heme iron [p. 605] in meat and as ionized iron in some plant products. Heme iron is more readily absorbed, apparently by endocytosis, but the mechanism is not well understood. Ionized iron (Fe^{2+}) is actively absorbed by apical cotransport with H^+ on a protein called the *divalent metal transporter 1 (DMT1)*. Inside the cell, enzymes convert heme iron to Fe^{2+}, and both pools of ionized iron leave the cell on a transporter called *ferroportin*.

Iron uptake by the body is regulated by a peptide hormone called *hepcidin*. When body stores of iron are high, the liver secretes hepcidin, which binds to ferroportin. The

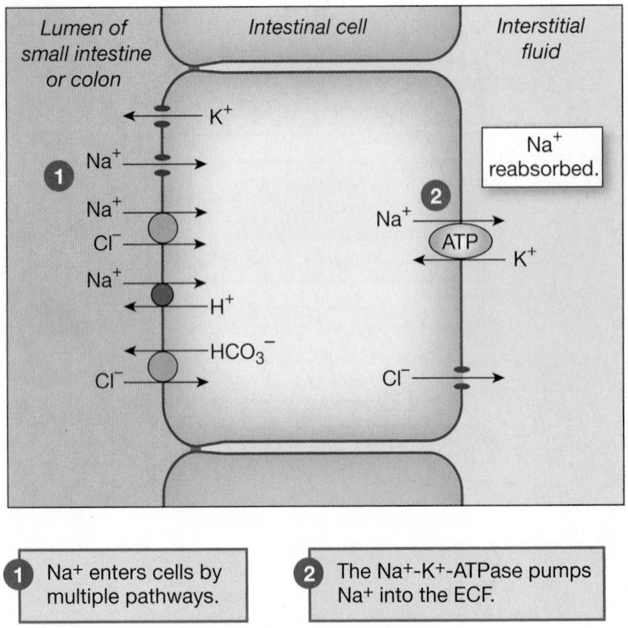

● **FIGURE 21-21** ***NaCl reabsorption in the small intestine and colon.*** A significant amount of Na^+ reabsorption in the small intestine also occurs through Na^+-coupled organic solute uptake across the apical membrane (not shown in this figure).

hepcidin-bound transporter is targeted for destruction by the enterocyte, which results in decreased iron uptake across the intestine. We discuss other aspects of iron metabolism in the body in Chapter 16 [p. 555].

Most Ca^{2+} absorption in the gut occurs by passive, unregulated movement through paracellular pathways. Hormonally regulated transepithelial Ca^{2+} transport takes place in the duodenum. Calcium enters the enterocyte through apical Ca^{2+} channels and is actively transported across the basolateral membrane by either a Ca^{2+}-ATPase or by the Na^+-Ca^{2+} antiporter. We describe calcium balance in detail in Chapter 22.

The Intestine Absorbs Ions and Water

Most water absorption takes place in the small intestine, with an additional 0.5 L per day absorbed in the colon. As with intestinal fluid secretion, water follows osmotic gradients created by solute absorption. Enterocytes in the small intestine and **colonocytes**, the epithelial cells on the luminal surface of the colon, absorb Na^+ using three membrane proteins (Fig. 21-21 ●): apical Na^+ channels, a Na^+-Cl^- symporter, and the NHE Na^+-H^+ exchanger. In the small intestine, a significant fraction of Na^+ absorption also takes place through Na^+-dependent organic solute uptake, such as the SGLT and Na^+-amino acid transporters (see Figs. 21-15 and 21-17). On the basolateral side of both enterocytes and colonocytes, the primary transporter for Na^+ is Na^+-K^+-ATPase. Chloride uptake uses the apical Cl^--HCO_3^- exchanger and a basolateral Cl^- channel. Potassium absorption in the intestine occurs by the paracellular pathway.

In the remainder of this chapter we follow some food as it passes through the GI tract. As a preview, look at Figure 21-22 ●, a summary of the main events that occur in each section of the GI tract. Food processing is traditionally divided into three phases: a cephalic phase, a gastric phase, and an intestinal phase.

CONCEPT CHECK

8. Recipes for homemade oral rehydration therapy usually include sugar (sucrose) and table salt. Explain how the salt enhances intestinal absorption of glucose.
9. Do bile salts digest triglycerides into monoglycerides and free fatty acids?

Answers: p. 723

THE CEPHALIC PHASE

Digestive processes in the body begin before food ever enters the mouth. Simply smelling, seeing, or even *thinking* about food can make our mouths water and our stomachs rumble. These long reflexes that begin in the brain create a feedforward response known as the **cephalic phase** of digestion (Fig. 21-23 ●). Anticipatory stimuli and the stimulus of food in the oral cavity activate neurons in the medulla oblongata. The medulla in turn sends an efferent signal through autonomic neurons to the salivary glands, and through the vagus nerve to the enteric nervous system. In response to these signals, the stomach, intestine, and accessory glandular organs begin secretion and increase motility in anticipation of the food to come.

Chemical and Mechanical Digestion Begins in the Mouth

When food first enters the mouth, it is met by a flood of the secretion we call *saliva*. Salivary secretion is under autonomic control and can be triggered by multiple stimuli, including the sight, smell, touch, and even thought of food. The water and mucus in saliva soften and lubricate food to make it easier to swallow. You can appreciate this function if you've ever tried to swallow a dry soda cracker without chewing it thoroughly. Saliva also dissolves food so that we can taste it.

Chemical digestion begins with the secretion of *salivary amylase* and a very small amount of salivary lipase. Amylase breaks starch into maltose after the enzyme is activated by Cl^- in saliva. If you chew on an unsalted soda cracker for a long time, you may be able to detect the conversion of the cracker's flour starch to maltose, which is sweeter.

The final function of saliva is protection. *Lysozyme* is an antibacterial salivary enzyme, and salivary *immunoglobulins* disable bacteria and viruses. In addition, saliva helps wash the teeth and keep the tongue free of food particles.

Mechanical digestion of food begins in the oral cavity with chewing. The lips, tongue, and teeth all contribute to the **mastication** [*masticare*, to chew] of food, creating a softened, moistened mass (*bolus*) that can be easily swallowed.

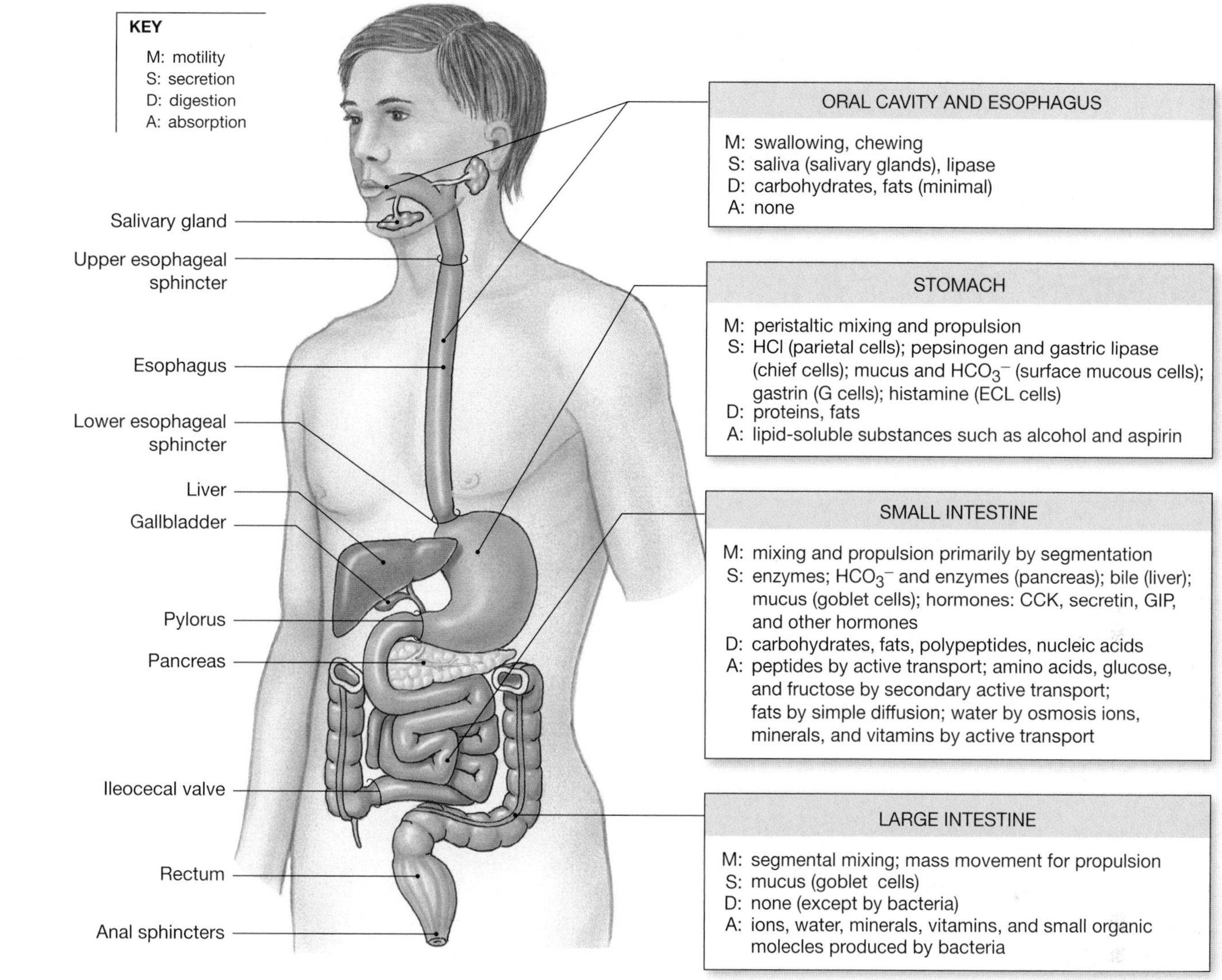
KEY
M: motility
S: secretion
D: digestion
A: absorption
Salivary gland
Upper esophageal sphincter
Esophagus
Lower esophageal sphincter
Liver
Gallbladder
Pylorus
Pancreas
Ileocecal valve
Rectum
Anal sphincters
ORAL CAVITY AND ESOPHAGUS
M: swallowing, chewing
S: saliva (salivary glands), lipase
D: carbohydrates, fats (minimal)
A: none
STOMACH
M: peristaltic mixing and propulsion
S: HCl (parietal cells); pepsinogen and gastric lipase (chief cells); mucus and HCO_3^- (surface mucous cells); gastrin (G cells); histamine (ECL cells)
D: proteins, fats
A: lipid-soluble substances such as alcohol and aspirin
SMALL INTESTINE
M: mixing and propulsion primarily by segmentation
S: enzymes; HCO_3^- and enzymes (pancreas); bile (liver); mucus (goblet cells); hormones: CCK, secretin, GIP, and other hormones
D: carbohydrates, fats, polypeptides, nucleic acids
A: peptides by active transport; amino acids, glucose, and fructose by secondary active transport; fats by simple diffusion; water by osmosis ions, minerals, and vitamins by active transport
LARGE INTESTINE
M: segmental mixing; mass movement for propulsion
S: mucus (goblet cells)
D: none (except by bacteria)
A: ions, water, minerals, vitamins, and small organic molecles produced by bacteria

● **FIGURE 21-22** ***Summary of motility, secretion, digestion, and absorption in different regions of the digestive system***

Swallowing Moves Food from Mouth to Stomach

Swallowing, or **deglutition** [*glutire,* to swallow], is a reflex action that pushes a bolus of food or liquid into the esophagus (Fig. 21-24 ●). The stimulus for swallowing is pressure created when the tongue pushes the bolus against the soft palate and the back of the mouth. Sensory input to a swallowing center in the medulla oblongata begins the reflex.

First, the **epiglottis** folds down over the opening of the larynx to prevent food and liquid from entering the airways. At the same time, respiration is inhibited, and the upper esophageal sphincter relaxes as the bolus enters the esophagus. Waves of peristaltic contraction then push the bolus toward the stomach, aided by gravity. Gravity is not required, however, as you know if you have ever participated in the party trick of swallowing while standing on your head.

The lower end of the esophagus lies just below the diaphragm and is separated from the stomach by the lower esophageal sphincter. This area is not a true sphincter but a region of relatively high muscle tension that acts as a barrier between the esophagus and the stomach. When food is swallowed, the tension relaxes, allowing the bolus to pass into the stomach.

If the lower esophageal sphincter does not stay contracted, gastric acid and pepsin can irritate the lining of the esophagus, leading to the pain and irritation of heartburn. The walls of the esophagus expand during inspiration, when the intrapleural pressure falls [p. 581]. Expansion creates subatmospheric pressure in the esophageal lumen and can suck acidic contents out of the stomach if the sphincter is relaxed. The churning action of the stomach when filled with food can also squirt acid back into the esophagus if the sphincter is not fully contracted.

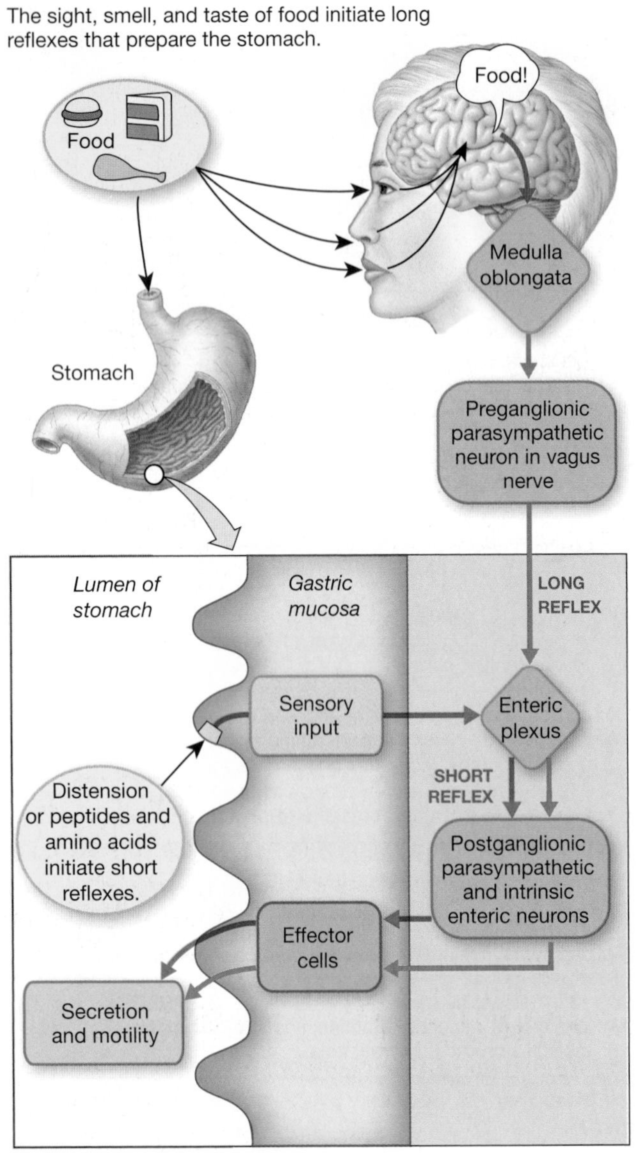

● **FIGURE 21-23** ***Long and short reflexes of the cephalic and gastric phases of digestion***

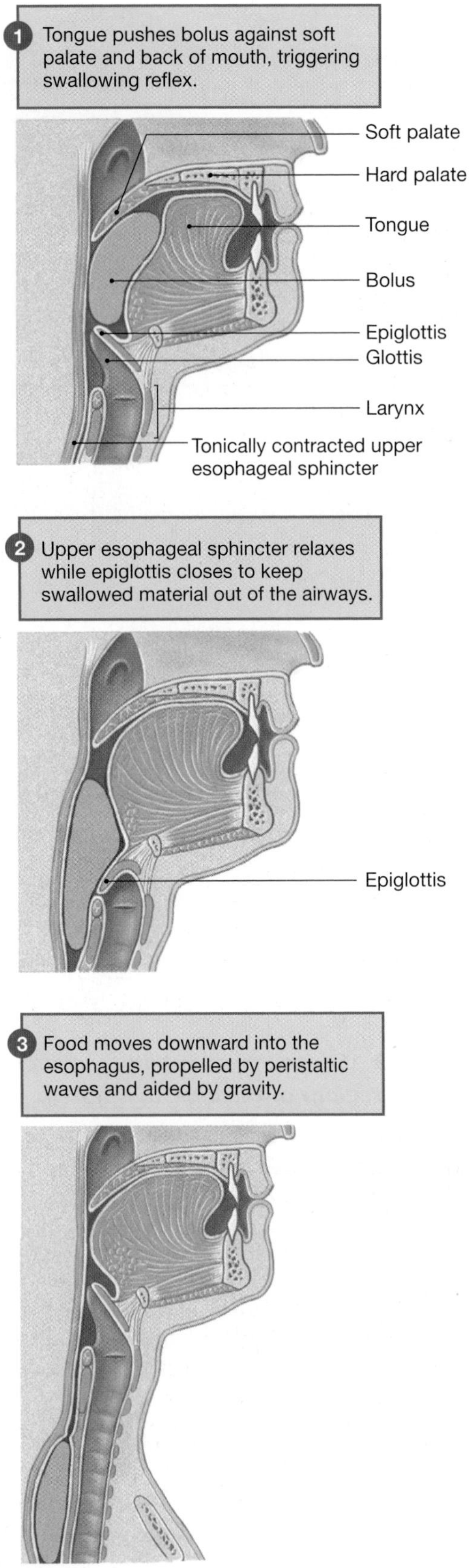

● **FIGURE 21-24** ***The swallowing reflex***

THE GASTRIC PHASE

About 3.5 liters of food, drink, and saliva enter the fundus of the stomach each day. The stomach has three general functions:

1. **Storage.** The stomach stores food and regulates its passage into the small intestine, where most digestion and absorption take place.
2. **Digestion.** The stomach chemically and mechanically digests food into the soupy mixture of uniformly small particles called chyme.
3. **Protection.** The stomach protects the body by destroying many of the bacteria and other pathogens that are swallowed with food or trapped in airway mucus. At the same time, the stomach must protect itself from being damaged by its own secretions.

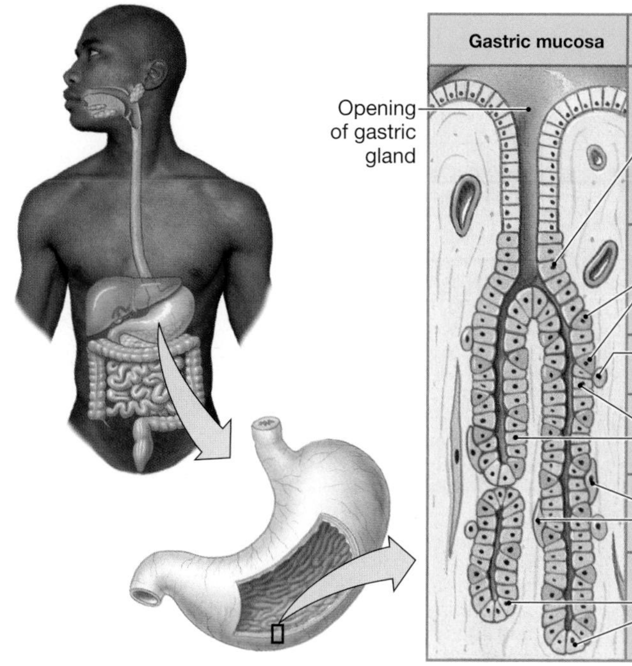

Cell Types	Substance Secreted	Stimulus for Release	Function of Secretion
Mucous neck cell	Mucus	Tonic secretion; with irritation of mucosa	Physical barrier between lumen and epithelium
	Bicarbonate	Secreted with mucus	Buffers gastric acid to prevent damage to epithelium
Parietal cells	Gastric acid (HCl)	Acetylcholine, gastrin, histamine	Activates pepsin; kills bacteria
	Intrinsic factor		Complexes with vitamin B_{12} to permit absorption
Enterochromaffin-like cell	Histamine	Acetylcholine, gastrin	Stimulates gastric acid secretion
Chief cells	Pepsin(ogen)	Acetylcholine, acid secretion	Digests proteins
	Gastric lipase		Digests fats
D cells	Somatostatin	Acid in the stomach	Inhibits gastric acid secretion
G cells	Gastrin	Acetylcholine, peptides and amino acids	Stimulates gastric acid secretion

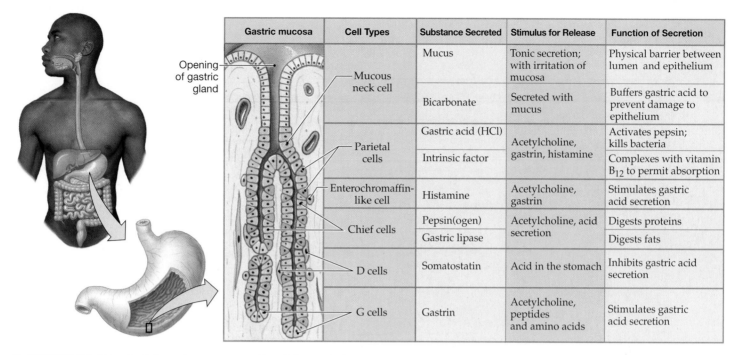

● **FIGURE 21-25** *Activity of secretory cells of the gastric mucosa*

Before food even arrives, digestive activity in the stomach begins with the long **vagal reflex** of the cephalic phase (Fig. 21-23). Then, when food enters the stomach, stimuli in the gastric lumen initiate a series of short reflexes that constitute the **gastric phase** of digestion.

In gastric phase reflexes, distension of the stomach and the presence of peptides or amino acids in the lumen activate endocrine cells and enteric neurons. Hormones, neurocrine secretions, and paracrine molecules then influence motility and secretion.

The Stomach Stores Food

When food arrives, the stomach relaxes and expands to hold the increased volume. This neurally mediated reflex is called *receptive relaxation.* The upper half of the stomach remains relatively quiet, holding food until it is ready to be digested. The storage function of the stomach is perhaps the least obvious aspect of digestion. However, whenever we ingest more than we need from a nutritional standpoint, the stomach must regulate the rate at which food enters the small intestine.

Without such regulation, the small intestine would not be able to digest and absorb the load presented to it, and significant amounts of unabsorbed chyme would pass into the large intestine. The epithelium of the large intestine is not designed for large-scale nutrient absorption, so most of the chyme would pass out in the feces, resulting in diarrhea. This "dumping syndrome" is one of the less pleasant side effects of surgery that removes portions of either the stomach or small intestine.

While the upper stomach is quietly holding food, the lower stomach is busy with digestion. In the distal half of the stomach, a series of peristaltic waves pushes the food down toward the pylorus, mixing food with acid and digestive enzymes. As large food particles are digested to the more uniform texture of chyme, each contractile wave squirts a small amount of chyme through the pylorus into the duodenum. Enhanced gastric motility during a meal is primarily under neural control and is stimulated by distension of the stomach.

The Stomach Secretes Acid and Enzymes

When food comes into the mouth, the feedforward cephalic vagal reflex begins secretion in the stomach. The various secretions, their stimuli for release, and their functions are summarized in Figure 21-25 ● and described below.

Acid Secretion **Parietal cells** deep in the gastric glands secrete **gastric acid** (HCl), which helps kill bacteria and other ingested microorganisms. Acid also *denatures* proteins [p. 43], destroying their tertiary structure by breaking disulfide and hydrogen bonds. Unfolding protein chains make the peptide bonds between amino acids accessible to enzymes.

Carbohydrate digestion that began in the mouth continues in the stomach until mixing exposes the amylase to gastric acid. Salivary amylase is inactivated at low pH.

Parietal cells also secrete *intrinsic factor.* As noted earlier, intrinsic factor forms complexes with vitamin B_{12} and is essential for B_{12} absorption in the intestine. In the absence of intrinsic factor, vitamin B_{12} deficiency causes the condition known as *pernicious anemia.* In this state, red blood cell synthesis (*erythropoiesis*), which depends on vitamin B_{12}, is severely diminished. Lack of intrinsic factor cannot be remedied directly, but patients with pernicious anemia can be given vitamin B_{12} shots.

21

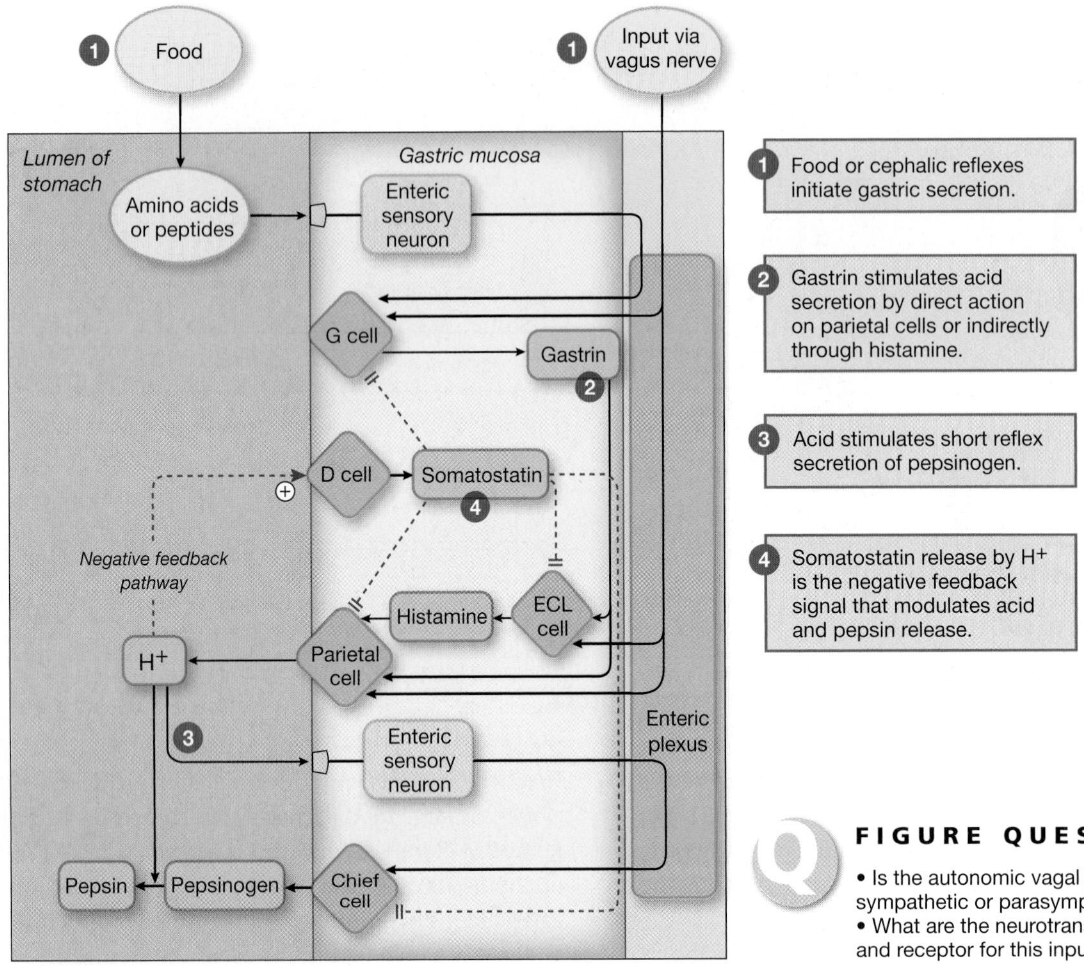

FIGURE QUESTIONS

- Is the autonomic vagal input sympathetic or parasympathetic?
- What are the neurotransmitter and receptor for this input?

● **FIGURE 21-26** ***Integration of cephalic and gastric phase secretion in the stomach.*** The cephalic phase is initiated by the sight, smell, sound, or thought of food or by the presence of food in the mouth. The gastric phase is initiated by the arrival of food in the stomach.

Enzyme Secretion **Chief cells** in the gastric glands secrete the inactive enzyme pepsinogen. Pepsinogen is cleaved to active pepsin in the lumen of the stomach by the action of H^+. Pepsin is an endopeptidase that carries out the initial digestion of proteins. It is particularly effective on collagen and therefore plays an important role in digesting meat.

Gastric lipase is co-secreted with pepsin. However, less than 10% of fat digestion takes place in the stomach.

Paracrine Secretion **Enterochromaffin-like** (ECL) **cells** secrete the paracrine histamine. Histamine promotes acid secretion by parietal cells. **D cells** secrete the paracrine somatostatin. Somatostatin is the primary negative feedback signal for gastric phase secretion. It shuts down acid secretion directly and indirectly and also inhibits pepsinogen secretion.

Hormone Secretion **G cells**, found deep in the gastric glands, secrete the hormone gastrin. Gastrin release is stimulated by the presence of amino acids and peptides in the stomach, by distension of the stomach, and by neural reflexes mediated by **gastrin-releasing peptide.** Coffee (even if decaffeinated) also stimulates gastrin release—one reason people with excess acid secretion syndromes are advised to avoid coffee.

The coordinated function of gastric secretion is illustrated in Figure 21-26 ●:

1. In a cephalic reflex, parasympathetic neurons from the vagus nerve stimulate G cells to release gastrin into the blood (Fig. 21-26 ①). The presence of amino acids or peptides in the lumen triggers a short reflex for gastrin release.
2. Gastrin in turn promotes acid release, both directly and indirectly by stimulating histamine release ②.
3. Histamine is released from ECL cells in response to gastrin and acetylcholine from the enteric nervous system ①. Histamine diffuses to its target, the parietal cells, and stimulates acid secretion by combining with *H_2 receptors* on parietal cells.
4. Acid in the stomach lumen stimulates pepsinogen release from chief cells through a short reflex ③. In the lumen,

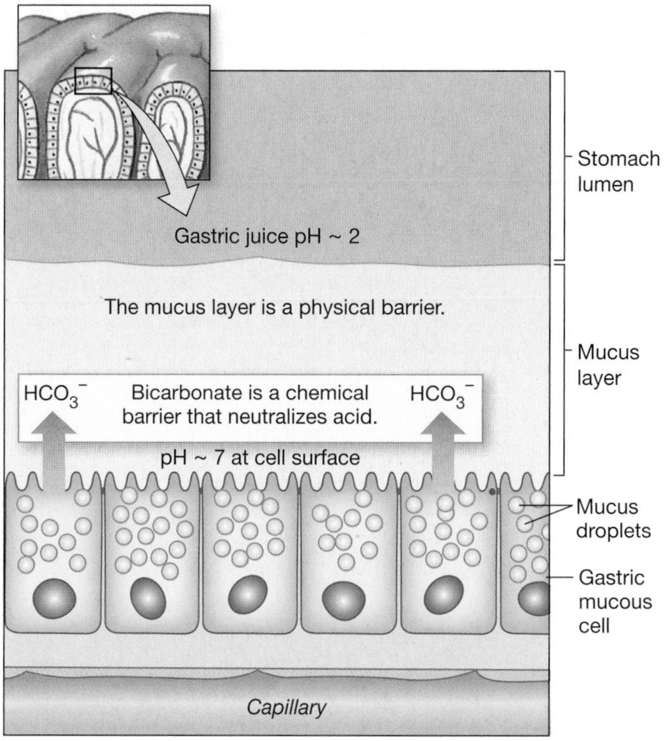
Stomach lumen
Gastric juice pH ~ 2
The mucus layer is a physical barrier.
Mucus layer
HCO_3^-
Bicarbonate is a chemical barrier that neutralizes acid.
HCO_3^-
pH ~ 7 at cell surface
Mucus droplets
Gastric mucous cell
Capillary

● **FIGURE 21-27** ***The mucus-bicarbonate barrier of the gastric mucosa***

acid converts pepsinogen into pepsin, and protein digestion begins.

5. Acid also triggers somatostatin release from D cells ④. Somatostatin acts via negative feedback to inhibit secretion of gastric acid, gastrin, histamine, and pepsinogen.

The Stomach Balances Digestion and Protection

Under normal conditions, the gastric mucosa is protected from autodigestion by a mucus-bicarbonate barrier. **Mucous cells** in the neck of gastric glands secrete both substances. The mucus forms a physical barrier, and the bicarbonate creates a chemical buffer barrier underlying the mucus (Fig. 21-27 ●). Researchers using microelectrodes have shown that the bicarbonate layer just above the cell surface in the stomach has a pH that is close to 7, even when the pH in the lumen is highly acidic at pH 2. Mucus secretion is increased when the stomach is irritated, such as by the ingestion of aspirin (acetylsalicylic acid) or alcohol.

Even the mucus-bicarbonate barrier can fail at times. In *Zollinger-Ellison syndrome,* patients secrete excessive levels of gastrin, usually from gastrin-secreting tumors in the pancreas. As a result, hyperacidity in the stomach overwhelms the normal protective mechanisms and causes a peptic ulcer. In peptic ulcers, acid and pepsin destroy the mucosa, creating holes that extend into the submucosa and muscularis of the stomach and duodenum. (*Acid reflux* [*re-* backward + *fluxus,* flow] into the esophagus can erode the mucosal layer there as well.)

Excess acid secretion is an uncommon cause of peptic ulcers. By far the most common causes are nonsteroidal anti-inflammatory drugs (NSAIDs), such as aspirin, and *Helicobacter pylori,* a bacterium that creates inflammation of the gastric mucosa (see the Running Problem in this chapter).

For many years the primary therapy for excess acid secretion, or *dyspepsia,* was the ingestion of *antacids,* agents that neutralize acid in the gastric lumen. But as molecular biologists explored the mechanism for acid secretion by parietal cells, the potential for new therapies became obvious. Today we have two classes of drugs to fight hyperacidity: H_2-receptor antagonists (cimetidine and ranitidine, for example) that block histamine action, and *proton pump inhibitors* (PPIs), which block H^+-K^+-ATPase (omeprazole and lansoprazole, for example).

THE INTESTINAL PHASE

The net result of the gastric phase is the digestion of proteins in the stomach by pepsin; the formation of chyme by the action of pepsin, acid, and peristaltic contractions; and the controlled entry of chyme into the small intestine, where further digestion and absorption can take place. Once chyme enters the small intestine, the **intestinal phase** of digestion begins. The initiation of the intestinal phase triggers a series of reflexes that feed back to regulate the delivery rate of chyme from the stomach, and feed forward to promote digestion, motility, and utilization of nutrients.

The feedback signals to the stomach are both neural and hormonal (Fig. 21-28 ●):

- Chyme in the intestine activates the enteric nervous system, which then slows gastric motility and secretion. In addition, three hormones reinforce the feedback signal: secretin, cholecystokinin (CCK), and gastric inhibitory peptide (GIP) (see Tbl. 21-1).
- Secretin is released by the presence of acidic chyme in the duodenum. Secretin inhibits acid production and gastric motility, slowing gastric emptying. In addition, secretin stimulates production of pancreatic HCO_3^- to neutralize the acidic chyme that has entered the intestine.
- If a meal contains fats, CCK is secreted into the bloodstream. CCK also slows gastric motility and acid secretion. Because fat digestion proceeds more slowly than either protein or carbohydrate digestion, it is crucial that the stomach allow only small amounts of fat into the intestine at one time.
- If the meal contains carbohydrates, the *incretin hormones* GIP and glucagon-like peptide 1 (GLP-1) are released. Both hormones feed forward to promote insulin release by the endocrine pancreas, allowing cells to prepare for glucose that is about to be absorbed. They also slow the entry of food into the intestine by decreasing gastric motility and acid secretion.

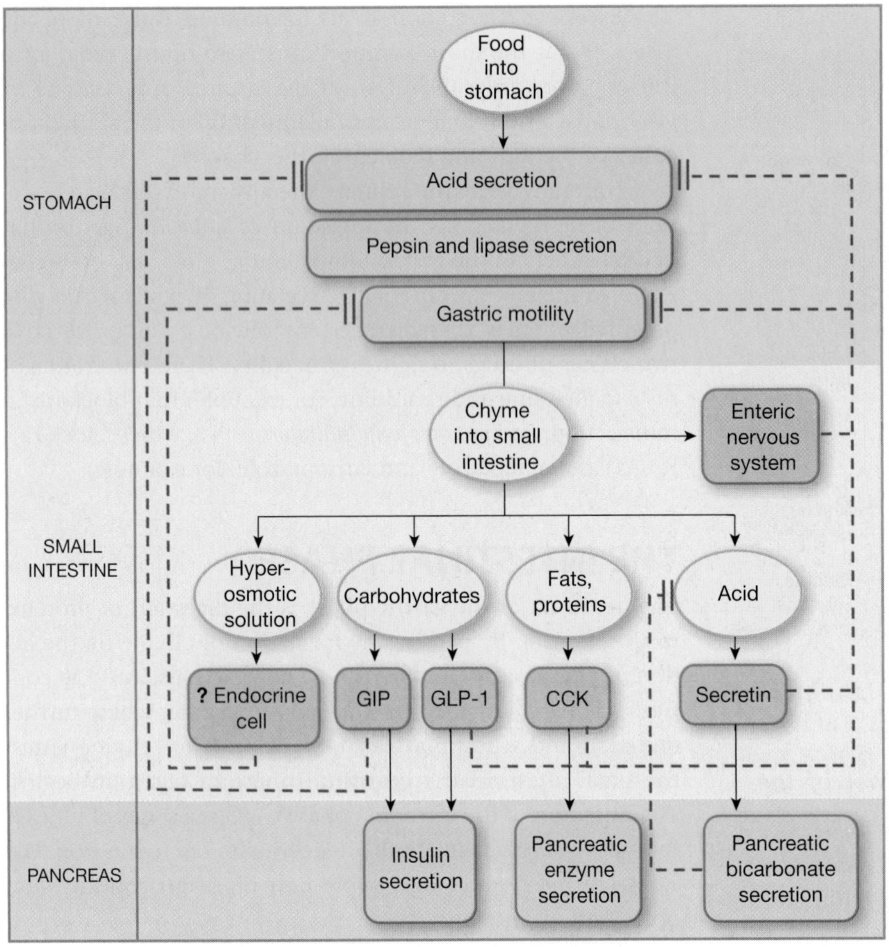

● **FIGURE 21-28** ***Chyme in the small intestine inhibits gastric motility and secretion.***

- The mixture of acid, enzymes, and digested food in chyme usually forms a hyperosmotic solution. Osmoreceptors in the intestine wall are sensitive to the osmolarity of the entering chyme. When stimulated by high osmolarity, the receptors inhibit gastric emptying in a reflex mediated by some unknown blood-borne substance.

Once food enters the small intestine, it is slowly propelled forward by a combination of slow-wave, segmental, and peristaltic contractions. These actions mix chyme with enzymes and expose digested nutrients to the mucosa for absorption. Forward movement of chyme through the intestine must be slow enough to allow digestion and absorption to go to completion. Parasympathetic innervation, gastrin, and CCK all promote intestinal motility, and sympathetic innervation inhibits it.

Bicarbonate Neutralizes Gastric Acid

About 5.5 liters of food, fluid, and secretions enter the small intestine each day, and about 3.5 liters of hepatic, pancreatic, and intestinal secretions are added there, making a total input of 9 liters into the lumen (see Fig. 21-1). The added secretions include bicarbonate, mucus, bile, and digestive enzymes.

1. *Bicarbonate secretion* into the small intestine neutralizes the highly acidic chyme that enters from the stomach. Most bicarbonate comes from the pancreas and is released in response to neural stimuli and secretin.
2. Intestinal goblet cells secrete mucus for protection and lubrication.
3. *Bile* release into the intestine occurs when gallbladder contraction is stimulated by CCK following ingestion of fats. Bile salts are not altered during fat digestion. When they reach the terminal section of the small intestine (the ileum), they encounter cells that transport them back into the circulation. From there, they return to the liver, are taken back up into the hepatocytes, and re-secreted. This recirculation of bile salts is essential to fat digestion because the body's pool of bile salts must cycle from two to five times for each meal. Bilirubin and other wastes secreted in bile are not reabsorbed and pass into the large intestine for excretion.
4. *Digestive enzymes* are produced by the intestinal epithelium and acinar cells of the exocrine pancreas. The brush border enzymes, which include peptidases, disaccharidases, and a protease called **enteropeptidase** (previously called *enterokinase*), are anchored to the luminal enterocyte membrane and are not swept out of the small intestine as chyme is propelled forward.

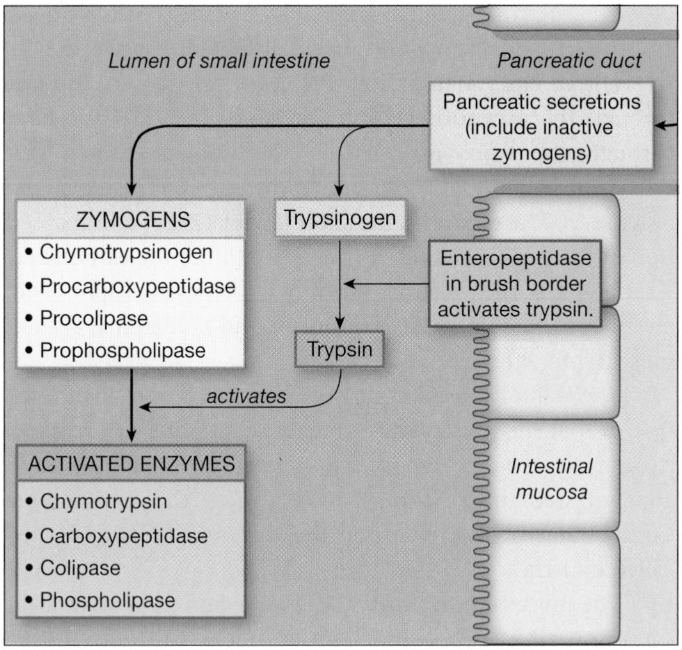

● **FIGURE 21-29** ***Activation of pancreatic zymogens.*** Inactive enzymes secreted by the pancreas are activated in a cascade. Trypsinogen is activated to trypsin by brush border enteropeptidase, and trypsin then activates other pancreatic enzymes.

The signals for pancreatic enzyme release include distension of the small intestine, the presence of food in the intestine, neural signals, and the hormone CCK. Pancreatic enzymes enter the intestine in a watery fluid that also contains bicarbonate. Most are secreted as zymogens that must be activated upon arrival in the intestine. This activation process is a cascade that begins when brush border enteropeptidase converts inactive trypsinogen to active trypsin (Fig. 21-29 ●). Trypsin then converts the other pancreatic zymogens to their active forms.

Most Fluid Is Absorbed in the Small Intestine

Of the 9 liters that enter the small intestine daily, most (7.5 liters) is reabsorbed there. The transport of organic nutrients and ions, which takes place mostly in the duodenum and jejunum, creates an osmotic gradient for water absorption. Most absorbed nutrients move into capillaries in the villi and from there into the *hepatic portal system* [p. 471]. This specialized region of the circulation has two sets of capillary beds: one that picks up absorbed nutrients at the intestine, and another that delivers the nutrients directly to the liver (Fig. 21-30 ●). Most digested fats go into the lymphatic system rather than into the blood.

The delivery of absorbed materials directly to the liver underscores the importance of that organ as a biological filter. Hepatocytes contain a variety of enzymes, such as the *cytochrome P450* isozymes, that metabolize drugs and xenobiotics and clear them from the bloodstream before they reach

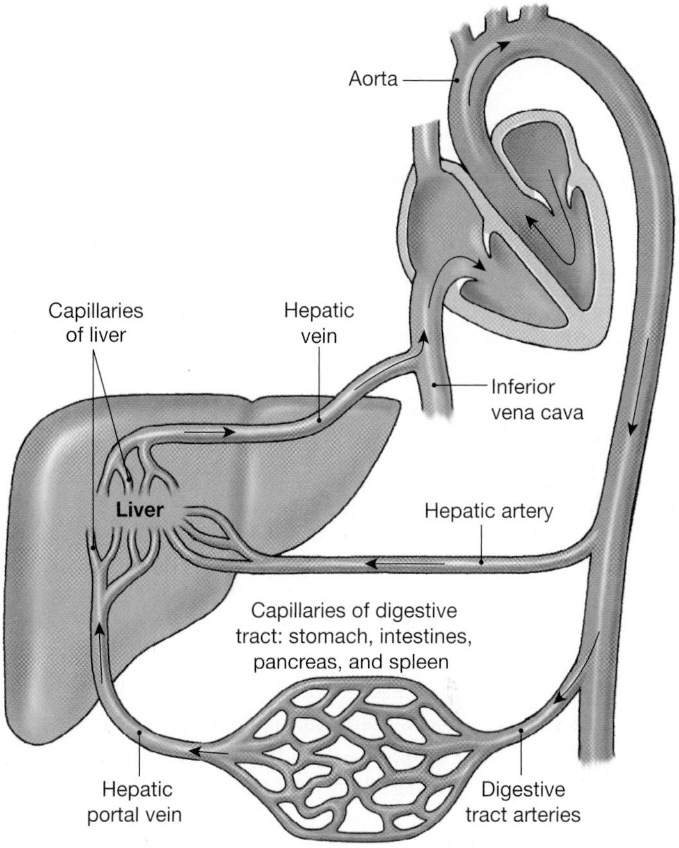

● **FIGURE 21-30** ***The hepatic portal system.*** Most nutrients absorbed by the intestine pass through the liver, which serves as a filter that can remove potentially harmful xenobiotics before they get into the systemic circulation.

the systemic circulation. Hepatic clearance is one reason a drug administered orally must often be given in higher doses than the same drug administered by IV infusion.

Most Digestion Occurs in the Small Intestine

Chyme entering the small intestine has undergone relatively little chemical digestion. Protein digestion started in the stomach, but pepsin entering the small intestine is soon inactivated at the higher intestinal pH. Pancreatic proteases and at least 17 additional proteases and peptidases in the brush border continue protein digestion, creating small peptides and free amino acids that can be absorbed.

Carbohydrate digestion in the small intestine finishes converting digestible polysaccharides and disaccharides into monosaccharides that can be absorbed. Pancreatic amylase continues to digest starch into maltose. Maltose and disaccharides from food, such as sucrose and lactose (milk sugar), are digested by the appropriate brush border disaccharidase to their absorbable end products: glucose, galactose, and fructose.

Fats enter the small intestine in the form of a coarse emulsion. In the duodenum, bile salts coat the fat droplets to stabilize them so that digestion can be carried out by pancreatic

21

CLINICAL FOCUS

LACTOSE INTOLERANCE

Lactose, or milk sugar, is a disaccharide composed of glucose and galactose. Ingested lactose must be digested before it can be absorbed, a task accomplished by the intestinal brush border enzyme *lactase*. Generally, lactase is found only in juvenile mammals, except in some humans of European descent. Those people inherit a dominant gene that allows them to produce lactase after childhood. Scientists believe the lactase gene provided a selective advantage to their ancestors, who developed a culture in which milk and milk products played an important role. In non-Western cultures, in which dairy products are not part of the diet after weaning, most adults lack the gene and synthesize less intestinal lactase. Decreased lactase activity is associated with a condition known as *lactose intolerance*. If a person with lactose intolerance drinks milk or eats dairy products, diarrhea may result. In addition, bacteria in the large intestine ferment lactose to gas and organic acids, leading to bloating and flatulence. The simplest remedy is to remove milk products from the diet, although milk predigested with lactase is available.

lipase. Cholesterol and fatty acids are absorbed as described earlier in this chapter.

CONCEPT CHECK

10. Bile acids are reabsorbed in the distal intestine by an apical Na^+-dependent bile acid transporter (ASBT) and a basolateral organic anion transporter (OAT). Draw one enterocyte; label lumen, ECF, basolateral and apical sides; and diagram bile acid reabsorption as described above.
11. List the actions of CCK on the digestive system, and explain how these functions coordinate to promote fat digestion and absorption. Answers: p. 723

The Large Intestine Concentrates Waste

By the end of the ileum, only about 1.5 liters of unabsorbed chyme remain. The colon absorbs most of this volume so that normally only about 0.1 liter of water is lost daily in feces. Chyme enters the large intestine through the **ileocecal valve.** This is a tonically contracted region of muscularis that narrows the opening between the ileum and the **cecum**, the initial section of the large intestine (Fig. 21-31 ●). The ileocecal valve relaxes each time a peristaltic wave reaches it. It also relaxes when food leaves the stomach as part of the *gastroileal reflex*.

The large intestine has seven regions. The cecum is a dead-end pouch with the *appendix*, a small fingerlike projection, at its ventral end. Material moves from the cecum upward through the **ascending colon**, horizontally across the body through the **transverse colon**, then down through the **descending colon** and **sigmoid colon** [*sigmoeides*, shaped like a sigma, Σ]. The **rectum** is the short (about 12 cm) terminal section of the large intestine. It is separated from the external environment by the **anus**, an opening closed by two sphincters, an internal smooth muscle sphincter and an external skeletal muscle sphincter.

The wall of the colon differs from that of the small intestine in that the muscularis of the large intestine has an inner circular layer but a discontinuous longitudinal muscle layer concentrated into three bands called the **tenia coli**. Contractions of the tenia pull the wall into bulging pockets called **haustra.**

The mucosa of the colon has two regions, like that of the small intestine. The luminal surface lacks villi and appears smooth. It is composed of colonocytes and mucus-secreting goblet cells. The crypts contain stem cells that divide to produce new epithelium, as well as goblet cells, endocrine cells, and maturing colonocytes.

Motility in the Large Intestine Chyme that enters the colon continues to be mixed by segmental contractions. Forward movement is minimal during mixing contractions and depends primarily on a unique colonic contraction known as **mass movement.** A wave of contraction decreases the diameter of a segment of colon and sends a substantial bolus of material forward. These contractions occur 3–4 times a day and are associated with eating and distension of the stomach through the *gastrocolic reflex*. Mass movement is responsible for the sudden distension of the rectum that triggers defecation.

The **defecation reflex** removes undigested feces from the body. Defecation resembles urination in that it is a spinal reflex triggered by distension of the organ wall. The movement of fecal material into the normally empty rectum triggers the reflex. Smooth muscle of the **internal anal sphincter** relaxes, and peristaltic contractions in the rectum push material toward the anus. At the same time, the external anal sphincter, which is under voluntary control, is consciously relaxed if the situation is appropriate. Defecation is often aided by conscious abdominal contractions and forced expiratory movements against a closed glottis (the *Valsalva maneuver*).

Defecation, like urination, is subject to emotional influence. Stress may increase intestinal motility and cause psychosomatic diarrhea in some individuals but may decrease motility and cause *constipation* in others. When feces are retained in the colon, either through consciously ignoring a defecation reflex or through decreased motility, continued water absorption creates hard, dry feces that are difficult to expel. One treatment for constipation is glycerin suppositories, small bullet-shaped

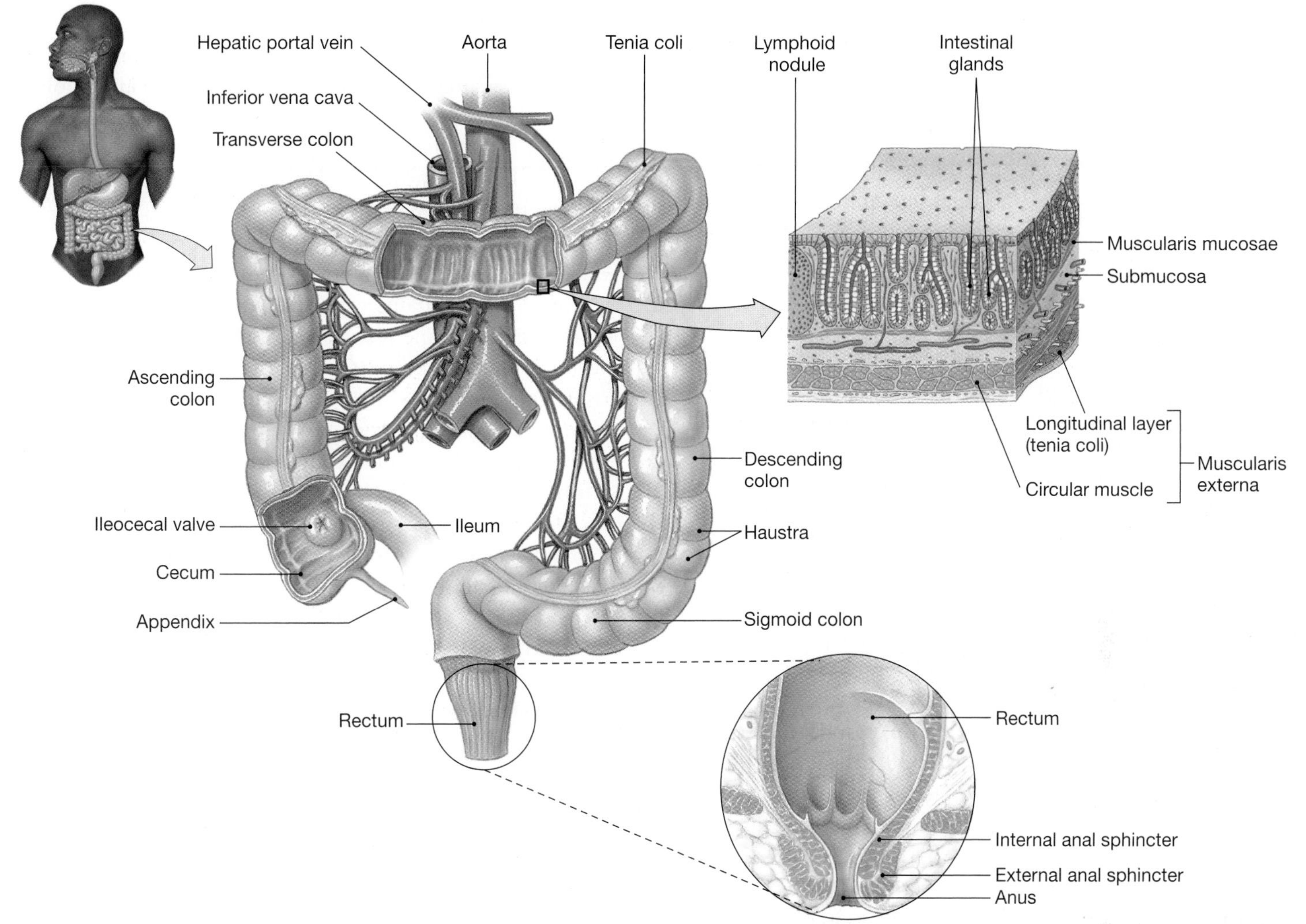

● **FIGURE 21-31** *Anatomy of the large intestine*

wads that are inserted through the anus into the rectum. Glycerin attracts water and helps soften the feces to promote defecation.

Digestion and Absorption in the Large Intestine

According to the traditional view of the large intestine, no significant digestion of organic molecules takes place there. However, in recent years this view has been revised. We now know that the numerous bacteria inhabiting the colon break down significant amounts of undigested complex carbohydrates and proteins through fermentation. The end products include lactate and short-chain fatty acids, such as butyric acid. Several of these products are lipophilic and can be absorbed by simple diffusion. The fatty acids, for example, are used by colonocytes as their preferred energy substrate.

Colonic bacteria also produce significant amounts of absorbable vitamins, especially vitamin K. Intestinal gases, such as hydrogen sulfide, that escape from the gastrointestinal tract are a less useful product. Some starchy foods, such as beans, are notorious for their tendency to produce intestinal gas (**flatus**).

Diarrhea Can Cause Dehydration

Diarrhea is a pathological state in which intestinal secretion of fluid is not balanced by absorption, resulting in watery stools. Diarrhea occurs if normal intestinal water absorption

RUNNING PROBLEM

Tonya's stomach still hurts later that night. Her roommate suggests that she try one of the new "acid blockers" she has seen advertised on TV. These drugs are more correctly known as H_2-receptor antagonists because they bind competitively to the H_2 receptors for histamine that are found on parietal cells. Fortunately, Tonya's roommate has just bought a package of these drugs. Two hours after taking the drug, Tonya feels much better.

Question 6:

How does blocking H_2 receptors stop acid production in the stomach?

mechanisms are disrupted or if there are unabsorbed osmotically active solutes that "hold" water in the lumen. Substances that cause *osmotic diarrhea* include undigested lactose and sorbitol, a sugar alcohol from plants. Sorbitol is used as an "artificial" sweetener in some chewing gums and in foods made for diabetics. Another unabsorbed solute that can cause osmotic diarrhea, intestinal cramping, and gas is Olestra, the "fake fat" made from vegetable oil and sugar.

In clinical settings, patients who need to have their bowels cleaned out before surgery or other procedures are often given four liters of an isotonic solution of polyethylene glycol and electrolytes to drink. Because polyethylene glycol cannot be absorbed, a large volume of unabsorbed solution passes into the colon, where it triggers copious diarrhea that removes all solid waste from the GI tract.

Secretory diarrheas occur when bacterial toxins, such as cholera toxin from *Vibrio cholerae* and *Escherichia coli* enterotoxin, enhance colonic Cl^- secretion (see Fig. 21-9). When excessive fluid secretion is coupled with increased motility, diarrhea results. Secretory diarrhea in response to intestinal infection can be viewed as adaptive because it helps flush pathogens out of the lumen. However, it also has the potential to cause dehydration if fluid loss is excessive.

The World Health Organization estimates that in developing countries, 4 million people die from diarrhea each year. In the United States, diarrhea in children causes about 200,000 hospitalizations a year. Oral replacement fluids for treatment of diarrheal salt and water loss can prevent the *morbidity* (illness) and *mortality* (death) associated with diarrhea. Oral rehydration solutions usually contain glucose or sucrose as well as Na^+, K^+, and Cl^- because the inclusion of a sugar enhances Na^+ absorption. If dehydration is severe, intravenous fluid therapy may be necessary.

CONCEPT CHECK

12. In secretory diarrhea, epithelial cells in the intestinal villi may be damaged or may slough off. In these cases, would it be better to use an oral rehydration solution containing glucose or one containing sucrose? Explain your reasoning. Answers: p. 723

IMMUNE FUNCTIONS OF THE GI TRACT

As you learned at the beginning of the chapter, the GI tract is the largest immune organ in the body. Its luminal surface is continuously exposed to disease-causing organisms, and the immune cells of the GALT must prevent these pathogens from entering the body through delicate absorptive tissues. The first lines of defense are the enzymes and immunoglobulins in saliva and the highly acidic environment of the stomach. If pathogens or toxic materials make it into the small intestine, sensory receptors and the immune cells of the GALT respond. Two common responses are diarrhea, just described, and vomiting.

M Cells Sample Gut Contents

The immune system of the intestinal mucosa consists of immune cells scattered throughout the mucosa, clusters of immune cells in Peyer's patches (see Fig. 21-3e), and specialized epithelial cells called **M cells** that overlie the Peyer's patches. The M cells provide information about the contents of the lumen to the immune cells of the GALT.

The microvilli of M cells are fewer in number and more widely spaced than in the typical intestinal cell. The apical surface of M cells contains clathrin-coated pits [p. 153] with embedded membrane receptors. When antigens bind to these receptors, the M cell uses transcytosis to transport them to its basolateral membrane, where they are released into the interstitial fluid. Macrophages and lymphocytes [p. 549] are waiting in the extracellular compartment for the M cell to present them with antigens.

If the antigens are substances that threaten the body, the immune cells swing into action. They secrete cytokines to attract additional immune cells that can attack the invaders and cytokines that trigger an inflammatory response. A third response to cytokines is increased Cl^-, fluid, and mucus secretion to flush the invaders from the GI tract.

In *inflammatory bowel diseases* (such as ulcerative colitis and Crohn's disease), the immune response is triggered inappropriately by the normal contents of the gut. One apparently successful experimental therapy for these diseases involves blocking the action of cytokines released by the gut-associated lymphoid tissues.

How certain pathogenic bacteria cross the barrier created by the intestinal epithelium has puzzled scientists for years. The discovery of M cells may provide the answer. It appears that some bacteria, such as *Salmonella* and *Shigella,* have evolved surface molecules that bind to M cell receptors. The M cells then obligingly transport the bacteria across the epithelial barrier and deposit them inside the body, where the immune system immediately reacts. Both bacteria cause diarrhea, and *Salmonella* also causes fever and vomiting.

Vomiting Is a Protective Reflex

Vomiting, or *emesis*, the forceful expulsion of gastric and duodenal contents from the mouth, is a protective reflex that removes toxic materials from the GI tract before they can be absorbed. However, excessive or prolonged vomiting, with its loss of gastric acid, can cause metabolic alkalosis [p. 673].

The vomiting reflex is coordinated through a vomiting center in the medulla. The reflex begins with stimulation of sensory receptors and is often (but not always) accompanied by nausea. A variety of stimuli from all over the body can trigger vomiting. They include chemicals in the blood, such as cytokines and certain drugs; pain; and disturbed equilibrium, such as occurs in a moving car or rocking boat. Tickling the back of the pharynx can also induce vomiting.

Efferent signals from the vomiting center initiate a wave of reverse peristalsis that begins in the small intestine and moves upward. The motility wave is aided by abdominal contraction that increases intra-abdominal pressure. The stomach relaxes so that the increased pressure forces gastric and intestinal contents back into the esophagus and out of the mouth.

During vomiting, respiration is inhibited. The epiglottis and soft palate close off the trachea and nasopharynx to prevent the *vomitus* from being inhaled (*aspirated*). Should acid or small food particles get into the airways, they could damage the respiratory system and cause *aspiration pneumonia*.

In the next chapter we look at the fates of nutrients once they have been absorbed from the digestive tract.

RUNNING PROBLEM CONCLUSION

Peptic Ulcers

The results are in. Tonya's tests confirm that an *H. pylori* infection is probably the cause of her duodenal ulcer. Tonya's physician gives her some antibiotics to take and changes her H_2-receptor antagonist to a proton pump inhibitor.

"Acid indigestion" and heartburn are two of the most common digestive disorders in the United States. Stroll the aisles of any pharmacy and look at the space devoted to over-the-counter medications for these conditions. Traditional antacids are buffers, such as calcium carbonate, sodium bicarbonate, aluminum hydroxide, and magnesium hydroxide, that neutralize H^+ in the stomach lumen. Newer therapies have been developed based on physiological studies of gastric acid secretion. To see acid secretion in action, do a Google search for *parietal cell animation*. Now check your understanding of this running problem by comparing your answers with the information in the following summary table.

	QUESTION	FACTS	INTEGRATION AND ANALYSIS
1	Why are peptic ulcers found in the duodenum rather than in the jejunum or ileum?	Peptic ulcers are caused by gastric acid and stomach enzymes. Chyme moving out of the stomach passes into the duodenum.	If protective mechanisms in the intestine fail, the duodenum is the first part of the small intestine to be exposed to gastric acid and enzymes.
2	What is the most common isotope of carbon in nature?	The atomic mass of an element indicates the most common isotope.	The most common isotope of carbon is ^{12}C.
3	How does the conversion of urea into ammonia protect *H. pylori* from the hostile environment of the stomach?	A base is an anion that combines with H^+. Ammonia, a base, combines with H^+ to create ammonium ions, NH_4^+. This ties up free H^+ and increases pH.	*H. pylori* has ammonia-producing enzymes that combine with H^+ to reduce acidity. In this way the bacteria protect themselves from being killed by the acidic environment of the stomach.
4	What component of Tonya's exhaled breath does this test measure? What result of her breath analysis would suggest that she has an *H. pylori* infection?	Ureases of *H. pylori* convert urea into carbon dioxide and ammonia. CO_2 made by normal metabolism will have ^{12}C, the most common isotope of carbon.	The breath test analyzes CO_2 in exhaled air. If Tonya has *H. pylori*, her exhaled CO_2 will include the unusual carbon isotope from the urea drink in addition to ^{12}C.
5	Write the chemical equations showing how the antacids sodium bicarbonate ($NaHCO_3$) and aluminum hydroxide ($Al(OH)_3$) buffer hydrochloric acid (HCl).	Buffers are molecules that combine with H^+. Bicarbonate (HCO_3^-) and OH^- are buffers.	$NaHCO_3 + HCl \rightarrow NaCl + H_2CO_3$ $Al(OH)_3 + 3\ HCl \rightarrow AlCl_3 + 3\ H_2O$
6	How does blocking H_2 receptors stop acid production in the stomach?	Histamine is a paracrine that binds to H_2 receptors and stimulates gastric acid secretion.	If H_2 receptors are blocked by antagonists, histamine cannot bind to them and stimulate acid secretion.

687 692 697 700 717 719

CHAPTER SUMMARY

The digestive system, like the renal system, plays a key role in *mass balance* in the body. Most material that enters the system, whether by mouth or by secretion, is absorbed before it reaches the end of the GI tract. In pathologies such as diarrhea, in which absorption and secretion are unbalanced, the loss of material through the GI tract can seriously disrupt *homeostasis*. Absorption and secretion in the GI tract provide numerous examples of *movement across membranes*, and most transport processes follow patterns you have encountered in the kidney and other systems. Finally, regulation of GI tract function illustrates the complex interactions that take place between endocrine and neural *control systems* and the immune system.

Digestive Function and Processes

1. The GI tract moves nutrients, water, and electrolytes from the external environment to the internal environment. (p. 687)
2. About 2 liters of fluid per day enter the GI tract through the mouth. Another 7 liters of water, ions, and proteins are secreted by the body. Nearly all of this volume is reabsorbed. (p. 687; Fig. 21-1)
3. The four processes of the digestive system are digestion, absorption, motility, and secretion. **Digestion** is chemical and mechanical breakdown of foods into absorbable units. **Absorption** is transfer of substances from the lumen of the GI tract to the ECF. **Motility** is movement of material through the GI tract. **Secretion** refers to the transfer of fluid and electrolytes from ECF to lumen or the release of substances from cells. (p. 688; Fig. 21-2)
4. The GI tract contains the largest collection of lymphoid tissue in the body, the **gut-associated lymphoid tissue (GALT)**. (p. 688)

Anatomy of the Digestive System

iP GI: Anatomy Review

5. **Chyme** is a soupy substance created as ingested food is broken down by mechanical and chemical digestion. (p. 689)
6. Food entering the digestive system passes through the mouth, pharynx, **esophagus, stomach (fundus, body, antrum), small intestine (duodenum, jejunum, ileum), large intestine (colon, rectum)**, and **anus**. (p. 689; Fig. 21-3a)
7. The **salivary glands**, **pancreas**, and **liver** add exocrine secretions containing enzymes and mucus to the lumen. (p. 689; Fig. 21-3a)
8. The wall of the GI tract consists of four layers: mucosa, submucosa, muscle layers, and serosa. (p. 689; Fig. 21-3d)
9. The **mucosa** faces the lumen and consists of epithelium, the **lamina propria**, and the **muscularis mucosa**. The lamina propria contains immune cells. Small **villi** and invaginations increase the surface area. (p. 692; Fig. 21-3c, e)
10. The **submucosa** contains blood vessels and lymph vessels and the **submucosal plexus** of the **enteric nervous system**. (p. 692; Fig. 21-3e)
11. The **muscularis externa** consists of a layer of circular muscle and a layer of longitudinal muscle. The **myenteric plexus** lies between these two muscle layers. (p. 692; Fig. 21-3c, e)
12. The **serosa** is the outer layer of the GI tract wall. It is a connective tissue membrane that is a continuation of the peritoneal membrane. (p. 693; Fig. 21-3d)

Motility

iP GI: Motility

13. Motility moves food from mouth to anus and mechanically mixes food. (p. 693)
14. GI smooth muscle cells are electrically connected by gap junctions. Some segments are **tonically contracted**, but others exhibit **phasic contractions**. (p. 693)
15. Intestinal muscle exhibits spontaneous **slow wave potentials**. When a slow wave reaches threshold, it fires action potentials and contracts. (p. 693; Fig. 21-4)
16. Slow waves originate in the **interstitial cells of Cajal**. (p. 693)
17. Between meals, the **migrating motor complex** moves food remnants from the upper GI tract to the lower regions. (p. 694)
18. **Peristaltic contractions** are progressive waves of contraction that occur mainly in the esophagus. (p. 694; Fig. 21-5a)
19. **Segmental contractions** are primarily mixing contractions. (p. 694; Fig. 21-5b)
20. GI motility is mediated by the enteric nervous system and modulated by hormones, paracrine signals, and neuropeptides. (p. 694)

Secretion

iP GI: Secretion

21. **Parietal cells** in gastric glands secrete hydrochloric acid. (p. 695; Fig. 21-6)
22. The pancreas secretes a watery $NaHCO_3$ solution from duct cells. (p. 695; Figs. 21-7, 21-8)
23. Intestinal cells secrete Cl^- using the **CFTR chloride channel**. Water and Na^+ follow passively down osmotic and electrochemical gradients. (p. 695; Fig. 21-9)
24. Digestive enzymes are secreted by exocrine glands or by gastric and intestinal epithelium. (p. 696)
25. Mucus from **mucous cells** and **goblet cells** forms a protective coating and lubricates contents of the gut. (p. 696)
26. **Saliva** is an exocrine secretion that contains water, ions, mucus, and proteins. Salivation is under autonomic control. (p. 697)
27. Bile made by **hepatocytes** contains **bile salts**, bilirubin, and cholesterol. Bile is stored and concentrated in the gallbladder (p. 699; Fig. 21-10)

Regulation of GI Function

iP GI: Control of the Digestive System

28. **Short reflexes** originate in the **enteric nervous system** and are integrated there. **Long reflexes** are integrated in the CNS. Long reflexes may originate in the ENS or outside it. (pp. 699–700; Fig. 21-11)
29. Generally, parasympathetic innervation is excitatory for GI function, and sympathetic innervation is inhibitory. (p. 700)
30. GI peptides excite or inhibit motility and secretion. Most stimuli for GI peptide secretion arise from the ingestion of food. (p. 701; Fig. 21-12)

31. GI paracrine molecules, such as histamine, interact with hormones and neural reflexes. (p. 700)
32. The enteric nervous system is called "the little brain" because it can integrate information without input from the CNS. **Intrinsic neurons** lie completely within the ENS. (p. 701)
33. Digestive hormones are divided into the gastrin family (**gastrin, cholecystokinin**), secretin family (**secretin, gastric inhibitory peptide, glucagon-like peptide 1**), and hormones that do not fit into either of those two families (**motilin**). (p. 702; Tbl. 21-1)

Digestion and Absorption

iP GI: Digestion and Absorption

34. Digestion combines mechanical and enzymatic breakdown of food. Digestion is not directly regulated but depends on secretion and motility. (p. 703)
35. Most nutrient absorption takes place in the small intestine. The large intestine absorbs water and ions. (p. 703)
36. **Amylase** digests starch to maltose. **Disaccharidases** digest disaccharides to monosaccharides. (pp. 703–704; Fig. 21-14)
37. Glucose absorption uses the SGLT Na^+-glucose symporter and GLUT2 transporter. Fructose uses the GLUT5 and GLUT2 transporters. (p. 704; Fig. 21-15)
38. **Endopeptidases** (also called proteases) break proteins into smaller peptides. **Exopeptidases** remove amino acids from peptides. (pp. 704–705; Fig. 21-16)
39. Amino acids are absorbed via Na^+- or H^+-dependent cotransport. Dipeptides and tripeptides are absorbed via H^+-dependent cotransport. Some larger peptides are absorbed intact via transcytosis. (p. 705; Fig. 21-17)
40. Fat digestion requires the enzyme **lipase** and the cofactor **colipase**. (pp. 705–706; Figs. 21-18, 21-20)
41. Fat digestion is facilitated by bile salts, which emulsify fats. As enzymatic and mechanical digestion proceed, fat droplets form **micelles**. (p. 706; Figs. 21-19, 21-20 ① ②)
42. Fat absorption occurs primarily by simple diffusion. Cholesterol is actively transported. (p. 706; Fig. 21-20 ③)
43. Monoglycerides and fatty acids reassemble into triglycerides in the intestinal cell, then combine with cholesterol and proteins into **chylomicrons**. Chylomicrons are absorbed into the lymph. (p. 706; Fig. 21-20 ④ ⑤)
44. Nucleic acids are digested and absorbed as nitrogenous bases and monosaccharides. (p. 706)
45. Fat-soluble vitamins are absorbed along with fats. Water-soluble vitamins are absorbed by mediated transport. Vitamin B_{12} absorption requires **intrinsic factor** secreted by the stomach. Mineral absorption usually occurs via active transport. (p. 707)

The Cephalic Phase

46. In the **cephalic phase** of digestion, the sight, smell, or taste of food initiates GI reflexes. (p. 708; Fig. 21-23)
47. Mechanical digestion begins with chewing, or **mastication**. Saliva moistens and lubricates food. Salivary amylase digests carbohydrates. (p. 708)
48. Swallowing, or **deglutition**, is a reflex integrated by a medullary center. (p. 709; Fig. 21-24)

The Gastric Phase

49. The stomach stores food, begins protein and fat digestion, and protects the body from swallowed pathogens. (p. 710)
50. The stomach secretes mucus and bicarbonate from **mucous cells**, gastric acid from parietal cells, pepsinogen from **chief cells**, somatostatin from **D cells**, histamine from **ECL cells**, and gastrin from **G cells**. (p. 712; Fig. 21-25)
51. Gastric function is integrated with the cephalic and intestinal phases of digestion. (p. 712; Figs. 21-26, 21-28)

The Intestinal Phase

52. Acid in the intestine, CCK, and secretin delay gastric emptying. (p. 713; Fig. 21-28)
53. The pancreas secretes bicarbonate to neutralize gastric acid. (p. 714)
54. Intestinal enzymes are part of the **brush border**. Most pancreatic enzymes are secreted as zymogens that need to be activated. (p. 715; Fig. 21-29)
55. Most absorption takes place in the small intestine. (p. 715)
56. Digestion and absorption of nutrients are completed in the small intestine. Most absorbed nutrients go directly to the liver via the hepatic portal system before entering the systemic circulation. (p. 715)
57. The large intestine concentrates the 1.5 liters of chyme that enter it daily. (p. 716)
58. Undigested material in the colon moves forward by **mass movement**. The **defecation reflex**, a spinal reflex subject to higher control, is triggered by sudden distension of the rectum. (p. 716)
59. Colonic bacteria use fermentation to digest organic material. (p. 717)
60. Cells of the colon can both absorb and secrete fluid. Excessive fluid secretion or decreased absorption causes diarrhea. (p. 717)

Immune Functions of the GI Tract

61. Protective mechanisms of the GI tract include acid and mucus production, vomiting, and diarrhea. (p. 718)
62. **M cells** sample gut contents and present antigens to cells of the GALT. (p. 718)
63. **Vomiting** is a protective reflex integrated in the medulla. (p. 718)

21

QUESTIONS

(Answers to the Review Questions begin on page A1.)

THE PHYSIOLOGY PLACE

Access more review material online at **The Physiology Place** web site. There you'll find review questions, problem-solving activities, case studies, flashcards, and direct links to both *Interactive Physiology*® and *PhysioEx*™. To access the site, go to *www.physiologyplace.com* and select *Human Physiology*, Fifth Edition.

LEVEL ONE REVIEWING FACTS AND TERMS

1. Define the four basic processes of the digestive system and give an example of each.
2. For most nutrients, the processes __________ and __________ are not regulated, whereas __________ and __________ are continuously regulated. Why do you think these differences exist? Defend your answer.

3. Match each of the following descriptions with the appropriate term(s):

(a) chyme is produced here	1. colon
(b) organ where most digestion occurs	2. stomach
(c) initial section of small intestine	3. small intestine
(d) this adds exocrine secretions to duodenum via a duct	4. duodenum
(e) sphincter between stomach and intestine	5. ileum
(f) enzymes produced here	6. jejunum
(g) distension of its walls triggers the defecation reflex	7. pancreas
	8. pylorus
	9. rectum
	10. liver

4. List the four layers of the GI tract walls. What type of tissue predominates in each layer?
5. Describe the functional types of epithelium lining the stomach and intestines.
6. What are Peyer's patches? M cells of the intestine?
7. What purposes does motility serve in the gastrointestinal tract? Which types of tissue contribute to gut motility? Which types of contraction do the tissues undergo?
8. What is a zymogen? What is a proenzyme? List two examples of each.
9. Match each of the following cells with the product(s) it secretes. Items may be used more than once.

(a) parietal cells	1. enzymes
(b) goblet cells	2. histamine
(c) brush border cells	3. mucus
(d) pancreatic cells	4. pepsinogen
(e) D cells	5. gastrin
(f) ECL cells	6. somatostatin
(g) chief cells	7. HCO_3^-
(h) G cells	8. HCl
	9. intrinsic factor

10. How does each of the following factors affect digestion? Briefly explain how and where each factor exerts its effects.
    (a) emulsification
    (b) neural activity
    (c) pH
    (d) size of food particles
11. Most digested nutrients are absorbed into the _________ of the _________ system, delivering nutrients to the _________ (organ). However, digested fats go into the _________ system because intestinal capillaries have a(n) _________ around them that most lipids are unable to cross.
12. What is the enteric nervous system, and what is its function?
13. What are short reflexes? What types of responses do they regulate? What is meant by the term *long reflex*?
14. What role do paracrines play in digestion? Give specific examples.

LEVEL TWO REVIEWING CONCEPTS

15. **Map exercise:** List the three major groups of biomolecules across the top of a large piece of paper. Down the left side of the paper write *mouth, stomach, small intestine, absorption*. For each biomolecule in each location, fill in the enzymes that digest the biomolecule, the products of digestion for each enzyme, and the location and mechanisms by which these products are absorbed.

    Map 2: Create a diagram or map using the following terms related to iron absorption:

DMT1	heme iron
endocytosis	hepcidin
enterocyte	ionized iron
ferroportin	liver

16. Define, compare, and contrast the following pairs or sets of terms:
    (a) mastication, deglutition
    (b) microvilli, villi
    (c) peristalsis, segmentation, migrating motor complex, mass movements, defecation, vomiting, diarrhea
    (d) chyme, feces
    (e) short reflexes, long reflexes
    (f) submucosal plexus, myenteric plexus, enteric nervous system, vagus nerve
    (g) cephalic, gastric, and intestinal phases of digestion
17. Diagram the mechanisms by which Na^+, K^+, and Cl^- are transported out of the intestine. Diagram the mechanisms by which H^+ and HCO_3^- are secreted into the lumen.
18. Compare the enteric nervous system with the cephalic brain. Give some specific examples of neurotransmitters, neuromodulators, and supporting cells in the two.
19. List and briefly describe the actions of the members of each of the three groups of GI hormones.
20. Explain how H_2-receptor antagonists and proton pump inhibitors decrease gastric acid secretion.

LEVEL THREE PROBLEM SOLVING

21. In the disease state called *hemochromatosis*, the hormone hepcidin is either absent or not functional. Use your understanding of iron homeostasis to predict what would happen to intestinal iron uptake and plasma levels of iron in this disease.
22. Erica's baby, Justin, has had a severe bout of diarrhea and is now dehydrated. Is his blood more likely to be acidotic or alkalotic? Why?
23. Mary Littlefeather arrives in her physician's office complaining of severe, steady pain in the upper right quadrant of her abdomen. The pain began shortly after she ate a meal of fried chicken, french fries, and peas. Lab tests and an ultrasound reveal the presence of gallstones in the common bile duct running from the liver, gallbladder, and pancreas into the small intestine.
    (a) Why was Mary's pain precipitated by the meal she ate?
    (b) Which of the following processes will be affected by the gallstones: micelle formation in the intestine, carbohydrate digestion in the intestine, protein absorption in the intestine. Explain your reasoning.
24. Using what you have learned about epithelial transport in this chapter and the renal chapters, draw a picture of the salivary duct cells and lumen. Arrange membrane channels and transporters on the apical and basolateral membranes so that the duct cell absorbs Na^+ and secretes K^+. With neural stimulation, the flow rate of saliva can increase from 0.4 mL/min to 2 mL/min. What do you think happens to the Na^+ and K^+ content of saliva at the higher flow rate?

LEVEL FOUR QUANTITATIVE PROBLEMS

25. Intestinal transport of the amino acid analog MIT (monoiodotyrosine) can be studied using the "everted sac" preparation. A length of intestine is turned inside out, filled with a solution containing MIT,

tied at both ends, and then placed in a bath containing nutrients, salts, and an equal concentration of MIT. Changes in the concentration of MIT are monitored in the bath (mucosal or apical side of the inverted intestine), in the intestinal cells (tissue), and within the sac (serosal or basolateral side of the intestine) over a 240-minute period. The results are displayed in the graph shown here. (Data from Nathans *et al.*, *Biochimica et Biophysica Acta* 41:271–282, 1960)

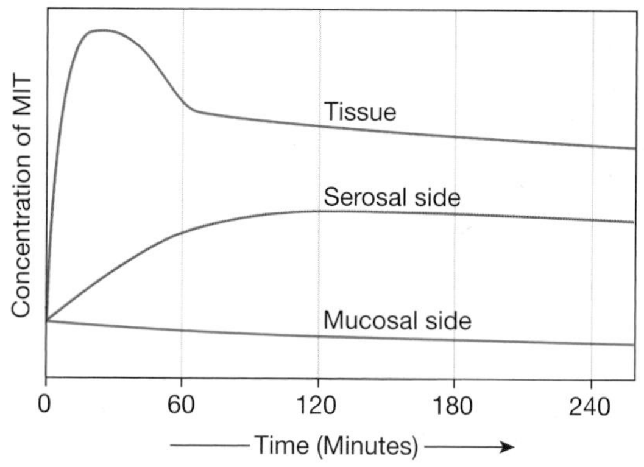

(a) Based on the data shown, is the transepithelial transport of MIT a passive process or an active process?

(b) Which way does MIT move: (1) apical to tissue to basolateral, or (2) basolateral to tissue to apical? Is this movement absorption or secretion?

(c) Is transport across the apical membrane active or passive? Explain your reasoning.

(d) Is transport across the basolateral membrane active or passive? Explain your reasoning.

ANSWERS

Answers to Concept Check Questions

Page 689

1. Digestion is the chemical and mechanical breakdown of food into absorbable units.
2. Digestion takes place in the GI tract lumen, which is external to the body; metabolism takes place in the body's internal environment.
3. Absorption moves material from the GI lumen into the ECF; secretion moves substances from the cells or the ECF into the lumen.

Page 693

4. The lumen of the digestive tract is on the apical or mucosal side of the intestinal epithelium.
5. Mouth → pharynx → esophagus → stomach (fundus, body, antrum) → small intestine (duodenum, jejunum, ileum) → large intestine (colon, rectum) → anus
6. Because the GI tract has a large, vulnerable surface area facing the external environment, it needs the immune cells of lymphoid tissue to combat potential invaders.

Page 694

7. Some sphincters are tonically contracted to close off the GI tract from the outside world and to keep material from passing freely from one section of the tract to another.

Page 708

8. Na^+ from table salt enhances the intestinal absorption of glucose because glucose must be cotransported with Na^+.
9. Bile salts do not digest triglycerides. They simply emulsify them into small particles so that lipase can digest them.

Page 716

10. The ASBT faces the lumen and brings Na^+ and bile acid into the enterocyte together. The OAT transports bile acid by itself out of the enterocyte and into the ECF.
11. CCK slows gastric motility and acid secretion, promotes release of pancreatic enzymes and bile, and promotes intestinal motility. Bile from the gallbladder and pancreatic lipase and colipase are necessary for efficient fat digestion. Fat digestion takes longer than digestion of other foodstuffs, and slowing gastric motility gives the intestine more time to digest fats. Decreasing gastric acid secretion also delays movement of chyme from stomach to intestine. Promoting intestinal motility ensures that bile salts can emulsify fats and that micelles will get adequate exposure to the brush border, where they are absorbed.

Page 718

12. Damage to epithelial cells means that brush border sucrase may be less effective or absent. In these cases, sucrose digestion would be impaired, so it would be better to use a solution containing glucose because this sugar need not be digested before being absorbed.

Answers to Figure Questions

Page 699

Figure 21-11: (a) The myenteric plexus controls smooth muscle contraction; the submucosal plexus controls smooth muscle contraction and endocrine and exocrine secretions by secretory cells. (b) Stretch receptors respond to stretch, osmoreceptors to osmolarity, and chemoreceptors to products of digestion.

Page 712

Figure 21-26: The vagal input is parasympathetic, which stimulates digestion. Neurotransmitter is ACh, and receptor is muscarinic.

22 Metabolism and Energy Balance

Stylized ribbon model of the leptin protein

BACKGROUND BASICS

Glycogen: **28** Brown fat: **82** Biological work: **95** Mass balance: **133** Metabolism: **105** Beta-oxidation: **115** GLUT transporters: **146** Receptor-mediated endocytosis: **153** Tyrosine kinase receptors: **186** Peptide hormones: **221** Blood pressure control: **533** Renal threshold for glucose: **639** Exocrine pancreas: **696** CCK: **702** GIP: **702** Chylomicrons: **706**

Probably no single abnormality has contributed more to our knowledge of the intermediary metabolism of animals than has the disease known as diabetes.

—Helen R. Downes, *The Chemistry of Living Cells*, 1955

RUNNING PROBLEM

Eating Disorders

Sara Inman and Nicole Baker had been best friends growing up but hadn't seen each other for several semesters. When Sara heard Nicole was in the hospital, she went to visit but wasn't prepared for what she saw. Nicole, who had always been thin, now was so emaciated that Sara hardly recognized her. Nicole had been taken to the emergency room when she fainted in a ballet class. When Dr. Ayani saw Nicole, her concern about her weight was as great as her concern about her broken wrist. At 5′6″, Nicole weighed only 95 pounds (normal healthy range for that height is 118–155 pounds). Dr. Ayani suspected an eating disorder, probably anorexia nervosa, and she ordered blood tests to confirm her suspicion.

725 727 729 732 745 752

Magazine covers at grocery store checkout stands reveal a lot about Americans. Headlines screaming "Lose 10 pounds in a week without dieting" or "CCK: the hormone that makes you thin" vie for attention with glossy photographs of fatty, high-calorie desserts dripping with chocolate and whipped cream. As one magazine article put it, we are a nation obsessed with staying trim and with eating—two mutually exclusive occupations. But what determines when, what, and how much we eat? The factors influencing food intake are an area of intense research because the act of eating is the main point at which our bodies exert control over energy input.

APPETITE AND SATIETY

The control of food intake is a complex process. The digestive system does not regulate energy intake, so we must depend on behavioral mechanisms, such as hunger and satiety [*satis,* enough], to tell us when and how much to eat. Psychological and social aspects of eating, such as parents who say "Clean your plate," complicate the physiological control of food intake. As a result, we still do not fully understand what governs when, what, and how much we eat. What follows is an overview of this increasingly complex and constantly changing field.

Our current model for behavioral regulation of food intake is based on two hypothalamic centers [Fig. 11-3, p. 388]: a **feeding center** that is tonically active and a **satiety center** that stops food intake by inhibiting the feeding center. Efferent signals from these centers cause changes in eating behavior and create sensations of hunger and fullness. Animals whose feeding center is destroyed cease to eat. If the satiety center is destroyed, animals overeat and become obese [*obesus,* plump or fat].

Studies using transgenic and knockout mice show that control of these hypothalamic centers is complex, influenced by cortical and limbic system input as well as by chemical signals. These chemical signals include multiple neuropeptides, "brain-gut" hormones secreted by the GI tract, and chemical signals called **adipocytokines**, which are secreted by adipose tissue.

There are two classic theories for regulation of food intake: the glucostatic theory and the lipostatic theory. The **glucostatic theory** states that glucose metabolism by hypothalamic centers regulates food intake. When blood glucose concentrations decrease, the satiety center is suppressed, and the feeding center is dominant. When glucose metabolism increases, the satiety center inhibits the feeding center.

The **lipostatic theory** of energy balance proposes that a signal from the body's fat stores to the brain modulates eating behavior so that the body maintains a particular weight. If fat stores are increased, eating decreases. In times of starvation, eating increases. Obesity results from disruption of this pathway.

The discovery of **leptin** [*leptos,* thin], a protein hormone synthesized in adipocytes, provided evidence for a negative-feedback signal between adipose tissue and the brain: as fat stores increase, adipose cells secrete more leptin, and food intake decreases. Leptin is synthesized in adipocytes under control of the *obese (ob) gene*. Mice that lack the *ob* gene (and therefore lack leptin) become obese, as do mice with defective leptin receptors. However, these findings did not translate well to humans, as only a small percentage of obese humans are leptin deficient. The majority of them have *elevated* leptin levels. As we are learning, leptin is only part of the story.

Another important signal molecule is **neuropeptide Y** (NPY), a brain neurotransmitter that seems to be the stimulus for food intake. In normal-weight animals, leptin inhibits NPY in a negative feedback pathway (Fig. 22-1 ●). The peptide **ghrelin**, secreted by the stomach, increases hunger when infused into human subjects. Other neuropeptides, hormones, and adipocytokines also influence NPY and the hypothalamic centers (Tbl. 22-1 ●). It is interesting to note that many of these peptides have other functions in addition to control of food intake. Ghrelin promotes release of growth hormone, for instance, and brain peptides called *orexins* appear to play a role in sleep. Our understanding of how all these factors interact is incomplete.

Appetite and eating are also influenced by sensory input through the nervous system. The simple acts of swallowing and chewing food help create a sensation of fullness. The sight, smell, and taste of food can either stimulate or suppress appetite.

In one interesting study researchers tried to determine whether chocolate craving is attributable to psychological factors or to physiological stimuli, such as chemicals in the

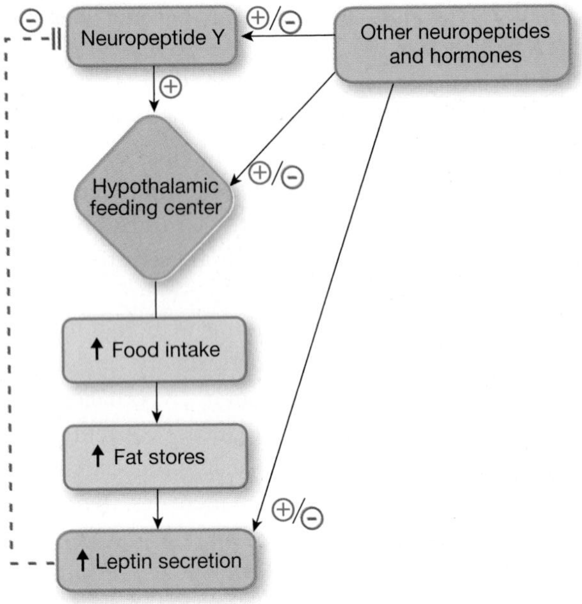

● **FIGURE 22-1** ***Peptide regulation of food intake is complex.***

TABLE 22-1 Some Peptides That Modulate Food Intake

PEPTIDE	SOURCE
Increase food intake	
Ghrelin	Stomach
Neuropeptide Y (NPY)	Hypothalamus
Orexins (also called hypocretins)	Hypothalamus
Decrease food intake	
CCK	Small intestine; neurons
Leptin	Adipose tissue
Obestatin	Stomach
Corticotropin-releasing hormone (CRH)	Hypothalamus
α-Melanocyte-stimulating hormone (α-MSH)	Hypothalamus
CART (cocaine- and amphetamine-regulated transcript)	Hypothalamus
Glucagon-like peptide-1 (GLP-1)	Intestines
PYY_{3-36}	Intestines

BIOTECHNOLOGY

NOVEL APPROACHES FOR DISCOVERING PEPTIDES

In the early days of molecular biology, scientists collected tissues that contained active peptides, isolated and purified the peptides, and then analyzed their amino acid sequence. Now, as we enter the age of proteomics, investigators are using reverse techniques to discover new proteins in the body. One group of researchers, for example, found the hunger-inducing orexin (or hypocretin) peptides by isolating mRNA expressed in a particular region of the hypothalamus. The investigators then used this mRNA to create the amino acid sequence of the prepropeptide. At the same time, a different group of scientists also discovered orexin peptides by working backwards from an "orphan" G protein–coupled receptor [p. 192] to find its peptide ligand. The endogenous hunger hormone ghrelin was discovered by a similar method. Pharmacologists testing synthetic peptides to stimulate the release of growth hormone found that their peptides were binding to a previously unknown receptor, and from that receptor they discovered ghrelin.

chocolate.* Subjects were given either dark chocolate, white chocolate (which contains none of the pharmacological agents of cocoa), cocoa capsules, or placebo capsules. The researchers found that white chocolate was the best substitute for the real thing. The results showed that aroma plays a significant role in satisfying chocolate craving, suggesting that one aspect of chocolate craving is psychological.

Psychological factors, such as eating or not eating when stressed, are known to play a significant role in regulating food intake. The eating disorder *anorexia nervosa* probably has both psychological and physiological components. The concept of *appetite* is closely linked to the psychology of eating, which may explain why dieters who crave smooth, cold ice cream cannot be satisfied by a crunchy carrot stick. A considerable amount of money is directed to research on eating behaviors.

CONCEPT CHECK

1. Explain the roles of the satiety and feeding centers. Where are they located?
2. Studies show that most obese humans have elevated leptin levels in their blood. Based on your understanding of endocrine disorders [p. 235], propose some reasons why leptin is not decreasing food intake in these people.

Answers: p. 755

*"Pharmacological versus sensory factors in the satiation of chocolate craving," *Physiology & Behavior* 56(3):419–422, 1994 Sep.

ENERGY BALANCE

Once food has been digested and absorbed, the body's chemical reactions—known collectively as metabolism—determine what happens to the nutrients in the food. Are they destined to burn off as heat? Become muscle? Or turn into extra pounds that make it difficult to zip up blue jeans? In this section we examine energy balance in the body.

Energy Input Equals Energy Output

The *first law of thermodynamics* [p. 97] states that the total amount of energy in the universe is constant. By extension, this statement means that all energy that goes into a biological system, such as the human body, can be accounted for. In the body, energy is primarily stored in the chemical bonds of molecules, so we can apply the concept of mass balance to energy balance:

$$\text{Body energy} = \text{energy intake} - \text{energy output} \quad (1)$$

Energy intake for humans consists of energy in the nutrients we eat, digest, and absorb. *Energy output* is a combination of work performed and energy returned to the environment as heat:

$$\text{Energy output} = \text{work} + \text{heat} \quad (2)$$

The work in equation 2 takes one of three forms [p. 95]:

1. *Transport work* moves molecules from one side of a membrane to the other. Transport processes bring materials into and out of the body and transfer them between compartments.
2. *Mechanical work* uses intracellular fibers and filaments to create movement. This form of work includes external work, such as movement created by skeletal muscle contraction, and internal work, such as the movement of cytoplasmic vesicles and the pumping of the heart.
3. *Chemical work* is used for growth, maintenance, and storage of information and energy. Chemical work in the body can be subdivided into synthesis and storage. Storage includes both *short-term energy storage* in high-energy phosphate compounds such as ATP and *long-term energy storage* in the chemical bonds of glycogen and fat.

In the human body, at least half the energy released in chemical reactions is lost to the environment as unregulated "waste" heat.

Most of the energy-consuming processes in the body are not under conscious control. Body movements, such as walking and exercise, are the only way people can voluntarily increase energy *output*. People can control their energy *intake*, however, by watching what they eat.

Although energy balance is a very simple concept, it is a difficult one for people to accept. Behavior modifications, such as eating less and exercising more, are among the most frequent instructions health care professionals give to patients. These instructions are also the most difficult to follow, and patient compliance is often low.

RUNNING PROBLEM

Sara and Nicole first met in ballet class at age 11. They were both serious about dance and worked hard to maintain the perfect thin ballet-dancer's body. Both girls occasionally took diet pills or laxatives, and it was almost a contest to see who could eat the least food. Sara was always impressed with Nicole's willpower, but then again, Nicole was a perfectionist. Two years ago, Sara found herself less interested in dance and went away to college. Nicole was accepted into a prestigious ballet company and remained focused on her dancing—and on her body image. Nicole's regimented diet became stricter, and if she felt she'd eaten too much, she would make herself throw up. Her weight kept dropping, but each time she looked in the mirror, she saw a fat girl looking back.

Question 1:

If you measured Nicole's leptin level, what would you expect to find?

Question 2:

Would you expect Nicole to have elevated or depressed levels of neuropeptide Y?

725 727 729 732 745 752

Energy Use Is Reflected by Oxygen Consumption

To compile an energy balance sheet for the human body, we must estimate both the energy content of food (energy intake) and the energy expenditure from heat loss and various types of work (energy output). The most direct way to measure the energy content of food is by **direct calorimetry.** In this procedure, food is burned in an instrument called a *bomb calorimeter,* and the heat released is trapped and measured. The heat released is a direct measure of the energy content of the burned food and is usually measured in kilocalories (kcal). One **kilocalorie** (kcal) is the amount of heat needed to raise the temperature of 1 liter of water by 1°C. A kilocalorie is the same as a *Calorie* (with a capital C).

Although direct calorimetry is a quick way of measuring the total energy content of food, the *metabolic* energy content of food is slightly less because most foods cannot be fully digested and absorbed. The metabolic energy content of proteins and carbohydrates is 4 kcal/g. Fats contain more than twice as much energy—9 kcal/g.

The caloric content of any food can be calculated by multiplying the number of grams of each component by its metabolic energy content. For example, if a bagel contains 2 g of fat, 7 g of protein, and 38 g of carbohydrates, its calorie content is (2 g fat × 9 kcal/g) + (7 g protein × 4 kcal/g) + (38 g carbohydrate × 4 kcal/g) = 198 kcal. In the United States, you can find the energy content for various foods on the *Nutrition Facts* label of food packages.

22

Oxygen Consumption Reflects Metabolic Rate Estimating an individual's energy expenditure, or **metabolic rate**, is more complex than figuring the caloric content of ingested food. Heat released by the body can be measured by enclosing a person in a sealed compartment. The difference between heat produced and the person's caloric intake is the energy used for chemical, mechanical, and transport work. Practically speaking, however, measuring total body heat release is not a very easy way to measure energy use.

Probably the most common method for estimating metabolic rate is to measure a person's **oxygen consumption**, the rate at which the body consumes oxygen as it metabolizes nutrients. Recall from Chapter 4 [p. 113] that metabolism of glucose to trap energy in the bonds of ATP is most efficient in the presence of adequate oxygen: $C_6H_{12}O_6 + O_2 + ADP + P_i \rightarrow CO_2 + H_2O + ATP + \text{heat}$. Studies have shown that oxygen consumption for different foods is relatively constant at a rate of 1 liter of oxygen consumed for each 4.5–5 kcal of energy released from the food being metabolized. The measurement of oxygen consumption is one form of **indirect calorimetry.**

Another method of estimating metabolic rate is to measure carbon dioxide production, either alone or in combination with oxygen consumption. The equation above shows that aerobic metabolism consumes O_2 and produces CO_2. However, the ratio of CO_2 produced to O_2 consumed varies with the composition of the diet. This ratio of CO_2 produced to O_2 consumed is known as the **respiratory quotient (RQ)** or the **respiratory exchange ratio (RER).** RQ varies from a high of 1.0 for a pure carbohydrate diet to 0.8 for pure protein and 0.7 for pure fat. The average American diet has an RQ of about 0.82.

Many Factors Influence Metabolic Rate Whether measured by O_2 consumption or by CO_2 production, metabolic rate can be highly variable from one person to another or from day to day in a single individual. An individual's lowest metabolic rate is considered the **basal metabolic rate (BMR).** In reality, metabolic rate would be lowest when an individual is asleep. However, because measuring the BMR of a sleeping person is difficult, metabolic rate is often measured after a 12-hour fast in a person who is awake but resting (a **resting metabolic rate, RMR**).

Metabolic rate (basal, resting, or with activity) is calculated by multiplying oxygen consumption by the number of kilocalories metabolized per liter of oxygen consumed:

$$\text{Metabolic rate (kcal/day)} = \text{liters of } O_2 \text{ consumed/day} \times \text{kcal/liter of } O_2$$

A mixed diet with an RQ of 0.8 requires one liter of O_2 for each 4.80 kcal metabolized. For a 70-kg male whose resting oxygen consumption is 430 L/day, this means:

$$\text{Resting metabolic rate} = 430 \text{ L } O_2\text{/day} \times 4.80 \text{ kcal/L } O_2 = 2064 \text{ kcal/day}$$

Factors that affect metabolic rate in humans include age, sex, amount of lean muscle mass, activity level, diet, hormones, and genetics.

1. **Age and sex.** Adult males have an average BMR of 1.0 kcal per hour per kilogram of body weight. Adult females have a lower rate than males: 0.9 kcal/hr/kg. The difference arises because women have a higher percentage of adipose tissue and less lean muscle mass. Metabolic rates in both sexes decline with age. Some of this decline is due to decreases in lean muscle mass.
2. **Amount of lean muscle mass.** Muscle has higher oxygen consumption than adipose tissue, even at rest. (Most of the volume of an adipose tissue cell is occupied by metabolically inactive lipid droplets.) This is one reason weight loss advice often includes weight training in addition to aerobic exercise. Weight training adds muscle mass to the body, which increases basal metabolic rate and results in more calories being burned at rest.
3. **Activity level.** Physical activity and muscle contraction increase metabolic rate over the basal rate. Sitting and lying down consume relatively little energy. Competitive rowing and cycling are among the activities that expend the most energy.
4. **Diet.** Resting metabolic rate increases after a meal, a phenomenon termed **diet-induced thermogenesis.** In other words, there is an energetic cost to the digestion and assimilation of food. Diet-induced thermogenesis is related to the type and amount of food ingested. Fats cause relatively little diet-induced thermogenesis, and proteins increase heat production the most. This phenomenon may support the claim of some nutritionists that eating a calorie of fat is different from eating a calorie of protein, although they contain the same amount of energy when measured by direct calorimetry.
5. **Hormones.** Basal metabolic rate is increased by thyroid hormones and by catecholamines (epinephrine and norepinephrine). Some of the peptides that regulate food intake also appear to influence metabolism.
6. **Genetics.** The effect of inherited traits on energy balance can be observed in the variety of normal body types. Some people have very efficient metabolism that converts food energy into energy stored in adipose tissue with little heat loss, while others can eat large amounts of food and never gain weight because their metabolism is less efficient.

Of the factors affecting metabolic rate, a person can voluntarily control only two: energy intake (how much food is eaten) and level of physical activity. If a person's activity includes strength training, which increases lean muscle mass, resting metabolic rate goes up. The addition of lean muscle mass to the body creates additional energy use, which in turn decreases the number of calories that go into storage.

RUNNING PROBLEM

When Nicole's blood test results came back, Dr. Ayani immediately wrote orders to start an intravenous infusion and heart monitoring. The laboratory report showed plasma potassium of 2.5 mEq/L (normal: 3.5–5.0 mEq/L), plasma HCO_3^- of 40 mEq/L (normal: 24–29), and plasma pH of 7.52 (normal: 7.38–7.42). Dr. Ayani admitted Nicole to the hospital for further treatment and evaluation, hoping to convince her that she needed help for her anorexia. Anorexia, meaning "no appetite," can have both physiological and psychological origins.

Question 3:
What is Nicole's K^+ disturbance called? What effect does it have on the resting membrane potential of her cells?

Question 4:
Why does Dr. Ayani want to monitor Nicole's cardiac function?

Question 5:
Based on her clinical values, what is Nicole's acid-base status?

Energy Is Stored in Fat and Glycogen

A person's daily energy requirement, expressed as caloric intake, varies with the needs and activity of the body. For example, during the 2008 Olympics, swimming champion Michael Phelps consumed more than 12,000 kcal per day. On the other hand, a woman engaged in normal activities may require only 2000 kcal/day.

Suppose that our woman's energy requirement could be met by ingesting only glucose. Glucose has an energy content of 4 kcal/g, which means that to get 2000 kcal, she would have to consume 500 g, or 1.1 pounds, of glucose each day. Our bodies cannot absorb crystalline glucose, however, so those 500 g of glucose would have to be dissolved in water. If the glucose were made as an isosmotic 5% solution, the 500 g would have to be dissolved in 10 liters of water—a substantial volume to drink in a day!

Fortunately, we do not usually ingest glucose as our primary fuel. Proteins, complex carbohydrates, and fats also provide energy. The glucose polymer glycogen [p. 28] is a more compact form of energy than an equal number of individual glucose molecules. Glycogen also requires less water for hydration.

For this reason, our cells convert glucose to glycogen for storage. Normally we keep about 100 g of glycogen in the liver and 200 g in skeletal muscles. But even this 300 g of glycogen can provide only enough energy for 10 to 15 hours. The brain alone requires 150 g of glucose per day.

Consequently, the body keeps most of its energy reserves in compact, high-energy fat molecules. One gram of fat has 9 kcal, more than twice the energy content of an equal amount of carbohydrate or protein. This feature makes adipose tissue very efficient at storing large amounts of energy in minimal space. Metabolically, however, the energy in fat is harder to access, and the metabolism of fats is slower than that of carbohydrates.

CONCEPT CHECK

3. Name seven factors that can influence a person's metabolic rate.
4. Why does the body store most of its extra energy in fat and not in glycogen?
5. Complete and balance the following equation for aerobic metabolism of one glucose molecule:

$$C_6H_{12}O_6 + O_2 \rightarrow ? + ?$$

6. What is the RQ for the balanced equation in Concept Check 5?

Answers: p. 755

METABOLISM

Chapter 4 introduced the basic pathways of cellular metabolism. **Metabolism** is the sum of all chemical reactions in the body. The reactions making up these pathways (1) extract energy from nutrients, (2) use energy for work, and (3) store excess energy so that it can be used later. Metabolic pathways that synthesize large molecules from smaller ones are called **anabolic pathways** [*ana-*, completion + *metabole,* change]. Those that break large molecules into smaller ones are called **catabolic** pathways [*cata-*, down or back].

The classification of a pathway is its net result, not what happens in any individual step of the pathway. For example, in the first step of *glycolysis* [p. 107], glucose adds a phosphate to become a larger molecule, glucose 6-phosphate. This single reaction is anabolic, but by the end of glycolysis the initial 6-carbon glucose molecule has been converted to two 3-carbon pyruvate molecules, which makes glycolysis a catabolic pathway.

In the human body, we divide metabolism into two states. The period of time following a meal, when the products of digestion are being absorbed, used, and stored, is called the **fed state** or the **absorptive state.** This is an anabolic state in which the energy of nutrient biomolecules is transferred to high-energy compounds or stored in the chemical bonds of other molecules.

Once nutrients from a recent meal are no longer in the bloodstream and available for use by the tissues, the body enters what is called the **fasted state** or the **postabsorptive state.** As the pool of available nutrients in the blood decreases, the body taps into its stored reserves. The postabsorptive state is catabolic because cells break down large molecules into smaller molecules. The energy released by breaking chemical bonds of large molecules is used to do work.

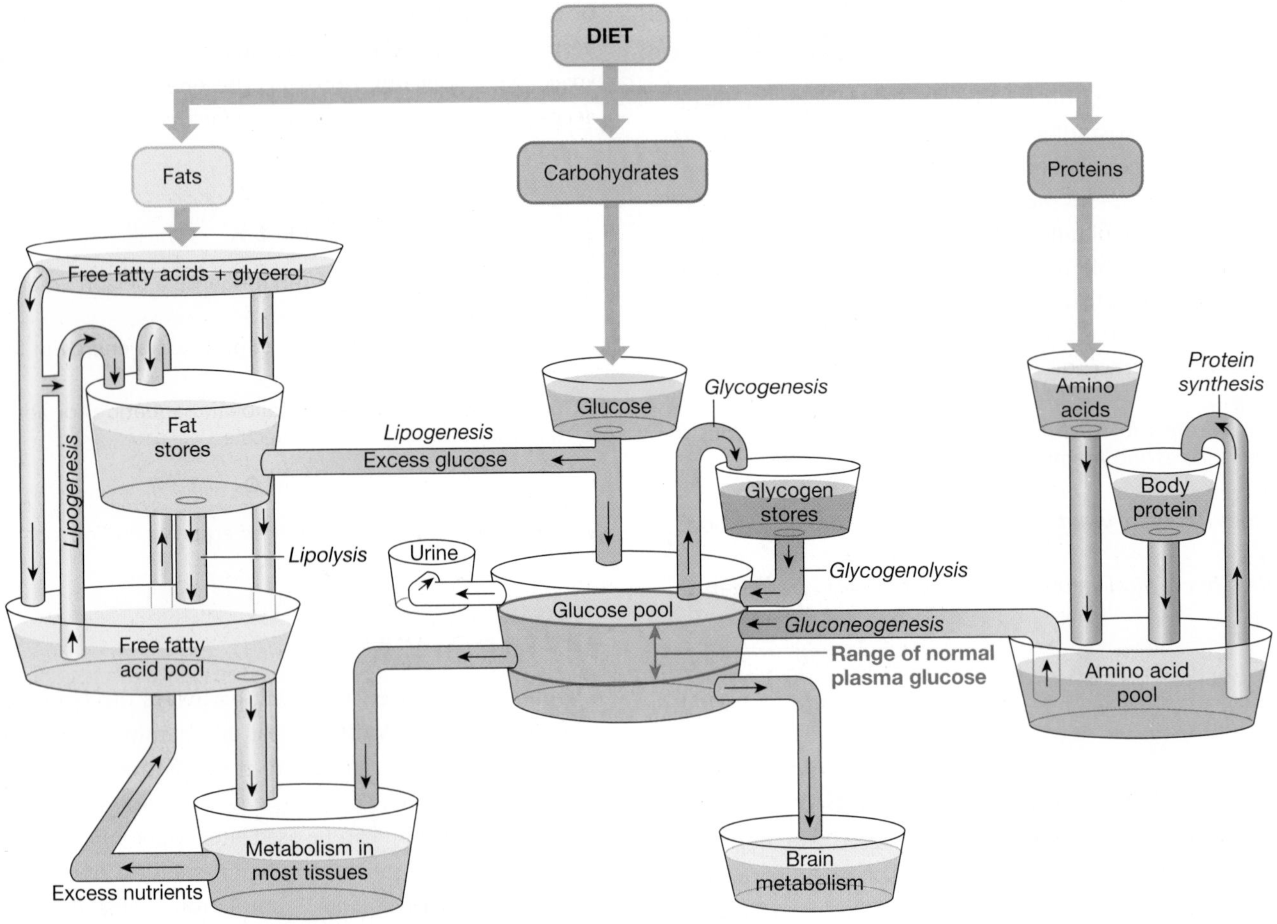

● **FIGURE 22-2** ***Summary of metabolism.*** Adapted from L. L. Langley, *Homeostasis* (New York: Reinhold, 1965).

Ingested Energy May Be Used or Stored

The biomolecules we ingest are destined to meet one of three fates:

1. *Energy.* Biomolecules can be metabolized immediately, with the energy released from broken chemical bonds trapped in ATP, phosphocreatine, and other high-energy compounds. This energy can then be used to do mechanical work.
2. *Synthesis.* Biomolecules entering cells can be used to synthesize basic components needed for growth and maintenance of cells and tissues.
3. *Storage.* If the amount of food ingested exceeds the body's requirements for energy and synthesis, the excess energy goes into storage in the bonds of glycogen and fat. Storage makes energy available for times of fasting.

The fate of an absorbed biomolecule depends on whether it is a carbohydrate, protein, or fat.

Figure 22-2 ● is a schematic diagram that follows these biomolecules from the diet into the three *nutrient pools* of the body: the free fatty acid pool, the glucose pool, and the amino acid pool. **Nutrient pools** are nutrients that are available for immediate use. They are located primarily in the plasma.

Free fatty acids form the primary pool of fats in the blood. They can be used as an energy source by many tissues but are also easily stored as fat (*triglycerides*) in adipose tissue. Carbohydrates are absorbed mostly as glucose. Plasma glucose concentration is the most closely regulated of the three nutrient pools because glucose is the only fuel the brain can metabolize, except in times of starvation. Notice from the locations of the exit "pipes" on the glucose pool in Figure 22-2 that if the pool falls below a certain level, only the brain has access to glucose. This conservation measure ensures that the brain has an adequate energy supply. Just as the circulatory system gives priority to supplying oxygen to the brain, metabolism also gives priority to the brain.

If the body's glucose pool is within the normal range, most tissues use glucose for their energy source. Excess glucose goes into storage as glycogen. The synthesis of glycogen from glucose is known as **glycogenesis.** Glycogen stores are limited, however, and additional excess glucose is converted to fat (**lipogenesis**).

If plasma glucose concentrations decrease, the body breaks down glycogen (**glycogenolysis**) to glucose. By balancing

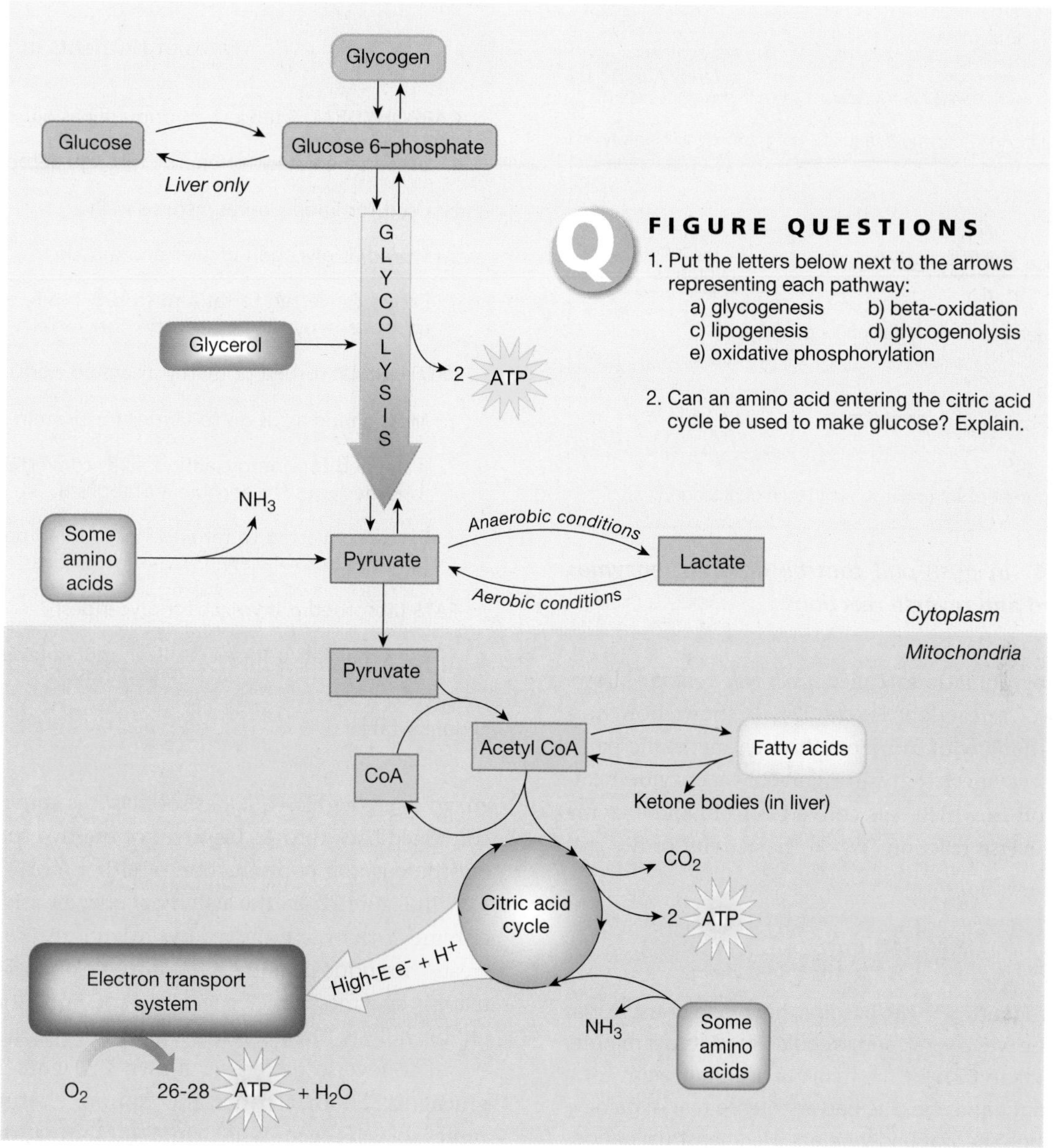

● **FIGURE 22-3** ***Summary of biochemical pathways for energy production.*** ATP yields are for one glucose entering glycolysis.

oxidative metabolism, glycogenesis, glycogenolysis, and lipogenesis, the body maintains plasma glucose concentrations within a narrow range.

If homeostasis fails and plasma glucose exceeds a critical level, as occurs in diabetes mellitus, excess glucose is excreted in the urine. Glucose excretion occurs only when the *renal threshold* for glucose reabsorption is exceeded [p. 139].

The amino acid pool of the body is used primarily for protein synthesis. However, if glucose intake is low, amino acids can be converted into glucose through the pathways known as **gluconeogenesis.** This word literally means "the birth (*genesis*) of new (*neo*) glucose" and refers to the synthesis of glucose from a noncarbohydrate precursor.

Amino acids are the main source for glucose through the gluconeogenesis pathways, but glycerol from triglycerides can also be used. Both gluconeogenesis and glycogenolysis are important backup sources for glucose during periods of fasting.

Hormones Alter Enzyme Activity to Control Metabolism

The most important biochemical pathways for energy production are illustrated in Figure 22-3 ●. This figure does not include all of the metabolic intermediates in each pathway (see Chapter 4 for detailed pathways). Instead, it emphasizes the points at which different pathways intersect, because these intersections are often key points at which metabolism is controlled.

One significant feature of metabolic regulation is the use of different enzymes to catalyze forward and reverse reactions.

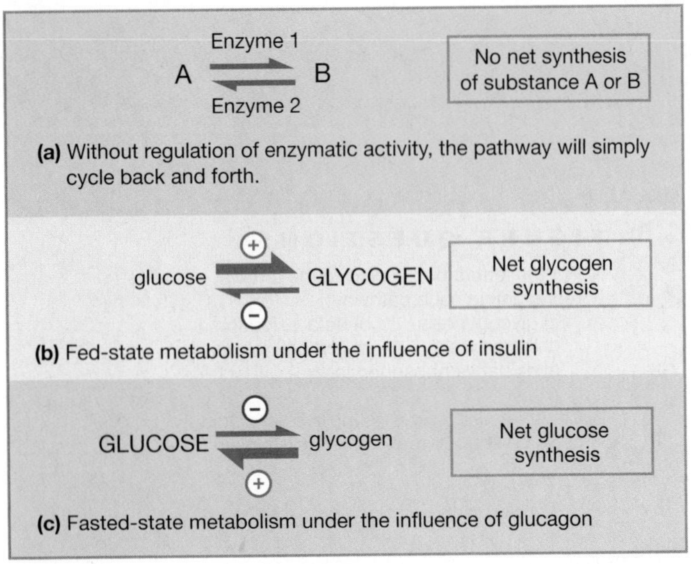

● **FIGURE 22-4** ***In push-pull control, different enzymes catalyze forward and reverse reactions.***

This dual control, sometimes called *push-pull control,* allows close regulation of a reaction. Figure 22-4 ● shows how hormones regulate the flow of nutrients through metabolic pathways by altering enzyme activity. In Figure 22-4a, enzyme 1 catalyzes the reaction in which A is converted to B, and enzyme 2 catalyzes the reverse reaction. When the activity of the two enzymes is roughly equal, as soon as A is converted into B, B is converted back into A. Turnover of the two substrates is rapid, but there is no net production of either A or B.

In Figure 22-4b, the activity of enzyme 1 is enhanced while enzyme 2 catalyzing the reverse reaction is inhibited. The pancreatic hormone insulin exerts this type of dual control by stimulating enzymes for glycogenesis and inhibiting enzymes for glycogenolysis. The net result is glycogen synthesis from glucose.

The reverse pattern is shown in Figure 22-4c, in which **glucagon**, another pancreatic hormone, stimulates the enzymes of glycogenolysis while inhibiting the enzymes for glycogenesis. The net result is glucose synthesis from glycogen.

RUNNING PROBLEM

When Nicole was admitted to the hospital, her blood pressure was 80/50 and her pulse was a weak and irregular 90 beats per minute. She weighed less than 85% of the minimal healthy weight for a woman of her height and age. She had an intense fear of gaining weight, even though she was underweight. Her menstrual periods were irregular, she had just suffered a fractured wrist from a fall that normally shouldn't have caused a fracture, and her hair was thinning. When Dr. Ayani questioned Nicole, she admitted that she had been feeling weak during dance rehearsals and had been having difficulty concentrating at times.

Question 6:
Based on what you learned in Chapters 14 and 15 about heart rate and blood pressure, speculate on why Nicole has low blood pressure with a rapid pulse.

Question 7:
Would you expect Nicole's renin and aldosterone levels to be normal, elevated, or depressed? How might these levels relate to her K^+ disturbance?

Question 8:
Give some possible reasons Nicole had been feeling weak during dance rehearsals.

725 727 729 732 745 752

TABLE 22-2 Fates of Nutrients in the Fed State

CARBOHYDRATES (absorbed primarily as glucose)
1. Used immediately for energy through aerobic pathways*
2. Used for lipoprotein synthesis in liver
3. Stored as glycogen in liver and muscle
4. Excess converted to fat and stored in adipose tissue (glucose → pyruvate → acetyl CoA → fatty acids)
PROTEINS (absorbed primarily as amino acids)
1. Most amino acids go to tissues for protein synthesis*
2. If needed for energy, amino acids converted in liver to intermediates for aerobic metabolism
3. Excess converted to fat and stored in adipose tissue (amino acids → acetyl CoA → fatty acids)
FATS (absorbed primarily as triglycerides)
1. Stored as fats primarily in liver and adipose tissue*

*Primary fate

Anabolic Metabolism Dominates in the Fed State

As we've noted, the fed state is anabolic: absorbed nutrients are being used for energy, synthesis, and storage. Table 22-2 ● summarizes the fates of nutrients in the fed state.

Carbohydrates Provide Energy Glucose absorbed after a meal enters the circulation of the hepatic portal system and is taken directly to the liver, where about 30% of all ingested glucose is metabolized. The remaining 70% continues in the bloodstream for distribution to the brain, muscles, and other organs and tissues.

Glucose moves from interstitial fluid into cells via GLUT transporters [p. 146]. Most glucose absorbed from a meal goes immediately into glycolysis and the citric acid cycle to make ATP. Some glucose is used by the liver for lipoprotein

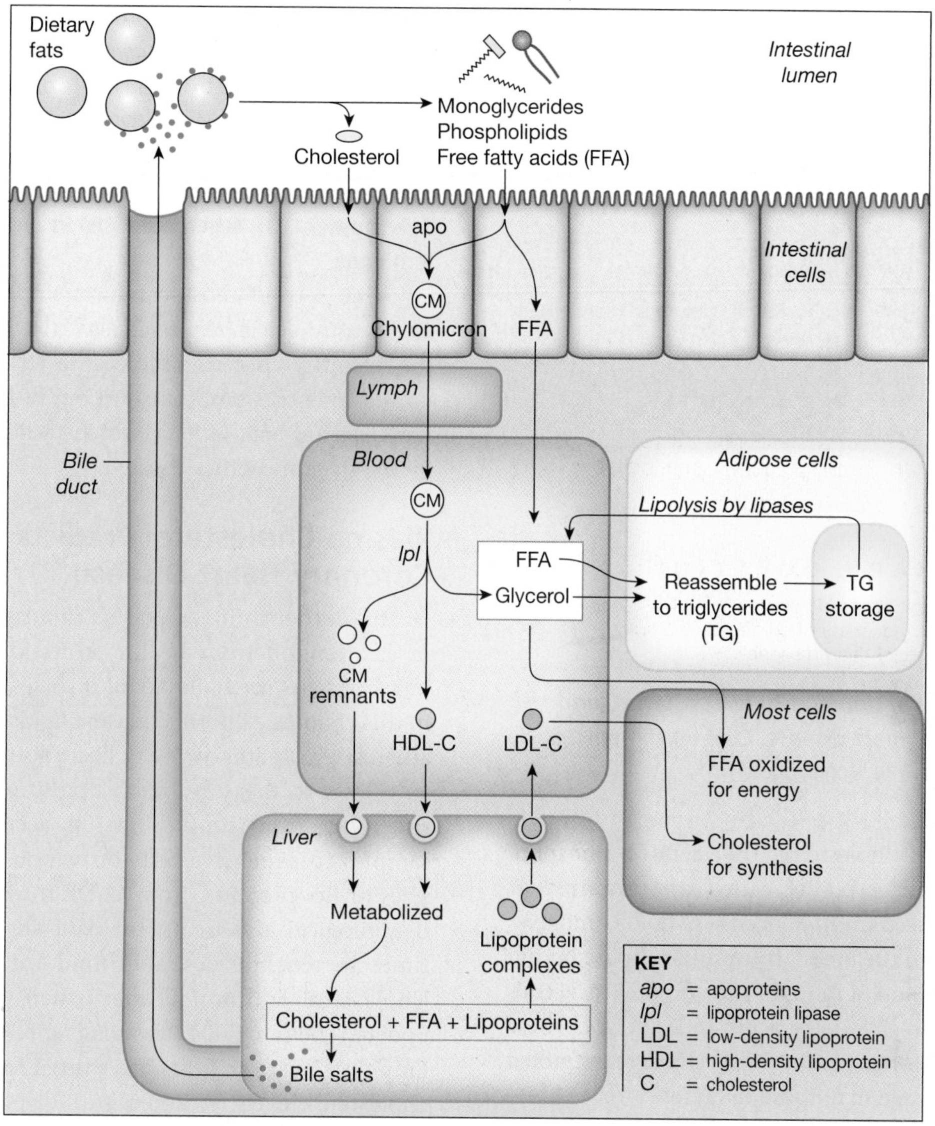

● **FIGURE 22-5** ***Transport and fate of dietary fats***

synthesis. Glucose that is not required for energy and synthesis is stored either as glycogen or fat. The body's ability to store glycogen is limited, so most excess glucose is converted to triglycerides and stored in adipose tissue.

CONCEPT CHECK

7. What is the difference between glycogenesis and gluconeogenesis?
8. Are GLUT transporters active or passive transporters?

Answers: p. 755

Amino Acids Make Proteins Most amino acids absorbed from a meal go to the tissues for protein synthesis. Like glucose, amino acids are taken first to the liver by the hepatic portal system. The liver uses them to synthesize lipoproteins and plasma proteins, such as albumin, clotting factors, and angiotensinogen.

Amino acids not taken up by the liver are used by cells to create structural or functional proteins, such as cytoskeletal elements, enzymes, and hormones. Amino acids are also incorporated into nonprotein molecules, such as amine hormones and neurotransmitters.

If glucose intake is low, amino acids can be used for energy. However, if more protein is ingested than is needed for synthesis and energy expenditures, excess amino acids are converted to fat. Some bodybuilders spend large amounts of money on amino acid supplements advertised to build bigger muscles. But these amino acids do not automatically go into protein synthesis. When amino acid intake exceeds the body's need for protein synthesis, excess amino acids are burned for energy or stored as fat.

Fats Store Energy Most ingested fats are assembled into *chylomicrons* in the intestinal epithelium [p. 706] and enter the venous circulation via the lymphatic vessels (Fig. 22-5 ●).

22

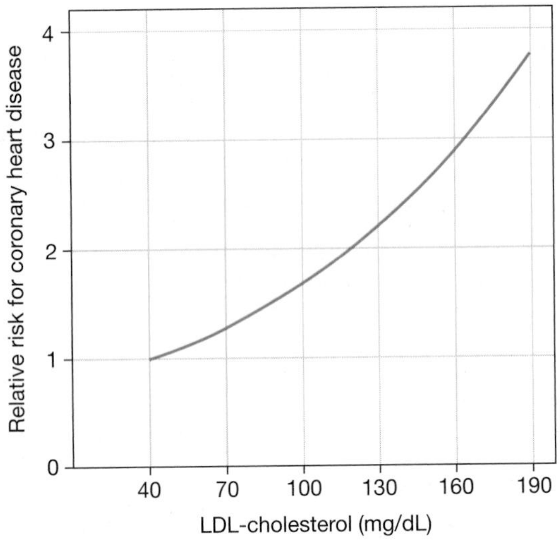

GRAPH QUESTION

Which 30 mg/dL decrease in LDL-C has the biggest effect on decreasing risk of coronary heart disease?

● **FIGURE 22-6** ***The relationship between LDL-C and risk of developing coronary heart disease.*** Data taken from Grundy et al., *Circulation* 110: 227–239, 2004 July 13.

Chylomicrons consist of cholesterol, triglycerides, phospholipids, and lipid-binding proteins called **apoproteins**, or *apolipoproteins* [*apo-*, derived from]. Once these lipid complexes begin to circulate through the blood, **lipoprotein lipase** bound to the capillary endothelium of muscles and adipose tissue converts their triglycerides to free fatty acids and glycerol. These molecules are then used for energy by most cells or reassembled into triglycerides for storage in adipose tissue.

Chylomicron remnants that remain in the circulation are taken up and metabolized by the liver (Fig. 22-5). Cholesterol from the remnants joins the liver's pool of lipids. If cholesterol is in excess, some may be converted to bile salts and excreted in the bile. The remaining cholesterol is added to newly synthesized cholesterol and fatty acids, and packaged into lipoprotein complexes for secretion into the blood.

The lipoprotein complexes that re-enter the blood contain varying amounts of triglycerides, phospholipids, cholesterol, and apoproteins. The more protein a complex contains, the heavier it is, with plasma lipoprotein complexes ranging from *very-low-density lipoprotein* (VLDL) to high-density lipoprotein (HDL). The combination of lipids with proteins makes cholesterol more soluble in plasma, but the complexes are unable to diffuse through cell membranes. Instead, they must be brought into cells by *receptor-mediated endocytosis* [p. 153]. The apoproteins in the complexes are specific for membrane receptors in different tissues.

Most lipoprotein in the blood is *low-density lipoprotein-cholesterol* [p. 537]. LDL-C is sometimes known as the "lethal cholesterol" because elevated concentrations of plasma LDL-C are associated with the development of atherosclerosis [p. 537]. LDL-C complexes contain *apoprotein B* (apoB), which combines with receptors that bring LDL-C into most cells of the body. Several inherited forms of *hypercholesterolemia* (elevated plasma cholesterol levels) have been linked to defective forms of apoB. These abnormal apoproteins may help explain the accelerated development of atherosclerosis in people with hypercholesterolemia.

The second most common lipoprotein in the blood is *high-density lipoprotein-cholesterol* (HDL-C), sometimes called the "healthy cholesterol" because HDL is the lipoprotein involved in cholesterol transport out of the plasma. HDL-C contains *apoprotein A* (apoA), which facilitates cholesterol uptake by the liver and other tissues.

Plasma Cholesterol Predicts Coronary Heart Disease

Of the nutrients in the plasma, lipids and glucose receive the most attention from health professionals. Abnormal glucose metabolism is the hallmark of diabetes mellitus, described later in this chapter. Abnormal plasma lipids are used as predictors of atherosclerosis and coronary heart disease (CHD) [p. 536].

Tests to measure blood lipids and assess cardiovascular risk range from simple but less accurate finger-stick blood samples to expensive tests on venous blood that look at all sizes of lipoproteins, from VLDL through HDL. As more epidemiological and treatment data are gathered, experts continue to redefine desirable lipid values. The U.S. National Cholesterol Education Panel issued guidelines in 2001 and updated them in 2004 (*www.nhlbi.nih.gov/guidelines/cholesterol*). Emphasis over the years has shifted from concern about total cholesterol levels (< 200 mg/dL of plasma is recommended) to the absolute amounts and relative proportions of the various subtypes.

Some studies indicate that elevated LDL-C is the single largest cholesterol risk factor for CHD (Fig. 22-6 ●), because oxidized LDL-C is taken up by macrophages and leads to the development of atherosclerotic plaques [Fig. 15-25, p. 538]. Desirable LDL-C values range from < 160 mg/dL for people at low risk for CHD to < 100 mg/dL for those considered at high risk (including those with diabetes). The HDL-C level in plasma has also been used to predict a person's risk of developing atherosclerosis. Like high LDL-C, low HDL-C (< 40 mg/dL) is associated with a higher risk of developing CHD. More recently, health professionals have started looking at the *non-HDL cholesterol value* (total cholesterol − HDL-C) as perhaps a better indicator of CHD risk.

Lifestyle modifications (improved diet, smoking cessation, and exercise) can be very effective in improving lipid profiles but can be difficult for patients to implement and sustain. All the pharmacological therapies developed to treat elevated cholesterol target some aspect of cholesterol absorption and metabolism, underscoring the principle of mass balance in

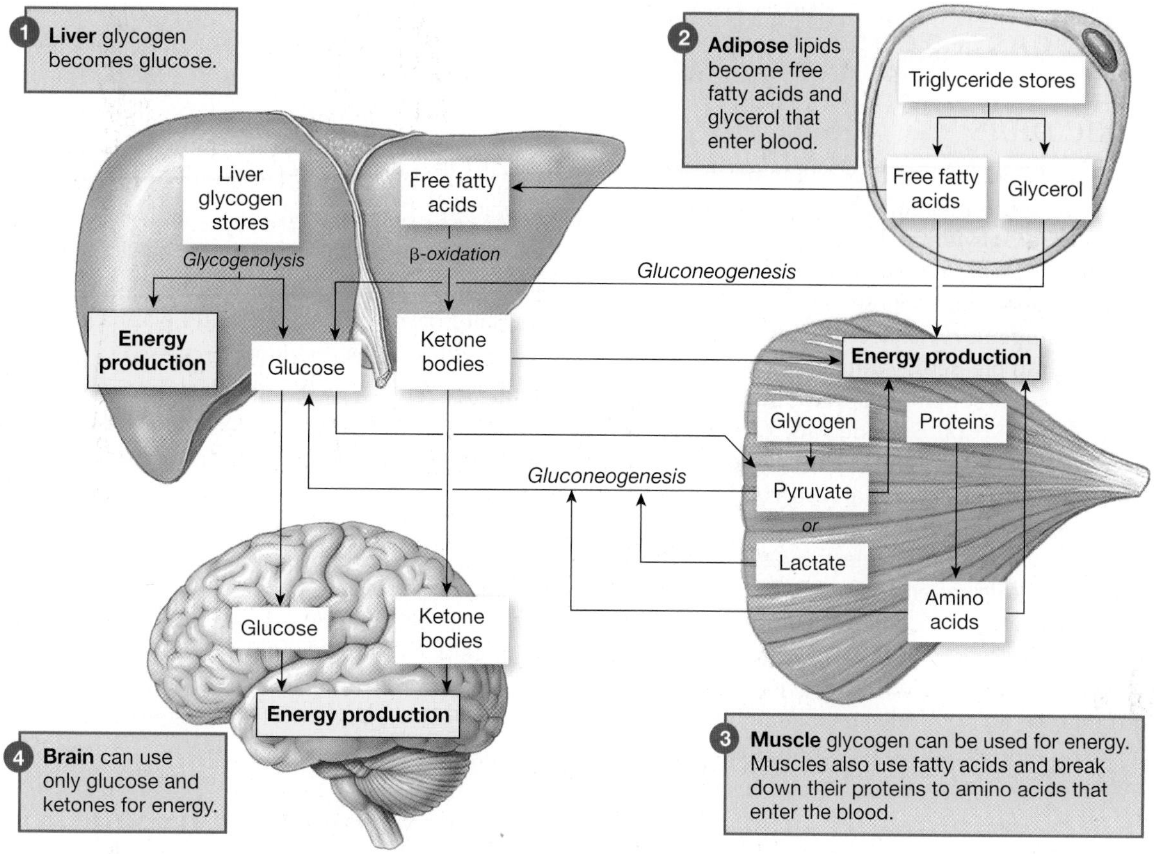

● **FIGURE 22-7** ***Fasted-state metabolism must maintain plasma glucose for the brain.***

cholesterol homeostasis. Decreasing cholesterol uptake or synthesis and increasing cholesterol clearance by metabolism or excretion are effective mechanisms for reducing the amount of cholesterol in the body.

The drugs known as *bile acid sequestrants* [*sequestrare,* to put in the hands of a trustee] bind to bile acids in the intestinal lumen, preventing their reabsorption, and increasing cholesterol excretion [p. 714]. In the absence of recycled bile salts, the liver increases bile acid synthesis from cholesterol, thereby decreasing plasma cholesterol when hepatic LDL receptors import cholesterol.

One of the newest lipid-lowering agents, *ezetimibe,* inhibits intestinal cholesterol transport [p. 706]. Another strategy for reducing intestinal cholesterol uptake is adding plant *sterols* (steroid-alcohols) and *stanols* (saturated sterols [p. 28]) to the diet by eating nuts, seeds, cereals, and vegetable oils. Sterols and stanols displace cholesterol in chylomicrons, which decreases cholesterol absorption.

The remaining lipid-lowering drugs all affect cholesterol metabolism in the liver. The drugs called *statins* inhibit the enzyme *HMG coA reductase,* which mediates cholesterol synthesis in hepatocytes. The *fibrates,* which stimulate a transcription factor called *PPARα* (pronounced *p-par-alpha*), and *niacin* (vitamin B_3, nicotinic acid) decrease LDL-C and increase HDL-C by mechanisms that are not well understood. All the drugs that alter hepatic cholesterol metabolism have a low incidence of liver toxicity and other significant side effects.

CONCEPT CHECK

9. Predict the predominant side effects of taking bile acid sequestrants and ezetimibe. Answers: p. 755

Catabolic Metabolism Dominates in the Fasted State

Once all nutrients from a meal have been digested, absorbed, and distributed to various cells, plasma concentrations of glucose begin to fall. This is the signal for the body to shift from fed (absorptive) state to fasted (postabsorptive) state metabolism. The goal of fasted-state metabolism is to maintain plasma glucose concentrations within an acceptable range so that the brain and neurons have adequate fuel.

The liver is the primary source of glucose production during the fasted state (Fig. 22-7 ● ①). Liver glycogen can provide enough glucose through glycogenolysis to meet 4–5 hours of the body's energy needs.

In the fasted state, adipose tissue breaks down its stores of triglycerides into fatty acids and glycerol (Fig. 22-7 ②).

CLINICAL FOCUS

KETOGENIC DIETS

Some people intentionally restrict or eliminate their intake of carbohydrates in an effort to lose weight. Diets very low in carbohydrate and high in fat and protein shift metabolism to β-oxidation of fats and production of ketone bodies. These diets are therefore known as *ketogenic diets*. People who go on these diets are often pleased by initial rapid weight loss, but it is due to glycogen breakdown and water loss, not body fat reduction. Sticking with ketogenic diets decreases caloric intake and eventually results in loss of body fat, but any diet that restricts calories can do the same. Among the risks associated with ketogenic diets are dehydration, electrolyte loss, inadequate intake of calcium and vitamins, gout, and kidney problems. The only recommended use of ketogenic diets is for children under 10 who have epilepsy that is not responding fully to drug therapy. For reasons that we do not understand, maintaining a state of ketosis in these children decreases the incidence of seizures.

Glycerol goes to the liver and can be converted to glucose. The fatty acids are released into the blood, from which they can be taken up by many tissues and used for energy production. Once inside cells, the long fatty acid carbon chains are chopped into two-carbon acyl units through the process of *β-oxidation* [p. 115]. In most tissues, these acyl units feed into the citric acid cycle through acetyl CoA and provide a substrate for ATP synthesis through oxidative phosphorylation.

If there is excessive fatty acid breakdown, the liver uses β-oxidation to create acidic **ketone bodies** (often called simply *ketones* in physiology and medicine). Ketone bodies enter the blood, creating a state of *ketosis*. The breath of people in ketosis has a fruity odor caused by acetone, a volatile ketone whose odor you might recognize from nail polish remover.

Normally neurons depend on glucose for energy but in cases of prolonged starvation, ketone bodies become a significant source of energy for the brain (Fig. 22-7 ④). Ketone bodies can be converted to acetyl CoA, which then enters the citric acid cycle. Unfortunately, the ketone bodies *acetoacetic acid* and *β-hydroxybutyric acid* are also moderately strong acids, and excessive ketone production leads to a state of *ketoacidosis* [p. 679].

In the fasted state, skeletal muscle glycogen can be metabolized to glucose, but not directly (Fig. 22-7 ③). Muscle cells, like most other cells, lack the enzyme that makes glucose from glucose 6-phosphate. Consequently, glucose 6-phosphate produced from glycogenolysis in skeletal muscle is metabolized to either pyruvate (aerobic conditions) or lactate (anaerobic conditions). Pyruvate and lactate are then transported to the liver, which uses them to make glucose via gluconeogenesis.

Additional glucose or ATP can also be made from amino acids, particularly those in muscle proteins (Fig. 22-7 ③). Enzymes remove amino groups from the amino acids (*deamination*) [p. 114] and convert the amino groups to urea, which is excreted. Some deaminated amino acids become citric acid cycle intermediates, enter the cycle, and produce ATP (see Fig. 22-3). This alternative ATP source spares plasma glucose for use by the brain. Other amino acids are processed to pyruvate, which goes to the liver and is made into glucose, as previously described.

With this summary of metabolic pathways as background, we now turn to the endocrine and neural regulation of metabolism.

CONCEPT CHECK

10. When amino acids are used for energy, which pathways in Figure 22-3 do they follow?
11. Cholesterol is soluble in lipids, so why does plasma cholesterol need the help of a membrane transporter to enter cells?

Answers: p. 755

HOMEOSTATIC CONTROL OF METABOLISM

The endocrine system has primary responsibility for metabolic regulation, although the nervous system does have some influence, particularly in terms of governing food intake. Hour-to-hour regulation depends primarily on the ratio of insulin to glucagon, two hormones secreted by endocrine cells of the pancreas. Both hormones have short half-lives and must be continuously secreted if they are to have a sustained effect.

The Pancreas Secretes Insulin and Glucagon

The endocrine cells of the pancreas make up less than 2% of the organ's total mass. Most pancreatic tissue is devoted to the production and exocrine secretion of digestive enzymes and bicarbonate [Fig. 21-7, p. 696]. In 1869, the German anatomist Paul Langerhans described small clusters of cells—now known as the **islets of Langerhans**—scattered throughout the body of the pancreas (Fig. 22-8b ●). The islets contain four distinct cell types, each associated with secretion of one or more peptide hormones.

Nearly three-quarters of the islet cells are **beta cells**, which produce *insulin* and a peptide called *amylin*. Another 20% are **alpha cells**, which secrete **glucagon.** Most of the remaining cells are *somatostatin*-secreting **D cells.** A few rare cells called *PP cells* (or *F cells*) produce *pancreatic polypeptide*.

Like all endocrine glands, the islets are closely associated with capillaries into which the hormones are released. Both sympathetic and parasympathetic neurons terminate on the

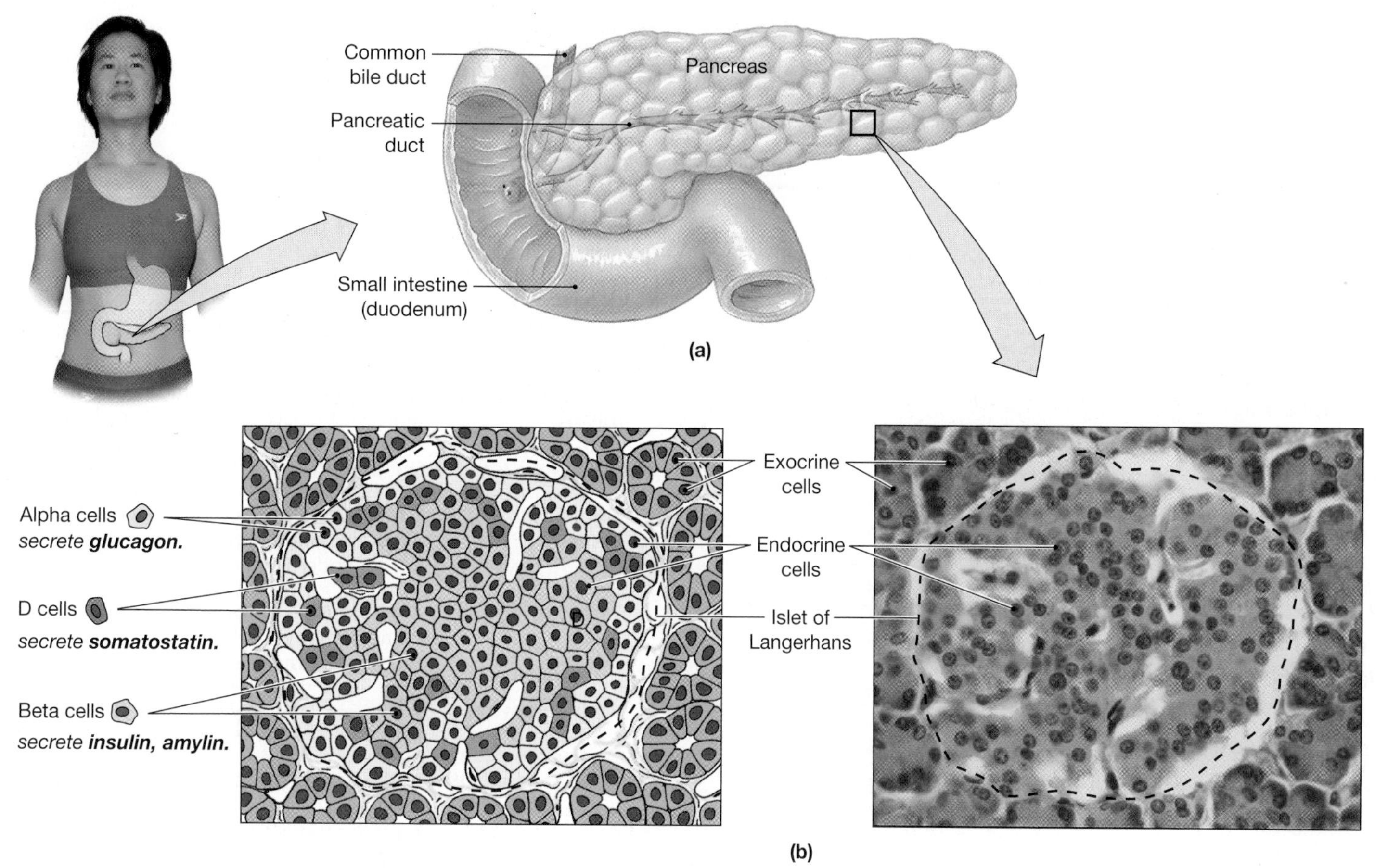

● **FIGURE 22-8** ***Anatomy of the pancreas.*** **(a)** Gross anatomy. **(b)** Cells of the islets of Langerhans, which constitute the endocrine pancreas.

islets, providing a means by which the nervous system can influence metabolism.

The Insulin-to-Glucagon Ratio Regulates Metabolism

As noted earlier, insulin and glucagon act in antagonistic fashion to keep plasma glucose concentrations within an acceptable range. Both hormones are present in the blood most of the time. The ratio of the two hormones determines which hormone dominates.

In the fed state, when the body is absorbing nutrients, insulin dominates, and the body undergoes net anabolism (Fig. 22-9a ●). Ingested glucose is used for energy production, and excess glucose is stored as glycogen or fat. Amino acids go primarily to protein synthesis.

In the fasted state, metabolic regulation prevents low plasma glucose concentrations (*hypoglycemia*). When glucagon predominates, the liver uses glycogen and nonglucose intermediates to synthesize glucose for release into the blood (Fig. 22-9b).

Figure 22-10 ● shows plasma glucagon, glucose, and insulin concentrations over the course of a day. In a normal person, fasting plasma glucose is maintained around 90 mg/dL of plasma. After absorption of nutrients from a meal, plasma

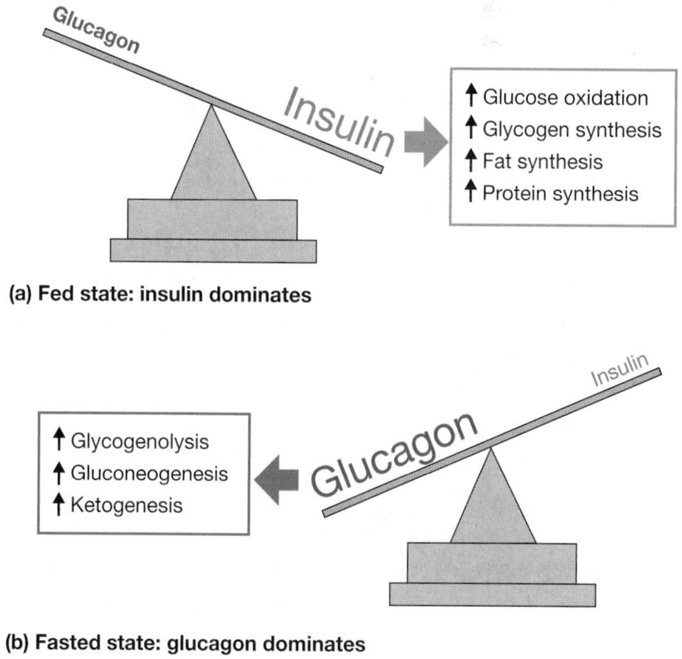

● **FIGURE 22-9** ***Metabolism is controlled by the insulin: glucagon ratio.***

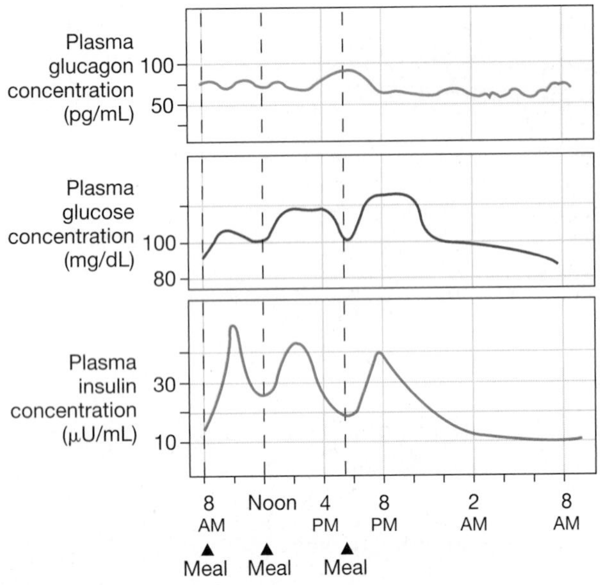

● **FIGURE 22-10** ***Glucose, glucagon, and insulin levels over a 24-hour period.*** One international unit (U) of insulin will decrease blood glucose by 30–50 mg/dL.

TABLE 22-3 Insulin

Cell of origin	Beta cells of pancreas
Chemical nature	51-amino acid peptide
Biosynthesis	Typical peptide
Transport in the circulation	Dissolved in plasma
Half-life	5 minutes
Factors affecting release	Plasma [glucose] > 100 mg/dL; ↑ blood amino acids; GLP-1 (feedforward reflex). Parasympathetic activity amplifies. Sympathetic activity inhibits.
Target cells or tissues	Liver, muscle, and adipose tissue primarily; brain, kidney, and intestine not insulin dependent
Target receptor	Membrane receptor with tyrosine kinase activity; pathway with insulin-receptor substrates
Whole body or tissue action	↓ Plasma [glucose] by ↑ transport into cells or ↑ metabolic use of glucose
Action at cellular level	↑ Glycogen synthesis; ↑ aerobic metabolism of glucose; ↑ protein and triglyceride synthesis
Action at molecular level	Inserts GLUT transporters in muscle and adipose cells; alters enzyme activity. Complex signal transduction pathway involved.
Feedback regulation	↓ Plasma [glucose] shuts off insulin release.
Other information	Growth hormone and cortisol are antagonistic.

glucose rises. The increase in glucose stimulates insulin release, which in turn promotes glucose transfer into cells. As a result, plasma glucose concentrations fall back toward the fasting level shortly after each meal.

During an overnight fast, plasma glucose concentrations fall to their lowest values, and insulin secretion also decreases. Glucagon secretion remains relatively steady during the 24-hour period, supporting the theory that it is the ratio of insulin to glucagon that determines the direction of metabolism.

Insulin Is the Dominant Hormone of the Fed State

Insulin is a typical peptide hormone (Tbl. 22-3 ●). It is synthesized as an inactive prohormone and activated prior to secretion [Fig. 7-4c, p. 223]. Glucose is an important stimulus for insulin secretion, but the following factors may stimulate, amplify, or inhibit secretion:

1. **Increased plasma glucose.** A major stimulus for insulin release is plasma glucose concentrations greater than 100 mg/dL. Glucose absorbed from the small intestine reaches pancreatic beta cells, where it is taken up by GLUT2 transporters [Fig. 5-35b, p. 170]. With more glucose available as substrate, ATP production increases and ATP-gated K^+ channels close. The cell depolarizes, voltage-gated Ca^{2+} channels open, and Ca^{2+} entry initiates exocytosis of insulin.
2. **Increased plasma amino acids.** Increased plasma amino acid concentrations following a meal also trigger insulin secretion.
3. **Feedforward effects of GI hormones.** Recently it has been shown that as much as 50% of insulin secretion is stimulated by the hormone *glucagon-like peptide-1 (GLP-1)*. GLP-1 and GIP (gastric inhibitory peptide) are *incretin* hormones produced by cells of the ileum and jejunum in response to nutrient ingestion. The incretins travel through the circulation to pancreatic beta cells and may reach them even before the first glucose is absorbed. The anticipatory release of insulin in response to these hormones prevents a sudden surge in plasma glucose concentrations when the meal is absorbed. Other GI hormones, such as CCK and gastrin, amplify insulin secretion.
4. **Parasympathetic activity.** Parasympathetic activity to the GI tract and pancreas increases during and following a meal. Parasympathetic input to beta cells stimulates insulin secretion.
5. **Sympathetic activity.** Insulin secretion is inhibited by sympathetic neurons. In times of stress, sympathetic input

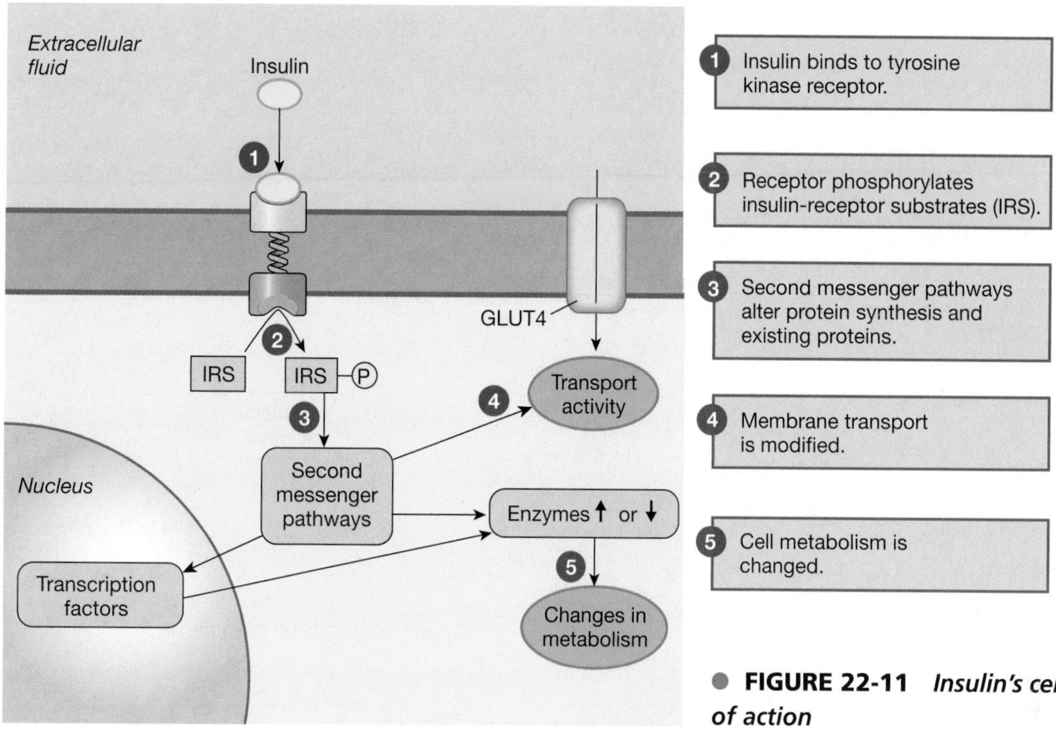
Extracellular fluid
Insulin
1
2
IRS
IRS -P
3
GLUT4
4
Transport activity
Nucleus
Second messenger pathways
Enzymes ↑ or ↓
5
Transcription factors
Changes in metabolism
1 Insulin binds to tyrosine kinase receptor.
2 Receptor phosphorylates insulin-receptor substrates (IRS).
3 Second messenger pathways alter protein synthesis and existing proteins.
4 Membrane transport is modified.
5 Cell metabolism is changed.

● **FIGURE 22-11** ***Insulin's cellular mechanism of action***

to the endocrine pancreas increases, reinforced by catecholamine release from the adrenal medulla (Tbl. 22-4 ●). Epinephrine and norepinephrine inhibit insulin secretion and switch metabolism to gluconeogenesis to provide extra fuel for the nervous system and skeletal muscles.

Insulin Promotes Anabolism

Like other peptide hormones, insulin combines with a membrane receptor on its target cells (Fig. 22-11 ●). The insulin receptor has *tyrosine kinase* activity, which initiates complex intracellular cascades whose details are still not completely understood. The activated insulin receptor phosphorylates proteins that include a group known as the **insulin-receptor substrates** (IRS). These proteins act through complicated pathways to influence transport and cellular metabolism. The enzymes that regulate metabolic pathways may be inhibited or activated directly, or their synthesis may be influenced indirectly through transcription factors.

The primary target tissues for insulin are the liver, adipose tissue, and skeletal muscles. The usual target cell response is increased glucose metabolism. In some target tissues, insulin also regulates the GLUT transporters. Other tissues, including the brain and transporting epithelia of the kidney and intestine, do not require insulin for glucose uptake and metabolism.

Insulin lowers plasma glucose in the following four ways:

1. **Insulin increases glucose transport into most, but not all, insulin-sensitive cells.** Adipose tissue and resting skeletal muscle require insulin for glucose uptake. Without insulin, their GLUT4 transporters are withdrawn

TABLE 22-4	Adrenal Catecholamines (Epinephrine and Norepinephrine)
Origin	Adrenal medulla (90% epinephrine and 10% norepinephrine)
Chemical nature	Amines made from tyrosine
Biosynthesis	Typical peptide
Transport in the circulation	Some bound to sulfate
Half-life	2 minutes
Factors affecting release	Primarily fight-or-flight reaction through CNS and autonomic nervous system; hypoglycemia
Target cells or tissues	Mainly neurons, pancreatic endocrine cells, heart, blood vessels, adipose tissue
Target receptor	G protein–coupled receptors; α and β subtypes
Second messenger	cAMP (α_2 and all β receptors); IP_3 (α_1 receptors)
Whole body or tissue action	↑ Plasma [glucose]; activate fight-or-flight and stress reactions; ↑ glucagon and ↓ insulin secretion
Onset and duration of action	Rapid and brief

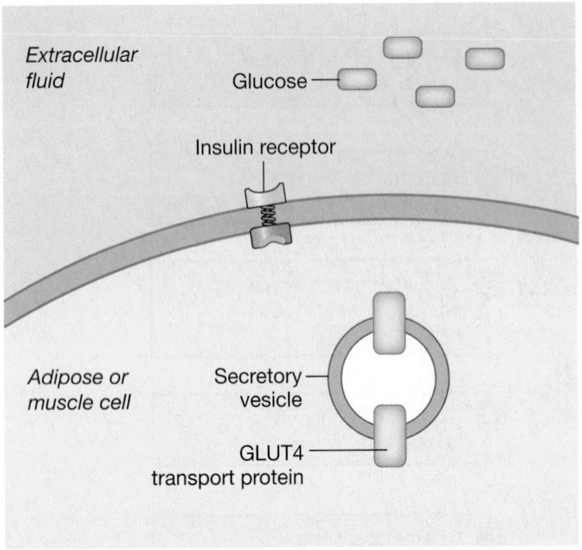

(a) In the absence of insulin, glucose cannot enter the cell.

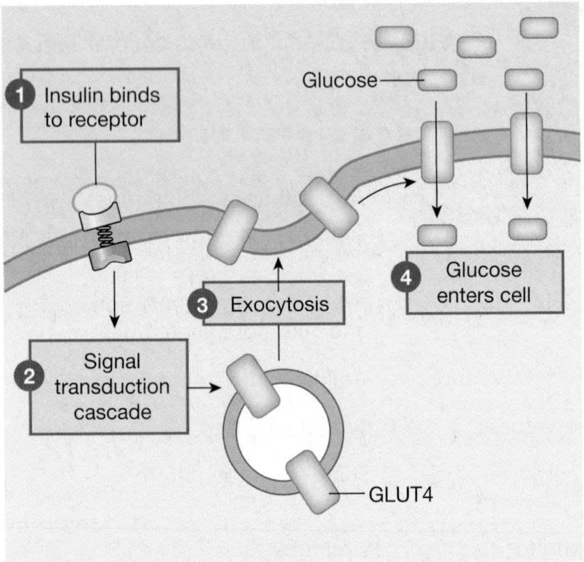

(b) Insulin signals the cell to insert GLUT4 transporters into the membrane, allowing glucose to enter cell.

● **FIGURE 22-12** ***Insulin enables glucose uptake by adipose tissue and resting skeletal muscle.***

from the membrane and stored in cytoplasmic vesicles (Fig. 22-12a ●). When insulin binds to the receptor and activates it, the resulting signal transduction cascade causes the vesicles to move to the cell membrane and insert the GLUT4 transporters by exocytosis (Fig. 22-12b). The cells then take up glucose from the interstitial fluid by facilitated diffusion.

Curiously, *exercising* skeletal muscle is not dependent on insulin activity for its glucose uptake. When muscles contract, GLUT4 transporters are inserted into the membrane even in the absence of insulin, and glucose uptake increases. The intracellular signal for this is unclear but appears to involve Ca^{2+} and decreased inorganic phosphate (P_i).

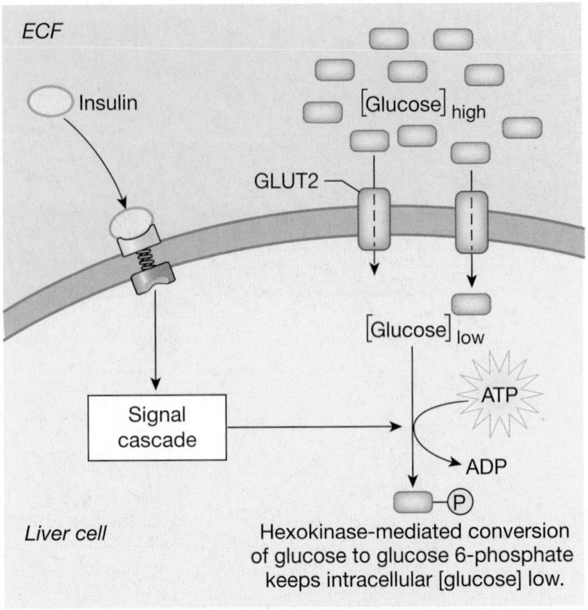

(a) Hepatocyte. In fed state, liver cell takes up glucose.

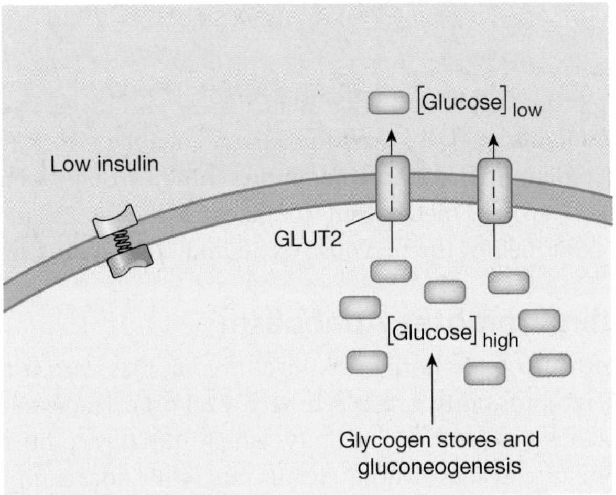

(b) Hepatocyte. In fasted state, liver cell makes glucose and transports it out into the blood.

● **FIGURE 22-13** ***Insulin indirectly alters glucose transport in hepatocytes.***

Glucose transport into liver cells (*hepatocytes*) is not *directly* insulin dependent but is influenced by the presence or absence of insulin. Hepatocytes have GLUT2 transporters that are always present in the cell membrane. In the fed state (Fig. 22-13a ●), insulin activates *hexokinase,* the enzyme that phosphorylates glucose to glucose 6-phosphate [p. 107]. This phosphorylation reaction keeps free intracellular glucose concentrations low relative to plasma concentrations, so that glucose continuously diffuses into the hepatocyte on the GLUT2 transporter.

In the fasted state, when insulin levels are low, glucose moves *out* of the liver and into the blood to help maintain glucose homeostasis. In this process (Fig. 22-13b), hepatocytes are converting glycogen stores and amino acids

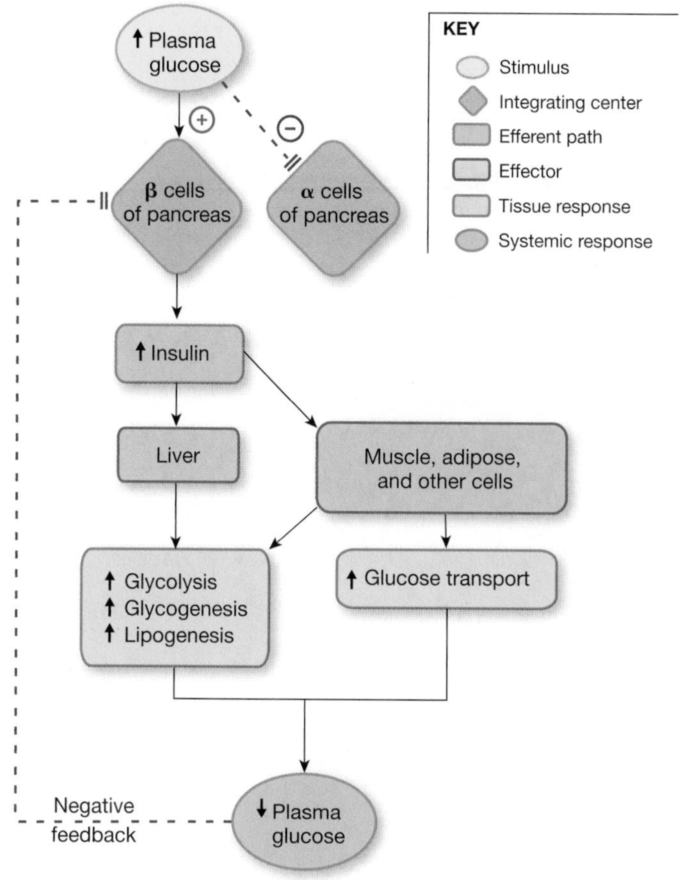

● **FIGURE 22-14** ***Insulin promotes glucose uptake and metabolism by cells.***

TABLE 22-5	Glucagon
Cell of origin	Alpha cells of pancreas
Chemical nature	29-amino acid peptide
Biosynthesis	Typical peptide
Transport in the circulation	Dissolved in plasma
Half-life	4–6 minutes
Factors affecting release	Enhanced secretion when plasma [glucose] < 65-70 mg/dL; ↑ blood amino acids
Target cells or tissues	Liver primarily
Target receptor/ second messenger	G protein–coupled receptor linked to cAMP
Whole body or tissue action	↑ Plasma [glucose] by glycogenolysis and gluconeogenesis; ↑ lipolysis leads to ketogenesis in liver
Action at molecular level	Alters existing enzymes and stimulates synthesis of new enzymes
Feedback regulation	↑ Plasma [glucose] shuts off glucagon secretion
Other information	Member of secretin family (along with VIP, GIP, and GLP-1)

to glucose. Newly formed glucose moves down its concentration gradient out of the cell using the same GLUT2 transporters operating in the reverse direction. If the GLUT transporters were pulled from the membrane during the fasted state, as they are in muscle and adipose tissue, glucose would have no way to leave the hepatocytes.

2. **Insulin enhances cellular utilization and storage of glucose** (Fig. 22-14 ●). Insulin activates enzymes for glucose utilization (*glycolysis*), and for glycogen and fat synthesis (*glycogenesis* and *lipogenesis*). Insulin simultaneously inhibits enzymes for glycogen breakdown (*glycogenolysis*), glucose synthesis (*gluconeogenesis*), and fat breakdown (*lipolysis*) to ensure that metabolism moves in the anabolic direction. If more glucose has been ingested than is needed for energy and synthesis, the excess is made into glycogen or fatty acids.
3. **Insulin enhances utilization of amino acids.** Insulin activates enzymes for protein synthesis and inhibits enzymes that promote protein breakdown. If a meal includes protein, amino acids in the ingested food are used for protein synthesis by both the liver and muscle. Excess amino acids are converted to fatty acids.
4. **Insulin promotes fat synthesis.** Insulin inhibits β-oxidation of fatty acids and promotes conversion of excess glucose or amino acids into triglycerides (*lipogenesis*). Excess triglyceride is stored as lipid droplets in adipose tissue.

In summary, insulin is an anabolic hormone because it promotes glycogen, protein, and fat synthesis. When insulin is absent or deficient, cells go into catabolic metabolism.

CONCEPT CHECK

12. What are the primary target tissues for insulin?
13. Why are glucose metabolism and glucose transport independent of insulin in renal and intestinal epithelium and in neurons?
14. What is the advantage to the body of inhibiting insulin release during a sympathetically mediated fight-or-flight response?

Answers: p. 755

Glucagon Is Dominant in the Fasted State

Glucagon, secreted by pancreatic alpha cells, is generally antagonistic to insulin in its effects on metabolism (Tbl. 22-5 ●). When plasma glucose concentrations decline after a meal, insulin secretion slows, and the effects of glucagon on tissue metabolism take on greater significance. As noted earlier, it is the ratio of insulin to glucagon that determines the direction of metabolism rather than an absolute amount of either hormone.

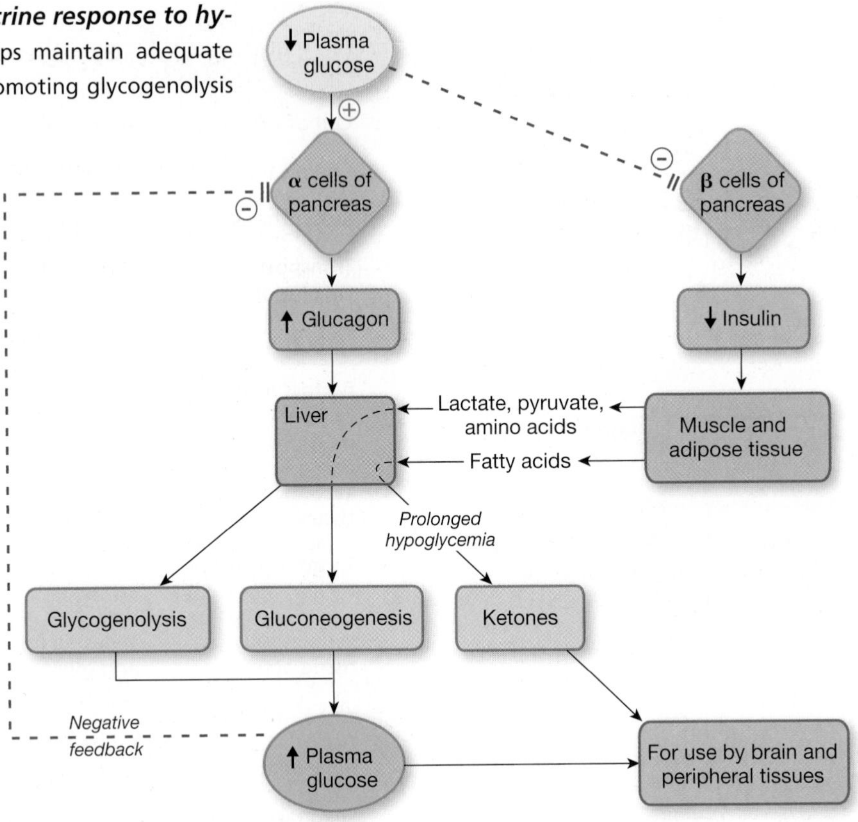

● **FIGURE 22-15** ***Endocrine response to hypoglycemia.*** Glucagon helps maintain adequate plasma glucose levels by promoting glycogenolysis and gluconeogenesis.

The function of glucagon action is preventing hypoglycemia, and the primary stimulus for glucagon release is plasma glucose concentration. When plasma glucose concentrations fall below 100 mg/dL, glucagon secretion rises dramatically. At glucose concentrations above 100 mg/dL, when insulin is being secreted, glucagon secretion is inhibited and remains at a low but relatively constant level (see Fig. 22-10). The strong relationship between insulin secretion and glucagon inhibition has led to speculation that alpha cells are regulated by some factor linked to insulin rather than by plasma glucose concentrations directly.

The liver is glucagon's primary target tissue (Fig. 22-15 ●). Glucagon stimulates glycogenolysis and gluconeogenesis to increase glucose output. It is estimated that during an overnight fast, 75% of the glucose produced by the liver comes from glycogen stores, and the remaining 25% from gluconeogenesis.

Glucagon release is also stimulated by plasma amino acids. This pathway prevents hypoglycemia after ingestion of a pure protein meal. Let's see how hypoglycemia might occur in the absence of glucagon.

If a meal contains protein but no carbohydrate, amino acids absorbed from the food cause insulin secretion. Even though no glucose has been absorbed, insulin-stimulated glucose uptake increases, and plasma glucose concentrations fall. Unless something counteracts this process, the brain's fuel supply is threatened by hypoglycemia.

Co-secretion of glucagon in this situation prevents hypoglycemia by stimulating hepatic glucose output. As a result, although only amino acids were ingested, both glucose and amino acids are made available to peripheral tissues.

CONCEPT CHECK

15. How are glycogenolysis and gluconeogenesis similar and how are they different? Answers: p. 755

Diabetes Mellitus Is a Family of Diseases

The most common pathology of the pancreatic endocrine system is the family of metabolic disorders known as **diabetes mellitus.** Diabetes is characterized by abnormally elevated plasma glucose concentrations (*hyperglycemia*) resulting from inadequate insulin secretion, abnormal target cell responsiveness [p. 235], or both. Chronic hyperglycemia and its associated metabolic abnormalities cause the many complications of diabetes, including damage to blood vessels, eyes, kidneys, and the nervous system.

Diabetes is reaching epidemic proportions in the United States. In 2007 the U.S. Centers for Disease Control estimated that 8% of the population had diabetes and that nearly another 20% had pre-diabetes, a condition that will likely become diabetes if those people do not alter their eating and exercise habits. Experts attribute the cause of the epidemic to our sedentary lifestyle, ample food, and overweight and obesity, which affect more than 50% of the population.

Diabetes has been known to affect humans since ancient times, and written accounts of the disorder highlight the calamitous consequences of insulin deficiency. Aretaeus the Cappadocian (C.E. 81–138) wrote of the "wonderful"* nature of this disease that consists of the "melting down of the flesh ... into urine," accompanied by terrible thirst that cannot be quenched. The copious production of glucose-laden urine gave the disease its name. *Diabetes* refers to the flow of fluid through a siphon, and *mellitus* comes from the word for honey. In the Middle Ages, diabetes was known as "the pissing evil."

The severe type of diabetes described by Aretaeus is **type 1 diabetes mellitus.** It is a condition of insulin deficiency resulting from beta cell destruction. Type 1 diabetes is most commonly an *autoimmune disease* in which the body fails to recognize the beta cells as "self" and destroys them with antibodies and white blood cells.

The other major variant of diabetes mellitus is **type 2 diabetes.** This type of diabetes is also known as *insulin-resistant diabetes* because in most patients, insulin levels in the blood are normal or even elevated initially. Later in the disease process, many type 2 diabetics become insulin deficient and require insulin injections. Type 2 diabetes is actually a whole family of diseases with a variety of causes.

Type 1 Diabetics Are Prone to Ketoacidosis

Type 1 diabetes is a complex disorder whose onset in genetically susceptible individuals is sometimes preceded by a viral infection. Many type 1 diabetics develop their disease in childhood, giving rise to the old name *juvenile-onset diabetes*. About 10% of all diabetics have type 1 diabetes.

Because individuals with type 1 diabetes are insulin deficient, the only treatment is insulin injections. Until the arrival of genetic engineering, most pharmaceutical insulin came from swine, cow, and sheep pancreases. However, once the gene for human insulin was cloned, biotechnology companies began to manufacture artificial human insulin for therapeutic use. In addition, scientists are developing techniques for implanting encapsulated beta cells in the body, in the hope that individuals with type 1 diabetes will no longer need to rely on regular insulin injections.

The events that follow ingestion of carbohydrate in an insulin-deficient diabetic create a picture of what happens to metabolism in the absence of insulin (Fig. 22-16 ●). Following a meal, nutrient absorption by the intestine proceeds normally because this process is insulin independent. However, nutrient uptake from the blood and cellular metabolism in many tissues are insulin dependent and therefore severely diminished in the absence of insulin. Lacking nutrients to metabolize, cells go into fasted-state metabolism:

1. *Protein metabolism.* Without glucose for energy and amino acids for protein synthesis, muscles break down their proteins to provide a substrate for ATP production. Amino acids leave the muscles and are transported to the liver.
2. *Fat metabolism.* Adipose tissue in fasted-state metabolism breaks down its fat stores. Fatty acids enter the blood for transport to the liver. The liver uses β-oxidation to break down fatty acids. However, this organ is limited in its ability to send fatty acids through the citric acid cycle, and the excess fatty acids are converted to ketones. Ketone bodies re-enter the circulation and can be used by other tissues (such as muscle and brain) for ATP synthesis. (The breakdown of muscle and adipose tissue in the absence of insulin leads to tissue loss and the "melting down of the flesh" described by Aretaeus.)
3. *Glucose metabolism.* In the absence of insulin, glucose remains in the blood, causing hyperglycemia. The liver, unable to take up and metabolize this glucose, initiates fasted-state pathways of glycogenolysis and gluconeogenesis. These pathways produce *additional* glucose from glycogen, amino acids, and glycerol. When the liver sends this glucose into the blood, hyperglycemia worsens.
4. *Brain metabolism.* Tissues that are not insulin dependent, such as most neurons in the brain, carry on metabolism as usual. However, neurons in the brain's satiety center *are* insulin sensitive. Therefore, in the absence of insulin, the satiety center is unable to take up plasma glucose. The center perceives the absence of intracellular glucose as starvation and allows the feeding center to increase food intake. The result is *polyphagia* (excessive eating), a classic symptom associated with untreated type 1 diabetes mellitus.
5. *Osmotic diuresis and polyuria.* If the hyperglycemia of diabetes causes plasma glucose concentrations to exceed the *renal threshold* for glucose, glucose reabsorption in the proximal tubule of the kidney becomes saturated [p. 151]. Consequently, some filtered glucose is not reabsorbed, and it is excreted in the urine (*glucosuria*).

   The presence of additional solute in the collecting duct lumen causes less water to be reabsorbed and more to be excreted (see Ch. 20, question 31, p. 684). This creates large volumes of urine (*polyuria*) and, if unchecked, causes dehydration. The loss of water in the urine due to unreabsorbed solutes is known as **osmotic diuresis.**
6. *Dehydration.* Dehydration resulting from osmotic diuresis leads to decreased circulating blood volume and decreased blood pressure. Falling blood pressure triggers homeostatic mechanisms for maintaining blood pressure, including secretion of vasopressin, thirst that causes constant drinking (*polydipsia*), and cardiovascular compensations [Fig. 20-17, p. 670].
7. *Metabolic acidosis.* Metabolic acidosis in diabetes has two potential sources: anaerobic metabolism and ketone body production. Tissues go into anaerobic glycolysis (which creates lactate) if cardiovascular compensation fails and blood pressure decreases to the point that perfusion of peripheral tissues becomes inadequate. Lactate leaves the cells and enters the blood, contributing to a state of metabolic acidosis.

*In the sense of "causing wonder."

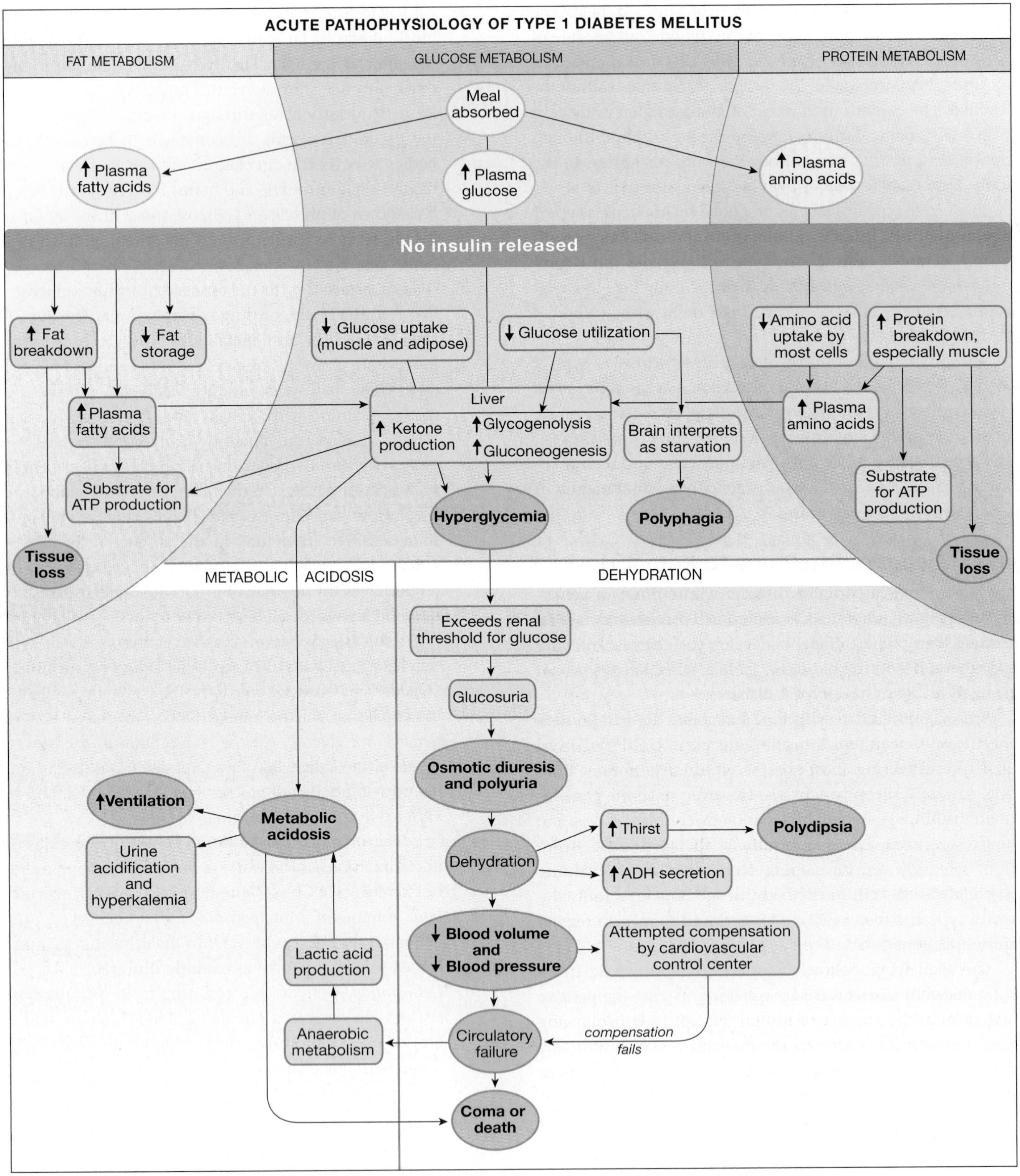

● **FIGURE 22-16** ***Acute pathophysiology of type 1 diabetes mellitus.*** Untreated type 1 diabetes is marked by tissue breakdown, glucosuria, polyuria, polydipsia, polyphagia, and metabolic ketoacidosis.

Note that anaerobic metabolism is only a secondary cause of metabolic acidosis in uncontrolled insulin-deficient diabetes. The primary cause is the production of acidic *ketone bodies* by the liver. Patients in *diabetic ketoacidosis* exhibit the signs of metabolic acidosis discussed in Chapter 20: increased ventilation, acidification of the urine, and hyperkalemia [p. 673]. If untreated, the combination of ketoacidosis and hypoxia from circulatory collapse can cause coma and even death. The treatment for a patient in diabetic ketoacidosis is insulin replacement, accompanied by fluid and electrolyte therapy to replenish lost volume and ions.

Type 2 Diabetics Often Have Elevated Insulin Levels

Type 2 diabetics account for 90% of all diabetics. A significant genetic predisposition to develop the disease exists among certain ethnic groups. For example, about 25% of Hispanics over age 45 have diabetes. The disease is more common in people over the age of 40, but there is growing concern about the increased diagnosis of type 2 diabetes in children and adolescents. About 80% of type 2 diabetics are obese.

A common hallmark of type 2 diabetes is **insulin resistance**, demonstrated by a delayed response to an ingested glucose load. This response can be detected by a procedure known as a *glucose tolerance test* (Fig. 22-17 ●). First, the subject's fasting plasma glucose concentration is determined (time 0). Then the person consumes either a special glucose drink or a typical meal. Plasma glucose is measured periodically for two or more hours.

Normal subjects have a fasting plasma glucose of 109 mg/dL or less. They show a slight increase in plasma glucose concentration soon after a meal, but the level rapidly returns to normal following insulin secretion. In diabetic patients, however, fasting plasma glucose concentrations are usually above normal, and they rise even higher as glucose is absorbed. Because the cells of the body are slow to remove glucose from the blood, plasma glucose stays elevated for two or more hours. This slow response suggests that insulin, even if present in the blood, is unable to carry out its normal function.

An abnormal glucose tolerance test simply shows that the body's response to an ingested glucose load is not normal. The test cannot distinguish between problems with insulin synthesis, insulin release, or the responsiveness of target tissues to insulin. Some type 2 diabetics have both resistance to insulin action and decreased insulin secretion. Others have normal-to-high insulin secretion but decreased target cell responsiveness.

In addition, although type 2 diabetics are hyperglycemic, they often have elevated glucagon levels as well. This seems contradictory until you realize that the pancreatic alpha cells, like muscle and adipose cells, require insulin for glucose uptake. This means that in diabetes, the alpha cells do not take up glucose, which prompts them to secrete glucagon. Glucagon then contributes to hyperglycemia by promoting glycogenolysis and gluconeogenesis.

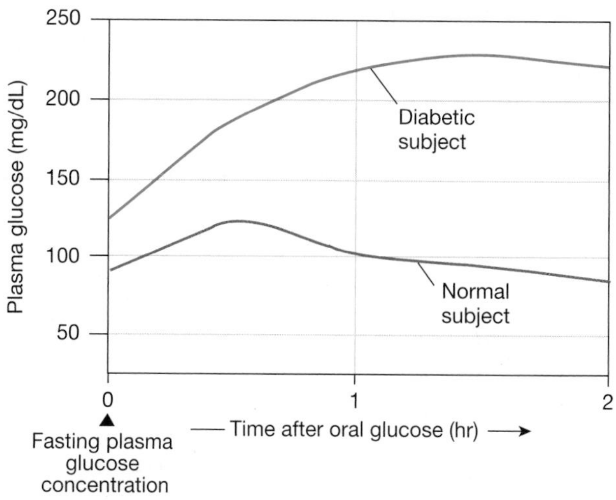

● **FIGURE 22-17** ***Normal and abnormal glucose tolerance tests.*** At time 0, the subject consumes a glucose drink or a meal. In diabetic individuals, the plasma glucose concentration remains above 200 mg/dL after two hours. Individuals with plasma glucose of 140–199 mg/dL after two hours have impaired glucose tolerance. Normal people have glucose concentrations below 140 mg/dL at the two-hour mark.

In type 2 diabetes, the acute symptoms of the disease are not nearly as severe as in type 1 because insulin is usually present, and the cells, although resistant to insulin's action, are able to carry out a certain amount of glucose metabolism. The liver, for example, does not have to turn to ketone production, with the result that ketosis is uncommon in type 2 diabetes.

RUNNING PROBLEM

The medical staff and Nicole's family decided to talk to her about her weight and eating habits. The disorder Dr. Ayani suspects, **anorexia nervosa** (AN), can have serious physiological consequences. As a result, AN has the highest death rate of any psychiatric disorder, and the mortality rate of young women ages 15–24 with AN is 12 times greater than that of the general population. The most common causes of death are cardiac arrest, electrolyte imbalance, and suicide. AN reportedly affects as many as 3% of females in industrialized nations at some point in their lifetime. (While 90% of AN cases are female, the number of male cases is increasing.) Successful treatment of AN includes providing nutrition, psychotherapy, and family therapy. Current research is investigating the usefulness of neuropeptide Y and other brain peptides in treating anorexia.

Question 9:
Why might an NPY agonist help in cases of anorexia?

725 727 729 732 745 752

TABLE 22-6 Drugs for Treating Diabetes

DRUG CLASS	EFFECT	MECHANISM OF ACTION
Sulfonylureas and meglitinides	Stimulate insulin secretion	Close beta cell K_{ATP} channels and depolarize the cell
α-Glucosidase inhibitors	Decrease intestinal glucose uptake	Block intestinal enzymes that digest complex carbohydrates
Biguanides (e.g., metformin)	Reduce plasma glucose by decreasing hepatic gluconeogenesis	Unclear
PPAR activators ("glitazones")	Increase gene transcription for proteins that promote glucose utilization and fatty acid metabolism	Activate PPARγ, a nuclear receptor activator
Amylin analogs (pramlintide)	Reduce plasma glucose	Delay gastric emptying, suppress glucagon secretion, and promote satiety
Incretin (GLP-1) analogs (exendin-4)	Reduce plasma glucose and induce weight loss	Stimulate insulin secretion, reduce glucagon secretion, delay gastric emptying, and promote satiety
DPP-4 inhibitors (sitagliptin)	Increase insulin secretion and decrease gastric emptying	Inhibit dipeptidyl peptidase-4, which breaks down GLP-1 and GIP

Nevertheless, overall metabolism is not normal, and patients with this condition develop a variety of diabetes-related problems because of abnormal glucose and fat metabolism. Complications of type 2 diabetes include atherosclerosis, neurological changes, renal failure, and blindness from diabetic retinopathy. As many as 70% of type 2 diabetics die from cardiovascular disease.

Because many people with type 2 diabetes are asymptomatic when diagnosed, they can be very difficult to treat. People who come in for their yearly checkup feeling fine, only to be told that they have diabetes, can be very resistant to making dramatic lifestyle changes when they do not feel sick. Unfortunately, by the time diabetic symptoms appear, damage to tissues and organs is well under way. Patient compliance at that point can slow the progress of the disease but cannot reverse the pathological changes. The goal of treatment is to correct hyperglycemia to prevent the complications described above.

The first therapy recommended for most type 2 diabetics and pre-diabetics, and for those individuals at high risk of developing the disease, is to lose weight and exercise. For some patients, simply losing weight eliminates their insulin resistance. Exercise decreases hyperglycemia because exercising skeletal muscle does not require insulin for glucose uptake.

Drugs used to treat type 2 diabetes may (1) stimulate beta-cell secretion of insulin, (2) slow the digestion or absorption of carbohydrates in the intestine, (3) inhibit hepatic glucose output, or (4) make target tissues more responsive to insulin (Tbl. 22-6 ●). Many of the newest anti-diabetic drugs mimic endogenous hormones. For example, *pramlintide,* approved by the U.S. Food and Drug Administration (FDA) in March 2005, is an analog of **amylin**, a peptide hormone that is co-secreted with insulin. Amylin helps regulate glucose homeostasis following a meal by slowing digestion and absorption of carbohydrates. Amylin also decreases food intake by a central effect on appetite, and it decreases secretion of glucagon.

Other hormone-based therapies recently approved by the FDA are incretin *mimetics* (agonists). *Exendin-4* (Byetta®) is a GLP-1 mimetic derived from a compound found in the venomous saliva of gila monsters. Exendin-4 has four primary effects: it increases insulin production, decreases production of glucagon, slows digestion, and increases satiety. It has also been associated with weight loss.

In normal physiology, the combined actions of amylin, GIP, and GLP-1 create a self-regulating cycle for glucose absorption and fed-state glucose metabolism. Glucose in the intestine following a meal causes feedforward release of GIP and GLP-1. The two incretins travel through the circulation to the pancreas, where they initiate insulin and amylin secretion. Amylin then acts on the GI tract to slow the rate at which food enters the intestine, while insulin acts on target tissues to promote glucose uptake and utilization.

Metabolic Syndrome Links Diabetes and Cardiovascular Disease

Clinicians have known for years that people who are overweight are prone to develop type 2 diabetes, atherosclerosis,

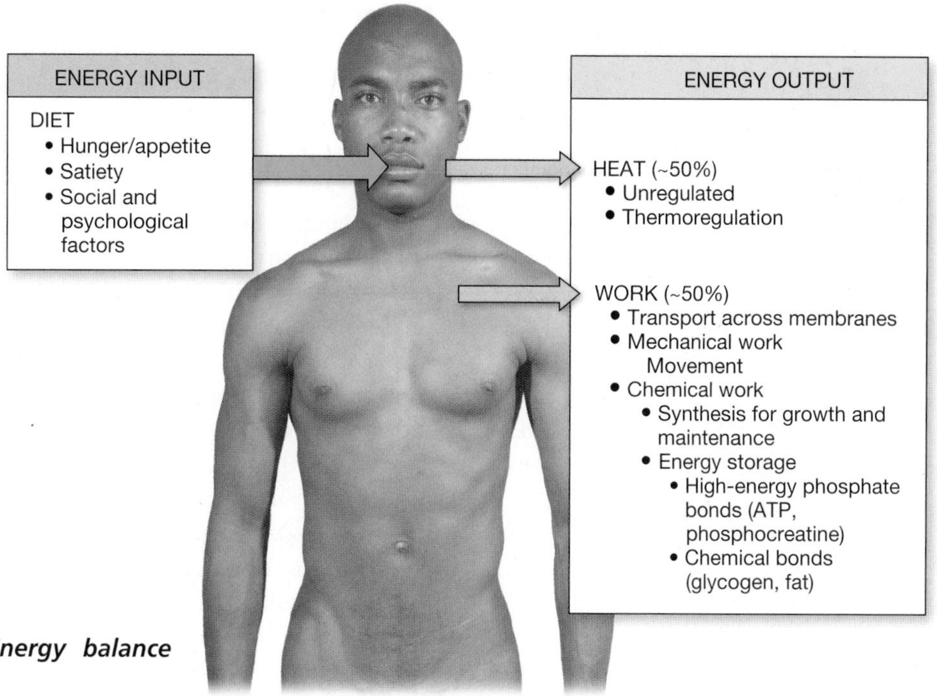
ENERGY INPUT
DIET
• Hunger/appetite
• Satiety
• Social and psychological factors
ENERGY OUTPUT
HEAT (~50%)
• Unregulated
• Thermoregulation
WORK (~50%)
• Transport across membranes
• Mechanical work
Movement
• Chemical work
• Synthesis for growth and maintenance
• Energy storage
• High-energy phosphate bonds (ATP, phosphocreatine)
• Chemical bonds (glycogen, fat)

● **FIGURE 22-18** *Energy balance in the body*

and high blood pressure. The combination of these three conditions has been formalized into a diagnosis called **metabolic syndrome**, which highlights the integrative nature of metabolic pathways. People with metabolic syndrome meet at least three of the following five criteria: central (visceral) obesity, blood pressure $\geq$ 130/85 mm Hg, fasting plasma glucose $\geq$ 110 mg/dL, elevated fasting plasma triglyceride levels, and low plasma HDL-C levels. *Central obesity* is defined as a waist circumference greater than 40″ in men and 35″ in women. Women who have an apple-shaped body (widest at the waist) are more prone to developing metabolic syndrome than women who have a pear-shaped body (widest at the hips).

The association between obesity, diabetes, and cardiovascular disease illustrates the fundamental disturbances in cellular metabolism that occur with obesity. One common mechanism known to play a role in both glucose metabolism and lipid metabolism involves the family of nuclear receptors called *peroxisome proliferator-activated receptors* (PPARs). Lipids and lipid-derived molecules bind to PPARs, which then turn on a variety of genes. The PPAR subtype called PPARγ (*p-par-gamma*) has been linked to adipocyte differentiation, type 2 diabetes, and foam cells, the endothelial macrophages that have ingested oxidized cholesterol. PPARα, mentioned earlier in the discussion of cholesterol metabolism, is important in hepatic cholesterol metabolism. The PPARs may be important clues to the link between obesity, type 2 diabetes, and atherosclerosis that has evaded scientists for so long.

CONCEPT CHECK

16. Why must insulin be administered as a shot and not as an oral pill?
17. Patients admitted to the hospital with acute diabetic ketoacidosis and dehydration are given insulin and fluids that contain K^+ and other ions. The acidosis is usually accompanied by hyperkalemia, so why is K^+ included in the rehydration fluids? (*Hint:* dehydrated patients may have a high *concentration* of K^+, but their total body fluid volume is low.)
18. In 2006 the FDA approved sitagliptin (Januvia®), a DPP-4 inhibitor. This drug blocks action of the enzyme *dipeptidyl peptidase-4*, which breaks down GLP-1 and GIP. Explain how sitagliptin is helpful in treating diabetes. Answers: p. 755

REGULATION OF BODY TEMPERATURE

Type 2 diabetes is an excellent example of the link between body weight and metabolism. The development of obesity may be linked to the efficiency with which the body converts food energy into cell and tissue components. According to one theory, people who are more efficient in transferring energy from food to fat are the ones who put on weight. In contrast, people who are less metabolically efficient can eat the same number of calories and not gain weight because more food energy is released as heat. Figure 22-18 ● summarizes the factors contributing to energy balance in the body. Much of what we know about the regulation of energy balance comes from studies on body temperature regulation.

22

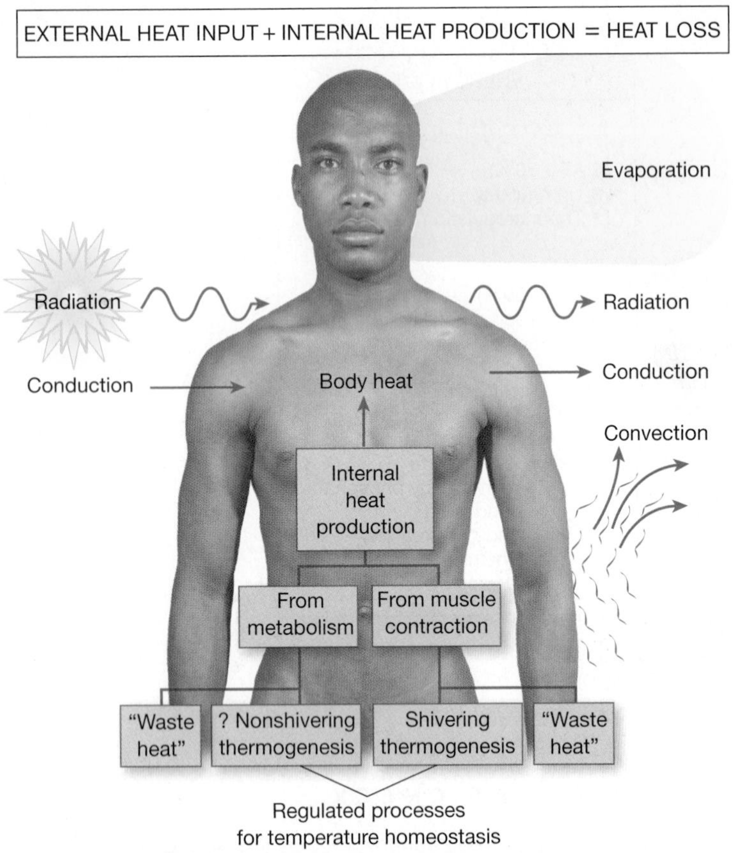

● **FIGURE 22-19** ***Heat balance in the body***

Body Temperature Balances Heat Production, Gain, and Loss

Temperature regulation in humans is linked to metabolic heat production (*thermogenesis*). Humans are **homeothermic** animals, which means our bodies regulate internal temperature within a relatively narrow range. Average body temperature is 37°C (98.6°F), with a normal range of 35.5°–37.7°C (96°–99.9°F).

These values are subject to considerable variation, both among individuals and throughout the day in a single individual. The site at which temperature is measured also makes a difference because core body temperature may be higher than temperature at the skin surface. Oral temperatures are about 0.5°C lower than rectal temperatures.

Several factors affect body temperature in a given individual. Body temperature increases with exercise or after a meal (because of *diet-induced thermogenesis*). Temperature also cycles throughout the day: the lowest (basal) body temperature occurs in the early morning, and the highest occurs in the early evening. Women of reproductive age also exhibit a monthly temperature cycle: basal body temperatures are about 0.5° C higher in the second half of the menstrual cycle (after ovulation) than before ovulation.

Heat Gain and Loss Are Balanced Temperature balance in the body, like energy balance, depends on a dynamic equilibrium between heat input and heat output (Fig. 22-19 ●). Heat input has two components: *internal heat production*, which includes heat from normal metabolism and heat released during muscle contraction, and *external heat input* from the environment through either *radiation* or *conduction*.

All objects with a temperature above absolute zero give off radiant energy (radiation) with infrared or visible wavelengths. This energy can be absorbed by other objects and constitutes **radiant heat gain** for those objects. You absorb radiant energy each time you sit in the sun or in front of a fire. **Conductive heat gain** is the transfer of heat between objects that are in contact with each other, such as the skin and a heating pad or the skin and hot water.

We lose heat from the body in four ways: conduction, radiation, convection, and evaporation. **Conductive heat loss** is the loss of body heat to a cooler object that is touching the body, such as an icepack or a cold stone bench. **Radiant heat loss** from the human body is estimated to account for nearly half the heat lost from a person at rest in a normal room. *Thermography* is a diagnostic imaging technique that measures radiant heat loss. Some cancerous tumors can be visually identified because they have higher metabolic activity and give off more heat than surrounding tissues.

Radiant and conductive heat loss is enhanced by **convective heat loss**, the process in which heat is carried away by warm air rising from the body's surface. Convective air currents are created wherever a temperature difference in the air exists: hot air rises and is replaced by cooler air. Convection helps move warmed air away from the skin's surface. Clothing, which traps air and prevents convective air currents, helps retain heat close to the body.

The fourth type of heat loss from the body is **evaporative heat loss**, which takes place as water evaporates at the skin's surface and in the respiratory tract. The conversion of water from the liquid state to the gaseous state requires the input of substantial amounts of heat energy. When water on the body evaporates, it removes heat from the body.

You can demonstrate the effect of evaporative cooling by wetting one arm and letting the water evaporate. As it dries, the wet arm feels much cooler than the rest of your body because heat is being drawn from the arm to vaporize the water. Similarly, the half-liter of water vapor that leaves the body through the lungs and skin each day takes with it a significant amount of body heat. Evaporative heat loss is affected by the humidity of surrounding air: less evaporation occurs at higher humidities.

Conductive, convective, and evaporative heat loss from the body is enhanced by the *bulk flow* of air across the body, such as air moved across the skin by a fan or breeze. The effect of wind on body temperature regulation in the winter is described by the *wind chill factor,* a combination of absolute environmental temperature and the effect of convective heat loss.

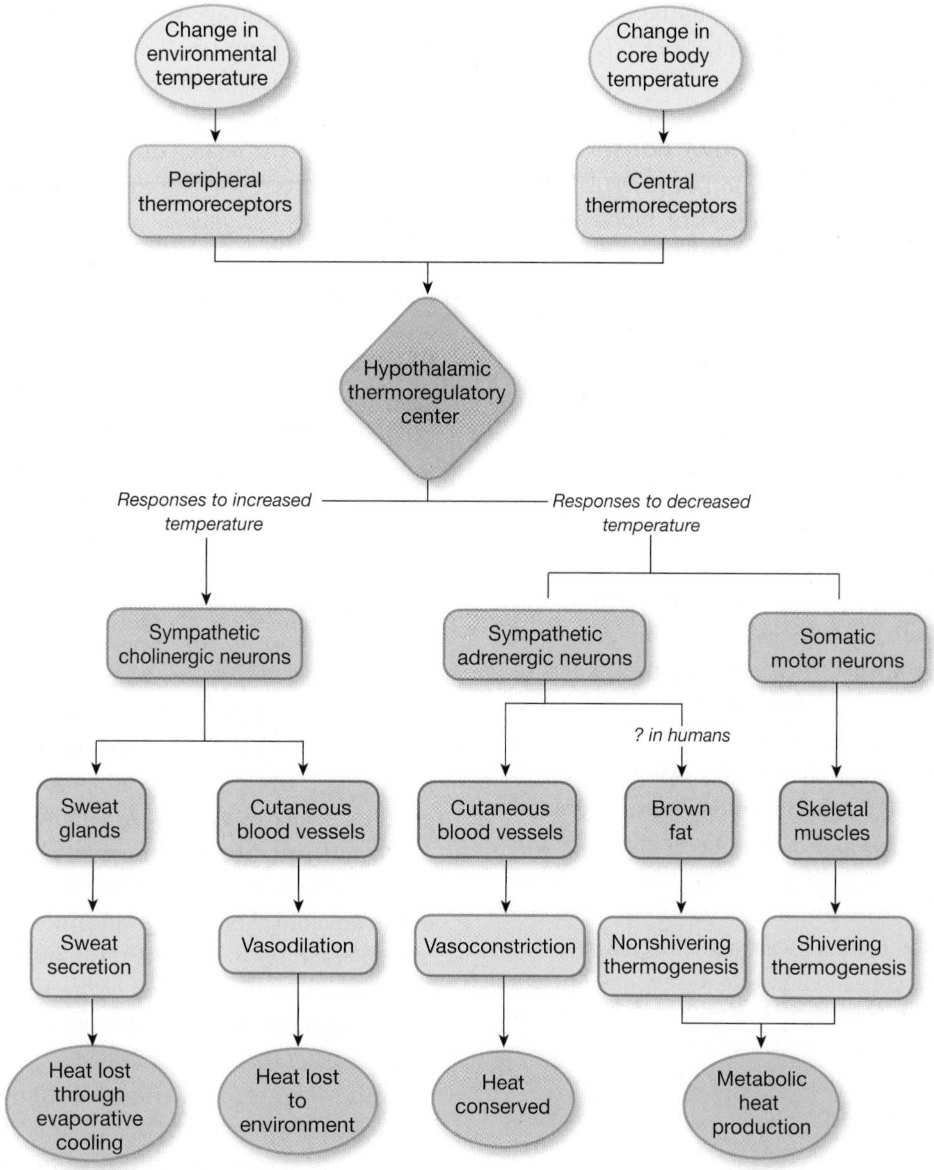

● **FIGURE 22-20** ***Thermoregulatory reflexes***

Body Temperature Is Homeostatically Regulated

The human body is usually warmer than its environment and therefore loses heat. However, normal metabolism generates enough heat to maintain body temperature when the environmental temperature stays between 27.8° and 30°C (82° and 86°F). This range is known as the **thermoneutral zone**.

In temperatures above the thermoneutral zone, the body has a net gain of heat because heat production exceeds heat loss. Below the thermoneutral zone, heat loss exceeds heat production. In both cases, the body must use homeostatic compensation to maintain a constant internal temperature.

A human without clothing can thermoregulate at environmental air temperatures between 10° and 55°C (50° and 131°F). Because we are seldom exposed to the higher end of that temperature range, the main physiological challenge in thermal regulation is posed by cold environments.

Humans have been described by some physiologists as tropical animals because we are genetically adapted for life in warm climates. But we have retained a certain amount of genetic flexibility, and the physiological mechanisms by which we thermoregulate have some ability to adapt to changing conditions.

The autonomic control of body temperature regulation is generally considered a function of *thermoregulatory centers* in the hypothalamus. Sensory neurons known as **thermoreceptors** are located peripherally in the skin and centrally in the anterior hypothalamus. These sensors monitor skin temperature and core body temperature, respectively, and send that information to the thermoregulatory center. The hypothalamic "thermostat" then compares the input signals with the desired temperature setpoint and coordinates an appropriate physiological response to raise or lower the core temperature (Fig. 22-20 ●). Heat loss from the body is promoted by dilation of blood vessels in the skin and by sweating. Heat gain is generated by shivering and possibly by nonshivering thermogenesis.

Alterations in Cutaneous Blood Flow Conserve or Release Heat Heat loss across the skin surface is regulated by controlling blood flow in *cutaneous* [*cutis,* skin] blood vessels (vessels near the skin's surface). These blood vessels can pick up heat from the environment by convection and transfer it to the body core, or they can lose heat to the surrounding air. Blood flow through cutaneous blood vessels varies from close to zero when heat must be conserved, to nearly one-third of cardiac output when heat must be released to the environment. Local control influences cutaneous blood flow to a certain degree, possibly through vasodilators produced by the vascular endothelium. However, neural regulation is the primary determining factor.

Most arterioles in the body are under tonic sympathetic control [p. 196]. If core body temperature falls, the hypothalamus selectively activates sympathetic neurons innervating cutaneous arterioles. The arterioles constrict, increasing their resistance to blood flow and diverting blood to lower-resistance blood vessels in the interior of the body. This response keeps warmer core blood away from the cooler skin surface, thereby reducing heat loss.

In warm temperatures, the opposite happens: cutaneous arterioles dilate to increase blood flow near the skin surface and enhance heat loss. In skin of the extremities, vasodilation results from decreased sympathetic input. In skin away from the extremities, vasodilation is mediated through specialized sympathetic neurons that secrete acetylcholine. It remains unclear whether the effect is direct or mediated by bradykinin or other paracrine vasodilator substances.

CONCEPT CHECK

19. What neurotransmitter and neurotransmitter receptor mediate cutaneous vasoconstriction?
20. What observations might have prompted researchers who discovered sympathetic neurons that secrete ACh to classify them as sympathetic rather than parasympathetic? [*Hint:* p. 389]

Answers: p. 756

Sweat Contributes to Heat Loss Surface heat loss is enhanced by the evaporation of sweat. By some estimates the human integument has 2–3 million sweat glands. The highest concentrations are found on the forehead, scalp, axillae (armpits), palms of the hands, and soles of the feet.

Sweat glands are made of transporting epithelium. Cells deep in the gland secrete an isotonic solution similar to interstitial fluid. As the fluid travels through the duct to the skin, NaCl is reabsorbed, resulting in hypotonic sweat. A typical value for sweat production is 1.5 L/hr. With acclimatization to hot weather, some people sweat at rates of 4–6 L/hr. However, they can maintain this high rate only for short periods unless they are drinking to replace lost fluid volume. Sweat production is regulated by cholinergic sympathetic neurons.

Cooling by evaporative heat loss depends on the evaporation of water from sweat on the skin's surface. Because water evaporates rapidly in dry environments but slowly or not at all in humid ones, the body's ability to withstand high temperatures is directly related to the relative humidity of the air. Meteorologists report the combination of heat and humidity as the *heat index* or *humidex*. Air moving across a sweaty skin surface enhances evaporation even with high humidity, which is one reason fans are useful in hot weather.

Movement and Metabolism Produce Heat

Heat production by the body falls into two broad categories: (1) unregulated heat production from voluntary muscle contraction and normal metabolic pathways, and (2) regulated heat production for maintaining temperature homeostasis in low environmental temperatures. Regulated heat production is further divided into shivering thermogenesis and nonshivering thermogenesis (Fig. 22-19).

In **shivering thermogenesis**, the body uses shivering (rhythmic tremors caused by skeletal muscle contraction) to generate heat. Signals from the hypothalamic thermoregulatory center initiate these skeletal muscle tremors. Shivering muscle generates five to six times as much heat as resting muscle. Shivering can be partially suppressed by voluntary control.

Nonshivering thermogenesis is metabolic heat production by means other than shivering. In laboratory animals such as the rat, cold exposure significantly increases heat production in brown fat [p. 82]. The mechanism for brown fat heat production is *mitochondrial uncoupling*. In this process, energy flowing through the electron transport system [p. 111] is released as heat rather than being trapped in ATP. Mitochondrial uncoupling in response to cold is promoted by thyroid hormones and by increased sympathetic activity.

The importance of nonshivering thermogenesis in adult humans is unclear. Humans are born with significant amounts of brown fat, found primarily in the *interscapular* area between the shoulder blades. In newborns, nonshivering thermogenesis in this brown fat contributes significantly to raising and maintaining body temperature. As children age, however, white fat gradually replaces most brown fat. The brown fat that remains is very difficult to study because the experimental methodology for doing so requires that the fat be extracted from the body.

The body's responses to high and low temperatures are summarized in Figure 22-21 ●. In cold environments, the body tries to reduce heat loss while increasing internal heat production. In hot temperatures, the opposite is true. Notice from Figure 22-21 that voluntary behavioral responses play a significant role in temperature regulation. We reduce activity during hot weather, thereby decreasing muscle heat production. In cold weather, we put on extra clothing, tuck our hands in our armpits, or curl up in a ball to slow heat loss.

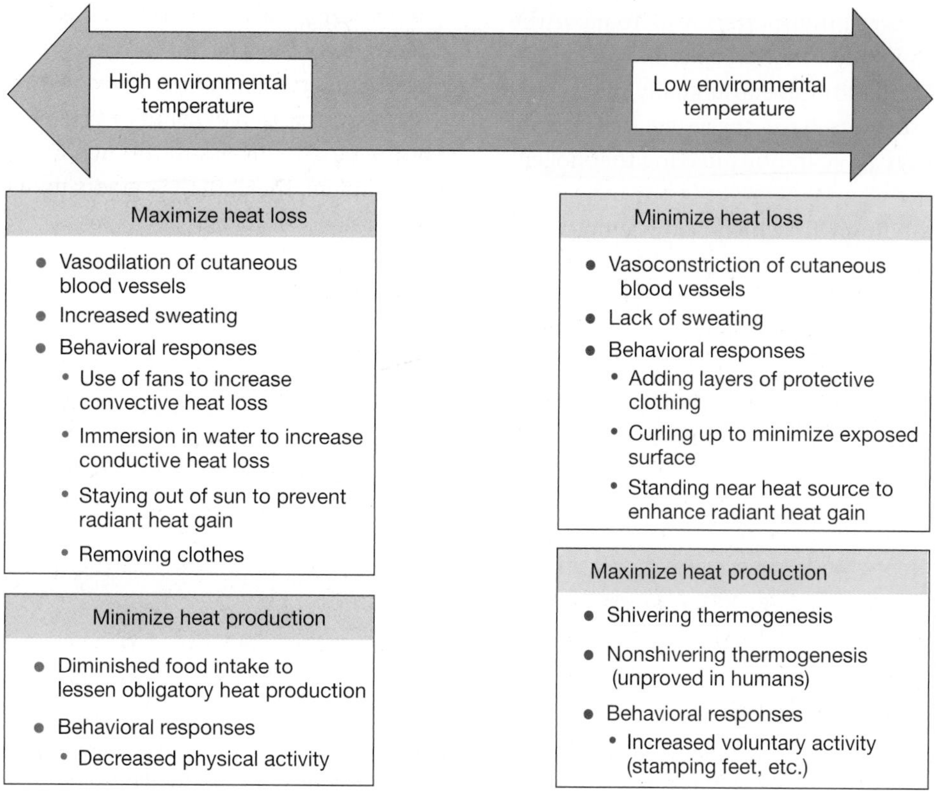

FIGURE 22-21 ***Homeostatic responses to environmental extremes***

The Body's Thermostat Can Be Reset

Variations in body temperature regulation can be either physiological or pathological. Examples of physiological variation include the circadian rhythm of body temperature mentioned earlier, menstrual cycle variations, postmenopausal hot flashes, and fever. These processes share a common mechanism: resetting of the hypothalamic thermostat.

Hot flashes appear to be transient decreases in the thermostat's setpoint caused by the absence of estrogen. When the setpoint is lower, a room temperature that had previously been comfortable suddenly feels too hot. This discomfort triggers the usual thermoregulatory responses to heat, including sweating and cutaneous vasodilation, which leads to flushing of the skin.

For many years *fever* was thought to be a pathological response to infection, but it is now considered part of the body's normal immune response. Toxins from bacteria and other pathogens trigger the release of chemicals known as **pyrogens** [*pyr,* fire] from various immunocytes. Pyrogens are fever-producing cytokines that also have many other effects.

Experimentally, some interleukins (IL-1, IL-6), some interferons, and tumor necrosis factor have all been shown to induce fever. They do so by resetting the hypothalamic thermostat to a higher setpoint. Normal room temperature feels too cold, and the patient begins to shiver, creating additional heat. Pyrogens may also increase nonshivering thermogenesis, causing body temperature to rise.

The adaptive significance of fever is still unclear, but it seems to enhance the activity of white blood cells involved in the immune response. For this reason, some people question whether patients with a fever should be given aspirin and other fever-reducing drugs simply for the sake of comfort. High fever can be dangerous, however, as a fever of 41°C (106° F) for more than a brief period causes brain damage.

Pathological conditions in which body temperature strays outside the normal range include different states of *hyperthermia* and *hypothermia*. Heat exhaustion and heat stroke are the most common forms of **hyperthermia**, a condition in which body temperature rises to abnormally high values. **Heat exhaustion** is marked by severe dehydration and core body temperatures of 37.5°–39°C (99.5°–102.2° F). Patients may experience muscle cramps, nausea, and headache. They are usually pale and sweating profusely. Heat exhaustion often occurs in people who are physically active in hot, humid climates to which they are not acclimatized. It also occurs in the elderly, whose ability to thermoregulate is diminished.

Heat stroke is a more severe form of hyperthermia, with higher core body temperatures. The skin is usually flushed and dry. Immediate and rapid cooling of these patients is important, as enzymes and other proteins begin to denature at temperatures above 41°C (106° F). Mortality in heat stroke is nearly 50%.

Malignant hyperthermia, in which body temperature becomes abnormally elevated, is a genetically linked condition. A defective Ca^{2+} channel in skeletal muscle releases too much

Ca^{2+} into the cytoplasm. As cell transporters work to move the Ca^{2+} back into mitochondria and the sarcoplasmic reticulum, the heat released from ATP hydrolysis substantially raises body temperature. Some investigators have suggested that a mild version of this process plays a role in nonshivering thermogenesis in mammals.

Hypothermia, a condition in which body temperature falls abnormally low, is also a dangerous condition. As core body temperature falls, enzymatic reactions slow, and the person loses consciousness. When metabolism slows, oxygen consumption also decreases.

Victims of drowning in cold water can sometimes be revived without brain damage if they have gone into a state of hypothermia. This observation led to the development of induced hypothermia for certain surgical procedures, such as heart surgery. The patient is cooled to 21°–24°C (70°–75°F) so that tissue oxygen demand can be met by artificial oxygenation of the blood as it passes through a bypass pump. After surgery is complete, the patient is gradually rewarmed.

CONCEPT CHECK

21. Why must a water bed be heated to allow a person to sleep on it comfortably?
22. Will a person who is exercising outside overheat faster when the air humidity is low or when it is high? Answers: p. 756

RUNNING PROBLEM CONCLUSION

Eating Disorders

Nicole finally agreed to undergo counseling and enter a treatment program for anorexia nervosa. She was lucky—her wrist would heal, and her medical complications could have been much worse. After seeing Nicole and discussing her anorexia, Sara realized that she also needed to see a counselor. Even though she was no longer dancing, Sara still used diet pills, diuretics, and laxatives when she became uncomfortable with her weight, and she had started binging and purging—eating much more than normal when she was stressed and then forcing herself to vomit to avoid gaining any weight. These are the behavioral patterns of *bulimia nervosa* (BN), a condition that is as serious as AN and that affects an estimated 4% of females. Its physiological effects and treatments are similar to those for AN.

To learn more about anorexia and bulimia, and for help finding a support group, see the National Association of Anorexia Nervosa and Associated Disorders web site at *www.anad.org* or *www.nationaleatingdisorders.org*.

	QUESTION	FACTS	INTEGRATION AND ANALYSIS
1	If you measured Nicole's leptin level, what would you expect to find?	Leptin is a hormone secreted by adipose tissue.	Nicole has little adipose tissue, so she would have a low leptin level.
2	Would you expect Nicole to have elevated or depressed levels of neuropeptide Y?	NPY is inhibited by leptin. NPY stimulates feeding centers.	Because her leptin level is low, you might predict that NPY would be elevated and feeding stimulated. However, the feeding center is affected by other factors besides NPY (Fig. 22-1). Brain studies of anorexic patients show high levels of CRH (Tbl. 22-1), which opposes NPY and depresses feeding.
3	What is Nicole's K^+ disturbance called? What effect does it have on the resting membrane potential of her cells?	Nicole's K^+ is 2.5 mEq/L, and normal is 3.5–5 mEq/L.	Low plasma K^+ is called hypokalemia. Hypokalemia causes the membrane potential to hyperpolarize [p. 272].
4	Why does Dr. Ayani want to monitor Nicole's cardiac function?	Cardiac muscle is an excitable tissue whose activity depends on changes in membrane potential.	Hypokalemia can alter the membrane potential of cardiac autorhythmic and contractile cells and cause a potentially fatal cardiac arrhythmia.
5	Based on her clinical values, what is Nicole's acid-base status?	Nicole's pH is 7.52, and her plasma HCO_3^- is elevated at 40 mEq/L.	Normal pH is 7.38–7.42, so she is in alkalosis. Her elevated HCO_3^- indicates a metabolic alkalosis. The cause is probably induced vomiting and loss of HCl from her stomach.

(continued)

QUESTION		FACTS	INTEGRATION AND ANALYSIS
6	Based on what you learned in Chapters 14 and 15 about heart rate and blood pressure, speculate on why Nicole has low blood pressure with a rapid pulse.	Her blood pressure is 80/50 (low), and her pulse is 90 (high).	Normally, increasing the heart rate would increase blood pressure. In this case, the increased pulse is a compensatory attempt to raise her low blood pressure. The low blood pressure probably results from dehydration.
7	Would you expect Nicole's renin and aldosterone levels to be normal, elevated, or depressed? How might these levels relate to her K^+ disturbance?	All the primary stimuli for renin secretion are associated with low blood pressure. Renin begins the RAAS pathway that stimulates aldosterone secretion.	Because Nicole's blood pressure is low, you would expect elevated renin and aldosterone levels. Aldosterone promotes renal K^+ secretion, which would lower her body load of K^+. She probably also has low dietary K^+ intake, which contributes to her hypokalemia.
8	Give some possible reasons Nicole had been feeling weak during dance rehearsals.	In fasted-state metabolism, the body breaks down skeletal muscle.	Loss of skeletal muscle proteins, hypokalemia, and possibly hypoglycemia could all be causes of Nicole's weakness.
9	Why might an NPY agonist help in cases of anorexia?	NPY stimulates the feeding center.	An NPY agonist might stimulate the feeding center and help Nicole want to eat.

725 727 729 732 745 752

CHAPTER SUMMARY

Energy balance in the body means that the body's energy intake equals its energy output. The same *balance principle* applies to metabolism: the amount of nutrient in each of the body's nutrient pools depends on intake and output. Glucose *homeostasis* is one of the most important goals of regulated metabolism, for without adequate glucose, the brain is unable to function. Flow of material through the biochemical pathways of metabolism depends on the *molecular interactions* of substrates and enzymes.

Appetite and Satiety

1. The hypothalamus contains a tonically active **feeding center** and a **satiety center** that inhibits the feeding center. (p. 725)
2. Blood glucose concentrations (the **glucostatic theory**) and body fat content (the **lipostatic theory**) influence food intake. (p. 725)
3. Food intake is influenced by a variety of peptides, including **leptin**, **neuropeptide Y**, and **ghrelin.** (p. 725; Fig. 22-1)

Energy Balance

4. In energy balance, energy intake equals energy output. (p. 727)
5. The body uses energy for transport, movement, and chemical work. (p. 727)
6. The energy content of food is measured by **direct calorimetry**. (p. 727)
7. Measuring **oxygen consumption** is the most common method of estimating energy expenditure. (p. 728)
8. The **respiratory quotient** (RQ) or **respiratory exchange ratio** (RER) is the ratio of CO_2 produced to O_2 consumed. RQ varies with diet. (p. 728)
9. **Basal metabolic rate** (BMR) is an individual's lowest metabolic rate. Metabolic rate (kcal/day) = L O_2 consumed/day × kcal/L O_2. (p. 728)
10. **Diet-induced thermogenesis** is an increase in heat production after eating. (p. 728)
11. Glycogen and fat are the two primary forms of energy storage in the human body. (p. 729)

Metabolism

12. **Metabolism** is all the chemical reactions that extract, use, or store energy. (p. 729; Figs. 22-2, 22-3)
13. **Anabolic pathways** synthesize small molecules into larger ones. **Catabolic pathways** break large molecules into smaller ones. (p. 729)
14. Metabolism is divided into the **fed** (absorptive) **state** and **fasted** (postabsorptive) **state**. The fed state is anabolic; the fasted state is catabolic. (p. 729)
15. **Glycogenesis** is glycogen synthesis. **Glycogenolysis** is glycogen breakdown. (p. 730; Fig. 22-4)
16. **Gluconeogenesis** is glucose synthesis from noncarbohydrate precursors, especially amino acids. (p. 731)
17. Ingested fats enter the circulation as chylomicrons. **Lipoprotein lipase** removes triglycerides, leaving chylomicron remnants to be taken up and metabolized by the liver. (p. 734; Fig. 22-5)

18. The liver secretes lipoprotein complexes, such as LDL-C. **Apoproteins** A and B are the ligands for receptor-mediated endocytosis of lipoprotein complexes. (p. 734; Fig. 22-5)
19. Elevated blood LDL-C and low blood HDL-C are risk factors for coronary heart disease. Therapies for lowering cholesterol decrease cholesterol uptake or synthesis or increase cholesterol clearance. (p. 734)
20. The function of fasted-state metabolism is to maintain adequate plasma glucose concentrations because glucose is normally the only fuel that the brain can metabolize. (p. 735; Fig. 22-7)
21. In the fasted state, the liver produces glucose from glycogen and amino acids. **Beta oxidation** of fatty acids forms acidic **ketone bodies**. (p. 736; Fig. 22-7)

Homeostatic Control of Metabolism

22. Hour-to-hour metabolic regulation depends on the ratio of insulin to glucagon. Insulin dominates the fed state and decreases plasma glucose. Glucagon dominates the fasted state and increases plasma glucose. (p. 736; Figs. 22-9, 22-10)
23. The **islets of Langerhans** secrete insulin and amylin from beta cells, glucagon from alpha cells, and somatostatin from D cells. (p. 736; Fig. 22-8)
24. Increased plasma glucose and amino acid levels stimulate insulin secretion. GI hormones and parasympathetic input amplify it. Sympathetic signals inhibit insulin secretion. (p. 738)
25. Insulin binds to a tyrosine kinase receptor and activates multiple **insulin-receptor substrates**. (p. 739; Fig. 22-11)
26. Major insulin target tissues are the liver, adipose tissue, and skeletal muscles. Some tissues are insulin independent. (p. 739)
27. Insulin increases glucose transport into muscle and adipose tissue, as well as glucose utilization and storage of glucose and fat. (pp. 739–741; Figs. 22-12, 22-14)
28. **Glucagon** stimulates glycogenolysis and gluconeogenesis. (p. 742; Fig. 22-15)
29. **Diabetes mellitus** is a family of disorders marked by abnormal secretion or activity of insulin that causes hyperglycemia. In **type 1 diabetes**, pancreatic beta cells are destroyed by antibodies. In **type 2 diabetes**, target tissues fail to respond normally to insulin. (pp. 742–743)
30. Type 1 diabetes is marked by catabolism of muscle and adipose tissue, glucosuria, polyuria, and metabolic ketoacidosis. Type 2 diabetics have less acute symptoms. In both types, complications include atherosclerosis, neurological changes, and problems with the eyes and kidneys. (pp. 743, 745; Fig. 22-16)
31. **Metabolic syndrome** is a condition in which people have central obesity, elevated fasting glucose levels, and elevated lipids. These people are at high risk for developing cardiovascular disease. (p. 747)

Regulation of Body Temperature

32. Body temperature homeostasis is controlled by the hypothalamus. (p. 749)
33. Heat loss from the body takes place by radiation, conduction, convection, and evaporation. Heat loss is promoted by cutaneous vasodilation and sweating. (p. 748; Fig. 22-19)
34. Heat is generated by **shivering thermogenesis** and by **nonshivering thermogenesis**. (p. 750; Figs. 22-19, 22-20)

QUESTIONS

(Answers to the Review Questions begin on page A1.)

THE PHYSIOLOGY PLACE

Access more review material online at **The Physiology Place** web site. There you'll find review questions, problem-solving activities, case studies, flashcards, and direct links to both *Interactive Physiology*® and *PhysioEx*™. To access the site, go to *www.physiologyplace.com* and select *Human Physiology*, Fifth Edition.

LEVEL ONE REVIEWING FACTS AND TERMS

1. Define metabolic, anabolic, and catabolic pathways.
2. List and briefly explain the three forms of biological work.
3. Define a kilocalorie. What is direct calorimetry?
4. What is the respiratory quotient (RQ)? What is a typical RQ value for an American diet?
5. Define basal metabolic rate (BMR). Under what conditions is it measured? Why does the average BMR differ in adult males and females? List at least four factors other than sex that may affect BMR in humans.
6. What are the three general fates of biomolecules in the body?
7. What are the main differences between metabolism in the absorptive and postabsorptive states?
8. What is a nutrient pool? What are the three primary nutrient pools of the body?
9. What is the primary goal of fasted-state metabolism?
10. Excess energy in the body is stored in what forms?
11. What are the three possible fates for ingested proteins? For ingested fats?
12. Name the two hormones that regulate glucose metabolism, and explain what effect each hormone has on blood glucose concentrations.
13. What noncarbohydrate molecules can be made into glucose? What are the pathways called through which these molecules are converted to glucose?
14. Under what circumstances are ketone bodies formed? From what biomolecule are ketone bodies formed? How are they used by the body, and why is their formation potentially dangerous?
15. Name two stimuli that increase insulin secretion, and one stimulus that inhibits insulin secretion.
16. What are the two types of diabetes mellitus? How do their causes and basic symptoms differ?
17. What factors release glucagon? What organ is the primary target of glucagon? What effect(s) do(es) glucagon produce?
18. Define the following terms and explain their physiological significance:

(a) lipoprotein lipase	(e) apoprotein
(b) amylin	(f) leptin
(c) ghrelin	(g) osmotic diuresis
(d) neuropeptide Y	(h) insulin resistance

19. What effect does insulin have on:
    - (a) glycolysis
    - (b) gluconeogenesis
    - (c) glycogenesis
    - (d) lipogenesis
    - (e) protein synthesis

LEVEL TWO REVIEWING CONCEPTS

20. Concept map: Draw a concept map that compares the fed state and the fasted state. For each state, compare metabolism in skeletal muscles, the brain, adipose tissue, and the liver. Indicate which hormones are active in each stage and at what points they exert their influence.
21. Examine the graphs of insulin and glucagon secretion in Figure 22-10. Why have some researchers concluded that the ratio of these two hormones determines whether glucose is stored or removed from storage?
22. Define, compare, and contrast or relate the terms in each of the following sets:
    - (a) glucose, glycogenolysis, glycogenesis, gluconeogenesis, glucagon, glycolysis
    - (b) shivering thermogenesis, nonshivering thermogenesis, diet-induced thermogenesis
    - (c) lipoproteins, chylomicrons, cholesterol, HDL-C, LDL-C, apoproteins
    - (d) direct and indirect calorimetry
    - (e) conductive heat loss, radiant heat loss, convective heat loss, evaporative heat loss
    - (f) absorptive and postabsorptive states
23. Describe (or map) the physiological events that lead to the following signs or symptoms in a type 1 diabetic:
    - (a) hyperglycemia
    - (b) glucosuria
    - (c) polyuria
    - (d) ketosis
    - (e) dehydration
    - (f) severe thirst
24. Both insulin and glucagon are released following ingestion of a protein meal that raises plasma amino acid levels. Why is the secretion of both hormones necessary?
25. Explain the current theory of the control of food intake. Use the following terms in your explanation: hypothalamus, feeding center, satiety center, appetite, leptin, NPY, neuropeptides.
26. Compare human thermoregulation in hot environments and cold environments.

LEVEL THREE PROBLEM SOLVING

27. Scott is a bodybuilder who consumes large amounts of amino acid supplements in the belief that they will increase his muscle mass. He believes that the amino acids he consumes are stored in his body until he needs them. Is Scott correct? Explain.
28. Draw and label a graph showing the effect of insulin secretion on plasma glucose concentration.
29. One of the debates in fluid therapy for diabetic ketoacidosis (DKA) is whether to administer bicarbonate (bicarb). Although it is generally accepted that bicarb should be given if the patient's blood pH is < 7.1 (life-threatening), most authorities do not give bicarb otherwise. One reason for not administering bicarb relates to the oxygen-binding capacity of hemoglobin. In DKA, patients have low levels of 2,3-DPG [p. 608]. When acidosis is corrected rapidly, 2,3-DPG is much slower to recover and may take 24 or more hours to return to normal.

    Draw and label a graph of the normal oxygen-dissociation curve [p. 607]. BRIEFLY explain and *draw in lines on the same graph to show:*
    - (a) what happens to oxygen release during DKA as a result of acidosis and low 2,3-DPG levels.
    - (b) what happens to oxygen release when the metabolic acidosis is rapidly corrected with bicarbonate.

LEVEL FOUR QUANTITATIVE PROBLEMS

30. One way to estimate obesity is to calculate a person's **body mass index** (BMI). A body mass index greater than 25 (for men) or 30 (for women) is considered a sign of obesity. Calculate your BMI: divide your body weight in kilograms by the square of your height in meters: kg/m^2. (To convert your weight from pounds to kilograms, use the conversion factor 1 kg/2.2 lb. To convert your height from inches to meters, use the factor 1 m/39.24 in.)
31. What is the calorie content of a serving of spaghetti and meatballs that contains 6 g fat, 30 g carbohydrate, and 8 g protein? What percentage of the calories comes from fat?

ANSWERS

Answers to Concept Check Questions

Page 726

1. The feeding center causes an animal to eat, and the satiety center causes an animal to cease eating. Both centers are located in the hypothalamus.
2. The problem might involve abnormal tissue responsiveness—a target cell with no leptin receptors or defective receptors. There might also be a problem with the signal transduction/second messenger pathway.

Page 729

3. These seven factors are age, sex, lean muscle mass, activity, diet, hormones, genetics.
4. One gram of fat contains more than twice the energy of 1 gram of glycogen.
5. $C_6H_{12}O_6 + 6\ O_2 \rightarrow 6\ CO_2 + 6\ H_2O$
6. $RQ = CO_2/O_2 = 6/6 = 1$

Page 733

7. Glycogenesis is glycogen synthesis; gluconeogenesis is synthesis of glucose from amino acids or glycerol.
8. GLUT transporters are passive facilitated diffusion transporters.

Page 735

9. Bile acid sequestrants and ezetimibe leave bile salts and cholesterol in the intestinal lumen to be excreted, so possible side effects are loose, fatty feces and inadequate absorption of fat-soluble vitamins.

Page 736

10. Amino acids used for energy become pyruvate or enter the citric acid cycle.
11. Plasma cholesterol is bound to a carrier protein and can't diffuse across the cell membrane.

Page 741

12. The primary target tissues for insulin are liver, muscle, and adipose tissue.
13. If glucose uptake depended on insulin, the intestine, kidney tubule, and neurons could not absorb glucose in the fasted state. Neurons use glucose exclusively for metabolism and must always be able to take it up.
14. During fight-or-flight, skeletal muscles need glucose for energy. Inhibiting insulin secretion causes the liver to release glucose into the blood and prevents adipose cells from taking it up, making more glucose available for exercising muscle, which does not require insulin for glucose uptake.

Page 742

15. Glycogenolysis and gluconeogenesis both produce glucose, but glycogenolysis does it via glycogen breakdown, whereas gluconeogenesis uses amino acids or glycerol to make new glucose.

Page 747

16. Insulin is a protein and is digested if administered orally.
17. Although dehydrated patients may have elevated plasma K^+ concentrations, their total *amount* of K^+ is below normal. If fluid volume is restored to normal with no K^+ added, a below-normal K^+ concentration results.
18. Sitagliptin inhibits DPP-4, the enzyme that breaks down GLP-1 and GIP. Prolonging the action of these two gut hormones enhances insulin release and slows digestion, which gives cells time to take up and use absorbed glucose.

Page 750

19. Norepinephrine binds to α-receptors to elicit vasoconstriction.
20. Researchers probably classified the neurons as sympathetic because of where they leave the spinal cord.

Page 753

21. Water cooler than body temperature draws heat away from the body through conductive heat transfer. If this loss exceeds the body's heat production, the person feels cold.
22. A person exercising in a humid environment loses the benefit of evaporative cooling and is likely to overheat faster.

Answers to Figure and Graph Questions

Page 731

Figure 22-3: 1. (a) next to up arrow from G-6-P to glycogen, (b) next to arrow from fatty acids to acetyl CoA, (c) next to arrow going from acetyl CoA to fatty acids, (d) next to down arrow from glycogen to G-6-P, (e) with electron transport system. 2. No, amino acids entering the citric acid cycle cannot be used to make glucose because the step from pyruvate to acetyl CoA is not reversible.

Page 734

Figure 22-6: The decrease from 190 to 160 mg/dL has the greatest effect.

25

Integrative Physiology III: Exercise

BACKGROUND BASICS

Aerobic and anaerobic metabolism: **107** Up-regulation: **44** Feedforward reflexes: **204** Catecholamines: **224** Muscle metabolism: **422** Myoglobin: **423** Isometric and isotonic contraction: **427** Presynaptic inhibition: **284** Motor control of movement: **446** Control of heart rate and contractility: **501** Venous return: **501** Control of cardiac output: **504** Starling's law of the heart: **501** Control of blood pressure: **533** Local control of blood flow: **523** Hemoglobin: **605** Alveolar ventilation: **588** Blood gases: **599** Respiratory chemoreceptors: **615** Dehydration: **669** Insulin: **736** Diabetes mellitus: **742** Thermoregulation: **749**

Computer analysis of microarray data showing gene expression.

One fascinating aspect of the physiology of the human being at work is that it provides basic information about the nature and the range of the functional capacity of different organ systems.

—Per-Olof Åstrand and Kaare Rodahl, *Textbook of Work Physiology*, 1977

RUNNING PROBLEM

Heat Stroke

"Dangerous heat continues for fifth straight day," reads the morning headline. Had Colleen Warren, 19, taken time to scan the story, she might have avoided the life-threatening health emergency she faced a few hours later. But Colleen overslept and rushed off to field hockey practice. The weather this week had been unbearably hot and humid, just as it had been all summer. The forecast today was for a high of 105°F, with high humidity. In her haste, Colleen forgot her water bottle. "No big deal," she thought as she hopped on her bike to pedal two miles to the practice field.

814
817
818
821
822
824

In July 2008 the world watched with great anticipation as Michael Phelps swam his way to a record eight gold medals at the 2008 Olympics. The work done by Phelps and the hundreds of other Olympic athletes from around the world represents one of the most common challenges to body homeostasis: exercise. Exercise comes in many forms. Distance running, swimming, and cycling are examples of a dynamic endurance exercise. Weight lifting and strength training are examples of resistance training. In this chapter we examine dynamic exercise as a challenge to homeostasis that is met with an integrated response from multiple body systems.

In many ways, exercise is the ideal example for teaching physiological integration. Everyone is familiar with it, and unlike high-altitude mountaineering or deep-sea diving, it involves no special environmental conditions. Moreover, exercise is a normal physiological state, not a pathological one—although it can be affected by disease and (if excessive) can result in injury.

In addition to being an excellent teaching example, exercise physiology is a very active area of integrative physiology research. The coordinated functioning of multiple body systems is still not well understood in many instances because of complex interactions between neural and local control mechanisms. Researchers use a combination of animal models and studies with human subjects, including elite athletes, in their quest to explain how the body adapts to the metabolic demands of exercise. Note that this chapter is not intended to be a complete discussion of exercise physiology. For further information, readers should consult an exercise physiology textbook.

METABOLISM AND EXERCISE

Exercise begins with skeletal muscle contraction, an active process that requires ATP for energy. But where does the ATP for muscle contraction come from? A small amount is in the muscle fiber when contraction begins (Fig. 25-1, ④ ●). As this ATP is used for muscle contraction and transformed into ADP, another phosphate compound, **phosphocreatine** (PCr), transfers energy from its high-energy phosphate bond to ADP. The transfer replenishes the muscle's supply of ATP [p. 420].

Together, the combination of muscle ATP and phosphocreatine is adequate to support only about 15 seconds of intense exercise, such as sprinting or power lifting. Subsequently, muscle fibers must manufacture additional ATP from energy stored in nutrients. Some of these molecules are contained within the muscle fiber itself. Others must be mobilized from the liver and adipose tissue, then transported to muscles through the circulation.

The primary substrates for energy production are carbohydrates and fats. Recall from Chapter 4 that the most efficient production of ATP occurs through aerobic pathways such as the glycolysis-citric acid cycle pathway [p. 107]. If the cell has adequate amounts of oxygen for oxidative phosphorylation, then both glucose and fatty acids can be metabolized to provide ATP (Fig. 25-1 ①, ②).

If the oxygen requirement of a muscle fiber exceeds its oxygen supply, energy production from fatty acids decreases dramatically, and glucose metabolism shifts to anaerobic pathways. In low-oxygen conditions, when the cell lacks oxygen for oxidative phosphorylation, the final product of glycolysis—pyruvate—is converted to lactate instead of being converted to acetyl CoA and entering the citric acid cycle [Fig. 25-1, ③ and p. 109]. In general, exercise that depends on anaerobic metabolism cannot be sustained for an extended period. Cells that obtain their ATP by anaerobic metabolism of glucose to lactate are said to be carrying out *glycolytic metabolism*.

Anaerobic metabolism has the advantage of speed, producing ATP 2.5 times as rapidly as aerobic pathways do (Fig. 25-2 ●). But this advantage comes with two distinct disadvantages: (1) anaerobic metabolism provides only 2 ATP per glucose, compared with an average of 30–32 ATP per glucose for oxidative metabolism, and (2) anaerobic metabolism contributes to a state of metabolic acidosis by producing H^+. (However, the CO_2 generated during exercise is a more significant source of acid.)

Where does glucose for aerobic and anaerobic ATP production come from? The body has three sources: the plasma glucose pool, intracellular stores of glycogen in muscles and liver, and "new" glucose made in the liver through *gluconeogenesis* [p. 116]. Muscle and liver glycogen stores provide enough energy substrate to release about 2000 kcal (equivalent to about 20 miles of running in the average person), more than adequate for the exercise that most of us do. However, glucose alone cannot provide sufficient ATP for

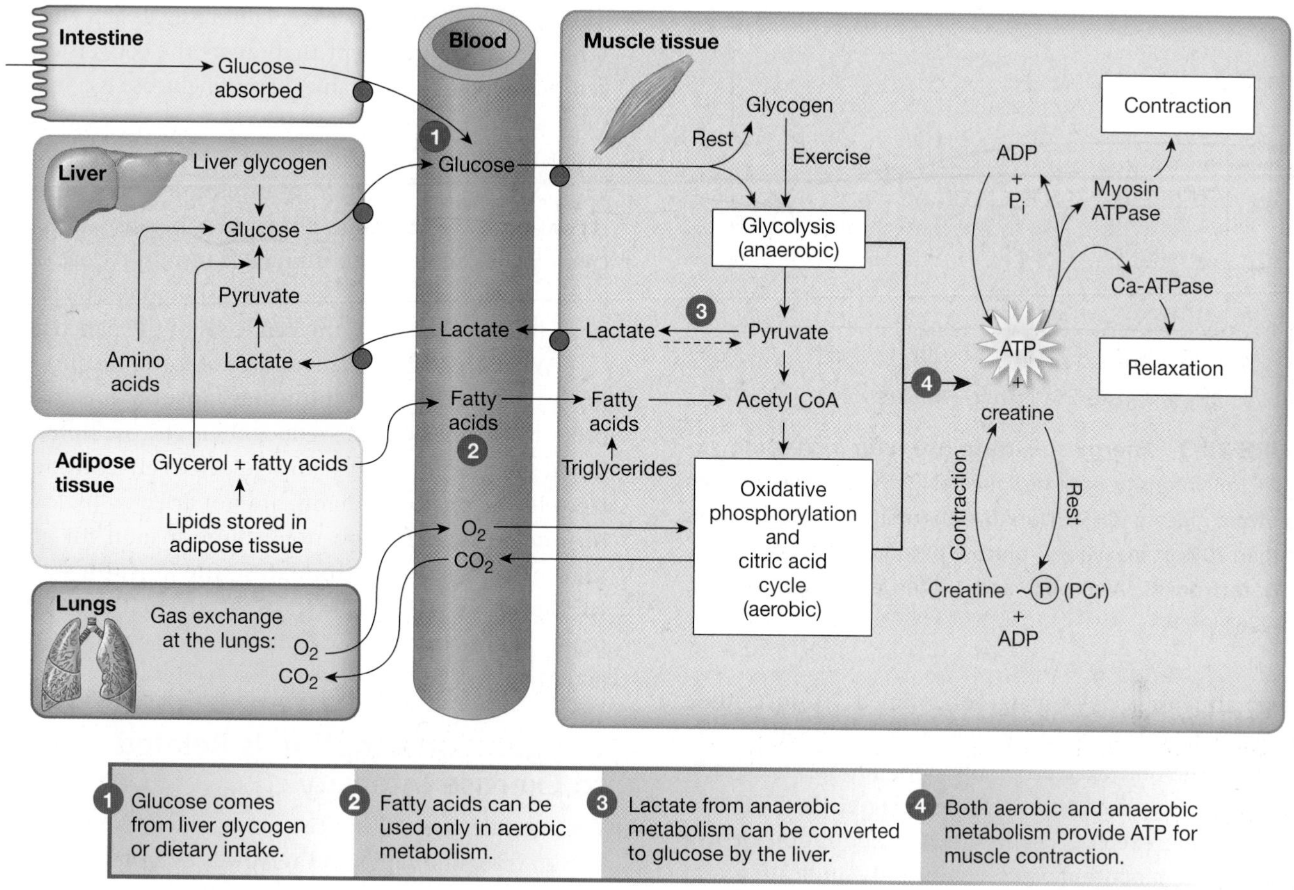

● **FIGURE 25-1** ***Overview of muscle metabolism.*** ATP for muscle contraction is continuously produced by aerobic metabolism of glucose and fatty acids. During short bursts of activity, when ATP demand exceeds the rate of aerobic ATP production, anaerobic glycolysis produces ATP, lactate, and H^+.

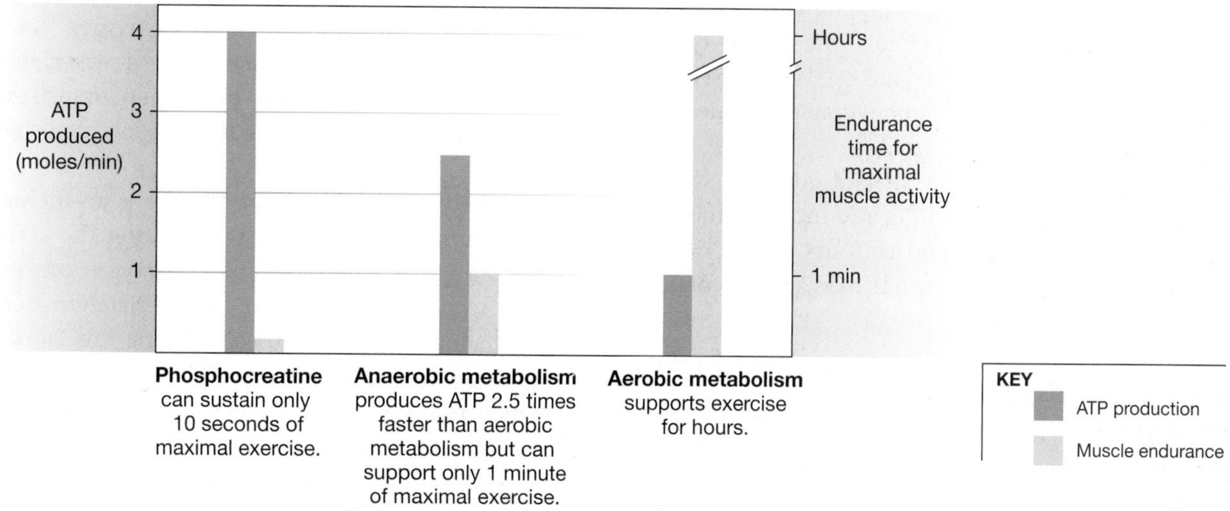

● **FIGURE 25-2** ***Anaerobic metabolism produces ATP 2.5 times faster than aerobic metabolism, but aerobic metabolism can support exercise for hours.***

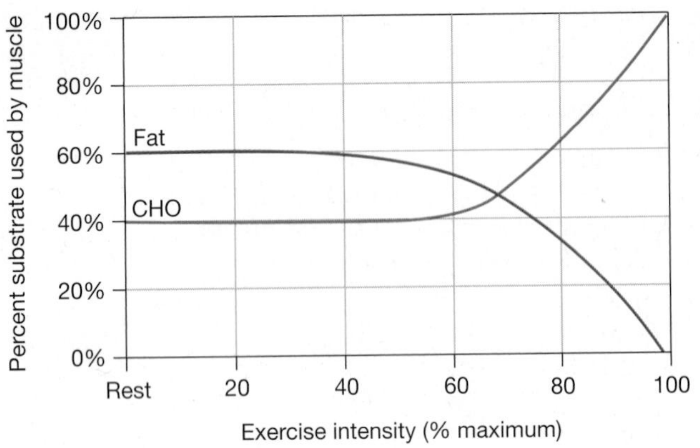

● **FIGURE 25-3** ***Energy substrate use with increasing exercise.*** At low-intensity exercise, muscles get more energy from fats than from glucose (CHO). During high-intensity exercise (levels greater than 70% of maximum), glucose becomes the main energy source. Data from G. A. Brooks and J. Mercier, *J. App. Physiol.* 76:2253–2261, 1994.

endurance athletes such as marathon runners. To meet their energy demands, they rely on the energy stored in fats.

In reality, aerobic exercise of any duration uses both fatty acids and glucose as substrates for ATP production. About 30 minutes after aerobic exercise begins, the concentration of free fatty acids in the blood increases significantly, indicating that fats are being mobilized from adipose tissue. However, the breakdown of fatty acids through the process of β-oxidation [p. 115] is slower than glucose metabolism through glycolysis, so muscle fibers use a combination of fatty acids and glucose to meet their energy needs.

At lower exercise intensities, most of the energy for ATP production comes from fats (Fig. 25-3 ●), which is one reason walking is a good way to lose weight. As exercise intensity increases and ATP is consumed more rapidly, the muscle fibers begin to use a larger proportion of glucose. When exercise exceeds about 70% of maximum, carbohydrates become the primary source of energy.

Aerobic training increases both fat and glycogen stores within muscle fibers. Endurance training also increases the activity of enzymes for β-oxidation and converts muscle fibers from fast-twitch glycolytic to fast-twitch oxidative-glycolytic [p. 422].

Hormones Regulate Metabolism During Exercise

Several hormones that affect glucose and fat metabolism change their pattern of secretion during exercise. Plasma concentrations of glucagon, cortisol, the catecholamines (epinephrine and norepinephrine), and growth hormone all increase during exercise. Cortisol and the catecholamines, along with growth hormone, promote the conversion of triglycerides to glycerol and fatty acids. Glucagon, catecholamines, and cortisol also mobilize liver glycogen and raise plasma glucose levels. A hormonal environment that favors the conversion of glycogen into glucose is desirable, because glucose is a major energy substrate for exercising muscle.

Curiously, although plasma glucose concentrations rise with exercise, the secretion of insulin decreases. This response is contrary to what you might predict, because normally an increase in plasma glucose stimulates insulin release. During exercise, however, insulin secretion is suppressed, probably by sympathetic input onto the beta cells of the pancreas.

What could be the advantage of lower insulin levels during exercise? For one thing, less insulin means that cells other than muscle fibers reduce their glucose uptake, sparing blood glucose for use by muscles. Actively contracting muscle cells, on the other hand, are not affected by low levels of insulin because they do not require insulin for glucose uptake. Contraction stimulates the insulin-independent translocation of GLUT4 transporters to the muscle membrane, increasing glucose uptake in proportion to contractile activity.

Oxygen Consumption Is Related to Exercise Intensity

The activities we call exercise range widely in intensity and duration, from the rapid and relatively brief burst of energy exerted by a sprinter or power lifter, to the sustained effort of a marathoner. Physiologists traditionally quantify the intensity of a period of exercise by measuring oxygen consumption (V_{O_2}). **Oxygen consumption** refers to the fact that oxygen is used up, or consumed, during oxidative phosphorylation, when it combines with hydrogen in the mitochondria to form water [p. 112].

Oxygen consumption is a measure of cellular respiration and is usually measured in liters of oxygen consumed per minute. A person's *maximal rate of oxygen consumption* (V_{O_2max}) is an indicator of the ability to perform endurance exercise. The greater the V_{O_2max}, the greater the person's predicted ability to do work.

A metabolic hallmark of exercise is an increase in oxygen consumption that persists even after the activity ceases (Fig. 25-4 ●). When exercise begins, oxygen consumption increases so rapidly that it is not immediately matched by the oxygen supplied to the muscles. During this lag time, ATP is provided by muscle ATP reserves, phosphocreatine, and aerobic metabolism supported by oxygen stored on muscle myoglobin and blood hemoglobin [p. 423].

The use of these muscle stores creates an *oxygen deficit* because their replacement requires aerobic metabolism and oxygen uptake. Once exercise stops, oxygen consumption is slow to resume its resting level. The **excess postexercise oxygen consumption** (EPOC; formerly called the oxygen debt) represents oxygen being used to metabolize lactate, restore ATP and phosphocreatine levels, and replenish the oxygen bound to

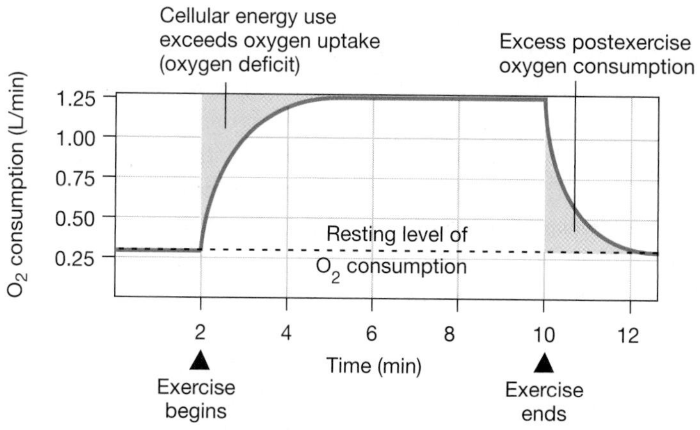

● **FIGURE 25-4** ***Oxygen supply to exercising cells lags behind energy use, creating an oxygen deficit.*** Excess post-exercise oxygen consumption compensates for the oxygen deficit.

myoglobin. Other factors that play a role in elevating postexercise oxygen consumption include increased body temperature and circulating catecholamines.

Several Factors Limit Exercise

What factors limit a person's exercise capacity? To some extent, the answer depends on the type of exercise. Resistance training such as strength training depends heavily on anaerobic metabolism to meet energy needs. The situation is more complex with aerobic or endurance exercise. Is the limiting factor for aerobic exercise the ability of the exercising muscle to use oxygen efficiently? Or is it the ability of the cardiovascular system to deliver oxygen to the tissues? Or the ability of the respiratory system to provide oxygen to the blood?

One possible limiting factor in exercise is the ability of muscle fibers to obtain and use oxygen. If muscle mitochondria are limited in number, or if they have insufficient oxygen supply, the muscle fibers are unable to produce ATP rapidly. Data suggest that muscle metabolism is not the limiting factor for maximum exercise capacity, but muscle metabolism has been shown to influence submaximal exercise capacity. This finding explains the increase in numbers of muscle mitochondria and capillaries with endurance training.

The question of whether the pulmonary system or the cardiovascular system limits maximal exercise was resolved when research showed that ventilation is only 65% of its maximum when cardiac output has reached 90% of its maximum. From that information, exercise physiologists concluded that the ability of the cardiovascular system to deliver oxygen and nutrients to the muscle at a rate that supports aerobic metabolism is a major factor in determining maximum oxygen consumption. One goal of training is to improve cardiac efficiency.

Next we examine the reflexes that integrate breathing and cardiovascular function during exercise.

RUNNING PROBLEM

By the time Colleen reached the practice field, she was already sweating and her face was flushed. At 9:00 A.M. the air temperature was 80°F and the humidity was 54%. Colleen took a quick drink of water from the large water container and ran out to the field.

Question 1:

"Humidity" is the percentage of water vapor present in air. Why is the thermoregulatory mechanism of sweating less efficient in humid environments?

VENTILATORY RESPONSES TO EXERCISE

Think about what happens to your breathing when you exercise. Exercise is associated with both increased rate and increased depth of breathing, resulting in enhanced alveolar ventilation [p. 588]. **Exercise hyperventilation**, or **hyperpnea**, results from a combination of feedforward signals from central command neurons in the motor cortex and sensory feedback from peripheral receptors.

When exercise begins, mechanoreceptors and proprioreceptors [p. 450] in muscles and joints send information about movement to the motor cortex. Descending pathways from the motor cortex to the respiratory control center of the medulla oblongata then immediately increase ventilation (Fig. 25-5 ●).

As muscle contraction continues, sensory information feeds back to the respiratory control center to ensure that ventilation and tissue oxygen use remain closely matched.

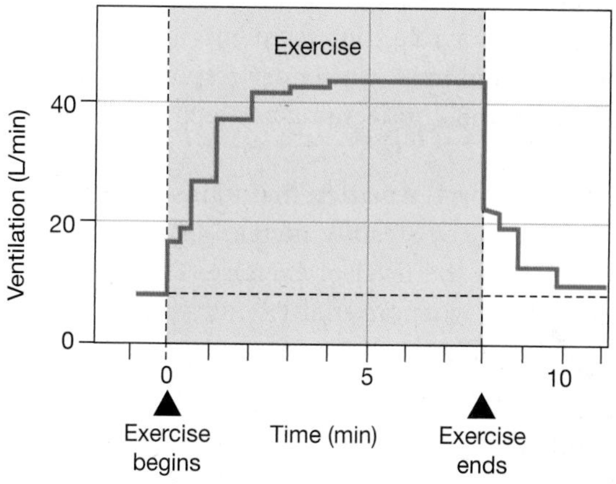

● **FIGURE 25-5** ***Ventilation rate jumps as soon as exercise begins, despite the fact that neither arterial P_{CO_2} nor P_{O_2} has changed.*** Modified from P. Dejours, *Handbook of Physiology* (Washington, D.C.: American Physiological Society, 1964).

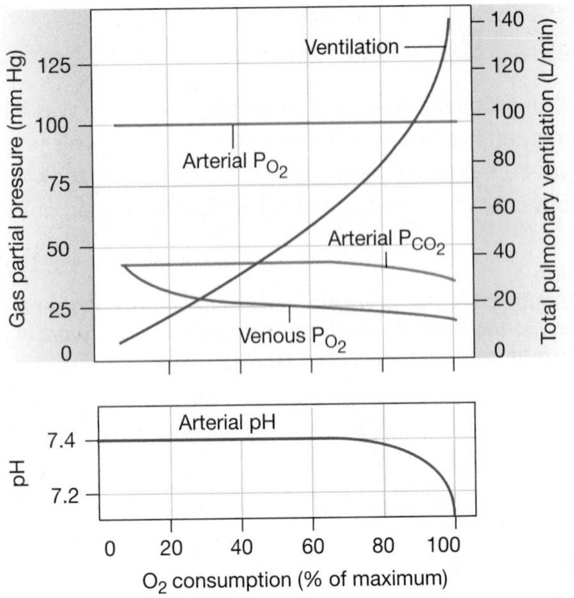

GRAPH QUESTIONS

(a) Ventilation increases with exercise. Why doesn't arterial P_{O_2} increase as well?
(b) What happens to O_2 delivery to cells with increasing exercise?
(c) Why does venous P_{O_2} decrease?
(d) Why doesn't arterial P_{CO_2} increase with exercise?
(e) Why does arterial P_{CO_2} decrease with maximum exercise?

● **FIGURE 25-6** ***Arterial blood gases and pH remain steady with submaximal exercise.*** (Adapted from *Textbook of Work Physiology*, Fourth Edition, P.O. Astrand *et al.*)

Sensory receptors involved in the secondary response probably include central, carotid, and aortic chemoreceptors that monitor P_{CO_2}, pH, and P_{O_2} [p. 615]; proprioceptors in the joints; and possibly receptors located within the exercising muscle itself. Pulmonary stretch receptors were once thought to play a role, but recipients of heart-lung transplants display a normal ventilatory response to exercise even though the neural connections between lung and brain are absent.

Exercise hyperventilation maintains nearly normal arterial P_{O_2} and P_{CO_2} by steadily increasing alveolar ventilation in proportion to the level of exercise. The compensation is so effective that when arterial P_{O_2}, P_{CO_2}, and pH are monitored during mild to moderate exercise, they show no significant change (Fig. 25-6 ●). This observation means that the once-accepted causes of increased ventilation during mild to moderate exercise—reduced arterial P_{O_2}, elevated arterial P_{CO_2}, and decreased plasma pH—must not be correct. Instead the chemoreceptors or medullary respiratory control center, or both, must be responding to other exercise-induced signals.

Several factors have been postulated to be these signals, including sympathetic input to the carotid body and changes in plasma K^+ concentration. During even mild exercise, extracellular K^+ increases as repeated action potentials in the muscle fibers allow K^+ to move out of cells. Carotid chemoreceptors are known to respond to increased K^+ by increasing ventilation. However, because K^+ concentration changes slowly, this mechanism does not explain the sharp initial rise in ventilation at the onset of activity.

It appears likely that the initial increase in ventilation is caused by sensory input from muscle mechanoreceptors combined with parallel descending pathways from the motor cortex to the respiratory control centers. Once exercise is under way, sensory input keeps ventilation matched to metabolic needs.

CONCEPT CHECK

1. If venous P_{O_2} decreases as exercise intensity increases, what do you know about the P_{O_2} of muscle cells as exercise intensity increases?

Answers: p. 827

CARDIOVASCULAR RESPONSES TO EXERCISE

When exercise begins, mechanosensory input from working limbs combines with descending pathways from the motor cortex to activate the cardiovascular control center in the medulla oblongata. The center responds with sympathetic discharge that increases cardiac output and causes vasoconstriction in many peripheral arterioles.

RUNNING PROBLEM

By 10:00 A.M. the temperature had risen to 93°F, with 50% humidity. Colleen felt dizzy and nauseated, but she pressed on. She had made the team by the skin of her teeth and felt she had to prove herself to her teammates. She took only a short drink of water during a break and hustled back onto the field. At 10:07 A.M. Colleen collapsed on the field. One of her teammates with training in first aid felt Colleen's skin. It was hot and dry. A call went in to emergency medical services.

Question 2:
Individuals with a heat emergency called heat exhaustion have cool, moist skin. Hot, dry skin indicates a more serious emergency called heat stroke. Why is heat exhaustion less serious than heat stroke? (Hint: How does skin temperature relate to the body's ability to regulate body temperature?)

814 817 818 821 822 824

Cardiac Output Increases During Exercise

During strenuous exercise, cardiac output rises dramatically. In untrained individuals, cardiac output goes up fourfold, from 5 L/min to 20 L/min. In trained athletes, it may go up six to eight times, reaching as much as 40 L/min. Because oxygen delivery by the cardiovascular system is the primary factor determining exercise tolerance, trained athletes are therefore capable of more strenuous exercise than untrained people.

As you learned in Chapter 14 [Fig. 14-31, p. 504], cardiac output is related to heart rate and stroke volume:

$$\text{Cardiac output (CO)} = \text{heart rate} \times \text{stroke volume}$$

If the factors that influence heart rate and stroke volume are considered, then

$$\text{CO} = (\text{SA node rate} + \text{autonomic nervous system input}) \times (\text{venous return} + \text{force of contraction})$$

Which of these factors has the greatest effect on cardiac output during exercise in a healthy heart? Venous return is enhanced by skeletal muscle contraction and deep inspiratory movements during exericse [p. 501], and it is tempting to postulate that the cardiac muscle fibers simply stretch in response to increased venous return, thereby increasing contractility.

However, overfilling of the ventricles is potentially dangerous, because overstretching may damage the fibers. One factor that counters increased venous return is increased heart rate. If the interval between contractions is shorter, the heart has less time to fill and is less likely to be damaged by excessive stretch.

The initial change in heart rate at the onset of exercise is due to decreased parasympathetic activity at the sinoatrial (SA) node [p. 486]. As cholinergic inhibition lessens, heart rate rises from its resting rate to around 100 beats per minute, the intrinsic pacemaker rate of the SA node. At that point, sympathetic output from the cardiovascular control center escalates.

Sympathetic stimulation has two effects on the heart. First, it increases contractility so that the heart squeezes out more blood per stroke (increased stroke volume). Second, sympathetic innervation increases heart rate so that the heart has less time to relax, protecting it from overfilling. In short, the combination of faster heart rate and greater stroke volume increases cardiac output during exercise.

Muscle Blood Flow Increases During Exercise

At rest, skeletal muscles receive less than a fourth of the cardiac output, or about 1.2 L/min. During exercise, a significant shift in peripheral blood flow takes place because of local and reflex reactions. During strenuous exercise in highly trained athletes, the combination of increased cardiac output and vasodilation can increase blood flow through exercising muscle to more than 22 L/min! The relative distribution of blood flow to tissues also shifts. About 88% of cardiac output is diverted to the exercising muscle, up from 21% at rest (Fig. 25-7 ●).

The redistribution of blood flow during exercise results from a combination of vasodilation in skeletal muscle arterioles and vasoconstriction in other tissues. At the onset of exercise, sympathetic signals from the cardiovascular control center cause vasoconstriction in peripheral tissues. As muscles become active, changes in the microenvironment of muscle tissue take place: tissue O_2 concentrations decrease, while temperature, CO_2, and acid in the interstitial fluid around muscle fibers increase. All these factors act as paracrines causing local vasodilation that overrides the sympathetic signal for vasoconstriction. The net result is shunting of blood flow from inactive tissues to the exercising muscles, where it is needed.

Blood Pressure Rises Slightly During Exercise

What happens to blood pressure during exercise? You learned in Chapter 15 that peripheral blood pressure is determined by a combination of cardiac output and peripheral resistance [p. 519]. Cardiac output increases during exercise, thereby contributing to increased blood pressure. The changes resulting from peripheral resistance are harder to predict, however, because some peripheral arterioles are constricting while others are dilating:

$$\text{Mean arterial blood pressure} = \text{cardiac output} \times \text{peripheral resistance}$$

Skeletal muscle vasodilation decreases peripheral resistance to blood flow. At the same time, sympathetically induced vasoconstriction in nonexercising tissues offsets the vasodilation, but only partially. Consequently, total peripheral resistance to blood flow falls dramatically as exercise commences, reaching a minimum at about 75% of V_{O_2max} (Fig. 25-8a ●).

If no other compensation occurred, this decrease in peripheral resistance would dramatically lower arterial blood pressure. However, increased cardiac output cancels out decreased peripheral resistance. When blood pressure is monitored during exercise, mean arterial blood pressure actually increases slightly as exercise intensity increases (Fig. 25-8b). The fact that it increases at all, however, suggests that the normal baroreceptor reflexes that control blood pressure are functioning differently during exercise.

CONCEPT CHECK

2. In Figure 25-8b, why does the line for mean blood pressure lie closer to diastolic pressure instead of being evenly centered between systolic and diastolic pressures? (*Hint:* What is the equation for calculating mean blood pressure?)

Answers: p. 827

25

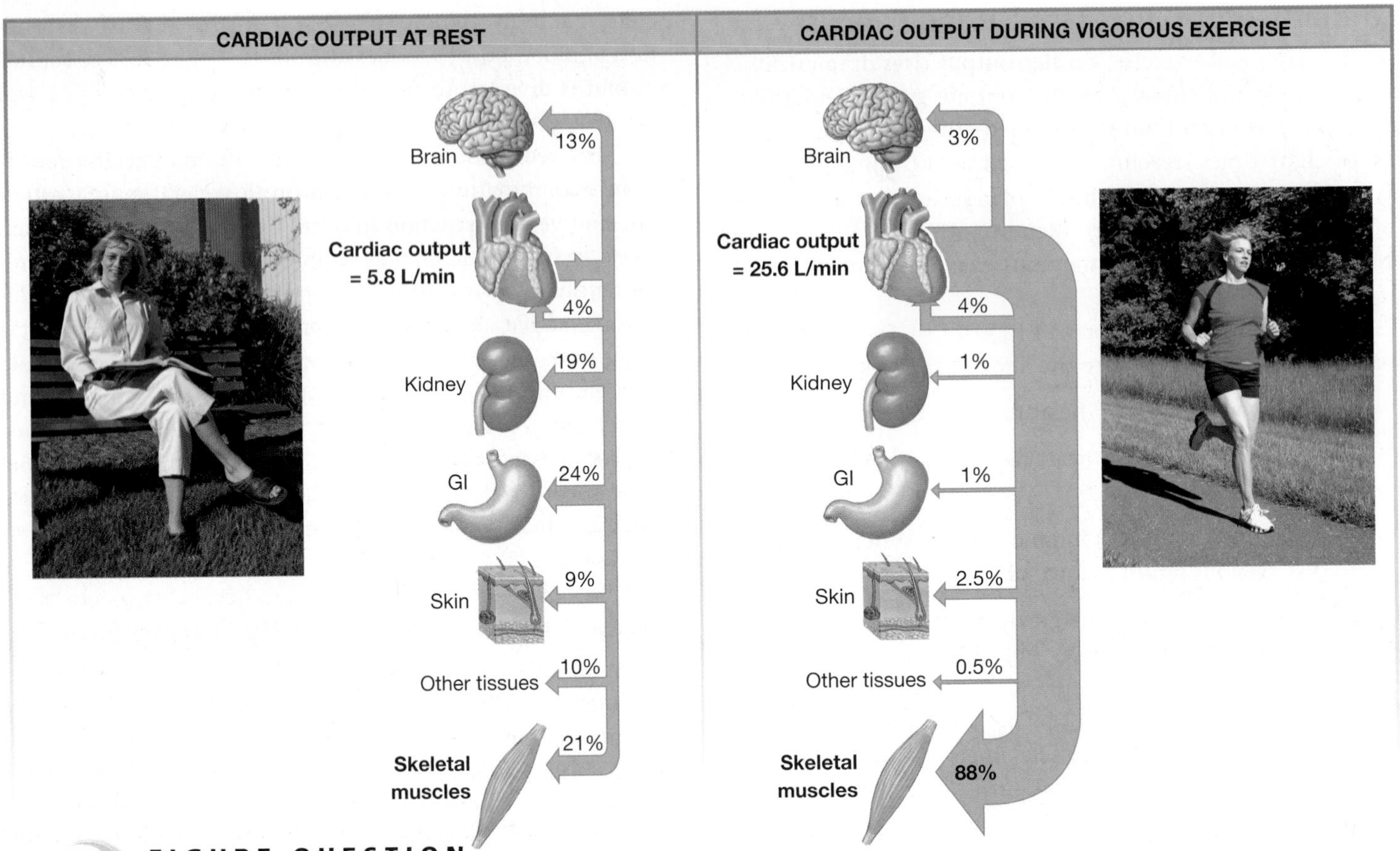

FIGURE QUESTION

The percentage of cardiac output to all tissues except muscle falls with exercise. In which tissues does actual blood flow decrease?

● **FIGURE 25-7** ***Blood flow is distributed differently at rest than during exercise.*** Vasoconstriction in nonexercising tissues combined with vasodilation in exercising muscle shunts blood to muscles.

The Baroreceptor Reflex Adjusts to Exercise

Normally, homeostasis of blood pressure is regulated through peripheral baroreceptors in the carotid and aortic bodies: an increase in blood pressure initiates responses that return blood pressure to normal. But during exercise, blood pressure increases without activating homeostatic compensation. What happens to the normal baroreceptor reflex during exercise?

There are several theories. According to one, signals from the motor cortex during exercise reset the arterial baroreceptor threshold to a higher pressure. Blood pressure can then increase slightly during exercise without triggering the homeostatic counter-regulatory responses.

Another theory suggests that signals in baroreceptor afferent neurons are blocked in the spinal cord by presynaptic inhibition [p. 284] at some point before the afferent neurons synapse with central nervous system neurons. This central inhibition inactivates the baroreceptor reflex during exercise.

A third theory is based on the postulated existence of muscle chemoreceptors that are sensitive to metabolites (probably H^+) produced during strenuous exercise. When stimulated, these chemoreceptors signal the CNS that tissue blood flow is not adequate to remove muscle metabolites or keep the muscle in aerobic metabolism. The chemoreceptor input is reinforced by sensory input from mechanoreceptors in the working limbs. The CNS response to this sensory input is to override the baroreceptor reflex and raise blood pressure to enhance muscle perfusion. The same hypothetical muscle chemoreceptors may play a role in ventilatory responses to exercise.

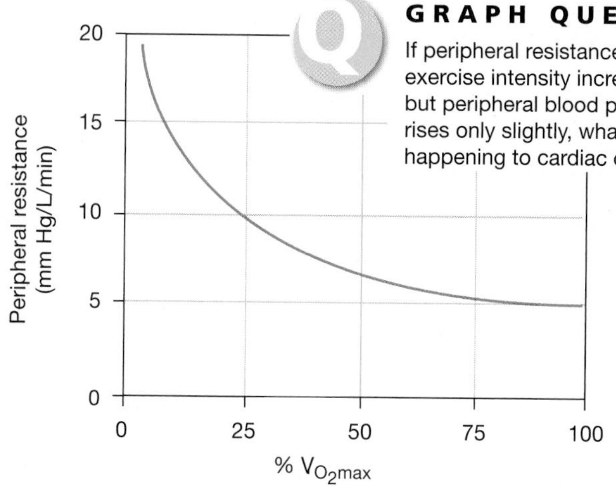

GRAPH QUESTION

If peripheral resistance falls as exercise intensity increases, but peripheral blood pressure rises only slightly, what must be happening to cardiac output?

(a) Peripheral resistance decreases due to vasodilation in exercising muscle.

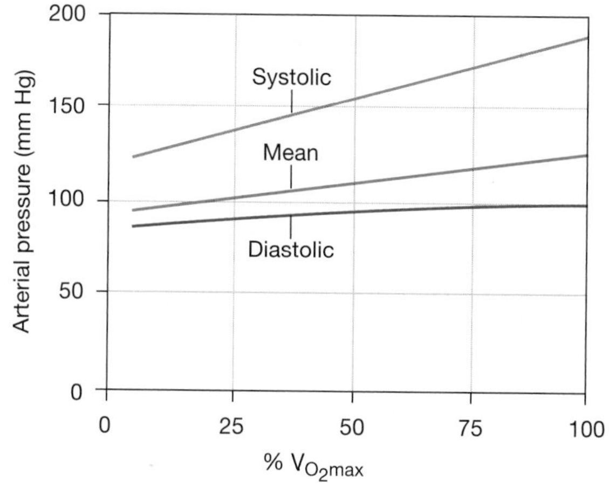

(b) Mean arterial blood pressure rises slightly despite drop in resistance.

● **FIGURE 25-8** ***Changes in peripheral resistance and arterial blood pressure during exercise***

RUNNING PROBLEM

While they waited for the ambulance, Colleen's coaches began to try to cool her down by misting her with cool water and using a fan to blow air across her body. When the paramedics reached Colleen on the field, they took her blood pressure, and it was extremely low. Her body temperature was 104°F. The paramedics rushed Colleen to the hospital.

Question 3:

Why was Colleen's blood pressure so low?

Question 4:

Why would misting and fanning help lower Colleen's body temperature?

814 817 818 821 822 824

FEEDFORWARD RESPONSES TO EXERCISE

Interestingly, there is a significant *feedforward* element [p. 204] in the physiological responses to exercise. It is easy to explain physiological changes that occur with exercise as reactions to the disruption of homeostasis. However, many of these changes occur in the absence of the normal stimuli or before the stimuli are present. For example, as you may know from your own experience, ventilation rates jump as soon as exercise begins (Fig. 25-5), even though experiments have shown that arterial P_{O_2} and P_{CO_2} do not change (Fig. 25-6).

How does the feedforward response work? One model says that as exercise begins, proprioceptors in the muscles and joints send information to the motor cortex of the brain. Descending signals from the motor cortex go not only to the exercising muscles but also along parallel pathways to the cardiovascular and respiratory control centers and to the limbic system of the brain.

Output from the limbic system and cardiovascular control center triggers generalized sympathetic discharge. As a result, an immediate slight increase in blood pressure marks the beginning of exercise. Sympathetic discharge causes widespread vasoconstriction, increasing blood pressure. Once exercise has begun, this increase in blood pressure compensates for decreases in blood pressure resulting from muscle vasodilation.

As exercise proceeds, reactive compensations become superimposed on the feedforward changes. For example, when exercise reaches 50% of aerobic capacity, muscle chemoreceptors detect the buildup of H^+, lactate, and other metabolites, and send this information to central command centers in the brain. The command centers then maintain changes in ventilation and circulation that were initiated in a feedforward manner. Thus, the integration of systems in exercise probably involves both common reflex pathways and some unique centrally mediated reflex pathways.

TEMPERATURE REGULATION DURING EXERCISE

As exercise continues, heat released through metabolism creates an additional challenge to homeostasis. Most of the energy released during metabolism is not converted into ATP but instead is released as heat. (Efficiency of energy conversion from organic substrates to ATP is only 20–25%.) With continued exercise, heat production exceeds heat loss, and core body temperature rises. In endurance events, body temperature can reach 40°–42°C (104°–108°F), which we would normally consider a fever.

This rise in body temperature during exercise triggers two thermoregulatory mechanisms: sweating and increased cutaneous blood flow [p. 750]. Both mechanisms help regulate

25

body temperature, but both can also disrupt homeostasis in other ways. While sweating lowers body temperature through evaporative cooling, the loss of fluid from the extracellular compartment can cause dehydration and significantly reduce circulating blood volume. Because sweat is a hypotonic fluid, the extra water loss increases body osmolarity. The combination of decreased ECF volume and increased osmolarity during extended exercise sets in motion the complex homeostatic pathway for dehydration described in Chapter 20, including thirst and renal conservation of water [Fig. 20-17, p. 671].

The other thermoregulatory mechanism—increased blood flow to the skin—causes body heat loss to the environment through convection [p. 748]. However, increased sympathetic output during exercise tends to vasoconstrict cutaneous blood vessels, which opposes the thermoregulatory response. The primary control of vasodilation in hairy regions of skin, such as trunk and limbs, during exercise appears to come from a sympathetic vasodilator system. Activation of these acetylcholine-secreting sympathetic neurons as body core temperature rises dilates some cutaneous blood vessels without altering sympathetic vasoconstriction in other body tissues.

Although cutaneous vasodilation is essential for thermoregulation, it can disrupt homeostasis by decreasing peripheral resistance and diverting blood flow from the muscles. In the face of these contradictory demands, the body initially gives preference to thermoregulation. However, if central venous pressure falls below a critical minimum, the body abandons thermoregulation in the interest of maintaining blood flow to the brain.

The degree to which the body can adjust to both demands depends on the type of exercise being performed and its intensity and duration. Strenuous exercise in hot, humid environments can severely impair normal thermoregulatory mechanisms and cause *heat stroke,* a potentially fatal condition. Unless prompt measures are taken to cool the body, core temperatures can go as high as 43°C (109°F).

It is possible for the body to adapt to repeated exercise in hot environments, however, through **acclimatization**. In this process, physiological mechanisms shift to fit a change in environmental conditions. As the body adjusts to exercise in the heat, sweating begins sooner and doubles or triples in volume, enhancing evaporative cooling. With acclimatization, sweat also becomes more dilute, as salt is reabsorbed from the sweat glands under the influence of increased aldosterone. Salt loss in an unacclimatized person exercising in the heat may reach 30 g NaCl per day, but that value decreases to as little as 3 g after a month of acclimatization.

CONCEPT CHECK

3. The active vasodilator nerves to the skin secrete ACh but are classified as sympathetic neurons. On what basis were they identified as sympathetic? Answers: p. 827

RUNNING PROBLEM

When Colleen arrived in the emergency room, she was quickly diagnosed with heat stroke, a life-threatening condition. She was immersed in a tub of cool water and given intravenous fluids.

Question 5:
What steps should Colleen have taken to avoid heat stroke? (Start at 9:00 A.M., when Colleen set out for the practice field.)

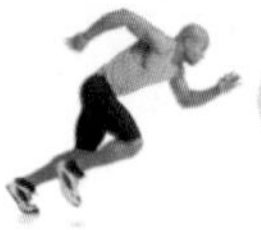

814 817 818 821 822 824

EXERCISE AND HEALTH

Physical activity has many positive effects on the human body. The lifestyles of humans have changed dramatically since we were hunter-gatherers, but our bodies still seem to work best with a certain level of physical activity. Several common pathological conditions—including high blood pressure, strokes, and diabetes mellitus—can be improved by physical activity. Even so, developing regular exercise habits is one lifestyle change that many people find difficult to make. In this section we look at the effects exercise has on several common health conditions.

Exercise Lowers the Risk of Cardiovascular Disease

As early as the 1950s, scientists showed that physically active men have a lower rate of heart attacks than do men who lead sedentary lives. These studies started many investigations into the exact relationship between cardiovascular disease and exercise. Scientists have subsequently demonstrated that exercise has positive benefits for both men and women. These benefits include lowering blood pressure, decreasing plasma triglyceride levels, and raising plasma HDL-cholesterol levels. High blood pressure is a major risk factor for strokes, and elevated triglycerides and low HDL-cholesterol levels are associated with development of atherosclerosis and increased risk of heart attack.

Overall, exercise reduces the risk of death or illness from a variety of cardiovascular diseases, although the exact mechanisms by which this occurs are still unclear. Even such mild exercise as walking has significant health benefits that could reduce the risk of developing cardiovascular diseases or diabetes and the complications of obesity in the estimated 40 million adult Americans with sedentary lifestyles.

Type 2 Diabetes Mellitus May Improve with Exercise

Regular exercise is now widely accepted as effective in preventing and alleviating type 2 diabetes mellitus and its complications, including microvascular retinopathy [p. 515], diabetic neuropathy [p. 348], and cardiovascular disease [p. 537]. With

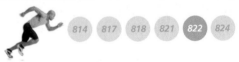

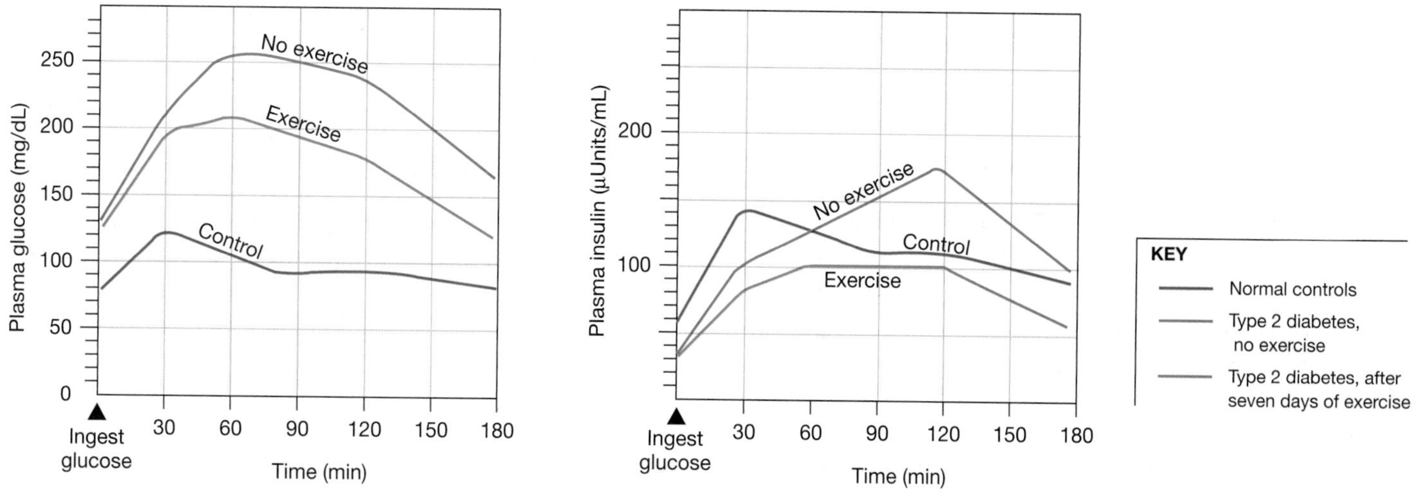

● **FIGURE 25-9** ***Exercise improves glucose tolerance and insulin secretion in diabetic men.*** **(a)** Plasma glucose levels in normal men (blue line), in men with type 2 diabetes who had not been exercising (red line), and in those same diabetic men after seven days of exercise (green line). **(b)** Plasma insulin levels in groups of men in the categories described in part (a). Data from B. R. Seals *et al.*, *J. App. Physiol.* 56(6):1521–1525, 1984; and M. A. Rogers *et al.*, *Diabetes Care* 11:613–618, 1988.

regular exercise, skeletal muscle fibers up-regulate both the number of GLUT4 glucose transporters and the number of insulin receptors on their membrane. The addition of insulin-independent GLUT4 transporters decreases the muscle's dependence on insulin for glucose uptake. Glucose uptake into the exercising muscle also helps correct the hyperglycemia of diabetes.

Up-regulation of insulin receptors with exercise makes the muscle fibers more sensitive to insulin. A smaller amount of insulin then can achieve a response that previously required more insulin. Because the cells are responding to lower insulin levels, the endocrine pancreas secretes less insulin. This lessens the stress on the pancreas, resulting in a lower incidence of type 2 diabetes mellitus.

Figure 25-9 ● shows the effects of seven days of exercise on glucose utilization and insulin secretion in men with mild type 2 diabetes. Individuals in the experiment underwent *glucose tolerance tests,* in which they ingested 100 g of glucose after an overnight fast. Their plasma glucose levels were assessed before and for 120 minutes after ingesting the glucose. Simultaneous measurements were made of plasma insulin.

The graph in Figure 25-9a shows glucose tolerance tests in control subjects (blue line) and in the diabetic men before and after exercise (red and green lines, respectively). Figure 25-9b shows concurrent insulin secretion in the three groups. After only seven days of exercise, both the glucose tolerance test and insulin secretion in exercising diabetic subjects had shifted to a pattern that was more like that of the normal control subjects. These results demonstrate the beneficial effect of exercise on glucose transport and metabolism, and support the recommendation that patients with type 2 diabetes maintain a regular exercise program.

Stress and the Immune System May Be Influenced by Exercise

Another topic that is receiving much attention is the interaction of exercise with the immune system. Epidemiological studies looking at large populations of people suggest that exercise is associated with a reduced incidence of disease and with increased longevity. Moreover, many people believe that exercise boosts immunity, prevents cancer, and helps HIV-infected patients combat AIDS.

To date, however, there are few rigidly controlled research studies that support those viewpoints. Actually, some evidence suggests that strenuous exercise is a form of stress that suppresses the immune response. Immune suppression may be due to corticosteroid release, or it may be due to release of interferon-γ during strenuous exercise.

Researchers have proposed that the relationship between exercise and immunity can be represented by a J-shaped curve (Fig. 25-10 ●). People who exercise moderately have slightly more effective immune systems than those who are sedentary, but people who exercise strenuously may experience a decrease in immune function because of the stress of the exercise.

Another area of exercise physiology filled with interesting though contradictory results is the effect of exercise on stress, depression, and other psychological parameters. Research has shown an inverse relationship between exercise and depression: people who exercise regularly are significantly less likely to be clinically depressed than are people who do not exercise regularly. Although the association exists, assigning cause and effect to the two parameters is difficult. Are the exercisers less

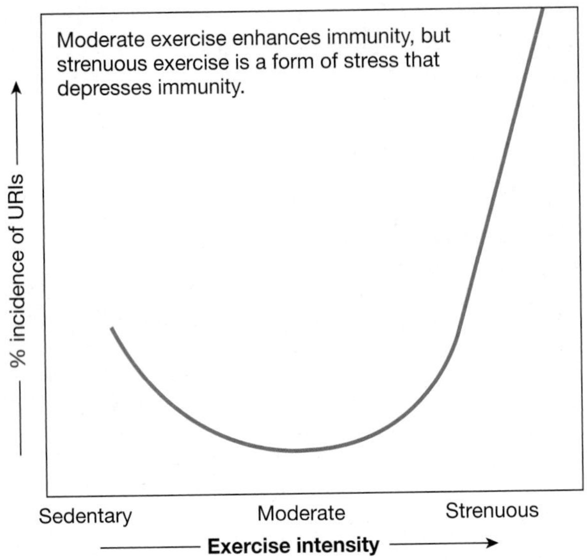
Moderate exercise enhances immunity, but strenuous exercise is a form of stress that depresses immunity.
% incidence of URIs
Sedentary
Moderate
Strenuous
Exercise intensity

● **FIGURE 25-10** ***The relationship between immune function and exercise.*** Individuals who exercise in moderation have fewer upper respiratory infections (URIs) than sedentary individuals or those who exercise strenuously.

depressed because they exercise? Or do depressed individuals exercise less because they are depressed?

Many published studies appear to show that regular exercise is effective in reducing depression. But a careful analysis of experimental design suggests that the conclusions of those studies may be overstated. The subjects in many of the experiments were being treated concurrently with drugs or psychotherapy, so it is difficult to attribute improvement in their condition solely to exercise. In addition, participation in exercise studies gives subjects a period of social interaction, another factor that might play a role in the reduction of stress and depression.

The assertion that exercise reduces depression has some support from studies that show that exercise increases serotonin in the brain. Drugs that enhance serotonin activity, such as the selective serotonin reuptake inhibitors [p. 322] are currently being used to treat depression, and a way to achieve the same result without drugs would be desirable. A number of clinical trials that look at exercise effects on depression and health are currently underway.

RUNNING PROBLEM CONCLUSION

Heat Stroke

After a day of treatment, Colleen recovered enough to be sent home. She was unable to practice with the team for the remainder of the season because victims of heat stroke are more sensitive to high temperature for some time after the episode.

Heat stroke can occur in athletes who overexert themselves in extremely hot weather, but it is also common in elderly individuals, whose thermoregulatory mechanisms are less efficient than those in younger people. To learn more about the symptoms and treatment of heat stroke, try a Google search. Then check your understanding of this problem by comparing your answers to those in the table below.

	QUESTION	FACTS	INTEGRATION AND ANALYSIS
1	Why is the thermoregulatory mechanism of sweating less efficient in humid environments?	"Humidity" is the percentage of water vapor present in air. Thermoregulation in warm environments includes sweating and evaporative cooling.	Evaporation is slower in humid air, so evaporative cooling is less effective in high humidity.
2	Individuals with a heat emergency called heat exhaustion have cool, moist skin. Hot, dry skin indicates a more serious emergency called heat stroke. Why is heat exhaustion less serious than heat stroke?	Sweating helps the body regulate temperature through evaporative cooling. As evaporation occurs, the skin surface cools.	Cool, moist skin indicates that the sweating mechanism is still functioning. Hot, dry skin indicates that the sweating mechanism has failed. Subjects with hot, dry skin are likely to have higher internal temperatures.
3	Why was Colleen's blood pressure so low?	Blood volume decreases when the body loses large amounts of water through sweating.	Colleen had been sweating but not replacing the fluid she lost. This caused her blood volume to decrease, with a corresponding decrease in blood pressure.
4	Why would misting and fanning help lower Colleen's body temperature?	Evaporation of water creates evaporative cooling.	Putting water on Colleen's skin, then using a fan to evaporate the water helps cool the skin.

(continued)

	QUESTION	FACTS	INTEGRATION AND ANALYSIS
5	What steps could Colleen have taken to avoid heat stroke? (Start at 9:00 A.M., when Colleen set out for the practice field.)	Heat stroke is caused by dehydration resulting from excessive sweating. Dehydration results in a drop in blood pressure. Peripheral blood vessels constrict in an effort to maintain pressure and blood flow to the brain. Constricted blood vessels in the skin cannot release excess heat. In addition, the sweating response is inhibited to prevent further fluid loss.	Colleen could have avoided heat stroke by: (1) consuming large amounts of fluid (water plus electrolytes) before and during practice; (2) avoiding unnecessary exercise such as bicycling to practice; (3) stopping activity at the first signs of heat emergency (dizziness and nausea); (4) seeking shade and drinking large amounts of fluid to replenish lost fluids; (5) applying cool wet towels or ice to lower body temperature.

814 817 818 821 822 824

CHAPTER SUMMARY

In this chapter you learned about exercise and the physiological challenges it presents. *Integration* and *coordination* between the body's *physiological control systems* allow the internal environment to remain relatively constant, despite the challenges to *homeostasis* that exercise presents.

Metabolism and Exercise

1. Exercising muscle requires a steady supply of ATP from metabolism or from conversion of phosphocreatine. (p. 814; Fig. 25-1)
2. Carbohydrates and fats are the primary energy substrates. Glucose can be metabolized through both oxidative and anaerobic pathways, but fatty acid metabolism requires oxygen. (p. 814; Fig. 25-1)
3. Anaerobic **glycolytic metabolism** converts glucose to lactate and H^+. Glycolytic metabolism is 2.5 times more rapid than aerobic pathways but is not as efficient at ATP production. (p. 814; Fig. 25-2)
4. Glucagon, cortisol, catecholamines, and growth hormone influence glucose and fatty acid metabolism during exercise. These hormones favor the conversion of glycogen to glucose. (p. 816)
5. Plasma glucose concentrations rise with exercise, but insulin secretion decreases. This response reduces glucose uptake by most cells, making more glucose available for exercising muscle. (p. 816)
6. The intensity of exercise is indicated by **oxygen consumption** (V_{O_2}). A person's maximal rate of oxygen consumption (V_{O_2max}) is an indicator of that person's ability to perform endurance exercise. (p. 816)
7. Oxygen consumption increases rapidly at the onset of exercise. **Excess postexercise oxygen consumption** is due to ongoing metabolism, increased body temperature, and circulating catecholamines. (p. 816; Fig. 25-4)
8. Muscle mitochondria increase in size and number with endurance training. (p. 817)
9. At maximal exertion, the ability of the cardiovascular system to deliver oxygen and nutrients appears to be the primary limiting factor. (p. 817)

Ventilatory Responses to Exercise

10. Exercise hyperventilation results from feedforward signals from the motor cortex and sensory feedback from peripheral sensory receptors. (p. 817; Fig. 25-5)
11. Arterial P_{O_2}, P_{CO_2}, and pH do not change significantly during mild to moderate exercise. (p. 818; Fig. 25-6)

Cardiovascular Responses to Exercise

12. Cardiac output increases with exercise because of increased venous return and sympathetic stimulation of heart rate and contractility. (p. 819; Fig. 25-7)
13. Blood flow through exercising muscle increases dramatically when skeletal muscle arterioles dilate. Arterioles in other tissues constrict. (p. 819; Fig. 25-7)
14. Decreased tissue O_2 and glucose or increased muscle temperature, CO_2, and acid act as paracrine signals and cause local vasodilation. (p. 819)
15. Mean arterial blood pressure increases slightly as exercise intensity increases. The baroreceptors that control blood pressure change their setpoints during exercise. (p. 820; Fig. 25-8)

Feedforward Responses to Exercise

16. When exercise begins, feedforward responses prevent significant disruption of homeostasis. (p. 821)

Temperature Regulation During Exercise

17. Heat released during exercise is dissipated by sweating and increased cutaneous blood flow. (p. 821)

Exercise and Health

18. Physical activity can help prevent or decrease the risk of developing high blood pressure, strokes, and type 2 diabetes mellitus. (p. 822)
19. Studies suggest that serotonin release during exercise may help alleviate depression. (p. 824)

QUESTIONS

(Answers to the Review Questions begin on page A1.)

THE PHYSIOLOGY PLACE

Access more review material online at **The Physiology Place** web site. There you'll find review questions, problem-solving activities, case studies, flashcards, and direct links to both *Interactive Physiology®* and *PhysioEx™*. To access the site, go to *www.physiologyplace.com* and select *Human Physiology,* Fifth Edition.

LEVEL ONE REVIEWING FACTS AND TERMS

1. Name the two muscle compounds that store energy in the form of high-energy phosphate bonds.
2. The most efficient ATP production is through *aerobic/anaerobic* pathways. When these pathways are being used, then *glucose/fatty acids/ both/neither* can be metabolized to provide ATP.
3. What are the differences between aerobic and anaerobic metabolism?
4. List three sources of glucose that can be metabolized to ATP, either directly or indirectly.
5. List four hormones that promote the conversion of triglycerides into fatty acids. What effects do these hormones have on plasma glucose levels?
6. What is meant by the term oxygen deficit, and how is it related to excessive postexercise oxygen consumption?
7. What organ system is the limiting factor for maximal exertion?
8. In endurance events, body temperature can reach 40°–42°C. What is normal body temperature? What two thermoregulatory mechanisms are triggered by this change in temperature during exercise?

LEVEL TWO REVIEWING CONCEPTS

9. Concept map: Map the metabolic, cardiovascular, and respiratory changes that occur during exercise. Include the signals to and from the nervous system, and show what specific areas signal and coordinate the exercise response.
10. What causes insulin secretion to decrease during exercise, and why is this decrease adaptive?
11. State two advantages and two disadvantages of anaerobic glycolysis.
12. Compare and contrast each of the terms in the following sets of terms, especially as they relate to exercise:
    (a) ATP, ADP, PCr
    (b) myoglobin, hemoglobin
13. Match the following brain areas with the response(s) that each controls. Brain areas may control one response, more than one response, or none at all. Some responses may be associated with more than one brain area.

(a) pons	1. changes in cardiac output
(b) medulla oblongata	2. vasoconstriction
(c) midbrain	3. exercise hyperventilation
(d) motor cortex	4. increased stroke volume
(e) hypothalamus	5. increased heart rate
(f) cerebellum	6. coordination of skeletal muscle movement
(g) brain not involved (i.e., local control)	

14. Specify whether each of the following parameters stays the same, increases, or decreases when a person becomes better conditioned for athletic activities:
    (a) heart rate during exercise
    (b) resting heart rate
    (c) cardiac output during exercise
    (d) resting cardiac output
    (e) breathing rate during exercise
    (f) blood flow to muscles during exercise
    (g) blood pressure during exercise
    (h) total peripheral resistance during exercise
15. Why doesn't increased venous return during exercise overstretch the heart muscle?
16. Diagram the three theories that explain why the normal baroreceptor reflex is absent during exercise.
17. List and briefly discuss the benefits of a lifestyle that includes regular exercise.
18. Explain how exercise decreases blood glucose in type 2 diabetes mellitus.

LEVEL THREE PROBLEM SOLVING

19. You have decided to manufacture a new sports drink that will help athletes, from football players to gymnasts. List at least four different ingredients you would include in your drink, and indicate why each is important for the athlete.

LEVEL FOUR QUANTITATIVE PROBLEMS

20. You are a well-conditioned athlete. At rest, your heart rate is 60 beats per minute and your stroke volume is 70 mL/beat. What is your cardiac output? At one point during exercise, your heart rate goes up to 120 beats/min. Does your cardiac output increase proportionately? Explain.

ANSWERS

Answers to Concept Check Questions

Page 818

1. If venous P_{O_2} decreases, P_{O_2} in the cells is also decreasing.

Page 819

2. The mean blood pressure line lies closer to the diastolic pressure line because the heart spends more time in diastole than systole.

Page 822

3. The neurons are classified as sympathetic because of where they originate along the spinal cord.

Answers to Figure and Graph Questions

Page 818

Figure 25-6: (a) Arterial P_{O_2} remains constant because pulmonary ventilation is matched to blood flow through the lungs. (b) Although arterial P_{O_2} is constant, oxygen delivery to cells increases due to increased cardiac output (not shown). (c) Venous P_{O_2} drops as exercise increases because cells remove more oxygen from hemoglobin as oxygen consumption increases. (d) Arterial P_{CO_2} does not increase because increased production is matched by increased ventilation. (e) As the person begins to hyperventilate, arterial (and alveolar) P_{CO_2} declines.

Page 820

Figure 25-7: Blood flow to an organ is calculated by multiplying cardiac output (L/min) times the percentage of flow to that organ. When rest and exercise values are compared, actual blood flow decreases only in the kidneys, GI tract, and "other tissues."

Page 821

Figure 25-8: Mean arterial pressure is cardiac output × resistance. If resistance is falling but MAP is increasing, then cardiac output must be increasing.

26 Reproduction and Development

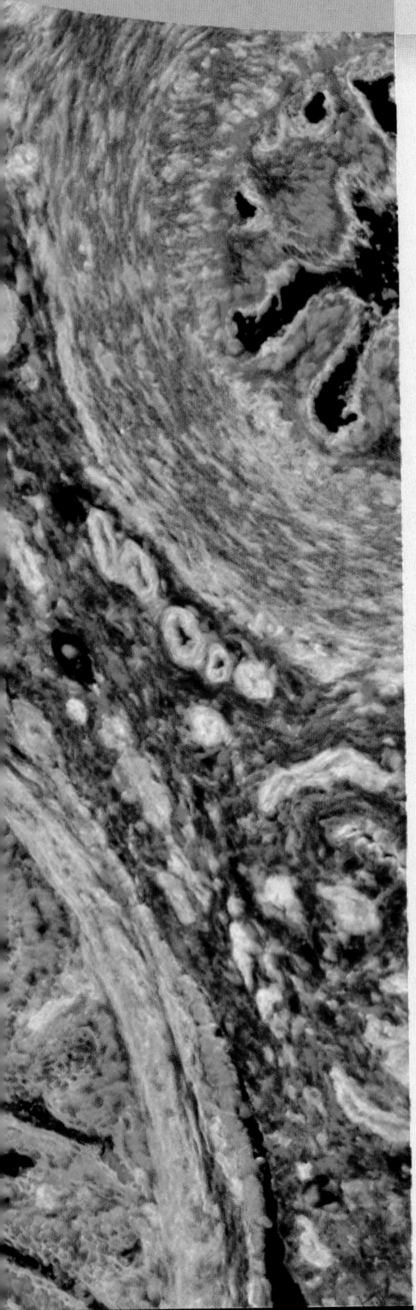

Rat oviduct

BACKGROUND BASICS

Prostaglandins: **193** Up-and down-regulation: **194** Positive and negative feedback: **203** Intestinal peptide absorption: **705** Oxytocin: **229** Hot flashes: **751** Flagella: **66** Steroids: **28** Agonist/antagonist: **41** Spinal reflex: **307** Hypothalamic-pituitary axis: **229** Prolactin: **233**

Birth, and copulation, and death. That's all the facts when you come to brass tacks.

—T.S. Eliot, ***Sweeney Agonistes***

RUNNING PROBLEM

Infertility

Peggy and Larry have just about everything to make them happy: successful careers, a loving marriage, a comfortable home. But one thing is missing: after five years of marriage, they have been unable to have a child. Today, Peggy and Larry have their first appointment with Charles Coddington, an infertility specialist. "Finding the cause of your infertility is going to require some painstaking detective work," Dr. Coddington explains. He will begin his workup of Peggy and Larry by asking detailed questions about their reproductive histories. Based on the answers to these questions, he will then order tests to pinpoint the problem.

829
841
850
851
855
860
862

Imagine growing up as a girl, then at the age of 12 or so, finding that your voice is deepening and your genitals are developing into those of a man. This scenario actually happens to a small number of men who have a condition known as *pseudohermaphroditism* [*pseudes,* false + *hermaphrodites,* the dual-sex offspring of Hermes and Aphrodite]. These men have the internal sex organs of a male but inherit a gene that causes a deficiency in one of the male hormones. Consequently, they are born with external genitalia that appear feminine, and they are raised as girls. At **puberty** [*pubertas,* adulthood], the period when a person makes the transition from being nonreproductive to being reproductive, pseudohermaphrodites begin to secrete more male hormones. As a result, they develop some, but not all, of the characteristics of men. Not surprisingly, a conflict arises: should these individuals change gender or remain female? Most choose to change and continue life as men.

Reproduction is one area of physiology in which we humans like to think of ourselves as significantly advanced over other animals. We mate for pleasure as well as procreation, and women are always sexually receptive (that is, not only during fertile periods). But just how different are we?

Like many other terrestrial animals, humans have internal fertilization that allows motile flagellated sperm to remain in an aqueous environment. To facilitate the process, we have mating and courtship rituals, as do other animals. Development is also internal, protecting the growing embryo from dehydration and cushioning it with a layer of fluid.

Humans are *sexually dimorphic* [*di-,* two + *morphos,* form], meaning that males and females are physically distinct. This distinction is sometimes blurred by dress and hairstyle, but these are cultural acquisitions. Although everyone agrees that male and female humans are physically dimorphic, we are still debating whether we are behaviorally and psychologically dimorphic as well.

Sex hormones play a significant role in the behavior of other mammals, acting on adults as well as influencing the brain of the developing embryo. Their role in humans is more controversial. Human fetuses are exposed to sex hormones while in the uterus, but it is unclear how much influence these hormones have on behavior later in life. Does the preference of little girls for dolls and of little boys for toy guns have a biological basis or a cultural basis? We have no answer yet, but growing evidence suggests that at least part of our brain structure is influenced by sex hormones before we ever leave the womb.

In this chapter we address the biology of human reproduction and development. We begin our discussion with gametes that fuse to form the fertilized egg, or **zygote.** As the zygote begins to divide (2-cell stage, 4-cell stage, etc.), it becomes first an **embryo** (weeks 0–8 of development), then a **fetus** (8 weeks until birth).

SEX DETERMINATION

The male and female sex organs consist of three sets of structures: the gonads, the internal genitalia, and the external genitalia. **Gonads** [*gonos,* seed] are the organs that produce **gametes** [*gamein,* to marry], the reproductive cells (eggs and sperm) that unite to form a new individual. The male gonads are the **testes** (singular *testis*), which produce **sperm** (*spermatozoa*). The female gonads are the **ovaries,** which produce eggs, or **ova** (singular *ovum*). The undifferentiated gonadal cells destined to produce eggs and sperm are called **germ cells.** The **internal genitalia** consist of accessory glands and ducts that connect the gonads with the outside environment. The **external genitalia** include all external reproductive structures.

Sexual development is programmed in the human genome. Each nucleated cell of the body except eggs and sperm contains 46 chromosomes. This set of chromosomes is called the *diploid number* because the chromosomes occur in pairs: 22 matched, or *homologous,* pairs of **autosomes** plus one pair of sex **chromosomes** (Fig. 26-1 ●). The 22 pairs of autosomal chromosomes direct development of the human body form and of variable characteristics such as hair color and blood type. The two sex chromosomes, designated as either X or Y, contain genes that direct development of internal and external sex organs. The X chromosome is larger than the Y chromosome and includes many genes that are missing from the Y chromosome.

Eggs and sperm are *haploid* cells with 23 chromosomes, one from each matched pair and one sex chromosome. When egg and sperm unite, the resulting zygote then contains a unique set of 46 chromosomes, with one chromosome of each matched pair coming from the mother and the other from the father.

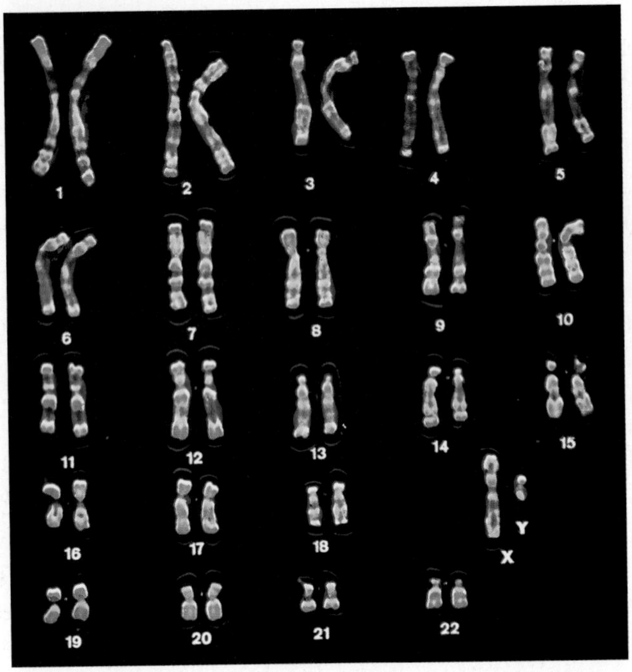

● **FIGURE 26-1** ***Humans have 23 pairs of chromosomes.*** They are arranged in homologous pairs in this figure. X and Y chromosomes (lower right) mean that these chromosomes came from a male.

Sex Chromosomes Determine Genetic Sex

The sex chromosomes a person inherits determine the genetic sex of that individual. Genetic females are XX, and genetic males are XY (Fig. 26-2 ●). Females inherit one X chromosome from each parent. Males inherit a Y chromosome from the father and an X chromosome from the mother. The

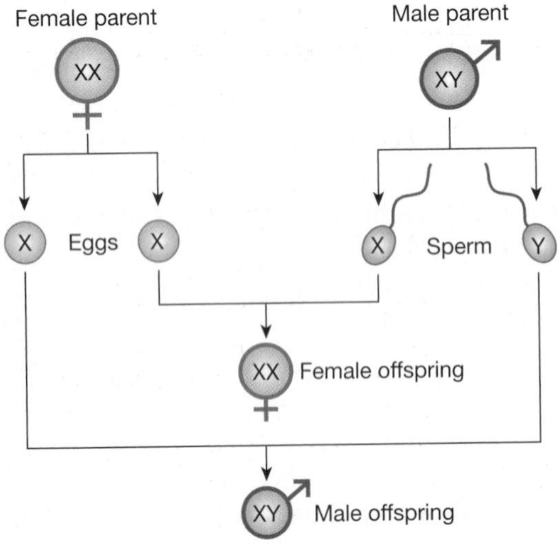

● **FIGURE 26-2** ***X and Y chromosomes determine sex.*** Each egg produced by a female (XX) has an X chromosome. Sperm produced by a male (XY) have either an X chromosome or a Y chromosome.

CLINICAL FOCUS

X-LINKED INHERITED DISORDERS

Normally, a person inherits two copies of the gene for a given trait: one copy from each parent. However, many genes found on the X chromosome, called *X-linked genes*, have no matching gene on the much smaller Y chromosome. Females always get two copies of X-linked genes, so the expression of X-linked traits follows the usual pattern of gene dominance and recession. Males, however, receive only one copy of an X-linked gene—on the X chromosome from their mother—so males *always* exhibit the traits associated with an X-linked gene. If the maternally inherited X-linked gene is defective, male offspring will exhibit the mutation. Among the identified X-linked diseases are Duchenne muscular dystrophy [p. 432], hemophilia [p. 564], and color-blindness.

Y chromosome is essential for development of the male reproductive organs.

If sex chromosomes are abnormally distributed at fertilization, the presence or absence of a Y chromosome determines whether development proceeds along male or female lines. The presence of a Y chromosome means the embryo will become male, even if the zygote also has multiple X chromosomes. For instance, an XXY zygote will become male. A zygote that inherits only a Y chromosome (YO) will die because the larger X chromosome contains essential genes that are missing from the Y chromosome.

In the absence of a Y chromosome, an embryo will develop into a female. For this reason, a zygote that gets only one X chromosome (XO; Turner's syndrome) will develop into a female. Two X chromosomes are needed for normal female reproductive function, however.

Once the ovaries develop in a female fetus, one X chromosome in each cell of her body inactivates and condenses into a clump of nuclear chromatin known as a *Barr body*. (Barr bodies in females can be seen in stained cheek epithelium.) The selection of the X chromosome that becomes inactive during development is random: some cells will have an active maternal X chromosome and others have an active paternal X chromosome. Because inactivation occurs early in development—before cell division is complete—all cells of a given tissue will usually have the same active X chromosome, either maternal or paternal.

CONCEPT CHECK

1. Name the male and female gonads and gametes.

Answers p. 866

TABLE 26-1 Sexual Differentiation

FEMALE	BIPOTENTIAL STRUCTURE	MALE
Clitoris	← Genital tubercle →	Glans penis
Labia minora, opening of vagina and urethra	← Urethral folds and groove →	Shaft of penis
Labia majora	← Labioscrotal swellings →	Shaft of penis and scrotum
Forms ovary	← Gonad (cortex) →	Regresses
Regresses	← Gonad (medulla) →	Forms testis
Regresses (testosterone absent)	← Wolffian duct →	Becomes epididymis, vas deferens, and seminal vesicle (testosterone present)
Becomes fallopian tube, uterus, cervix, and upper ⅓ of vagina (AMH absent)	← Müllerian duct →	Regresses (AMH present)

Sexual Differentiation Occurs Early in Development

The sex of an early embryo is difficult to determine because reproductive structures do not begin to differentiate until the seventh week of development. Before differentiation, the embryonic tissues are considered *bipotential* because they cannot be morphologically identified as male or female.

The bipotential gonad has an outer cortex and an inner medulla (Fig. 26-3a ●). Under the influence of the appropriate developmental signal (described below), the medulla will develop into a testis ①. In the absence of that signal, the cortex will differentiate into ovarian tissue.

The bipotential internal genitalia consist of two pairs of accessory ducts: **Wolffian ducts** derived from the embryonic kidney, and **Müllerian ducts.** As development proceeds along either male or female lines, one pair of ducts develops while the other degenerates (Fig. 26-3a ②).

The bipotential external genitalia consist of a *genital tubercle, urethral folds, urethral groove,* and *labioscrotal swellings* (Fig. 26-3b). These structures differentiate into the male and female reproductive structures as development progresses (Tbl. 26-1 ●).

What directs some single-cell zygotes to become males, and others to become females? Sex determination depends on the presence or absence of the *sex-determining **r**egion of the **Y** chromosome,* or **SRY gene.** In the absence of the SRY gene and its products, the gonads develop into ovaries. In the presence of a functional SRY gene, the bipotential gonads develop into testes.

Male Embryonic Development The SRY gene produces a protein (**SRY protein** or *testis-determining factor*) that binds to DNA and activates additional genes, including SOX9, WT1 (Wilms' tumor protein), and SF1 (steroidogenic factor). The protein products of these genes direct development of the gonadal medulla into a testis (Fig. 26-4 ●). Note that testicular development does *not* require male sex hormones such as **testosterone.** The developing embryo cannot secrete testosterone until after the gonads differentiate into testes.

Once the testes differentiate, they begin to secrete three hormones that influence development of the male internal and external genitalia. Testicular **Sertoli cells** secrete glycoprotein **anti-Müllerian hormone** (AMH; also called *Müllerian-inhibiting substance*). Testicular **Leydig cells** secrete testosterone and its derivative **dihydrotestosterone (DHT).** These two **androgens** [*andro-*, male] are the dominant steroid hormones in males. Testosterone and DHT both bind to the same *androgen receptor,* but the two ligands elicit different responses.

In the developing fetus, anti-Müllerian hormone causes the embryonic Müllerian ducts to regress (Fig. 26-3a, ② male). Testosterone converts the Wolffian ducts into male accessory structures: epididymis, vas deferens, and seminal vesicle (③ male and Tbl. 26-1). Later in fetal development, testosterone controls migration of the testes from the abdomen into the *scrotum,* or scrotal sac. The remaining male sex characteristics, such as differentiation of the external genitalia, are controlled primarily by DHT.

The importance of DHT in male development came to light in studies of the male pseudohermaphrodites described in the opening of this chapter. These men inherit a defective gene for **5α-reductase**, the enzyme that catalyzes the conversion of testosterone to DHT [Fig. 23-2, p. 759]. Despite normal testosterone secretion, these men have inadequate levels of DHT, and as a result the male external genitalia and prostate gland fail to develop fully during fetal development. At birth, the infants appear to be female and are raised as such. However, at puberty, the testes again begin to secrete testosterone, causing masculinization of the external genitalia, pubic hair growth (although scanty facial and body hair), and deepening voice. By studying the 5α-reductase defect in these individuals, scientists have been able to separate the effects of testosterone from those of DHT.

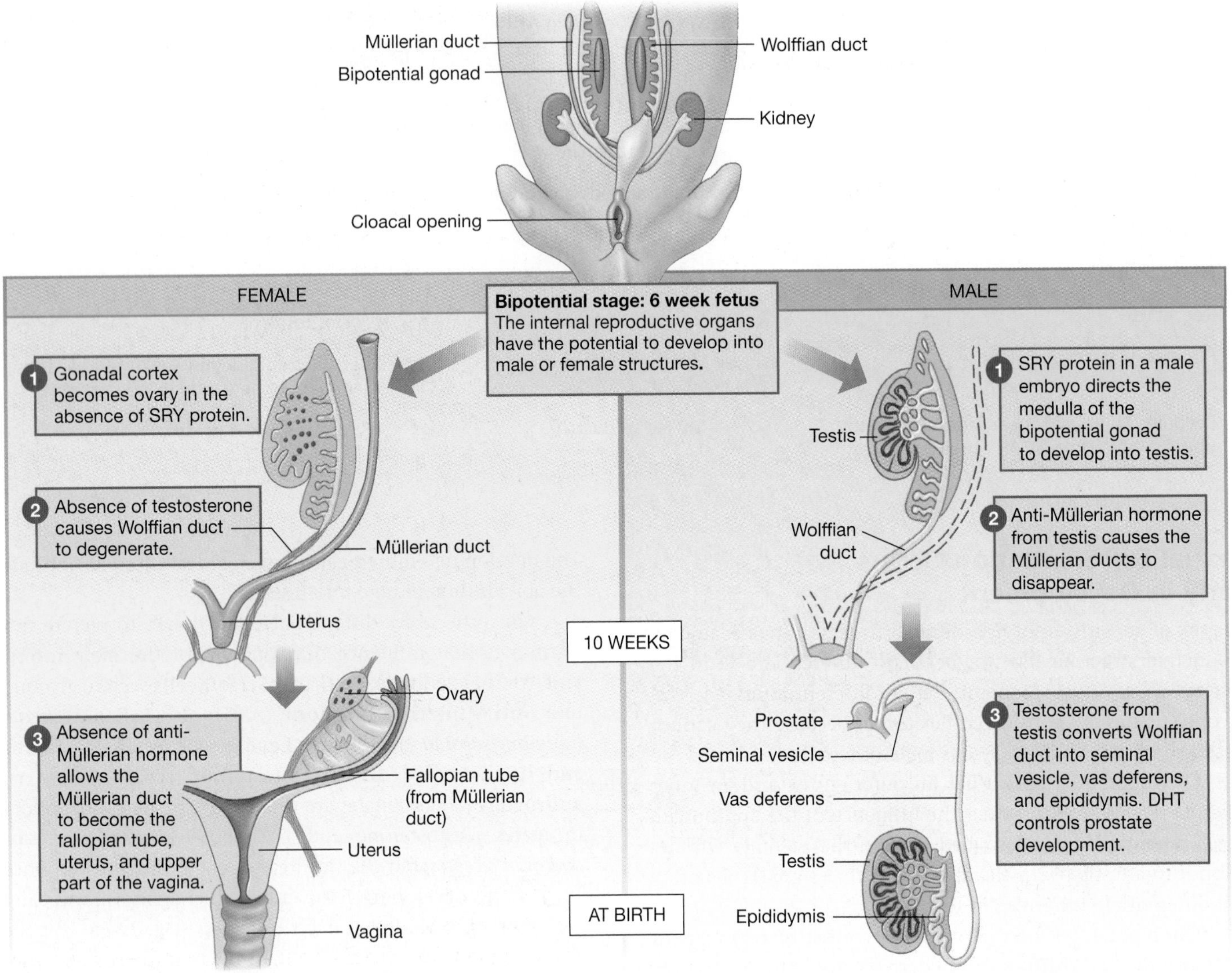

(a) DEVELOPMENT OF INTERNAL ORGANS

FIGURE 26-3 *Sexual development in the human embryo*

Exposure of nongenital tissues to testosterone during embryonic development is known to have masculinizing effects, such as altering the brain's responsiveness to certain hormones. One controversial aspect of the masculinizing effects of testosterone is its influence on human sexual behavior and gender identity. It is well documented that in many nonhuman mammals, adult sexual behavior depends on the absence or presence of testosterone during critical periods of brain development. However, a similar cause-effect relationship has never been proved in humans. In human behavior, it is very difficult to separate biological influences from environmental factors, and it will probably be years before this question is resolved.

Female Embryonic Development In female embryos, which have no SRY gene, the cortex of the bipotential gonad develops into ovarian tissue (Fig. 26-3a, ① female). Without inhibition from testicular AMH, the Müllerian ducts develop into the upper portion of the **vagina**, the **uterus**, and the **fallopian tubes** (after the anatomist Fallopius, who first described them; also known as **oviducts**). Without testosterone, the Wolffian ducts degenerate, and without DHT the external genitalia take on female characteristics. In other words, absence of the SRY gene and testicular hormones creates a female.

CONCEPT CHECK

2. Where in a target cell would you expect to find receptors for androgens? Where would you expect to find receptors for AMH?
3. Why was King Henry VIII of England wrong to blame his wives when they were unable to produce a male heir to the throne?
4. Which sex will a zygote become if it inherits only one X chromosome (XO)?
5. If the testes are removed from an early male embryo, why does it develop a uterus and fallopian tubes rather than the normal male accessory structures? Will the embryo have male or female external genitalia? Explain.

Answers p. 866

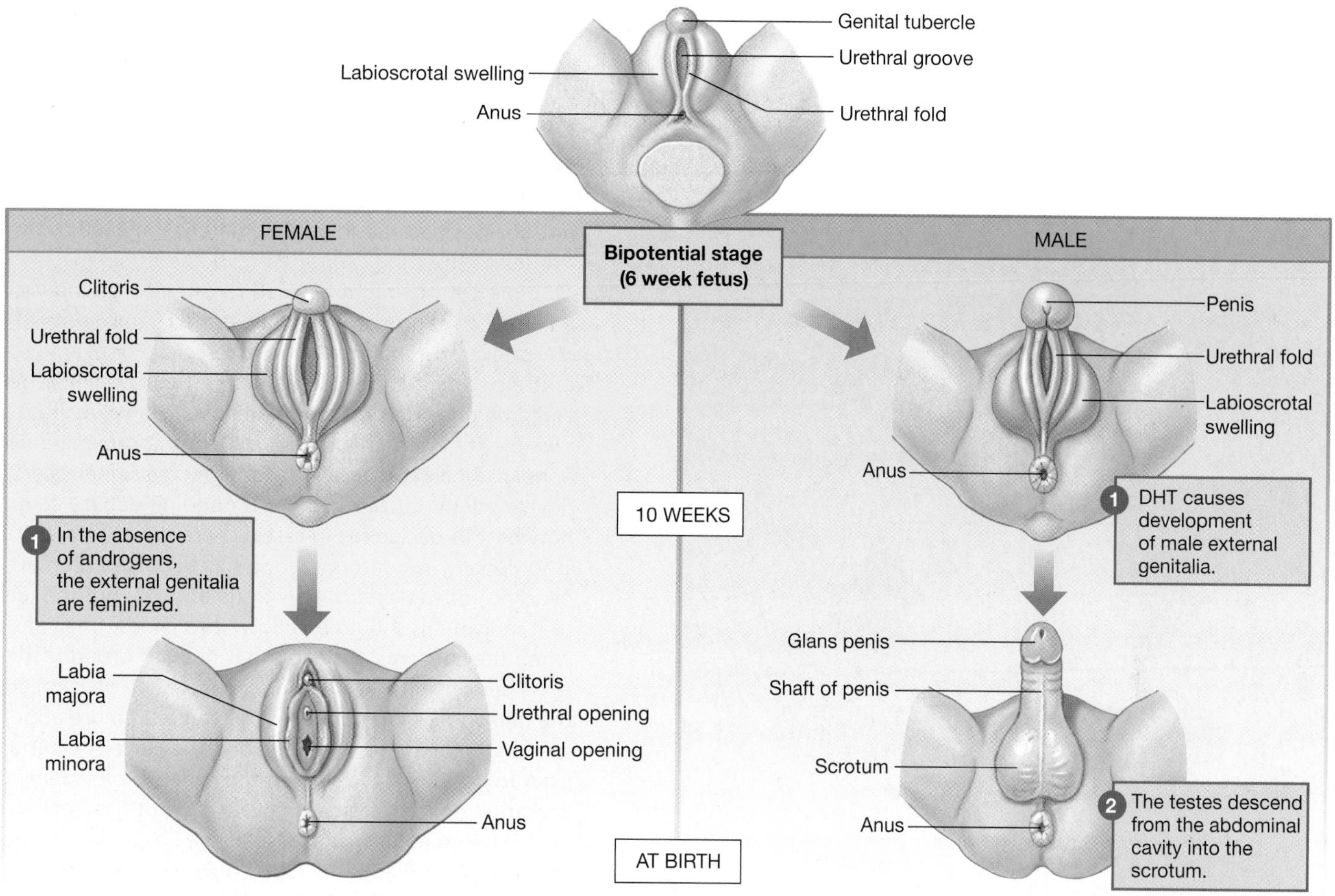

(b) DEVELOPMENT OF EXTERNAL GENITALIA

● **FIGURE 26-3** *(continued)*

BASIC PATTERNS OF REPRODUCTION

The testis and ovary both produce hormones and gametes, and they share other similarities, as might be expected of organs having the same origin. However, male and female gametes are very different from each other. Eggs are some of the largest cells in the body [Fig. 3-10, p. 62]. They are nonmotile and must be moved through the reproductive tract on currents created by smooth muscle contraction or the beating of cilia. Sperm, in contrast, are quite small. They are the only flagellated cells in the body and are highly motile so that they can swim up the female reproductive tract in their search for an egg to fertilize.

The timing of gamete production, or **gametogenesis**, is also very different in males and females. Most evidence indicates that women are born with all the eggs, or **oocytes**, they will ever have. During the reproductive years, eggs mature in a cyclic pattern and are released from the ovaries roughly once a month. After about 40 years female reproductive cycles cease (*menopause*).

Men, by contrast, manufacture sperm continuously from the time they reach reproductive maturity. Sperm and testosterone production diminishes with age but does not cease as women's reproductive cycles do.

Gametogenesis Begins *in Utero*

Figure 26-5 ● compares the male and female patterns of gametogenesis. In both sexes, germ cells of the embryonic gonads first undergo a series of mitotic divisions to increase their numbers ①. After that, the germ cells are ready to undergo **meiosis**, the cell division process through which gametes are formed.

In the first step of meiosis, the cell's DNA replicates until each chromosome is duplicated and the cell, now called a **primary spermatocyte** or **primary oocyte**, contains twice the normal amount of DNA ②. However, cell and chromosomal division do not take place as they do in mitosis. Instead, each duplicated chromosome forms two identical **sister chromatids**, linked together at a region known as the **centromere**. The primary gametes are then ready to undergo meiotic divisions to create four haploid cells.

In the **first meiotic division**, one primary gamete divides into two *secondary gametes* (**secondary spermatocyte** or **secondary**

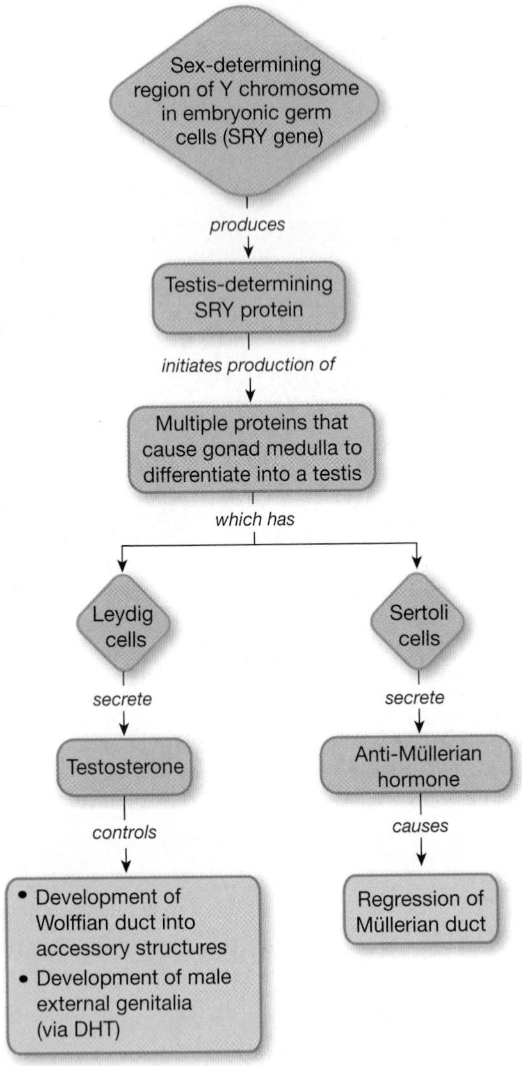

● **FIGURE 26-4** ***The SRY gene directs male development.***

CLINICAL FOCUS

DETERMINING SEX

The first question new parents typically ask about their child is, "Is it a boy or a girl?" Sometimes the answer is not obvious because in approximately 1 in 3000 births, the sex of the child cannot easily be determined. Multiple criteria might be used to establish an individual's sex: genetic, chromosomal, gonadal, morphological, or even psychological characteristics. For example, presence of a Y chromosome with a functional SRY gene could be one criterion for "maleness." However, it is possible for an infant to have a Y chromosome and not appear to be male because of a defect in some aspect of development. Currently there is ongoing debate about how best to decide sex in cases where there is doubt. Traditionally, sex determination has been based on appearance of the external genitalia at birth, but the idea that individuals should be allowed to choose their sex when they become old enough is gaining ground. The sex a person considers himself or herself to be is called the person's *gender identity*. You can read more about causes of ambiguous genitalia and the current criteria used to decide a child's sex in the American Academy of Pediatrics policy statement "Evaluation of the Newborn with Developmental Anomalies of the External Genitalia," *Pediatrics* 106(1):138–142, 2000 (July) (available online at *http://pediatrics.aappublications.org*).

oocyte) ③. Each secondary gamete gets half of the body's 46 chromosomes, which remain as paired sister chromatids.

In the **second meiotic division**, the sister chromatids separate ④. In males, the second meiotic division goes to completion, resulting in haploid sperm. In females, the result of the second meiotic division depends on whether or not the egg is fertilized. In addition, the timing of mitotic and meiotic divisions is very different in males and females. Now let's take a closer look at male and female gametogenesis.

Male Gametogenesis At birth, the testes of a newborn boy have not progressed beyond the mitosis stage and contain only immature germ cells (Fig. 26-5 ①). After birth, the gonads become *quiescent* (relatively inactive) until puberty, the period in the early teen years when the gonads mature.

At puberty, germ cell mitosis resumes ①. From that point onward, the germ cells, known as **spermatogonia** (singular *spermatogonium*), have two possible fates. Some continue to undergo mitosis throughout the male's reproductive life. Others are destined to undergo meiosis and become primary spermatocytes.

Through meiosis, one primary spermatocyte creates four sperm. In the first meiotic division, each primary spermatocyte divides into two secondary spermatocytes ③. In the second meiotic division, each secondary spermatocyte divides into two spermatids, each with 23 single chromosomes, the haploid number characteristic of a gamete ④. The spermatids then mature into sperm.

Female Gametogenesis In the embryonic ovary, germ cells are called **oögonia** (singular *oögonium*) (Fig. 26-5 ①). Oögonia complete mitotic replication and the DNA duplication stage of meiosis by the fifth month of fetal development ②. At this time, germ cell mitosis ceases and no further oocytes can be formed. At birth each ovary contains about half a million primary gametes, or **primary oocytes.**

The oocyte's first meiotic division takes place following puberty ③. Each primary oocyte divides into two cells, a large **egg** (**secondary oocyte**) and a tiny **first polar body**. Despite the size difference, egg and polar body each contain 23 duplicated chromosomes. This first polar body disintegrates.

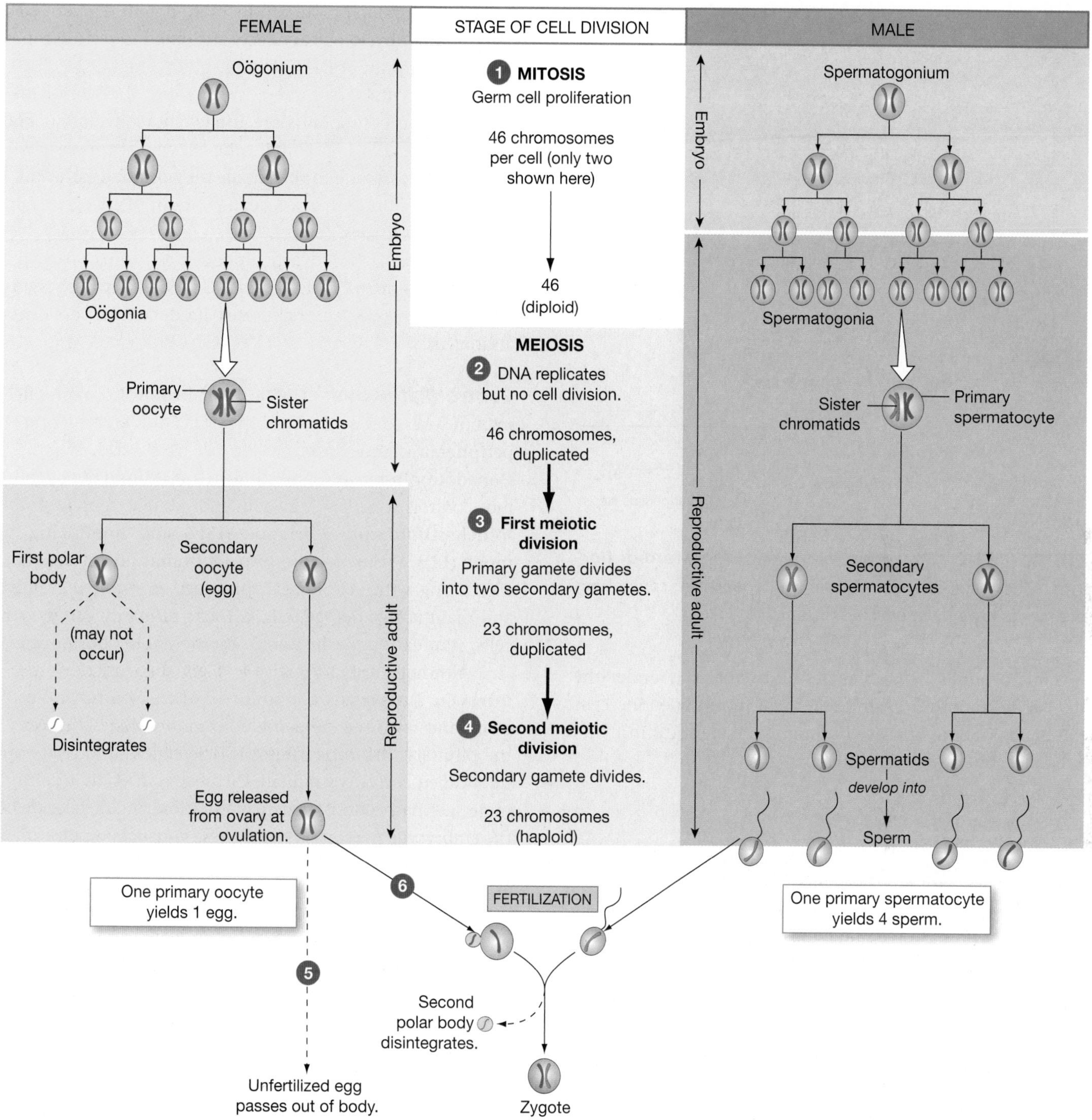

● **FIGURE 26-5** ***Gametogenesis.*** For simplicity, this figure shows only one of the body's 22 pairs of autosomes. Germ cells first undergo mitosis, then go through meiosis.

Meanwhile, the egg begins the second meiotic division ④. After the sister chromatids separate from each other, meiosis pauses. The final step of meiosis, in which sister chromatids in the egg go to separate cells, does not take place unless the egg is fertilized.

The ovary releases the mature egg during a process known as **ovulation**. If the egg is not fertilized, meiosis never goes to completion, and the egg disintegrates or passes out of the body ⑤. If fertilization by a sperm occurs, the final step of meiosis takes place ⑥. Half the sister chromatids remain in the fertilized egg (zygote), while the other half are released in a **second polar body.** The second polar body, like the first, degenerates. As a result of meiosis, each primary oocyte gives rise to only one egg.

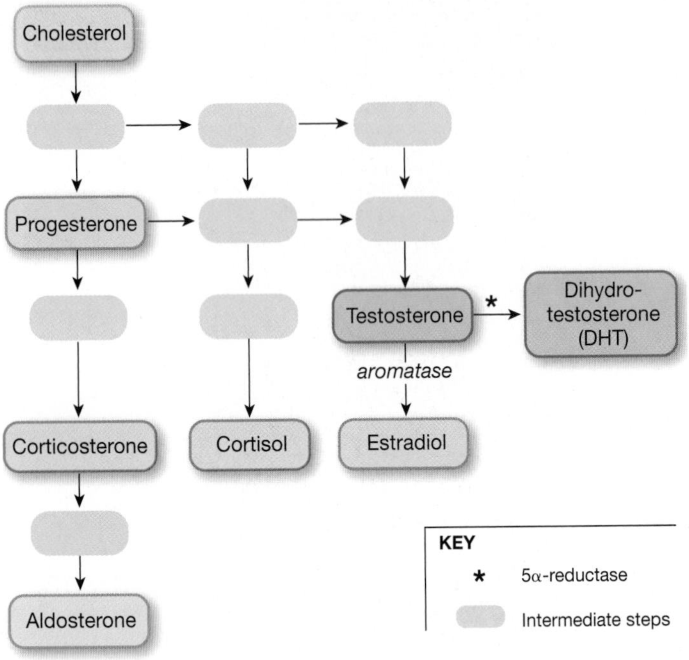

● **FIGURE 26-6** ***Synthesis pathways for steroid hormones.*** The blank boxes represent intermediate compounds whose names have been omitted for simplicity.

Gametogenesis in both males and females is under the control of hormones from the brain and from endocrine cells in the gonads. Some of these hormones are identical in males and females, but others are different.

CONCEPT CHECK

6. At what stage of development is the gamete in a newborn male? In a newborn female?
7. Compare the amount of DNA in the first polar body with the amount of DNA in the second polar body.
8. How many gametes are formed from one primary oocyte? From one primary spermatocyte? Answers p. 866

The Brain Directs Reproduction

The reproductive system has some of the most complex control pathways of the body, in which multiple hormones interact in an ever-changing fashion. The pathways that regulate reproduction begin with secretion of peptide hormones by the hypothalamus and anterior pituitary. These trophic hormones control gonadal secretion of the steroid sex hormones, including androgens, **estrogens**, and **progesterone**. The steroid hormones are closely related to one another and arise from the same steroid precursors (Fig. 26-6 ●). Both sexes produce both androgens and estrogens, but androgens predominate in males, and estrogens are dominant in females.

In men, most testosterone is secreted by the testes, but about 5% comes from the adrenal cortex. Testosterone is converted in peripheral tissues to its more potent derivative DHT. Some of the physiological effects attributed to testosterone are actually the result of DHT activity.

Males synthesize some estrogens, but the feminizing effects of these compounds are usually not obvious in males. Both testes and ovaries contain the enzyme **aromatase**, which converts testosterone to the female sex hormone **estradiol**, the main estrogen in humans. A small amount of estrogen is made in peripheral tissues.

In women, the ovary produces estrogens (particularly estradiol and *estrone*) and *progestins*, particularly progesterone. The ovary and the adrenal cortex produce small amounts of androgens.

Control Pathways The hormonal control of reproduction in both sexes follows the basic hypothalamus-anterior pituitary-peripheral gland pattern (Fig. 26-7 ● and p. 230). **Gonadotropin-releasing hormone** (GnRH*) from the hypothalamus controls secretion of two anterior pituitary **gonadotropins: follicle-stimulating hormone (FSH)** and **luteinizing hormone (LH).** FSH and LH in turn act trophically on the gonads. FSH, along with steroid sex hormones, is required to initiate and maintain gametogenesis. LH acts primarily on endocrine cells, stimulating production of the steroid sex hormones.

Although primary control of gonadal function arises in the brain, the gonads also influence their own function. Both ovary and testis secrete peptide hormones that act directly on the pituitary. **Inhibins** inhibit FSH secretion, and related peptides called **activins** stimulate FSH secretion. Activins also promote spermatogenesis, oocyte maturation, and development of the embryonic nervous system. These gonadal peptides are produced in nongonadal tissues as well, and their other functions are still being investigated.

AMH, introduced earlier in the discussion of sexual differentiation during development, is also made by cells of both ovary and testis after birth. The inhibins, activins, and AMH are part of a large family of related growth and differentiation factors known as the *transforming growth factor-β* family.

Feedback Pathways The feedback loops of the reproductive system also become quite complex. The feedback pathways for trophic hormones follow the general pattern of long-loop and short-loop feedback described in Chapter 7 [p. 231]. Gonadal hormones alter secretion of GnRH, FSH, and LH in a long-loop response, and the pituitary gonadotropins inhibit GnRH release from the hypothalamus by a short-loop path (Fig. 26-7).

When circulating levels of gonadal steroids are low, the pituitary secretes FSH and LH (Tbl. 26-2 ●). Once steroid secre-

*GnRH is sometimes called *luteinizing hormone releasing hormone* (LHRH) because it was first thought to have its primary effect on LH.

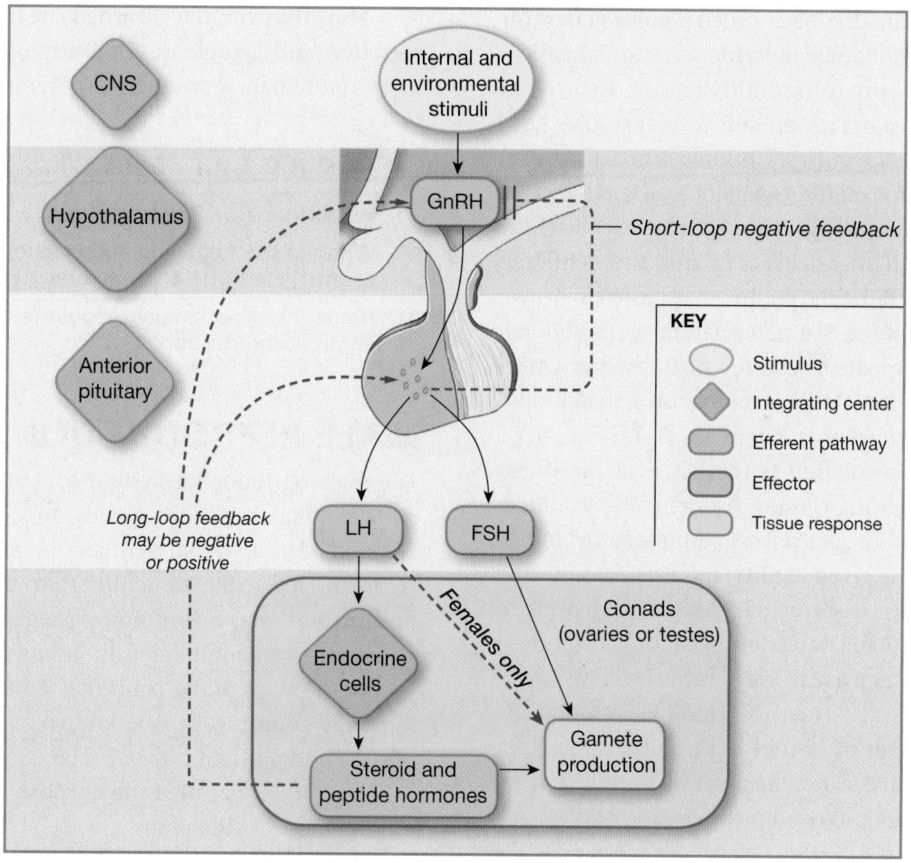

● **FIGURE 26-7** ***The general pattern for hormonal control of reproduction***

tion reaches a certain level, negative feedback usually inhibits gonadotropin release. Androgens always maintain negative feedback on gonadotropin release: as androgen levels go up, FSH and LH secretion decreases.

In contrast, estrogen alternates between positive and negative feedback. Lower concentrations of estrogen have a negative feedback effect. However, if estrogen rises rapidly to a threshold level or above for at least 36 hours, feedback changes from negative to positive, and gonadotropin release (particularly LH) is *stimulated*. The paradoxical effects of estrogen on gonadotropin release play a significant role in the female reproductive cycle, as you will learn later in this chapter.

Scientists still do not fully understand the mechanism underlying the change from negative to positive feedback with estrogen. Some evidence suggests that high levels of estrogen increase the number of GnRH receptors in the anterior pituitary, making it more sensitive to GnRH (up-regulation of receptors [p. 194]). Other evidence points to estrogen influencing GnRH release by altering the release of a peptide called *kisspeptin* from hypothalamic neurons.

Pulsatile GnRH Release Tonic GnRH release from the hypothalamus occurs in small pulses every 1–3 hours in both males and females. The region of the hypothalamus that contains

TABLE 26-2 Effects of Sex Steroids on Gonadotropin Release

STEROID HORMONE	EFFECT	GONADOTROPIN LEVEL
Low estrogen or androgen	Absence of negative feedback	Increases
Moderate estrogen or androgen	Negative feedback	Decreases
High androgen	Negative feedback	Decreases
Sustained high estrogen	Positive feedback	Increases

the GnRH neuron cell bodies has been called a **pulse generator** because it coordinates the periodic pulsatile secretion of GnRH.

Scientists wondered why tonic GnRH release occurred in pulses rather than in a steady fashion, but several studies have shown the significance of the pulses. Children who suffer from a GnRH deficiency will not mature sexually in the absence of gonadotropin stimulation of the gonads. If treated with steady infusions of GnRH through drug-delivery pumps, these children still fail to mature sexually. But if the pumps are adjusted to deliver GnRH in pulses similar to those that occur naturally, the children will go through puberty. Apparently, steady high levels of GnRH cause down-regulation of the GnRH receptors on gonadotropin cells, making the pituitary unable to respond to GnRH.

This receptor down-regulation is the basis for the therapeutic use of GnRH in treating certain disorders. For example, patients with prostate and breast cancers stimulated by androgens or estrogens may be given GnRH agonists to slow the growth of the cancer cells. It seems paradoxical to give these patients a drug that stimulates secretion of androgens and estrogens, but after a brief increase in FSH and LH, the pituitary becomes insensitive to GnRH. Then FSH and LH secretion decreases, and gonadal output of steroid hormones also falls. In essence, the GnRH agonist creates chemical castration that reverses when the drug is no longer administered.

Environmental Factors Influence Reproduction

Among the least-understood influences on reproductive hormones and gametogenesis are environmental effects. In men, factors that influence gametogenesis are difficult to monitor short of requesting periodic sperm counts. Disruption of the normal reproductive cycle in women is easier to study because physiological uterine bleeding in the menstrual cycle is easily monitored.

Factors that affect reproductive function in women include stress, nutritional status, and changes in the day-night cycle, such as those that occur with travel across time zones or with shift work. The hormone **melatonin** from the pineal gland [p. 224] mediates reproduction in seasonally breeding animals, such as birds and deer, and researchers are investigating whether melatonin also plays a role in seasonal and daily rhythms in humans.

Environmental estrogens are also receiving a lot of attention. These are naturally occurring compounds, such as the *phytoestrogens* of plants, or synthetic compounds that have been released into the environment. Some of these compounds bind to estrogen receptors in both sexes and mimic estrogen's effects. Others are anti-estrogens that block estrogen receptors or interfere with second messenger pathways or protein synthesis. Growing evidence suggests that some of these endocrine disruptors can adversely influence developing embryos and even have their effects passed down to subsequent generations.

Now that you have learned the basic patterns of hormone secretion and gamete development, let's look in detail at the male and female reproductive systems.

CONCEPT CHECK

9. What does aromatase do?
10. What do the following abbreviations stand for? (Spelling counts!) FSH, DHT, SRY, LH, GnRH, AMH
11. Name the hypothalamic and anterior pituitary hormones that control reproduction. Answers p. 866

MALE REPRODUCTION

The male reproductive system consists of the testes, the internal genitalia (accessory glands and ducts), and the external genitalia. The external genitalia consist of the **penis** and the **scrotum**, a saclike structure that contains the testes. The **urethra** serves as a common passageway for sperm and urine, although not simultaneously. It runs through the ventral aspect of the shaft of the penis (Fig. 26-8 ●) and is surrounded by a spongy column of tissue known as the **corpus spongiosum** [*corpus,* body; plural *corpora*]. The corpus spongiosum and two columns of tissue called the **corpora cavernosa** constitute the erectile tissue of the penis.

The tip of the penis is enlarged into a region called the **glans** that at birth is covered by a layer of skin called the **foreskin,** or **prepuce.** In some cultures, the foreskin is removed surgically in a procedure called **circumcision.** In the United States, this practice goes through cycles of popularity. Proponents of the procedure claim that it is necessary for good hygiene, and they cite evidence suggesting that the incidence of penile cancer, sexually transmitted diseases, and urinary tract infections is lower in circumcised men. Opponents claim that it is cruel to subject newborn boys to an unnecessary and possibly painful procedure.

The scrotum is an external sac into which the testes migrate during fetal development. This location outside the abdominal cavity is necessary because normal sperm development requires a temperature that is 2°–3° F lower than core body temperature. Men who have borderline or low sperm counts are advised to switch from jockey-style underwear, which keeps the scrotum close to the body, to boxer shorts, which allow the testes to stay cooler.

The failure of one or both testes to descend is known as **cryptorchidism** [*crypto,* hidden + *orchis,* testicle] and occurs in 1–3% of newborn males. If left alone, about 80% of cryptorchid testes spontaneously descend later. Those that remain in the abdomen through puberty become sterile and are unable to produce sperm.

Although cryptorchid testes lose their sperm-producing potential, they can produce androgens, indicating that hormone production is not as temperature sensitive as sperm

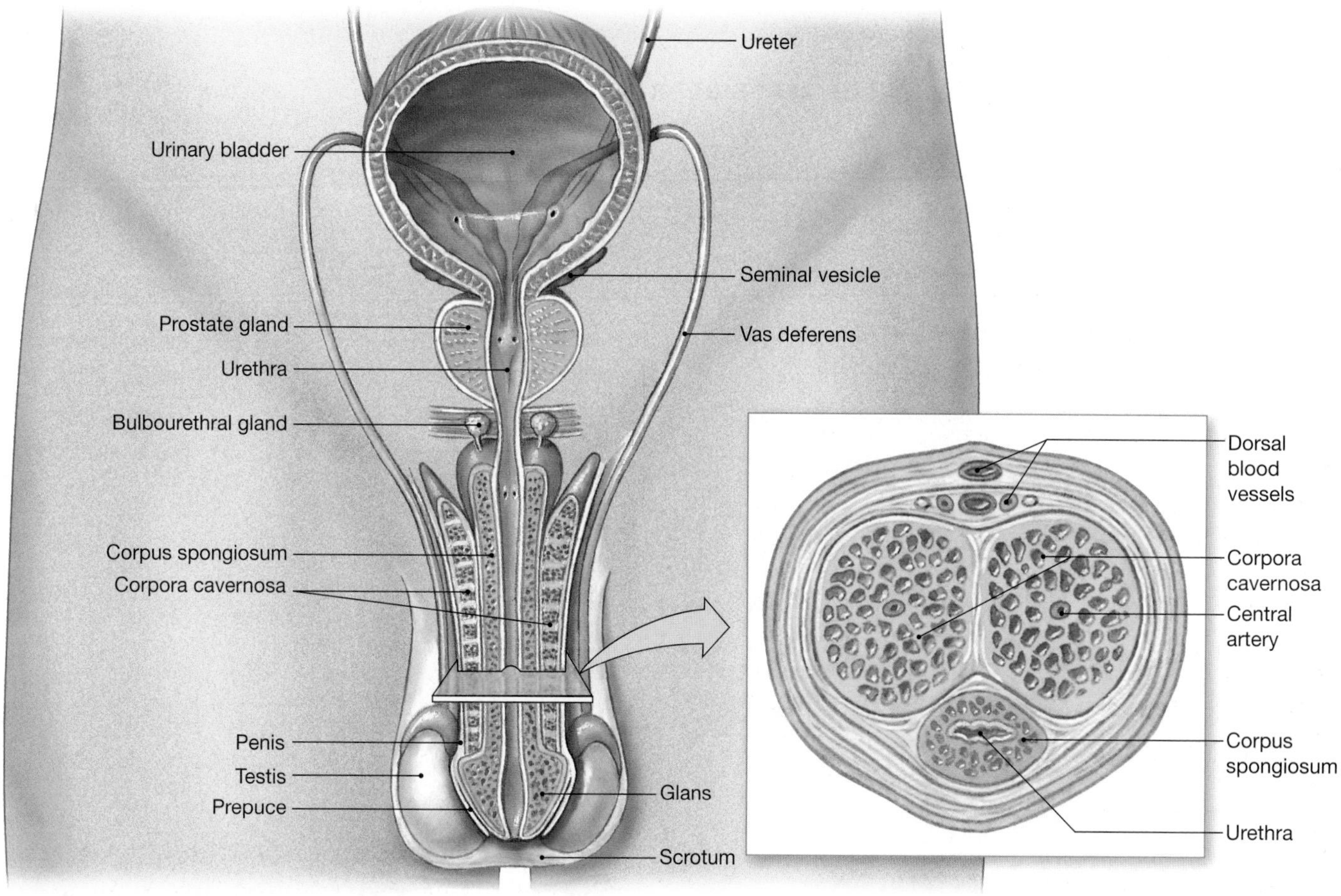

● **FIGURE 26-8** ***Reproductive anatomy of the male***

production. Because undescended testes are prone to become cancerous, authorities recommend that they be moved to the scrotum with testosterone treatment or, if necessary, surgically.

The male accessory glands and ducts include the **prostate gland**, the **seminal vesicles**, and the **bulbourethral (Cowper's) glands.** The bulbourethral glands and seminal vesicles empty their secretions into the urethra through ducts. The individual glands of the prostate open directly into the urethral lumen.

The prostate gland is the best known of the three accessory glands because of its medical significance. Cancer of the prostate is the second most common form of cancer in men (next to lung cancer), and *benign prostatic hypertrophy* (enlargement) creates problems for many men after age 50. Because the prostate gland completely encircles the urethra, its enlargement causes difficulty in urinating by narrowing the passageway.

Fetal development of the prostate gland, like that of the external genitalia, is under the control of dihydrotestosterone. Discovery of the role of DHT in prostate growth led to the development of *finasteride,* a 5α-reductase inhibitor that blocks DHT production. This drug was the first nonsurgical treatment for benign prostatic hypertrophy. Studies are currently under way to determine if lowering (but not eliminating) DHT levels will decrease the incidence of cancer of the prostate gland.

Testes Produce Sperm and Hormones

The human testes are paired ovoid structures about 5 cm by 2.5 cm (Fig. 26-9a ●). The word *testis* means "witness" in Latin, and its application to the male gonad comes from the fact that in ancient Rome, men taking an oath placed one hand on their genitals.

The testes have a tough outer fibrous capsule that encloses masses of coiled **seminiferous tubules** clustered into 250–300 compartments (Fig. 26-9b). Between tubules is interstitial tissue consisting primarily of blood vessels and the testosterone-producing Leydig cells (Fig. 26-9c). The seminiferous tubules constitute nearly 80% of the testicular mass in an adult. Each individual tubule is 0.3–1 meter long, and, if stretched out and laid end to end, the entire mass would extend for about the length of two and a half football fields.

The seminiferous tubules leave the testis and join the **epididymis** [*epi-,* upon + *didymos,* twin], a single duct that forms a tightly coiled cord on the surface of the testicular capsule (Fig. 26-9b). The epididymis becomes the **vas deferens** [*vas,* vessel + *deferre,* to carry away from], also known as the **ductus deferens**. This duct passes into the abdomen, where it eventually empties into the urethra, the passageway from the urinary bladder to the external environment (see Fig. 26-8).

ANATOMY SUMMARY

THE MALE REPRODUCTIVE SYSTEM

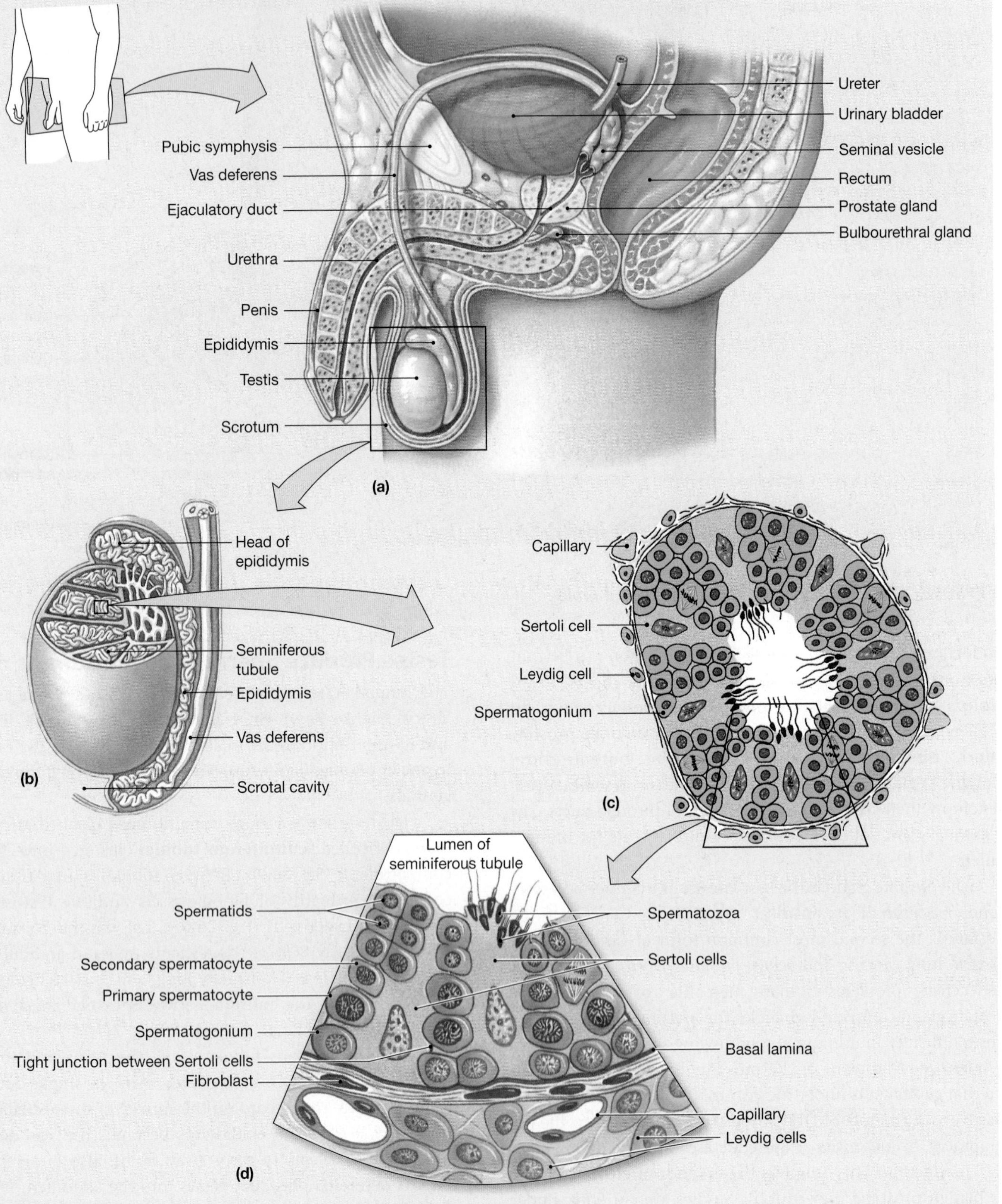
Ureter
Urinary bladder
Seminal vesicle
Rectum
Prostate gland
Bulbourethral gland
Pubic symphysis
Vas deferens
Ejaculatory duct
Urethra
Penis
Epididymis
Testis
Scrotum
(a)
Head of epididymis
Seminiferous tubule
Epididymis
Vas deferens
Scrotal cavity
(b)
Capillary
Sertoli cell
Leydig cell
Spermatogonium
(c)
Lumen of seminiferous tubule
Spermatids
Secondary spermatocyte
Primary spermatocyte
Spermatogonium
Tight junction between Sertoli cells
Fibroblast
Spermatozoa
Sertoli cells
Basal lamina
Capillary
Leydig cells
(d)

FIGURE 26-9

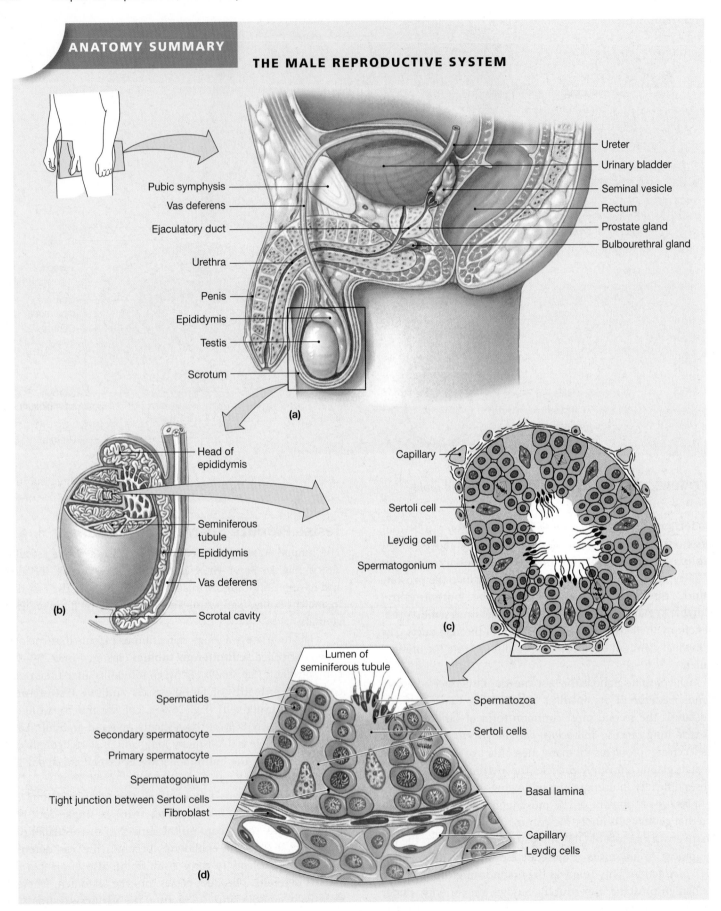

Seminiferous Tubules The seminiferous tubules are the site of sperm production and contain two types of cells: spermatogonia in various stages of becoming sperm and **Sertoli cells** (Fig. 26-9c, d). The developing spermatocytes stack in columns from the outer edge of the tubule to the lumen. Between each column is a single Sertoli cell that extends from the outer edge of the tubule to the lumen. Surrounding the outside of the tubule is a basal lamina (Fig. 26-9d) that acts as a barrier, preventing certain large molecules in the interstitial fluid from entering the tubule but allowing testosterone to enter easily.

Adjacent Sertoli cells in a tubule are linked to each other by tight junctions that form an additional barrier between the lumen of the tubule and the interstitial fluid outside the tubule. These tight junctions are sometimes called the **blood-testis barrier** because functionally they behave much like the impermeable capillaries of the blood-brain barrier, restricting movement of molecules between two compartments. The basal lamina and tight junctions create three compartments: the tubule lumen, a *basal compartment* on the basolateral side of the Sertoli cells, and the interstitial fluid. Because of the barriers between these compartments, the luminal fluid has a composition different from that of interstitial fluid, with low concentrations of glucose and high concentrations of K^+ and steroid hormones.

RUNNING PROBLEM

Infertility can be caused by problems in either the man or the woman. Sometimes, however, both partners have problems that contribute to their infertility. In general, male infertility is caused by low sperm counts, abnormalities in sperm morphology, or abnormalities in the reproductive structures that carry sperm. Female infertility may be caused by problems in hormonal pathways that govern maturation and release of eggs or by abnormalities of the reproductive structures (cervix, uterus, ovaries, oviducts). Because tests of male fertility are simple to perform, Dr. Coddington first analyzes Larry's sperm. In this test, trained technicians examine a fresh sperm sample under a microscope. They note the shape and motility of the sperm and estimate the concentration of sperm in the sample.

Question 1:
Name (in order) the male reproductive structures that carry sperm from the testes to the external environment.

Question 2:
A new technique for the treatment of male infertility involves retrieval of sperm from the epididymis. The retrieved sperm can be used to fertilize an egg, which is then implanted in the uterus. Which causes of male infertility might make this treatment necessary?

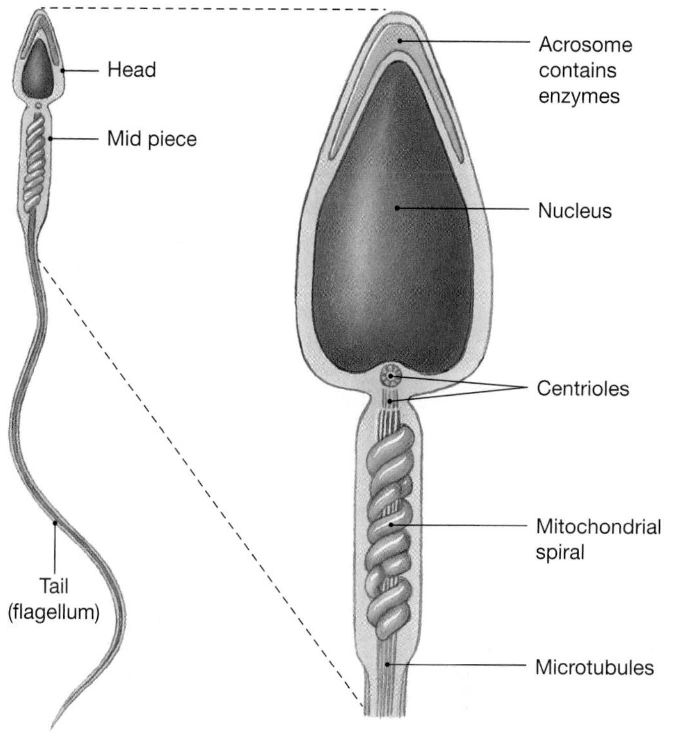

● **FIGURE 26-10** ***A sperm consists of a head with enzymes and DNA, a long tail, and mitochondria to power movement of the tail.***

Sperm Production Spermatogonia, the germ cells that undergo meiotic division to become sperm, are found clustered near the basal ends of the Sertoli cells, just inside the basal lamina of the seminiferous tubules (Fig. 26-9c, d). In this basal compartment, they undergo mitotic divisions that produce additional germ cells. Some of the spermatogonia remain near the outer edge of the tubule to produce future spermatogonia. Other spermatogonia enter meiosis and become primary spermatocytes.

As spermatocytes differentiate into sperm, they move inward toward the tubule lumen, continuously surrounded by Sertoli cells. The tight junctions of the blood-testis barrier break and reform around the migrating cells, ensuring that the barrier remains intact. By the time spermatocytes reach the luminal ends of Sertoli cells, they have divided twice and become spermatids.

Spermatids remain embedded in the apical membrane of Sertoli cells while they complete the transformation into sperm, losing most of their cytoplasm and developing a flagellated tail (Fig. 26-10 ●). The chromatin of the nucleus condenses into a dense structure, while a lysosome-like vesicle called an **acrosome** flattens out to form a cap over the tip of the nucleus. The acrosome contains enzymes essential for fertilization. Mitochondria to produce energy for sperm movement concentrate in the midpiece of the sperm body, along with microtubules that extend into the tail [p. 65]. The result is a small, motile gamete that bears little resemblance to the parent spermatid.

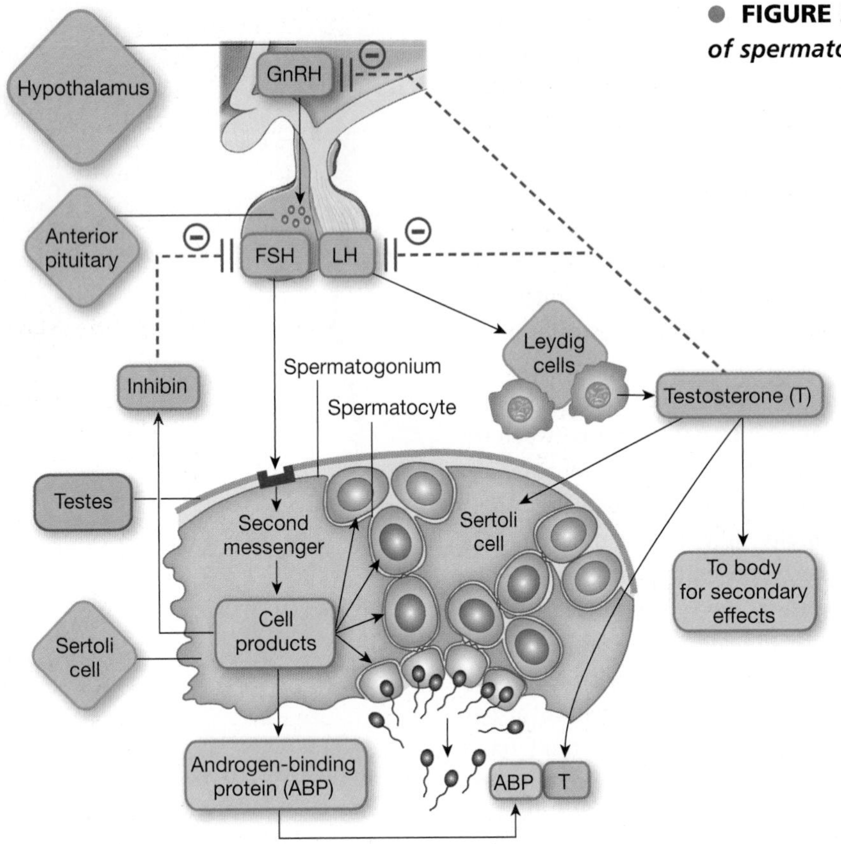

● **FIGURE 26-11** ***Hormonal control of spermatogenesis***

Sperm are released into the lumen of the seminiferous tubule, along with secreted fluid. From there, they are free to move out of the testis. The entire development process—from spermatogonium division until sperm release—takes about 64 days. At any given time, different regions of the tubule contain spermatocytes in different stages of development. The staggering of developmental stages allows sperm production to remain nearly constant at a rate of *200 million* sperm per day. That may sound like an extraordinarily high number, but it is about the number of sperm released in a single ejaculation.

Sperm just released from Sertoli cells are not yet mature and are incapable of swimming. They are pushed out of the tubule lumen by other sperm and by bulk flow of fluid secreted by Sertoli cells. Sperm entering the epididymis complete their maturation during the 12 or so days of their transit time, aided by protein secretions from epididymal cells.

Sertoli Cells The function of Sertoli cells is to regulate sperm development. Another name for Sertoli cells is *sustentacular cells* because they provide sustenance, or nourishment, for the developing spermatogonia. Sertoli cells manufacture and secrete proteins that range from the hormones inhibin and activin to growth factors, enzymes, and **androgen-binding protein** (ABP). ABP is secreted into the seminiferous tubule lumen, where it binds to testosterone (Fig. 26-11 ●). Protein binding makes testosterone less lipophilic so that it cannot diffuse out of the tubule lumen.

Leydig Cells

Leydig cells, located in the interstitial tissue between seminiferous tubules (Fig. 26-9c, d), secrete testosterone. They are first active in the fetus, when testosterone is needed to direct development of male characteristics. After birth, the cells become inactive until puberty, when they resume testosterone production. The Leydig cells also convert some testosterone to estradiol.

Spermatogenesis Requires Gonadotropins and Testosterone

The hormonal control of spermatogenesis follows the general pattern described previously: hypothalamic GnRH promotes release of LH and FSH from the anterior pituitary (Fig. 26-11). FSH and LH in turn stimulate the testes. The gonadotropins were named originally for their effect on the female ovary, but the same names have been retained in the male.

GnRH release is pulsatile, peaking every 1.5 hours, and LH release follows the same pattern. FSH levels are not as obviously related to GnRH secretion because FSH secretion is also influenced by inhibin and activin.

The target of FSH is Sertoli cells because (unlike oocytes) male germ cells do not have FSH receptors. FSH stimulates Sertoli synthesis of paracrine molecules needed for spermatogonia mitosis and spermatogenesis. In addition, FSH stimulates production of androgen-binding protein and inhibin.

The primary target of LH is the Leydig cells, which produce testosterone. In turn, testosterone feeds back to inhibit LH release.

Testosterone is essential for spermatogenesis, but its actions also appear to be mediated by Sertoli cells. Spermatocytes have no androgen receptors and cannot respond directly to testosterone, but they do have receptors for androgen-binding protein. Sertoli cells, which produce androgen-binding protein, have androgen receptors.

Spermatogenesis is a very difficult process to study *in vivo* or *in vitro*, and the available animal models may not accurately reflect the situation in the human testis. For these reasons, it may be some time before we can say with certainty how testosterone and FSH regulate spermatogenesis.

CONCEPT CHECK

12. What do Sertoli cells secrete? What do Leydig cells secrete?
13. Because GnRH agonists cause down-regulation of GnRH receptors, what would be the advantages and disadvantages of using these drugs as a male contraceptive?
14. Name another important lipophilic molecule that binds to protein to make it more soluble in body fluid. Answers p. 867

Male Accessory Glands Contribute Secretions to Semen

The male reproductive tract has three accessory glands—bulbourethral glands, seminal vesicles, and prostate—whose primary function is to secrete various fluid mixtures. When sperm leave the vas deferens during ejaculation, they are joined by these secretions, resulting in a sperm-fluid mixture known as **semen**. About 99% of the volume of semen is fluid added from the accessory glands.

Accessory gland contributions to the composition of semen are listed in Table 26-3 ●. Semen provides a liquid medium for delivering sperm. The bulbourethral glands contribute mucus for lubrication and buffers to neutralize the usually acidic environment of the vagina. Seminal vesicles contribute prostaglandins [p. 193] that appear to influence sperm motility and transport in both male and female reproductive tracts. Prostaglandins were originally believed to come from the prostate gland, and the name was well established by the time their true source was discovered. Both the prostate and seminal vesicles contribute nutrients for sperm metabolism.

In addition to providing a medium for sperm, accessory gland secretions help protect the male reproductive tract from pathogens that might ascend the urethra from the external environment. The secretions physically flush out the urethra and supply immunoglobulins, lysozyme, and other compounds with antibacterial action. One interesting component of semen is zinc. Its role in reproduction is unclear, but concentrations of zinc below a certain level are associated with male infertility.

Androgens Influence Secondary Sex Characteristics

Androgens have a number of effects on the body in addition to gametogenesis. These effects are divided into primary and secondary sex characteristics. **Primary sex characteristics** are the internal sexual organs and external genitalia that distinguish males from females. As you have already learned, androgens are responsible for the differentiation of male genitalia during embryonic development and for their growth during puberty.

The **secondary sex characteristics** are other traits that distinguish males from females. The male body shape is sometimes described as an inverted triangle, with broad shoulders and narrow waist and hips. The female body is usually more pear shaped, with broad hips and narrow shoulders. Androgens are responsible for such typically male traits as beard and body hair growth, muscular development, thickening of the vocal chords with subsequent lowering of the voice, and behavioral effects, such as the sex drive, also called **libido** [*libido*, desire, lust].

Androgens are anabolic hormones that promote protein synthesis, which gives them their street name of *anabolic steroids*. The illicit use of these drugs by athletes has been widespread despite possible adverse side effects such as liver tumors, infertility, and excessive aggression (*'roid rage*). One of the more interesting side effects is the apparent addictiveness of anabolic steroids. Withdrawal from the drugs may be associated with behavioral changes that include depression, psychosis, or aggression. These psychiatric disturbances suggest

TABLE 26-3 Composition of Semen

COMPONENT	FUNCTION	SOURCE
Sperm	Gametes	Seminiferous tubules
Mucus	Lubricant	Bulbourethral glands
Water	Provides liquid medium	All accessory glands
Buffers	Neutralize acidic environment of the vagina	Prostate, bulbourethral glands
Nutrients	Nourish sperm	
Fructose		Seminal vesicles
Citric acid		Prostate
Vitamin C		Seminal vesicles
Carnitine		Epididymis
Enzymes	Clot semen in vagina, then liquefy the clot	Seminal vesicles and prostate
Zinc	Unknown; possible association with fertility	Unknown
Prostaglandins	Smooth muscle contraction; may aid sperm transport	Seminal vesicles

that human brain function can be modulated by sex steroids, just as the brain function of other animals can. Fortunately, many side effects of anabolic steroids are reversible once their use is discontinued.

CONCEPT CHECK

15. Explain why the use of exogenous anabolic steroids might shrink a man's testes and make him temporarily infertile.

Answers p. 867

FEMALE REPRODUCTION

Female reproduction is an example of a physiological process that is cyclic rather than steady state. The cycles of gamete production in the ovary and the interactions of reproductive hormones and feedback pathways are part of one of the most complex control systems of the human body.

Females Have Ovaries and a Uterus

The female external genitalia are known collectively as either the **vulva** or the **pudendum** [*vulva,* womb; *pudere,* to be ashamed]. They are shown in Figure 26-12a ●, the view seen by a health care worker who is about to do a pelvic exam or take a Pap smear [p. 54].

Starting at the periphery are the **labia majora** [*labium,* lip], folds of skin that arise from the same embryonic tissue as the scrotum. Within the labia majora are the **labia minora**, derived from embryonic tissues that in the male give rise to the shaft of the penis (see Fig. 26-3). The **clitoris** is a small bud of erectile, sensory tissue at the anterior end of the vulva, enclosed by the labia minora and an additional fold of tissue equivalent to the foreskin of the penis.

In females, the urethra opens to the external environment between the clitoris and the vagina [*vagina,* sheath], the cavity that acts as receptacle for the penis during copulation. At birth, the external opening of the vagina is partially closed by a thin ring of tissue called the **hymen**, or *maidenhead.* The hymen is external to the vagina, not within it, so the normal use of tampons during menstruation will not rupture the hymen. However, it can be stretched by normal activities such as horseback riding and therefore is not an accurate indicator of a woman's virginity.

Now let's follow the path of sperm deposited in the vagina during intercourse. To continue into the female reproductive tract, sperm must pass through the narrow opening of the **cervix**, the neck of the uterus that protrudes slightly into the upper end of the vagina (Fig. 26-12b, c). The cervical canal is lined with mucous glands whose secretions create a barrier between the vagina and uterus. Sperm that make it through the cervical canal arrive in the lumen of the uterus, or *womb,* a hollow, muscular organ slightly smaller than a woman's clenched fist.

The uterus is the structure in which fertilized eggs implant and develop during pregnancy. It is composed of three tissue layers (Fig. 26-12f): a thin outer connective tissue covering, a thick middle layer of smooth muscle known as the **myometrium**, and an inner layer known as the **endometrium** [*metra,* womb]. The endometrium consists of an epithelium with glands that dip into a connective tissue layer below. The thickness and character of the endometrium vary during the menstrual cycle. Cells of the epithelial lining alternately proliferate and slough off, accompanied by a small amount of bleeding in the process known as **menstruation** [*menstruus,* monthly].

Sperm swimming upward through the uterus leave its cavity through openings into the two fallopian tubes (Fig. 26-12c). The fallopian tubes are 20–25 cm long and about the diameter of a drinking straw. Their walls have two layers of smooth muscle, longitudinal and circular, similar to the walls of the intestine. A ciliated epithelium lines the inside of the tubes. Fluid movement created by the cilia and aided by muscular contractions transports an egg along the fallopian tube toward the uterus. If sperm moving up the tube encounter an egg moving down the tube, fertilization may occur. Pathological conditions in which ciliary function is absent are associated with female infertility and with pregnancies in which the embryo implants in the fallopian tube rather than the uterus.

The flared open end of the fallopian tube divides into fingerlike projections called **fimbriae** [*fimbriae,* fringe]. The fimbriae (Fig. 26-12c) are held close to the adjacent ovary by connective tissue, which helps ensure that eggs released from the surface of the ovary will be swept into the tube rather than floating off into the abdominal cavity.

The Ovary Produces Eggs and Hormones

The ovary is an elliptical structure, about 2–4 cm long (Fig. 26-12d). It has an outer connective tissue layer and an inner connective tissue framework known as the **stroma** [*stroma,* mattress]. Most of the ovary consists of a thick outer *cortex* filled with ovarian follicles in various stages of development or decline. The small central *medulla* contains nerves and blood vessels.

The ovary, like the testis, produces both gametes and hormones. As mentioned earlier, about 7 million oögonia in the embryonic ovary develop into half a million primary oocytes. Each primary oocyte is enclosed in a **primary follicle** with a single layer of **granulosa cells** separated by a basement membrane from an outer layer of cells known as the **theca** [*theke,* case or cover] (Fig. 26-12e).

A Menstrual Cycle Lasts About One Month

Female humans produce gametes in monthly cycles (average 28 days; normal range 24–35 days). These cycles are commonly called **menstrual cycles** because they are marked by a 3–7 day period of bloody uterine discharge known as the **menses** [*menses,* months], or **menstruation**. The menstrual cycle can be described by following changes that occur in follicles of the ovary, the **ovarian cycle**, or by following changes in the endometrial lining of the uterus, the **uterine cycle.** Figure 26-13 ● is a summary figure showing a typical menstrual cycle and its phases.

ANATOMY SUMMARY

THE FEMALE REPRODUCTIVE SYSTEM

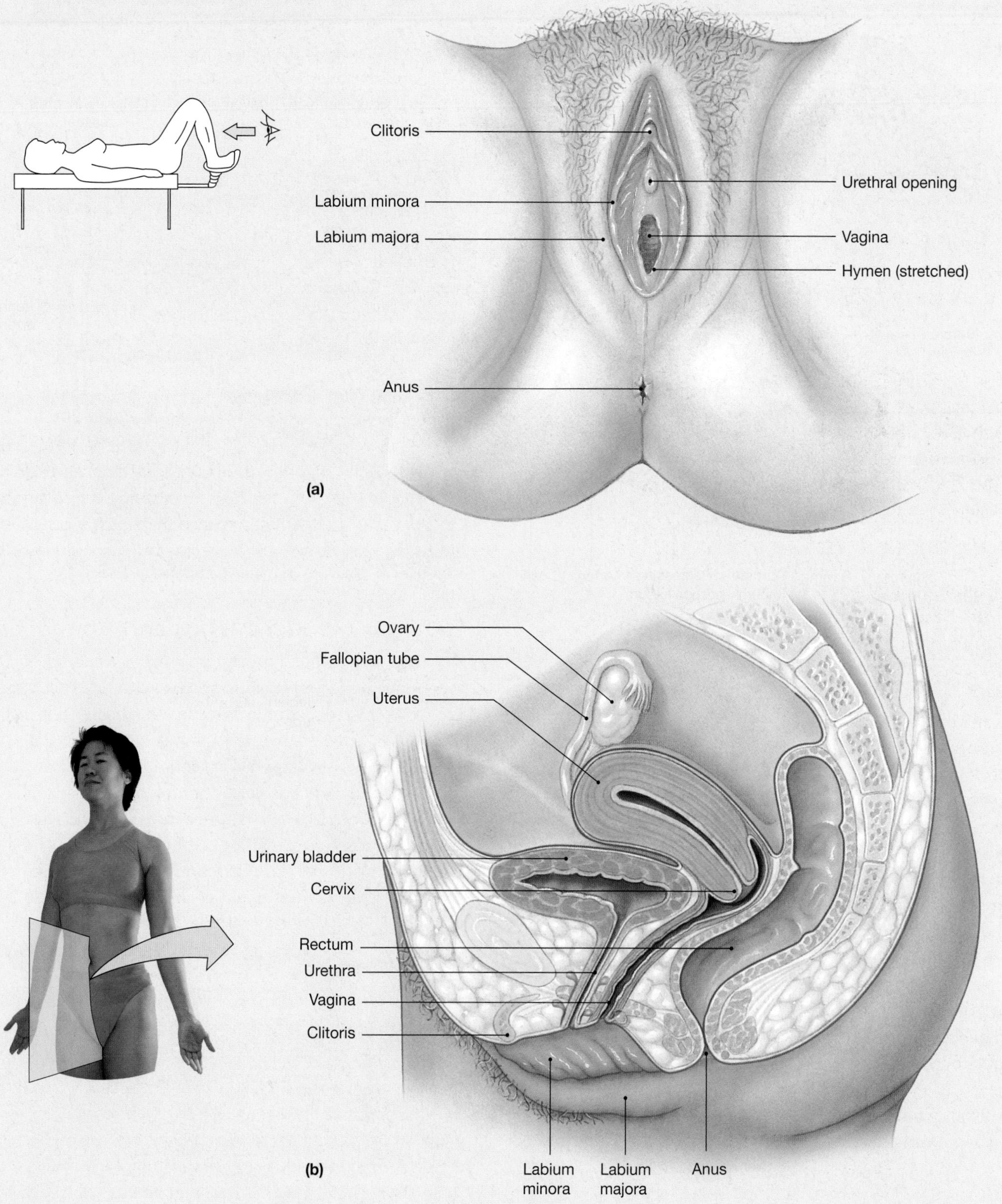
Clitoris
Urethral opening
Labium minora
Labium majora
Vagina
Hymen (stretched)
Anus
(a)
Ovary
Fallopian tube
Uterus
Urinary bladder
Cervix
Rectum
Urethra
Vagina
Clitoris
(b)
Labium minora
Labium majora
Anus

FIGURE 26-12

STRUCTURE OF THE UTERUS AND OVARY

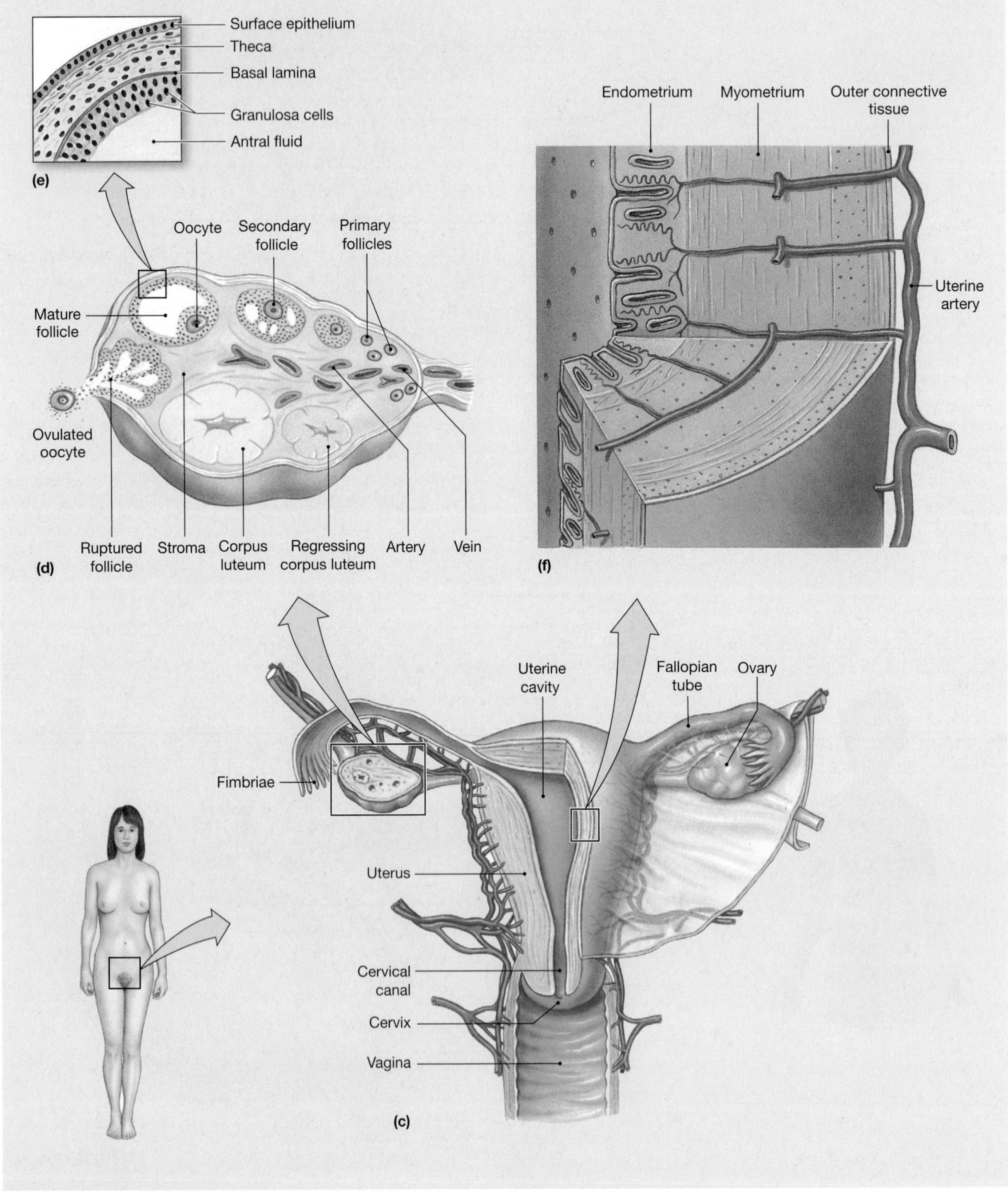
Surface epithelium
Theca
Basal lamina
Granulosa cells
Antral fluid
(e)
Oocyte
Secondary follicle
Primary follicles
Mature follicle
Ovulated oocyte
Ruptured follicle
Stroma
Corpus luteum
Regressing corpus luteum
Artery
Vein
(d)
Endometrium
Myometrium
Outer connective tissue
Uterine artery
(f)
Uterine cavity
Fallopian tube
Ovary
Fimbriae
Uterus
Cervical canal
Cervix
Vagina
(c)

FIGURE 26-12 *(continued)*

Notice that the ovarian cycle is divided into three phases:

1. **Follicular phase.** The first part of the ovarian cycle, known as the **follicular phase**, is a period of follicular growth in the ovary. This phase is the most variable in length and lasts from 10 days to 3 weeks.
2. **Ovulation.** Once one or more follicles have ripened, the ovary releases the oocyte(s) during **ovulation**.
3. **Luteal phase.** The phase of the ovarian cycle following ovulation is known as the *postovulatory* or **luteal phase**. The second name comes from the transformation of a ruptured follicle into a **corpus luteum** [*corpus*, body + *luteus*, yellow], named for its yellow pigment and lipid deposits. The corpus luteum secretes hormones that continue the preparations for pregnancy. If a pregnancy does not occur, the corpus luteum ceases to function after about two weeks, and the ovarian cycle begins again.

The endometrial lining of the uterus also goes through a cycle—the uterine cycle—regulated by ovarian hormones:

1. **Menses.** The beginning of the follicular phase in the ovary corresponds to menstrual bleeding from the uterus.
2. **Proliferative phase.** The latter part of the ovary's follicular phase corresponds to the **proliferative phase** in the uterus, during which the endometrium adds a new layer of cells in anticipation of pregnancy.
3. **Secretory phase.** After ovulation, hormones from the corpus luteum convert the thickened endometrium into a secretory structure. This means that the luteal phase of the ovarian cycle corresponds to the **secretory phase** of the uterine cycle. If no pregnancy occurs, the superficial layers of the secretory endometrium are lost during menstruation as the uterine cycle begins again.

Hormonal Control of the Menstrual Cycle Is Complex

The ovarian and uterine cycles are under the primary control of various hormones:

- GnRH from the hypothalamus
- FSH and LH from the anterior pituitary
- Estrogen, progesterone, inhibin, and AMH from the ovary

During the follicular phase, the dominant steroid hormone is estrogen (Fig. 26-13). Ovulation is triggered by surges in LH and FSH. In the luteal phase, progesterone is dominant, although estrogen is still present.

Now let's go through an ovarian cycle in detail.

Early Follicular Phase The first day of menstruation is day 1 of a cycle. This point was chosen to start the cycle because the bleeding of menstruation is an easily observed physical sign. Just before the beginning of each cycle, gonadotropin secretion from the anterior pituitary increases. Under the influence of FSH, several follicles in the ovaries begin to mature (second row of Fig. 26-13 and Tbl. 26-4 ●).

TABLE 26-4 Development of Ovarian Follicles

To help visualize these stages, see the ovarian cycle row in Figure 26-13 and the layers of the follicle in Figure 26-12e. The zona pellucida (see Fig. 26-16) is a glycoprotein coat that protects the ovum.

OVARIAN PHASE	FOLLICLE STAGE	OVUM	ZONA PELLUCIDA	GRANULOSA CELLS	ANTRUM	BASAL LAMINA	THECA
Before FSH stimulation	Primary follicle	Primary oocyte	Minimal	Single layer	None	Separates granulosa and theca	Single cell layer plus blood vessels
Early follicular phase	Secondary follicle	Primary oocyte	Increased in width	2–6 cell layer	None	Present	Single cell layer
Late follicular phase	Tertiary follicle	Primary oocyte, then secondary oocyte with division arrested	Present	3–4 cell layer	Develops within granulosa layer and fills with fluid; swells to 15–20 mm in diameter	Present	*Inner layer:* secretory and small blood vessels *Outer layer:* connective tissue, smooth muscle cells, large blood vessels
Luteal phase	Corpus luteum	None	None	Converted to luteal cells	Fills with migrating cells	Disappears	Converted to luteal cells
Post-luteal phase	Corpus albicans	None	None	Cells degenerate	None	None	Cells degenerate

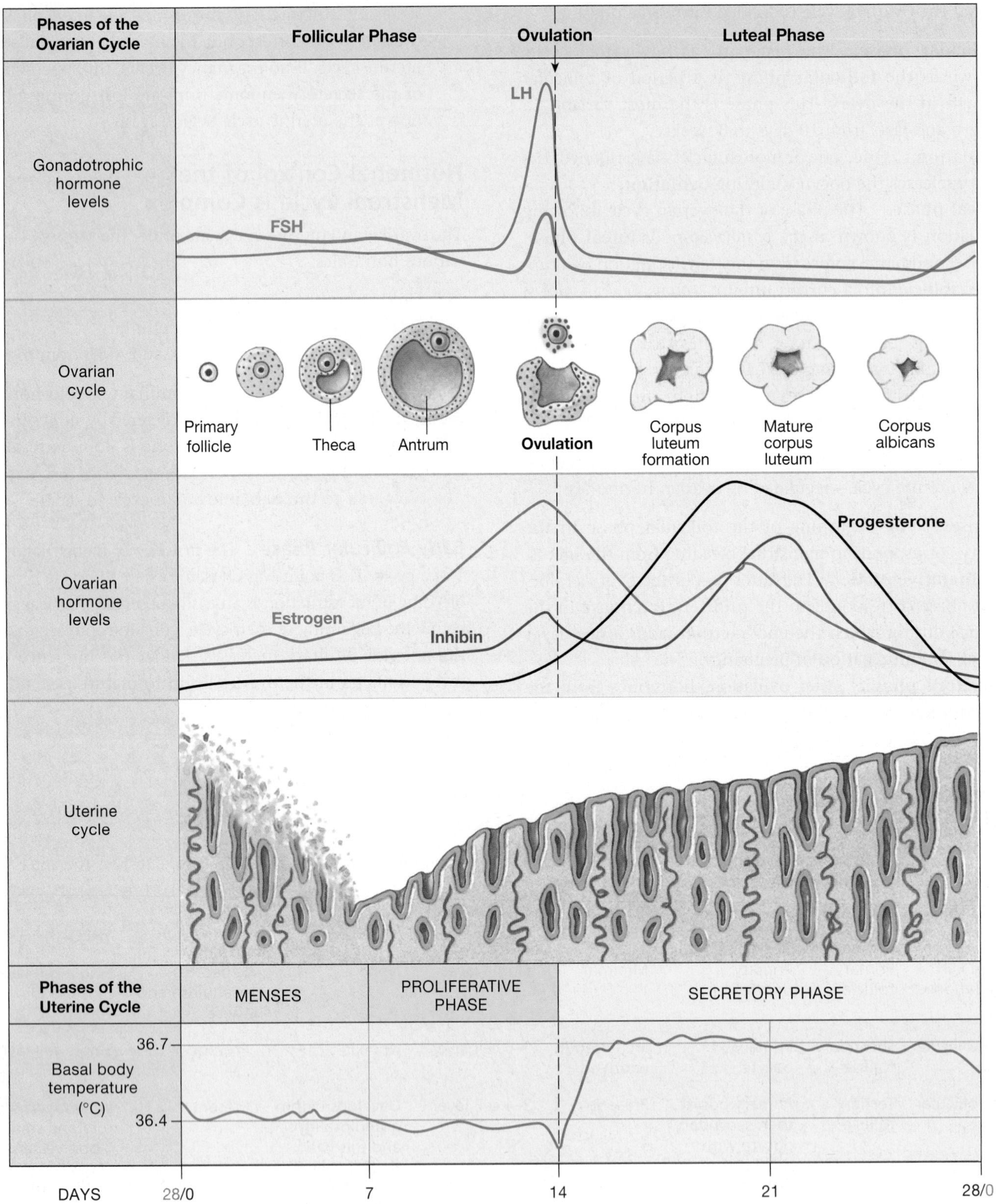

Phases of the Ovarian Cycle
Follicular Phase
Ovulation
Luteal Phase
Gonadotrophic hormone levels
LH
FSH
Ovarian cycle
Primary follicle
Theca
Antrum
Ovulation
Corpus luteum formation
Mature corpus luteum
Corpus albicans
Ovarian hormone levels
Progesterone
Estrogen
Inhibin
Uterine cycle
Phases of the Uterine Cycle
MENSES
PROLIFERATIVE PHASE
SECRETORY PHASE
Basal body temperature (°C)
36.7
36.4
DAYS
28/0
7
14
21
28/0

● **FIGURE 26-13** ***The menstrual cycle.*** This 28-day menstrual cycle is divided into phases based on events in the uterus and ovary.

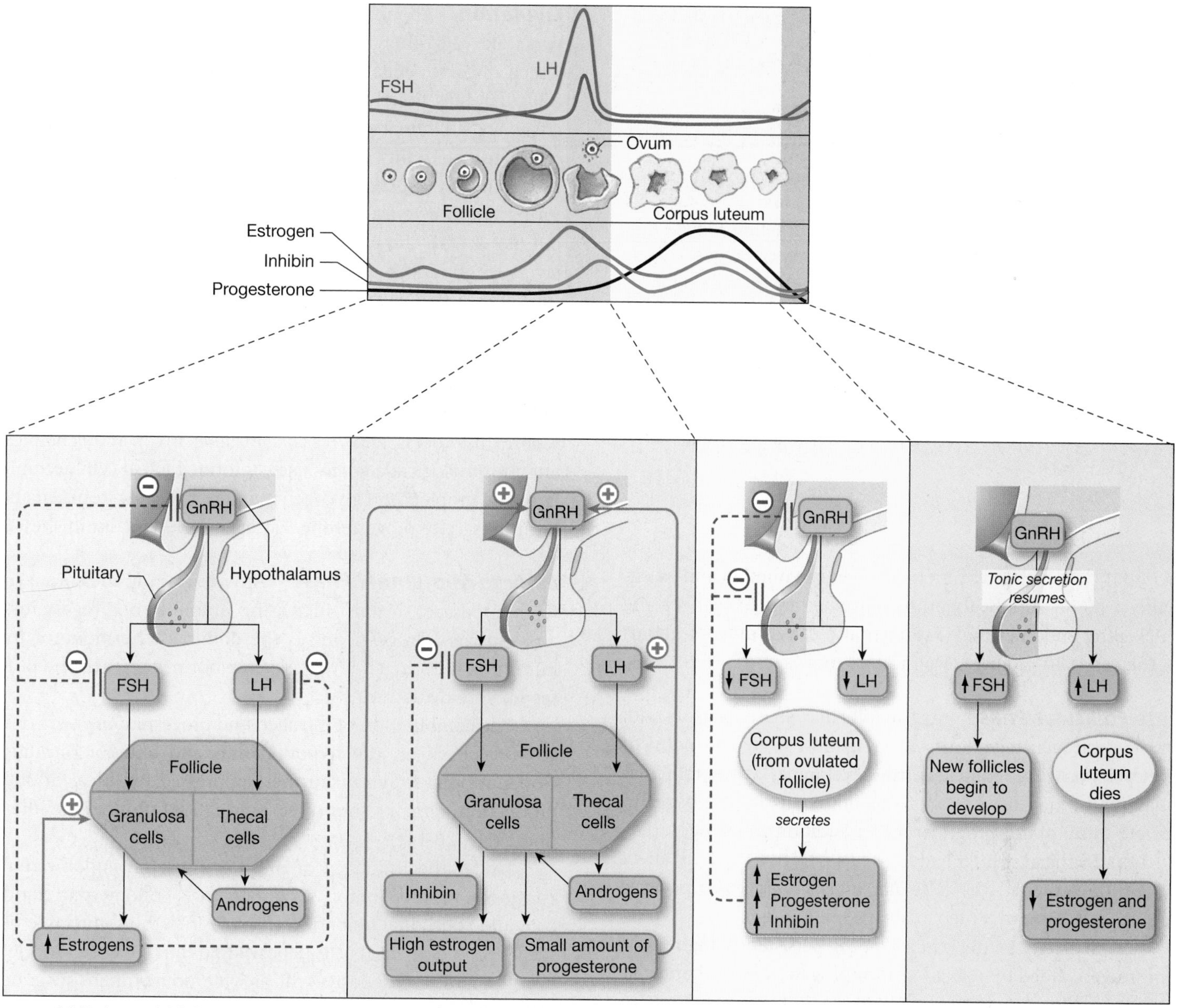

(a) Early to mid-follicular phase **(b)** Late follicular phase and ovulation **(c)** Early to mid-luteal phase **(d)** Late luteal phase

● **FIGURE 26-14** ***Hormonal control of the menstrual cycle***

As the follicles grow, their granulosa cells (under the influence of FSH) and their thecal cells (under the influence of LH) start to produce steroid hormones. Granulosa cells also begin to secrete AMH. This AMH decreases follicle sensitivity to FSH, which apparently prevents recruitment of additional primary follicles once one group has started developing. Physicians are testing whether blood AMH levels are an accurate indicator of ovarian function.

Thecal cells synthesize androgens that diffuse into the neighboring granulosa cells, where aromatase converts them to estrogens (Fig. 26-14a ●). Gradually increasing estrogen levels in the circulation have several effects. Estrogen exerts negative feedback on pituitary FSH and LH secretion, which prevents the development of additional follicles in the same cycle. At the same time, estrogen stimulates additional estrogen production by the granulosa cells. This positive feedback loop allows the follicles to continue estrogen production even though FSH and LH levels decrease.

As the follicles enlarge, granulosa cells secrete fluid that collects in a central cavity in the follicle known as the **antrum** [*antron,* cave]. Antral fluid (see Fig. 26-12e) contains hormones and enzymes needed for ovulation. At each stage of follicular development, some follicles undergo *atresia* (hormonally regulated cell death). Only a few follicles reach the final stage, and usually only one dominant follicle develops until ovulation.

In the uterus, menstruation ends during the early follicular phase. Under the influence of estrogen from developing follicles, the endometrium begins to grow, or proliferate. This

EMERGING CONCEPTS

AMH AND OVARIAN FUNCTION

Although anti-Müllerian hormone (AMH) is best known for its role in male development, scientists discovered that AMH is also produced by granulose cells of ovarian follicles in the first part of the late follicular phase. AMH decreases the sensitivity of developing follicles to FSH and apparently acts as a brake to keep too many follicles developing at one time. Evidence from rodents and humans suggests that blood levels of AMH may be able to serve as a marker for several reproductive problems, including some forms of infertility and the condition known as *polycystic ovary syndrome (PCOS)*, in which ovarian follicles form fluid-filled cysts.

period is characterized by an increase in cell number and by enhanced blood supply to bring nutrients and oxygen to the thickening endometrium. Estrogen also causes mucous glands of the cervix to produce clear, watery mucus.

Late Follicular Phase As the follicular phase nears its end, ovarian estrogen secretion peaks (Fig. 26-13). By this point of the cycle, only one follicle is still developing. As the follicular phase ends, granulosa cells of this dominant follicle begin to secrete inhibin and progesterone in addition to estrogen (Fig. 26-14b). Estrogen, which had exerted a negative feedback effect on GnRH earlier in the follicular phase, changes to positive feedback, leading to a preovulatory GnRH surge.

Immediately before ovulation, the persistently high levels of estrogen, aided by rising levels of progesterone, enhance pituitary responsiveness to GnRH. As a result, LH secretion increases dramatically, a phenomenon known as the *LH surge*. FSH surges also, but to a lesser degree, presumably because it is being suppressed by inhibin and estrogen.

The LH surge is an essential part of ovulation. Without it, the final steps of oocyte maturation cannot take place. Meiosis resumes in the developing follicle with the first meiotic division, which converts the primary oocyte into a secondary oocyte (egg) and a polar body, which is extruded (see Fig. 26-5). While this division is taking place, antral fluid collects and the follicle grows to its greatest size, preparing to release the egg.

High levels of estrogen in the late follicular phase prepare the uterus for a possible pregnancy. The endometrium grows to a final thickness of 3–4 mm. Just before ovulation, the cervical glands produce copious amounts of thin, stringy mucus to facilitate sperm entry. The stage is set for ovulation.

Ovulation About 16–24 hours after LH peaks, ovulation occurs (Fig. 26-14b). The mature follicle secretes *collagenase,* which dissolves collagen in the connective tissue holding the follicular cells together. The breakdown products of collagen create an inflammatory reaction, attracting leukocytes that secrete prostaglandins into the follicle. The prostaglandins may cause smooth muscle cells in the outer theca to contract, rupturing the follicle wall at its weakest point. Antral fluid spurts out along with the egg, which is surrounded by two to three layers of granulosa cells. The egg is swept into the fallopian tube and carried away to be fertilized or to die.

In addition to promoting follicular rupture, the LH surge causes follicular thecal cells to migrate into the antral space, mingling with the former granulosa cells and filling the cavity. Both cell types then transform into *luteal cells* of the corpus luteum. This process, known as *luteinization,* involves biochemical and morphological changes. Newly formed luteal cells accumulate lipid droplets and glycogen granules in their cytoplasm and begin to secrete progesterone. Estrogen synthesis diminishes.

Early to Mid-Luteal Phase After ovulation, the corpus luteum produces steadily increasing amounts of progesterone and estrogen. Progesterone is the dominant hormone of the luteal phase. Estrogen levels increase but never reach the peak seen before ovulation.

The combination of estrogen and progesterone exerts negative feedback on the hypothalamus and anterior pituitary. Gonadotropin secretion, further suppressed by luteal inhibin production, remains shut down throughout most of the luteal phase (Fig. 26-14c).

Under the influence of progesterone, the endometrium continues its preparation for pregnancy. Endometrial glands coil, and additional blood vessels grow into the connective tissue layer. Endometrial cells deposit lipids and glycogen in their cytoplasm. These deposits will provide nourishment for a developing embryo while the **placenta**, the fetal-maternal connection, is developing.

RUNNING PROBLEM

The results of Larry's sperm analysis are normal. Dr. Coddington is therefore able to rule out sperm abnormalities as a cause of Peggy and Larry's infertility. Peggy is instructed to take her body temperature daily and record the results on a chart. This temperature tracking is intended to determine whether or not she is ovulating. Following ovulation, body temperature rises slightly and remains elevated through the remainder of the menstrual cycle.

Question 3:

For which causes of female infertility is temperature tracking useful? For which causes is it not useful?

829 841 850 851 855 860 862

Progesterone also causes cervical mucus to thicken. Thicker mucus creates a plug that blocks the cervical opening, preventing bacteria as well as sperm from entering the uterus.

One interesting effect of progesterone is its thermogenic ability. During the luteal phase of an ovulatory cycle, a woman's basal body temperature, taken immediately upon awakening and before getting out of bed, jumps 0.3°–0.5° F and remains elevated until menstruation. Because this change in the temperature setpoint occurs after ovulation, it cannot be used effectively to predict ovulation. However, it is a simple way to assess whether a woman is having ovulatory or *anovulatory* (non-ovulating) cycles.

Late Luteal Phase and Menstruation The corpus luteum has an intrinsic life span of approximately 12 days. If pregnancy does not occur, the corpus luteum spontaneously undergoes *apoptosis* [p. 85] to become an inactive structure called a **corpus albicans** [*albus,* white]. As the luteal cells degenerate, progesterone and estrogen production decrease (Fig. 26-14d). This decrease removes the negative feedback signal to the pituitary and hypothalamus, and secretion of FSH and LH increases.

Maintenance of a secretory endometrium depends on the presence of progesterone. When the corpus luteum degenerates and hormone production decreases, blood vessels in the surface layer of the endometrium contract. Without oxygen and nutrients, the surface cells die. About two days after the corpus luteum ceases to function, or 14 days after ovulation, the endometrium begins to slough its surface layer, and menstruation begins.

Menstrual discharge from the uterus totals about 40 mL of blood and 35 mL of serous fluid and cellular debris. There are usually few clots of blood in the menstrual flow because of the presence of *plasmin* [p. 562], which breaks up clots. Menstruation continues for 3–7 days, well into the follicular phase of the next ovulatory cycle.

Hormones Influence Female Secondary Sex Characteristics

Estrogens control the development of primary sex characteristics in females, just as androgens control them in males. Estrogens also control the most prominent female secondary sex traits: breast development and the pattern of fat distribution (hips and upper thighs). Other female secondary sex characteristics, however, are governed by androgens produced in the adrenal cortex. Pubic and axillary (armpit) hair growth and libido (sex drive) are under the control of adrenal androgens.

CONCEPT CHECK

16. Name the phases of the ovarian cycle and the corresponding phases of the uterine cycle.
17. What side effects would you predict in female athletes who take anabolic steroids to build muscles?
18. Aromatase converts testosterone to estrogen. What would happen to the ovarian cycle of a woman given an aromatase inhibitor?
19. On what day of the menstrual cycle will a woman with the following cycle lengths ovulate? (a) 28 days (b) 23 days (c) 31 days

Answers p. 867

PROCREATION

Reproduction throughout the animal kingdom is marked by species-specific behaviors designed to ensure that egg and sperm meet. For aquatic animals that release gametes into the water, coordinated timing is everything. Interaction between males and females of these species may be limited to chemical communication by pheromones.

In terrestrial vertebrates, internal fertilization requires interactive behaviors and specialized adaptations of the genitalia. For example, the female must have an internal receptacle for sperm (the vagina in humans), and the male must possess an organ (the penis in humans) that can place sperm in the receptacle. The human penis is *flaccid* (soft and limp) in its resting state, not capable of penetrating the narrow opening of the vagina. In the male sex act, the penis first stiffens and enlarges during **erection**, and then releases sperm from the ducts of the reproductive tract during **ejaculation**. Without these events, fertilization cannot take place.

RUNNING PROBLEM

Results of the temperature tracking for several months reveal that Peggy is ovulating regularly. Dr. Coddington therefore believes that her ovaries are functioning normally. Other possible causes for this couple's infertility include abnormalities in Peggy's cervix, fallopian tubes, or uterus. Dr. Coddington next decides to order a postcoital test. In this test, the couple is instructed to have intercourse 12 hours before the physician visit. Cervical mucus is then analyzed. This test will also analyze the interaction between sperm and mucus.

Question 4:

What abnormalities in the cervix, fallopian tubes, and uterus could cause infertility?

The Human Sexual Response Has Four Phases

The human sex act—also known as sexual intercourse, copulation, or **coitus** [*coitio,* a coming together]—is highly variable in some ways and highly stereotypical in other ways.

Human sexual response in both sexes is divided into four phases: (1) excitement, (2) plateau, (3) orgasm, and (4) resolution. In the excitement phase, various erotic stimuli prepare the genitalia for the act of copulation. For the male, excitement involves erection of the penis. For the female, it includes erection of the clitoris and vaginal lubrication. In both sexes, erection is a state of vasocongestion in which arterial blood flow into spongy erectile tissue exceeds venous outflow.

Erotic stimuli include sexually arousing tactile stimuli as well as psychological stimuli. Because the latter vary widely among individuals and among cultures, what is erotic to one person or in one culture may be considered disgusting by another individual or in another culture. Regions of the body that possess receptors for sexually arousing tactile stimuli are called **erogenous zones** and include the genitalia as well as the lips, tongue, nipples, and ear lobes.

In the plateau phase, changes that started during excitement intensify and peak in an **orgasm** (climax). In both sexes, orgasm is a series of muscular contractions accompanied by intense pleasurable sensations and increased blood pressure, heart rate, and respiration rate. In females, the uterus and walls of the vagina contract. In males, the contractions usually result in the ejaculation of semen from the penis. Female orgasm is not required for pregnancy.

The final phase of the sexual response is resolution, a period during which the physiological parameters that changed in the first three phases slowly return to normal.

The Male Sex Act Includes Erection and Ejaculation

A key element to successful copulation is the ability of the male to achieve and sustain an erection. Sexual excitement from either tactile or psychological stimuli triggers the **erection reflex,** a spinal reflex that is subject to control from higher centers in the brain. The urination and defecation reflexes are similar types of reflexes [pp. 644, 716].

In its simplest form, the erection reflex begins with tactile stimuli sensed by mechanoreceptors in the glans penis or other erogenous zones (Fig. 26-15 ●). Sensory neurons signal the spinal integration center, which inhibits vasoconstrictive sympathetic input on penile arterioles. Simultaneously, nitric oxide produced by increased parasympathetic input actively dilates the penile arterioles. As arterial blood flows into the open spaces of the erectile tissue, it passively compresses the veins and traps blood. The erectile tissue becomes engorged, stiffening and lengthening the penis within 5–10 seconds.

The climax of the male sexual act coincides with emission and ejaculation. **Emission** is the movement of sperm out of the vas deferens and into the urethra, where they are joined by secretions from the accessory glands to make semen. The average semen volume is 3 mL (range 2–6 mL), of which less than 10% is sperm.

During ejaculation, semen in the urethra is expelled to the exterior by a series of rapid muscular contractions accompanied by sensations of intense pleasure—the orgasm. A sphincter at the base of the bladder contracts to prevent sperm from entering the bladder and urine from joining the semen.

Both erection and ejaculation can occur in the absence of mechanical stimulation. Sexually arousing thoughts, sights, sounds, emotions, and dreams can all initiate sexual arousal and even lead to orgasm in both men and women. In addition, nonsexual penile erection accompanies rapid eye movement (REM) sleep.

Sexual Dysfunction Affects Males and Females

The inability to obtain or sustain a penile erection is known as **erectile dysfunction** (ED) or *impotence.* Erectile dysfunction is a matter of global concern because inability to achieve and sustain an erection disrupts the sex act for both men and women. Organic (physiological and anatomical) causes of ED include neural and hormonal problems, vascular insufficiency, and drug-induced ED. A variety of psychological causes can also contribute to ED.

Alcohol inhibits sexual performance in both men and women, as noted by Shakespeare in *Macbeth* (II, iii). When Macduff asks, "What three things does drink especially provoke?" the porter answers, "Marry, sir, nose-painting, sleep, and urine. Lechery, sir, it provokes and unprovokes: it provokes the desire, but it takes away the performance." Several antidepressant drugs list loss of libido among their side effects.

Erectile dysfunction in men over age 40 is now considered a marker for cardiovascular disease and atherosclerosis, and sometimes ED is the first clinical sign of these conditions. Erections occur when neurotransmitters from pelvic nerves increase endothelial production of nitric oxide (NO), which increases cGMP and results in vasodilation of penile arterioles. Endothelial dysfunction and failure to produce adequate NO occur in atherosclerosis and diabetes mellitus, making ED an early manifestation of vascular pathology.

In 1998 the U.S. Food and Drug Administration (FDA) approved sildenafil (Viagra®) for the treatment of erectile dysfunction. Sildenafil and similar drugs in the same class prolong the effects of nitric oxide by blocking *phosphodiesterase-5* (PDE-5), the enzyme that degrades cGMP. Clinical trials have shown that phosphodiesterase inhibitors are very effective in correcting ED but are not without side effects. The U.S. Federal Aviation Administration issued an order that pilots should not take sildenafil within six hours of flying because 3% of men report impaired color vision (a blue or greenish haze). This impairment occurs because sildenafil also inhibits an enzyme in the retina.

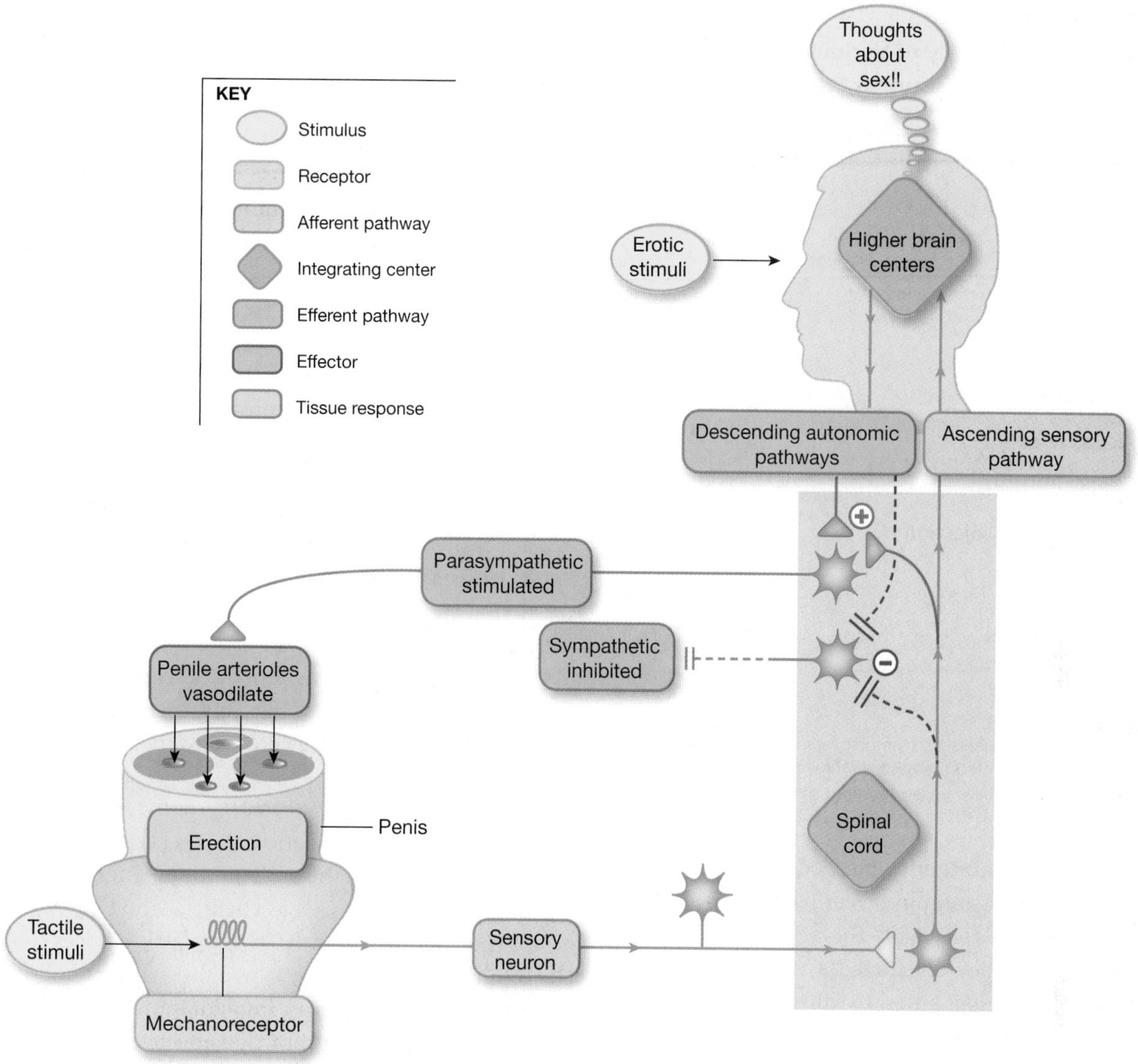
KEY
Stimulus
Receptor
Afferent pathway
Integrating center
Efferent pathway
Effector
Tissue response
Thoughts about sex!!
Erotic stimuli
Higher brain centers
Descending autonomic pathways
Ascending sensory pathway
Parasympathetic stimulated
Sympathetic inhibited
Penile arterioles vasodilate
Erection
Penis
Spinal cord
Tactile stimuli
Sensory neuron
Mechanoreceptor

● **FIGURE 26-15** ***The erection reflex.*** Erection can take place without input from higher brain centers. It can also be stimulated (and inhibited) by descending pathways from the cerebral cortex.

When the FDA approved PDE-5 inhibitors for male erectile dysfunction, women wondered if the drug, which promotes the erection reflex, would improve their sexual response. Although women do have clitoral erections, the female sexual response is more complicated. Studies on the efficacy of PDE-5 inhibitors for orgasmic dysfunction in women have had mixed results. Instead, pharmaceutical companies are testing other drugs for female sexual dysfunction. The most promising candidates, now in late clinical trials, are based on testosterone, the androgen that creates libido in both sexes.

Contraceptives Are Designed to Prevent Pregnancy

One disadvantage of sexual intercourse for pleasure rather than reproduction is the possibility of an unplanned pregnancy. On average, 85% of young women who have sexual intercourse without using any form of birth control will get pregnant within a year. Many women, however, get pregnant after just a single unprotected encounter. Couples who hope to avoid unwanted pregnancies generally use some form of birth control, or **contraception.**

Contraceptive practices fall into several broad groups. **Abstinence**, the total avoidance of sexual intercourse, is the surest method to avoid pregnancy (and sexually transmitted diseases). Some couples practice abstinence only during times of suspected fertility.

Interventional methods of contraception include (1) barrier methods, which prevent union of eggs and sperm; (2) methods that prevent implantation of the fertilized egg; and (3) hormonal treatments that decrease or stop gamete production. The efficacy of interventional contraceptives depends in part on how consistently and correctly they are used (Tbl. 26-5 ●).

TABLE 26-5 Efficacy of Various Contraceptive Methods

METHOD	PREGNANCY RATE WITH TYPICAL USE*
No contraception	85%
Spermicides	29%
Abstinence during times of predicted fertility	25%
Diaphragm, cervical cap, or sponge	16–32%†
Oral contraceptive pills	8%
Intrauterine devices (IUDs)	< 1%
Contraceptive hormone injection	< 1%
Male condom	15%
Female condom	21%
Sterilization	< 1%

*Rates reflect unintentional pregnancies in the first year of using the method. Data are from *www.contraceptivetechnology.org/table.html* (Accessed 8/22/08).
†Lower rates are in women who have never delivered a child.

Barrier Methods Contraceptive methods based on chemical or physical barriers are among the earliest recorded means of birth control. Once people made the association between pregnancy and semen, they concocted a variety of physical barriers and *spermicides* [*cida,* killer] to kill sperm. An ancient Egyptian papyrus with the earliest known references to birth control describes the use of vaginal plugs made of leaves, feathers, figs, and alum held together with crocodile and elephant dung. Sea sponges soaked in vinegar and disks of oiled silk have also been used at one time or another. In subsequent centuries women used douches of garlic, turpentine, and rose petals to rinse the vagina after intercourse. As you can imagine, many of these methods also caused vaginal or uterine infections.

Modern versions of the female barrier include the **diaphragm,** introduced into the United States in 1916. These rubber domes and a smaller version called a *cervical cap* are usually filled with a spermicidal cream, then inserted into the top of the vagina so they cover the cervix. One advantage to the diaphragm is that it is nonhormonal. When used properly and regularly, diaphragms are highly effective (97–99%). However, they are not always used because they must be inserted close to the time of intercourse, and consequently about 20% of women who depend on diaphragms for contraception are pregnant within the first year. Another female barrier contraceptive that was recently re-introduced is the **contraceptive sponge,** which contains a spermicidal chemical.

The male barrier contraceptive is the **condom,** a closed sheath that fits closely over the penis to catch ejaculated semen. Males have used condoms made from animal bladders and intestines for centuries. Condoms lost popularity when oral contraceptives came into widespread use in the 1960s and 1970s, but in recent years they have regained favor because they combine pregnancy protection with protection from many sexually transmitted diseases. However, latex condoms may cause allergic reactions, and there is evidence that HIV can pass through pores in some condoms currently produced. A female version of the condom is also commercially available. It covers the cervix and completely lines the vagina, providing more protection from sexually transmitted diseases.

Sterilization is the most effective contraceptive method for sexually active people, but it is a surgical procedure and is not easily reversed. Female sterilization is called **tubal ligation.** It consists of tying off and cutting the fallopian tubes. A woman with a tubal ligation still ovulates, but the eggs remain in the abdomen. The male form of sterilization is the **vasectomy,** in which the vas deferens is tied and clipped. Sperm are still made in the seminiferous tubules, but because they cannot leave the reproductive tract, they are reabsorbed.

Implantation Prevention Some contraceptive methods do not prevent fertilization but do keep a fertilized egg from establishing itself in the endometrium. They include **intrauterine devices (IUDs)** as well as chemicals that change the properties of the endometrium. IUDs are plastic devices that are inserted into the uterine cavity, where they create a mild inflammatory reaction that prevents implantation. They have low failure rates (0.5% per year) but side effects that range from pain and bleeding to infertility caused by pelvic inflammatory disease and blockage of the fallopian tubes.

Hormonal Treatments Techniques for decreasing gamete production depend on altering the hormonal milieu of the body. In centuries past, women would eat or drink various plant concoctions for contraception. Some of these substances actually worked because the plants contained estrogen-like compounds. Modern pharmacology has improved on this method, and now women can choose between oral contraceptive pills, injections lasting three months, or a vaginal contraceptive ring (NuvaRing®).

The **oral contraceptives,** also known as *birth control pills,* were first made available in 1960. They rely on various combinations of estrogen and progesterone that inhibit gonadotropin secretion from the pituitary. Without adequate FSH and LH, ovulation is suppressed. In addition, progesterones in the contraceptive pills thicken the cervical mucus and help prevent sperm penetration. These hormonal methods of contraception are highly effective when used correctly but also carry some risks, including an increased incidence of blood clots and strokes (especially in women who smoke).

Development of a male hormonal contraceptive has been slow because of undesirable side effects. Contraceptives that block testosterone secretion or action are also likely to decrease the male libido or even cause impotence. Both side effects are unacceptable to men who would be most interested in using the contraceptive. Some early male oral contraceptives irreversibly suppressed sperm production, which was also unacceptable. It now appears, however, that a combination of oral progestin to suppress sperm production plus injected testosterone to maintain libido is a promising candidate for a male hormonal contraceptive.

Contraceptive vaccines are based on antibodies against various components of the male and female reproductive systems, such as antisperm or antiovum antibodies. These contraceptives appear to be long lasting and reversible, and they can be administered as shots. Some contraceptive vaccines are being tested in clinical trials.

Infertility Is the Inability to Conceive

While some couples are trying to prevent pregnancy, others are spending thousands of dollars trying to get pregnant using **assisted reproductive technology** (ART). *Infertility* is the inability of a couple to conceive a child after a year of unprotected intercourse. For years, infertile couples had no choice but adoption if they wanted to have a child, but incredible strides have been made in this field since the 1970s. As a result, many infertile couples today are able to have children.

Infertility can arise from a problem in the male, the female, or both. Male infertility usually results from a low sperm count or an abnormally high number of defective sperm. Female infertility can be mechanical (blocked fallopian tubes or other structural problems) or hormonal, leading to decreased or absent ovulation. One problem involving both partners is that the woman may produce antibodies to her partner's sperm. In addition, not all pregnancies go to a successful conclusion. By some estimates, as many as a third of all pregnancies spontaneously terminate—many within the first weeks, before the woman is even aware that she was pregnant.

Some of the most dramatic advances have been made in the field of *in vitro* fertilization, in which a woman's ovaries are hormonally manipulated to ovulate multiple eggs at one time. The eggs are collected surgically and fertilized outside the body. The developing embryos are then placed in the woman's uterus, which has been primed for pregnancy by hormonal therapy. Because of the expense and complicated nature of the procedure, multiple embryos are usually placed in the uterus at one time, which may result in multiple births. *In vitro* fertilization has allowed some infertile couples to have children, with a 2005 success rate in the United States ranging from 43% for women younger than 35 and 18% for women older than 40.

RUNNING PROBLEM

Analysis of Peggy's postcoital cervical mucus shows that sperm are present but not moving. Dr. Coddington explains that it is likely that Peggy's cervical mucus contains antibodies that destroy Larry's sperm.

Question 5:

Speculate on how this kind of infertility problem might be treated.

829 841 850 851 855 860 862

PREGNANCY AND PARTURITION

Now let's return to a recently ovulated egg and some sperm deposited in the vagina and follow them through fertilization, pregnancy, and **parturition**, the birth process.

Fertilization Requires Capacitation

Once an egg is released from the ruptured follicle, it is swept into the fallopian tube by beating cilia. Meanwhile, sperm deposited in the vagina must go through their final maturation step, **capacitation**, which enables the sperm to swim rapidly and fertilize an egg. The process apparently involves the reorganization of molecules in the outer membrane of the sperm head.

Normally, capacitation takes place in the female reproductive tract, which presents a problem for *in vitro* fertilization. Those sperm must be artificially capacitated by placing them in physiological saline supplemented with human serum. Much of what we know about human fertilization has come from infertility research aimed at improving the success rate of *in vitro* fertilization.

Fertilization of an egg by a sperm is the result of a chance encounter, possibly aided by chemical attractants produced by the egg. An egg can be fertilized for only about 12–24 hours after ovulation. Sperm in the female reproductive tract remain viable for four to six days.

Fertilization normally takes place in the distal part of the fallopian tube. Of the millions of sperm in a single ejaculation, only about 100 reach this point. To fertilize the egg, a sperm must penetrate both an outer layer of loosely connected granulosa cells (the *corona radiata*) and a protective glycoprotein coat called the **zona pellucida** (Fig. 26-16 ●). To get past these barriers, capacitated sperm release powerful enzymes from the acrosome in the sperm head, a process known as the **acrosomal reaction**. The enzymes dissolve cell junctions and the zona pellucida, allowing the sperm to wiggle their way toward the egg. The first sperm to reach the egg quickly finds sperm-binding receptors on the oocyte membrane and fuses its membrane to the egg membrane (Fig. 26-17 ●). The fused section of membrane opens, and the sperm nucleus sinks into the egg's cytoplasm. Fusion of the egg and sperm membranes signals the egg to resume meiosis and complete its second division. The final meiotic division creates a

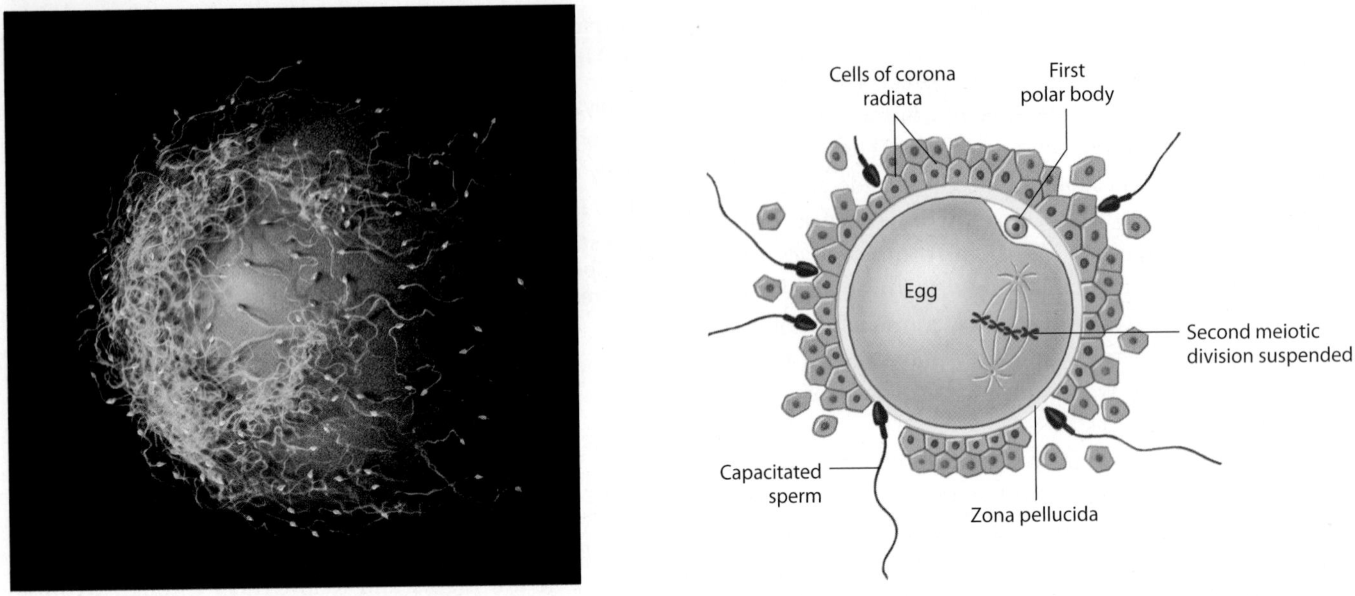
Cells of corona radiata
First polar body
Egg
Second meiotic division suspended
Capacitated sperm
Zona pellucida

(a)

(b) Capacitated sperm release enzymes from their acrosomes in order to penetrate the cells and zona pellucida surrounding the egg.

● **FIGURE 26-16** ***The first sperm to fuse with the egg fertilizes it.*** The photograph shows the tremendous difference in the sizes of human sperm and egg.

second polar body, which is ejected. At this point, the 23 chromosomes of the sperm join the 23 chromosomes of the egg, creating a zygote nucleus with a full set of genetic material.

The fusion of sperm and oocyte membrane prevents **polyspermy**, in which more than one sperm fertilizes an egg, by triggering a chemical reaction called the **cortical reaction**. Membrane-bound **cortical granules** in the peripheral cytoplasm of the egg release their contents into the space just outside the egg membrane. These chemicals rapidly alter the membrane and surrounding zona pellucida so that additional sperm cannot penetrate or bind.

Once the egg is fertilized and becomes a zygote, it begins mitotic division as it slowly makes its way along the fallopian tube to the uterus, where it will settle for the remainder of the **gestation** period [*gestare*, to carry in the womb].

The Developing Embryo Implants in the Endometrium

The dividing embryo takes four or five days to move through the fallopian tube into the uterine cavity (Fig. 26-18 ●). Under the influence of progesterone, smooth muscle of the tube relaxes, and transport proceeds slowly. By the time the developing embryo reaches the uterus, it consists of a hollow ball of about 100 cells called a **blastocyst**.

Some of the outer layer of blastocyst cells will become the **chorion**, an *extraembryonic membrane* that will enclose the embryo and form the placenta (Fig. 26-19a ●). The inner cell mass of the blastocyst will develop into the embryo and into other extraembryonic membranes. These membranes include the **amnion**, which secretes *amniotic fluid* in which the developing embryo floats; the **allantois**, which becomes part of the umbilical

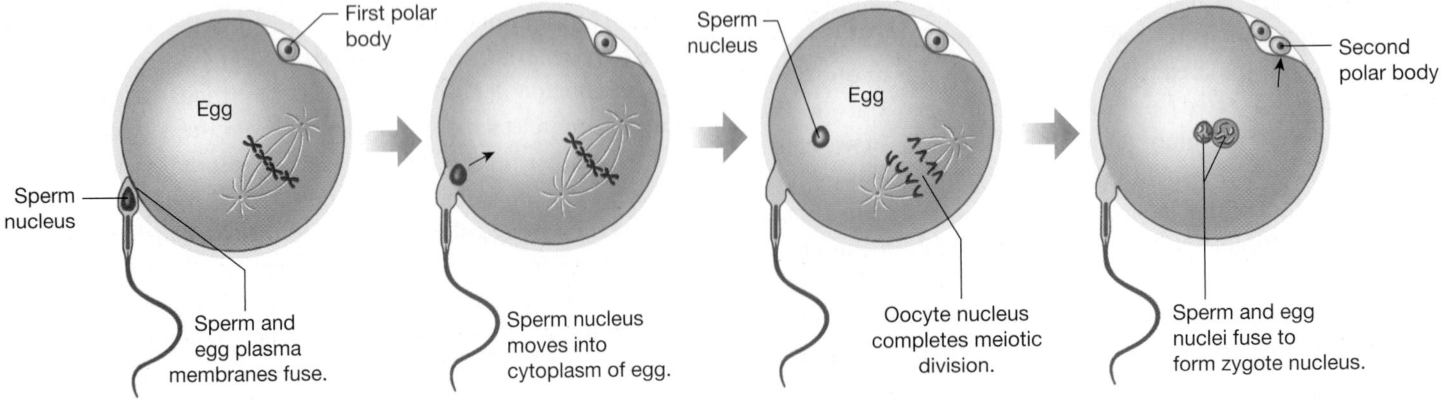
First polar body
Egg
Sperm nucleus
Sperm and egg plasma membranes fuse.
Sperm nucleus moves into cytoplasm of egg.
Sperm nucleus
Egg
Oocyte nucleus completes meiotic division.
Second polar body
Sperm and egg nuclei fuse to form zygote nucleus.

● **FIGURE 26-17** ***Sperm and egg fuse to form a zygote.***

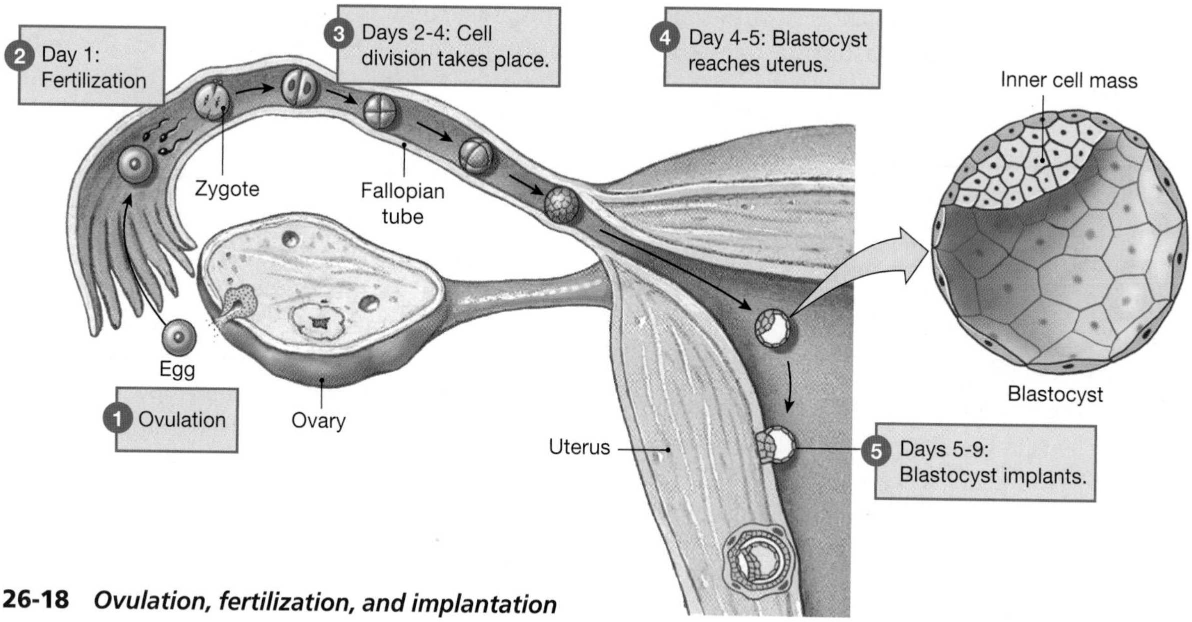

● **FIGURE 26-18** ***Ovulation, fertilization, and implantation***

cord that links the embryo to the mother; and the **yolk sac**, which degenerates early in human development.

Implantation of the blastocyst into the uterine wall normally takes place about 7 days after fertilization. The blastocyst secretes enzymes that allow it to invade the endometrium, like a parasite burrowing into its host. As it does so, endometrial cells grow out around the blastocyst until it is completely engulfed.

As the blastocyst continues dividing and becomes an embryo, cells that will become the placenta form fingerlike **chorionic villi** that penetrate into the vascularized endometrium. Enzymes from the villi break down the walls of maternal blood vessels until the villi are surrounded by pools of maternal blood (Fig. 26-19b). The blood of the embryo and that of the mother do not mix, but nutrients, gases, and wastes are exchanged across the

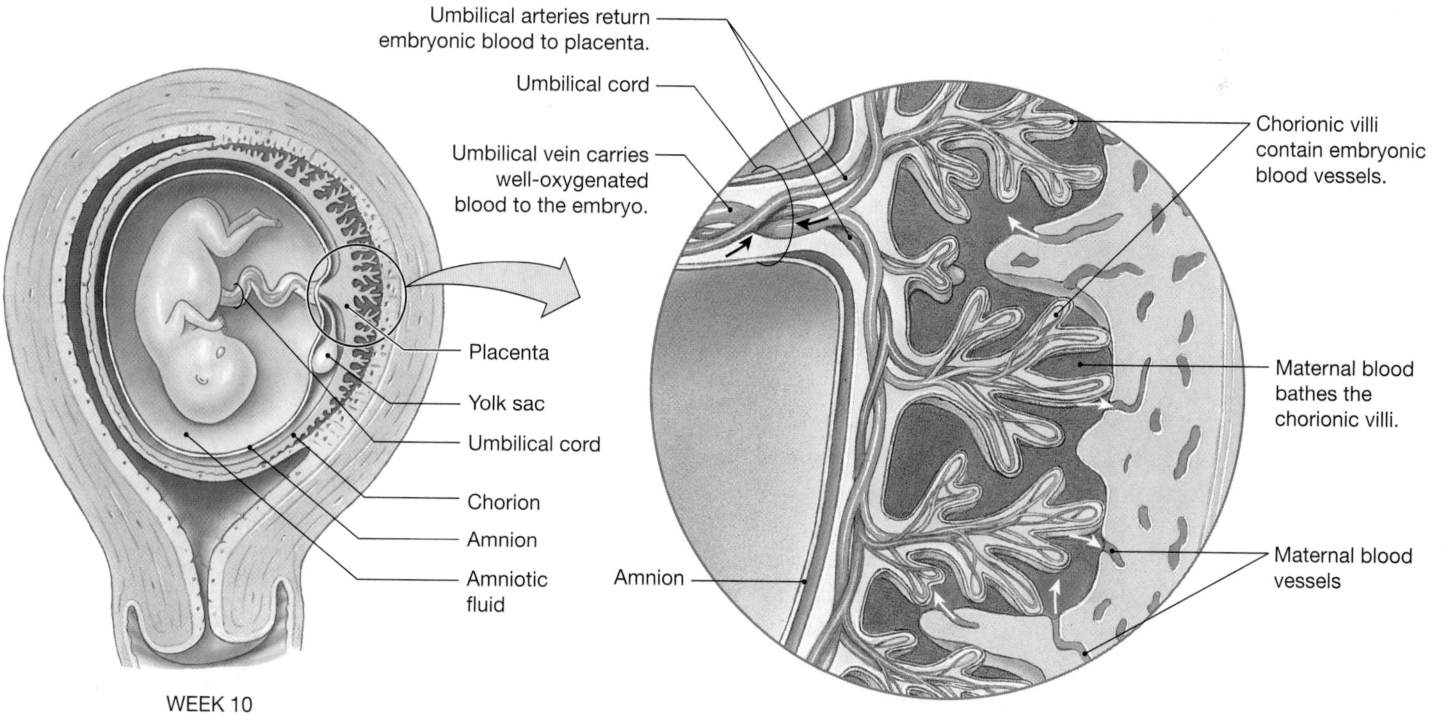

(a) The developing embryo floats in amniotic fluid. It obtains oxygen and nutrients from the mother through the placenta and umbilical cord.

(b) Some material is exchanged across placental membranes by diffusion, but other material must be transported.

● **FIGURE 26-19** ***The placenta***

membranes of the villi. Many of these substances move by simple diffusion, but some, such as maternal antibodies, are transported across the membrane.

The placenta continues to grow during pregnancy until, by delivery, it is about 20 cm in diameter (the size of a small dinner plate). The placenta receives as much as 10% of the total maternal cardiac output. The tremendous blood flow to the placenta is one reason sudden abnormal separation of the placenta from the uterine wall is a medical emergency.

The Placenta Secretes Hormones During Pregnancy

As the blastocyst implants in the uterine wall and the placenta begins to form, the corpus luteum is nearing the end of its preprogrammed 12-day life span. Unless the developing embryo sends a hormonal signal, the corpus luteum will disintegrate, progesterone and estrogen levels will drop, and the embryo will be flushed from the body along with the surface layers of endometrium during menstruation. Several hormones that prevent menstruation during pregnancy are secreted by the placenta, including human chorionic gonadotropin, human placental lactogen, estrogen, and progesterone.

Human Chorionic Gonadotropin The corpus luteum remains active during early pregnancy because of **human chorionic gonadotropin** (hCG), a peptide hormone secreted by the chorionic villi and developing placenta. Human chorionic gonadotropin is structurally related to LH, and it binds to LH receptors. Under the influence of hCG, the corpus luteum keeps producing progesterone to keep the endometrium intact.

By the seventh week of development, however, the placenta has taken over progesterone production, and the corpus luteum is no longer needed. At that point, it finally degenerates. Human chorionic gonadotropin production by the placenta peaks at three months of development, then diminishes.

A second function of hCG is stimulation of testosterone production by the developing testes in male fetuses. As you learned in the opening sections of this chapter, fetal testosterone and its metabolite DHT are essential for expression of male characteristics and for descent of the testes into the scrotum before birth.

Human chorionic gonadotropin is the chemical detected by pregnancy tests. Because hCG can induce ovulation in rabbits, years ago the urine from a woman who suspected she was pregnant was injected into a rabbit. The rabbit's ovaries were then inspected for signs of ovulation. It took several days for the women to learn the results of this test. Today, with modern biochemical techniques, women can perform their own pregnancy tests in a few minutes in the privacy of their home.

Human Placental Lactogen (hPL) Another peptide hormone produced by the placenta is **human placental lactogen** (hPL), also known as *human chorionic somatomammotropin* (hCS). This hormone, structurally related to growth hormone and prolactin, was initially believed to be necessary for breast development during pregnancy and for milk production (**lactation**). Although hPL probably does contribute to lactation, women who do not make hPL during pregnancy because of a genetic defect still have adequate breast development and milk production.

A second role for hPL is alteration of the mother's glucose and fatty acid metabolism to support fetal growth. Maternal glucose moves across the membranes of the placenta by facilitated diffusion and enters the fetal circulation. During pregnancy, about 4% of women develop *gestational diabetes mellitus,* with elevated blood glucose levels caused by insulin resistance, similar to type 2 diabetes. After delivery, glucose metabolism in most of these women returns to normal, but these mothers and their babies are at higher risk of developing type 2 diabetes later in life.

Estrogen and Progesterone Estrogen and progesterone are produced continuously during pregnancy, first by the corpus luteum under the influence of hCG and then by the placenta. With high circulating levels of these steroid hormones, feedback suppression of the pituitary continues throughout pregnancy, preventing another set of follicles from beginning development.

During pregnancy, estrogen contributes to the development of the milk-secreting ducts of the breasts. Progesterone is essential for maintaining the endometrium and in addition helps suppress uterine contractions. The placenta makes a variety of other hormones, including inhibin and prorenin, but the function of most of them remains unclear.

Pregnancy Ends with Labor and Delivery

Parturition normally occurs between the 38th and 40th weeks of gestation. What triggers this process? For many years, researchers developed animal models of the signals that initiate parturition, only to discover recently that many of those models do not apply to humans. Parturition begins with **labor**, the rhythmic contractions of the uterus that push the fetus out into the world. Signals that initiate these contractions could begin with either the mother or the fetus, or they could be a combination of signals from both.

In many nonhuman mammals, a decrease in estrogen and progesterone levels marks the beginning of parturition. A decrease in progesterone levels is logical, as progesterone inhibits uterine contractions. In humans, however, levels of these hormones do not decrease until labor is well under way.

Another possible labor trigger is oxytocin, the peptide hormone that causes uterine muscle contraction. As a pregnancy nears full term, the number of uterine oxytocin receptors increases. However, studies have shown that oxytocin secretion does not increase until after labor begins. Synthetic oxytocin is often used to induce labor in pregnant women, but it is not always effective. Apparently, the start of labor requires something more than adequate amounts of oxytocin.

● **FIGURE 26-20** ***Parturition: the birth process.*** **(a)** As labor begins, the fetus is normally head down in the uterus. **(b)** Rhythmic uterine contractions push the head against the softened cervix, stretching and dilating it. **(c)** Once the cervix is fully dilated and stretched, the uterine contractions push the fetus out through the vagina. **(d)** Shortly after the fetus is delivered, the placenta detaches from the uterine wall and is expelled.

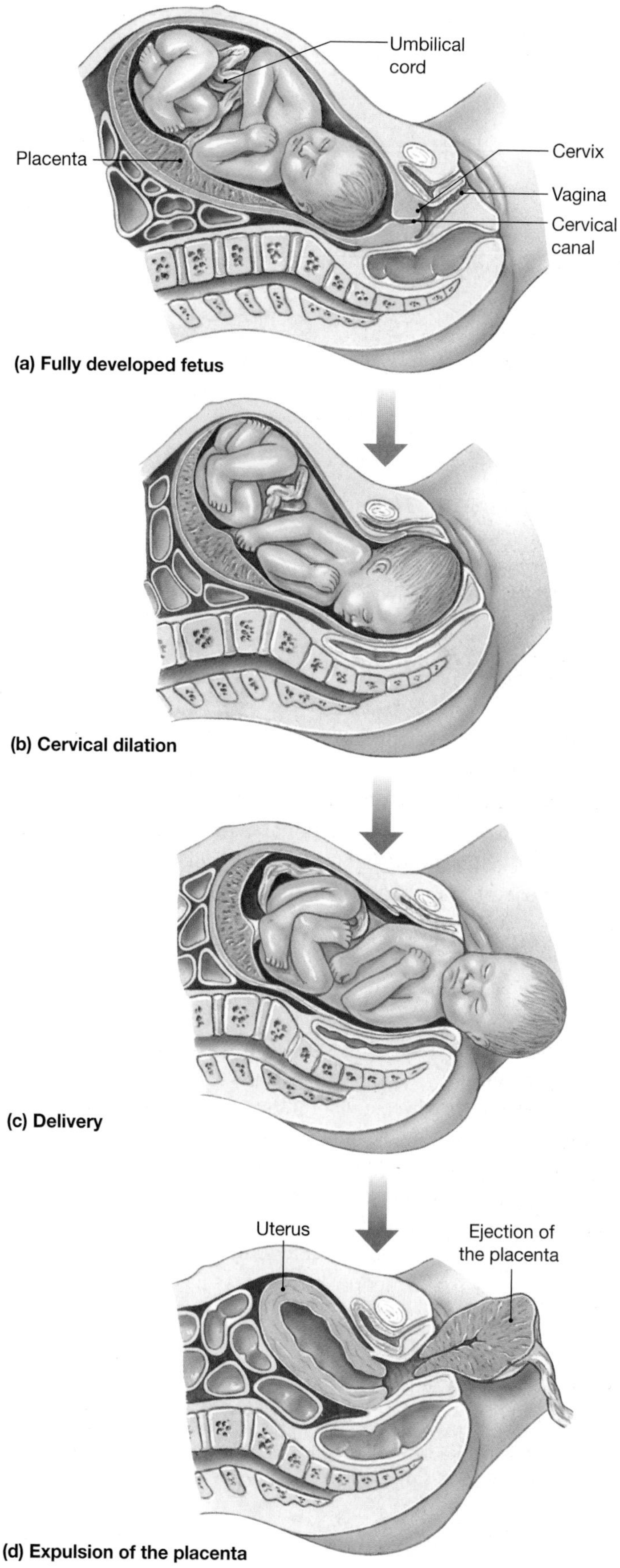
Umbilical cord
Placenta
Cervix
Vagina
Cervical canal
(a) Fully developed fetus
(b) Cervical dilation
(c) Delivery
Uterus
Ejection of the placenta
(d) Expulsion of the placenta

Another possibility for the induction of labor is that the fetus somehow signals that it has completed development. One theory supported by clinical evidence is that corticotropin-releasing hormone (CRH) secreted by the placenta is the signal to begin labor. (CRH is also a hypothalamic releasing factor that controls release of ACTH from the anterior pituitary.) In the weeks prior to delivery, maternal blood CRH levels increase rapidly. In addition, women with elevated CRH levels as early as 15 weeks of gestation are more likely to go into premature labor.

Although we do not know for certain what initiates parturition, we do understand the sequence of events. In the days prior to the onset of active labor, the cervix softens ("ripens") and ligaments holding the pelvic bones together loosen. The control of these processes is not clear and may be due to estrogen or the peptide hormone **relaxin**, which is secreted by ovaries and the placenta.

Once the contractions of labor begin, a positive feedback loop consisting of mechanical and hormonal factors is set into motion. The fetus is normally oriented head down (Fig. 26-20a ●). At the beginning of labor it repositions itself lower in the abdomen ("the baby has dropped") and begins to push on the softened cervix (Fig. 26-20b).

Cervical stretch triggers uterine contractions that move in a wave from the top of the uterus down, pushing the fetus farther into the pelvis. The lower portion of the uterus stays relaxed, and the cervix stretches and dilates. Cervical stretch starts a positive feedback cycle of escalating contractions (Fig. 26-21 ●). The contractions are reinforced by secretion of oxytocin from the posterior pituitary [p. 228], with continued cervical stretch reinforcing oxytocin secretion.

Prostaglandins are produced in the uterus in response to oxytocin and CRH secretion. Prostaglandins are very effective at causing uterine muscle contractions at any time. They are the primary cause of menstrual cramps and have been used to induce abortion in early pregnancy. During labor and delivery, prostaglandins reinforce the uterine contractions induced by oxytocin (Fig. 26-21).

As the contractions of labor intensify, the fetus moves down though the vagina and out into the world (Fig. 26-20c), still attached to the placenta. The placenta then detaches from the uterine wall and is expelled a short time later (Fig. 26-20d). Uterine contractions clamp the maternal blood vessels and help prevent excessive bleeding, although typically the mother loses about 240 mL of blood.

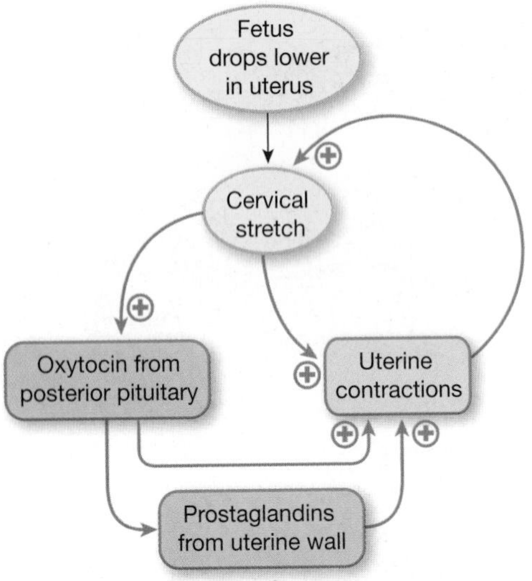

● **FIGURE 26-21** ***The positive feedback loop of parturition.*** Initiation of this loop requires a uterus that is ready to respond to these stimuli. The loop stops when the fetus is delivered and the cervix is no longer being stretched.

The Mammary Glands Secrete Milk During Lactation

A newborn has lost its source of maternal nourishment through the placenta and must rely on an external source of food instead. Primates, who normally have only one or two offspring at a time, have two functional mammary glands. A mammary gland is composed of about 20 milk-secreting lobules, each made of branched hollow ducts of secretory epithelium surrounded by *myoepithelial* contractile cells (Fig. 26-22 ●). Interestingly, the mammary gland epithelium is closely related to the secretory epithelium of sweat glands, so milk secretion and sweat secretion share some common features.

RUNNING PROBLEM

Assisted reproductive technologies (ART) are one treatment option currently available to infertile couples. All ART techniques involve either artificially stimulating the ovaries to produce eggs or using an egg from an egg donor. The eggs are harvested surgically and often are fertilized *in vitro*. The zygote may be placed in the fallopian tube immediately or may be allowed to develop into an early embryo before being placed into the uterus. A different technique used to overcome infertility is *intrauterine insemination*. In this procedure, sperm that have been washed to remove antigenic material are introduced into the uterus through a tube inserted through the cervix so that fertilization takes place *in vivo*.

Question 6:

Based on the results of their infertility workup, which intervention—ART or intrauterine insemination—should be recommended for Peggy and Larry? Why?

829 841 850 851 855 860 862

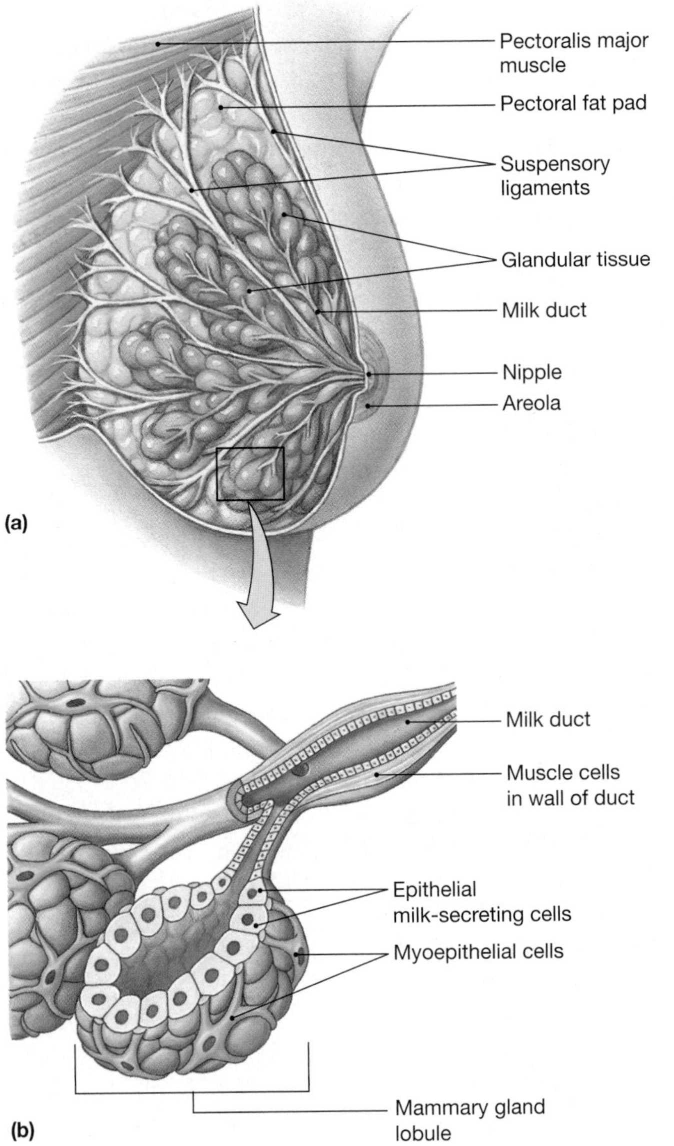

● **FIGURE 26-22** ***Mammary glands.*** Epithelial cells of the mammary glands secrete milk into the lumen of the gland.

During puberty, the breasts begin to develop under the influence of estrogen. The milk ducts grow and branch, and fat is deposited behind the glandular tissue. During pregnancy, the glands develop further under the direction of estrogen, growth hormone, and cortisol. The final development step also requires progesterone, which converts the duct epithelium into a secretory structure. This process is similar to progesterone's effect on the uterus, in which progesterone makes the endometrium into a secretory tissue during the luteal phase.

Although estrogen and progesterone stimulate mammary development, they inhibit secretion of milk. Milk production is stimulated by prolactin from the anterior pituitary [p. 233]. Prolactin is an unusual pituitary hormone in that its secretion is primarily controlled by **prolactin-inhibiting hormone** (PIH) from the hypothalamus. Good evidence suggests that PIH is actually *dopamine,* an amine neurohormone related to epinephrine and norepinephrine [p. 225].

During the later stages of pregnancy, PIH secretion falls, and prolactin reaches levels 10 or more times those found in nonpregnant women. Prior to delivery, when estrogen and progesterone are also high, the mammary glands produce only small amounts of a thin, low-fat secretion called **colostrum.** After delivery, when estrogen and progesterone decrease, the glands produce greater amounts of milk that contains 4% fat and substantial amounts of calcium. Proteins in colostrum and milk include maternal immunoglobulins, secreted into the duct and absorbed intact by the infant's intestinal epithelium [p. 705]. This process transfers some of the mother's immunity to the infant during its first weeks of life.

Suckling, the mechanical stimulus of the infant nursing at the breast, reinforces the inhibition of PIH begun in the last weeks of pregnancy (Fig. 26-23 ●). In the absence of PIH, prolactin secretion increases, resulting in milk production. Pregnancy is not a requirement for lactation, and some women who have adopted babies have been successful in breast-feeding.

The ejection of milk from the glands, known as the **let-down reflex,** requires the presence of oxytocin from the posterior pituitary. Oxytocin initiates smooth muscle contraction in the uterus and breasts. In the *postpartum* (after delivery) uterus, oxytocin-induced contractions help return the uterus to its prepregnancy size.

In the lactating breast, oxytocin causes contraction of myoepithelial cells surrounding the mammary glands. This contraction creates high pressure that sends the milk squirting into the infant's mouth. Although prolactin release requires the mechanical stimulus of suckling, oxytocin release can be stimulated by various cerebral stimuli, including the thought of the child. Many nursing mothers experience inappropriate milk release triggered by hearing someone else's child cry.

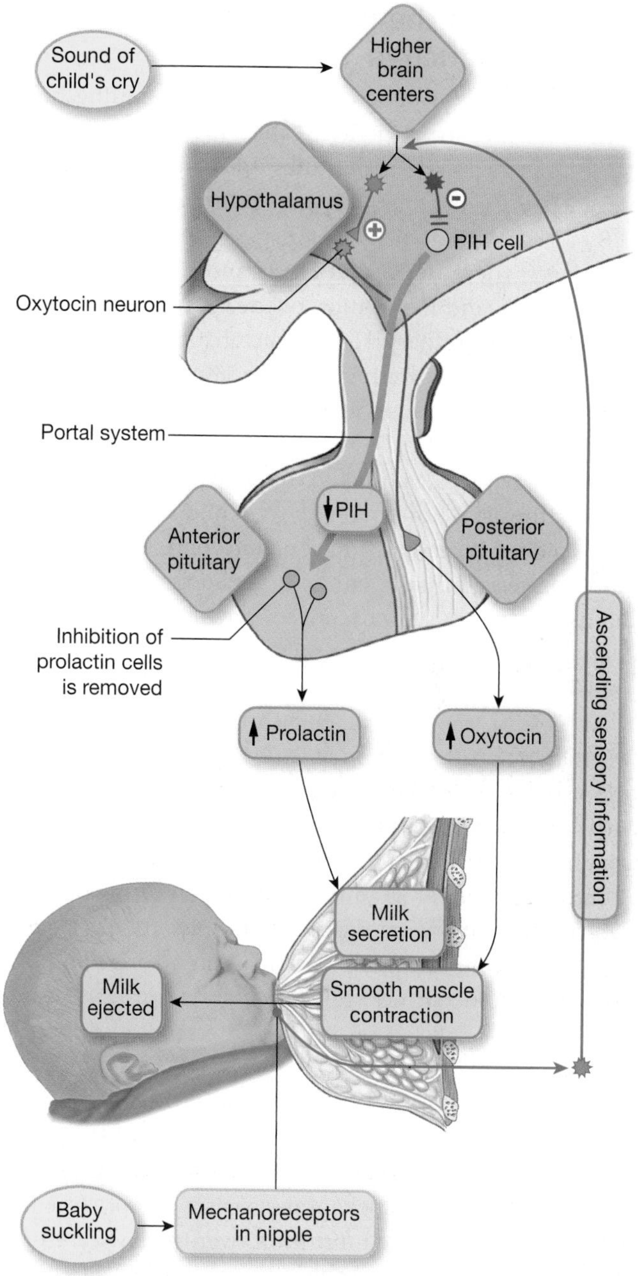

● **FIGURE 26-23** ***The hormonal control of milk secretion and release***

Prolactin Has Other Physiological Roles

Although we discussed prolactin in the context of nursing mothers, all non-nursing women and men have tonic prolactin secretion that exhibits a diurnal cycle, peaking during sleep. Prolactin is related to growth hormone and plays a role in other reproductive and nonreproductive processes. For example, prolactin is synthesized in the uterine endometrium during normal menstrual cycles. Male knockout mice who lack prolactin or a prolactin receptor have decreased fertility.

Some interesting research has established a role for prolactin in neuroimmuno-modulation [p. 806]. Both prolactin and growth hormone appear to be necessary for normal differentiation of T lymphocytes in the thymus gland, an observation supported by impaired immune function in animals with *hypoprolactinemia.* In contrast, several autoimmune diseases, including multiple sclerosis, systemic lupus erythematosus, and autoimmune thyroiditis, have been linked to elevated levels of prolactin.

GROWTH AND AGING

The reproductive years begin with the events surrounding puberty and end with decreasing gonadal hormone production.

Puberty Marks the Beginning of the Reproductive Years

In girls, the onset of puberty is marked by budding breasts and the first menstrual period, called **menarche**, a time of ritual significance in many cultures. In the United States, the average age at menarche is 12 years (normal range is considered 8 to 13 years).

In boys, the onset of puberty is more subtle. The signs include growth and maturation of the external genitalia; development of secondary sex characteristics, such as pubic and facial hair and lowering of voice pitch; change in body shape; and growth in height. The age range for male puberty is 9 to 14 years.

Puberty requires maturation of the hypothalamic-pituitary control pathway. Before puberty, the child has low levels of both steroid sex hormones and gonadotropins. Because low sex hormone levels normally enhance gonadotropin release, the combination of low steroids and low gonadotropins indicates that the hypothalamus and pituitary are not yet sensitive to steroid levels in the blood.

At puberty, the hypothalamic GnRH-secreting neurons increase their pulsatile secretion of GnRH, which in turn increases gonadotropin release. The signals responsible for the onset of puberty are complex, but several of them appear to be mediated by the hypothalamic neuropeptide *kisspeptin*. One theory says that the genetically programmed maturation of hypothalamic neurons initiates puberty. We know that puberty has a genetic basis because inherited patterns of maturation are common. If a woman did not start her menstrual periods until she was 16, for example, it is likely that her daughters will also have late menarche.

The hormone *leptin* [p. 725] also contributes to the onset of puberty. Undernourished women with little adipose tissue and low leptin levels often stop having menstrual periods (*amenorrhea*), and knockout mice without leptin are infertile. Presumably improved nutrition over the last century increased individuals' prepubertal fat stores and leptin secretion, which could interact with other factors to initiate puberty.

Menopause and Andropause Are a Consequence of Aging

Several centuries ago in America, many people died of acute illnesses while still reproductively active. Now modern medicine has overcome most acute illnesses, and most of us will live well past the time we are likely to have children.

Women's reproductive cycles stop completely at the time known as **menopause**. The physiology of menopause has been well studied. After about 40 years of menstrual cycles, a woman's periods become irregular (*perimenopause*) and finally cease. The cessation of reproductive cycles is due not to the pituitary but to the ovaries, which can no longer respond to gonadotropins. In the absence of negative feedback, gonadotropin levels increase dramatically in an effort to stimulate the ovaries into maturing more follicles.

The absence of estrogen in postmenopausal women leads to symptoms of varying severity. These may include hot flashes [p. 751], atrophy of genitalia and breasts, and osteoporosis as calcium is lost from bones [p. 777]. Hormone replacement therapy (HRT) for women in menopause traditionally consists of estrogen or a combination of estrogen and progesterone. This treatment has become controversial, however, because of studies that suggest that its risks outweigh its benefits.

A newer drug therapy for menopause uses *selective estrogen receptor modulators* (SERMs). These drugs bind with different affinities to the two estrogen receptor subtypes, which allows the drugs to mimic the beneficial effects of estrogen on bone while avoiding the potentially detrimental effects on breasts and uterus.

In men, testosterone production decreases with age, and about half of men over the age of 50 have symptoms of **andropause**, a term coined to be the equivalent of female menopause. The existence of physiological andropause in men is still controversial because the physical and psychological symptoms of aging men are not clearly linked to a decline in testosterone. Many men remain reproductively active as they age, and it is not uncommon for men in their fifties or sixties to have children with younger women. Postmenopausal women also remain sexually active, although not reproductively active, and some report a more fulfilling sex life once the fear of unwanted pregnancy has been removed.

RUNNING PROBLEM CONCLUSION

Infertility

In this running problem you learned how the cause of infertility is diagnosed in a typical couple. To learn more about infertility, see literature from the American Society for Reproductive Medicine at *www.asrm.org* or go to Medline Plus (*www.nlm.nih.gov/medlineplus*) and look under Health Topics.

Now test your understanding of the running problem by checking your answers against the information in this summary table.

(continued)

	QUESTION	FACTS	INTEGRATION AND ANALYSIS
1	Name (in order) the male reproductive structures that carry sperm from the testes to the external environment.	The male reproductive structures include the testes, accessory glandular organs, a series of ducts, and the external genitalia.	Sperm leaving the testes pass into the epididymis, then into the vas deferens, and finally exit the body via the urethra.
2	Which causes of male infertility might make retrieval of sperm from the epididymis necessary?	The epididymis is the first duct the sperm enter upon leaving the testes.	If the infertility problem is due to blockage or congenital defects in the vas deferens or urethra, removal of sperm from the epididymis might be useful. If the problem is caused by low sperm count or abnormal sperm morphology, this technique would probably not be useful.
3	For which causes of female infertility is temperature tracking useful? For which causes is it not useful?	Basal body temperature rises slightly following ovulation.	Temperature tracking is a useful way to tell if a woman is ovulating, but it cannot reveal structural problems in the female reproductive tract.
4	What abnormalities in the cervix, fallopian tubes, and uterus could cause infertility?	The cervix, fallopian tubes, and uterus are hollow structures through which sperm must pass.	Any blockage of these organs resulting from disease or congenital defects would prevent normal movement of sperm and cause infertility. Hormonal problems might cause the endometrium to develop incompletely, preventing implantation of the embryo.
5	Speculate on how infertility due to cervical mucus antibodies against sperm might be treated.	Antibodies in the cervical mucus react with antigenic material in the semen or on the sperm, causing the sperm to become immobile.	If the antigenic material can be removed from the semen, this might help the problem of sperm immobilization. A semen sample can be washed to remove nonsperm components. If the antigens are part of the sperm, this method will not work.
6	Should ART or intrauterine insemination be recommended for Peggy and Larry? Why?	ART is used when ovulation is abnormal. Intrauterine insemination is used when ovulation is normal.	Intrauterine insemination can be used to overcome cervical factors, as this technique bypasses the cervix. Because Peggy can ovulate, intrauterine insemination should be recommended for Peggy and Larry.

829
841
850
851
855
860
862

CHAPTER SUMMARY

In this chapter you learned how the human species perpetuates itself through reproduction. The reproductive system has some of the most complex *control systems* of the body, in which multiple hormones interact in an ever-changing fashion. *Homeostasis* in the adult reproductive system is anything but steady state, particularly during the female menstrual cycle, when the *feedback effects* of estrogen change from negative to positive and back again. An example of *positive feedback* occurs with oxytocin secretion during labor and delivery. The testis provides a nice example of *compartmentation*, with the lumen of the seminiferous tubules, where sperm develop, isolated from the rest of the extracellular compartment.

Sex Determination

1. The sex organs consist of **gonads, internal genitalia**, and **external genitalia.** (p. 829)
2. **Testes** produce **sperm**. **Ovaries** produce eggs, or **ova.** Embryonic cells that will produce **gametes** (eggs and sperm) are called **germ cells.** (p. 829)
3. Humans have 46 chromosomes. (p. 829; Fig. 26-1)
4. The genetic sex of an individual depends on the **sex chromosomes:** females are XX, and males are XY. In the absence of a Y chromosome, an embryo will develop into a female. (p. 830; Fig. 26-2)
5. The **SRY gene** on the Y chromosomes produces **SRY protein**, a *testis-determining factor* that converts the bipotential gonad into a testis. In the absence of SRY protein, the gonad becomes an ovary. (p. 831)

6. Testicular **Sertoli cells** secrete **anti-Müllerian hormone** (AMH), which causes the **Müllerian ducts** to regress. **Leydig cells** secrete **testosterone**, which converts **Wolffian ducts** to male accessory structures. **Dihydrotestosterone** (DHT) promotes development of the prostate gland and external genitalia. (p. 831; Figs. 26-3, 26-4)
7. Absence of testosterone and AMH causes Müllerian ducts to develop into **fallopian tubes (oviducts)**, **uterus**, and **vagina**. In females, the Wolffian ducts regress. (p. 832; Figs. 26-3, 26-4)

Basic Patterns of Reproduction

8. **Gametogenesis** begins with mitotic divisions of **spermatogonia** and **oögonia**. The first step of meiosis creates **primary spermatocytes** and **primary oocytes**. The first meiotic division creates two identical **secondary spermatocytes** in males or a large secondary oocyte (egg) and a tiny **first polar body** in females. (p. 833; Fig. 26-5)
9. The second meiotic division in males creates haploid **spermatids** that mature into sperm. In females, the second meiotic division does not take place unless the egg is fertilized. (p. 834; Fig. 26-5)
10. In both sexes, **gonadotropin-releasing hormone** (GnRH) controls the secretion of **follicle-stimulating hormone** (FSH) and **luteinizing hormone** (LH) from the anterior pituitary. FSH and steroid sex hormones regulate gametogenesis in gonadal gamete-producing cells. LH stimulates production of steroid sex hormones. (p. 836; Fig. 26-7)
11. The steroid sex hormones include **androgens**, **estrogens**, and **progesterone**. **Aromatase** converts androgens to estrogens. **Inhibin** inhibits secretion of FSH, and **activin** stimulates FSH secretion. (p. 836; Fig. 26-6)
12. Gonadal steroids generally suppress secretion of GnRH, FSH, and LH. However, if estrogen rises rapidly above a threshold level for at least 36 hours, its feedback changes to positive and stimulates gonadotropin release. (p. 836)
13. After puberty, tonic GnRH release occurs in small pulses every 1–3 hours from a region of the hypothalamus called a **pulse generator**. (p. 838)

Male Reproduction

14. The **corpus spongiosum** and **corpora cavernosa** make up the erectile tissue of the penis. The **glans** is covered by the **foreskin**. The urethra runs though the **penis**. (p. 838; Fig. 26-8)
15. The testes migrate into the scrotum during fetal development. Failure of one or both testes to descend is known as **cryptorchidism**. (p. 838)
16. The testes consist of **seminiferous tubules** and interstitial tissue containing blood vessels and Leydig cells. The seminiferous tubules join the **epididymis**, which becomes the **vas deferens**. The vas deferens empties into the urethra. (p. 839; Fig. 26-9b)
17. A seminiferous tubule contains spermatogonia, spermatocytes, and Sertoli cells. Tight junctions between Sertoli cells form a **blood-testis barrier**. (p. 841; Fig. 26-9c, d)
18. Spermatogonia in the tubule undergo meiosis, becoming primary spermatocytes, spermatids, and finally sperm in about 64 days. (p. 842; Fig. 26-9)
19. Sertoli cells regulate sperm development. They also produce inhibin, activin, growth factors, enzymes, and **androgen-binding protein**. (p. 842; Fig. 26-11)
20. Leydig cells produce 95% of a male's testosterone. The other 5% comes from the adrenal cortex. (p. 842)
21. FSH stimulates Sertoli cell production of androgen-binding protein, inhibin, and paracrine molecules. Leydig cells produce testosterone under the direction of LH. (p. 842; Fig. 26-11)
22. The **prostate gland**, **seminal vesicles**, and **bulbourethral glands** secrete the fluid component of **semen**. (p. 843)
23. **Primary sex characteristics** are the internal sexual organs and external genitalia. **Secondary sex characteristics** are other features of the body, such as body shape. (p. 843)

Female Reproduction

24. Female external genitalia, called the **vulva** or **pudendum**, are the **labia majora**, **labia minora**, and **clitoris**. The urethra opening is between the clitoris and the vagina. (p. 844; Fig. 26-12a)
25. The uterine tissue layers are outer connective tissue, **myometrium**, and **endometrium**. (p. 844; Fig. 26-12f)
26. Fallopian tubes are lined with ciliated epithelium. The bulk of an ovary consists of ovarian follicles. (p. 844; Fig. 26-12d)
27. Eggs are produced in monthly **menstrual cycles**. (p. 844; Fig. 26-13)
28. In the **ovarian cycle**, the **follicular phase** is a period of follicular growth. **Ovulation** is the release of an egg from its follicle. In the **luteal phase**, the ruptured follicle becomes a **corpus luteum**. (p. 845; Fig. 26-13)
29. The **menses** begin the **uterine cycle**. This is followed by a **proliferative phase**, with endometrial thickening. Following ovulation, the endometrium goes into a **secretory phase**. (p. 845; Fig. 26-13)
30. Follicular **granulosa cells** secrete estrogen. As the follicular phase ends, a surge in LH is necessary for oocyte maturation. (p. 845; Fig. 26-13)
31. The corpus luteum secretes progesterone and some estrogen, which exert negative feedback on the hypothalamus-anterior pituitary. (p. 851; Fig. 26-14c, d)
32. Estrogens and androgen control primary and secondary sex characteristics in females. (p. 851)

Procreation

33. The human sex act is divided into four phases; (1) excitement, (2) plateau, (3) orgasm, and (4) resolution. (p. 852)
34. The male **erection reflex** is a spinal reflex that can be influenced by higher brain centers. Parasympathetic input mediated by nitric oxide actively vasodilates the penile arterioles. (p. 852; Fig. 26-15)
35. **Emission** is the movement of sperm out of the vas deferens and into the urethra. **Ejaculation** is the expulsion of semen to the external environment. (p. 852)
36. Contraceptive methods include **abstinence**, **barrier methods**, **implantation prevention**, and **hormonal treatments**. (pp. 853–854)
37. Infertility can arise from a problem in the male, the female, or both. *In vitro* fertilization has allowed some infertile couples to have children. (p. 855)

Pregnancy and Parturition

38. Sperm must go through **capacitation** before they can fertilize an egg. (p. 855)
39. Fertilization normally takes place in the fallopian tube. Capacitated sperm release acrosomal enzymes (the **acrosomal reaction**) to dissolve cell junctions and the **zona pellucida** of the egg. The first sperm to reach the egg fertilizes it. (p. 855; Figs. 26-16, 26-17)
40. Fusion of egg and sperm membranes initiates a **cortical reaction** that prevents **polyspermy**. (p. 856)
41. The developing embryo is a hollow **blastocyst** when it reaches the uterus. Once the blastocyst implants, it develops extraembryonic membranes. (p. 856; Figs. 26-18, 26-19a)

42. The **chorionic villi** of the placenta are surrounded by pools of maternal blood where nutrients, gases, and wastes are exchanged between mother and embryo. (p. 857; Fig. 26-19b)
43. The corpus luteum remains active during early pregnancy because of **human chorionic gonadotropin** (hCG) produced by the developing embryo. (p. 858)
44. The placenta secretes hCG, estrogen, progesterone, and **human placental lactogen**. This last hormone plays a role in maternal metabolism. (p. 858)
45. Estrogen during pregnancy contributes to development of milk-secreting ducts in the breasts. Progesterone is essential for maintaining the endometrium and, along with **relaxin**, helps suppress uterine contractions. (p. 859)
46. **Parturition** normally occurs in the 38th–40th weeks of gestation. It begins with **labor** and ends with delivery of the fetus and placenta. A positive feedback loop of oxytocin secretion causes uterine muscle contraction. (p. 858; Figs. 26-20, 26-21)
47. Following delivery, the mammary glands produce milk under the influence of prolactin. Milk is released during nursing by oxytocin, causing mammary gland myoepithelial cells to contract. (p. 860; Figs. 26-22, 26-23)
48. Prolactin plays a role in immune function in both sexes. (p. 861)

Growth and Aging

49. In girls, puberty begins with **menarche**, the first menstrual period, at age 8–13 years. The age range for the onset of puberty in boys is 9 to 14 years. (p. 862)
50. The cessation of reproductive cycles in women is known as the **menopause.** Some men exhibit symptoms of testosterone deficiency. (p. 863)

QUESTIONS

(Answers to the Review Questions begin on page A1.)

THE PHYSIOLOGY PLACE

Access more review material online at **The Physiology Place** web site. There you'll find review questions, problem-solving activities, case studies, flashcards, and direct links to both *Interactive Physiology®* and *PhysioEx™*. To access the site, go to *www.physiologyplace.com* and select *Human Physiology*, Fifth Edition.

LEVEL ONE REVIEWING FACTS AND TERMS

1. Match each of the following items with all the terms it applies to:

(a) X or Y	1. chromosomes other than sex chromosomes
(b) inactivated X chromosome	2. fertilized egg
(c) XX	3. sperm or ova
(d) XY	4. sex chromosomes
(e) XX or XY	5. germ cells
(f) autosomes	6. male chromosomes
	7. female chromosomes
	8. Barr body

2. The Y chromosome contains a region for male sex determination that is known as the __________ gene.
3. List the functions of the gonads. How do the products of gonadal function differ in males and females?
4. Trace the anatomical routes to the external environment followed by a newly formed sperm and by an ovulated egg. Name all structures the gametes pass through on their journey.
5. Define each of the following terms and describe its significance to reproductive physiology:
   (a) aromatase
   (b) blood-testis barrier
   (c) androgen-binding protein
   (d) first polar body
   (e) acrosome
6. Decide whether each of the following statements is true or false, and defend your answer.
   (a) All testosterone is produced in the testes.
   (b) Each sex hormone is produced only by members of one sex.
   (c) Anabolic steroid use appears to be addictive, and withdrawal symptoms include psychological disturbances.
   (d) High levels of estrogen in the late follicular phase help prepare the uterus for menstruation.
   (e) Progesterone is the dominant hormone of the luteal phase of the ovarian cycle.
7. What is semen? What are its main components, and where are they produced?
8. List and give a specific example of the various methods of contraception. Which is/are most effective? Least effective?

LEVEL TWO REVIEWING CONCEPTS

9. **Concept maps:** Map the following groups of terms. You may add additional terms.

List 1	**List 2**
AMH	antrum
DHT	corpus luteum
Leydig cells	endometrium
Müllerian ducts	follicle
Sertoli cells	granulosa cells
sperm	myometrium
spermatids	ovum
spermatocytes	thecal cells
spermatogonia	
SRY	
testosterone	
Wolffian ducts	

10. Diagram the hormonal control of gametogenesis in males.
11. Diagram the menstrual cycle, distinguishing between the ovarian cycle and the uterine cycle. Include all relevant hormones.
12. Why are X-linked traits exhibited more frequently by males than females?
13. Define and relate each of the following terms in each group:
    (a) gamete, zygote, germ cell, embryo, fetus
    (b) coitus, erection, ejaculation, orgasm, emission, erogenous zones

(c) capacitation, zona pellucida, acrosomal reaction, cortical reaction, cortical granules

(d) puberty, menarche, menopause, andropause

14. Compare the actions of each of the following hormones in males and females:

(a) FSH
(b) inhibin
(c) activin
(d) GnRH
(e) LH
(f) DHT
(g) estrogen
(h) testosterone
(i) progesterone

15. Compare and contrast the events of the four phases of sexual intercourse in males and in females.

16. Discuss the roles of each of the following hormones in pregnancy, labor and delivery, and mammary gland development and lactation:

(a) human chorionic gonadotropin
(b) luteinizing hormone
(c) human placental lactogen
(d) estrogen
(e) progesterone
(f) relaxin
(g) prolactin

LEVEL THREE PROBLEM SOLVING

17. Down syndrome is a chromosomal defect known as "trisomy" (three copies instead of two) of chromosome 21. The extra chromosome usually comes from the mother. Speculate what causes trisomy, using what you have learned about the events surrounding fertilization.

18. Sometimes the follicle fails to rupture at ovulation, even though it appears to have gone through all stages of development. This condition results in benign ovarian cysts, and the unruptured follicles can be palpated as bumps on the surface of the ovary. If the cysts persist, symptoms of this condition often mimic pregnancy, with missed menstrual periods and tender breasts. Explain how these symptoms occur, using diagrams as needed.

19. An XY individual inherits a mutation that results in completely nonfunctional androgen receptors.

(a) Is this person genetically male or female?

(b) Will this person have functional ovaries, functional testes, or incompletely developed or nonfunctional gonads?

(c) Will this person have Wolffian ducts or their derivatives? Müllerian ducts or their derivatives?

(d) Will this person have the external appearance of a male or a female?

20. The babies of mothers with gestational diabetes mellitus tend to weigh more at birth. They are also at risk of developing hypoglycemia immediately following birth. Use what you have learned about diabetes and insulin to explain these two observations. *Hint:* these babies have normal insulin responses.

LEVEL FOUR QUANTITATIVE PROBLEMS

21. The following graph shows the results of an experiment in which normal men were given testosterone over a period of months (indicated by the beige bar from A to E). Control values of hormones were measured prior to the start of the experiment. From time B to time C, the men were also given FSH. From time D to time E, they were also given LH. Based on the information given, answer the following questions.

(a) Why did testosterone level increase beginning at point A?

(b) Why did LH and FSH levels decrease beginning at point A?

(c) Predict what happened to the men's sperm production in the A–B interval, the B–C interval, and the D–E interval.

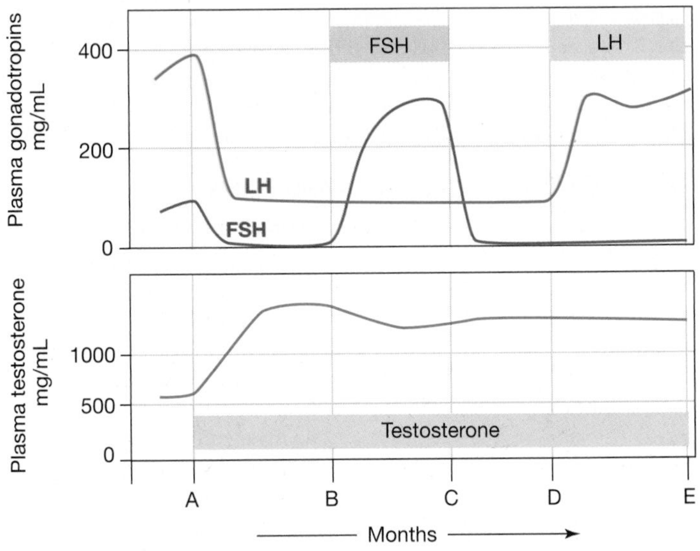

ANSWERS

Answers to Concept Check Questions

Page 830

1. Female gonad: ovary; female gamete: egg, or ovum. Male gonad: testis; male gametes: sperm.

Page 832

2. Primary androgen receptors are in the cytoplasm or nucleus of the target cell. AMH has membrane receptors.

3. The male parent donates the chromosome that determines sex of the zygote; therefore, the wives were not at fault.

4. An XO fetus will be a female because she lacks a Y chromosome.

5. Lack of AMH from the testes allows Müllerian ducts to develop into uterus and fallopian tubes. External genitalia will be female because there is no DHT for development of male genitalia.

Page 836

6. A newborn male's gametes are spermatogonia; a newborn female's gametes are primary oocytes.

7. The first polar body has twice as much DNA as the second polar body.

8. Each primary oocyte forms one egg; each primary spermatocyte forms four sperm.

Page 838

9. Aromatase converts testosterone to estradiol.
10. FSH = follicle-stimulating hormone, DHT = dihydrotestosterone, SRY = sex-determining region of Y chromosome, LH = luteinizing hormone, GnRH = gonadotropin-releasing hormone, AMH = anti-Müllerian hormone.
11. Hypothalamic GnRH, and FSH and LH from the anterior pituitary, control reproduction.

Page 843

12. Sertoli cells secrete inhibin, activin, androgen-binding protein, enzymes, and growth factors. Leydig cells secrete testosterone.
13. The advantage is that GnRH agonists decrease FSH and LH, so the testes stop producing sperm. The disadvantage is that the testes also stop producing testosterone, which causes decreased sex drive.
14. Cholesterol and steroid hormones such as cortisol are examples of lipophilic molecules that bind to protein carriers.

Page 844

15. Exogenous anabolic steroids (androgens) shut down FSH and LH secretion. In response, the testes shrink and stop producing sperm.

Page 851

16. Ovarian cycle: follicular phase, ovulation, and luteal phase. The menses and proliferative phases of the uterine cycle correspond to the follicular phase and ovulation; the secretory uterine phase corresponds to the luteal phase.
17. Women who take anabolic steroids may experience growth of facial and body hair, deepening of the voice, increased libido, and irregular menstrual cycles.
18. A woman given an aromatase inhibitor would have decreased estrogen production.
19. Ovulation occurs about 14 days before the end of the cycle, which would be (a) day 14, (b) day 9, or (c) day 17.

APPENDIX A Answers to Review Questions

CHAPTER 1

LEVEL ONE Reviewing Facts and Terms

1. The normal functioning of a living organism. Anatomy is the study of structure.
2. See Fig. 1-1.
3. See Tbl. 1-1.
4. Physiology integrates body function across all levels of organization and emphasizes the coordinated function of body systems.
5. The maintenance of internal stability. Examples: body temperature and water balance.
6. Homeostasis and control systems; structure-function relationships; biological energy; communication.

LEVEL TWO Reviewing Concepts

7. Maps are highly individual. Evaluate your map by comparing it to some done by classmates or to ask your instructor for comments.
8. (a) Tissues – collections of cells that carry out related functions. Organs – collections of tissues that form structural and functional units. (b) *x*-axis – independent variable; *y*-axis – dependent variable. (c) Independent variable is manipulated to change the dependent variable. (d) Teleological – functional approach, the "why" of a system. Mechanistic approach – physiological mechanisms, the "how" of a system. (e) Internal environment – extracellular fluid; external environment – the world outside the body. (f) Blind study: subjects do not know the treatment they are receiving. Double-blind study: neither subjects nor experimenters know which is the active treatment. Crossover study: each subject serves as both control and experimental.
9. Nasal and oral cavities, external ear, lacrimal ducts, sweat, sebaceous, and mammary gland ducts, lumens of esophagus, stomach, small and large intestines, ducts of the salivary glands, pancreas, liver and gall bladder, urinary tract organs, reproductive organs, respiratory organs.
10. Coordinate: endocrine and nervous systems. Protection: integumentary, digestive, cardiovascular, and immune systems. Exchange with external environment: respiratory exchanges gases; digestive system takes in nutrients; digestive and urinary eliminate waste products. Integumentary loses water and solutes.

LEVEL THREE Problem Solving

11. (a) incorrect mechanistic answer (b) correct teleological answer (c) correct teleological answer (d) correct mechanistic answer
12. Other problems: requirement of an aqueous environment for fertilization (internal fertilization in mammals; many other terrestrial animals return to water to breed); aqueous environment for embryonic development (eggs in birds, some reptiles and insects; internal development in mammals, some reptiles, and insects); physical support (exoskeletons in insects, internal skeletons in vertebrates)

LEVEL FOUR Quantitative Problems

13. (a) independent – time; dependent – body length (b) There was no control. (c) Should be a line graph with time in days on *x*-axis and body length on *y*-axis. (d) Growth slowest from days 0–3 and most rapid for days 6–9 and days 18–21.
14. (a) independent solution concentration; dependent volume change (b) The volume measurements before soaking provide a baseline but there is no control. (c) A scatter plot with best-fit line would allow you to estimate volume change at intermediate salt concentrations, such as 5%.
15. (a) scatter plot (b) Is there a relationship between midarm muscle circumference and aerobic fitness? (c) There appears to be no relationship between midarm muscle circumference and aerobic fitness.
16. (a) There is no "correct" answer. For peer critiques of the study, see *New England Journal of Medicine* 347(2):132–33 and 137–39, 2002, July 11. (b) The subjects believed that the surgery had helped (a placebo effect) or other interventions, such as physical therapy, helped. (c) The study is directly applicable to a limited population: male veterans, under age 76, predominantly white, with osteoarthritis or degenerative joint disease. (d) blind study (e) The investigators were trying to determine whether a placebo effect could account for post-surgical improvement.

CHAPTER 2

LEVEL ONE Reviewing Facts and Terms

1. carbon, hydrogen, and oxygen
2. molecule
3. (a) proton (b) neutron (c) −1
4. protons
5. calcium, carbon, oxygen, sodium, nitrogen, potassium, hydrogen, and phosphorous
6. *protons* and *electrons; neutrons*
7. *radiation; nuclear medicine*
8. paired
9. *ion*
10. (a) 2 (b) 4 (c) 1 (d) 3
11. *nonpolar; polar.* Polar compounds dissolve more readily.
12. pH – H^+ concentration. *Acidic* – pH < 7; *basic* or *alkaline* – pH > 7.
13. *buffer*
14. proteins (collagen, hemoglobin), carbohydrates (glucose, sucrose), lipids (cholesterol, phospholipids), and nucleic acids (ATP, DNA, RNA)
15. (a) 4 (b) 5 (c) 6 (d) 1 (e) 3
16. *lipoproteins; glycoproteins*
17. (a) 1 (b) 5 (c) 4 (d) 2 (e) 3
18. (a) 3 (b) 1 (c) 5 (d) 2 (e) 4, 6
19. one or more phosphate groups, a 5-carbon sugar, and a base
20. *ligand*
21. (a) 4 (b) 3 (c) 2

22. *cofactor*
23. *denatured*

LEVEL TWO Reviewing Concepts

24. See Fig. 2-1 to start List 1.
25. (a) 11 electrons (b) electrical charge = 0 (c) 12 neutrons (d) an ion or cation (e) +1 (f) Na^+ (g) a neon atom (h) Ne
26. 10^{-3} M = *pH 3; acidic.* 10^{-10} M = *pH 10; basic*
27. ATP – usable energy in a high-energy bond. DNA stores genetic information. RNA translates genetic information into proteins. cAMP – transfer of signals into cells. NAD and FAD transfer energy.
28. Primary structure – amino acid sequence. Secondary structure – α-helix or β-pleated sheet. Tertiary structure – three-dimensional shape (globular or fibrous). Quaternary structure – combination of subunits.
29. DNA – double – stranded molecule with adenine, guanine, cytosine, and thymine linked in α-helix; sugar is deoxyribose. RNA – single – stranded molecule with uracil instead of thymine and the sugar ribose.
30. Purines – two carbon rings. Pyrimidines – one carbon ring.
31. Structurally related proteins with similar functions but differing affinities
32. (a) 4, 5 (b) 3 (c) 2, 1

LEVEL THREE Problem Solving

33. Nucleotides contain all of the elements listed. Carbohydrates have a C:H:O ratio of 1:2:1. Fats are mostly C and H with little O. Proteins do not have P and have less N relative to C.
34. More H^+ means a decrease in pH.
35. Atomic mass −131; atomic number −54. Element – xenon.

LEVEL FOUR Quantitative Problems

36. (a) $C_6H_{12}O_6$ (glucose); m.w. 180 (b) CO_2; m.w. 44 (c) H_2O; m.w. 18 (d) $C_3H_7O_2N$ (alanine); m.w. 89 (e) $C_5H_{10}O_5$; m.w. 150
37. 0.9% = 0.9 g/100 mL. Dissolve 9 g NaCl in water to yield 1 L of solution.
38. (a) 6.02×10^{23} molecules of NaCl (b) 1000 millimoles (c) 1 equivalent (d) 5.85% solution
39. 5% glucose = 5 g/100 mL or 10 g/200 mL solution. Molarity: 5 g/100 mL = 50 g/L × 1 mole/180 g = 0.278 moles/L or 278 millimoles/L (278 mM). 500 mL of 5% glucose would have 25 g glucose × 1 mole/180 g = 139 millimoles glucose.
40. Myoglobin has a higher affinity for O_2 because at lower oxygen concentrations, more myoglobin has O_2 bound to it.

CHAPTER 3

LEVEL ONE Reviewing Facts and Terms

1. Create a barrier between cell and ECF; regulate exchange of material between cell and ECF; transfer information between the cell and other cells; provide structural support
2. *fluid mosaic model; phospholipids; proteins; carbohydrates*
3. phospholipids and proteins
4. Inclusions – particles of insoluble material, such as glycogen, protein fibers, and ribosomes. Organelles, such as mitochondria and Golgi complex, are separated from cytosol by membranes.
5. A flexible, changeable, three-dimensional scaffold of actin, microfilaments, intermediate filaments, and microtubules. Functions: mechanical strength; stabilizes position of organelles; transports material; links cells together; movement.
6. (a) 2 (b) 3 (c) 1 (d) 4
7. *serous secretions; mucous secretions*
8. (a) 3 (b) 5 (c) 4 (d) 1 (e) 2
9. very acidic conditions
10. *endocrine*
11. connective tissue (tendons that hold muscles to bones); epithelium (skin); neural tissue (the brain); and muscular tissue (heart and skeletal muscles).
12. *skin*
13. (a) 1 (b) 1 (c) 4 (d) 3 (e) 4 (f) 4 (g) 4 (h) 1 (i) 1
14. sweat glands – sweat; apocrine glands – waxy or milky secretions; sebaceous glands – a mixture of lipids
15. mitochondrial matrix – the internal compartment. Tissue matrix – noncellular material found outside cells.

LEVEL TWO Reviewing Concepts

16. Map: See Figs. 3-11, 3-12, 3-13, and 3-14.
17. Adhesive junctions (skin) – allow twisting and stretching of tissue. Tight junctions (epithelia) – prevent movement of materials between cells. Gap junctions (some muscles) – allow material to pass directly from cytoplasm of one cell to another.
18. Rough endoplasmic reticulum (RER) is where proteins are made, so pancreatic cells would have more.
19. Vesicles – membranous spheres. Examples: lysosomes, peroxisomes, secretory vesicles.
20. Stratified has many cell layers; simple epithelium only has one layer.
21. See Fig. 3-25. Tight junctions prevent movement of material between cells; leaky junctions allow some material to pass between cells.
22. *intracellular fluid*; *interstitial fluid*; *plasma*. Interstitial fluid and plasma are ECF.
23. Cholesterol molecules fill space between phospholipid tails.
24. Bone is rigid due to calcification; cartilage is firm but elastic. Bones are the primary support structure for the body; cartilage forms the ear, nose, larynx, and spine and helps hold bones together at the joints.
25. (a) lumen – hollow inside of an organ or tube; wall – cell layer. (b) Cytoplasm – everything inside the cell except the nucleus; cytosol – semi-gelatinous, intracellular fluid. (c) Myosin – motor protein filament; keratin – structural protein fiber.
26. Apoptosis – it is a normal part of development.
27. (a) cell junctions: 1 (gap junctions), 2 (tight junction proteins), 4 (strength of desmosomes) (b) cell membrane: 1 (receptors), 2 (enzymes), 3 (barrier), 4 (fluidity), 5 (ATP-dependent transporters) (c) cytoskeleton: 2 (microtubules direct movement), 4 (strength), 5 (ATP required for actin-myosin interaction) (d) organelles: 2 (mRNA binds to ribosomes), 3 (membrane-bounded organelles), 5 (ATP-dependent processes) (e) cilia: 2 (microtubules and dynein), 4 (flexibility), 5 (ATP-dependent movement)
28. The matrix can be disassembled and re-assembled.

LEVEL THREE Problem Solving

29. Cilia sweep mucus and particles up and out of the airways. When they fail, inhaled pathogens are more likely to reach the lungs, resulting in infections, inflammation, or cancer. The smoker's cough removes the mucus that would normally be swept away by the cilia.
30. Many epithelia are vulnerable to damage and need to be replaced frequently. Cells undergoing frequent mitosis are more likely to develop abnormal cell division.
31. MMPs are enzymes that dissolve the extracellular matrix, so blocking them might inhibit tissue growth and repair.

CHAPTER 4

LEVEL ONE Reviewing Facts and Terms

1. transport work (moving substances across membranes); chemical work (making proteins); and mechanical work (muscle contraction).
2. potential energy = stored energy; kinetic energy = energy of motion.
3. First Law – there is a fixed amount of energy in the universe. Second Law – without input of energy, an open system will become progressively less organized.
4. *metabolism*
5. *reactants; substrates; rate*
6. *enzymes; decreasing*
7. 1. (d) 2. (a) 3. (f) 4. (c)
8. *-ase*
9. *coenzymes; vitamins*
10. *reduced; oxidized*
11. *dehydration; hydrolysis*
12. *deamination; transamination*. They are converted to urea and uric acid.
13. *catabolic; anabolic*. Kilocalories.
14. *feedback inhibition.*
15. H^+ transported into the inner compartment stores energy in a concentration gradient. When the ions move back across the membrane, the released energy is trapped in the high-energy bond of ATP.
16. NADH and $FADH_2$.
17. *lipolysis; beta-oxidation*. Acetyl CoA goes into the citric acid cycle.
18. Carbohydrates and proteins have 4 kilocalories per gram; fat has 9.
19. smooth endoplasmic reticulum

LEVEL TWO Reviewing Concepts

20. Map 1, start with Fig. 4-13. Use Figs. 4-26 and 4-27 for map 2.
21. Perform work, transfer to another molecule, or be released as heat.
22. 1. (b) 2. (a) 3. (b) 4. (a) 5. (c) 6. (c) or (a)
23. When inactive, they cannot harm the cell if accidentally released.
24. Aerobic breakdown – 30–32 ATP; anaerobic breakdown – 2 ATP. Anaerobic is faster and does not require oxygen, but energy yield is less.
25. Glycogen to G-6-P via glucose uses one ATP, but conversion of glycogen directly to G-6-P does not need ATP.
26. Transcription – synthesis of RNA from the sense strand of DNA. Translation – conversion of information coded in mRNA into a string of amino acids.
27. Anticodons are part of tRNA. Amino acids attach to tRNA.
28. The energy in ATP's high-energy bond is potential energy.
29. If the reaction requires ATP, the activation energy must be large compared to a reaction that does not require ATP.

LEVEL THREE Problem Solving

30. They could use certain amino acids or fatty acids.
31. mRNA: GCGAUGUUCAGUCCAUGGCAUUGC. Anticodons: UAC (tyrosine), AGU (serine), AGG (arginine), GUA (valine).

LEVEL FOUR Quantitative Problems

32. Exergonic
33. 149 amino acids

CHAPTER 5

LEVEL ONE Reviewing Facts and Terms

1. structural proteins (link cell to matrix); transporters (water channels); receptors (hormone receptors); and enzymes (intestinal digestive enzymes)
2. active – requires direct or indirect use of energy. Passive – uses energy stored in a concentration gradient.
3. passive: simple and facilitated diffusion, osmosis. Active: phagocytosis, exocytosis, and endocytosis.
4. greater concentration gradient, smaller distance, higher temperature, and smaller molecular size
5. (a) 2, 4 (b) 1, 6 (c) 2, 3 (d) 2, 5
6. simple diffusion, protein-mediated transport, or in vesicular transport
7. *symport; antiport; uniport*
8. *direct* and *indirect*
9. *penetrating; nonpenetrating*
10. (d), (a), (b), (c).
11. osmolarity – concentration of osmotically active particles, expressed as osmol/L or milliosmoles per liter
12. hypotonic – net influx of water into the cell. Hypertonic – net water loss. Tonicity is determined by relative concentrations of nonpenetrating solutes in cell versus solution.
13. (1) like charges repel, opposites attract; (2) every positive ion has a matching negative ion; (3) energy must be used to separate ions or electrons and protons; and (4) conductors allow ions to move through them, while insulators keep ions separated
14. (a) 7 (b) 1, 4 (c) 6 (d) 5 (e) 8 (f) 3 (g) 2
15. *equilibrium potential*
16. *conductor; insulator*

LEVEL TWO Reviewing Concepts

17. Use Fig. 5-4, 5-7, 5-9, 5-21, and 5-23 to create your map.
18. See Fig. 5-3.
19. Lipid solubility, so that a molecule can pass through the lipid core of the membrane; diffusion is slower across thicker membranes and faster when there is more surface area.
20. Specificity: enzyme or transporter works on one molecule or class of molecules. Competition: similar substrates can compete for the protein binding site. Saturation: rate reaches a maximum when all binding sites are filled. GLUT is specific for hexose sugars. If glucose and fructose are both present, they compete for GLUT binding sites. If enough sugar is present, transport saturates.
21. (a) hypotonic (b) into the cells

22. active transport
23. (a) hyperosmotic. (convert molarity to osmolarity.) (b) True. Water moves from B to A.
24. Chemical gradient = concentration gradient. Electrical gradient = separation of electrical charge. Electrochemical gradient includes both concentration and electrical gradients.

LEVEL THREE Problem Solving

25. Apical side: Na^+ leak channels but no water pores. Basolateral side: Na^+-K^+-ATPase and K^+ leak channels. May also have water channels.
26. Insulin could increase the number or affinity of GLUT proteins or could act on cell metabolism to keep the intracellular glucose concentration low.
27. Both bind ligands at a specific binding site. Enzymes alter their substrates. Transporters move substrates unchanged across a membrane.
28. Must be converted from mM to mOsM. (a) hyperosmotic, isotonic (b) hyposmotic, hypotonic (c) isosmotic, hypotonic (d) hyperosmotic, isotonic (e) hyperosmotic, hypotonic
29. Sugars are added to proteins inside the organelle/vesicle, therefore will face the ECF after being inserted into the membrane.

LEVEL FOUR Quantitative Problems

30. 296 mOsM
31. (a) ICF = 29.5 L; interstitium = 9.8 L. (b) Total solute = 12.432 osmoles; ECF = 3.7 osmoles; ICF = 8.732 osmoles; plasma = 0.799 osmoles.
32. 154 mOsM.
33. (a) increases (b) decreases (c) increase (d) decrease
34. Simple diffusion (a). Not active transport because C_{in} never exceeds C_{out}.

CHAPTER 6

LEVEL ONE Reviewing Facts and Terms

1. neurons and blood
2. nervous and endocrine systems
3. chemical (available to all cells) and electrical
4. *homeostasis*
5. Examples: blood pressure, body temperature, heart rate, blood glucose
6. Receptors receive signals. Targets respond to signals.
7. *first messenger, receptor, effectors*
8. (a) adenylyl cyclase, (b) guanylyl cyclase, (c) phospholipase C
9. *phosphate, ATP*
10. stimulus, receptor, afferent pathway, integrating center, efferent pathway, effector, response
11. central – located within the central nervous system; peripheral – found outside the CNS
12. (a) 3 (b) 1 (c) 4 (d) 5
13. *nucleus, cytosol, cell membrane*
14. *circadian rhythm, brain*
15. *decreased*
16. It may down-regulate receptor number or decrease receptor affinity for the substrate.
17. *opposite*

LEVEL TWO Reviewing Concepts

18. (a) *Gap junctions* connect two cells using protein channels called *connexons*, made from *connexin* subunits. (b) All are chemicals secreted into the ECF. *Paracrines* act on nearby cells; *autocrines* act on the cell that secretes them. *Cytokines* are peptide autocrine and paracrine signals or *hormones*. *Neurocrines* are chemicals secreted by neurons. (c) *Agonists* have the same action as another molecule; *antagonists* act to oppose another molecule. (d) *Transduction* – a signal molecule transfers information from ECF to the cytoplasm. *Cascade* – a series of steps. *Amplification* – one signal molecule creates a larger signal.
19. ligand-gated channels (ATP-gated K^+ channel); integrin receptors (platelet receptors); receptor enzymes (tyrosine kinase receptor); G-protein-coupled receptors (adenylyl cyclase/cAMP-linked receptors).
20. The father of American physiology. (1) The nervous system keeps body functions within normal limits. (2) Some functions have tonic control rather than on-off control. (3) Some signals act in opposition to each other. (4) Cell response depends on the cell's receptor to a signal.
21. Efferent: output signal from integrating center to target (nerve or hormone). Afferent: input pathway from stimulus to integrating center (sensory nerve). Effector: target cell or tissue that carries out the response (muscle). Stimulus: change that begins a response (touching a hot stove). Receptor (sensor): cell that perceives the stimulus (temperature receptor). Integrating center: cell or cells that receive information, decides whether and how it should be acted upon, and send a signal to initiate a response (the brain). Response: what target cell does to react to the stimulus (pull hand away from hot stove).
22. Negative feedback – feedback signal turns response loop off; helps maintain homeostasis. Positive feedback – feedback keeps the response loop going; makes a change bigger. Feedforward – starts response loop before the stimulus does; minimizes change.
23. Neural control is faster than endocrine and better for short-acting responses. Endocrine can affect widely separated tissues with a single signal and better for long-acting responses.
24. (a) negative (b) positive (c) negative (d) negative
25. (a) tissues that respond to glucagon (b) breast (c) bladder (d) sweat glands
26. (a) pancreatic endocrine cells that secrete glucagon (c) nervous system (d) nervous system

LEVEL THREE Problem Solving

27. (a) stimulus = decrease in body temperature to decrease; receptor = temperature receptors; afferent = sensory neurons; integrating center = CNS; efferent = efferent neurons; effectors = muscles used to pull up afghan; response = afghan conserves heat
(b) stimulus = smell of sticky buns; receptor = odor receptors in the nose; afferent = sensory neurons; integrating center = CNS; efferent = skeletal muscles; response = walk to bakery, buy, and eat buns
28. (a) *antagonistic* (b) Neurotransmitters act on nearby cells (paracrine action). Neurohormones act on distant targets. (c) Epinephrine is secreted in larger amounts because it will be diluted by the blood volume before reaching its target.

LEVEL FOUR Quantitative Problems

29. (a) amplification and a cascade (b) (1000 × 4000) or 4,000,000 GMP

CHAPTER 7

LEVEL ONE *Reviewing Facts and Terms*

1. *endocrinology*
2. Alter the rate of enzymatic reactions, control transport of molecules into and out of cells, or change gene expression and protein synthesis in target cells.
3. See Fig. 7-2.
4. (a) 4 (b) 5 (c) 1 (d) 2 (e) 3
5. (d) – (b) – (c) – (a)
6. *blood; distant target; very low*
7. the time required for half a dose of hormone to disappear from the blood
8. *kidneys* and *liver; urine* and *bile*
9. *factors*
10. Peptides – three or more amino acids; example: insulin. Steroids – derived from cholesterol; example: estrogen. Amino acid-derived – made from single amino acids; example: thyroid hormone
11. (a) peptide (b) peptide (c) steroid (d) peptide (e) peptide (f) steroid (g) peptide (h) all classes (i) steroid (j) steroid
12. Steroid hormones usually initiate new protein synthesis, which takes time; peptides modify existing proteins.
13. *transcription* factor; *genes; proteins*
14. *cell membrane*
15. *tryptophan; tyrosine*
16. *trophic*
17. *negative feedback*
18. synthesized by and secreted from neurons
19. oxytocin and vasopressin, both peptide neurohormones
20. The portal system is composed of hypothalamic capillaries that take up hormones and deliver them directly to capillaries in the anterior pituitary. The direct connection allows very small amounts of hypothalamic hormone to control the anterior pituitary endocrine cells.
21. See Fig. 7-13.
22. Long-loop – peripheral endocrine gland turns off pituitary and hypothalamic hormone secretion. Short-loop – anterior pituitary turns off hypothalamus.
23. *synergism; permissiveness; antagonistic*

LEVEL TWO *Reviewing Concepts*

24. (a) Paracrines – local; cytokines – local or long distance; hormones – long distance. Cytokines – peptides; hormones – peptides, steroids, or amines. Cytokines – made on demand; peptides – made in advance and stored. (b) Primary pathology arises in the last endocrine gland of the pathway. Secondary pathology arises in a gland secreting a trophic hormone. (c) Hypersecretion – too much hormone; hyposecretion – too little hormone. (d) Both secrete peptide hormones. Anterior pituitary gland – true endocrine gland; posterior pituitary – neural tissue.
25. See Table 7-1.
26. Use Fig. 7-3 for List 1 and Figs. 7-12 and 7-13 for List 2.

LEVEL THREE *Problem Solving*

27. The meanings of the words given have not changed significantly. Enzymes, hormone receptors, and transport proteins are all proteins that bind ligands.
28. Patient A – cortisol hypersecretion results from ACTH hypersecretion. When dexamethasone suppresses ACTH secretion, the adrenal gland is no longer stimulated and cortisol secretion decreases. Patient B – problem in the adrenal gland. His normal negative feedback pathways do not operate, and the adrenal gland continues oversecreting cortisol even though ACTH secretion has been suppressed by dexamethasone.
29. (a) See Fig. 26-11. (b) Both LH and testosterone needed for gamete formation. Testosterone will not directly suppress gamete formation but it does have a negative feedback effect and shuts off LH secretion. LH is needed for gamete production, so its absence would suppress gamete synthesis.

LEVEL FOUR *Quantitative Problems*

30. Half-life is 3 hours.
31. (a) Group A (b) Group B (c) Group A
32. *x*-axis – plasma glucose; *y*-axis – insulin secretion. As *X* increases, *Y* increases.

CHAPTER 8

LEVEL ONE *Reviewing Facts and Terms*

1. Afferents carry messages from sensory receptors to CNS. Cell bodies are located close to the CNS. Interneurons are completely contained within the CNS and are often extensively branched. Efferents carry signals from the CNS to effectors. They have short, branched dendrites and long axons.
2. *skeletal muscles; autonomic*
3. *sympathetic* or *parasympathetic*
4. (a) 3 (b) 1 (c) 2 (d) 5 (e) 4
5. neurons and glial cells
6. See Figs. 8-2 and 8-4.
7. (c) (Answer (b) is only partly correct because not all axonal transport uses microtubules and not all substances moved will be secreted.)
8. (a) 1, 4 (b) 2, 3, 5, 6
9. (a) 3 (b) 1 (c) 4, 6 (d) 2 (e) 5, 6 (f) 5
10. Na^+ channels (voltage-gated along axon and ligand-gated or mechanically gated on dendrites); voltage-gated K^+ channels along axon; (3) voltage-gated Ca^{2+} channels in axon terminal; chemically gated Cl^- channels
11. e - b - d - a - c
12. (b) and (d)
13. *K^+, Na^+, Na^+*
14. *Na^+*
15. *K^+*
16. *Na^+*
17. *K^+*
18. Insulating membranes around neurons that prevents current leak
19. diameter of the axon and the presence or absence of myelin
20. enzymatic degradation, reabsorption and diffusion
21. See Figs. 8-9, 8-10, and 8-12.

LEVEL TWO *Reviewing Concepts*

22. See Figs. 8-1 and 8-5.
23. (d)
24. See Tbl. 8-4.
25. f - c - g - e - b - k - c - a - h - i - d

26. (a) depolarize (b) hyperpolarize (c) repolarize (d) depolarize. See Fig. 5-34.
27. (a) depolarize (b) hyperpolarize (c) hyperpolarize (d) depolarize
28. (a) Threshold signals trigger action potentials. Suprathreshold will also trigger action potentials but subthreshold will not unless summed. Action potentials are all-or-none events. Overshoot – portion of the action potential above 0 mV. Undershoot – after-hyperpolarization portion of the action potential (see Figs. 8-8, 8-9, 8-12). (b) Graded potentials may be depolarizing or hyperpolarizing. Graded potential in a postsynaptic cell is an EPSP if depolarizing and an IPSP if hyperpolarizing. (c) No stimulus can trigger another action potential during the absolute refractory period but a suprathreshold stimulus can trigger an action potential during the relative refractory period. (d) See question 1 answer. (e) Sensory are afferents; all others are efferents. (f) Fast synaptic potentials result from neurotransmitters altering ion channel gating, occur rapidly, and are short-lived. Slow synaptic potentials are mediated through second messengers, may involve protein modification, and last longer. (g) Temporal summation – multiple stimuli arrive at the trigger zone close together in time. Spatial summation – multiple stimuli from different locations arrive simultaneously at the trigger zone. (h) Divergence – a single neuron branches and its collaterals synapse on multiple targets. Convergence – many presynaptic neurons provide input to a smaller number of postsynaptic neurons.
29. Strength is coded by the frequency of action potentials; duration is coded by the duration of a train of repeated action potentials.
30. (b)

LEVEL THREE Problem Solving

31. All the necessary synapses have not yet been made between neurons or between neurons and effectors.
32. Inactivation gates also respond to depolarization but they close more slowly than the activation gates open, allowing ions to flow for a short period of time.
33. (b), (d), and (h)
34. (a) thermal (b) chemical (c) chemical (d) chemical (e) chemical (f) mechanical
35. Unmyelinated axons have many ion channels, so more ions cross during an action potential and must be returned to their original compartments by the Na^+-K^+-ATPase, using energy from ATP.

LEVEL FOUR Quantitative Problems

36. (a) −80 mV (b) +63 mV (c) −86 mV (d) −73 mV
37. (a)(12 × 2 mV = 24) + (3 × −3 mV = −9) = signal strength of +15. V_m = −70 + 15 = −55. Threshold is −50, so no action potential. (V_m must be equal to or more positive than threshold.) (b) Signal = +13. V_m = −57. Action potential will fire. (c) Signal = +19. V_m = −51. No action potential.

CHAPTER 9

LEVEL ONE Reviewing Facts and Terms

1. *plasticity*
2. *cognitive; affective*
3. *cerebrum*
4. *skull; vertebral column*
5. From the bones inward: dura mater, arachnoid membrane, pia mater
6. buoyancy reduces brain's weight; cushion between the brain and bone; chemical protection by creating a closely regulated ECF for brain cells
7. (a) HCO_3^- is lower in CSF (b) Ca^{2+} is lower in CSF (c) glucose is lower in CSF (d) H^+ is higher in CSF (e) Na^+ is the same in CSF and plasma (f) K^+ is lower in CSF
8. *glucose; hypoglycemia; oxygen; 15%*
9. (a) 5 (b) 7 (c) 9 (d) 3 (e) 1 (f) 2 (g) 6 (h) 8 (i) 4
10. Capillaries that are less leaky due to tight junctions between endothelial cells. Function – regulate substances allowed into brain tissue.
11. Gray matter: nerve cell bodies, dendrites, and axon terminals. Forms nuclei or layers in the brain and spinal cord. Information passes from neuron to neuron. White matter: mostly myelinated axons; tracts carry information up and down the spinal cord.
12. (a) Sensory areas – perception. (b) Motor cortex – movement. (c) Association areas integrate information and direct voluntary behavior.
13. Asymmetrical distribution of function between the two lobes of the cerebrum. Left brain – language and verbal functions; right brain – spatial skills.
14. See Tbl. 9-1. Mnemonic: **O**h **O**nce **O**ne **T**akes **T**he **A**natomy **F**inal, **V**ery **G**ood **V**acations **S**ound **H**eavenly.
15. REM (rapid eye movement) sleep – when most dreaming takes place. Rapid, low-amplitude EEG waves, flaccid paralysis, and depression of homeostatic function. Slow-wave (deep) sleep – high amplitude, low frequency EEG waves and unconscious body movements.
16. Homeostasis of body temperature and osmolarity, reproduction functions, hunger and satiety, and cardiovascular function. Emotional input from the limbic system.
17. *amygdala*
18. Associative and nonassociative. Habituation – a person responds less and less to a repeated stimulus; sensitization – an enhanced response to a dangerous or unpleasant stimulus.
19. Broca's area and Wernicke's area

LEVEL TWO Reviewing Concepts

20. Include information from Tbl. 9-1 and Figs. 9-4, 9-5, and 9-7.
21. Secreted into the ventricles and flows into the subarachnoid space around the brain and spinal cord before being reabsorbed by the cerebral arachnoid membrane.
22. sensory system, behavioral state system, and cognitive system
23. Wernicke's area – understand language; Broca's area – produce language.
24. (a) Diffuse modulatory – attention, motivation, wakefulness, memory, motor control, mood, and metabolism. Reticular formation – arousal and sleep, muscle tone, breathing, blood pressure, and pain. Reticular activating system – helps maintain consciousness. Limbic system – links higher cognitive functions with more primitive emotions such as fear. (b) Short-term memory – disappears unless consolidated; long-term memory – stored for recall. Long-term includes reflexive, or unconscious, memory, and declarative, or conscious, memory. (c) Nuclei – clusters of nerve cell bodies in the CNS; ganglia – clusters of nerve cell bodies outside the CNS. (d) Tracts – bundles of axons within the CNS; nerves – bundles of

axons outside the CNS. Horns – extensions of spinal cord gray matter that connect to peripheral nerves. Nerve fibers – bundles of axons. Roots – branches of peripheral nerves that enter or exit the spinal cord.

25. Primary somatic sensory cortex – parietal lobe. Visual cortex – processes information from eyes. Auditory cortex – processes information from ears. Olfactory cortex – processes information from nose. Frontal lobe motor cortices – control skeletal muscle movements. Association areas – integrate sensory information into perception.
26. (a) Lower frequency: wave peaks farther apart. b) Larger amplitude: taller peaks. (c) Higher frequency: peaks closer together.
27. Drives increase arousal, initiate goal-oriented behavior, and coordinate disparate behaviors to achieve goals.
28. new synapses and changes in effectiveness of synaptic transmission

LEVEL THREE Problem Solving

29. Expressive aphasia – could understand people but unable to communicate in any way that made sense. Speech centers are in the left brain. If music centers are in the right brain, then perhaps information from Wernicke's area can be integrated by the right brain so that Mr. Anderson can musically string together words so that they make sense.
30. Learning probably occurred, but need not be translated into behavioral responses. The participants who didn't buckle their seat belts learned that wearing seat belts was important but did not consider this knowledge important enough to act on.
31. Sleep-deprived dogs are producing a substance that induces sleep. Controls: putting CSF from normal dogs into sleep-deprived dogs, CSF from normal dogs into normal dogs, and CSF from sleep-deprived dogs into other sleep-deprived dogs.
32. (a) No, other information that should be taken into consideration include genetics, age, and general health. (b) The application of this study would be limited to women of similar age, background, and health. Other factors you would be interested in would include the ethnicity of the participants, factors as listed in (a), and geographical location.

CHAPTER 10

LEVEL ONE Reviewing Facts and Terms

1. Carries information from sensory receptors to the CNS.
2. The ability to tell where our body is in space and to sense the relative locations of different body parts.
3. A sensor and a sensory neuron. Could be one cell or two.
4. Mechanoreceptors – pressure, sound, stretch, etc. Chemoreceptors – specific chemicals. Photoreceptors– photons of light. Thermoreceptors – heat and cold.
5. *sensory field*
6. (a) 3 (b) 2 (c) 1, 2 (d) 2, 3 (e) 4
7. *transduction; adequate stimulus; threshold*
8. *Receptor potentials* are graded potentials.
9. Adequate stimulus – form of energy to which a receptor is most sensitive.
10. *cortex*. Exceptions – olfaction and hearing.
11. Sensory neurons surrounding a sensory field are inhibited, which enhances contrast between the stimulus and surrounding areas.
12. Tonic receptors, such as for heat, adapt slowly and respond to stimuli that need to be constantly monitored. Phasic receptors adapt rapidly and stop responding unless the stimulus changes. An example is smell.
13. *referred pain*
14. Sweet (nutritious foods), salty (Na^+), bitter (may contain toxins), sour (H^+), and umami (nutritious).
15. Sound waves per second – *hertz (Hz)*. Loudness – a function of the *wave amplitude* and measured in *decibels (dB)*. Range of hearing: *20–20,000 Hz*. Most acute hearing: *1000–3000 Hz*.
16. Basilar membrane. Spatial coding – association of wave frequencies with different areas of the membrane.
17. Correct: a.
18. Signals from cochlea to *medulla*, with collaterals to *reticular formation* and *cerebellum*. Synapses in *midbrain* and *thalamus* before projecting to *auditory cortex* in the *cerebrum*.
19. *Semicircular canals* – rotation; *otolith organs* – linear forces.
20. b, a, d, c, e
21. *Red, blue,* and *green; cones; color-blindness*
22. Rods and cones (photoreceptors), bipolar cells, ganglion cells, horizontal cells, and amacrine cells. Photoreceptors transduce light energy. Remaining cells carry out signal processing.

LEVEL TWO Reviewing Concepts

23. (a) Special senses have receptors localized in the head. Somatic senses have receptors located all over the body. (b) See Tbl. 10-4. (c) Sharp pain – small, myelinated Aδ fibers. Dull pain – small, unmyelinated C fibers. (d) Conductive loss: sound cannot be transmitted through the external or middle ear. Sensorineural loss: inner ear is damaged. Central hearing loss: auditory pathways are damaged. (e) Minimal convergence of retinal neurons in the fovea results in the sharpest vision. Minimal convergence of primary somatic sensory neurons creates smaller receptive fields and two-point discrimination is better. Regions with more convergence have less acute vision or poor two-point discrimination.
24. Seven distinct areas: 1, 2, 3, 1+2, 1+3, 2+3, and 1+2+3.
25. Ascending pathways for pain go to the limbic system (emotional distress) and hypothalamus (nausea and vomiting).
26. Olfactory receptors – olfactory bulb – secondary sensory neuron – higher-order neurons – olfactory cortex, with parallel pathways to amygdala and hippocampus. G_{olf} – G protein of olfactory receptors.
27. Bitter, sweet, and umami: membrane receptors on taste buds, with different G protein-linked receptors and signal transduction pathways for each ligand. Salty and sour ions (Na^+ and H^+) enter receptor cell through ion channels.
28. a, g, j, h, c, e, i, b, f, d
29. See Figs. 10-25, 10-26, and 10-27.
30. The lens changes shape due to contraction/relaxation of the ciliary muscles. Loss of this reflex – presbyopia.
31. Presbyopia – loss of accommodation due to stiffening of the lens with age. Myopia or near-sightedness – longer-than-normal distance between lens and retina; hyperopia or far-sightedness – shorter-than-normal distance. Color blindness – defective cones.
32. Intensity – action potential frequency. Duration – duration of a train of action potentials.
33. See Tbl. 10-1 and the section for each special sense.

34. Start with Fig. 10-30 and the basic components of vision. Work in details and related terms from the text.

LEVEL THREE Problem Solving

35. Testing touch-pressure, mediated through free nerve endings and Merkel receptors. Feeling only one probe means both needles are within the same receptive field.
36. Walk a straight line, stand on one leg with the eyes closed, recite the alphabet backwards.
37. Test hearing first. If children cannot hear well, they cannot imitate speech.
38. Absence of the consensual reflex upon stimulating the left eye suggests damage to the left retina and/or to the left optic nerve.
39. To dilate: a sympathetic agonist (a) or something that blocks muscarinic receptors (b). To constrict: a cholinergic agonist (c), a nicotinic agonist (e), or an anticholinesterase (d), which prevents breakdown of ACh.
40. Circular muscles form a ring on the inner part of the iris, surrounding the pupil. When these muscles contract, the pupil gets smaller. The radial muscles extend from the outer edge of the iris to the circular muscles. When the radial muscles contract, they pull on the relaxed circular muscles and expand the diameter of the pupil (dilation).
41. Loss of rods explains loss of night vision.

LEVEL FOUR Quantitative Problems

42. (a) 0.02 m (b) 1/0.02 m = 1/0.3048 + 1/Q. Q = 21.4 mm so lens must round to make F smaller.

CHAPTER 11

LEVEL ONE Reviewing Facts and Terms

1. Somatic motor – skeletal muscles. Autonomic – smooth and cardiac muscle, glands, some adipose tissue.
2. *Visceral* nervous system because it controls internal organs (viscera) and functions such as heart rate and digestion.
3. Sympathetic and parasympathetic divisions. Sympathetic neurons exit the spinal cord in the thoracic and lumbar regions; ganglia are close to the spinal cord. Parasympathetic exit from the brain stem or sacral region; ganglia on or close to their targets. Sympathetic – fight-or-flight; parasympathetic – rest-and-digest.
4. adrenal medulla
5. *Cholinergic* – acetylcholine; *adrenergic* or *noradrenergic* – norepinephrine.
6. Diffuse away from the synapse, digested by enzymes in the synapse, taken back into the presynaptic neuron, or bind to a membrane receptor.
7. *monoamine oxidase, MAO*
8. excitatory, single neuron, and synapse with skeletal muscle
9. enzyme that breaks down ACh
10. nicotinic cholinergic receptors

LEVEL TWO Reviewing Concepts

11. Divergence allows one signal to affect multiple targets.
12. (a) neuroeffector junction – distal ends of autonomic axons, anywhere there is a varicosity; neuromuscular junction – axon terminals of the somatic motor neuron. (b) Alpha and beta adrenergic; nicotinic and muscarinic cholinergic. Nicotinic – on skeletal muscle and postganglionic autonomic neurons. Adrenergic and muscarinic receptors – autonomic targets.
13. Use Figs. 11-10 and 11-11 to create this map.
14. (a) Autonomic ganglia – nerve cell bodies of postganglionic autonomic neurons. CNS nuclei – nerve cell bodies in the brain and spinal cord. (b) Both have true endocrine tissue and neuroendocrine tissue. (c) Boutons – ends of axons; varicosities – strung out along the ends of autonomic neurons.
15. (a) 1, 2 (b) 3 (c) 4 (d) 3
16. (d), (e)

LEVEL THREE Problem Solving

17. The electrochemical gradient for Na^+ is greater than that for K^+.
18. (a) endocytosis (b) parasympathetic autonomic (c) acetylcholine
19. Skeletal muscles would become paralyzed. Monkey could not flee.

LEVEL FOUR Quantitative Problems

20. Increased 1991–1997, then began to decrease. Little change from 2003 to 2005. (b) Most likely – white females. Least likely – black females.

CHAPTER 12

LEVEL ONE Reviewing Facts and Terms

1. Smooth, cardiac, and skeletal, which are attached to bones.
2. cardiac and skeletal muscle
3. skeletal muscle
4. (a) false (b) true (c) true (d) true
5. connective tissue, sarcolemma, myofibrils, thick and thin filaments
6. *sarcoplasmic reticulum;* Ca^{2+} ions
7. *action potentials*
8. Actin, myosin, troponin, tropomyosin, titin and nebulin. Myosin produces the power stroke.
9. Z disk – ends of a sarcomere. I band – Z disk in the middle. A band (thick filaments) – darkest; H zone – lighter region of A band. M line divides A band in half; thick filaments link to each other.
10. They keep actin and myosin in alignment. Titin helps stretched muscles return to resting length.
11. *A band; myosin.* Z disks approach each other.
12. Contraction occurs when thin and thick filaments slide past each other as myosin binds to actin, swivels, and pulls actin toward the center of the sarcomere.
13. Ca^{2+} binds to troponin, which repositions tropomyosin, uncovering actin's myosin-binding sites.
14. acetylcholine
15. The region of a muscle fiber where the synapse occurs. Contains ACh receptors. Influx of Na^+ through ACh receptor-channels depolarizes muscle.
16. Fast-twitch glycolytic fibers: a, b, e; Fast-twitch oxidative-glycolytic fibers: d, f, g; Slow-twitch oxidative fibers: c, d, f, h
17. *twitch*

18. ATP binding – myosin dissociates from actin. ATP hydrolysis – myosin head swings and binds to a new actin. Release of P_i initiates the power stroke.
19. *motor unit; recruitment*
20. *single-unit* (visceral) and *multi-unit*

LEVEL TWO Reviewing Concepts

21. Use Figs. 12-3 to 12-6.
22. Action potential activates DHP receptors that open SR Ca^{2+} channels.
23. Generate ATP by energy transfer from phosphocreatine. Oxidative fibers use oxygen to make ATP from glucose and fatty acids; glycolytic fibers get ATP primarily from anaerobic glycolysis.
24. Fatigue – a reversible state in which a muscle can no longer generate or sustain the expected force. May involve changes in ion concentrations, depletion of nutrients, or excitation-contraction coupling. Increase size and number of mitochondria or increase blood supply.
25. The body uses different types of motor units and recruits different numbers of motor units. Small movements use motor units with fewer muscle fibers; gross movements use motor units with more fibers.
26. See Tbl. 12-3.
27. Use Figs. 12-9 to 12-11.
28. Stores and releases Ca^{2+} on command. Smooth muscle uses Ca^{2+} from the ECF.
29. (a) Fast-twitch oxidative-glycolytic – smaller, some myoglobin, use both oxidative and glycolytic metabolism, more fatigue-resistant. Fast-twitch glycolytic fibers – largest, rely primarily on anaerobic glycolysis, least fatigue-resistant. Slow-twitch – develop tension more slowly, maintain tension longer, the most fatigue-resistant, depend primarily on oxidative phosphorylation, more mitochondria, greater vascularity, large amounts of myoglobin, smallest in diameter. (b) twitch – a single contraction-relaxation cycle. Tetanus – contraction with little to no relaxation. (c) Both result from inward Na^+ current and outward K^+ current through voltage-gated channels. Motor neuron action potential triggers ACh release. Muscle action potential triggers Ca^{2+} release from the sarcoplasmic reticulum. (d) Motor neuron temporal summation determines whether or not the neuron fires an action potential. Muscle cell summation increases force of contraction. (e) Isotonic contraction moves a load. Isometric contraction creates tension without moving a load. (f) Slow-wave potentials – cycles of depolarization and repolarization in smooth muscle cells. Pacemaker potentials – repetitive depolarizations to threshold in some smooth muscle and cardiac muscle. (g) Skeletal muscle – sarcoplasmic reticulum. Smooth muscle – ECF and sarcoplasmic reticulum.
30. Ca^{2+} release from smooth muscle SR uses an IP_3-activated channel. Influx from ECF uses mechanically, chemically, or voltage-gated channels.

LEVEL THREE Problem Solving

31. (a) Adding ATP allows cross bridges to detach. If insufficient Ca^{2+} is available, the muscle will relax. (b) With ATP and Ca^{2+}, the muscle will continue in the contraction cycle until it is completely contracted.
32. Curare must interfere with a process that follows ACh release: diffusion of ACh across the synaptic cleft, ACh binding to receptors, and opening of the receptor-channel. Curare binds to the ACh receptor and stops the channel from opening.
33. Muscle length is related to bone length. Assuming these athletes are lean, differences in weight are correlated with muscle strength, so heavier athletes should have stronger muscles. More important factors are the relative endurance and strength required for a given sport. Any given muscle will have a combination of three fiber types, with the exact ratios depending upon genetics and specific type of athletic training. (a) Basketball: endurance and strength. Leg muscles – fast-twitch glycolytic fibers, to generate strength, and fast-twitch oxidative, for endurance. The arm and shoulder muscles – fast-twitch glycolytic, because shooting requires fast and precise contraction. (b) Steer wrestler: great strength but less endurance. Fast-twitch glycolytic fibers. (c) Figure skaters: strength and endurance. Trunk muscles – slow-twitch oxidative fibers for endurance. Leg muscles – fast-twitch oxidative, for moving across the ice, and fast-twitch glycolytic, for powering jumps. (d) Gymnastics – great strength in arms and legs, and great endurance in trunk and limb muscles. Arm and leg muscles – fast-twitch glycolytic fibers. Limb and trunk muscles – slow-twitch oxidative fibers.

LEVEL FOUR Quantitative Problems

34. The data suggest lactate accumulation or loss of PCr. Find the original paper at *http://jap.physiology.org*
35. (a) 7.5 kg of force, a 125% increase. (b) an additional 28 kg of force. This is less than if the weight is placed in the hand.

CHAPTER 13

LEVEL ONE Reviewing Facts and Terms

1. *stimulus*
2. *skeletal; autonomic*
3. *convergence*
4. *presynaptic inhibition*
5. *visceral* reflexes because many of them involve internal organs (the viscera)
6. Spinal reflexes: urination and defecation. Cranial reflexes: control of heart rate, blood pressure, and body temperature.
7. Limbic system. Emotional reflexes: blushing, heart rate, gastrointestinal function
8. Two neuron-neuron synapses in the spinal cord and the autonomic ganglion, and one neuron-target synapse.
9. Golgi tendon organ, the muscle spindle, and joint capsule mechanoreceptors
10. *tone*
11. Increase. This reflex prevents damage from overstretching.
12. (a) 2, 3, 5, 6 (b) 1, 2, 6 (c) 1, 2, 4
13. *stretch; contraction; contraction; decreases; alpha motor* neuron
14. Two neurons and one synapse between them (monosynaptic). The knee jerk (patellar tendon) reflex is an example.
15. Reflex movements, such as the knee jerk, can be integrated in the spinal cord; voluntary movements, such as playing the piano; and rhythmic movements, such as walking, must involve the brain. Reflex movements are involuntary; the initiation, modulation, and termination of rhythmic movements are voluntary.

LEVEL TWO Reviewing Concepts

16. Alpha-gamma coactivation allows muscle spindles to continue functioning when the muscle contracts. When the muscle contracts, the ends of the spindles also contract to maintain stretch on the central portion of the spindle.
17. Neurotransmitter release will decrease when M's neurotransmitter hyperpolarizes P.
18. (a) Assessing the components that regulate limb movement, including quadriceps muscle, the nerves that control it, and the area of the spinal cord where the reflex integrates. (b) The reflex would probably be less apparent. The origin of this inhibition is the primary motor cortex. The inhibitory cells will produce IPSPs in the spinal motor neuron. (c) If the brain is distracted by some other task, the inhibitory signals will presumably stop.

LEVEL THREE Problem Solving

19. (a) Prevents Ca^{2+}-activated transmitter release. (b) Cell hyperpolarizes and voltage-gated Ca^{2+} channels in terminal will not open. (c) Same as (b).
20. See Figs. 13-12 and 13-13. Parts of the brain include the brain stem, cerebellum, basal ganglia, thalamus, cerebral cortex (visual cortex, association areas, motor cortex).
21. (a) Fright activates the sympathetic nervous system fight-or-flight response. (b) Limbic system processes fear. Other functions include regulating drives such as sex, rage, aggression and hunger, and reflexes including urination, defecation, and blushing. Limbic system influences autonomic motor output. Heart, blood vessels, respiratory muscles, smooth muscle, and glands are some of the target organs involved. (c) Smooth muscles attach to the base of each hair and pull them upright. See Focus on Skin, p. 86.
22. Both toxins are produced by bacteria of the Clostridium genus. *Clostridium tetani* enter the body through a cut. *Clostridium botulini* enter the body through ingestion. Both toxins produce skeletal muscle paralysis. Tetanus toxin inhibits secretion of glycine from interneurons that normally inhibit somatic motor neurons. This releases the neurons from inhibition, so they trigger prolonged contractions in skeletal muscles, or spastic paralysis. Botulinum toxin blocks secretion of acetylcholine from somatic motor neurons, so skeletal muscles cannot contract, which is flaccid paralysis.

CHAPTER 14

LEVEL ONE Reviewing Facts and Terms

1. (a) first European to describe the closed circulatory system (b) described the relationship between ventricular muscle stretch and force of contraction (c) described capillaries
2. transport of materials entering and leaving the body, defense, and cell-to-cell communication
3. a – e – d – b – f – c
4. *pressure; left ventricle; aorta; right atrium; friction*
5. *decreases*
6. *intercalated disks; gap junctions*
7. SA node to internodal pathways to AV node to bundle of His (left and right branches) to Purkinje fibers to ventricular myocardium
8. (a) ESV – volume of blood in ventricle at end of contraction; EDV – volume of blood in the ventricle at beginning of contraction (b) Sympathetic increases heart rate; parasympathetic decreases heart rate. (c) Diastole = relaxation; systole = contraction (d) Pulmonary goes to the lungs; systemic goes to rest of body. (e) SA node is the (atrial) pacemaker; AV node transmits signals from atria to ventricles.
9. (a) 11 (b) 12 (c) 3 (d) 14 (e) 8 (f) 1 (g) 10 (h) 2 (i) 6 (j) 4
10. Vibrations from AV closure cause the "lub" sound and from semilunar valve closure causes the "dup" sound.
11. (a) heart rate (b) end-diastolic volume (c) stroke volume (d) cardiac output (e) blood volume

LEVEL TWO Reviewing Concepts

12. (a) Refer to Fig. 14-1. (b) Use Figs. 14-31 and 14-27 as starting point for a map.
13. See Figs. 14-24 and 14-26.
14. See Tbl. 12-3. Cardiac muscle has strong cell-to-cell junctions, gap junctions for electrical conduction, and the modification of some muscle cells into autorhythmic cells.
15. The long refractory period prevents a new action potential until the heart muscle has relaxed.
16. See Fig. 14-21. Atrial relaxation and ventricular contraction overlap during the QRS complex.
17. (a) 3; 5 in the last part (b) 5 (c) 3 (d) 5 (e) 2 (f) 2 (g) 5 (h) 6
18. Heart rate, heart rhythm (regular or irregular), conduction velocity, and the electrical condition of heart tissue. An ECG does not give any direct information about force of contraction.
19. An effect on force of contraction. Norepinephrine and cardiac glycosides

LEVEL THREE Problem Solving

20. Calcium channel blockers slow heart rate by blocking Ca^{2+} entry and decrease force of contraction by decreasing Ca^{2+}-induced Ca^{2+} release. Beta blockers decrease effect of norepinephrine and epinephrine, preventing increased heart rate and force of contraction.
21. (a) His heart muscle has been damaged by lack of oxygen and the cells are unable to contract as strongly. Thus, less blood is being pumped out of the ventricle each time the heart contracts. (b) Leads are recording electrodes placed on the surface of the body to measure electrical activity. (c) Leads are effective because electricity is conducted through body fluids to the skin surface.
22. A conduction problem at the AV node or in the ventricular conduction system might cause a long P-R interval.
23. Destroying the AV node will prevent rapid atrial signals from being passed to the ventricles. A ventricular pacemaker is implanted so that the ventricles have an electrical signal telling them to contract at an appropriate rate. Rapid atrial depolarization rate is dangerous because it if the rate is too fast, only some action potentials will initiate contractions because of the refractory period of muscle. This can cause an arrhythmia.

LEVEL FOUR Quantitative Problems

24. SV/EDV = 0.25. If SV = 40 mL, EDV = 160 mL. SV = EDV − ESV, so ESV = 120 mL. CO = HR × SV = 4 L/min.
25. (a) 162.2 cm H_2O (b) 108.1 cm H_2O
26. 5200 mL/min or 5.2 L/min
27. 85 mL
28. (a) 1 min (b) 12 sec

CHAPTER 15

LEVEL ONE Reviewing Facts and Terms

1. brain and heart
2. (a) 6, 9 (b) 1, 2 (c) 4, 7 (d) 3, 5, 6, 8 (e) 3, 4
3. endothelium (capillary exchange and paracrine secretion); elastic tissue (recoil); smooth muscle (contraction); fibrous connective tissue (resistance to stretch).
4. arterioles
5. *120 mm Hg; diastole; 80 mm Hg; 120/80*
6. *pulse*. Pulse pressure = systolic pressure – diastolic pressure
7. One-way valves in the veins, skeletal muscle pump, and low pressure in the thorax during breathing
8. Elevated blood pressure can cause a weakened blood vessel to rupture and bleed.
9. Korotkoff sounds occur when cuff pressure is lower than systolic pressure but higher than diastolic pressure.
10. See Tbl. 15-2. Sympathetic neurons (α-receptors) vasoconstrict and epinephrine on β_2-receptors in certain organs vasodilates.
11. A region of increased blood flow. Active – increased blood flow is in response to an increase in metabolism. Reactive – increase in flow follows a period of decreased blood flow.
12. *Sympathetic* innervation causes vasoconstriction.
13. (a) 1, 5 (b) 2, 6 (c) 1, 2, 4 (d) 3, 8 (e) none of the above
14. Digestive tract, liver, kidneys, and skeletal muscles. Kidneys have the highest flow on a per unit weight basis.
15. Capillary density is proportional to the tissue's metabolic rate. Cartilage – lowest; muscles and glands – highest.
16. (a) diffusion (b) diffusion or transcytosis (c) facilitated diffusion (d) osmosis
17. immune, circulatory, and digestive systems
18. Edema is excess fluid in the interstitial space. Causes include lower capillary oncotic pressure due to decreased plasma proteins or blockage of the lymphatic vessels by a tumor or other pathology.
19. (a) blood flow though a tissue (b) the contribution of plasma proteins to the osmotic pressure of the plasma (c) a decrease in blood vessel diameter (d) growth of new blood vessels, especially capillaries, into a tissue (e) small vessels between arterioles and venules that can act as bypass channels (f) cells surrounding the capillary endothelium that regulate capillary leakiness
20. *HDL* and *LDL*. LDL-C is bad in elevated amounts.

LEVEL TWO Reviewing Concepts

21. Use Fig 15-10 as the starting point.
22. (a) Pores of lymphatic capillaries are larger. Lymphatic capillaries have contractile fibers to help fluid flow; systemic capillaries depend on systemic blood pressure for flow. (b) Sympathetic division raises blood pressure by increasing cardiac output and causing vasoconstriction. Parasympathetic division can decrease heart rate. (c) Lymph fluid is similar to blood plasma minus most plasma proteins. Blood also has nearly half its volume occupied by blood cells. (d) Continuous capillaries have smaller pores and regulate the movement of substances better than fenestrated capillaries. Fenestrated can open large gaps to allow proteins and blood cells to pass. (e) Hydrostatic pressure forces fluid out of capillaries; colloid osmotic pressure of plasma proteins draws fluid into capillaries.
23. Preventing Ca^{2+} entry decreases ability of cardiac and smooth muscles to contract. Decreasing Ca^{2+} entry into autorhythmic cells decreases heart rate. Neurons and other cells are unaffected because they have types of calcium channels not affected by the drugs.
24. The ability of vascular smooth muscle to regulate its own contraction. Probably results from Ca^{2+} influx when the muscle is stretched.
25. Left ventricular failure causes blood to pool in the lungs, increasing pulmonary capillary hydrostatic pressure. This may cause pulmonary edema and shortness of breath when oxygen has trouble diffusing into the body. Blood backing up into the systemic circulation increases venous pressure.

LEVEL THREE Problem Solving

26. (a) Uncontrollable: male, middle-aged, family history of cardiovascular disease on both sides of his family. Controllable: elevated blood pressure. (b) Yes, because blood pressure > 140 or diastolic pressure > 90 on several occasions. It would be useful to confirm that this was not "white coat hypertension" by having him take his blood pressure for a week or so at locations away from the doctor's office, such as at a drug store. (c) Beta blockers block β_1 receptors in the heart, thus lowering cardiac output and MAP.
27. (a) MAP increases, flow through vessels 1 and 2 decreases, flow through 3 and 4 increases. (b) Pressure increase → arterial baroreceptor → cardiovascular control center → arteriolar vasodilation ans decreased CO → decreased pressure (c) decreases
28. sight of blood → cerebral cortex → CVCC in the medulla oblongata → increased parasympathetic and decreased sympathetic output → decreased heart rate and vasodilation → decreased blood pressure
29. Cells (endothelium) in the intact wall detect changes in oxygen and communicate these changes to the smooth muscle.
30. Atropine is an ACh antagonist, possibly by binding to ACh receptor.
31. (a) increases (b) resistance increases and pressure increases
32. (a) In Fig. 14-1 draw a connection from pulmonary artery to aorta. In Fig. 14-7d you can see a remnant of the closed ductus as a small ligament connecting the aorta and pulmonary artery. (b) The lungs are not functioning. (c) systemic (d) left side (e) from the aorta into the pulmonary artery

LEVEL FOUR Quantitative Problems

33. increases 16-fold
34. Answers will vary. For a 50-kg individual with a resting pulse of 70 bpm, she will pump her weight in blood in about 10 minutes.
35. MAP = 87 mm Hg; pulse pressure = 42 mm Hg
36. 250 mL oxygen/min = CO × (200 − 160 mL oxygen/L blood). CO = 6.25 L/min

CHAPTER 16

LEVEL ONE Reviewing Facts and Terms

1. *plasma; water*
2. albumins (most prevalent), globulins, and fibrinogen. Functions: Table 16-1.

3. erythrocytes (transport O_2 and CO_2); leukocytes or white blood cells (defense); platelets (clotting)
4. *hematopoiesis*. Embryo – yolk sac, liver, spleen, and bone marrow. At birth – restricted to the bone marrow. By adulthood – only in axial skeleton and proximal ends of long bones.
5. Colony-stimulating factors stimulate hematopoiesis. Cytokines are released by one cell to act on another cell. Interleukins are cytokines released by leukocytes to act on other leukocytes. All influence growth and differentiation of blood cells. Examples: see Tbl. 16-2.
6. RBC – erythropoiesis; WBC – leukopoiesis; platelets – thrombopoiesis.
7. *erythropoietin*. Produced primarily in the kidney in response to low oxygen.
8. Hematocrit – % total blood volume occupied by packed (centrifuged) red cells. Men: 40–54%; women: 37–47%.
9. Erythroblast is an immature, large, nucleated precursor of the erythrocyte. Characteristics: biconcave disk shape, no nucleus, and red color due to hemoglobin.
10. iron
11. (a) yellow color to the skin due to elevated bilirubin (b) low level of hemoglobin (c) plasma protein that acts as a carrier for iron (d) inherited defects of the coagulation cascade, resulting in decreased clotting ability
12. *anticoagulants*

LEVEL TWO Reviewing Concepts

13. List 1: see Fig. 16-11. List 2: see Fig. 16-13. List 3: see Fig. 16-7.
14. Intrinsic pathway – exposed collagen and other triggers activate factor XII. Extrinsic pathway – damaged tissue exposes tissue factor (III), which activates factor VII. The two pathways unite at the common pathway to initiate the formation of thrombin. See Fig. 16-12.
15. Activated platelets cannot stick to undamaged regions of endothelium that release prostacyclin and nitric oxide (NO).

LEVEL THREE Problem Solving

16. Rachel is pale and tired because she is anemic. Bruising is a sign that platelet count is low. Proteins and vitamins promote hemoglobin synthesis and the production of new blood cell components. Iron is also necessary for hemoglobin synthesis. Avoid crowds to prevent being exposed to infections because her WBC count and ability to fight infection are decreased. By day 20, all blood counts are back into the low-normal range.
17. (a) transferrin (b) the liver, which stores iron (c) withdraw blood. This illustrates mass balance: if input exceeds output, restore body load by increasing output.
18. Some other factor essential for RBC synthesis, such as iron, folic acid, or vitamin B_{12}, must be lacking.

LEVEL FOUR Quantitative Problems

19. 200-lb man: blood 6.4 L and plasma about 3.1 L. 130-lb woman: blood 4.1 L and plasma about 2.4 L.
20. blood volume 3.5 L and total erythrocyte volume is 1.4 L.

CHAPTER 17

LEVEL ONE Reviewing Facts and Terms

1. gas exchange, vocalization, pH regulation, and protection
2. Cellular respiration – oxygen and nutrients are used for energy production. External respiration – gas exchange between atmosphere and cells.
3. Quiet inspiration – external intercostals, scalenes, and diaphragm. Quiet expiration – no significant muscle contraction. Active expiration – internal intercostals and abdominal muscles. These are all skeletal muscles.
4. Lubrication between lungs and internal thoracic surface
5. Nose and mouth, pharynx, larynx, trachea, main bronchus, secondary bronchi, bronchioles, epithelium of the alveoli, interstitial fluid, and capillary endothelium
6. See Fig. 17-2g. Type I – gas exchange; type II – surfactant. Macrophages ingest foreign material. Capillary endothelium is almost fused to the alveolar epithelium, and the space between alveoli is almost filled with capillaries.
7. Right ventricle to pulmonary trunk, to left and right pulmonary arteries, smaller arteries, arterioles, capillaries, venules, small veins, pulmonary veins, left atrium. Contains about 0.5 L of blood. Arterial pressure is 25/8, compared with 120/80 for systemic.
8. Warmed, humidified, and cleaned (filtered)
9. *diaphragm*
10. See Fig. 17-11.
11. Surfactant decreases surface tension of water and makes it easier for lungs to inflate and stay inflated.
12. radius of the airways
13. (a) 1 (b) 2 (c) 1 (d) 2
14. (a) See Fig. 17-8. (b) V_T = 0.5 L, IRV = 1.25 L, ERV = 1.0 L. (c) 3 breaths/15 sec = 0.2 br/sec × 60 sec/min = 12 br/min

LEVEL TWO Reviewing Concepts

15. (a) Compliance – ability to stretch; elastance – measure of recoil. (b) Ventilation – air exchange between atmosphere and lungs. Inspiration – air movement into lungs. Expiration – air movement out of lungs. (c) Intrapleural pressure – always subatmospheric (except during forced expiration, when it may become positive); alveolar pressures vary from subatmospheric to above atmospheric. (d) Total pulmonary ventilation – volume of air entering or leaving airways in a given period of time. Alveolar ventilation – volume of air entering or leaving alveoli in a given period of time. (e) Type I – thin cells for gas exchange; Type II – synthesize and secrete surfactant. (f) pulmonary – from right heart to lung and back to left atrium. Systemic – left heart to most tissues and back to right atrium.
16. Bronchoconstrictors: histamine, leukotrienes, acetylcholine (muscarinic); bronchodilators: carbon dioxide, epinephrine (β_2)
17. See Figs. 17-9 and 17-11.
18. (a) decrease (b) decrease (c) decrease (d) increase (e) decrease (f) increase
19. Pneumothorax – air in the pleural cavity. Spirometer – device used to measure ventilation. Auscultation – listening for body sounds. Hypoventilation – decreased pulmonary ventilation. Bronchoconstriction – decrease in bronchiole radius. Minute volume – total

pulmonary ventilation. Partial pressure of gas – portion of total pressure in a mixture of gases that is contributed by a specific gas.

20. (a) *vital capacity*. Sum of tidal volume and expiratory and inspiratory reserve volumes. (b) No, because lung function decreases with age as elastance and compliance diminish.
21. b – b – d – d
22. *x*-axis – time; *y*-axis – P_{O_2}. During inspiration, the P_{O_2} of the primary bronchi will increase, as fresh air (P_{O_2} = 160 mm Hg) pushes the stale air (P_{O_2} = 100 mm Hg) into the alveoli. During expiration, the P_{O_2} will decrease, as the oxygen-depleted air exits. The curve will vary from 100 mm Hg to 160 mm Hg.
23. (a) Work increases. (b) Lungs inflate more easily. (c) Elastance decreases. (d) Airway resistance is not affected.
24. (a) decrease (b) increase (c) decrease

LEVEL THREE Problem Solving

25. Resting alveolar ventilation = 3575 mL/min. Exercising: (a) 5500 mL/min (b) 5525 mL/min (c) 5625 mL/min. Increasing both rate and depth has the largest effect and is what would happen in real life.
26. (a) 9600 mL/min. (b) Dilating bronchioles reduces airway resistance. The patient is able to force more air out of the lungs on expiration, which increases her ERV and decreases her RV. (c) Respiratory rate is normal, but lung volumes are abnormal. Her high RV is confirmed by the X-ray. In obstructive lung diseases such as asthma, the bronchioles collapse on expiration, trapping air in the lungs and resulting in hyperinflation. Her low IRV accounts for most of the low vital capacity, and is to be expected in someone with asthma, where the lungs are already overinflated at the beginning of inspiration. Her higher tidal volume may be the result of the effort she must exert to breathe.

LEVEL FOUR Quantitative Problems

27. $P_1V_1 = P_2V_2$. New volume = 200 mL
28. (a) O_2 = 160 mm Hg, nitrogen = 593 mm Hg, CO_2 = 3 mm Hg. (b) O_2 = 304 mm Hg, nitrogen = 99 mm Hg, CO_2 = 342 mm Hg, H_2 = 15 mm Hg. (c) O_2 = 76 mm Hg, nitrogen = 114 mm Hg, argon = 8 mm Hg, CO_2 = 190 mm Hg.
29. Total pulmonary ventilation = 4800 mL/min. Before an exam, ventilation is 7200 mL/min. Alveolar ventilation is 3360 mL/min (at rest) and 5040 mL/min (before exam).
30. Tidal volume = 417 mL/breath. IRV = 3383 mL
31. Lung volume is 1.1 L. (Did you forget to subtract the volume of the spirometer?)

CHAPTER 18

LEVEL ONE Reviewing Facts and Terms

1. Pressure gradients, solubility in water, alveolar capillary perfusion, blood pH, temperature.
2. *98%*. Remainder is dissolved in plasma.
3. P_{O_2}, temperature, pH, and the amount of hemoglobin available for binding (most important).
4. Four globular protein chains, each wrapped around a central heme group with iron.
5. *medulla* and *pons*. Dorsal – neurons for inspiration; ventral – neurons for inspiration and active expiration. Central pattern generator – group of neurons that interact spontaneously to control rhythmic contraction of certain muscle groups.
6. Medullary chemoreceptors increase ventilation when P_{CO_2} increases. Carotid and aortic chemoreceptors respond to P_{CO_2}, pH, and P_{O_2} < 60 mm Hg. P_{CO_2} is most important.
7. They include irritant-mediated bronchoconstriction and the cough reflex.
8. partial pressure gradients
9. Decreased atmospheric P_{O_2}, decreased alveolar perfusion, loss of hemoglobin, increased thickness of respiratory membrane, decreased respiratory surface area, increased diffusion distance.

LEVEL TWO Reviewing Concepts

10. Start with Fig. 18-13.
11. Most oxygen is bound to hemoglobin, not dissolved in the plasma.
12. (a) Most O_2 is transported bound to hemoglobin but most CO_2 is converted to bicarbonate. (b) Concentration is amount of gas per volume of solution, measured in units such as moles per liter. While solution partial pressure and concentration are proportional, concentration is affected by the gas solubility, and therefore is not the same as partial pressure.
13. decrease
14. Hypoxia – low oxygen inside cells. COPD – chronic obstructive pulmonary disease (chronic bronchitis and emphysema). Hypercapnia – elevated CO_2.
15. Oxygen is not very soluble in water, and the metabolic requirement for oxygen in most multicellular animals would not be met without an oxygen-transport molecule.
16. (a) *x*-axis – ventilation in L/min; *y*-axis – arterial P_{O_2}, in mm Hg. See Fig. 18-9. (b) *x*-axis – arterial P_{CO_2} in mm Hg; *y*-axis – ventilation in L/min. As arterial P_{CO_2} increases, ventilation increases. Because there is maximum ventilation determined by properties of muscles involved in ventilation, slope of curve should decrease as it approaches this maximum.
17. (a) increases (b) increases
18. Normal, because P_{O_2} depends on the P_{O_2} of the alveoli, not on how much Hb is available for oxygen transport.
19. (a) See Fig. 18-21. (b) See Fig. 18-15.

LEVEL THREE Problem Solving

20. Increased dead space decreases alveolar ventilation. (a) increases (b) decreases (c) increases (d) decreases
21. (a) has slightly reduced dissolved O_2 but at P_{O_2} = 80, Hb saturation is still about 95%. If oxygen content is 197 mL O_2/L at P_{O_2} =100 and 98% saturation, then oxygen content at P_{O_2} = 80 mm Hg and 95% saturation is 190 mL O_2/L blood (197 × (0.95/0.98)), with Hb constant). Person (b) has reduced hemoglobin of 12 g/dL but it is still 98% saturated, so oxygen content would be 157.6 mL O_2/L blood (197 × (12/15)). The increased P_{O_2} did not compensate for the decreased hemoglobin content.
22. (a) decrease (b) decrease (c) decrease
23. (a) Respiratory movements originate above the level of the cut, which could include any area of the brain. (b) Ventilation depends upon signals from the medulla and/or pons. (c) Respiratory rhythm is controlled by the medulla alone, but other important aspects of respiration depend upon signals originating in the pons or higher.

24. With chronic elevated P_{CO_2}, the chemoreceptor response adapts and CO_2 is no longer a chemical drive for ventilation. The primary chemical signal for ventilation becomes low oxygen (below 60 mm Hg). Thus, when the patient is given O_2, there is no chemical drive for ventilation, and the patient stops breathing.
25. (a) alveoli – 96%; exercising cell – 23% (b) At rest Bzork only uses about 20% of the oxygen that his hemoglobin can carry. With exercise, his oxygen consumption increases, and his hemoglobin releases more than 3/4 of the oxygen it can carry.
26. All three lines show that as P_{CO_2} increases, ventilation increases. Line A shows that a decrease in P_{CO_2} potentiates this increase in ventilation (when compared to Line B). Line C shows that ingestion of alcohol lessens the effect of increasing P_{CO_2} on ventilation. Because alcohol is a CNS-depressant, we can hypothesize that the pathway that links increased P_{CO_2} and increased ventilation is integrated in the CNS.
27. apical – faces airspace; basolateral – faces interstitial fluid. Apical side has ENaC and aquaporins; basolateral side has aquaporins and Na^+-K^+-ATPase. Na^+ enters the cell through ENaC, then is pumped out the basolateral side. (Cl^- follows to maintain electrical neutrality.) Translocation of NaCl allows water to follow by osmosis.

LEVEL FOUR Quantitative Problems

28. 1.65 mL O_2/gm Hb
29. 247.5 mL O_2/min
30. Nothing. The percent saturation of Hb is unchanged at any given P_{O_2}. However, with less Hb available, less oxygen will be transported.

CHAPTER 19

LEVEL ONE Reviewing Facts and Terms

1. Color (concentration), odor (infection or excreted substances), clarity (presence of cells), taste (presence of glucose), and froth (presence of proteins)
2. Regulation of extracellular fluid volume (to maintain adequate blood pressure), regulation of osmolarity, maintenance of ion balance (neuron function), regulation of pH (proteins denature if pH not maintained), excretion of wastes and foreign substances (to prevent toxic effects), and production of hormones (that regulate RBC synthesis, Ca^{2+} and Na^+ balance).
3. 20–25%
4. Nephrons through ureters to urinary bladder (storage), leaving through the urethra
5. (a), (e), (b), (g), (f), (d), (c), (h)
6. glomerular capillary endothelium, basal lamina, and epithelium of Bowman's capsule. Blood cells and most plasma proteins are excluded.
7. Capillary hydrostatic pressure promotes filtration. Fluid pressure in Bowman's capsule and colloid osmotic (oncotic) pressure of plasma oppose it. Net driving force is the sum of these pressures.
8. GFR – glomerular filtration rate. 125 mL/min or 180 L/day.
9. (a) Found where distal tubule passes between afferent and efferent arterioles. Composed of macula densa cells in the distal tubule and granular cells in arteriole wall. (b) Macula densa paracrine signals control autoregulation of GFR and renin secretion. (c) Alter the size of filtration slits. (d) Specialized epithelial cells that surround glomerular capillaries. Changes in slit size alter GFR. (e) An internal smooth muscle sphincter that is passively contracted and an external skeletal muscle sphincter that is tonically (actively) contracted. (f) Outer layer of the kidney that contains renal corpuscles, proximal and distal tubules, and parts of the loop of Henle and collecting ducts.
10. 80% occurs in the proximal tubule. Reabsorbed molecules go into the peritubular capillaries and the systemic venous circulation. If filtered and not reabsorbed, a molecule is excreted in the urine.
11. (a) 2, 3 (b) 3, 4 (c) 3, 5 (d) 1 (e) 5
12. penicillin, K^+, and H^+
13. creatinine
14. urination

LEVEL TWO Reviewing Concepts

15. Use Figs. 19-5, 19-6, 19-7, 19-8, and 19-9.
16. (a) Filtration and secretion both move material from blood to tubule lumen, but filtration is a bulk flow process while secretion is a selective process. Excretion is also bulk flow but involves movement from the kidney lumen to the outside world. (b) Transport maximum – the maximum rate at which carriers are saturated by substrate. Renal threshold – plasma concentration at which saturation occurs. (c) Creatinine and inulin – compounds used to determine GFR. Penicillin and probenecid – xenobiotics that are secreted. (d) Clearance – rate at which plasma is cleared of a substance (mL plasma cleared of substance *X*/min). GFR – filtration rate of plasma (mL plasma filtered/min). Excretion – removal of urine, mL urine/min.
17. Allows rapid removal of foreign substances that are filtered but not reabsorbed.
18. Afferent arteriole constricts, GFR decreases. Efferent arteriole constricts, GFR increases.
19. See Fig. 19-18. Toilet training allows higher brain centers to inhibit the reflex until an appropriate time. Higher brain centers can also initiate the reflex.
20. Bladder smooth muscle contracts under parasympathetic control, so blocking muscarinic receptors decreases bladder contraction.

LEVEL THREE Problem Solving

21. (a) Inulin is filtered, secreted, and excreted. No evidence for reabsorption is presented. (b) The line indicating net secretion will be close to the filtration line until the slope changes, after which the secretion line is horizontal (no further increase in rate due to saturation).
22. See Fig. 19-12. Place transporters as described. Cl^- moves between the cells.
23. Dialysis fluid should resemble plasma without waste substances, such as urea. This will allow diffusion of solutes and water from the blood into the dialysis fluid but diffusion will stop at the desired concentration. To remove excess water from the blood, the dialysis fluid can be made more concentrated.

LEVEL FOUR Quantitative Problems

24. 1 L/min
25. First specimen clearance = 1000 L plasma/day. Normally creatinine clearance = GFR. However, this value is not at all realistic for GFR (normal average is 180 L/day). The repeat test has 4000 mg of creatinine and gives a clearance of 200 L/day, which is within normal limits. The abnormal values on the first test were probably a laboratory error. Dwight's kidney function is normal.
26. For any solute that filters: plasma concentration × GFR = filtration rate. At the transport maximum: filtration rate = reabsorption rate of T_m. By substitution: plasma concentration × GFR = T_m. The renal threshold represents the plasma concentration at which the transporters are working at their maximum (T_m). By substitution: renal threshold × GFR = T_m. Mermaid's GFR is 250 mL/min and T_m is 50 mg/min, so renal threshold is 0.2 mg glucose/mL plasma. Clearance = excretion rate/plasma concentration. At 15 mg glucose/mL plasma, 3750 mg/min filter and 50 mg/min reabsorb, so 3700 mg/min are excreted.

CHAPTER 20

LEVEL ONE Reviewing Facts and Terms

1. Electrolytes are ions, which can conduct electric current through a solution. Examples: Na^+, K^+, Ca^{2+}, H^+, HPO_4^{2-} and HCO_3^-.
2. Organs: kidneys, lungs, heart, blood vessels, digestive tract. Hormones: vasopressin (ADH), aldosterone, atrial natriuretic peptides (ANP), RAAS pathway.
3. Entry: ingested and a small amount from metabolism. Loss: exhaled air, evaporation and perspiration from skin, excreted by kidneys, and in feces.
4. See Tbl. 20-1.
5. Descending limb: permeable to water but lacks transporters for salts. Ascending limb: impermeable to water but reabsorbs NaCl.
6. ECF volume: Na^+; pH: H^+
7. More K^+ leaves the cell, and membrane potential becomes more negative (hyperpolarizes). The heart is most likely to be affected.
8. salt and water
9. ADH = antidiuretic hormone; ANP = atrial natriuretic peptide; ACE = angiotensin-converting enzyme; ANG II = angiotensin II; JG (apparatus) = juxtaglomerular; P cell = principal cell; I cell = intercalated cell.
10. Use the following figures: Figs. 19-12, 19-13, 20-10b, 20-12, 20-21, and 20-22.
11. pH alters protein structure (enzyme activity, membrane transporters, neural function). Buffers, renal and respiratory compensation.
12. Acids from CO_2, metabolism, and food are more likely. Sources of bases include some foods.
13. A molecule that moderates changes in pH. Intracellular: proteins, HPO_4^{2-}, and hemoglobin. Extracellular: HCO_3^-.
14. Kidneys excrete or reabsorb H^+ or HCO_3^-. Ammonia and phosphates.
15. $CO_2 + H_2O \rightarrow H_2CO_3^- \rightarrow H^+ + HCO_3^-$. Carbonic anhydrase. High in renal tubule cells and RBCs.
16. Arterial P_{CO_2} decreases, pH increases, and plasma H^+ concentration decreases.

LEVEL TWO Reviewing Concepts

17. Use the information in Tbl. 20-1 and compile multiple pathways into a single map similar to Fig. 20-17. Include all steps of the reflex.
18. Combine information from Figs. 20-19 through 20-22.
19. See Fig. 20-10.
20. Combine Figs. 20-5 and 20-6.
21. (a) ANP – peptide from atrial myocardial cells. Causes Na^+ and water excretion; inhibits ADH secretion. (b) Aldosterone – steroid from adrenal cortex. Increases distal nephron Na^+ reabsorption and K^+ excretion. (c) Renin – enzyme from JG cells. Converts plasma angiotensinogen to ANG I. (d) ANG II – peptide hormone made from ANG I. Increases blood pressure by actions on arterioles, brain, and adrenal cortex. (e) ADH – hypothalamic peptide. Increases distal nephron water reabsorption. (f) ACE – enzyme on vascular endothelium. Converts ANG I to ANG II.
22. Vasoconstriction, increased cardiac output, water conservation by kidneys, and increased thirst. If blood pressure falls too low, oxygen supply to the brain will decrease, resulting in damage or death.
23. (a) Both are in the distal nephron. P cells are associated with aldosterone-mediated Na^+ reabsorption; I cells are involved with acid-base regulation. (b) All are parts of the RAAS system. Renin and ACE – enzymes; ANG II and aldosterone – hormones. See Fig. 20-13. (c) In both, body pH falls below 7.38. Respiratory – results from CO_2 retention (from any number of causes); metabolic – results from excessive production of metabolic acids. Respiratory compensation – renal H^+ excretion and HCO_3^- retention. Metabolic compensation – increased ventilation, renal H^+ excretion, and HCO_3^- retention. Respiratory – arterial P_{CO_2} is elevated; metabolic – P_{CO_2} usually decreased. (d) Proximal tubule – not regulated; distal nephron – regulated by vasopressin. Ascending limb – impermeable to water. (e) Both – pH goes above 7.42. Metabolic – may be caused by excessive ingestion of bicarbonate-containing antacids or vomiting; respiratory – hyperventilation. Metabolic compensation – decrease ventilation, decreased renal H^+ excretion, increased HCO_3^- excretion. Respiratory compensation – decreased renal H^+ excretion, increased HCO_3^- excretion.
24. The cells concentrate organic solutes to increase their internal osmolarity.

LEVEL THREE Problem Solving

25. (a) Acute respiratory acidosis (b) Chronic respiratory acidosis (c) Renal compensation has increased his pH by H^+ excretion and HCO_3^- reabsorption. His P_{CO_2} is elevated because of his emphysema.
26. These drugs decrease ADH-mediated water reabsorption. Useful in people who secrete too much vasopressin (SIADH, or syndrome of inappropriate ADH secretion) or in hyponatremia, such as the woman in this chapter's Running Problem.
27. (a) metabolic alkalosis, partially compensated. (b) After vomiting acid (H^+), her body was left with HCO_3^-. (c) Hypoventilation increases P_{CO_2}, HCO_3^-, and H^+. Increased H^+ decreases pH (compensation). Hypoventilation also decreases arterial P_{O_2} and decreases the total oxygen content of blood (see Fig. 17-15).
28. Blood pressure is high, plasma Na^+ and osmolarity are low. Use Tbl. 20-1 to select reflex pathways for the map.

LEVEL FOUR Quantitative Problems

29. (a) pH = 6.1 + log 24/(0.03 × 40) = 7.40 (b) 7.34
30. 428.6 mL. (600 mosmol/? L = 1400 mosmol/L)
31. (a) 400 mg glucose/100 mL × 130 mL/min = 520 mg glucose/min filters. (b) Can reabsorb up to T_m so 400 mg/min reabsorbed. (c) Excreted = filtered – reabsorbed = 120 mg/min × 1440 min/day = 172.8 g/day excreted. (d) Convert grams to milliosmoles: 172.8 g × mole/180 g × 1000 mosmol/mole = 960 mosmol glucose excreted/day. Concentration = amount/volume. 1200 mosmol/L = 960 mosmol/? liters. Will require 0.8 L additional volume.

CHAPTER 21

LEVEL ONE Reviewing Facts and Terms

1. Digestion – chemical or mechanical breakdown of nutrients (proteins). Absorption – transport from lumen to ECF (water); secretion – transport from ECF to lumen (enzymes). Motility – movement of material through the digestive tract.
2. *Absorption* and *digestion; secretion* and *motility*. By not regulating absorption and digestion, the body ensures that it will always absorb the maximum available nutrients.
3. (a) 2 (b) 3 (c) 4 (d) 7, 10 (e) 8 (f) 2, 3, 7 (g) 9
4. Layers (lumen outward): mucosa (epithelium, connective tissue and smooth muscle), submucosa (connective tissue), musculature (smooth muscle), serosa (connective tissue).
5. Secretory epithelium (endocrine and exocrine) lines the stomach; absorptive epithelium with a few secretory cells lines the intestines.
6. Peyer's patches – nodes of lymphoid tissue. M cells – epithelial cells that transfer information from gut lumen to Peyer's patches.
7. Moves food through the GI tract and helps mix food with secretions. Results from contraction of longitudinal and circular muscle layers to create propulsive peristaltic movements or mixing segmental movements.
8. An inactive digestive proenzyme. Must have a segment of protein chain removed to activate. Examples: pepsinogen-pepsin, trypsinogen-trypsin.
9. (a) 8, 9 (b) 3 (c) 1, 3, 7 (d) 1, 7 (e) 6 (f) 2 (g) 4 (h) 5
10. (a) Increases surface area for enzymes to work; stomach and small intestine. (b) Motility and secretion along the length of the digestive tract. (c) Acidic pH in stomach helps break down food and digest microorganisms. (d) Size determines the surface area upon which enzymes can act.
11. *capillaries; hepatic portal system; liver; lymphatic; basement membrane (basal lamina)*
12. ENS: network of neurons within the GI tract that can sense a stimulus, integrate information, and create an appropriate response without integration or input from the CNS. Also interacts with the CNS through sensory and autonomic neurons.
13. Short reflexes – mediated entirely within the ENS; regulate secretion and motility. Long reflexes – GI reflexes integrated in the CNS.
14. Paracrines help mediate secretion and motility. Examples: serotonin (5-HT) and histamine.

LEVEL TWO Reviewing Concepts

15. Map 2: use Fig. 21-22 and add details. Map 2: Use the information on p. 707.
16. (a) Mastication – chewing, deglutition – swallowing. (b) Villi – folds of intestine; microvilli – folds of cell membrane. Both increase surface area. (c) All patterns of GI muscle contraction. Migrating motor complex – move material from stomach to large intestine between meals. Peristalsis – progressive waves of contraction. Segmental contraction – contraction and relaxation of short intestinal segments. Mass movements – push material into rectum, triggering defecation. Vomiting – forceful expulsion of GI contents from the mouth. Diarrhea – excessive amounts of watery stool. (d) Chyme – semidigested food and secretions, produced in the stomach. Feces – solid waste material that remains after digestion and absorption are complete, produced in the large intestine. (e) Short reflexes – integrated within the ENS. Long reflexes – integrated within the CNS. (f) Submucosal plexus – ENS in the submucosal layer; myenteric plexus – ENS that lies between muscle layers of the GI tract wall. Vagus nerve – carries sensory and efferent signals between the brain and ENS. (g) Cephalic phase – digestive reflexes triggered by stimuli received in the brain. Gastric phase – short reflexes that begin with food entering the stomach. Intestinal phase – begins when chyme enters the small intestine.
17. See Figs. 21-6, 21-8, 21-9, and 21-21.
18. Both use similar neurotransmitters and neuromodulators (serotonin, VIP, NO). Enteric support cells similar to CNS astroglia. GI capillaries not very permeable, like blood-brain barrier. Both act as integrating centers.
19. See Tbl. 21-1 for specific hormones.
20. See Figs. 21-6 and 21-26.

LEVEL THREE Problem Solving

21. Hepcidin causes enterocytes to destroy ferroportin transporters. If hepcidin is absent or not functional, intestinal iron uptake cannot be down-regulated when iron levels become too high, so these patients have elevated plasma levels of iron.
22. Severe diarrhea → loss of small intestine HCO_3^- → metabolic acidosis
23. (a) Ingestion of a fatty meal triggers contraction of the gall bladder to release bile salts, but the blocked bile duct prevented bile secretion, causing pain. (b) Micelle formation – decreased due to lack of bile salts. Carbohydrate digestion – decreased because pancreatic secretions with amylase not able to pass blockage. Protein absorption – decreased slightly because of low pancreatic secretion, but protein digestion is also done by brush border enzymes, so it does not stop completely when the bile duct is blocked. Therefore, some digested proteins will be absorbed.
24. Apical membrane has Na^+ and K^+ leak channels. Basolateral membrane has the Na^+-K^+-ATPase. At high flow, saliva has more Na^+ and less K^+.

LEVEL FOUR Quantitative Problems

25. (a) MIT started out with equal concentrations in both solutions but by the end of the experiment, it was more concentrated on the serosal side. Therefore, MIT must be moving by active transport. (b) MIT moves apical to basolateral, which is absorption. (c) Transport across the apical membrane goes from bath into tissue. Tissue MIT is more concentrated than bath. Therefore, this

must be active transport. (d) Transport across the basolateral membrane goes from tissue into the sac. Tissue MIT is more concentrated than sac fluid so this must be passive transport.

CHAPTER 22

LEVEL ONE Reviewing Facts and Terms

1. Metabolism – all pathways for synthesis or energy production, use, or storage. Anabolic – primarily synthetic; catabolic – break down large molecules into smaller ones.
2. Transport (moving molecules across membranes), mechanical work (movement of muscles), chemical work (protein synthesis).
3. The amount of heat required to raise the temperature of 1 L water by 1°C. In direct calorimetry, food is burned to see how much energy it contains.
4. The ratio of CO_2 produced to O_2 used in cellular metabolism. Typical RQ is 0.82.
5. BMR – an individual's lowest metabolic rate, measured at rest after sleep and a 12-hour fast. Higher in adult males because females have more adipose tissue with a lower respiration rate. Factors that affect BMR: age, physical activity, lean muscle mass, diet, hormones, and genetics.
6. Broken down for energy, used for synthesis, or stored.
7. Absorptive state – anabolic reactions and nutrient storage. Postabsorptive – mobilizes stored nutrients for energy and synthesis.
8. A group of nutrients (glucose, free fatty acids, and amino acids), mostly in the blood, available for cell use.
9. To maintain adequate glucose supply for the brain.
10. Glycogen and adipose tissue fat
11. Proteins: protein synthesis, energy, and conversion to fat for storage. Fats: lipid synthesis, energy, and storage as fats.
12. Insulin decreases blood glucose and glucagon increases it.
13. Amino acids and glycerol. Gluconeogenesis.
14. Excessive breakdown of fatty acids, as occurs in starvation. Can be burned as fuel by neurons and other tissues. Many ketone bodies are strong acids and can cause metabolic acidosis.
15. Increased plasma glucose and parasympathetic input stimulate, sympathetic input inhibits.
16. Type 1: absolute lack of insulin. Type 2: cells do not respond normally to insulin. Both: elevated fasting blood glucose levels. Type 1: body uses fats and proteins for fuel. Type 2: not as severe because the cells can use some glucose.
17. Low plasma glucose or increased plasma amino acids stimulate. Primary target – liver, which increases glycogenolysis and gluconeogenesis.
18. (a) capillary endothelium enzyme that converts triglycerides into free fatty acids and monoglycerides. (b) co-secreted with insulin; slows gastric emptying and gastric acid secretion. (c) "hunger hormone" secreted by the stomach. (d) hypothalamic peptide that increases food intake. (e) protein components of lipoproteins. Apoprotein B on LDL-C facilitates transport into most cells. (f) "satiety hormone" produced by adipocytes. (g) loss of water in the urine due to high amounts of urine solutes. Hyperglycemia causes dehydration through osmotic diuresis. (h) target cells fail to respond normally to insulin.
19. (a) stimulates (b) inhibits (c) stimulates (d) stimulates (e) stimulates

LEVEL TWO Reviewing Concepts

20. Use Figs. 22-2, 22-5, or 22-6. Try different colors for each organ or hormone.
21. Glucagon varies only slightly during the day, while insulin cycles according to food intake. So it appears that the ratio rather than an absolute amount of hormone determines the direction of metabolism.
22. (a) Glucose – monosaccharide. Glycogenolysis – glycogen breakdown. Glycogenesis – glycogen production from glucose. Gluconeogenesis – glucose synthesis from amino acids and fats. Glucagon – hormone that increases plasma glucose. Glycolysis – first pathway in glucose metabolism for ATP production. (b) Thermogenesis – heat production by cells. Shivering thermogenesis – muscle twitches produce heat as a by-product. Non-shivering thermogenesis occurs in all cells. Diet-induced thermogenesis – heat generated by digestive and anabolic reactions during the absorptive state. (c) Lipoproteins – transport molecules. Chylomicrons – lipoprotein complexes assembled in intestinal epithelium and absorbed into lymphatic system. Cholesterol – steroid component of cell membranes and precursor to steroid hormones. HDL-C – takes cholesterol into liver cells, where it is metabolized or excreted. LDL-C – elevated concentrations are associated with atherosclerosis. Apoprotein – protein component of lipoproteins. (d) Calorimetry – measurement of energy content and a means of determining metabolic rate. Direct calorimetry – measuring heat production when food is burned. Indirect calorimetry – measures oxygen consumption or CO_2 production. (e) Conductive heat loss – loss of body heat to a cooler object. Radiant heat loss – loss from production of infrared electromagnetic waves. Convective heat loss – upward movement of warm air and its replacement by cooler air. Evaporative heat loss – heat lost when water evaporates. (f) absorptive state – following a meal, when anabolism exceeds catabolism. Postabsorptive state – catabolism exceeds anabolism.
23. (a) Hyperglycemia results from the lack of insulin production. (b) Glucosuria results when filtered glucose exceeds the kidney's capacity to reabsorb it. (c) Polyuria results from osmotic diuresis caused by glucosuria. (d) Ketosis results from increased fatty acid metabolism. (e) Dehydration is a consequence of polyuria due to osmotic diuresis. (f) Severe thirst is a consequence of dehydration.
24. If a person ingests a pure protein meal and only insulin is released, blood glucose concentrations might fall too low. Glucagon co-secretion ensures that blood glucose remains within normal levels.
25. See Fig. 22-1.
26. See Figs. 22-19 and 22-20.

LEVEL THREE Problem Solving

27. Amino acids in excess of what's needed for protein synthesis store as glycogen or fat.
28. As insulin secretion (x-axis) increases, plasma glucose (y-axis) decreases.
29. See Fig. 18-9 on p. 607. (a) See Fig. 18-10 on p. 608. Acidosis shifts the curve to the right. Low DPG, however, would shift the curve to the left (like Fig. 18-11 on p. 608). The net effect of both conditions simultaneously would be close to normal oxygen binding. (b) As pH approaches normal, the curve shifts back to the left.

With DPG still low, the curve would be between the left shift for low DPG and normal. Oxygen release after treatment would therefore be less than normal.

LEVEL FOUR Quantitative Problems

30. Answers vary. A 64-inch woman weighing 50 kg has a BMI of 19.
31. Fat: 6 g × 9 kcal/g = 54 kcal. Carbohydrate: 30 g × 4 kcal/g = 120 kcal. Protein: 8 g H 4 kcal/g = 32 kcal. Total = 206 kcal. 54/206 = 26% of calories from fat.

CHAPTER 23

LEVEL ONE Reviewing Facts and Terms

1. zona glomerulosa (aldosterone), zona fasciculata (glucocorticoids), zona reticularis (sex steroids, primarily androgens).
2. (a) corticotropin releasing hormone (hypothalamus) → adrenocorticotropic hormone (anterior pituitary) → cortisol (adrenal cortex) feeds back to inhibit secretion of both CRH and ACTH. (b) growth hormone releasing hormone and somatostatin (hypothalamus) → growth hormone (anterior pituitary) (c) decreased blood Ca^{2+} → parathyroid hormone (parathyroid glands) → ↑ blood Ca^{2+} by increasing reabsorption of bone, among other effects → negative feedback inhibits secretion of PTH. (d) Thyrotropin releasing hormone (hypothalamus) → thyroid stimulating hormone (thyrotropin) (anterior pituitary) → triiodothyronine (T_3) and thyroxine (T_4) (thyroid gland) → negative feedback to hypothalamus and anterior pituitary
3. Conditions: adequate diet, absence of chronic stress, and adequate amounts of thyroid and growth hormones. Other important hormones: insulin, somatomedins, and sex hormones at puberty.
4. Triiodothyronine (T_3) and tetraiodothyronine (T_4 or thyroxine). T_3 is the more active; most of it is made from T_4 in peripheral tissues.
5. (a) Include ACTH (cortisol secretion) and MSH (not significant in humans). (b) Bone loss that occurs when bone reabsorption exceeds bone deposition. (c) The inorganic portion of bone matrix, mostly calcium salts. (d) Steroid hormones that regulate minerals, i.e., aldosterone. (e) Small spicules of bone that surround red marrow cavities, in areas of spongy bone. (f) Pro-opiomelanocortin, inactive precursor to ACTH and other molecules. (g) Growth zones in long bones, comprised of cartilage.
6. Functions: blood clotting, cardiac muscle excitability and contraction, skeletal and smooth muscle contraction, second messenger systems, exocytosis, tight junctions, strength of bones and teeth.
7. In this table, A indicates anabolism, C indicates catabolism. CHO = carbohydrate

HORMONE	PROTEIN	CHO	FAT
Cortisol	C (skeletal muscle)	C	C
Thyroid	A (children) C (adults)	C	C
GH	A	C	C
Insulin	A	A	A
Glucagon	C	C	C

LEVEL TWO Reviewing Concepts

8. (a) See Fig. 7-20c, p. 237. (b) See Fig. 7-20b, p. 237. (c) Substitute thyroid pathway hormones into Fig. 7-20c. (d) Substitute thyroid pathway hormones into Fig. 7-21a, p. 238.
9. (a) Hypothalamic CRH stimulates anterior pituitary secretion of ACTH, which stimulates adrenal cortex (zona fasciculata) secretion of glucocorticoids such as cortisol. (b) Thyroid gland follicle cells secrete colloid from which thyroid hormones are produced; C cells secrete calcitonin. (c) Thyroid hormone synthesis is controlled by TSH, whose release is controlled by TRH. In the thyroid gland, tyrosine and iodine combine on thyroglobulin to make thyroid hormones. Thyroid-binding globulin (TBG) carries thyroid hormones in the blood. Target cell deiodinase removes iodine from T_4 to make T_3. (d) Growth hormone releasing hormone (GHRH) stimulates anterior pituitary secretion of growth hormone (GH or somatotropin). Somatostatin (GHIH) inhibits production of GH. Growth hormone binding protein binds about half the GH in the blood. Insulin-like growth factors (IGFs) from the liver act with GH to promote growth. (e) Dwarfism results from severe GH deficiency in childhood. Giantism results from hypersecretion of GH during childhood. Acromegaly is lengthening of jaw and growth in hands and feet, caused by hypersecretion of GH in adults. (f) Hyperplasia – increased cell number. Hypertrophy – increased cell size. (g) Osteoblasts – bone cells that secrete organic bone matrix. Chondrocytes – cartilage cells. Osteoclasts – bone-destroying cells. (h) PTH increases blood Ca^{2+} by stimulating bone and renal reabsorption, and intestinal absorption of Ca^{2+}. Calcitriol (1,25-dihydroxycholecalciferol) is a vitamin D derivative that mediates PTH effect on intestinal absorption of Ca^{2+}. Calcitonin decreases bone reabsorption of Ca^{2+}. Estrogen promotes bone deposition.
10. Thyroid hormones have intracellular receptors so you expect 60–90 minute onset of action. However, effects on metabolic rate are apparent within a few minutes and are thought to be related to changes in ion transport across cell and mitochondrial membranes.
11. Equivalent = ion's molarity × the number of charges/ion. Ca^{2+}: 2.5 mmoles × 2 = 5 mEq.
12. See Fig. 23-18. The cell uses carbonic anhydrase to make H^+ from $CO_2 + H_2O$. Apical membrane: H^+-ATPase secretes H^+; basolateral membrane secretes HCO_3^- with Cl^--HCO_3^- antiporter or Na^+-HCO_3^- symporter

LEVEL THREE Problem Solving

13. Physiological stress stimulates secretion of cortisol, which increases blood glucose. Increased insulin opposes this effect.
14. Normal response: dexamethasone → ACTH suppression → decrease in cortisol. Patient A: no response to dexamethasone suggests there is adrenal hypersecretion that is insensitive to ACTH. Patient B: dexamethasone decreases cortisol, suggesting that the problem is in the pituitary.
15. Mr. A – elevated TSH. Ms. B – low TSH. Mrs. C – elevated TSH. (a) Not possible to determine if the lab slip has the results of Mr. A or Mrs. C without knowing the thyroid hormone levels. (b) Ms. B can be ruled out, because her TSH would be low if the tentative diagnosis is correct.
16. (a) People in all age groups showed vitamin D insufficiency at the end of winter. Deficiency was most pronounced in the 18–29 age

group and least pronounced in the 50+ age group. At the end of summer, fewer subjects were deficient in vitamin D. Variables: season when blood collected, age group, and % of people with vitamin D insufficiency. (b) Energy from the sun is required for precursors in the skin to be converted to vitamin D. Days are shorter in the winter, and at northern latitudes like Boston, people spend less time outside during the winter. This explains the difference between the two seasons. Fewer than half the people tested were deficient, however, suggesting that most people consumed enough vitamin D. The biggest seasonal difference was in the 18–29 age group, who probably spent more time outside in the summer than members of other groups. (c) Multivitamin supplements contain vitamin D and their consumption should reduce vitamin D insufficiency.

LEVEL FOUR Quantitative Problems

17. (a) 5 mg Ca^{2+}/L plasma × 125 mL plasma filtered/min × 1440 min/day = 900 mg Ca^{2+} filtered/day (b) To remain in Ca^{2+} balance, he must excrete 170 mg/day. (c) 900 mg filtered –170 mg excreted = 730 mg reabsorbed. 730/900 = 81%.

CHAPTER 24

LEVEL ONE Reviewing Facts and Terms

1. The body's ability to defend itself against disease-causing pathogens. Memory – immune cells remember prior exposure to an antigen and create a stronger immune response. Specificity – antibodies that target specific antigens.
2. thymus gland, bone marrow, spleen, lymph nodes, and diffuse lymphoid tissues
3. Protect the body against foreign pathogens; remove dead or damaged tissues and cells; recognize and remove abnormal "self" cells.
4. Viruses bud off the host cell or kill and rupture it. Viruses damage host cells by killing them, taking over their metabolism, or causing them to become cancerous and reproduce uncontrollably.
5. Detect the pathogen, recognize it as foreign, organize a response, and recruit assistance from other cells. If a pathogen cannot be destroyed, it may be suppressed.
6. (a) severe IgE-mediated allergic reaction with widespread vasodilation, circulatory collapse, and bronchoconstriction. (b) To clump together. When blood cells are exposed to an antibody, an antibody-antigen reaction may cause the blood cells to agglutinate. (c) Outside the blood vessels. Many immune reactions are extravascular. (d) Release of cytoplasmic granule chemicals into the ECF. (e) Opsonins that coat pathogens; released in the early stages of injury or infection. (f) One cell of a clone divides to make many identical cells. (g) Ability of the immune system to find and destroy abnormal cells (especially cancerous).
7. histiocytes, Kupffer cells, osteoclasts, microglia
8. monocytes and macrophages, which ingest and destroy invaders and abnormal cells
9. (a) 5 (b) 1 (c) 3 (d) 6 (e) 2 (f) 4
10. Physical: skin, mucous membranes, respiratory mucociliary escalator. Chemical: lysozymes, opsonins, enzymes, and antibodies.
11. B-lymphocytes secrete antibodies; T-lymphocytes and NK cells kill infected cells. T-lymphocytes bind to antigen presented by MHC-complexes; NK cells can also bind to antibodies coating foreign cells.
12. The ability of the body's immune system to ignore the body's own cells. Occurs because T lymphocytes that react with "self" cells are eliminated by clonal deletion. If self-tolerance fails, the body makes antibodies against itself (autoimmune disease).
13. The ability of the nervous system to influence immune function, either positively or negatively.
14. Stress – nonspecific stimulus that disturbs homeostasis. Stressor – stimulus that causes stress. General adaptation syndrome – stress response that includes activation of the adrenal glands (fight-or-flight response by adrenal medulla and cortisol secretion by the cortex).

LEVEL TWO Reviewing Concepts

15. Use figures and tables of the chapter to create the map.
16. When lymph nodes trap bacteria, a localized inflammatory response (swelling and cytokine activation of nociceptors) results in swollen, sore nodes.
17. Histamine – opens pores in capillaries so immune cells and proteins can leave the blood. IL-1 – increases capillary permeability, stimulates acute phase proteins, causes fever. Acute phase proteins – opsonins. Bradykinin – vasodilator; stimulates pain receptors. Complement – opsonins, chemotaxins, histamine release, membrane attack complex. Interferon-γ – activates macrophages. These molecules work together so they are not antagonistic. If their combined effect is greater than the sum of their individual effects, they are synergistic.
18. (a) Pathogen – any organism that causes disease. Microbes – microscopic organisms, pathogens or not. Pyrogens – fever-causing chemicals. Antigens – substances that trigger an immune response and react with products of the response. Antibodies – disease-fighting chemicals produced by the body. Antibiotics – drugs that destroy bacteria and fungi. (b) Infection – illness caused by pathogens, especially viruses or bacteria. Inflammation – nonspecific response to cell damage or invaders, including nonpathogens such as a splinter. Allergy – inflammatory response to a nonpathogenic invader, such as plant pollen. Autoimmune disease – body creates antibodies to its own cells. (c) Allergens – nonpathogenic substances that create allergic reactions. Bacteria – cellular organisms. Viruses and retroviruses – acellular parasites that must invade the host's cells to reproduce. Retroviruses – cause host cell to make viral DNA so the virus can reproduce. (d) Chemotaxins – chemicals that attract immune cells. Cytokines – peptides made on demand and secreted for action on other cells. Opsonins – proteins that coat and tag foreign material so that it can be recognized by the immune system. Interleukins – cytokines initially thought to act only on leukocytes. Interferons – lymphocyte cytokines that aid in the immune response. Bradykinin – paracrine vasodilator. (e) Innate immunity – nonspecific, present from birth; acquired – directed at specific invaders. Acquired can be divided into cell-mediated and humoral (antibodies). (f) Immediate hypersensitivity response – mediated by antibodies; occurs within minutes of exposure to allergen. Delayed – may take several days to develop; mediated by helper T cells and macrophages. (g) All chemicals of the immune response. Membrane attack complex and perforin are membrane pore proteins. Perforins allow granzymes (cytotoxic enzymes) to enter the cell.
19. See Fig. 24-12. Fc region – determines antibody class; Fab region – antigen-binding sites that confer the antibody's specificity.
20. See Fig. 24-17.
21. See Fig. 24-18.
22. See Fig. 24-19.

LEVEL THREE Problem Solving

23. Type O – universal donor because these RBCs lack A or B surface antigens and do not trigger an immune response. Type AB – universal recipient because these RBCs have both A and B antigens and no A or B antibodies.
24. Maxie and baby are both OO. Snidley could be either BB or BO. Baby received an O gene from Maxie, and could have received the other O gene from Snidely. Thus, it is possible that Snidley is the father of Maxie's baby.
25. Emotional stress → increases cortisol secretion → immune system suppression. Also likely that students are spending more time inside and having closer contact with fellow students.
26. Barbara's immune cells recognize her connective tissue as an antigen, and attack it. Autoimmune diseases often begin in association with an infection and are thought to represent cross-reactivity of antibodies that developed because of the infection. Stress suppresses the immune system.
27. Increase in neutrophils – bacterial infection. Increase in eosinophils – parasitic infection.

CHAPTER 25

LEVEL ONE Reviewing Facts and Terms

1. ATP and phosphocreatine
2. *aerobic; both glucose and fatty acids*
3. Aerobic metabolism: requires O_2; glucose goes through glycolysis and citric acid cycle; produces 30–32 ATP/glucose through oxidative phosphorylation. Anaerobic: no O_2 used; glucose undergoes glycolysis to lactic acid; produces only 2 ATP/glucose.
4. glycogen, plasma glucose, glucose produced through gluconeogenesis
5. Cortisol, growth hormone, epinephrine, and norepinephrine all increase plasma glucose.
6. At the beginning of exercise, muscle ATP use exceeds aerobic ATP production so cellular stores of ATP are used. This creates an oxygen deficit reflected by increased oxygen consumption after exercise ceases.
7. cardiovascular system
8. Normal – 37°C. Sweating and cutaneous vasodilation

LEVEL TWO Reviewing Concepts

9. Look for figures in Chs. 4, 15, 17, 18, 23, and 25.
10. Sympathetic input on pancreatic beta cells decreases insulin secretion. Less insulin → liver produces glucose; insulin-sensitive tissues do not take up blood glucose → blood glucose available for brain and exercising muscle (glucose uptake does not require insulin).
11. Advantages: fast; uses readily available glucose. Disadvantages: low ATP yield per glucose; contributes to metabolic acidosis.
12. (a) ATP – energy for muscle contraction. ADP – accepts high-energy phosphate from PCr and becomes ATP. (b) Myoglobin–muscle O_2-binding protein that aids O_2 diffusion from blood to mitochondria. Hemoglobin – RBC O_2-binding pigment that transports O_2 from lungs to cells.
13. (a) 3 (b) 1, 2, 3, 4, 5 (c) 1, 2, 4, 5, 6 (d) 6 (e) no match (f) 6 (g) 1 (venous return), 4
14. a) increases (b) decreases (c) increases (d) increases (e) increases (f) increases (g) stays the same (h) decreases
15. Increased heart rate shortens filling time and helps offset increased end diastolic volume that might be expected from increased venous return.
16. (1) the baroreceptor reflex resets to a higher setpoint, (2) afferent signals from the baroreceptors are being blocked in transit up the spinal cord, or (3) chemo- and mechanoreceptor input from exercising tissues overrides the baroreceptor input.
17. Regular exercise lowers risk of heart attacks, lowers blood pressure, creates better lipid profiles, and lowers risk of developing type 2 diabetes.
18. Exercising muscle does not require insulin for glucose uptake, so regular exercise can help keep blood glucose levels normal.

LEVEL THREE Problem Solving

19. Water, NaCl, and K^+ to replace fluid and ions lost in sweat plus a carbohydrate that is easily absorbed and metabolized to form ATP

LEVEL FOUR Quantitative Problems

20. CO = 60 beats/minute × 70 mL/beat = 4200 mL/min. If heart rate doubles, CO goes to 8400 mL/min, or doubles also.

CHAPTER 26

LEVEL ONE Reviewing Facts and Terms

1. (a) 3, 4, 5 (b) 8 (c) 2, 7 (d) 2, 6 (e) 2 (f) 1
2. *SRY*
3. Gonads produce gametes and secrete sex hormones. Female gamete – egg (ovum); male – sperm. Female gonadal hormones – estrogen, progesterone, androgens, and inhibin; male – androgens and inhibin.
4. Newly formed sperm: seminiferous tubule → epididymis → ductus (vas) deferens → ejaculatory duct (passing the seminal vesicles, prostate gland, and bulbourethral glands) → urethra. Ovulated egg: fallopian tube → uterine cavity → cervix → vagina
5. (a) converts androgens to estrogens (b) tight junctions that prevent free movement of substances between blood and seminiferous tubule lumen (c) Sertoli cell protein secreted into seminiferous tubule lumen, where it binds and concentrates androgens (d) formed by the first meiotic division of a primary oocyte; disintegrates and has no function (e) lysosome-like structure in the head of sperm; contains enzymes essential for fertilization
6. (a) False. Some is produced in the adrenal glands of both sexes. (b) False. Both sexes produce them. (c) True. (d) False. High levels of late follicular estrogen help prepare the uterus for implantation of a fertilized ovum. (e) True.
7. A sperm-fluid mixture made mostly by the accessory glands. See Tbl. 26-3 for components.
8. The most effective contraception is abstinence. Least effective forms rely on avoiding intercourse during times when the female thinks she might be fertile.

LEVEL TWO Reviewing Concepts

9. List 1: use Figs. 26-3, 26-4, and 26-5. List 2: use Figs. 26-12, 26-13, and 26-14.
10. See Fig. 26-11.
11. See Fig. 26-14.

12. Males have one Y chromosome, which often does not have a gene to match one found on the X chromosome. Thus, a male may inherit a recessive X trait and will exhibit it, while a female who inherits the same recessive trait will not exhibit it if her second X chromosome has the dominant gene for the trait.
13. (a) gamete – eggs and sperm. zygote – formed from the fusion of egg and sperm; undergoes mitosis to become an embryo. In 8th week of pregnancy, embryo becomes a fetus. (b) Coitus – intercourse. Erection – stiffening and enlargement of the penis. Male orgasm – sperm move into the urethra during emission, then out of the body in semen during ejaculation. Erogenous zones – portions of the body with receptors for sexually arousing stimuli. (c) Capacitation – sperm maturation necessary before it can fertilize an egg. Acrosomal reaction – enzymes help sperm penetrate the zona pellucida around an egg. Cortical reaction – granules in egg cytoplasm release their contents at fertilization to change the egg membrane properties. (d) Puberty – time of sexually maturation. Menarche – the first menstrual period. Menopause – female reproductive cycles cease. Andropause – controversial male equivalent of menopause.
14. (a) FSH – stimulates gamete production in both sexes. (b) Inhibin – inhibits FSH secretion. (c) Activin – stimulates FSH secretion. (d) GnRH – stimulates release of FSH and LH. (e) LH – stimulates gonadal sex hormone production; in females, also necessary for gamete maturation. (f) DHT – testosterone metabolite responsible for fetal development of male genitalia. (g) Estrogen – present in both sexes but dominant in females; female gamete formation and some secondary characteristics. (h) Testosterone in males – gamete formation. Both sexes – some secondary sex traits such as hair growth. (i) Progesterone – females only; helps prepare the uterus for pregnancy.
15. The four phases are similar in both sexes. Excitement – penis and clitoris become erect due to increased blood flow. The vagina secretes fluids for lubrication. In male orgasm, ejaculation takes place, while in female orgasm the uterus and vaginal walls contract.
16. (a) hCG – keeps the corpus luteum from dying. (b) LH – no direct role in pregnancy. (c) HPL – regulation of maternal metabolism during pregnancy. (d) Estrogen – breast development; negative feedback signal to prevent new follicles from developing. (e) Progesterone – maintenance of the uterine lining; prevents uterine contractions; mammary gland development. (f) Relaxin – prevents uterine contractions. (g) PIH levels decrease so that prolactin levels will increase, allowing milk production.

LEVEL THREE Problem Solving

17. Normally after fertilization the second polar body, containing a haploid set of chromosomes, is released from the zygote. If all or some of the second polar body chromosomes are retained, the embryo will have three copies of a chromosome instead of just two.
18. If the unovulated cysts continue to secrete estrogen and do not develop into corpora lutea, the uterine lining will continue to grow and the breasts will develop, just as during pregnancy.
19. (a) Male (b) nonfunctional testes (c) no ducts of either type (d) female
20. During pregnancy the mother's blood glucose is available to the fetus, which metabolizes the extra energy and gains weight. The fetus also up-regulates insulin secretion to handle the glucose coming across the placenta. After birth, when insulin is still high but glucose drops to normal, the baby may become hypoglycemic.

LEVEL FOUR Quantitative Problems

21. (a) because it was being administered to the subjects. (b) negative feedback by testosterone. (c) Sperm production decreased in the A-B interval because FSH and LH decreased. It increased toward the end of the B-C interval because FSH allowed sperm production to resume. Sperm production did not increase significantly during the D-E interval.

APPENDIX B

Physics and Math

Richard D. Hill and Daniel Biller,
University of Texas

INTRODUCTION

This appendix discusses selected aspects of **biophysics**, the study of physics as it applies to biological systems. Because living systems are in a continual exchange of force and energy, it is necessary to define these important concepts. According to the seventeenth-century scientist Sir Isaac Newton, a body at rest tends to stay at rest, and a body in motion tends to continue moving in a straight line unless the body is acted upon by some force (Newton's First Law). Newton further defined **force** as an influence, measurable in both intensity and direction, that operates on a body in such a manner as to produce an alteration of its state of rest or motion. Put another way, force gives **energy** to a quantity, or mass, thereby enabling it to do work. In general, a driving force multiplied by a quantity yields energy, or work. For example: force × distance = work.

Energy exists in two general forms: kinetic energy and potential energy. **Kinetic energy** [*kinein,* to move] is the energy possessed by a mass in motion. **Potential energy** is energy possessed by a mass because of its position. Kinetic energy (*KE*) is equal to one-half the mass (*m*) of a body in motion multiplied by the square of the velocity (*v*) of the body:

$$KE = \tfrac{1}{2} m v^2$$

Potential energy (*PE*) is equal to the mass (*m*) of a body multiplied by acceleration due to gravity (*g*) times the height (*h*) of the body above the earth's surface:

$$PE = mgh \quad \text{where } g = 10 \text{ m/s}^2$$

Both kinetic and potential energy are measured in joules.

BASIC UNITS OF MEASUREMENT

For physical concepts to be useful in scientific endeavors, they must be measurable and should be expressed in standard units of measurement. Some fundamental units of measure include the following:

Length (*l*): Length is measured in meters (m).
Time (*t*): Time is measured in seconds (s).
Mass (*m*): Mass is measured in kilograms (kg), and is defined as the weight of a body in a gravitational field.
Temperature (*T*): Absolute temperature is measured on the Kelvin (K) scale,

where K = degrees Celsius (°C) + 273.15
and °C = (degrees Fahrenheit − 32)/1.8

Electric current (*I*): Electric current is measured in amperes (A).
Amount of substance (*n*): The amount of a substance is measured in moles (mol).

Using these fundamental units of measure, we can now establish standard units for physical concepts (Table B-1 ●). Although these are the standard units for these concepts at this time, they are not the only units ever used to describe them. For instance, force can also be measured in dynes, energy can be measured in calories, pressure can be measured in torr or mm Hg, and power can be measured in horsepower. However, all of these units can be converted into a standard unit counterpart, and vice versa.

The remainder of this appendix discusses some biologically relevant applications of physical concepts. This discussion includes topics such as bioelectrical principles, osmotic principles, and behaviors of gases and liquids relevant to living organisms.

BIOELECTRICAL PRINCIPLES

Living systems are composed of different molecules, many of which exist in a charged state. Cells are filled with charged particles such as proteins and organic acids, and ions are in continual flux across the cell membrane. Therefore, electrical forces are important to life.

When molecules gain or lose electrons, they develop positive or negative charges. A basic principle of electricity is that opposite charges attract and like charges repel. A force must act on a charged particle (a mass) to bring about changes in its position. Therefore, there must be a force acting on charged particles to

TABLE B-1 Standard Units for Physical Concepts

MEASURED CONCEPT	STANDARD (SI*) UNIT	MATHEMATICAL DERIVATION/ DEFINITION
Force	Newton (N)	1 N = 1 KG M/s^2
Energy/Work/Heat	Joule (J)	1 J = 1 N H m
Power	Watt (W)	1 W = 1 J/s
Electrical charge	Coulomb (C)	1 C = 1 A H s
Potential	Volt (V)	1 V = 1 J/C
Resistance	Ohm (Ω)	1 Ω = 1 V/A
Capacitance	Farad (F)	1 F = 1 C/V
Pressure	Pascal (Pa)	1 Pa = 1 N/m^2

*SI = Système International d'Unités

cause attraction or repulsion, and this electrical force can be measured. Electrical force increases as the strength (number) of charges increases, and it decreases as the distance between the charges increases. This observation has been called **Coulomb's law**, and can be written:

$$F = q_1 q_2 / \varepsilon d^2$$

where q_1 and q_2 are the electrical charges (coulombs), d is the distance between the charges (meters), ε is the dielectric constant, and F is the force of attraction or repulsion, depending on the type of charge on the particles.

When opposite charges are separated, a force acts over a distance to draw them together. As the charges move together, work is being done by the charged particles and energy is being released (Fig. B-1 ●). Conversely, to separate the united charges, energy must be added and work done. If charges are separated and kept apart, they have the potential to do work. This electrical potential is called **voltage.** Voltage is measured in **volts (V).**

If electrical charges are separated and there is a potential difference between them, then the force between the charges allows electrons to flow. Electron flow is called an electric **current.** The **Faraday constant** (F) is an expression of the electrical charge carried by one mole of electrons and is equal to 96,485 coulombs/mole.

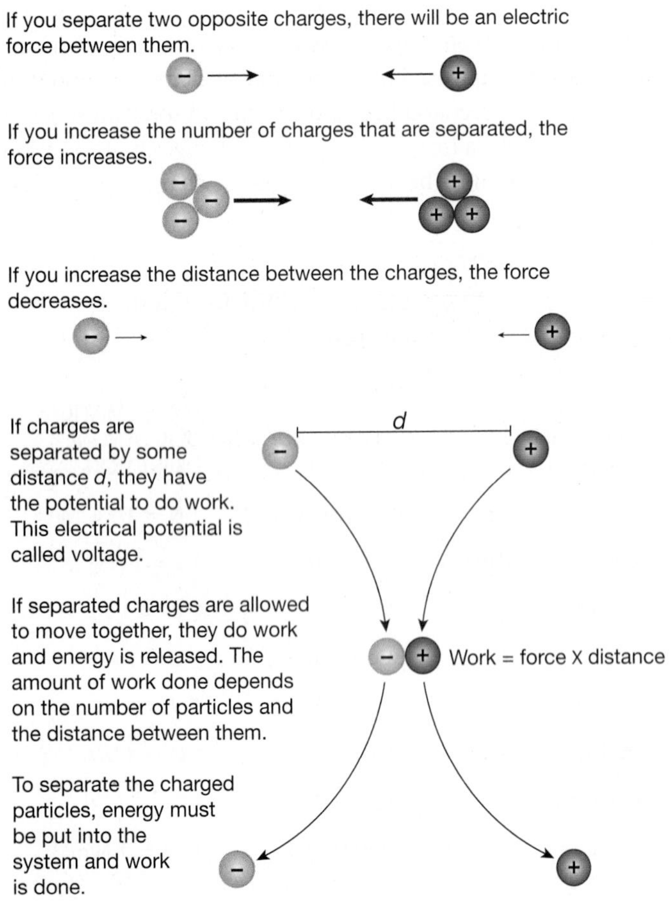
If you separate two opposite charges, there will be an electric force between them.
If you increase the number of charges that are separated, the force increases.
If you increase the distance between the charges, the force decreases.
If charges are separated by some distance d, they have the potential to do work. This electrical potential is called voltage.
d
If separated charges are allowed to move together, they do work and energy is released. The amount of work done depends on the number of particles and the distance between them.
Work = force X distance
To separate the charged particles, energy must be put into the system and work is done.

● **FIGURE B-1** ***Electrical force***

The amount of current that flows depends on the nature of the material between the charges. If a material hinders electron flow, then it is said to offer **resistance (R)**, measured in ohms. Current is inversely proportional to resistance, such that current decreases as resistance increases. If a material offers high resistance to electron flow, then that material is called an **insulator.** If resistance is low, and current flows relatively freely, then the material is called a **conductor.** Current, voltage, and resistance are related by **Ohm's law**, which states:

$$V = IR$$

where V = potential difference in volts
I = current in amperes
R = resistance in ohms

In biological systems, pure water is not a good conductor, but water containing dissolved NaCl is a fairly good conductor because ions provide charges to carry the current. In biological membranes, the lipids have few or no charged groups, so they offer high resistance to current flow across them. Thus, different cells can have different electrical properties depending on their membrane lipid composition and the permeability of their membranes to ions.

OSMOTIC PRINCIPLES

Freezing point, vapor pressure, boiling point, and osmotic pressure are properties of solutions collectively called **colligative properties.** These properties depend on the number of solute particles present in a solution. **Osmotic pressure** is the force that drives the diffusion of water across a membrane. Because there are no solutes in pure water, it has no osmotic pressure. However, if one adds a solute like NaCl, the greater the concentration (c) of a solute dissolved in water, the greater the osmotic pressure. The osmotic pressure (π) varies directly with the concentration of solute (number of particles (n) per volume (V)):

$$\pi = (n/V)RT$$
$$\pi = cRT$$

where R is the ideal gas constant (8.3145 joules/K mol) and T is the absolute temperature in Kelvin. Osmotic pressure can be measured by determining the mechanical pressure that must be applied to a solution so that osmosis ceases.

Water balance in the body is under the control of osmotic pressure gradients (concentration gradients). Most cell membranes allow water to pass freely, primarily through open channels. To control the movement of water, the body either removes these channels from the membrane or control solute movement that creates concentration gradients.

RELEVANT BEHAVIORS OF GASES AND LIQUIDS

The respiratory and circulatory systems of the human body obey the physical laws that govern the behavior of gases and liquids. This section discusses some of the important laws that govern these behaviors and how our body systems utilize these laws.

Gases The **ideal gas law** states:

$$PV = nRT$$

where P = pressure of gases in the system
V = volume of the system
n = number of moles in gas
T = temperature
R = ideal gas constant (8.3145 J/K mol)

If n and T are kept constant for all pressures and volumes in a system of gases, then any two pressures and volumes in that system are related by Boyle's Law,

$$P_1V_1 = P_2V_2$$

where P represents pressure and V represents volume.

This principle is relevant to the human lungs because the concentration of gas in the lungs is relatively equal to that in the atmosphere. In addition, body temperature is maintained at a constant temperature by homeostatic mechanisms. Therefore, if the volume of the lungs is changed, then the pressure in the lungs changes inversely. For example, an increase in pressure causes a decrease in volume, and vice versa.

Liquids **Fluid pressure** (or hydrostatic pressure) is the pressure exerted by a fluid on a real or hypothetical body. In other words, the pressure exists whether or not there is a body submerged in the fluid. Fluid exerts a pressure (P) on an object submerged in it at a certain depth from the surface (h). **Pascal's law** allows us to find the fluid pressure at a specified depth for any given fluid. It states:

$$P = \rho gh$$

where P = fluid pressure (measured in pascals, Pa)
ρ = density of the fluid
g = acceleration due to gravity (10 m/s^2)
h = depth below the surface of the fluid

Fluid pressure is unrelated to the shape of the container in which the fluid is situated.

REVIEW OF LOGARITHMS

Understanding logarithms ("logs") is important in biology because of the definition of pH:

$$\text{pH} = -\log_{10}[\text{H}^+]$$

This equation is read as "pH is equal to the negative log to the base 10 of the hydrogen ion concentration." But what is a logarithm?

A logarithm is the exponent to which you would have to raise the base (10) to get the number in which you are interested. For example, to get the number 100, you would have to square the base (10):

$$10^2 = 100$$

The base 10 was raised to the second power; therefore, the log of 100 is 2:

$$\log 100 = 2$$

Some other simple examples include:

$10^1 = 10$ The log of 10 is 1.
$10^0 = 1$ The log of 1 is 0.
$10^{-1} = 0.1$ The log of 0.1 is -1.

What about numbers that fall between the powers of 10? If the log of 10 is 1 and the log of 100 is 2, the log of 70 would be between 1 and 2. The actual value can be looked up on a log table or ascertained with most calculators.

To calculate pH, you need to know another rule of logs that says:

$$-\log x = \log(1/x)$$

and a rule of exponents that says:

$$1/10^x = 10^{-x}$$

Suppose you have a solution whose hydrogen ion concentration $[\text{H}^+]$ is 10^{-7} mEq/L. What is the pH of this solution?

$$\text{pH} = -\log[\text{H}^+]$$
$$\text{pH} = -\log[10^{-7}]$$

Using the rule of logs, this can be rewritten as

$$\text{pH} = \log(1/10^{-7})$$

Using the rule of exponents, this can be rewritten as

$$\text{pH} = \log 10^7$$

The log of 10^7 is 7, so the solution has a pH of 7.

Natural logarithms (ln) are logs in the base e. The mathematical constant e is approximately equal to 2.7183.

APPENDIX C

Genetics

Richard D. Hill, *University of Texas*

WHAT IS DNA?

Deoxyribonucleic acid (DNA) is the macromolecule that stores the information necessary to build structural and functional cellular components. It also provides the basis for inheritance when DNA is passed from parent to offspring. The union of these concepts about DNA allows us to devise a working definition of a gene. A **gene** (1) is a segment of DNA that codes for the synthesis of a protein, and (2) acts as a unit of inheritance that can be transmitted from generation to generation. The external appearance (**phenotype**) of an organism is determined to a large extent by the genes it inherits (**genotype**). Thus, one can begin to see how variation at the DNA level can cause variation at the level of the entire organism. These concepts form the basis of **genetics** and evolutionary theory.

NUCLEOTIDES AND BASE-PAIRING

DNA belongs to a group of macromolecules called **nucleic acids. Ribonucleic acid (RNA)** is also a nucleic acid. Nucleic acids are polymers made from monomers [*mono-*, one] called **nucleotides.** Each nucleotide consists of a *nucleoside* (a pentose, or 5-carbon, sugar covalently bound to a nitrogenous base) and a phosphoric acid with at least one phosphate group (Fig. C-1a ●). Nitrogenous bases in nucleic acids are classified as either **purines** or **pyrimidines.** The purine bases are **guanine (G)** and **adenine (A)**; the pyrimidine bases are **cytosine (C)**, **thymine (T)**, found in DNA only, and **uracil (U)**, found in RNA only. To remember which DNA bases are pyrimidines, look at the first syllable. The word "pyrimidine" and names of the DNA pyrimidine bases all have a "y" in the first syllable.

When nucleotides link together to form polymers such as DNA and RNA, the phosphate group of one nucleotide bonds covalently to the sugar group of the adjacent nucleotide (Fig. C-1b, c). The end of the polymer that has an unbound sugar is called the 3′ ("three prime") end. The end of the polymer with the unbound phosphate is called the 5′ end.

DNA STRUCTURE

In humans, many millions of nucleotides are joined together to form DNA. Eukaryotic DNA is commonly in the form of a double-stranded double helix (Fig. C-2 ●) that looks like a twisted ladder or twisted zipper. The sugar-phosphate sides, or backbone, are the same for every DNA molecule, but the sequence of the nucleotides is unique for each individual organism.

The backbone of the double helix is formed by covalent **phosphodiester bonds** that link a deoxyribose sugar from one nucleotide to the phosphate group on the adjacent nucleotide. The "rungs" of the double helix are created when the nitrogenous bases on one DNA strand form hydrogen bonds with nitrogenous bases on the adjoining DNA strand. This phenomenon is called **base-pairing.** The base-pairing rules are as follows:

1. Purines pair only with pyrimidines.
2. Guanine (G) forms three hydrogen bonds with cytosine (C) in both DNA and RNA.
3. Adenine (A) forms with two hydrogen bonds with thymine (T) in DNA or with uracil (U) in RNA.

The number of hydrogen bonds is directly related to the amount of energy necessary to break the base pair. Thus, more energy is required to break G:::C bonds (each ":" represents a hydrogen bond) than A::T bonds. This fact can be useful experimentally to make general conjectures about the similarity of two DNA samples.

The two strands of DNA are bound in **antiparallel** orientation, so that the 3′ end of one strand is bound to the 5′ end of the second strand (see Fig. C-1c). This organization has important implications for DNA replication.

DNA Replication Is Semi-Conservative

In order to be transmitted from one generation to the next, DNA must be replicated. Furthermore, the process of replication must be accurate and fast enough for a living system. The base-pairing rules for nitrogenous bases provide a means for making an appropriate replication system.

In DNA replication, special proteins unzip the DNA double helix and build new DNA by pairing new nucleotide molecules to the two existing DNA strands. The result of this replication is two double-stranded DNA molecules, such that each DNA molecule contains one DNA strand from the template and one newly synthesized DNA strand. This form of replication is called **semi-conservative replication.**

Replication of DNA is bidirectional. A portion of DNA that is "unzipped" and has enzymes performing replication is called a **replication fork** (Fig. C-2). Replication begins at many points (**replicons**), and it continues along both parent strands simultaneously until all the replication forks join.

Nucleotides bond together to form new strands of DNA with the help of an enzyme called **DNA polymerase.** DNA polymerase can only add nucleotides to the 3′ end of a growing strand of DNA. For this reason, DNA is said to replicate in a 5′ to 3′ direction. The antiparallel orientation of the DNA strands and the directionality of DNA polymerase force replication into two different modes: **leading strand replication** and **lagging strand**

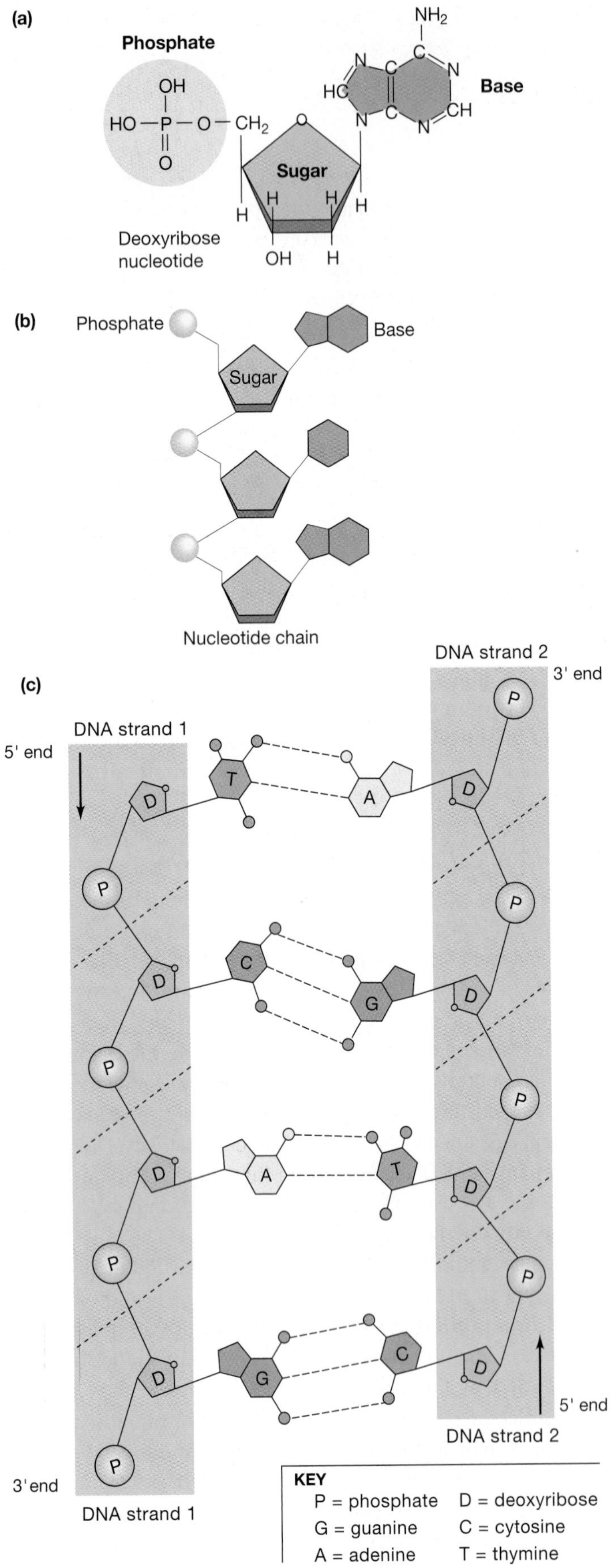
(a)
Phosphate
OH
HO—P—O—CH2
O
Sugar
Base
NH2
Deoxyribose
nucleotide
(b)
Phosphate
Sugar
Base
Nucleotide chain
(c)
DNA strand 1
5' end
3'end
DNA strand 1
DNA strand 2
3' end
5' end
DNA strand 2
KEY
P = phosphate
G = guanine
A = adenine
D = deoxyribose
C = cytosine
T = thymine

● **FIGURE C-1** ***Nucleotides and DNA*** **(a)** A nucleotide is composed of a pentose sugar, a nitrogenous base, and a phosphate group. **(b)** Nucleotides link sugar to phosphate to form nucleic acids. The end with an unbound sugar is designated the 3′ end; the end with the unbound phosphate is the 5′ end. **(c)** Hydrogen binding between complementary base pairs links two nucleotide strands to form the double helix of DNA. Adenine always pairs to thymine, and guanine pairs to cytosine.

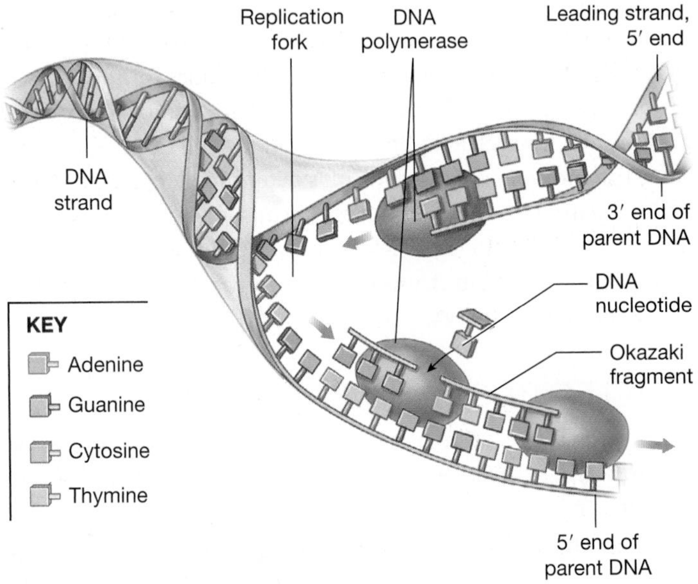
Replication fork
DNA polymerase
Leading strand, 5′ end
DNA strand
3′ end of parent DNA
DNA nucleotide
Okazaki fragment
5′ end of parent DNA
KEY
Adenine
Guanine
Cytosine
Thymine

● **FIGURE C-2** ***DNA replication***

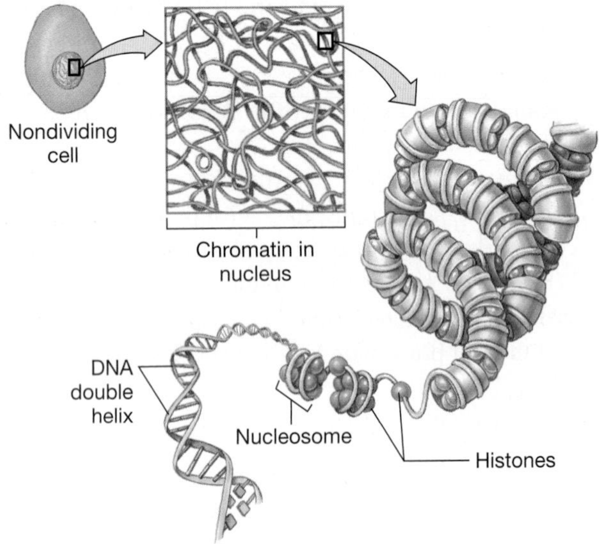
Nondividing cell
Chromatin in nucleus
DNA double helix
Nucleosome
Histones

● **FIGURE C-3** ***Levels of organization of DNA***

TABLE C-1 The Amino Acids of the Human Body

Each amino acid has both a three-letter abbreviation of its name and a single-letter abbreviation, used to spell out the sequence of amino acids in large proteins. The essential amino acids are marked with a star. These nine amino acids cannot be made by the body and must be obtained from the diet.

AMINO ACID	THREE-LETTER ABBREVIATION	ONE-LETTER SYMBOL
Alanine	Ala	A
Arginine	Arg	R
Asparagine	Asn	N
Asparagine or aspartic acid	Asx	B
Aspartic acid	Asp	D
Cysteine	Cys	C
Glutamic acid	Glu	E
Glutamine	Gln	Q
Glutamine or glutamic acid	Glx	Z
Glycine	Gly	G
*Histidine	His	H
*Isoleucine	Ile	I
*Lysine	Lys	K
*Methionine	Met	M
*Phenylalanine	Phe	F
Proline	Pro	P
Serine	Ser	S
*Threonine	Thr	T
*Tryptophan	Trp	W
*Tyrosine	Tyr	Y
*Valine	Val	V

*Essential amino acids

replication. The DNA polymerase can replicate continuously along only one parent strand of DNA: the parent strand in the 3′ to 5′ orientation. The DNA replicated continuously is called the **leading strand.**

The DNA replication along the other parent strand is discontinuous because of the strand's 5′ to 3′ orientation. DNA replication on this strand occurs in short fragments called **Okazaki fragments** that are synthesized in the direction away from the replication fork. Another enzyme known as **DNA ligase** later connects these fragments into a continuous strand. The DNA replicated in this way is called the **lagging strand.** Because the 5′ ends of the lagging strand of DNA cannot be replicated by DNA polymerase, a specialized enzyme called **telomerase** has arisen to replicate the 5′ ends.

Much of the accuracy of DNA replication comes from base pairing, but on occasion, mistakes in replication happen. However, several quality control mechanisms are in place to keep the error rate at 1 error/10^9 to 10^{12} base pairs. **Genome** (the entire amount of DNA in an organism) sizes in eukaryotes range from 10^9 to 10^{11} base pairs per genome, so this error rate is low enough to prevent many lethal mutations, yet still allows genetic variation to arise.

APPENDIX D Anatomical Positions of the Body

ANTERIOR (situated in front of): in humans, toward the front of the body (see VENTRAL).
POSTERIOR (situated behind): in humans, toward the back of the body (see DORSAL).
MEDIAL (middle, as in *median strip*): located nearer to the midline of the body (the line that divides the body into mirror-image halves)
LATERAL (side, as in a *football lateral*): located toward the sides of the body
DISTAL (distant): farther away from the point of reference or from the center of the body
PROXIMAL (closer, as in *proximity*): closer to the center of the body
SUPERIOR (higher): located toward the head or the upper part of the body
INFERIOR (lower): located away from the head or from the upper part of the body
PRONE: lying on the stomach, face downward
SUPINE: lying on the back, face up
DORSAL: refers to the back of the body
VENTRAL: refers to the front of the body
IPSILATERAL: on the same side as
CONTRALATERAL: on the opposite side from

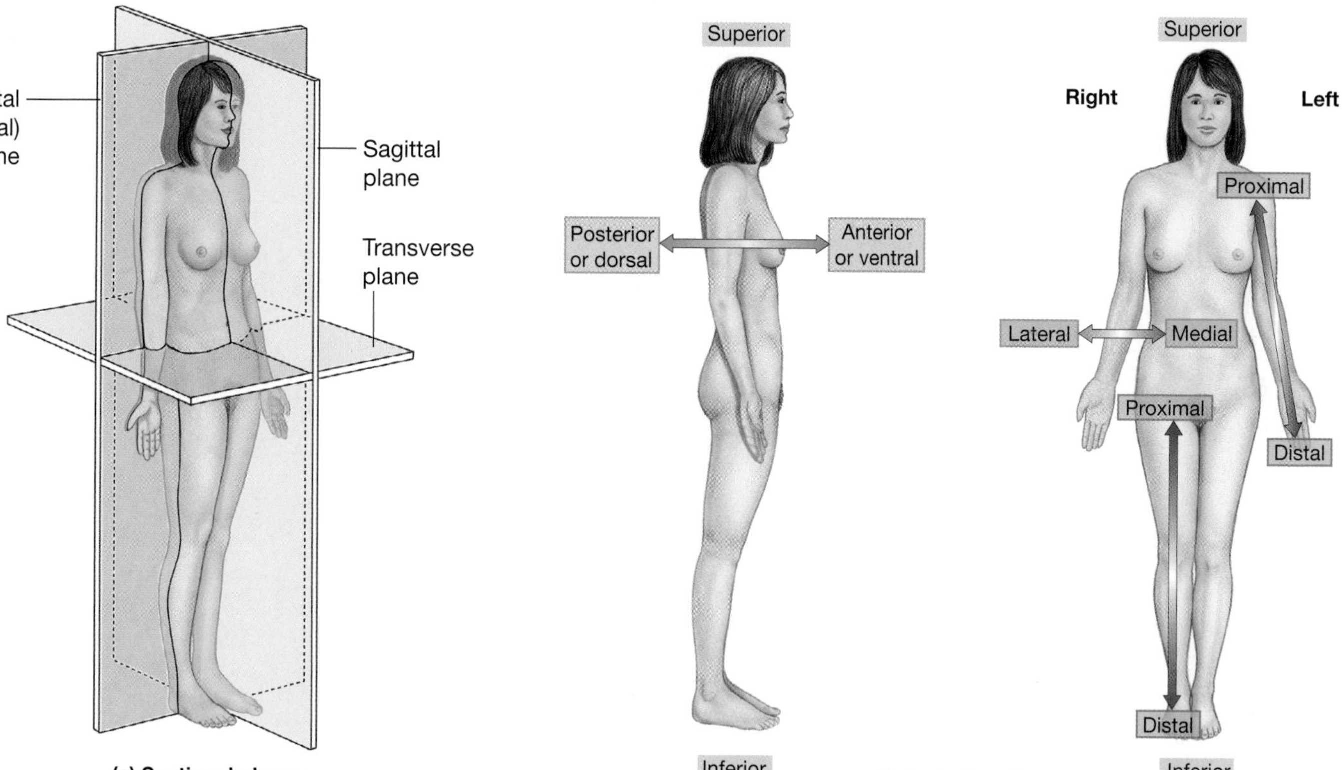

(a) Sectional planes (b) Body directions

Glossary/Index

NOTE: A *t* following a page number indicates tabular material and an *f* indicates a figure.

cytosolic receptors, 182, 183*f*
cytotoxic cell, 788, 789*f*
cytotoxic T cell A lymphocyte that kills its target cells (Ch 24), 789*f*, 799, 799–800, 799*f*, 801–802, 802*f*

Da. *See* dalton
DAG. *See* diacylglycerol
Dalton, John, 22
dalton (Da) 1 dalton = 1 atomic mass unit (Ch 2), 22
Dalton's Law The total pressure of a mixture of gases is determined by the sum of the pressures of the individual gases (Ch 17), 576, 576*t*, 577*t*
darbepoietin, 561, 565
data Information or facts gathered during an experiment (Ch 1), 10
daughter cells, A-25*f*
daughter chromosome, A-25*f*
dB. *See* decibel
D cell Pancreatic endocrine cell that secretes somatostatin (Ch 21, 22), 711*f*, 712, 712*f*, 713, 736, 737*f*
DDAVP Synonym for one form of vasopressin (Ch 21), 705
ddC, 785
dead space Those portions of the respiratory system that do not exchange gases with the blood (Ch 17), 587, 587*f*, 588
deafness (hearing loss), 361–362
  noise damage and, 355
deaminase, 104*t*
deamination Removal of an amino group from a molecule (Ch 4, 22), 104, 114, 114*f*, 736
1-deamino-8-D-arginine vasopressin (DDAVP), 705
decibel (dB) Measure of sound wave intensity (Ch 10), 355, 357*f*
deciliter (dL) 1/10 of a liter or 100 mL (Ch 2), 37
declarative memory Memory that depends on the use of higher level cognitive skills such as inference, comparison, and evaluation. Synonym: explicit memory (Ch 9), 324, 324*t*
deep sleep, 319, 319*f*
deep somatic pain, 347–348
defecation, 689, 716
defecation reflex, 689, 716
degenerative diseases, 87
deglutition Swallowing (Ch 21), 709, 710*f*
degradation
  hormone, 221
  protein, 44
degranulation Process in which immune cells release the contents of their granules (Ch 24), 788, 792, 796, 797*f*, 800, 801*f*, 803*f*
dehydratases, 104*t*
dehydration, 159, 569, 669–672, 671*f*
  avoidance behavior in prevention of, 668
  diabetes mellitus and, 655, 743, 744*f*
  diarrhea causing, 653, 669, 717–718
  exercise and, 822
  homeostatic response to, 669–672, 671*f*
  pathological, 670*t*
dehydration reaction, 104, 104*t*
dehydration synthesis Reaction in which two molecules are joined with the loss of a water molecule (Ch 4), 104
  in protein synthesis, 124
dehydroepiandrosterone (DHEA), 759*f*, 760
dehydrogenase, 104*t*
deiodinase Tissue enzyme that converts T_4 to T_3 by removal of an iodine (Ch 23), 765
delayed gastric emptying, 694
delayed hypersensitivity reaction Allergic reaction mediated by T cells that may take several days to develop (Ch 24), 803
delta (δ) chain, 605
delta wave High-amplitude, low-frequency brain waves of deep sleep (Ch 9), 319, 319*f*
dementia, 325
demyelinating disease Disease in which myelin is destroyed, slowing the conduction of action potentials (Ch 8), 271*f*, 272
denaturation, 43, 44*f*, 101, 711
  pH changes causing, 672
dendrite Thin, branched processes that receive and transfer incoming information to an integrating region within the neuron (Ch 8), 249, 250*f*, 251, 251*f*
dendritic cell Antigen-presenting immune cells with long, thin processes (Ch 24), 788, 789*f*, 790
dendritic spine Projections of the dendrite membrane that increase surface area (Ch 8), 251, 285, 285*f*
denervation hypersensitivity Up-regulation of neurotransmitter receptors following denervation creates greater than expected response to exogenous neurotransmitter (Ch 11), 396
dense bodies Attachment proteins for smooth muscle actin fibers (Ch 12), 434, 435*f*
dense connective tissue, 81, 81*f*, 82*t*, 83*f*
deoxygenated blood, 470
deoxyribonucleic acid. *See* DNA
deoxyribose, 33*f*, 34, A-24*f*
dependent variable The Y-axis variable that is dependent on the manipulated or independent variable (Ch 1), 8, 10
dephosphorylation, 185
  in smooth muscle relaxation, 436, 437*f*
depolarization A decrease in the membrane potential difference of a cell (Ch 8, 14, 18), 169, 169*f*, 257
  action potential and, 262*f*, 263
    demyelination affecting, 271*f*, 272
    sodium channels and, 263, 264*f*, 265*f*
  in cardiac cycle, 491, 493*f*
  graded potential and, 258, 259, 260, 260*f*
  of myocardial autorhythmic cell, 485–486, 488–489, 489*f*, 490*f*
  of myocardial contractile cell, 484
depression (mood disorder), 287, 322
  exercise and, 823–824
depression (synaptic), long-term, 286, 287
depth of field, 368
dermis, 86*f*
descending colon, 716, 717*f*
descending limb of loop of Henle, 625, 627*f*
descending tract Neurons that carry information from the brain to the spinal cord (Ch 9), 307, 307*f*, 310, 461
descending ventricles, 301, 304*f*
desensitization Reversible form of receptor down-regulation achieved using modulators (Ch 6), 194
desmopressin A form of vasopressin (Ch 16), 657
desmosome A type of cell-to-cell junction (Ch 3, 14), 73*f*, 74, 75*f*, 86*f*
  in intercalated disk, 481, 481*f*
deuterium Hydrogen atom with atomic mass of 2 (Ch 2), 21*f*, 22
dextran Glucose storage polymer of yeast and bacteria (Ch 2), 28, 29*f*
dextrose A six-carbon sugar; also known as glucose (Ch 2), 28
DHP receptor. *See* dihydropyridine (DHP) receptor
DHT. *See* dihydrotestosterone
diabetes insipidus Disease characterized by lack of vasopressin (Ch 4, 20), 195*t*
diabetes mellitus Disease characterized by lack of or abnormal action of insulin (Ch 1, 4, 6, 7, 10, 15, 19, 20, 21, 22, 24, 25, 26), 5, 179, 182, 195, 198, 201, 205, 210, 216, 217, 623, 655, 731, 742–747, 744*f*, 745*f*, 805*t*, 806
  autonomic neuropathy and, 348, 396
  cardiovascular disease and, 536–537, 537, 746, 746–747
  chromium and, 24
  delayed gastric emptying and, 694
  discovery of insulin and, 217
  drugs in treatment of, 195, 746, 746*t*
  exercise and, 746, 822–823, 823*f*
  gastroparesis and, 694
  gestational, 858
  hemoglobin monitoring and, 555
  kidneys and, 631, 638, 655
  metabolic syndrome and, 746–747
  neuronal function affected in, 306
  osmotic diuresis and, 655
  type 1, 182, 195, 210, 743, 743–745, 744*f*, 805*t*, 806
  type 2, 182, 195, 210, 743, 745–746, 745*f*
    agouti mice as model for, 763
  urine testing in, 623
diabetic autonomic neuropathy Disturbances of neuronal function as a complication of diabetes mellitus (Ch 11), 348, 396
diabetic gastroparesis, 694
diabetic ketoacidosis, 745. *See also* ketoacidosis
diabetic nephropathy, 631
diabetic neuropathy, 348, 396
diabetic retinopathy, 515
diacylglycerol (DAG) A second messenger (Ch 6), 185*t*, 186*t*, 188, 188*f*
dialysis, 637
diaphragm (birth control), 854, 854*t*
diaphragm (muscle) The skeletal muscle that forms the floor of the thoracic cage (Ch 17), 54, 55*f*, 476*f*, 477*f*, 570, 572*f*, 579, 580, 580*f*, 581
diaphysis The shaft of a long bone (Ch 23), 772, 772*f*
diarrhea Excessive amounts of watery stool (Ch 6, 20, 21), 195*t*, 653, 669, 688, 716, 717–718
diastole The time during which cardiac muscle relaxes (Ch 14), 494, 494–495, 496*f*, 499*f*
diastolic pressure Lowest pressure in the circulatory system, associated with relaxation of the ventricles (Ch 15), 516, 518*f*
Dicer, 119
diencephalon Brain portion between brain stem and cerebrum, consisting of thalamus and hypothalamus (Ch 9), 300*f*, 301, 309*f*, 311, 311*f*
diet
  growth and, 769
  metabolic rate and, 728
dietary fat. *See also* lipid
  as energy source, 733–734, 733*f*
dietary fiber, 703
diet-induced thermogenesis An increase in resting metabolic rate following a meal (Ch 22), 728, 748
differential white cell count (Ch 16), 552, 552*f*
differentiation Developmental process during which cells take on different forms and functions (Ch 3), 62, 85
  nerve cell, 255
diffuse endocrine system Hormones secreted by isolated endocrine cells (Ch 7), 217
diffuse lymphoid tissue, 788
diffuse modulatory system Clusters of brain stem neurons that influence large areas of the brain (Ch 9), 317–318, 317*t*, 318*f*
diffusion Movement of molecules from an area of higher concentration to an area of lower concentration (Ch 5, 15, 17, 18), 136–141, 137*f*, 138*f*, 139*t*, 140*f*
  across membranes, 136, 137*f*, 139–141, 139*t*, 140*f*
  capillary exchange by, 528
  energy of molecular movement for, 136–139, 137*f*, 138*f*, 139*t*
  equilibrium and, 137, 138*f*
  facilitated, 141, 145–146, 145*f*, 146*f*
  Fick's law of, 140–141, 140*f*, 598
  of gases, 598–599, 599*f*
  properties of, 137–138, 139*t*
  rate of, 138, 139–140, 139*t*
  simple, 139–141, 139*t*, 140*f*
diffusion barrier, of enteric nervous system, 701

during contraction, 412–413, 413–415, 414*f*, 415–416, 416*f*
in vitro motility assay for, 417
smooth muscle, 434, 435, 435*f*, 436, 437*f*
myosin ATPase, 415
smooth muscle, 435, 436*f*
myosin-binding site, 409
myosin crossbridge. *See* crossbridge
myosin light chain, 434, 435, 436*f*
myosin light chain kinase (MLCK) Enzyme that phosphorylates light protein chains of myosin in smooth muscle (Ch 12), 435, 436*f*
myosin light protein chain, 434, 435, 436*f*
myosin phosphatase Enzyme that dephosphorylates light protein chains of myosin in smooth muscle (Ch 12), 436, 437*f*
myotatic unit Collection of synergistic and antagonistic muscles that act in a coordinated fashion to control a single joint (Ch 13), 454–455
myxedema, 766, 766*f*

Na^+. *See* sodium ion
Na^+-Ca^+ exchanger. *See* sodium-calcium exchanger
Na^+-glucose secondary active symporter (transporter). *See* sodium-glucose secondary active symporter (transporter)
Na^+-H^+ exchanger. *See* sodium-hydrogen exchanger
Na^+-K^+-ATPase. *See* sodium-potassium ATPase
Na^+-K^+-$2Cl^-$ transporter. *See* sodium-potassium-chloride symporter (transporter)
nAchr. *See* nicotinic receptor
NaCl. *See* sodium chloride
NAD (nicotinamide adenine dinucleotide) Molecule that captures and transfers energy with high-energy electrons (Ch 2), 33*f*, 34, 111
NADH, 99, 99*f*, 105, 107, 108, 109*f*, 111, 111*f*, 113, 113*f*
NADPH, 99, 99*f*, 105
naive lymphocyte A lymphocyte that has not yet been exposed to its specific antigen (Ch 24), 787, 794
nasal cavity, 572*f*
nasolacrimal duct, 366*f*
natriuresis Sodium (Na^+) loss in the urine (Ch 20), 665
natriuretic peptide, 665–666, 666*f*
as vasodilator, 522*t*
natural killer cell (NK cell) A type of lymphocyte that apparently attacks certain tumor and virus-infected cells (Ch 24), 789*f*, 790, 792, 794, 799*f*, 802
natural logarithm, B-3
nausea, 694, 718
NCAM. *See* nerve-cell adhesion molecule
NCX. *See* sodium-calcium exchanger
near point of accommodation, 369
near-sightedness (myopia), 370, 371*f*
nebulin Inelastic giant protein that aligns filaments of the sarcomere (Ch 12), 409, 410*f*, 411*f*, 412, 414*f*
necrosis Cell death due to toxins, physical damage, or lack of oxygen. The dying cell releases enzymes that may damage neighboring cells (Ch 3), 85
negative feedback A homeostatic feedback loop designed to keep the system at or near a setpoint (Ch 6, 7, 13), 203, 203*f*, 235, 235*f*, 236, 447
endocrine pathology and, 235–236, 235*f*, 237*f*
in endocrine reflex, 226, 227, 227*f*
hypersecretion and, 235, 237*f*
hyposecretion and, 235, 237*f*
long- and short-loop, 231, 231*f*, 760*f*
in neural reflex, 447
in reproduction control, 836–837, 837*f*, 837*t*
neostigmine, 395*t*
nephrin Protein of podocyte filtration slit membrane (Ch 19), 631
nephron Microscopic tubule that is the functional unit of the kidney (Ch 19), 624, 624–625, 626–627*f*
distal, 625, 654–655, 655*f*, 678, 678*f*
function of, 625–629, 628*f*. *See also* kidney(s), functions of
structure of, 624–625, 626–627*f*
nephropathy, diabetic, 631
Nernst equation The equation that determines the equilibrium potential for a single ion based on the ion concentrations inside and outside the cell (Ch 5, 8), 168, 256, 256*t*
nerve A collection of axons running between the central nervous system and the peripheral target cells (Ch 3, 8), 84, 84*t*, 250
repairing damage to, 288*f*, 289
nerve cell. *See* neuron
nerve-cell adhesion molecule (NCAM) Membrane proteins in nerve cells that aid cell growth (Ch 3), 72, 72*t*, 287
nerve conduction test, 273, 275
nerve cord, 298, 298*f*
nerve ending, free, 335, 335*f*, 345, 345*f*, 345*t*
nociceptive pain mediated by, 346
nerve fiber Synonym: axon (Ch 8), 247*t*. *See also* axon
somatosensory, 346–347, 346*t*
nerve net, 297, 298*f*
nerve root, 306, 307*f*
nervous control, 198–209, 199*f*
neural/neuroendocrine/endocrine comparisons and, 205–209, 206*f*, 207*f*, 208*t*, 209*t*
nervous reflex. *See* neural reflex
nervous system Network of billions or trillions of nerve cells linked together in a highly organized manner to form the rapid control system of the body (Ch 1, 6, 8, 9, 10, 11, 14, 20), 2–3, 3*f*, 4*t*, 196, 247
autonomic, 247*t*, 248*f*, 249
cells of, 249–255, 250*f*, 251*f*, 254*f*. *See also specific type*
cell-to-cell communication and, 180, 181*f*, 273–281
integration of information and, 281–289, 282*f*, 283*f*
chemical signals in development of, 287–288, 288*f*
endocrine reflex and, 228. *See also* neuroendocrine reflex
evolution of, 297–299, 298*f*
immune system/endocrine system interactions and, 806–808, 807*f*, 808*f*
modulation of heart rate and, 486–487, 487*f*, 500–501, 500*f*
movement integration and, 458–463, 459*f*, 459*t*, 460*f*, 461*f*, 462*f*
organization of, 247–249, 248*f*
pH changes and, 673
reflex control systems and, 198–209, 199*f*
neural/neuroendocrine/endocrine comparisons and, 205–209, 206*f*, 207*f*, 208*t*, 209*t*
role of, 196
net diffusion. *See* diffusion
net filtration pressure, glomerular filtration and, 631–632
net free energy change of reaction, 98
reversibility and, 100, 100*f*
neural circuit, 309
neural crest cells Embryonic cells that form the peripheral nervous system (Ch 9), 299*f*, 300
neural information transfer. *See also* synaptic transmission
integration of, 281–289, 282*f*, 283*f*
neural networks, 247, 298, 299, 309
emergent properties of, 247, 297
in spinal cord, 306
neural pathway, 309. *See also specific type*
multiple neurons in, 283–284, 283*f*, 284*f*, 285*f*
neural plate, 299, 299*f*
neural reflex, 206, 206*f*, 207*f*, 208, 208–209, 208*t*, 209*t*, 247, 273, 314, 314*f*, 447–448, 447*t*, 448*f*
CNS as integrating center for, 248*f*, 249, 447
neural signal
demyelination affecting, 271*f*, 272
inactivation of, 280–281, 281*f*
neural stem cell, 85–88, 253–255, 300
neural tissue, 84, 84*t*
metabolic requirements of, 305–306
neural tube Embryonic cells that develop into the CNS (Ch 9), 299–300, 299*f*, 300*f*, 301
neurocrine Any molecule secreted by a nerve cell (Ch 6, 8), 180, 275, 275–278, 276*t*
neuroeffector junction Synapse between an autonomic neuron and its target muscle or gland (Ch 11), 392
neuroendocrine control Signal molecule secreted by a neuron into the blood, where it functions as a hormone (Ch 6), 206*f*, 209. *See also* neuroendocrine reflex
neuro-endocrine-immune interactions, 806–808, 807*f*, 808*f*
neuroendocrine reflex, 206*f*, 207*f*, 209, 209*t*, 226
neuroendocrine signal, 316, 317
neuroepithelium, 255
neurofilament Intermediate filament of neurons (Ch 3), 63, 65*t*
neuroglia. *See* glial cells
neurohormone A hormone that is produced and secreted by a neuron (Ch 6, 7, 9), 180, 181*f*, 206, 207*f*, 217, 228, 275
anterior pituitary, 229, 230*f*
posterior pituitary, 228–229, 229*f*
neurohormone reflex, 206, 207*f*, 209
neurohypophysis. *See* posterior pituitary gland
neuroimmunomodulation The ability of the nervous system to influence immune function (Ch 24), 806–808, 807*f*, 808*f*
prolactin and, 861
neuromodulator Chemicals that alter the response of a neuron more slowly than neurotransmitters (Ch 6, 9, 21), 180, 275, 317*t*. *See also* neurotransmitter
in enteric nervous system, 701
neuromuscular junction The synapse of a somatic motor neuron and a skeletal muscle fiber (Ch 8, 11, 12), 398–399, 399*f*
in muscle contraction, 412, 414*f*, 417–419, 418*f*
neuron A nerve cell, capable of generating and transmitting electrical signals (Ch 3, 7, 8, 9, 10), 62*f*, 84, 180, 181*f*, 247, 249–253, 250*f*, 251*f*. *See also specific type and* neural network
autonomic, 248*f*, 249, 250, 386, 388–389, 388*f*, 396
calcium affecting excitability of, 773
cell body of, 247*t*, 250–251, 250*f*
of cerebral cortex, 312, 313*f*
composition of membrane of, 57*t*
electrical signals in, 147, 247, 252–253, 252*f*
emergent properties of, 247, 297, 309
energy source for, 306
function of, 249–250
gap junctions in, 84, 247, 273–274
glial cells supporting, 253, 254*f*, 255*f*
injury to, 251, 288–289, 289*f*
metabolic requirements and, 305–306
multiple, in neural pathway, 283–284, 283*f*, 284*f*, 285*f*
nervous system evolution and, 297–298, 298*f*
pH imbalance affecting, 673
resting membrane potential of, 167
size of, speed of action potential and, 270, 270*f*
stem cell differentiation into, 255

obstructive lung disease, 591. *See also* chronic obstructive pulmonary disease
obstructive sleep apnea, 591, 614
occipital lobe, 308–309*f*, 312, 315*f*
occluding junction A cell-cell junction that prevents movement of material between cells (Ch 3), 72, 73–74, 73*f*, 75*f*
occludin proteins Proteins in tight junctions (Ch 3), 73*f*, 74, 75*f*
occlusion (blockage), 516
ocular smooth muscle, 432
oculomotor nerve, 310*t*
Oddi, sphincter of, 689
odorant, 336, 350*f*
odorant receptor, 351
off-center/on-surround field, 377
-ogen (suffix), 41, 696
OH (hydroxyl free radical), 23
ohm (ω), B-1*t*, B-2
Ohm's law, B-2
oils. *See* lipid
Okazaki fragments, C-2*f*, C-3
oleic acid, 30*f*
  taste and, 355
Olestra, 707, 718
olfaction Pertaining to the sense of smell (Ch 9, 10), 315, 315*f*, 334*t*, 338, 349–351, 350*f*, 351*f*
  sensory receptors in, 200*f*, 349, 350*f*, 351, 351*f*
    phasic, 342
olfactory bulb Part of the brain that receives input from primary olfactory neurons (Ch 10), 338, 338*f*, 349, 350*f*, 351*f*
olfactory cortex, 315, 315*f*, 338, 338*f*, 349–351, 351*f*
olfactory epithelium, 350*f*, 351
olfactory nerve, 310*t*, 338, 349, 350*f*, 351*f*
olfactory pathways, 338*f*, 351, 351*f*
olfactory receptor cells, 349, 350*f*, 351, 351*f*
olfactory tract, 349, 350*f*, 351, 351*f*
oligodendrocyte CNS glial cell that forms myelin around several axons (Ch 8), 253, 254*f*
oligopeptide (Ch 2), 31*f*, 32, 705
oligopeptide transporter, 705
-ome (suffix), 6
omeprazole, 713
-omics (suffix), 6
on-center/off-surround field, 377
oncogenic virus, 785
oncotic pressure. *See* colloid osmotic pressure
oocyte Developing female germ cells that have begun meiosis (Ch 26), 833, 834–835, 835*f*, 844, 845*t*, 846*f*
oögonia Germ cells of the ovary (Ch 26), 834, 835*f*, 844
open channel (leak channel/pore), 143*f*, 144. *See also* leak channel
open system
  diffusion in, 138
  human body as, 97
  mass balance in, 133, 133*f*
opiate/opioid peptide, 277, 348–349, 349
opioid receptor, 348–349
opsin Visual pigment forms from rhodopsin when light strikes it; opsin initiates a signal transduction cascade (Ch 10), 374*f*, 375, 376*f*
opsonins Proteins that coat pathogens to make them targets for immune cells (Ch 24), 792, 793*t*, 796, 797*f*, 800, 801, 801*f*
optic chiasm Portion of the brain where some fibers from each eye cross to opposite sides of the brain (Ch 10), 367, 378, 378*f*
optic disk Region of the retina where the optic nerve and blood vessels exit the eye (Ch 10), 367, 367*f*, 372
optic nerve, 310*t*, 367, 367*f*, 372, 373*f*, 378, 378*f*
optics The physical relationship between light and lenses (Ch 10), 368–371, 369*f*, 370*f*, 371*f*
optic tract Neurons leading from the eyes to the visual cortex (Ch 10), 308*f*, 378, 378*f*
oral cavity, 689, 690*f*
  digestion in, 708, 709*f*, 710*f*
oral contraceptive, 854–855, 854*t*
oral temperature, 748
orbit Bony cavity that protects the eye (Ch 10), 366, 366*f*
orexin, 725, 726, 726*t*
organ Group of tissues that carries out related functions (Ch 1, 3), 2, 2*f*, 87
  mechanical properties of, 7
organ of Corti Portion of the cochlea that contains the hair cells (Ch 10), 357, 359*f*
organelle Assorted intracellular structures that each take on one or more of the cell's functions (Ch 3), 7, 63, 63*f*, 64*f*, 67–70. *See also specific type*
  membranous, 63, 63*f*
  nonmembranous, 63
  in transporting epithelia, 78
organic anion transporter (OAT), 151, 645
organic molecules Molecules that contain carbon (Ch 2), 28
organisms, 2, 2*f*
  living, properties of, 94, 94*t*
organophosphate insecticides, 395
organotherapy, 217
organ systems, 2, 2*f*, 4*t*
orgasm A series of involuntary muscular contractions during the sex act, accompanied by sensations of intense pleasure (Ch 26), 852
origin of a muscle The end of the muscle attached closest to the trunk or to the more stationary bone (Ch 12), 408
oropharynx receptor An unidentified receptor that monitors oral water intake (Ch 20), 667
orphan receptor One that has no known ligand (Ch 6), 192
orthostatic hypotension Low blood pressure that occurs when going from the supine position to standing up (Ch 15), 535, 536*f*
oscillation, around setpoint, 203, 203*f*
osmolality Concentration expressed as osmoles solute per kilogram of water (Ch 5), 160
osmolarity Concentration expressed in osmoles per liter (Ch 5, 19, 20), 159–160, 160*t*, 163*t*, 164*t*, 651
  comparing, 160, 160*t*
  dehydration and, 671*f*, 672
  disturbances of, 668–669, 668*f*
    integrated response to, 567*f*, 652, 652*f*, 668–672, 668*f*, 670*t*, 671*f*
  extracellular fluid, 651, 659
    aldosterone secretion and, 663
  filtrate, nephron modification of, 628–629, 628*t*, 629*f*
  of intravenous solutions, 163, 164*t*
  medullary interstitial, 654, 659
  regulation of, 623, 651, 668–672, 668*f*, 670*t*, 671*f*
  rules for, 163*t*
  thirst and, 667
  tonicity differentiated from, 161
  of urine, 654–655, 655*f*
  water balance and, 657, 657*f*
osmole, 160
osmometer An instrument for measuring osmolarity of a fluid (Ch 5), 161
osmoreceptor Sensory receptor that monitors extracellular fluid osmolarity (Ch 20, 21), 200*f*, 387, 657, 658*f*, 667, 670*t*, 714
osmosis The movement of water across a membrane in response to a solute concentration gradient (Ch 5), 159, 159*f*
osmotic diarrhea, 718
osmotic diuresis Water loss in the urine due to unreabsorbed solute in the tubule lumen (Ch 20, 22), 655, 743, 744*f*
osmotic equilibrium, 134, 159, 159*f*
osmotic pressure The pressure that exactly opposes a given concentration gradient (Ch 5, 15, 24, Appendix B), 159, 159*f*, 529, 549, B-2
  colloid, 529, 530*f*
    edema and, 531, 532
    glomerular filtration and, 631, 631*f*
osmotic principles, B-2
osteoblast Cells that produce bone (Ch 3, 23), 82*t*, 771–772, 772*f*, 774
osteocalcin, 772
osteoclast Large, mobile, multinucleate cell that is responsible for bone resorption (Ch 23), 82*t*, 774, 774*f*, 775, 788
osteocyte A less active form of osteoblast (Ch 23), 772
osteoid, 772
osteonectin, 772
osteopenia, 777
osteoporosis Pathological condition marked by bone resorption exceeding bone deposition (Ch 23), 777
osteoprotegerin, 775
otitis media Bacterial infection of the middle ear (Ch 10), 354
otolith Small calcium carbonate crystals whose movement activates hair cells for equilibrium (Ch 10), 363, 364*f*, 365*f*
otolith membrane Gelatinous mass within which otoliths are embedded (Ch 10), 363, 364*f*
otolith organ The utricle and saccule of the vestibular apparatus that sense linear acceleration and head position (Ch 10), 363
ouabain Cardiac glycoside that specifically inhibits the Na^+-K^+-ATPase (Ch 14), 503
outer ear, 354, 356*f*
outer segment, 374, 374*f*, 375
output signal, 198, 199*f*
ova. *See* ovum
oval window Membrane between the middle ear and cochlea where sound is converted from sound waves to fluid waves (Ch 10), 355, 356*f*, 358*f*, 359*f*
  in sound transduction, 356, 358*f*
ovarian cycle The monthly cycle of egg development in the ovary (Ch 26), 844, 847, 847*t*, 848*f*
ovarian follicle, 844, 845*t*, 847–850, 847*t*, 848*f*, 849*f*
ovary The female gonad (Ch 26), 218–219*f*, 224*f*, 829, 844, 845*f*
  development of, 831, 831*t*, 832, 832*f*
overshoot, 262, 262*f*
oviduct. *See* Fallopian tube
ovulation Release of a mature egg from its follicle in the ovary (Ch 26), 835, 847, 848*f*, 850, 851
ovum The female gamete. Synonym: egg (Ch 26), 62*f*, 829, 833, 845*t*, 847*t*, 849*f*
  fertilization of, 829, 835, 835*f*, 844, 855–856, 856*f*, 857*f*
    in vitro, 855, 860
oxaloacetate, 110, 111*f*
oxidase, 104*t*
oxidation, 103–104, 104*t*
  beta, 115, 115*f*, 736, 741
    exercise and, 816
oxidation-reduction reaction Involves the transfer of electrons or protons (H^+) between chemicals (Ch 4), 103–104, 104*t*
oxidative-glycolytic muscle fibers, 422–423, 424*t*
oxidative muscle fibers, 422–423, 423*f*, 424*t*
oxidative pathway, 107
oxidative phosphorylation Mitochondrial pathway that consumes oxygen and high-energy electrons and produces ATP and water (Ch 4), 112, 112*f*
oxidative stress, 253

pulmonary circulation That portion of the circulation that carries blood to and from the lungs (Ch 14, 17), 471, 575–576
pulmonary edema Excessive interstitial fluid volume in the lungs (Ch 18), 539, 576, 602
alveolar ventilation/gas exchange and, 602, 602*f*
high-altitude (HAPE), 603
pulmonary fibrosis, 584–585
alveolar ventilation/gas exchange and, 601–602, 602*f*
pulmonary function tests, 578, 591
pulmonary trunk The single artery that receives blood from the right ventricle; splits into left and right pulmonary arteries (Ch 14, 16), 478, 478*t*, 575
pulmonary valve The semilunar valve between the right ventricle and the pulmonary trunk (Ch 14), 477*f*, 479, 480*f*
pulmonary vein Vessel that carries well-oxygenated blood from the lung to the left heart (Ch 14), 470, 470*f*, 476*f*, 477*f*, 478*t*, 575
pulmonary ventilation, total, 587–589, 587*f*, 588*t*, 589*t*
pulse Pressure wave that is transmitted through the fluid of the cardiovascular system (Ch 15), 516
pulse generator Region of the hypothalamus that coordinates the pulsatile secretion of GnRH (Ch 26), 838
pulse oximeter, 601
pulse pressure The strength of the pulse wave, defined as the systolic pressure minus the diastolic pressure (Ch 15), 516, 518, 518*f*
pumps. *See* ATPase
pupil, 366*f*, 367, 367–368, 367*f*
autonomic control of, 390*f*
pupillary reflex Constriction of the pupil in response to light (Ch 10), 367–368
purine, 33*f*, 34, 639, A-23
as neurotransmitter, 276*t*, 277
receptors for, 276*t*, 277
purinergic receptor A receptor that binds to purines, such as AMP or ATP (Ch 8), 276*t*, 277
Purkinje fiber Specialized myocardial cell that rapidly conducts electrical signals to the apex of the heart (Ch 14), 488, 490*f*
pus, 791
push-pull control, 732, 732*f*
P wave Wave of the ECG that represents atrial depolarization (Ch 14), 491, 492*f*, 493*f*
pyloric sphincter. *See* pylorus
pyloric valve, 689
pylorus The region of increased muscle tone separating the stomach and small intestine (Ch 21), 689, 690*f*, 709*f*
pyramid Region of the medulla where neurons from one side of the body cross to the other (Ch 9, 13), 311, 461, 461*f*
pyramidal cell, 317
pyramidal tract Descending pathways for movement that pass through the pyramids (Ch 13), 461
pyrimidine, 33*f*, 34, A-23
pyrogen Fever-causing substances (Ch 22, 24), 751, 789, 793*t*
pyruvate
in citric acid cycle, 110–111, 110*f*, 111*f*, 113*f*
in glycolysis, 108–109, 108*f*, 109*f*, 113*f*, 731*f*
in lactate production, 109, 110*f*, 731*f*
PYY_{3-36}, 726*t*

QRS complex Wave complex that represents ventricular depolarization and atrial repolarization (Ch 14), 491, 492*f*, 494, 499*f*
QT interval From the beginning of the Q wave to the end of the T wave. Corresponds to ventricular contraction (Ch 12), 492*f*
long, 258, 494
quaternary structure, of protein Arrangement of a protein with multiple peptide chains (Ch 2), 31*f*, 32–33
quiet breathing, 578, 579, 580, 581, 581*f*, 584
quisqualate, 276*t*
Q wave First wave of ventricular depolarization (Ch 14), 491, 492*f*, 493*f*

RAAS. *See* renin-angiotensin-aldosterone system
rabies, 783
Rabs, 154
radiant heat gain, 748, 748*f*
radiant heat loss, 748, 748*f*
radiation Energy emitted by unstable isotopes (Ch 2), 23
radiation (heat), 748, 748*f*
radioactive iodine, 23, 234, 768
radioisotope Unstable isotopes that emit energy (Ch 2), 23
radio waves, 371
raloxifene, 777
ramping, 614, 614*f*
ranitidine, 276*t*, 713
RANKL, 775
Ranvier, nodes of Unmyelinated regions on myelinated axons (Ch 8), 253, 254*f*, 255*f*
rapid eye movement sleep, 319, 319*f*
Ray, Felix, 334
reabsorption Movement of filtered material from the lumen of the nephron to the blood (Ch 19), 625, 628, 628*f*, 635–639, 635*f*, 636*f*, 637*f*, 638*f*
active and passive, 635–637, 635*f*, 636*f*
of bicarbonate, 676–678, 677*f*
peritubular capillary pressures and, 639
saturation and, 637–639, 637*f*, 638*f*
urine concentration and, 654–655, 655*f*
vasopressin affecting, 655–657, 656*f*, 657*f*
reactant, 97, 97*t*
reaction rate, 45, 45*f*, 97
enzymes affecting, 45, 102
substrate concentration affecting, 44, 102
reactive hyperemia An increase in tissue blood flow following a period of low perfusion (Ch 15), 523*f*, 524
reactive oxygen species, 253
receiving segment, 694, 694*f*
receptive aphasia Inability to understand spoken or visual information due to damage to Wernicke's area (Ch 9), 326
receptive field The region within which a sensory neuron can sense a stimulus (Ch 10), 336–338, 337*f*
receptive relaxation, 711
receptor (1) A cellular protein that binds to a ligand; (2) A cell or group of cells that continually monitor changes in the internal or external environment (Ch 2, 5, 6, 10, 11), 39, 141, 142*f*, 181, 182, 183*f*, 199–200, 200*f*, 201, 202*f*
agonists and antagonists and, 193–194, 193*f*
conversion of stimuli by, 336
diseases/drugs associated with abnormalities of, 195–196, 195*t*
down-regulation of, 194, 236
hormone, 180, 181*f*, 220
abnormal, 236
isoforms of, 194, 194*f*
membrane, 141, 142*f*, 182, 183*f*, 190*f*
multiple
neurotransmitter amplification and, 278–279
for one ligand, 194, 194*f*
multiple ligands for, 193
multiple meanings for, 199, 200*f*
neuroimmunomodulation and, 807
nociceptors, 346, 456, 456*f*
odorant, 351
phasic, 341–342, 342*f*
in reflex control pathway, 199, 199–200, 199*f*, 200*f*, 201, 202*f*
sensitivity of, 335–336
sensory, 86*f*, 199, 199–200, 199*f*, 200*f*, 201, 202*f*, 248, 248*f*, 334–335, 335*f*
for somatic senses, 335, 335*f*, 343
specificity and competition and, 193
taste, 200*f*, 352–353, 352*f*, 354*f*
temperature, 200*f*, 336, 336*t*, 346, 387
termination of activity of, 195
tonic, 341, 342*f*
touch, 344–345, 345*f*, 345*t*
up-regulation of, 194–195
receptor adaptation A repeated stimulus loses its ability to stimulate a receptor (Ch 10), 341–342, 342*f*
receptor-channel, 182, 183*f*, 189, 189*f*
receptor-enzyme A class of membrane proteins that bind ligands on the extracellular side and activate enzymes (usually tyrosine kinase or guanylyl cyclase) on the intracellular side (Ch 6), 182, 183*f*, 186, 187*f*
receptor-mediated endocytosis A ligand binds to a membrane protein, which triggers endocytosis of the membrane-receptor complex (Ch 5, 22), 153, 153*f*, 734
receptor potential Graded potential in a special senses receptor (Ch 10), 336
receptor proteins, 181, 182*f*, 183*f*. *See also* receptor
diseases/drugs associated with alterations in, 195–196, 195*t*
recessive genetic disorder, 102, 116, 126
reciprocal inhibition The relaxation of antagonistic muscles during a contraction reflex (Ch 13), 455, 455*f*, 456
recognition of self Ability of the immune system to recognize self and not create an immune response. This ability is lost in autoimmune diseases (Ch 24), 805–806
recombinant human EPO, blood doping and, 561, 565
recombinant human growth hormone (hGH), 770, 770–771
recording electrode, 166, 166*f*
recruitment Addition of motor units to increase the force of contraction in a muscle (Ch 12), 427
rectal temperature, 748
rectifying synapse, 273
rectum The distal segment of the large intestine (Ch 21), 689, 690*f*, 709*f*, 716, 717*f*
red blood cell (RBC). *See* erythrocyte
red blood cell antigens, 804–805, 804*f*, 805*t*
red blood cell membrane, composition of, 57*t*
red bone marrow, 551
red cell count, 552*f*
"red muscle" Muscle that has lots of mitochondria and good blood supply so that it can carry out oxidative metabolism (Ch 12), 423, 424*t*
red pulp, 787*f*
reduced molecule, 103
reductase, 104*t*
5-α-reductase Enzyme that converts testosterone to DHT (Ch 26), 831, 836*f*
reduction reaction, 103–104, 104*t*
reference electrode, 166, 166*f*
referred pain Pain that is felt in a location away from the actual site of the stimulus (Ch 10), 348, 348*f*
reflex Any long-distance pathway that receives input about a change, integrates the information, and uses the nervous system, endocrine system, or both to react appropriately (Ch 6, 11, 13), 447. *See also* reflex control pathway
abnormal, 451
autonomic, 338, 387–388, 387*f*, 388*f*, 447, 447*t*, 449, 449*f*
endocrine, 206, 206*f*, 207*f*, 208, 208*t*, 209*t*

valine, C-3*t*
valley fever, 784
Valsalva maneuver Abdominal contraction and forced expiratory movement against a closed glottis (Ch 21), 716
valve
cardiac, 469, 477*f*, 479–481, 480*f*
lymphatic, 531
venous, 469, 470*f*, 516, 518*f*
valvular stenosis, 497
van der Waals force Weak attractive force that occurs between two polar molecules or a polar molecule and an ion (Ch 2), 27, 32, 32*f*
Van Gogh, Vincent, 334
vanilloid receptor, 346
varenicline (Chantix®), for nicotine addiction, 389, 401
variability, 11
variable resistance, 514
variables
dependent, 8, 10
independent, 8, 10
regulated, 7, 196, 196*f*
Cannon's postulates describing, 196–198, 197*f*
varicella-zoster virus, 785
varicosity Swollen regions along autonomic axons that store and release neurotransmitter (Ch 8, 11), 250, 392, 392*f*, 393*f*
vasa recta Peritubular capillaries in the kidney that dip into the medulla and then go back up to the cortex, forming hairpin loops (Ch 19, 20), 625, 627*f*, 659, 661
vascular endothelial growth factor (VEGF), 516
vascular smooth muscle The smooth muscle of blood vessels (Ch 15), 432, 514, 514*f*
myogenic autoregulation of, 523
paracrines affecting contraction of, 523–524, 523*f*
sympathetic control of, 524, 525*f*
vasculature The blood vessels (Ch 14), 469. *See also* blood vessel
vas deferens Tube that carries sperm from the epididymis to the urethra. Synonym: ductus deferens (Ch 26), 839, 839*f*, 840*f*, 852
development of, 831, 831*t*, 832*f*
ligation of in vasectomy, 854
vasectomy, 854
vasoactive intestinal peptide (VIP), 702
as vasodilator, 522*t*
vasoconstriction Contraction of circular vascular smooth muscle that narrows the lumen of a blood vessel (Ch 6, 11, 14, 15, 19, 25), 194, 194*f*, 474, 514, 522*t*, 524, 525*f*
angiotensin II causing, 522*t*, 524, 665
exercise and, 818, 819, 820*f*, 821, 822
in hemostasis, 559–560, 559*f*
resistance and, 474, 474*f*, 526, 527*f*
in thermoregulation, 750, 822
vasodilation Relaxation of circular vascular smooth muscle that widens the lumen of a blood vessel (Ch 6, 11, 14, 15), 194, 194*f*, 474, 514, 522*t*, 524, 525*f*
exercise and, 819, 820*f*, 821, 821*f*, 822
nitrates causing, 192
resistance and, 474
in thermoregulation, 750, 822
vasopressin. *See* antidiuretic hormone
vasopressin receptor, 656, 657*f*
abnormal, 195*t*
vasopressin receptor antagonists, 684
vasovagal syncope Fainting due to a sudden decrease in blood pressure as a result of an emotional stimulus (Ch 15), 513, 534
vault Organelles of RNA-protein; the function of vaults is still unclear (Ch 3), 63
VC. *See* vital capacity
vegetative nervous system (Ch 11), 386. *See also* autonomic nervous system
VEGF (vascular endothelial growth factor) Growth factors that regulate angiogenesis (Ch 15), 516
veiled cell, 789*f*. *See also* dendritic cell
vein Blood vessels that return blood to the heart (Ch 14, 15), 469, 470*f*, 471, 513*f*, 514, 514*f*, 515
blood flow velocity in, 529*f*
compression of, venous return and, 502–503
pressure in, 471*f*, 516, 518*f*
sympathetic control of, 390*f*, 502
valves in, 469, 470*f*, 516, 518*f*
velocity of flow The distance a fixed volume will travel in a given period of time (Ch 14, 15), 475–478, 475*f*
in capillaries, 526, 527–528, 529*f*
velocity of muscle contraction, load and, 430, 431*f*
venae cavae, 470*f*, 471, 476*f*, 477*f*, 478*t*
blood flow velocity in, 529*f*
pressure in, 471*f*
venesection, 547
venipuncture, 515
venous blood
pH of, 600*t*
P_{O_2} and P_{CO_2} of, 600, 600*t*, 611*f*
exercise and, 818, 818*f*
venous return The amount of blood that enters the heart from the venous circulation (Ch 14, 15), 501–502, 504*f*, 505
exercise and, 819
venous sinus, in brain, 301, 302*f*, 304*f*
venous valve, 469, 470*f*, 516, 518*f*
ventilation The movement of air between the atmosphere and the lungs (Ch 17, 18, 20, 25), 570, 578–591
in acid-base balance, 675–676, 675*f*
air conditioning (warming/humidifying/filtering) and, 571–574, 575*f*
air flow/pressure gradients and, 577, 579–580
airway resistance and, 586, 586*t*
alveolar, 588–589, 588*t*, 589*t*
breathing pattern and, 588*t*, 589, 617
gas composition and, 589, 589*f*
alveolar blood flow and, 589–591, 590*f*, 590*t*
alveolar pressure and, 580–582, 580*f*, 581*f*
auscultation in evaluation of, 591
disease states and, 584–585
efficiency of, 587–589, 587*f*, 588*t*, 589*t*
exercise and, 817–818, 817*f*, 818*f*
gas composition in alveoli and, 589, 589*f*
higher brain center control of, 612*f*, 613, 613*f*, 617
intrapleural pressure and, 582–584, 583*f*
lung compliance and elastance and, 584–585
lung volume changes during, 578–579, 578*f*, 579*f*
maximum voluntary, 589, 589*t*
muscles of, 572*f*, 579, 580*f*, 581
normal values for, 587, 589*t*
pH disturbances and, 675–676, 675*f*
positive-pressure, 586
pressure gradients and, 577, 579–580
pulmonary function tests and, 578, 591
reflex control of, 612–613, 612*f*
regulation of, 612–617, 612*f*
spirometry in evaluation of, 578, 578*f*, 579*f*, 591
surfactant and, 585–586, 585*f*
total pulmonary, 587, 587*f*, 588*t*, 589*t*
types and patterns of, 588*t*, 617
work of breathing and, 585–586, 585*f*
ventilation-perfusion matching, 589–591, 590*f*, 590*t*
ventral horn Region of the spinal cord that contains efferent nuclei (Ch 9), 306, 307*f*
ventral respiratory group (VRG) Medullary neurons for active expiration and greater-than-normal inspiration (Ch 18), 613–614, 613*f*
ventral root Section of a spinal nerve that carries information from the central nervous system to the muscles and glands (Ch 9), 306, 307*f*
ventricle (brain) Hollow spaces in the brain filled with circulating cerebrospinal fluid (Ch 9), 301, 303, 304*f*
ventricle (cardiac) Lower chamber of the heart that pumps blood into the blood vessels (Ch 14), 469, 470*f*, 476*f*, 477*f*, 478*t*
ventricular contraction, 480*f*, 495–496, 496*f*, 497*f*, 498, 499*f*
blood pressure and, 514, 516, 517*f*, 518*f*
premature (PVC), 494
ventricular diastole, 494–495, 496*f*, 499*f*
ventricular ejection, 496, 496*f*
ventricular fibrillation, 488, 495*f*
ventricular filling, 495, 496*f*, 497*f*, 498
ventricular relaxation, 480*f*, 496–497, 496*f*, 497*f*, 498
blood pressure and, 514, 516, 517*f*
ventricular systole, 499*f*
venule The smallest vessels in the venous circulation (Ch 15), 513*f*, 514*f*, 515
blood flow velocity in, 529*f*
pressure in, 471*f*, 518*f*
verbal skills, cerebral lateralization and, 314, 316*f*
vertebrae, 301, 302*f*
vertebral column, 301
vertigo, 339
positional, 365
very-low-density lipoprotein (VLDL), 734
vesicle A sac-like, membrane-bound organelle used for storage and transport (Ch 3, 4, 5), 68, 69–70, 69*f*, 70*f*, 125*f*, 126, 152
vesicular transport The movement of vesicles within the cell with the aid of the cytoskeleton (Ch 5), 152–154, 152*f*, 153*f*
transcytosis and, 157, 157*f*
vestibular apparatus Portion of the inner ear that contains sensory receptors for balance and equilibrium (Ch 10), 355, 356*f*, 363, 364*f*, 366*f*, 458
vestibular disorder, 365. *See also* Ménière's disease
vestibular duct, 357, 358*f*, 359*f*
vestibular nerve, 363, 366*f*
sectioning, for Ménière's disease, 371
vestibular nuclei, 365, 366*f*
vestibulocochlear nerve, 310*t*, 355, 356, 361, 362*f*
vestigial endocrine structures, 240
Viagra® (sildenafil), 852
Vibrio cholerae, 718
villi Fingerlike projections of the intestinal surface (Ch 21), 690*f*, 691*f*, 692, 703
villi (arachnoid) (Ch 9), 303, 304*f*
villi (chorionic), 857, 857*f*
VIP. *See* vasoactive intestinal peptide
viral load, in HIV infection/AIDS, 807
virus, 783, 784–785, 784*f*, 784*t*
immune response to, 800–803, 802*f*
visceral nervous system. *See* autonomic nervous system
visceral pain, 348
visceral (autonomic) reflex, 338, 387–388, 387*f*, 388*f*, 447, 447*t*, 449, 449*f*
visceral response, 316, 317, 449, 449*f*. *See also* autonomic nervous system; visceral (autonomic) reflex
visceral smooth muscle Smooth muscle of the internal organs (Ch 12), 433, 433*f*
control of movement in, 463
viscosity Thickness or resistance to flow of a solution (Ch 14, 17), 473
air flow and, 586, 586*t*
visible light, 371, 372*f*
vision, 315, 315*f*, 334*t*, 365–378
pathways for, 367, 368*f*
sensory receptors for, 200*f*, 336, 336*t*, 365, 372, 372–376, 373*f*, 374*f*, 376*f*

Photo Credits

Chapter 1 CO-1 Alfred Pasieka/Photo Researchers

Chapter 2 CO-2 Michael W. Davidson/Photo Researchers

Chapter 3 CO-3 Michael W. Davidson/Molecular Expressions **3-8:** D. E. Saslowsky, J. Lawrence, X. Ren, D. A. Brown, R. M. Henderson, J. M. Edwardson, Placental alkaline phosphatase is efficiently targeted to rafts in supported lipid bilayers, Journal of Biological Chemistry, pages 26966-70, Vol. 277:30, 26 July 2002. ©2002 Journal of Biological Chemistry, American Society for Biochemistry and Molecular Biology, Inc., Bethesda, MD, 20814 **3-13b** Robert W. Riess **3-14b** Fawcett/Hirokawa/Heuser/Science Source/Photo Researchers, Inc. **3-16** CNRI/Science Source/Photo Researchers **3-17** Robert W. Riess **3-18b** Brad J. Marsh, David N. Mastronarde, Karolyn F. Buttle, Kathryn E. Howell, and J. Richard McIntosh, Inaugural Article: Organellar relationships in the Golgi region of the pancreatic beta cell line, HIT-T15, visualized by high resolution electron tomography. Proceedings of the National Academy of Sciences of the United States of America. Fig. 2, pages 2399-2406, Vol. 98:5, 27 February 2001. ©2001 by the National Academy of Sciences **3-19** Don Fawcett/Photo Researchers **3-20** Biophoto Associates/Photo Researchers **3-21** (top) H. Wartenberg/H. Jastrow's EM Atlas, *www.drjastrow.de* **3-21** (bottom) Photo Researchers **3-23** Todd Derksen **3-26b** Custom Medical Stock Photo **3-27** Todd Derksen **3-29** Ward's Natural Science Establishment **3-30c** John D. Cunningham/Visuals Unlimited **3-31** Frederic H. Martini **3-33a, b** SPL/ Photo Researchers

Chapter 4 CO-4 P. Motta & T. Naguro/Photo Researchers

Chapter 5 CO-5 Dennis Kunkel/Phototake

Chapter 6 CO-6 Veronique Blanc and Qin Wang/Wellcome Images UN01 Dmitri Gordienko/Wellcome Images

Chapter 7 CO-7 Dennis Kunkel/Phototake **7-1** Dee Silverthorn

Chapter 8 CO-8 C.J. Guerin, MRC Toxicology Unit/Photo Researchers **8-17a** Todd Derksen **8-17b** David M. Phillips/Visuals Unlimited **8-27** Tom Deerinck/Visuals Unlimited **8-30** Harris K.M., Stevens J.K., Dendritic spines of CA1 pyramidal cells in the rat hippocampus: serial electron microscopy with reference to their biophysical characteristics. *J.Neurosci.* (1989) 9:2982-2997. Image supplied by Synapse Web, Kristen M. Harris, PI; Image resurfacing by Josef Spacek. **8-33** Timothy M. Gomez, University of Wisconsin-Madison

Chapter 9 CO-9 Steve Gschmeissner/Photo Researchers **9-12b** Robert Brons/BPS **9-17** Marcus Raichle, Washington University School of Medicine

Chapter 10 CO-10 David Furness/Wellcome Images **10-16b** Todd Derksen **10-30b** Webvision, John Moran Eye Center, University of Utah

Chapter 11 CO-11 Kent Wood/Photo Researchers

Chapter 12 CO-12 Biology Media/Photo Researchers **12-1a** Ward's Natural Science Establishment **12-1b** Phototake NYC **12-1c** Todd Derksen **12-8** Phototake NYC **12-14** D. Comack, ed. Ham's Histology 9th ed. Philadelphia: J.B. Lippincott, 1987. By permission. **12-14** Frederic H. Martini **12-26** Biophoto Associates/Photo Researchers.

Chapter 13 CO-13 Veronique Blanc and Qin Wang/Wellcome Images

Chapter 14 CO-14 Quest/Photo Researchers

Chapter 15 CO-15 Susumu Nishinaga/Photo Researchers **15-21** CDC/Lyle Conrad

Chapter 16 CO-16 National Cancer Institute/Photo Researchers **16-5a** Todd Derksen **16-6a, b, c** Visuals Unlimited **16-8** Photo Researchers **16-9b, c** Todd Derksen **16-14** Susumu Nishinaga/Photo Researchers

Chapter 17 CO-17 Biophoto Associates/Photo Researchers **17-5** Frederic H. Martini

Chapter 18 CO-18 CNRI/Photo Researchers

Chapter 19 CO-19 Susumu Nishinaga/Photo Researchers **19-1AS** Todd Derksen **19-5** Todd Derksen

Chapter 20 CO-20 Veronique Blanc and Qin Wang/Wellcome Images

Chapter 21 CO-21 Thomas Deerinck, NCMIR/Photo Researchers

Chapter 22 CO-22 Alfred Pasieka/Photo Researchers **22-8b** Ward's Natural Science Establishment

Chapter 23 CO-23 Fred Hossler/Visuals Unlimited/Getty Images **23-1c** Ward's Natural Science Establishment **23-5a** Biophoto Associates/Science Source/Photo Researchers **23-5b** Biophoto Associates/Photo Researchers **23-10a** Martin Rotker/Phototake **23-10b** Alison Wright/CORBIS **23-10c** Ralph Eagle/Science Source/Photo Researchers **23-14** American Journal of Medicine **23-15** Ralph T. Hutchings **23-21** Dr. Michael Klein/Peter Arnold

Chapter 24 CO-24 Dennis Kunkel/Visuals Unlimited/Getty Images

Chapter 25 CO-25 Veronique Blanc and Qin Wang/Wellcome Images

Chapter 26 CO-26 Michael W. Davidson/Molecular Expressions **26-1** CNRI/Science Photo Library/Photo Researchers **26-26a** Francis Leroy/Biocosmos/Science Photo Library/Custom Medical Stock Photo

Chapter Icons **Running man** Photodisc/Getty Images **Compass** iStockpoto **DNA** iStockphoto **Microscope** Andy Sotiriou/Photodisc/Getty Images **Magnifying glass** Stockbyte/Getty Images